STRATIGRAPHICAL
PALAEONTOLOGY

STRATIGRAPHICAL PALAEONTOLOGY

A Study of Ancient Life-Provinces

BY

E. NEAVERSON, D.Sc. (LONDON), F.G.S.

Formerly Lecturer in Palaeontology
University of Liverpool

SECOND EDITION
REVISED AND ENLARGED

OXFORD
AT THE CLARENDON PRESS

Oxford University Press, Amen House, London E.C.4

GLASGOW NEW YORK TORONTO MELBOURNE WELLINGTON
BOMBAY CALCUTTA MADRAS KARACHI LAHORE DACCA
CAPE TOWN SALISBURY NAIROBI IBADAN ACCRA
KUALA LUMPUR HONG KONG

First edition 1928. Macmillan & Co. Ltd.
Second edition 1955

PRINTED LITHOGRAPHICALLY IN GREAT BRITAIN
AT THE UNIVERSITY PRESS, OXFORD
BY VIVIAN RIDLER, PRINTER TO THE UNIVERSITY
FROM SHEETS OF THE SECOND EDITION
1962

PREFACE

THE plan of this book, as first published in 1928, was frankly an experiment. At that time references to fossils in works on stratigraphy were so inadequate that a connected account of the palaeontological succession was obviously desirable. Judging by a bulky correspondence, the aim of the book was achieved, and when, towards the end of the last war, the remaining stock was destroyed as a result of enemy action, numerous inquiries were received concerning the possibility of a new edition.

In revising the work two outstanding criticisms of the original had to be taken into account. One was that a chapter on the morphology of fossils was out of place in a volume of this nature. The other was to the effect that the book did not justify its title because only British fossils were discussed. These criticisms have been met by the omission of the first item, and the addition of synopses of extra-British marine faunas. The vertebrate land-faunas of the several continents now form the subject of three new chapters. With the original scope of the work thus extended, one could hardly avoid discussing, in a final chapter, the relations of the continents and oceans as revealed by their past faunas. The book therefore becomes a study of ancient life-provinces.

The criticism that one man cannot write with equal authority on all the aspects of this vast subject is undoubtedly true; but, under the conditions prevailing in the geological schools of our universities, one man often has to present the whole subject to his students. This volume is the outcome of such presentation over many years, and of experience in building up a collection of rocks and fossils to illustrate the course. With the gradual accumulation of evidence the interpretation to be placed on the geographical distribution of fossil faunas has so changed that the writer's outlook on some of the major questions of geology is entirely opposed to that current in his student days. This is the case particularly with regard to the relations of the continents and oceans. It is hoped that the interpretation here presented will lead to further investigation and revaluation as additional information becomes available.

It should, perhaps, be mentioned here that certain widely used geological terms are avoided (except in quotations) because they are ambiguous. A case in point is the term 'geosyncline'. As long ago as 1926, J. W. Evans stated that 'the expression has been employed too loosely for it to retain any scientific meaning'. Its recent extension to the deposition of the Coal Measures, which is far outside the original definition, emphasizes the case for its suppression. Again, the term 'normal' should be left to the mathematicians, and replaced in geological literature by 'ordinary', 'usual', 'average', or 'standard', according to context. For 'normality', as applied to faunas and facies, is the natural outcome of circumstance; all faunas are 'normal' for the conditions in which they exist, and there is no such thing as an abnormal fauna. For much the same reason the term 'facies-fauna' is unnecessary, because, strictly it applies to all faunas. Such loose expressions, and there are many nowadays, only lead to needless confusion.

While the text has been altered considerably, the illustrations remain substantially the same as in the first edition. In response to many requests, the photographs and most of Miss Ball's drawings have been retained, and a few figures of extra-British fossils have been added. Discussion of faunal regions has led to the inclusion of maps to indicate the distribution of facies in certain critical areas. They are not palaeogeographical maps, but they do indicate the transgression and regression of the seas during the periods represented by the stratigraphical systems. More detailed maps of the same kind may easily be compiled, and it is hoped that students will do this for themselves, for much may be learned in this way.

The volume is compiled from the works of many authors to which references are given throughout the text. More intimate aid by friends in the University of Liverpool and elsewhere is gratefully acknowledged; special thanks are due to Dr. J. C. Harper, Dr. L. F. Spath, Dr. C. J. Stubblefield, and Prof. J. McLean Thompson for information concerning Ordovician faunas, Triassic ammonoids, Trilobites, and Neozoic plants respectively, and to Miss G. Williams for help in the library. For illustrations, the writer is again indebted to the Councils of the Palaeontographical Society, and the Liverpool Biological Society, H.M. Geological Survey of Great Britain, the Geological Survey of India, and of the United States of America, also to the works of W. S. Bisat, P. G. H. Boswell, S. S. Buckman, T. Davidson, F. E. Edwards, G. L. Elles, F. W. Harmer, G. W. Lamplugh, W. D. Lang, J. Lycett, A. Pavlow, A. C. Seward, D. Sharpe, J. P. Smith, L. F. Spath, H. U. Sverdrup, A. E. Trueman, J. W. Tutcher, J. H. F. Umbgrove, J. Walton, S. V. Wood, H. Woods, A. S. Woodward, and T. Wright. Finally, I wish to record my appreciation of the courtesy, patience, and skill shown by all at the Clarendon Press during the preparation of the volume.

Prestatyn   E. N.
March 1955

CONTENTS

LIST OF PLATES

(Grouped at end of volume)

LIST OF ILLUSTRATIONS

to the north-east coast. Many of his stratigraphical terms are still in use, and his famous map of 1815 formed the groundwork on which subsequent geological maps were based.

The rocks thus investigated provide admirable material for testing the principles enunciated by Smith. They crop out for long distances and their stratigraphical relations are not obscured by serious disturbance. It is otherwise with the Palaeozoic rocks below, of which the Permian, the Carboniferous, and part of the Devonian systems were recognized by Smith, though he did not apply these names to them. The publication of Smith's work led Murchison and Sedgwick (among others) to investigate these greatly disturbed rocks, with the result that the basic principles were fully confirmed, and the Palaeozoic rocks below the Devonian were divided into a lower and an upper series—Sedgwick's Cambrian and Murchison's Silurian respectively. Details of the subsequent unfortunate controversy concerning the upper limit of the Cambrian and the lower limit of the Silurian need not be given here. Suffice it to say that the brilliant work of Lapworth long afterwards established the fact that the beds in dispute contained a distinct fauna, equal in importance to those of the Cambrian and Silurian strata. Thus the Ordovician system was instituted and the main classification of the Palaeozoic rocks as now accepted was established.

For some years the younger systems, from the Triassic upwards, were grouped under the term Neozoic by Lyell and others. But in 1841 J. Phillips divided these systems between his Mesozoic and Cainozoic groups. Since then the term Neozoic has fallen into disuse in Britain, even though the name Cainozoic has proved unpopular. We may, however, regard the separation of the Mesozoic as an emendation of the Neozoic group, and the latter can still be used appropriately for the systems usually classified in the archaic Tertiary and Quaternary groups. The Neozoic rocks as thus restricted were found difficult to classify on account of their exposure in disconnected outcrops. In 1830 Lyell proposed a scheme based on the percentage of living species of mollusca in the various deposits. This classification still stands but slightly modified, though the subdivisions are now recognized by their actual fossil species and not by percentage of living forms.

It is not possible here to trace in detail the gradual growth of the classification of British sedimentary rocks. Many modifications of varied extent were made before such a grouping as that given in the accompanying table met with general acceptance. And space will not allow of due reference to the share taken by many continental workers in the early history of geology. All students will do well to read the history of their science, if only to appreciate the pioneer work done when communications were slow and tedious. Even in the light of present-day knowledge the geologist cannot fail to be impressed by the achievements of the early writers. He will perceive, moreover, that many additions to knowledge now attributed to later

Group	System	Series	Characteristic Fossil-groups
NEOZOIC	NEOGENE	Holocene Pleistocene Pliocene Miocene	Mammals
NEOZOIC	PALAEOGENE	Oligocene Eocene	
MESOZOIC	CRETACEOUS	Upper Cretaceous Lower Cretaceous	Ammonites · Fishes · Reptiles
MESOZOIC	JURASSIC	Oolitic Liassic	
MESOZOIC	TRIAS	Keuper Bunter	
PALAEOZOIC	PERMIAN		Goniatites
PALAEOZOIC	CARBONIFEROUS	Coal Measures Avonian	
PALAEOZOIC	DEVONIAN		
PALAEOZOIC	SILURIAN	Ludlow Wenlock Valentian	Graptolites · Trilobites
PALAEOZOIC	ORDOVICIAN	Ashgill Caradoc Llandeilo Arenig	
PALAEOZOIC	CAMBRIAN	Tremadocian Olenidian Paradoxidian Olenellidian	
PRE-CAMBRIAN			No fossils of correlative value

Classification of Sedimentary Rocks

workers could have been credited to the pioneers had the information been originally expressed appositely.

Even in the early days of palaeontological study fossils were regarded from one of two aspects according to the inclination of the observer. The biologist studied fossil organisms as individual forms of life, classified them by comparison with existing genera and species, and attempted to work out their relation to conditions of environment and habitat. The geologist treated fossils mainly as a means of determining the relative age of the rocks. As the result of experience he soon found that a trilobite does not occur with an ammonite, or a deinosaur with an elephant; further collecting showed that various kinds of trilobites or ammonites are confined to different strata. Thus accumulated knowledge enabled lists of fossils characteristic of major rock-formations to be compiled, and later allowed minor subdivisions to be recognized. The labours of both biologists and geologists furnished a voluminous literature which obviously cannot be reviewed here. It is desirable, however, to indicate the influence of a few of these works on the general progress of the science.

In 1812 Cuvier, the French biologist, published his *Researches on Fossil Bones* and thereby established the position of comparative anatomy as an independent science. This great work also exerted tremendous influences on palaeontological thought during the next few decades. On the one hand, it attracted many students to geology and palaeontology, and thus contributed to the ensuing rapid advance of investigation in those subjects. Its influence in another direction, however, probably retarded progress. Cuvier, in common with his contemporaries, regarded specific characters as constant and immutable, and held that the various individual faunas entombed in the rocks were special creations that were, each in its turn, extinguished by catastrophic revolutions. Notwithstanding the ideas of evolutional change advanced by Lamarck a few years previously, Cuvier's theory dominated palaeontological thought until the publication (in 1859) of Darwin's *Origin of Species*. A few years, however, sufficed for the almost general acceptance of Darwin's conception, and then began the modern period of palaeontological research. In the light of evolutional theories the gradual increase in complexity of organization shown by fossils in passing from earlier to later rocks assumed a new significance, and the mutual interdependence of palaeontology and stratigraphy was still more emphasized. Just as stratigraphy makes use of fossils for determining the age of the rocks, so palaeontology needs the stratigraphical law of superposition in order to obtain a chronological succession as ancillary to work on the evolution of animal groups.

The modern period of stratigraphical research may be said to date from the publication of Oppel's *Juraformation* in 1856–8. In this work the Jurassic strata of England and France are compared with those of south-west Germany on a palaeontological basis, the law of faunal dissimilarity being applied to the smallest groups of strata that could be recognized by their fossils. Thus Oppel deduced a series of palaeontological subdivisions which he termed **zones,** each being based upon the time-range of certain typical fossils, one of which, the index fossil, gives its name to the zone. Though minute subdivision of strata had been suggested by some previous writers, Oppel's exact zonal method set an example of precision which led directly

to the detailed study of local developments in the various systems, especially
the Jurassic. During the last century the zonal method has been applied
to most of the fossiliferous formations, and mapping on this basis has fully
justified the principle of detailed subdivision. Thus, by means of graptolite
zones in the Ordovician and Silurian rocks, Lapworth worked out the complex structure of the southern Uplands of Scotland, and showed that this
area had been misinterpreted by former observers. Many other instances
might be given where zonal mapping has solved structural problems, and
the method has also been used by O. T. Jones to trace the course of lead
and zinc lodes of which the position in graptolite zones had been ascertained in other localities.

In its original connotation, a stratigraphical zone is a bed, or a series of
beds, characterized by an assemblage of fossils of which one typical and
abundant species is taken as index. In most cases this concept is still
evident in the use of the term, but at various times some authors have
employed other criteria, so that certain so-called zones are determined by
different means. The Micraster zones of the Chalk, for instance, are based
on the sequence of developmental changes observed in several features of
the shell during the evolution of the genus *Micraster* (p. 508). The zones
of the Coal Measures, based on communities of non-marine lamellibranchs,
are determined by computing the average at different stages of development in a large number of individuals (p. 289). Arthur Vaughan's zones of
the Carboniferous Limestone Series are based on the successive appearance
of coral-genera; these are on a larger scale for they are divided into 'subzones', each of which is essentially equivalent to the original concept of the
zone (p. 274). The same may be said of Bisat's use of the Carboniferous
goniatite genera for zonal classification, and of the subdivision of the Cambrian system by means of trilobites, which are equivalent to stages. Thus,
it is evident that 'zones' are not of the same rank throughout the stratigraphical column. Moreover, in the Lower Palaeozoic graptolite zones, great
differences in thickness are apparent, due to the vagaries of depositional
processes at different localities.

It is perhaps only natural that the Jurassic strata should have been 'zoned'
to a much greater extent than other systems. Oppel recognized thirty-three
zones in this system, but S. S. Buckman and others have increased this
number tenfold. Since, however, many of Buckman's 'hemerae' (i.e.
time-intervals during which the zones were deposited) are hypothetical, it
is possible that the total may eventually be substantially reduced. Buckman
has also proposed a series of palaeontological 'ages' for the Jurassic to replace—or alternatively to parallel—the older stratigraphical terms, which
were originally based mainly on lithological characters. The fact that these
'ages' correspond closely with Oppel's zones is a great tribute to the accuracy
of Oppel's work, since the recognition of the smaller stratigraphical entities
demands a minute discrimination of species for which Buckman himself

is largely responsible. The ammonite-zones of the Cretaceous have been grouped on similar lines by L. F. Spath.

This proposal of a separate chronological nomenclature is the logical outcome of one important result accruing from the application of zonal methods to stratigraphy, namely, the recognition that lithological planes are not reliable indexes of time-intervals (see p. 29). The idea is not confined to workers in Mesozoic rocks, since H. S. Williams proposed in 1894 a scheme for the Cambrian system, based on the time-ranges of certain trilobites; his suggestion was, however, not adopted in its entirety. There seems no reason to doubt that future stratigraphical classification will be based, to an increasing extent, on palaeontological horizons. But there also appears no reason to fear either nomenclatural confusion or the overthrow of the present rock-systems and their main subdivisions. These seem well established on the law of faunal dissimilarity, which it is now necessary to discuss, along with certain principles of correlation.

In comparing the rocks of two separated districts the geologist has to rely entirely on the fossils present in those rocks. Supposing the fossil-assemblages to be identical, the rocks are held to be contemporaneous (or synchronous), even if they occur in such widely separated countries as England and America. It was once suggested that faunal migration is such a slow process that by the time a fauna reached the opposite quarter of the globe its original centre of dispersal would be occupied by a very different faunal development. Hence, it was argued, a British fauna regarded as Devonian might be contemporaneous with a Silurian fauna in a widely distant country. It was admitted that the same general order of faunal succession exists in all parts of the world, and the term Homotaxy was suggested for this phenomenon. Later it was realized that the time needed for migration is negligible compared with the period taken by the deposition of a rock-series, so that essentially similar faunas are nowadays held to be contemporaneous, and not merely homotaxial.

Though any fossil should (theoretically) give precise evidence of age, some are more useful than others to the general geologist. The most reliable are those with a restricted vertical range and a wide horizontal distribution, since they enable rocks from widely separated localities to be correlated. Thus graptolites and ammonites are almost ideal zone-fossils, while such slowly evolving groups as lamellibranchs and gastropods are but little used for purposes of correlation. The relative value of fossil groups as time-indexes is discussed in greater detail in Chapter II. Some fossils have such a restricted time-range that they are absolutely conclusive when found; but it cannot be too strongly emphasized that the whole fauna is the actual basis of correlation, especially where the major rock-series are concerned. Therefore collection should not be confined to the index-fossils, especially as much other important information can be gained from a study of the fauna as a whole.

The simplest case of correlation is that in which identical faunas occur in different localities. Stratigraphical divisions may then be recognized by the sum total of their contained species. Smaller divisions may be determined by a statistical method, the number or percentage of restricted species being compared with those of longer range. Or the relations of a fauna to contiguous assemblages may be inferred by a comparison of the number of species common to higher and lower beds. This was the only method available in the early days of stratigraphical study, but is now rarely practised. It should be noted also that absolute faunal identity rarely occurs, owing to differences (which may be only slight) in the physical conditions prevailing in different areas during the life of the organisms.

The incoming of new forms in abundance is now generally accepted as the most reliable criterion for determining the lower limit of each series of rocks. For instance, the Devonian is marked by the incoming of ammonoids and fishes, and the Neozoic by the appearance in force of eutherian Mammalia. Rigid adherence to this rule, however, is not always convenient in practice, since such a line of demarcation would sometimes occur in the middle of strata showing constant lithological characters; and in mapping reliance is often placed on local lithology (after the fauna of a rock type has been ascertained) owing to the uncertain occurrence of fossils. Thus in this country graptolites first appear in the Tremadoc Series, which pass up gradually from the upper series of the Cambrian. The succeeding Arenig Series is separated from the Tremadoc Slates by a marked physical break which is readily mapped. Consequently the Tremadoc Slates are retained as the uppermost series of the Cambrian system, though in Scandinavia (where there is no interruption) equivalent strata are placed at the base of the Ordovician. Similarly, fishes occur below the line taken as the base of the Devonian system, but they are not abundant, and convenience of mapping makes desirable a slight departure from the palaeontological basis of division.

These principles are not so strongly applicable to the 'zone', which is generally marked by the dominance of a definite species with a wide horizontal distribution. Members of slowly evolving groups often range through several zones—sometimes, indeed, through one series into another. Hence faunas of the smaller stratigraphical divisions are often closely related to those of contiguous zones. Moreover, such faunas are more liable to differentiation by local conditions of habitat which are obscured in the larger faunal groupings. Zonal correlation is therefore more reliably based upon progressive modifications of characters observed in appropriate fossils.

The established facts of evolution show that organisms are constantly changing, generally in some definite direction. It is obvious that recognizable stages in the evolution of particular lines of descent acquire special significance when their exact stratigraphical occurrence has been ascertained. Thus certain zones of the White Chalk are based on minute progressive changes in various features of the test of the echinoid *Micraster* (p. 508). The greater part of the Silurian system is divided into zones characterized by progressive changes in the graptolites grouped under the term *Monograptus*. These are only two instances, out of many that might be given, which go to show the peculiar value of those fossils whose evolutional history is known. Furthermore, in many cases evolution has proceeded on closely similar lines and at approximately the same rate in closely allied—but not identical—lineages, equivalent stages in development giving a similar appearance to the organisms. Where this occurs in widely separated localities similarity of expression in the faunas may be relied upon for correlation of the rocks. For instance, the Middle Cambrian strata of North America, north-west Europe, and Bohemia, contain species of the trilobite *Paradoxides* that are closely allied but not identical. These 'complementary' or 'vicarious' species produce faunal similarity which is almost as good as absolute identity.

Since evolutional change is generally in the direction of increased structural complexity, it follows that in any lineage, or series of parallel lineages, the more specialized forms will be zonally later than the simple forms. The simple rugose coral usually cited as *Zaphrentis* makes its first appearance in the British area at a low horizon of the Carboniferous Limestone. For some vertical distance it is unaccompanied by other rugose corals, and then marks the Zaphrentis zone. At successively higher levels it is associated with other forms showing increased complexity of internal structure, and the dominance of certain of these types is taken to mark various succeeding zones. This occurrence is shown diagrammatically in Fig. 7 (p. 76), and is further discussed in Chapter II. It is to be noted that *Zaphrentis* persists apparently unchanged (except in minor features) throughout the series, so that the mere occurrence of that genus does not necessarily indicate the Zaphrentis zone; its associates must be taken into account. The persistence of root-stocks through a rock-series is a frequent phenomenon. The occurrence of the ammonoids *Phylloceras* and *Lytoceras* throughout the Mesozoic, and that of the echinoid *Cidaris* from the Lias onwards, may be cited; but these genera are not at present used as zonal indexes.

Persistent types are not necessarily root-stocks. The brachiopod *Lingula*, though of comparatively simple organization, is specialized in several features and lives in a special habitat. Its persistence is probably due to the absence of competition with other organisms in its 'safe' environment. The eel-like form of certain fishes, often described as 'degenerate', is also probably an adaptation to special conditions of life, which has arisen in different lineages when there was need for it.

Sedimentary rocks are mainly of marine origin, and therefore much of the present British land area was at different times part of the sea floor. Moreover, since deposition takes place on approximately horizontal planes, it is evident that, quite apart from the carving out of the present topographical features by agents of denudation, many British deposits have suffered serious displacement since the time of their formation. Let us consider for a moment some of the effects of a possible future re-submergence. On the continental shelf, where sedimentation has been proceeding for a considerable period, there would be simply a continuation of that process and the rocks would in general be conformable to those at present being formed. On the present land area, however, horizontal deposits would be laid down directly upon rocks of widely separated ages, tilted or dipping in various directions and at different angles. In short there would be abundant evidence of a great physical break or unconformity. Such interruptions of the geological sequence have long been recognized, and in many cases the physical unconformity is accompanied by a faunal break. On this account unconformities are often taken as the lines of demarcation between groups, series, or stages, according to their magnitude, and they have the advantage that they are readily mapped. Coarse beach-deposits formed on the subsidence of land areas, eroded surfaces bored by marine mollusca, and abrupt differences in the lithological character of succeeding beds, often mark unconformable junctions.

Deposition, however, is not universal under marine conditions. Observations of the present sea floor have shown that large areas of bare rock exist where current-action (or other factors) prevents the accumulation of detrital material. Subsequent deflection of the currents might result in the deposition of sediment in those areas. Supposing such alternation of conditions to have occurred several times, it becomes evident that breaks in the succession of rocks may occur in a series of horizontal strata without changes in the relative level of land and sea. In a rock-series such interruptions would not necessarily be apparent on physical grounds, but might be detected by possible breaks in the continuity of faunal elements. The best criterion would be the absence of a stage in the evolutional sequence of a lineage that is complete at a neighbouring locality. Breaks of this kind are distinguished as non-sequences, but the difference from unconformities is merely one of degree, and possibly of location.

Zonal methods have disclosed the presence of many indubitable non-sequences, in the Jurassic rocks especially. But, it may be noted, care should be taken lest an inferred non-sequence should prove to be merely failure on the part of an investigator to collect the characteristic fossils owing to lack of exposures or other causes. It has recently been suggested that some of the supposed non-sequences are due rather to limitations in the geographical distribution of organisms than to erosive phenomena (combined with intraformational earth movements) as originally postulated by Buckman. Referring to this matter Dr. W. D. Lang writes: 'The rigid application of the principle of dissimilar faunas contravenes the facts of distribution as seen among recent organisms.' Possibly the effects of currents on faunal distribution, and more especially on the occurrence of fossils, may meet some of the objections. But no rigid rule can be laid down, and each case must be considered on its merits. The fact that the question has been raised is, however, an incentive to assiduous zonal collecting combined with careful surveying on maps of large scale. Dr. Lang's descriptions and maps of parts of the Dorset coast (p. 484) may well serve as models for similar work in the other parts of the country.

Fossils, like living animals and plants, are identified by the sum-total of their characters. Each form is given a name which serves as a means of reference to the features by which it may be recognized. The name itself is not always descriptive of the characters, for a fossil may be named after its type-locality, after its discoverer, or in honour of some other person. But once established, the name implies the collection of characters shown by the organism and is the most convenient device for avoiding the repetition of long descriptions. The method in use is the familiar Linnean system, and its only serious disadvantage is that it tends to give the idea that species are fixed and immutable entities. Indeed this was the prevalent view when the system was devised. Now that the fact of evolution has become firmly established the difficulty is being gradually removed by revision of the original diagnosis to give the necessary elasticity.

Furthermore, since many fossils differ slightly from named forms, some means of indicating minor variations is necessary. The insertion of 'aff.' in the specific name, e.g. *Hoplites* aff. *dentatus* (J. Sow.) (Pl. XVI), indicates affinity but not identity with the named species, whereas 'cf.' as in *Rasenia* cf. *involuta* Salf. (Pl. XIV), denotes a certain degree of similarity, but does not necessarily imply genetic affinity. Where the genus is determinable but the species is indeterminate (owing to poor preservation or other causes), the abbreviation 'sp.' may be written after the generic name. It is to be noted also that the name of the author is considered an integral part of the specific name; it is enclosed in brackets, or alternatively, the abbreviation 'sp.' is written after it, in those cases where the species has been assigned to a different genus by a later author.

Nowadays the author of a species indicates the particular specimen which he takes as the **type** or standard of reference. Such types should always be preserved in a national museum or other place of safety easily accessible to students. The best means of identifying fossils is by direct comparison with these described types. But as this is not always possible, fossils must generally be compared with adequate illustrations of described species; descriptions alone are likely to mislead. Hence the student needs to know something of the sources where such illustrations may be found.

In the early days of palaeontological research several authors aspired to describe and illustrate all the fossils (or all those belonging to one great group) found in some particular country. Naturally these works are left unfinished, and there is usually no system in the arrangement of species; furthermore, the descriptions must now be interpreted in the light of present-day knowledge. Nevertheless, the illustrations are often extremely accurate, and the works should always be consulted when the exact interpretation of early established species is desired. A British work of this character is *Mineral Conchology of Great Britain*, by J. Sowerby (1812–22) and his son J. de C. Sowerby (1822–46). About 1,250 fossil shells are described and illustrated on 648 engraved and coloured plates.

Among other works of this kind, and also important to British students, are:

Paléontologie française, by A. d'Orbigny, 1840–55, which includes Jurassic and Cretaceous Corals, Echinoderms, Polyzoa, Brachiopoda and Mollusca, and Eocene Echinoids.

Petrefacta Germaniae, by G. A. Goldfuss and G. Münster, 2 vols., 1826–40, descriptive of Sponges, Corals, Echinoderms, and Mollusca.

Description des coquilles fossiles des environs de Paris, by P. G. Deshayes, 2 vols. and Atlas, 1824–37. This work, descriptive of Neozoic Mollusca, is of special value to students of British Eocene strata, since the illustration of English Eocene fossils is notoriously incomplete.

The species described in these early works are most easily traced by means of various catalogues and indexes subsequently published. Such are:

British Fossils, by J. Morris, 2nd ed. 1854, which records all British species established at that date, with geological age and references to literature.

Index Palaeontologicus, by H. G. Bronn, 1848–9. This is now being replaced by *Fossilium Catalogus*, edited by F. Frech (1913 onwards), containing lists of species compiled by specialists in the various fossil groups.

Index Animalium, by C. D. Sherborn. Vol. i, 1902, includes all genera and 'species' of animals (living and fossil) published between 1758 and 1800. Vol. ii to 1850. *Nomenclator Zoologicus*, edited by S. A. Neave, gives a list of the names of zoological genera and subgenera from the 10th ed. of Linnaeus, 1758, to the end of 1935; it is published by the Zool. Soc. Lond. 1939–40.

Here may also be mentioned the *Zoological Record*, an annual publication of the Zoological Society of London, which contains lists of all new genera and species of animals published during the year.

There are also various serial publications, such as the *Monographs of the Palaeontographical Society of London*. These provide complete descriptions, including revision of previous publications, of particular groups of fossils. Usually the chosen group is a biological one, such as the Graptolites or the Trilobites, which is described for one or all of the geological systems in which it occurs. Sometimes, however, the whole fauna of one system is described; e.g. the Devonian Fauna. These monographs furnish the student with a summary of knowledge of the particular group up to the date of publication, and the general worker is able to avoid much bibliographical research by means of them. Reference to appropriate monographs (abbreviated to *Mon. Pal. Soc.*) will be found at the end of Chapters III to XVII.

Many descriptions and figures of fossils are published in the *Quarterly Journal of the Geological Society of London* (*Q. J.G.S.* in subsequent pages), the *Geological Magazine*, the *Philosophical Transactions of the Royal Society of London*, the *Transactions of the Royal Society of Edinburgh*, and other journals issued by various geological and biological societies. References to these are appended where necessary to the appropriate chapters.

The publications of the Geological Survey of Great Britain furnish an excellent account of the stratigraphy of the country. Many memoirs contain figures of fossils, but, although much information may be gleaned concerning their geological distribution, the identification of the various forms must be made independently. For this reason the *Memoirs of the Geological Survey* are but rarely mentioned in the following pages; the exception consists of a series of palaeontological memoirs, those already published dealing with Carboniferous fossils (see end of Chaps. VII and VIII).

The usefulness of a fossil does not end with its accurate identification nor with the determination of its age. Much other information may be gained from it—especially in conjunction with its associates. Its mode of preservation, combined with the lithological characters of the surrounding deposit, tells much concerning the conditions under which the rock was formed, and the changes that have occurred subsequent to its formation. The mode of occurrence of fossils also furnishes evidence of events preceding and during burial; even a bed of comminuted shells has its value in this connexion, though it may not provide cabinet specimens. The general structural features of the faunal elements indicate, by analogy with living forms, the probable mode of life of the ancient organisms. Many of these features (which are discussed more fully in subsequent pages) may be observed to most advantage in the field. It may safely be said that much valuable evidence has been lost because full attention has not been given to these questions. Literature may be searched in vain for information on the interrelations of fossils and rocks; and most of us can recall annoying omissions in our own work. Hence it cannot be too strongly emphasized that full and accurate observation in the field, equally careful labelling of specimens, and detailed mapping, are essential if a reliable history of the earth and its past inhabitants is ever to be written.

The palaeontological succession provided by British strata has played a prominent part in the formation of a stratigraphical classification applicable in general terms throughout the world. We have noted that the principles of stratigraphy were first formulated by William Smith in 1816 as a result of prolonged observations in the west of England. Several of the stratigraphical systems are named from typical districts in Britain where the rocks were first investigated, and others carry more or less descriptive terms given to them by British geologists.

But Britain has only an area of some 121,000 square miles out of approximately 60 millions of square miles of land-surface on the globe. It is not surprising, therefore, that certain reservations and modifications are necessary when the British stratigraphical classification is applied to the geological succession in other countries. Just as there are great variations in the physical conditions of various regions today, so the lithological characters of the rocks show that similar differences existed during former geological periods. Moreover, the physical conditions obtaining in a particular area at any given time depend largely on the geological history of that and contiguous regions. They determine to a large extent the type of fauna which occupies the area, and consequently the contemporaneous faunas of two distant regions may show conspicuous differences.

This circumstance may, at first sight, seem to contravene the dictum that strata can be correlated by means of their fossil-contents. Actually, however, the evolution of animals and plants appears to have proceeded on the same general lines throughout the world, and groups of organisms seem to have attained recognizable grades of development at certain geological periods. On this account general correlation can often be made by means of equivalent stages in the morphological development of appropriate organisms—stages nowadays expressed as genera. This general likeness may be enhanced by the migration of some forms from one region to another. At the same time the faunas of different regions are often found to have acquired local peculiarities in some minor features, and thus many species, and even some genera have a more or less restricted geographical distribution. In a general way, therefore, the floras and faunas of certain regions may be grouped in life-provinces.

As a background to the study of ancient life-provinces some knowledge of the general geology of the land-masses is necessary; such general information may be gained from the following regional studies, apart from the more detailed papers cited in these works and at the end of each chapter below.

Géologie Stratigraphique, by M. Gignoux, 4th ed., Paris, 1950. More details are given by E. Haug in his famous *Traité de Géologie*, Paris, 1911, but many of his interpretations are not now accepted.

Geologie von Europa, by S. v. Bubnoff, Berlin, 1926–36.

Geologie von Sibirien, by W. A. Obrutschew, Berlin, 1929.

Geology of India, by D. N. Wadia, London, 1939.

Geology of China, by J. S. Lee, London, 1939.

Geologie Afrikas, by E. Krenkel, 4 vols., Berlin, 1925–8.

Lexicon de Stratigraphie, vol. i, Africa, by S. H. Haughton, London, 1938.

Geology of South Africa, by A. L. Dutoit, Edinburgh, 1926.

Geology of the British Empire, by F. R. C. Reed, 2nd ed., London, 1950.

Historical Geology of the Antillean–Caribbean Region, by C. Schuchert, New York, 1935.

Stratigraphy of the Eastern and Central United States, by C. Schuchert, New York, 1943.

Geology von Groenland, by L. Koch, Berlin, 1935, summarizing a large series of papers in *Meddelser om Groenland,* Copenhagen 1880–1950 (in progress).

Geologie Sudamerikas, by H. Gerth, Berlin, 1932–5.

Geology of the Commonwealth of Australia, by T. W. E. David and W. R. Browne, London, 1950.

Geology of Indonesia, by R. W. v. Bemmelen, The Hague, 1949.

A brief historical review of 'The Relationship of Palaeontology to Stratigraphy' by C. J. Stubblefield, *The Advancement of Science,* No. 42, pp. 149–59, 1954, may also be read with advantage at this stage.

I

THE PRESERVATION AND DISTRIBUTION OF FOSSILS

NOWADAYS the term 'fossil' is restricted to the recognizable remains and traces of past life found in rocks, though formerly it also included objects of inorganic origin. The state of preservation of these organic relics varies greatly in different strata according to a variety of circumstances. The nature of the organism, its habitat and mode of life, the conditions of its burial, and events subsequent to its entombment, all have their peculiar influence on the state in which the fossil is found today.

THE NATURE OF THE ORGANISM. Since the soft tissues of animals and plants usually perish very quickly it is obvious that the whole organism can seldom, if ever, be preserved in the fossil state. Perhaps the nearest approach to complete preservation is that of fossil insects enclosed in amber from Oligocene deposits of the Baltic area. Traces of 'soft' coelenterates have been found as imprints, but this occurrence is due to exceptionally favourable conditions of burial and the nature of the surrounding deposit. As a general rule organisms that secrete no hard skeletal matter are almost entirely lost to palaeontological study.

Some skeletons, such as those of vertebrates, arthropods, and many sponges, are made up of separate hard parts held together by soft tissues. On the death of the animal the several parts of the skeleton often become scattered, and their exact identification is a matter of some difficulty. In the case of animals like the trilobites that periodically cast their (external) skeleton, it is probable that many of the fragments found in rocks represent parts of the 'moulted' covering rather than exoskeletons dismembered after the death of the individuals. Despite the fact that these remains are often fragmentary, they frequently occur in such abundance as to impart a special character to the deposits which enclose them. At the present time loose siliceous spicules of sponges are said to accumulate on the sea floor off Kerguelen at a depth of 120 fathoms, forming a 'spicular ooze'. Some cherts among the stratified rocks are considered to have been formed in the same way, the spicules becoming cemented together by a secondary deposit of silica. Such beds of sponge-chert occur in the British Carboniferous Limestone, in the Portland Limestones (Upper Jurassic), and in some Lower Cretaceous rocks. Fragments of trilobites are often profuse in Lower Palaeozoic strata, in one instance in the Ordovician rocks of North Wales, imparting a distinct phosphatic character to the deposit; it may be noted that the tests of trilobites from the Cambrian rocks of Wales are said to contain 20 per cent. of calcium phosphate, a proportion which agrees well with published analyses of modern crustacean tests. Vertebrate remains often occur in 'bone beds' whose distinctive characters will be considered subsequently. In contrast with these compound and incoherent skeletons, the tests of corals and polyzoa, the shells of molluscs and brachiopods, are coherent and usually preserve their original shape; moreover, the latter shells often afford information concerning anatomical details by impressions of muscles, &c., on the internal surfaces.

Again, the hard parts of organisms are by no means of equal durability. The skeletal structures of animals are formed mainly of silica, calcium carbonate, or of chitin, and each of these substances has peculiar limitations with regard to its capacity for preservation.

Radiolaria and many sponges form siliceous skeletons, the silica being secreted in its colloid condition, which is soluble in alkaline water. The presence of beds of flint and chert in many stratified rocks is ascribed, at least in part, to the redeposition of silica, after solution of radiolarian and poriferan tests. Some cherts indeed still enclose tests and spicules respectively of these organisms.

Two forms of calcium carbonate, namely, calcite and aragonite, are concerned in the building up of calcareous skeletons. Calcite is the more durable form, but both are readily soluble in acidulated water. The skeletons of alcyonarian corals, most brachiopods, echinoderms, and some molluscs (e.g. *Ostrea* and *Pecten*) are made of calcite, while aragonite constitutes those of madreporarian corals, gastropods, and cephalopods. Some shells of bivalved mollusca (e.g. *Pinna*, *Mytilus*, *Spondylus*) have an inner layer of aragonite and an outer layer of calcite. In connexion with the distribution of calcite and aragonite in animal skeletons, the investigations of Clarke and Wheeler on the inorganic constituents of marine invertebrates have emphasized the importance of magnesium carbonate in some skeletons. This substance is isomorphous with calcite, and always occurs in some quantity in calcitic shells, while aragonitic shells or tests are practically free from magnesia. The magnesian carbonate, being less soluble than the calcium salt, may increase the durability of the shells containing it, while its presence may have some bearing in another connexion—that of the formation of dolomite. Skeletons of vertebrate animals contain a considerable proportion of calcium phosphate, which increases their durability; teeth contain up to 60 per cent. of this compound and are most frequently preserved as fossils.

Chitin is an organic substance that is less soluble than calcium carbonate, but is very brittle. It can only be preserved when excluded from atmospheric action, and even then, like other organic compounds, it tends to become carbonized. Chitin forms the skeleton of many larval forms which later in life secrete calcium carbonate, and is especially characteristic of the arthropoda, being mixed with the carbonate and phosphate of calcium in many large crustacea.

The woody tissues of plants, composed of cellulose and allied substances, may be regarded as organic skeletal structures. These are usually carbonized in the fossil state, and when present in sufficient quantity form deposits of peat, lignite, or coal according to the degree of carbonization. In some instances, however, exceptional circumstances during and after burial may result in the preservation of the cellular structure.

Other characters of certain organisms directly influence their precise mode of occurrence in the fossil state. Thus, brachiopod shells are generally found with the valves closed. The muscles that open and close the valves are so placed that the shell is closed when the principal muscles are relaxed. Hence the shell remains closed after the animal dies, and is so preserved in the fossil state. On the other hand, the muscles of bivalved mollusca merely close the shell by retraction; on relaxation of the muscles the shell is opened by the action of a ligament on the hinge-line. When the shell is quickly buried, especially in burrowing forms, the valves remain closed in the fossil. If the muscles decay before burial, the shell opens and may be preserved with the valves united by the ligament, but burial may be delayed until the ligament decays and then the two valves are completely separated.

THE HABITAT AND MODE OF LIFE of an organism may often affect its chances of preservation after death. It is evident that a skeleton exposed to the destructive action of atmospheric agencies will soon disintegrate. Hence early and effective burial is essential for fossilization. Since there are comparatively few places on land where deposition of sedimentary material is in progress to any extent, it follows that remains of terrestrial animals have but little chance of preservation. The great majority remain on the surface after death and in a short time are entirely decomposed. In this way the extreme rarity of skeletons from the Triassic rocks of this country may be explained, though the presence of animals is manifest in the marly 'footprint-beds' representing marginal lake-deposits.

In the case of freshwater organisms the conditions are more favourable for preservation, since burial is more certain. Not only do the freshwater deposits contain remains of the fauna and flora proper to them, but transported remains of land-dwelling animals and plants are often preserved in them. Transport by streams also accounts for the association of land and freshwater species with marine fossils. The wood of Conifers is found in Jurassic oyster-beds, while stems and leaves of 'tree-ferns' are associated with brachiopods and molluscs in some beds of the Carboniferous Limestone. Such relics of organisms drifted far from their original home must be rightly interpreted if confusion is to be avoided. Freshwater deposits, however, are among the first to suffer from subsequent earth-movements and have frequently been lost almost entirely by denudation. An interesting instance of local escape from destruction is seen in the freshwater bed at the base of the Carboniferous Limestone series at Horton-in-Ribblesdale, described by E. J. Garwood.

Since the sea is the chief repository of the detrital products of denudation, and deposition is most rapid near the shore-line, prompt burial is most certain in those areas near the coast that are not subjected to wave action. It may also be noted that the coastal belt is most favourably situated for subsequent elevation. Of all fossil records the most complete is that of the animals inhabiting the littoral region (from the shore-line to a depth of about 20 fathoms). This area exhibits the greatest variety of physical conditions and its fauna is correspondingly varied. These conditions are discussed in more detail later, but it is necessary here to show that the habits of some of the animals influence their fossil occurrence. Thus brachiopods and echinoids are mainly gregarious animals, living in masses or groups, the former being fixed to the substratum by their pedicles. The 'nests' of rhynchonellids and terebratulids in the Jurassic Marlstone of the Midlands, and of *Hemicidaris* in the Corallian Limestones of Wiltshire, is a reflection of this gregarious habit. Living colonies of these groups of animals frequently migrate wholesale to a fresh locality, and this circumstance may help to explain the sporadic occurrence of many echinoids and brachiopods in the fossil state. The frequent occurrence of oyster-beds in Jurassic and later rocks also reflects the gregarious habits of ostrean mollusca.

The massive, colonial, reef-like growth of many corals and calcareous algae is another mode of life exceedingly favourable for fossilization. Indeed, in many instances this habit of growth is responsible for the building up of considerable limestone formations at various horizons in the geological column. It must be emphasized that the so-called coral reefs seldom consist entirely of corals; some are constituted largely of the limy secretions of calcareous algae, while other invertebrates adherent to or sheltering in the reef structure may form a considerable bulk. Modern coral reefs consist essentially of the skeletons of true corals (Zoantharia) but such calcareous algae as *Lithothamnion* and *Halimeda* often surpass the corals in abundance, while the hydrozoan *Millepora* contributes largely to the formation of some coral reefs. Reef-like masses of zoantharian corals occur in some of the British Mesozoic deposits, especially in the Lower Oolites and Corallian, but they are generally more or less local in extent. Likewise in the Carboniferous Limestone similar masses of compound corals are important constituents of the rock. In the older Palaeozoic systems, however, the Tabulate corals are the chief reef-builders, and are abundantly represented in the Wenlock and Devonian Limestones. Some Devonian reefs are made almost entirely of Stromatoporoid colonies, the Stromatoporoidea being an extinct group usually classified with the Hydrozoa. The importance of calcareous algae in their capacity of rock-builders was realized in continental countries as early as 1858, when Unger showed that *Lithothamnion* contributed largely to the formation of the Neozoic Leithakalk of the Vienna basin. These organisms were somewhat neglected by British geologists until E. J. Garwood (in 1913) drew attention to their abundance in certain British strata. Thus *Girvanella* and *Solenopora* occur abundantly in Ordovician Limestones of Scotland and in the Wenlock Limestone of Shropshire. In the Carboniferous Limestone the genera *Girvanella*, *Solenopora*, *Mitcheldeania*, and *Ortonella* form considerable masses of limestone and are often of distinct stratigraphical value, since they have a wide geographical distribution and some are restricted to definite horizons. Masses of *Solenopora* often attain a large size in certain Jurassic rocks of Gloucestershire, but calcareous algae are not yet recognized in British Cretaceous and Neozoic strata.

The coralloid habit of growth is simulated by a remarkable extinct group of bivalved mollusca which is typical of Cretaceous Limestones extending along the borders of the Mediterranean Sea into Asia. These bivalves, known collectively as the rudistids or hippurites, are fixed to the substratum by cementation; the fixed valve takes the shape of an inverted cone, while the free valve remains flat, forming a lid. The whole structure indeed resembles operculate corals rather than mollusca. These shells are abundantly preserved, and contribute largely to the bulk of the Mediterranean Cretaceous Limestone. The same habit is acquired by certain sessile brachiopods, such as *Richthofenia*, which occurs in the Permian deposits of the Salt Range in India.

The sessile condition and presumably gregarious habit of the Palaeozoic crinoids may account for the local abundance of their remains in Silurian and Carboniferous Limestones. The massive stems of these organisms are familiar objects in 'crinoid limestones', where they often occur almost to the exclusion of other material. Since, however, the crinoid skeleton is composed of numerous parts articulated together, the fossil remains are nearly always fragmentary, complete specimens being preserved only in the most favourable circumstances.

Burrowing animals are also favourably situated for preservation, and many animals that live in the sandy or muddy sea floor are represented in the fossil state. The Jurassic genus *Pleuromya* is a well-known molluscan example; *Lingula* among brachiopods and the spatangid sea-urchins furnish other instances. Among fossil terrestrial insects beetles are said to be most numerous, because of their burrowing habits during life, but the possession of durable elytra is also an important factor. An occasional habit of certain fishes may be mentioned here because it seems to explain certain occurrences of fossil forms without invoking catastrophic events. On the drying up of pools during drought some freshwater fishes are known to bury themselves in the soft mud at the bottom, there to await replenishment of the water. If the drought be prolonged, however, the fishes die and are favourably situated for fossilization. This circumstance seems to account most satisfactorily for the abundance of well-preserved fishes in certain beds of the Old Red Sandstone in the north of Scotland and in Triassic deposits of Nottinghamshire.

Some adherent fossils owe their preservation to the protection afforded by large forms to which they are fixed. Fragile colonies of polyzoa attached to massive echinoid tests or oyster shells, and certain small brachiopods cemented to similar objects, are thus preserved. Sometimes colonies of polyzoa grow to such a size that they envelop the object to which they are fixed, and then the role of protector and protected is reversed. Gastropods thus enveloped by polyzoa are commonly found in the Aymestry Limestone, while barnacles form a covering to many molluscan shells in Pliocene deposits. The occurrence of small gastropods inside the tests of large Cretaceous echinoids, and of small shells in the body-chamber of Jurassic ammonites, is accidental, but here again the larger fossil has a protective influence.

CONDITIONS OF BURIAL. Rapid burial being essential for the effective fossilization of organic remains, it will now be shown that the ultimate state of preservation and the mode of occurrence of fossils are influenced to no small extent by the conditions which obtain at the time of their entombment. This really opens up the whole question of sedimentation and conditions of deposition, whose adequate discussion demands a large volume to itself. In this place it is possible only to describe the general properties of the chief types of deposit and the influence of the rate of deposition.

Sediments are nowadays classified as sands, silts, and clays on the basis of the average diameter of their constituent particles. Thus an incoherent deposit whose grains have an average diameter of between 2 mm. and 0·1 mm. is called a sand, the grains being mainly of the mineral quartz. Pure sands rarely occur in Nature, some admixture of finer material being general. Even so, arenaceous deposits are porous, and on this account any shelly substance they may contain is likely to be dissolved by percolating water. Where shells escape this solvent action their surfaces often become pitted by reason of the greater hardness of the surrounding sand grains. Consequently burial in sandy material does not usually result in ideal preservation—a decided disadvantage, since sandy deposits are of wide distribution in the littoral or coastal regions, and so are likely to enclose abundant shells of marine invertebrate animals.

The chief disadvantages of sands are absent from clays, which are impervious to water, and, being formed of soft, fine-grained material, are capable of preserving the detail of fine ornament. The physical properties of clays, however, act disadvantageously in other directions. As the fine particles become closely pressed together, the weight of the overlying deposit eventually becomes too great for most shells, which consequently become flattened. The development of concretionary nodules after the accumulation of the sediment but before the shells are flattened may, however, result in preservation without crushing. Thus ammonites enclosed in cementstone nodules generally preserve their original shape, while those in surrounding clays are often crushed. Graptolites, as usually preserved in shales, are generally flattened on the bedding-planes of the rock, but occasionally specimens are preserved in their original shape. Such 'solid' specimens have long been known from limestones in Sweden, and more recently have been found in calcareous concretions, in mudstones of Ludlow age, on the Denbighshire Moors, North Wales. Chemical changes during the decay of the organic contents cause the formation of sulphuretted hydrogen and other gases. Ultimately such unstable minerals as marcasite may be formed, resulting in the complete disintegration of the fossil when it is exposed to atmospheric action.

Calcareous deposits, considered in the present connexion, possess some characters shown by arenaceous and argillaceous deposits respectively. Like sandy deposits they are porous to a marked degree, but the calcareous material is finely divided and, on this account, is usually more soluble than calcite (but not aragonite) shells. The fine-grained limy material may be compared with argillaceous sediments, since it is not harder than the enclosed animal shells and therefore does not deface their surfaces. Moreover, shells preserved in calcareous deposits are not usually crushed, but they are sometimes difficult to extract from the rock.

While arenaceous, argillaceous, and calcareous deposits reflect the broad general conditions of burial, it must be understood that the preservation of fossils is capable of infinite variety, owing to local peculiarities of deposition. Indeed, most rock-series (when examined in detail), present some problems of this nature that are difficult to explain in the present state of knowledge. Moreover, it is sometimes hard to say if the mode of preservation of particular fossils is due to contemporaneous conditions of deposition or to subsequent alteration.

The familiar 'coal-balls', restricted to certain seams in the Lower Coal Measures of Lancashire and Yorkshire, provide an interesting local type of preservation. 'Coal-balls' are calcareous nodules that contain plant debris so exquisitely preserved that the cell structure can be minutely studied in thin section. Stopes and Watson consider that the vegetation (xerophytic swamp plants) was preserved by salt water, which also acted as a source of the calcium and magnesium salts required for petrifaction. Parts of the plants decayed and liberated organic carbon, which combined with the inorganic salts to form carbonates. Mud of marine origin containing drifted plant remains from an upland habitat (along with marine shells) covered the plant deposits and now forms the roofs of the seams in which the coal-balls occur. Stocks had previously concluded that the calcareous concretions were precipitated in a bacterial jelly formed by the anaerobic decay of vegetable debris in stagnant sea-water.

A similar instance of plant preservation, but in silica instead of calcium carbonate, occurs in the Devonian rocks of Rhynie, Aberdeenshire. In this case a peat-bed is enclosed in chert (an impure form of silica), the material of which is considered to have its origin in contemporaneous volcanic emanations.

The rate at which sedimentation is affected also has considerable influence on the state of preservation and the mode of occurrence of fossils. Deposition may take place so rapidly that organisms are buried in the position of life, or so slowly that the skeletal parts are rolled on the sea bottom for a long time before being covered. In the latter case the surface ornament and delicate margins are damaged, the valves of lamellibranch shells become separated, and the tests of echinoids and arthropods are dismembered. Furthermore, such adherent animals as polyzoa and barnacles may be found on the inner surface of shells. The long accumulation of organic remains during a period of slow deposition is one cause of the so-called 'condensed deposits', in which the fossils often bulk larger than the actual sedimentary material. Many 'fossil bands', isolated by thicknesses of quickly deposited barren strata, are of this nature. The state of preservation of the fossils in these beds depends upon the amount of movement they underwent before being buried. Many of the Productus-bands in the Carboniferous Limestone of North Wales contain shells that are little damaged, but in others the surface ornament is so worn that specific identification is almost impossible and fractured edges are rounded. It is evident that condensed deposits caused by local paucity of sedimentation may be represented in another area by a considerable thickness of strata.

The accumulation of shells and other organic debris may be hastened by the action of water and wind in building up shell banks. This phenomenon is well illustrated at the present day on the coast of Holland, where the prevailing westerly gales pile up huge quantities of shells. It is paralleled by the Pliocene 'Red Crag' of East Anglia, a deposit which Harmer considers to have been formed in a similar manner by the easterly gales presumed to have been prevalent over Britain in Pliocene times. 'Bone-beds' may be of this nature—accumulation of vertebrate remains sorted out by current-action; the famous Ludlow Bone-bed of Silurian age and the Rhaetic bone-beds afford well-known British examples. Rolled bones also form a considerable part of the so-called 'coprolite beds' of the Lower Greensand at Potton (Beds.), the Cambridge Greensand, and those at the base of the Pliocene Crags of East Anglia. In these deposits the solution and subsequent redeposition of phosphatic material has resulted in the formation of nodules rich in phosphates.

EVENTS SUBSEQUENT TO BURIAL are of no less importance in the preservation and occurrence of fossils than the above-mentioned factors. Indeed, organic remains may be of suitable character and in favourable situation for preservation and may be safely buried, yet after-events may cause them to be totally destroyed. On the other hand, the durability of some fossils may be considerably increased by modification subsequent to entombment. These factors may conveniently be considered from two aspects: (1) chemical, and (2) mechanical.

(1) The least altered of all fossil shells are those in the later geological formations, such as the Pliocene Crags of East Anglia. These shells are practically in their original state apart from the removal of all organic matter. Exceptionally, arthropods and graptolites are found in ancient rocks, practically unaltered in composition, and plant tissue forming the 'paper-coal' of Russia is said to be unchanged. Most fossils, however, have been chemically altered by the action of water percolating through the strata and generally bearing carbon dioxide in solution. The degree of alteration naturally varies with the facility offered by the nature of the rock to percolating water, and with the solubility of the original shell. Solution is almost inevitable for shells entombed in sandy strata, and only external and internal moulds remain available for study. These, however, are most useful fossils, for surface-ornamentation can be restored to relief (by means of wax squeezes) from the external moulds, while the internal moulds, by revealing details of hinge structure, muscle-impressions, and other internal features, are often as instructive as perfect shells. Many examples of this type of preservation might be cited: familiar instances occur in the decalcified Ordovician Sandstones of Shropshire, in the carious Portland Limestones of the southern counties, and in the Triassic Sandstones of Scotland.

A clay matrix provides the only medium in which shells can be preserved unchanged. But even in this impervious material, the nature of the shell substance affects its mode of preservation. The differences in stability of calcite and aragonite have already been mentioned, and it is worthy of note that oyster shells, which are made of calcite, are among the most durable of molluscan remains. But aragonite shells are generally dissolved, and in limestones the shell substance is often replaced by a mosaic of calcite crystals, all structure having been destroyed during the solution of the original shell. Some shells, e.g. *Mytilus* and *Spondylus*, have an inner layer of aragonite and an outer layer of calcite; in these cases the aragonite is generally removed, while the calcite persists unaltered. The replacement of aragonite by crystalline calcite is a common type of alteration, but the reverse does not occur.

After deposition consolidation of the sedimentary material takes place. In arenaceous and calcareous rocks this involves cementation, with which the process of 'infilling', affecting the fossils, is comparable. Empty shells often become filled with crystalline calcite or opaline silica, and, owing to the slow and undisturbing quality of the process, details of internal structure may be clearly preserved. It is thus possible to make preparations showing, for instance, the internal loops and spires of brachiopods when this type of preservation occurs. The chambers of foraminiferal shells often occur with an infilling of glauconite, and many isolated grains of this mineral occurring in sediments have been recognized as internal moulds of such shells. Internal moulds made of phosphatic material often occur in association with glauconite. Marcasite and iron pyrites are other minerals that frequently occur in cavities of fossils, while such vein minerals as Galena, Blende, Malachite, and Haematite, very occasionally replace the original substance of the skeleton.

The process of infilling not only takes place in the larger cavities, but the original tissue of shells may become impregnated with fresh mineral matter, generally calcium carbonate or silica, which often greatly increases their durability. Tests of echinoderms are extremely porous, and, in limestones, fresh calcium carbonate is deposited in crystalline continuity with that of the original structure, making the latter more massive and durable, often without seriously obscuring superficial details. Where the process is carried to excess, as in many pyritous moulds of Jurassic ammonites, the surface ornamentation may be entirely obliterated. This is often seen when the nature of the infilling mineral differs from that of the original, and obviously the extent of damage depends upon the available quantity of the secondary mineral. Some siliceous replacements present curious concentric surface markings, due to imperfect crystallization in rings (beekite structure), which obscure, but do not always destroy, the external markings of the fossil.

A more complete degree of replacement occurs where the secondary mineral was deposited at the same time as the original material was removed. In this case even the microscopic structure of the fossil is preserved in great perfection. Silicification of plant tissues is a familiar instance, and some silicified shells in the Upper Greensand of Blackdown retain their minute structure. The 'coal-balls' already mentioned furnish an example of similar deposition of calcareous material. Some pyritic fossils may be of this type, but the opaque character of the mineral hides any details of structure that may be preserved. Selenite is recorded as replacing calcite in the guards of Kimmeridgian belemnites, and a similar replacement in oyster shells occurs in the Great Oolite Clays of Wiltshire.

While these metasomatic processes depend largely on the mineral solution available during deposition or subsequent replacement, it has been suggested that differences in minute structure of organisms result in 'selective mineralization'. Thus in many silicified limestones of Lower Carboniferous age crinoids frequently retain their calcareous condition while other organisms are completely silicified. Moreover masses of crinoidal chert often contain only external and internal moulds of crinoid stems, while corals are entirely replaced by silica. In general, silicification appears more rarely in echinoderms than in most other fossil groups. Wickes recorded replacement by beekite in corals, stromatoporoids, sponges, some brachiopods, lamellibranchs, and a few gastropods; he regarded crustacea, echinoids, most cephalopods (except belemnites) and some brachiopods as apparently immune, and concluded that immunity or otherwise does not follow the distinction between aragonite and calcite skeletons, but that it may be influenced by minute structural details. Subsequently Strachan commented on the immunity of vertebrate remains, crustacea, and many cephalopods, and concluded that 'the calcareous structures chiefly affected and replaced by beekite are those which possess a netted or spicular structure (such as corals and sponges), or a honeycombed structure (such molluscs as the lamellibranchs), and which leave a gelatinous colloid residue (described by Carpenter as "animal glue") when digested with acid'. Further, he remarked: 'The fact that aragonite is more easily dissolved and replaced than calcite depends almost entirely on the nature of the organic matter of the shell.'

An interesting instance of differential mineralization is seen in the Oil Shales of Kimmeridge, where the molluscan remains retain their calcareous material, but plates of the free-swimming crinoid *Saccocoma* are pyritized. While Liassic crinoids, and also ammonite shells in various formations, are often replaced or encrusted by pyrite, the occurrence in the oil shales of pyritized crinoids along with calcareous mollusca seems to indicate the influence of some factors not yet recognized.

(2) The preservation and occurrence of fossils are influenced mechanically in several ways. In ordinary circumstances desiccation and the consequent shrinking of rocks will often result in distortion of the fossils they contain. This is especially marked in shales and clays, where hollow shells are frequently flattened out and otherwise distorted. In some instances the calcareous material of molluscan shells has been dissolved, and subsequent pressure has imprinted the external sculpture upon the internal mould; this has been observed at some localities in the Oxford and Atherfield Clays.

In the case of orogenic disturbances also, the fossils are readily affected; for instance, a brachiopod may be so altered by compression that it may be mistaken for a bivalved mollusc. Where the compression is so strong that it induces cleavage in the rocks, the fossils become much distorted or even entirely destroyed. The familiar distorted trilobites in the cleaved Tremadoc Slates of North Wales afford a sufficient example.

The regional influence of orogenic movement on the occurrence of fossils must not be forgotten. Intense pressure on a regional scale may result in (*a*) overfolding—in which the succession of faunas in the lower limb will appear inverted; (*b*) overthrusting—when older beds may be thrust bodily over newer strata; Pre-Cambrian beds rest on Cambrian in the North-west Highlands of Scotland. In such cases applications of the law of superposition fails, and only careful palaeontological work will reveal the true succession.

Earth-movements may also bring an area of deposition under the destructive action of denuding agents. In this way strata may disappear leaving no trace of their former presence—though in some circumstances certain evidence remains. But before pursuing this theme it should be noted that denudation does not necessarily imply elevation above sea level. At the present time large areas of the sea bottom consist of bare rock swept clean by currents which doubtless perform some amount of erosion. It is probable that changes in the direction of the currents would result in a resumption of deposition in these areas. Similarly some breaks in the palaeontological succession, termed non-sequences, were doubtless caused by submarine denudation, without the intervention of earth-movements. During denudation the fossils suffer more or less, according to their durability. The most stable may survive transportation to an area of deposition, and may be entombed along with members of a younger fauna. Such survivors, usually rolled and waterworn, are known as 'derived' fossils, and are of frequent occurrence throughout the geological sequence. Obviously the younger assemblage of fossils will 'date' the deposit; the older fauna gives evidence both of the destruction involved in the formation of the newer bed, and of the strata exposed at the time of its deposition. As an example the Detritus Bed at the base of the East Anglian Pliocene Crags may be cited. The constituents of the bed include:

(a) Phosphatic nodules (so-called coprolites) yielding some twenty species of turtles, fishes, and crustacea, all of Sheppey (Eocene) type.

(b) Sandstone nodules or 'box-stones' containing a marine fauna perhaps of Miocene age.

(c) Rocks of various ages earlier than the Crag.

(d) Large Chalk flints—many unrolled.

(e) Rolled and waterworn bones (usually much mineralized) of whales and other mammalia—may be of Pliocene or Miocene age.

(f) Wood and other remains of uncertain age.

Thus various Neozoic and Upper Cretaceous rocks were exposed and denuded away during the formation of the Pliocene Detritus Bed.

From this brief outline it will be gathered that much may be learned from the mode of preservation and occurrence of fossils. At the same time the subject presents many problems that have not yet been solved.

In connexion with field-work it may be pointed out that some formations were deposited under practically uniform conditions over widespread areas, but some slight difference in a depositional factor or in subsequent chemical change may result in a characteristic mode of fossil occurrence in some part of a series of strata. Thus the Oxford Clay as a whole would be difficult to subdivide by lithological features. Classification into two stages is, however, possible without identification of fossils, since shells in the lower zones are flattened and retain their calcareous condition, while those of the higher zones are almost invariably solid and infilled with pyritic material. In Palaeozoic strata graptolite zones may often be traced by similar means. It must be remembered, however, that careful determination of the fossils is necessary for complete accuracy.

FAUNAS IN RELATION TO HABITAT. In discussing the relation of various forms of life to their environment it is convenient (if not inevitable) to separate the land-dwellers from the aquatic organisms. The last-named may be further subdivided into freshwater and marine groups. Though most people are more familiar with the living land fauna than with marine animals, the latter are the more important from the geological point of view, since most known sedimentary rocks were deposited under marine conditions. The remains of marine animals, therefore, constitute the **standard faunas** in geology.

The seaward margins of the land masses of the globe are bordered by a gently sloping shallow region known as the **continental shelf**. This area receives the detrital matter (derived by denudation from the land) carried down by rivers. Its limit is generally taken at the 100-fathom line, outside which the gradient increases more rapidly (**the continental slope**) and a much greater depth is reached within a comparatively short horizontal distance. The deposits outside the continental slope (**abyssal deposits**), being formed mainly by organic agency, are characterized by a general absence of detrital material and are thereby strongly contrasted with the inshore sediments. The animals inhabiting the deeps are specially adapted for the peculiar conditions under which they live, and in many ways are different from animals living in the coastal regions. It may be said at once that no known British sedimentary rock gives conclusive evidence of abyssal origin; even where the lithology seems to indicate deposition at great depths, the characters of the fossils negative this view. The marine sedimentary rocks, as they are at present known, represent deposition within the detrital area in epicontinental seas of greatly varying depth. In the present discussion, therefore, the term 'deep water' must be read with this limitation.

It may, indeed, be useful in some cases to distinguish three broad regions of depth in the epicontinental seas. The **littoral** belt may be said to extend from the shore line to a depth of 15 or 20 fathoms, representing almost the distribution of seaweeds. This region shows a great variety of bottom conditions and periodic changes in temperature and salinity. A **sublittoral** belt, with a depth limit of about 80 fathoms, is characterized by a general absence of vegetation, more uniform bottom conditions, and less pronounced differences in temperature and salinity. Between 80 and 500 fathoms is the **continental deep-sea** region, with nearly constant temperature and salinity, and a bottom consisting mainly of bare rock, which, however, may be covered by a little fine mud. This region takes in the seaward margin of the continental shelf and the shallower portion of the continental slope.

The deposition of material in the detrital area must now be considered in greater detail. As the waters of a river enter the sea, their velocity is checked and their transporting power consequently decreases. The load of detrital matter is therefore deposited, the larger and heavier particles near the shore, the finer grades farther out. Thus deposits of different lithological character are formed at the same time—shingle, sand, silt, mud—at varying distances from the land margin. It was formerly considered that mud was characteristic of fairly deep water away from the influence of waves or shore currents. But beds of sand and silt close inshore also contain mud particles, owing to flocculation by the salts dissolved in the sea-water and precipitation by the agency of organic matter or iron hydroxide. In a subsiding area the sea, encroaching upon the land, will deposit succeeding beds of detritus slightly landward of the corresponding bed below, while in an area of elevation the deposits are arranged in a seaward direction (Fig. 1). In mapping such deposits there is a tendency to group together the beds of similar lithological character, but it is evident that the lithological planes are not true time-planes, though they are 'bedding planes' as that term is commonly used. The true time-planes are only revealed by the evidence of fossils and are more difficult to follow, demanding accurate and detailed study of the faunas; moreover, the fauna may vary to some extent in the several rocks of the same period as a result of differing habitat.

Nevertheless such work is possible and profitable, as in the careful investigation (by S. S. Buckman) of the series of sands occupying the uppermost portion of the Lias and the lowermost part of the Inferior Oolite of the west of England. The sands extending from the Dorset coast to the Cotteswolds have been named the Bridport Sands, Yeovil Sands, Midford Sands, or the Cotteswolds Sands according to the locality at which they occur. Their age, however, varies from place to place, and they mark an area of shallowing which moved gradually southwards from the Cotteswolds, the time-planes crossing the lithological planes. On the other hand, some rocks—e.g. the graptolite-bearing mud-stones of the Ordovician and Silurian—are remarkably uniform in lithological character and fossil-content over considerable areas. Sufficient has been said, however, to show that marine conditions of deposition may vary considerably from place to place; and it is now our purpose to consider the influence of varying habitat upon the fauna.

The work of C. G. H. Peterson (1913) on marine shallow-water faunas has furnished much information concerning the effect of physical conditions on existing animals. The more important conclusions may be summarized thus: (1) certain characteristic animal assemblages exist under, and are bounded by, definite physical conditions; (2) changes in physical conditions cause changes in the characteristic animal assemblages, but certain animals may be found in more than one assemblage; (3) the physical changes to be correlated with variations of fauna are those of temperature, salinity, clearness of water, and character of sea bottom. Depth in itself seems to be less important than these factors.

These conclusions are of supreme interest to geologists, since deductions concerning environments of past times depend upon the fundamental principle that 'the present is the key to the past'. Thus some changes in

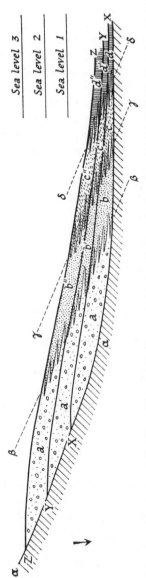

Diagram showing appoximate disposition of littoral sediments on a subsiding sea-bottom. The time-planes ZZ, YY, XX will be strongly marked only if there are pauses in sedimentation. The planes $\alpha\alpha$, $\beta\beta$, $\gamma\gamma$, etc., mark off lithological divisions from one another, and may, when the sediments are consolidated, be mistaken for bedding-planes. The steeper the shore-line, the greater will be the discordance between the time-planes and the lithological planes.

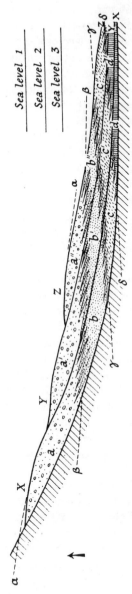

As above, but indicating conditions on a rising sea-bottom. The deposits a, b, c, d are again contemporaneous, as are also a′, b′, c′, d′, etc. The planes XX, YY, ZZ are true time-planes, and $\alpha\alpha$, $\beta\beta$, $\gamma\gamma$, $\delta\delta$ mark off lithological divisions, and may be interpreted later as 'bedding-planes'.

FIG. I. GENERAL DISPOSITION OF LITTORAL DEPOSITS. *Reproduced from* Trans. Liverpool Biol. Soc., *vol. xxxv, p. 8, 1921, by permission of the Society and the author, P. G. H. Boswell*

conditions of deposition are reflected in the lithology of strata, and are often accompanied by variations in the contained faunas. And, conversely, many fossil faunas afford important information concerning the conditions prevalent at the time and place of their life.

Many fossils represent organisms that are entirely extinct, and sometimes their exact taxonomic position is uncertain. It is unsafe in these cases to assume that extinct forms necessarily flourished in the same habitat as modern representatives of the same group. Conclusions in this connexion must be checked by reference to other members of the same fauna. Thus the majority of modern stalked crinoids inhabit the ocean deeps, but most Palaeozoic forms must have lived in comparatively shallow water, judging by the characters of the associated brachiopods, mollusca, and other organisms, and by the lithological features of the deposits.

Nevertheless, adaptive morphological features of the animals generally furnish a clue to their mode of life and the conditions under which they lived. Though the exact affinities of the graptolites are not known, their general morphology is comparable with that of certain living hydrozoa and polyzoa, and it is inferred that their habits of life must have been similar. Again, the reef-building tabulate corals of Palaeozoic rocks give evidence of a habitat similar to that of modern reef-building madreporarians, since their structure corresponds generally with that of the living corals. This agreement between habitat and form is not confined to members of the same phylum. For instance, certain large sessile bivalved mollusca, the Hippurites, simulate corals in reefs of Cretaceous age in the Mediterranean area while *Richthofenia*, a brachiopod with a similar coralloid habit, occurs in Permian deposits of the Salt Range in northern India.

Interesting conclusions have been reached by L. Dollo from a study of adaptive structures in many animal groups. Reference may be made especially to certain members of the order Merostomata illustrated in Fig. 2. The Silurian eurypterid *Erettopterus* has a flattened bilobed tail obviously adapted for use as an organ of propulsion; its prominent eyes, situated near the margin of the head-shield, give the widest range of vision possible to these creatures. These characters are in strong contrast with the corresponding features of the living King Crab *Limulus*, whose habits, moreover, are known. This form lives on the sea bottom in the coastal waters of southeastern Asia and eastern North America. It has a long, thin tail-spine which it fixes in the mud and uses as a lever while turning the body in search of food. The eyes are placed near the centre of the head-shield, where they are not likely to be harmed during the mud-grubbing process; they are certainly useless in the search for food but probably serve to warn the animal of the approach of enemies. The central position of the eye and the spine-like tail are typical of bottom-living arthropods, while the flattened tail and marginal eyes of *Erettopterus* are characteristic of many forms which habitually swim through the water. Between these two extremes there are

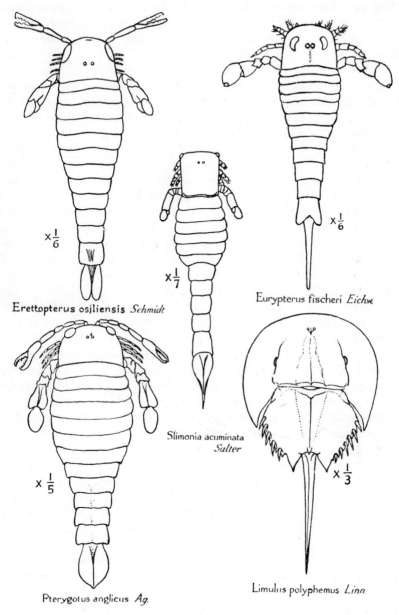

$\times \frac{1}{6}$

Erettopterus osjliensis *Schmidt*

$\times \frac{1}{7}$

Slimonia acuminata
Salter

Eurypterus fischeri *Eichw.*

$\times \frac{1}{6}$

$\times \frac{1}{5}$

$\times \frac{1}{3}$

Pterygotus anglicus *Ag.*

Limulus polyphemus *Linn.*

FIG. 2. ADAPTATIONAL FORM AMONG THE MEROSTOMATA (*after Dollo*)

many gradations, some of which may still be illustrated by fossil Mero-stomes. *Pterygotus*, an early Devonian genus, has the marginal eyes of swimming animals but its flattened tail is pointed, while *Slimonia*, whose tail has a longer spine, is less adapted for a swimming mode of life. *Eurypterus* and *Bunodes*, of Upper Silurian age, are obviously bottom-living forms, but the last-named genus has no eyes and probably lived buried in the mud. Similar adaptive characters are seen in various trilobites and ostracoderm fishes (as well as in many living animals) and afford evidence concerning their general mode of life.

Dollo was led further to the general conception of Irreversibility in Evolution, which may be briefly stated as follows. In the course of its racial development an organism never returns exactly to its former state even if former conditions of existence are reproduced. If organs are lost through adaptation to a new mode of life, those organs are never developed again, but, when the necessity arises, other organs are modified to perform the same function. But the organism generally preserves some trace of the modification through which it passed when changing from one mode of existence to another. The mode of life pursued by ancestral forms may then be inferred from such persistent adaptive characters.

Organisms vary widely in their reaction to physical conditions. Some modern invertebrates are capable of living under a variety of conditions or of surviving considerable changes of environment. The brachiopod genus *Lingula* and the common edible mussel (*Mytilus*), besides other mollusca, can live in diluted sea-water, though they do not survive if placed in completely fresh water. This wide margin of adaptibility is eminently characteristic of animals with comparative simplicity of organization. Highly specialized organisms, as a rule, are more sensitive to change; and since they have lost the power to respond quickly to environmental variations, they often become extinct after a comparatively short space of time. Their short vertical range renders them suitable as correlative fossils (p. 6), and a careful examination of their morphological features and of their matrices often gives valuable evidence concerning their ecological limitations.

Marine faunas are not only more important from the geological stand-point, but they are more varied biologically than land and freshwater faunas, since they include representatives of all the large animal groups. Indeed some groups of animals, such as the echinoderms, brachiopods, and cephalo-pods, are exclusively marine. As a basis for discussion fossil marine assemblages may be broadly grouped into two facies corresponding in a general way with the deposits of the shallower and deeper water of the epicontinental seas.

A most instructive example of widespread ancient animal-assemblages is seen in the Ordovician and Silurian strata of Britain. The folding of the Cambrian rocks produced a wide basin in which two distinct facies of the later rocks were formed.

(*a*) A graptolitic facies of shales and mudstones in which the principal fossils are graptolites: this type of deposit is developed in North Wales, the Lake District, and the Moffat area in southern Scotland.

(*b*) A 'shelly' facies represented by sandstones and limestones with occasional shales, in which the dominant fossils are brachiopods, trilobites, and corals; this facies occurs on the landward margin of the graptolitic deposits in South Wales, the Welsh borders of Shropshire and Hereford, and the Girvan district in southern Scotland.

It was formerly considered that the graptolite faunas represented deposition in very deep water, but this opinion is now discarded in favour of the view that graptolitic shales were laid down in the deeper parts of the epicontinental seas. The factors controlling their formation seem to have been quietness of the water and the absence of coarse sediment—conditions which are often associated with depth but which may occur close inshore. The deposits have lately been compared with 'lagoon-deposits' formed in enclosed areas of the ocean with only slight current-action and out of the range of detritus-bearing streams. In view, however, of the great areas covered by graptolitic deposits of the same age, some of these rock types might also be explained by reference to the conditions obtaining in the modern Sargasso Sea if the question of depth be left out of consideration. It is generally accepted that graptolites lived attached to floating seaweeds, and these would furnish the carbonaceous material so often characteristic of the black graptolitic shales. Currents encircling the 'quiet' area suffice to explain the dispersal and consequent wide distribution of the graptolites as well as their occasional presence in the shallow-water shelly facies. In the latter connexion it may be mentioned that Valentian graptolites occur near Minsterley (Salop), associated with a shelly fauna in sandy shales which contain pebbles up to half an inch in diameter. This is only one instance of the occurrence of graptolites in rocks of undoubted shallow-water origin; incidentally it demonstrates how the two faunas may be correlated in point of age.

The shallow-water 'shelly' facies exhibits the usual variations consequent upon local peculiarities in physical conditions. It is interesting to note that the general aspect of the Welsh shelly faunas is different from that of Scottish deposits. This question, however, is probably connected with factors governing dispersal of the organisms, and is more appropriately discussed in connexion with Ordovician faunal provinces (p. 177). The Welsh shelly faunas also differ from the corresponding Shropshire assemblages in that the individuals of the whole Welsh fauna are of smaller size. This dwarfing of all members of the fauna may be taken as reflecting development under unfavourable conditions in the area immediately adjacent to the graptolitic facies.

Similar dwarfing is shown in the British Permian fauna, but the cause in this case is a change towards increasing salinity of the sea-water, indicated by beds of rock-salt and gypsum, which are associated with the fossiliferous beds. This approach to 'Dead Sea conditions' not only caused a dwarfing of the whole fauna, but encouraged the development of spiny outgrowths, giving various species a grotesque appearance. During the succeeding period of time (Triassic) the British area was continental, and when subsidence caused a return of the sea in Rhaetic times, the incoming fauna became dwarfed, but gradually assumed ordinary proportions as conditions became more favourable. The reverse series of changes, that from marine to brackish conditions, also has its effect in modifying the fauna. The lower beds of the Upper Silurian of Shropshire contain an abundance of brachiopods, together with a subordinate proportion of bivalved mollusca. In higher beds the proportions are gradually reversed, and eventually the majority of the fossils are mollusca allied to the mussels, while the only brachiopods are species of *Lingula*. This illustrates a transition from marine to brackish-water conditions, and in the overlying Devonian marls almost all marine species disappear. These examples suffice to show that an increase or decrease in the salinity of sea-water is important in its effect on marine organisms.

The evidence of fossils is hardly needed for information concerning the clearness of the water, since the lithology of the strata generally forms a sufficient guide. It is interesting, however, to attempt an explanation of the effect of turbid water upon certain elements of the fauna. Some groups of animals are habitually absent from a muddy habitat, or, if present, are rare and have a stunted appearance. Echinoids, for instance, are rare and of small size in clayey deposits such as the Lias or the Oxford Clay, but the dwarfing is not general throughout the fauna. In some animals a quantity of finely divided solid particles in suspension in the water has a tendency to impede the proper functioning of the breathing organs. Observations made after the construction of a breakwater had modified the physical conditions in Plymouth Sound have shown that crabs of narrow frontal breadth have more efficient filtration of water than those of wide frontal breadth, and survive in turbid water while the latter succumb. A rain of ash from Vesuvius in 1906 caused great mortality among the fauna in the Bay of Naples. The mortality was selective, some groups suffering more than others, but the echinoids were entirely wiped out because the fine ash in suspension had clogged the madreporite and thus prevented the aeration of the body-fluids. Considerations of this kind may help to explain some instances of sporadic distribution among fossils. Echinoids are rare in the Portland Limestones of this country, while they are numerous in the Chalk, though the lithology (in hand specimens) of some samples does not indicate serious differences of deposition. Treated with dilute hydrochloric acid the Portland Stone yields a fair proportion of finely divided insoluble material, while the Chalk leaves little residue. The Chalk was formed largely by chemical precipitation of calcium carbonate in a clear sea (judging by the paucity of detrital material), but the Portland Stone gives evidence of deposition in turbid waters. Thus the frequently quoted fact that echinoids habitually live in clusters and migrate wholesale to a fresh locality may, perhaps, be partially explained. The reef-building corals, sponges, polyzoa, and brachiopods generally avoid turbid waters, which are usually tenanted by mollusca and arthropods. Simple corals, however, are often found in shales, such as those which are interbedded with the Carboniferous Limestone in various districts. Along with the coral-genera *Zaphrentis* and *Cyathaxonia*, the polyzoon *Fenestella* and certain brachiopods such as *Brachythyris* and *Orbiculoidea* often occur in association, but most of the species characteristic of the limestone beds are absent. Turbidity of seawater, therefore, is often responsible for a 'lack of balance' among the various elements of the fauna in a given district.

Temperature leaves little impress upon the marine rocks, and its influence as an environmental factor upon fossil faunas is more uncertainly known. Its chief effect would seem to be that of governing (to some extent) the geographical distribution of organisms (pp. 45-46). It is, however, known that the secretion of calcium carbonate by living organisms takes place more quickly and abundantly in the warmer seas, and in this connexion the restriction of reef-building corals to tropical seas is of considerable interest. These organisms require a clear sea with a temperature of at least 65° F. and a depth of not more than 20 or 30 fathoms. The distribution of fossil reef-building corals and of the Cretaceous reef-building mollusca has been cited as evidence of tropical conditions in discussions concerning the climates of former periods.

The present limit of coral-reef formation extends to about 30° latitude north and south of the equator. In Eocene and Oligocene time numerous reef-corals allied to contemporary West Indian forms flourished in the Mediterranean region and extended in Europe to localities now at the 50th parallel of latitude. The relationship of these to the main reef-belt of the period is discussed with the Palaeogene faunas in Chapter XV. W. J. Arkell (1928, 1935) has described the spread of Jurassic coral-reefs in England, extending from Wiltshire to Yorkshire (lat. 55° N.), and on the mainland of Europe from France and Portugal to Swabia and Stramberg (see p. 474). The English reefs contain far fewer species than the corresponding reefs of Europe, and Arkell suggests that migration and colonization was limited to a small number of hardy forms that could become established before they were overwhelmed by recurring floods of clastic sediment. Not the least important feature of Arkell's work is the recognition of a unique assemblage of mollusca and echinoids constantly associated with the reef-structures but differing from the fauna of contemporary non-coralline deposits near by. Later in the Jurassic succession masses of *Isastraea oblonga* are recorded from Kimmeridgian deposits in Sutherland, Scotland in lat. 58° N. Triassic reef-corals recorded from Alaska (lat. 60° N.) are noted on p. 427.

The Carboniferous reef-coral assemblage of North Wales again, is restricted to a small number of genera (Neaverson 1946); similar corals are recorded from the Carboniferous Limestone of the Midland Valley of Scotland (lat. 56° N.). The familiar Silurian reef-corals, preserved in the Wenlock Limestone of Shropshire (lat. 52°. 30° N.) in position of growth, provide another example of the former presence of coral reefs far north of the present limit for these structures. It is evident that, for the greater part of geological time since the Cambrian period, the temperature gradient between equator and poles was less steep than at present, and there is no evidence of polar ice-caps during those periods.

The intensity of light in sea-water is probably an important factor affecting the bathymetrical range of organisms, though it is not certain if it is sufficient by itself to explain such distribution of a species in different marine areas. Two general light-regions recognized by oceanographers are based on the distribution of plants: the **photic region,** where the intensity of the sunlight is sufficient for the process of photosynthesis in plants, and the **aphotic region,** where the light is insufficient for this process to be carried on. The depth-limit between the two regions varies with locality and purity of water, but is usually taken at about 200 fathoms. Some authors recognize a dysphotic (dusk) region between the two.

The obvious connexion with the fauna concerns the character of the visual organs, and may be illustrated by reference to fishes. Many bottom-dwellers from abyssal depths have large eyes, often larger than those of bottom-fishes living in the strong light of the coastal banks. In the case of pelagic fishes there seems to be a striking change at a depth of about 250 fathoms. Above this, pelagic fishes have well-developed eyes, but in lower regions the visual organs are typically imperfect and may be entirely atrophied. Some deep-dwelling fishes are caught near the surface at night, having adopted the 'nocturnal habit' of rising to the surface for feeding; these possess eyes that are considerably larger than those of species which constantly live at great depths.

Among fossil organisms certain trilobites such as *Agnostus* and *Trinucleus* are blind. This condition is regarded as a secondary specialization due to absence of light in their habitat. The Ordovician genus *Trinucleus* probably arose from the earlier *Orometopus*, which possessed functional eyes. From a study of various species of *Trinucleus* F. R. C. Reed (1916) concludes that these trilobites lived burrowing in the mud, and the aphotic conditions of this habitat rendered compound eyes unnecessary, and they were therefore lost. This led to other changes in the head-shield. For instance, the fixed and free cheeks fused along the line of the facial suture which became obliterated, and a line of weakness was formed in the broadened fringe of the head-shield to facilitate moulting. Changes in the habits of some species resulted in a renewal of simple visual organs (ocelli) from rudiments of compound eyes persisting from larval to adult life, but these again were lost when they proved to be of no value. The trilobite *Aeglina*, with enormous eyes, is regarded as a 'nocturnal' animal, which migrated nightly from considerable depths to the surface in search of food.

One of the most variable factors influencing modern shallow-water marine faunas is the nature of the sea bottom. In the littoral region especially, the bottom conditions form the basis of subdivision into the low-tide area, the barnacle belt, the fucoid belt, the laminarian belt, the zosteran belt, hard bottom, sandy bottom, and so on, each with its own particular assemblage of organisms. The composition of the fauna in each case is dependent to a large extent on the structure of the animals, since some must have a solid substratum, while others require loose material. It is not possible here to give details of all these habitats; a few illustrations must suffice. It will be realized, too, that other factors vary in different localities with the same bottom conditions causing local variations in the fauna, which, however, preserves its general characteristics. Petersen indeed expresses wonder 'that there are some species common to all these localities and different conditions'.

On bare rock are found large numbers of attached organisms, which are not adapted for life on loose incoherent material. The majority of these live in situations more or less exposed to wave action or other movement of water, since their food must be brought to them. Barnacles and limpets are found fixed to rocks in the low-tide area, with vagrant periwinkles (*Littorina*) and *Purpura*. Dense masses of mussels (*Mytilus*) also frequent the low-tide area, being fixed to the substratum by a byssus. Brachiopods adhere to bare rock in deeper water by means of their pedicles, and other forms usually living on a hard bottom include sponges, corals, polyzoa, and various mollusca (*Anomia, Chiton, Lima, Buccinum,* &c.), besides those cited above. Some freely moving animals, especially echinoderms and crustacea, habitually live in rocky places. Among fossil faunas, that of the Carboniferous Limestone consists largely of attached animals. Its dominant forms are brachiopods, corals and crinoids, freely moving organisms (except foraminifera) being in a decided minority.

The fauna of the densely vegetated Laminarian and Zosteran belts also includes many hydroids, sponges, polyzoa, and the tube-worm *Spirorbis*. The algal substratum is not a biological necessity for these organisms, but merely increases the area available for attachment. Along with the adherent animals are many species which shelter in the algal growth, including crustaceans, gastropods, bivalved mollusca, and star-fishes. Some of these possess special adaptive structures for gripping and climbing; the bent legs and claws of some crustaceans and the flexible 'foot' of the gastropods may be cited as examples. This fauna varies also according to its situation in places sheltered from, or exposed to, wave action respectively.

Burrowing animals predominate on the sandy and muddy bottoms, though each facies has its own characteristic assemblage. Burrowing mollusca, as exemplified by the genera *Mya, Tellina, Solen,* &c., are provided with two elongated siphons, the openings of which are always raised above the sea floor. The presence of these siphons is indicated on the interior of the shell by the pallial sinus, and so fossil siphonate bivalves may be recognized. The brachiopod *Lingula* also lives in a narrow hole in the sand, being fixed to the bottom by means of its long pedicle. Some gastropods of the family Naticidae burrow some distance down and feed on small mussels, boring through the thin shells to obtain the succulent animals. Among echinoids, the spatangids, or heart-urchins, burrow deeply, and maintain circulation of the water round their tests by rapid vibration of certain of their spines which are specially adapted for the purpose. *Astropecten,* a burrowing star-fish, causes water currents in a similar way, and has conical structures adapted for digging—a circumstance which compels it to feed in a different way from other asteroids. Worms and a few vertebrates (the lancelet and sand-eels) also burrow; but crabs, which also seem to prefer a sandy substratum, do not make a general habit of burrowing. The fauna of the argillaceous Portland Limestones includes many burrowing molluscs, but corals, echinoids, and brachiopods are extremely rare.

The fauna of the continental deep-sea area must also be briefly mentioned. The bottom is generally rocky, and attached animals predominate in the fauna—sponges, coelenterates, polyzoa, brachiopods, and tube-worms being abundant. The sponges are nearly all siliceous, in contrast with those of the littoral region, which are mainly calcareous. Species of *Lima* attached by a byssus, and crinoids, are also locally characteristic. The free forms include crustaceans and star-fishes. The fauna of the continental slope in the North Atlantic is also noteworthy for the occurrence of the echinoid family Echinothuridae with flexible shells. Fossil urchins of the same family are recorded from the Chalk of Gravesend, and the fauna of the Upper Chalk as a whole appears to be analogous to the assemblage of the continental deep-sea region.

Before leaving the subject of marine faunas it should be emphasized that the application of ecology to fossil assemblages is often obscure, and much work is required before palaeoecology can be established on a satisfactory basis. It may be well, therefore, to mention some important deposits whose origin is imperfectly known.

Black shales which contain much pyrite (sulphide of iron) occur at several geological horizons, notably in the Cambrian of North Wales, in the graptolitic facies of the Ordovician and Silurian, in the Rhaetic Beds, the Lias and the Oil Shales of Kimmeridge. The abundance of pyrite indicates that sulphuretted hydrogen, a product of decomposing organic matter, was originally present in the shales. These deposits are therefore generally supposed to have formed under conditions similar to those obtaining in the Black Sea at the present day. There the quantity of air in the water rapidly decreases downwards, until below 125 fathoms no animal life is known to exist. The anaerobic action of sulphur bacteria causes the formation of sulphuretted hydrogen, which effectually restricts organisms to the surface waters. It will be noticed that depth is an important factor in the Black Sea, while the transgressive Rhaetic Beds were probably formed in quite shallow water. It is evident, then, that comparison with 'Black Sea conditions' should be made with due restraint. Black muds fetid with sulphuretted hydrogen have been dredged from the shallow waters of the Irish Sea, while black 'buttery' muds, permeated with the same odorous compound and oil globules, are forming between tide levels on the salt marshes of East Anglia. Microscopic examination of the last-mentioned deposits shows that much of the bulk consists of organic matter, such as algae and animal plankton, in various stages of decomposition. This clings to small detrital quartz grains, which then float in the moving water, but rapidly sink when movement ceases. It seems probable that some of the ancient black shales are comparable with these slimy muds now forming in shallow land-locked bays like the Wash. In any case the subject seems worthy of further investigation.

Sandstones belonging to various systems from the Cambrian onwards often contain abundant green grains which give the deposit a distinctive colour. These grains are often collectively known as glauconite, but are variable in composition, in optical properties, and magnetic permeability. Many of them are infillings of foraminiferal shells, and were probably formed by precipitation in the presence of decaying organic matter, but their precise mode of origin is still obscure. Glauconite is often associated with phosphatic deposits.

The Jurassic ironstones of the English Midlands were once thought to be replacements of limestones, but are now regarded as original deposits. Bacteria are tentatively suggested as agents of precipitation, since the presence of large well-developed molluscan shells seems to preclude the precipitation of iron compounds in large quantities at any given time. Similarly, the massive Carboniferous cherts of north Flintshire are now thought to be siliceous sediments deposited as a colloid precipitate of silica. In this case the precipitation seems to have been inimical to life, since no indigenous fauna is known; the only fossils are at the base of the deposit and belong to the underlying limestone, the top of which has suffered replacement by the silica. Some cherts, however, like those of the Cretaceous Greensands, were formed by solution and redeposition of silica derived from organic skeletons of sponges and possibly other organisms.

Such intricate problems of deposition are perhaps mainly chemical in their nature, but they have a direct bearing upon palaeontology, since they indicate the conditions of life in the sea at various geological periods.

Freshwater faunas are much less diverse in character than marine faunas, since whole groups of animals such as the Echinodermata, the Anthozoa, the Brachiopoda, and the Cephalopoda, are ordinarily absent from fresh water. The dominant invertebrate groups are Mollusca and Arthropoda, which, as a rule, are poorly represented by genera and species, though often most prolific in individuals. The freshwater mollusca include bivalves (lamellibranchs) and univalves (mainly pulmonate gastropods), whose shells are characteristically thin and fragile. The Arthropoda comprise ostracods and crustaceans, groups which are equally well represented in marine faunas by similar forms and can only be distinguished with difficulty. Indeed, it might even be stated that fossil freshwater faunas are more satisfactorily identified as such by the absence of exclusively marine animals than by the occurrence of peculiar types. Thus the lamellibranchs *Archanodon* from the Old Red Sandstone, and *Carbonicola* from the Coal Measures, are regarded as freshwater types chiefly because their associates do not include marine forms. The freshwater bivalves (e.g. *Unio*) frequently show characteristically eroded umbones, and this is the case in *Archanodon*. From the absence of marine associates there is some reason to believe that the Devonian eurypterids and fishes inhabited brackish or fresh water. But Silurian eurypterids are associated in North America and Gotland with brachiopods, cephalopods, and graptolites, and are therefore considered to have inhabited salt water. Their successors, however, may have changed their habitat in Devonian and Carboniferous times, though the freshwater origin of the Old Red Sandstone is still a matter of opinion (see p. 248).

Plant life is abundantly represented in fresh water by diatoms and algae, as well as by vascular plants which grow by the margin of the land surface. Remains of these, however, are frequently mingled with fragments of land plants transported by wind or streams into the area of deposition. The intensive study of fossil seeds thus preserved has recently thrown new light upon Neozoic floras.

Freshwater vertebrates include fishes and amphibians, and some modern fishes inhabit both fresh and salt water at different periods of their existence. The Devonian genera *Dipterus*, *Pterichthys*, and *Osteolepis* occur in marine strata in Germany, and in the Old Red Sandstone of Scotland. Some authors who uphold the freshwater origin of the Old Red Sandstone appeal to the modern distribution in order to explain this discrepancy, while others maintain that the Scottish deposits were formed in lagoons which communicated with the sea. Freshwater strata often contain remains of land vertebrates in consequence of their close proximity to the land-surface; indeed, it is safe to say that our knowledge of fossil land vertebrates is almost entirely based on material of this transported character.

Terrestrial faunas are marked by the greatest variety of highly specialized types among plants and vertebrate animals. On the other hand, invertebrate land-dwellers are represented by only three groups, worms, molluscs, and arthropods, and the former are generally not capable of fossilization. The land mollusca are mainly pulmonate gastropods (snails and slugs). Their shells are less massive than those of most marine gastropods; slugs, indeed, secrete so little calcium carbonate that the fossil preservation of their shells is extremely doubtful. The Arthropoda living on land are sufficiently exemplified by the large and diverse group of Insects. Their chitinous coverings are less soluble than calcareous molluscan shells, but they are extremely brittle and are only occasionally found fossil, and then usually in deposits of freshwater origin. The same applies to other arthropod groups which are perhaps less abundantly represented.

The Vertebrates are highly diversified in consequence of the great range of physical conditions obtaining on the land. The dominant existing group is the Mammalia, which arose in early Neozoic time from primitive swamp dwelling animals, and which now shows remarkable structural adaptations for life in every conceivable habitat. It is only necessary to mention the arboreal apes and monkeys, the plain-dwelling horses and ruminants, the burrowing rodents, the amphibious beavers, and the carnivores, to realize the extraordinary extent of this adaptive radiation. The Mammalia, however, are not the only group of vertebrates to become diversified in this way. The Mesozoic reptilian land fauna similarly became fitted for life in various terrestrial habitats (pp. 550-75).

The most highly specialized land plants of the present day have an arborescent habit, and reproduce by means of seeds, contrasting strongly with the aquatic algae, which reproduce by means of spores and do not develop woody tissue to any extent. The rigid tree-like form is a means, not only for exposing the leaves to light and air, but also for mechanical protection and structural stability, the need for which is essentially an outcome of life on land. The adoption of the seed-habit obviates the necessity for the presence of external water during the process of fertilization, a condition which still obtains in the algae of our seas and rivers, in that amphibious group the Vascular Cryptogams, and in certain gymnosperms.

The arborescent habit is first seen in plants of the Devonian and Carboniferous floras. The well-known *Calamites*, *Lepidodendron* and *Sigillaria*, from the Coal Measures, supply abundant evidence of the size and tree-like characters in Vascular Cryptogams of Carboniferous age. As this group is now represented only by the lowly horsetails (*Equisetum*) and club-mosses (*Lycopodium* and *Selaginella*), which develop no woody tissue, some controversy raged for many years concerning the affinities of the Carboniferous plants just mentioned. They were eventually excluded from the gymnosperms, which apparently have affected the arborescent habit since their earliest record. Some early flowering plants, of Lower Cretaceous age, also developed woody tissue. This developmental trend, therefore, was not always confined (as now) to the highly organized gymnosperms and angiosperms, but was adopted by various groups whenever there was need for it.

Several groups of land plants have shown a tendency to adopt the seed-habit at different periods of geological time. Evidence has accumulated during the last few decades which goes to show that the majority of the

Palaeozoic fern-like plants were reproduced by seeds. This led to the establishment of a separate group in plant classification—the pteridosperms—in recognition of this advanced degree of specialization in plants which retain most of the general characters of Vascular Cryptogams. One important peculiarity of the seeds of pteridosperms is the absence of an embryo, which suggests that the nursing of the infant plant was not performed by the seed in these early periods. Another feature is the great complexity of the seeds, probably connected with the spermatozoid method of fertilization. These characters may indicate imperfect adaptation to land conditions (though in many respects the plants were well adapted for terrestrial life), and their limitations may have contributed to the extinction of the group at the close of Palaeozoic times. The pteridosperms do not, however, represent the highest stage of evolution reached in the Palaeozoic flora. The extensive family of the Cordaiteae, ranging back to Devonian time, resembles certain conifers of the southern hemisphere in general habit and anatomical structure; the reproductive organs are more advanced than those of the pteridosperms, while the seeds are on the same level as those of the latter group. The Cordaiteae lingered on into Mesozoic time and gradually died out.

During Mesozoic time the Cycadophytes were the dominant members of the land flora and are well represented in Britain and other parts of Europe, but far more abundantly in Dakota, Maryland, and Wyoming (U.S.A.). In general aspect they resemble the shorter-stemmed Cycads of the present day, but bore their fructifications laterally, scattered in great numbers among the bases of the leaves. Two important characters of the reproductive organs may be mentioned here: (1) they were organized on the same general plan as the typical flower of the angiosperms; (2) the fruit enclosed a seed the interior of which was almost entirely filled by the embryo. These are very advanced characters, and contrast sharply with the cryptogamic aspect of the stamens and gynoecium. During Cretaceous time the seed-bearing Cycadophytes dwindled away, their place being taken at once by the angiosperms, which have formed the dominant feature of floras from that period to the present day. The less advanced Cycads did not come into such direct competition with the ascendant race, and have survived in tropical climates as an interesting 'link with the past'. Space will not permit a discussion of modern plant associations, but botanists know that plants of widely differing relationships develop characteristic structural features that admit of ready correlation with their habitat. Such terms as xerophytes ('dry-loving' plants), halophytes ('salt' plants), heath plants, and hygrophytes (marsh plants) illustrate the close association of structure with environment.

The adaptation of organisms to their habitat furnishes a study of absorbing interest on account of its probable connexion with problems of evolution. For over a century controversy has raged over the question as to the efficacy of environment as a factor in evolution. While most palaeontologists have maintained throughout that physical conditions of habitat, variations of food-supply, and other environmental factors have a decided modifying influence on the evolution of faunas and floras, biologists have always been divided on the question. In recent years, however, there seems to have been a more decided trend of opinion in its favour. Thus C. T. Regan has shown that fishes of the same genus have developed on different lines in various isolated localities, giving rise to local communities or species. Each community has its own peculiar features, which are probably 'the expression of physiological differences and are the result of differences in the environment or in the activities of the fish'. Further, he expresses the opinion that 'the first step in the origin of a new species is not a change of structure, but the formation of a community either with new habits or in a new or a restricted environment'.

Two geological examples must suffice to illustrate the point at issue. The Upper Ordovician (Ashgillian) rocks of Wales, the Lake District, south Scotland, and eastern Ireland contain many trilobites of the genera *Cheirurus*, *Lichas*, and *Remopleurides*, and yet have few species in common. The general resemblance of these faunas is generic in character, but specific differences tend to obscure the faunal relationship that undoubtedly exists. Again, it is well known that the Jurassic deposits of Yorkshire show marked general lithological differences when compared with those of southern England. The ammonite faunas of these two areas also show striking contrasts. And though these differences are often said to be due to differences in the age of the deposits, this explanation does not seem entirely satisfactory.

The evidence seems to suggest that while true genera may be taken to represent stages in development along particular lines of descent, species are modifications which have arisen in response to local conditions of environment, and are more or less isolated geographically. The ordinary method of discrimination of species by means of external characters, while genera are distinguished by internal features, appears to support this view. If this interpretation be correct, it is incumbent upon the geologist to apply himself, more than ever before, to the study of palae-ecology in the field.

GEOGRAPHICAL DISTRIBUTION AND MIGRATION. A cursory examination is sufficient to show that the present distribution of plants and animals does not apply to former geological periods. This is partly due to the fact that certain groups of organisms have become entirely extinct, but also to the circumstance that the geographical distribution of surviving groups has changed with the progress of time. During the Jurassic period the brachiopods had a world-wide distribution and were exceedingly abundant in the seas of the British area; at the present day the group, numbering only about 150 species (of which eleven are found around Britain) has its headquarters in the Sea of Japan, and its importance in most existing marine faunas is almost negligible. *Nautilus*, too, is abundant in British Jurassic strata, but is now restricted to a limited area in the Indo-Pacific Ocean. Of lamellibranch genera, *Trigonia*, with a world-wide distribution in Mesozoic time, is now found only in the Australian region, while *Pholadomya* with a similar Mesozoic range is now represented by a single species in the Antilles. Many molluscan genera that are abundant in British Eocene rocks are now typical of subtropical seas. The bivalved genus *Chama* lives in the West Indies, Canary Islands, the Mediterranean Sea, and off the coasts of India, while *Crassatella* is characteristic of Australia, New Zealand, the Philippines, India, and West Africa. Among univalves the genera *Conus, Voluta, Pyrula, Cypraea*, and *Fusus*, though of wide geographical extent, are typical of warm climates.

The archaic fishes *Protopterus, Lepidosiren*, and *Ceratodus* are found living only in the rivers of Africa, South America, and Australia respectively, though they represent groups with a wide horizontal range in former geological periods. Among terrestrial forms, the marsupial mammals are represented in British Jurassic strata, though, as is well known, they are now restricted to Australia and South America. The occurrence of fossil elephants, hippopotamus, lion, hyena, and other animals in British Pleistocene deposits indicates important faunal changes in comparatively recent times.

Plants also share in the gradual change of location. The Cycadales were cosmopolitan in Jurassic time but are now confined to tropical or subtropical regions, while *Ginkgo* (the maidenhair tree), found fossil in all latitudes from Spitzbergen to Tasmania, now lives in the wild state only in China and Japan. The Malayan ferns *Matonia* and *Dipteris* are the sole survivors of a group that attained considerable importance in European Mesozoic floras. Similarly the Araucariae, an order of Conifers world-wide in the Jurassic epoch, are now confined to the southern hemisphere, while the giant *Sequoia* of California occurs fossil in European Neozoic strata. Such genera as *Eucalyptus, Cinnamomum, Liriodendron*, and *Magnolia*, besides various palms, also flourished in Europe during early Neozoic time, but subsequently took part in the universal migration southwards.

The limitation of various organisms to certain restricted areas has been shown to depend partly upon ecological conditions—the relation between the organism and its environment—to which many local peculiarities of distribution are due. But there is also the wider question of regional distribution (chorology), for which differences of food supply and habitat are not sufficient to account. Indeed, two widely separated areas may have similar physical conditions and yet greatly differ faunistically. Obviously there are other factors at work, and of these, isolation probably does more than anything else to cause faunal differences, or at least to maintain them.

Isolation may be caused by various circumstances, the most obvious of which is the existence of topographical barriers, and it may be recalled that in the oceans an area of deep water is just as effective as a land barrier in separating littoral faunas, while a desert often rivals the sea in the prevention of terrestrial migration. Other circumstances which influence the distribution of organisms will be discussed at a later stage.

The operation of the various factors has caused a distribution of organisms into 'faunal provinces' whose boundaries have been broadly defined. The limits of the provinces do not always harmonize for diverse groups of animals or plants and, as already noted, the distribution of each group, has varied in successive periods of time. The subject is much too large for detailed discussion here, but the general distribution of marine mollusca and terrestrial mammals may be briefly outlined.

The marine mollusca are usually considered to be distributed among eighteen provinces. These again may be arranged in six climatic belts, thus:

I. THE ARCTIC BELT

The **Arctic Province** is circumpolar, extending north of the Aleutian Islands in the Pacific along the boundary of floating ice in the Atlantic to Iceland and the northern coasts of Europe and Asia. In the Glacial period the fauna of this province extended over much of Europe, Siberia, and North America now occupied by North Temperate faunas.

II. THE NORTH TEMPERATE BELT

The **Boreal Province** comprises the coasts of Massachusetts and Nova Scotia, Iceland, Faröe, Shetland, and Norway (North Cape to Naze).

The **Celtic Province** includes the British coasts with those of Denmark, southern Sweden, and the Baltic Sea.

The **Aleutian Province** stretches southwards from Alaska along the coast of British Columbia.

III. THE NORTHERN SUBTROPICAL BELT

The **Lusitanian Province** includes the Bay of Biscay, the coast of Portugal, the Mediterranean Sea and the north-west African coast, Madeira, Azores, and the Canaries.

The **Aralo-Caspian Province** is confined to the inland seas of Aral and Caspian.

The **Japonic Province** comprises the seas around Japan and Korea.

The **Californian Province** extends along the western coast of the United States of America.

The **Transatlantic Province,** extending along the eastern coast of North America from Massachusetts to Florida, is separated from the Lusitanian Province by the deep waters of the Atlantic.

IV. THE TROPICAL BELT

The **Caribbean Province** includes the Gulf of Mexico and the eastern coasts of South America as far south as Rio.

The **West African Province** extends from the Tropic of Cancer to that of Capricorn.

The **Indo-Pacific Province,** the most extensive of all, comprises the east coast of Africa as far south as Madagascar, the coasts of India, Malaya, and north Australia, and a large area eastwards in the Pacific.

The **Panamic Province** extends from the Gulf of California down the Pacific coast of America to Payta in Peru.

V. THE SOUTHERN SUBTROPICAL BELT

The **Patagonian Province** occupies the eastern coast of South America from Rio to Terra del Fuego.

The **South African Province** comprises both eastern and western coasts of Africa south of the Tropic of Capricorn.

The **Australian Province** includes the southern shores of Australia, with Tasmania, New Zealand, and neighbouring islands.

The **Peruvian Province** occupies the western coast of South America from Callao to Valparaiso.

VI. THE SOUTH TEMPERATE BELT

The **Magellanic Province,** includes Terra del Fuego, with the Falkland Islands and Kerguelen.

No useful purpose would be served by detailing the faunas of all these provinces, since many of them have little (if any) connexion with British geology. A few, however, may be noted in a general way.

The gradual southward migration of Arctic and Boreal mollusca furnishes a means of subdividing the Pliocene deposits of Britain. One of the earliest arrivals is a gastropod of the genus *Neptunaea*, which was followed at a later period by species of *Buccinum, Purpura, Sipho, Bela, Littorina, Admete*, and the bivalves *Yoldia, Arctica*, and *Glycimeris*, all characteristic of northern waters. European and American faunas have few species in common, but some of the British Pliocene immigrants show relations with American forms, though most agree with Scandinavian species. The Pliocene mollusca are discussed more fully in Chapter XVI.

The Celtic Province has few peculiar species but has character of its own, since it is a 'coalition' of Boreal and Lusitanian elements. Thus such southern genera as *Trivia, Ocinebra, Trochus, Aporrhais*, and *Turritella* are associated with the northern *Buccinum, Purpura*, and other forms. The sea-urchins also belong to genera which are widely distributed through western Europe—*Spatangus purpureus*, Müller, *Echinocardium cordatum* (Pennant), and *Echinocyamus pusillus* (Müller), the latter being the only clypeasteroid of northern seas.

The subtropical provinces have many genera but few species in common. Thus the Lusitanian province has practically none of the species typical of the Transatlantic province, from which it is separated by the deep waters of the Atlantic Ocean. Similarly the Caribbean and Panamic provinces, separated only by a narrow isthmus, are said to have no species in common.

The Indo-Pacific Province is of much interest on account of the resemblance between its fauna and that of certain Eocene strata of Britain. Many genera are peculiar to this province, e.g. *Nautilus, Rostellaria, Terebellum, Pterocera, Rimella, Cucullaea,* and *Anatina,* which occur as far north as the Red Sea but do not range into the Mediterranean. Other genera like *Conus, Cypraea, Murex, Mitra, Cerithium,* and *Chama* have many species in the Red Sea, but are sparsely represented in the Mediterranean. It will be seen later that many of these genera occur in the Eocene deposits of Britain. It may further be noted that the existing coral reefs occur mainly in the Indo-Pacific and Caribbean provinces.

Faunal provinces have been detected in the Cambrian and several later geological systems. The Cambrian trilobites of Wales and the English Midlands are closely related to those of Scandinavia and Bohemia, and also show generic similarity with those of the eastern part of the United States of North America. The trilobites of the north-west Highlands of Scotland, however, are very different, resembling those typical of Newfoundland and the Pacific States of America. Thus there is evidence of two faunal provinces which are discussed in Chapter III. Eastern Asia has certain trilobites, such as the genus *Redlichia,* which are rare or unknown elsewhere; consequently that area is often regarded as forming a distinct life-province. Each of these regions seems to contain a number of sub-provinces marked by less conspicuous differences, but the same limits do not hold for different animal groups. The Ordovician faunas also furnish evidence concerning the existence of life-provinces, but Silurian assemblages seem to be more uniformly distributed, though certain trilobite genera are confined to the southern hemisphere.

Long ago Neumayr based a series of 'climatic belts' on the distribution of Mesozoic ammonites and reef-building corals. While Neumayr's interpretation has been considerably modified, recent investigation has confirmed certain broad faunal distinctions between the Mediterranean and other regions. Furthermore the distinction is not confined to ammonites and corals, for there are regional differences in the distribution of lamellibranchs. The Lower Cretaceous rocks of the southern hemisphere, for instance, contain a peculiar group of Trigoniae—the Pseudo-quadratae, which, along with other lamellibranchs, are unknown in Europe. The Mediterranean region with its east and west extensions (the 'Tethys' of Suess) is marked by the abundance of the coralloid rudistids, which are rare outside that region. It must be remembered that geographical limits of distribution—especially of fossil organisms—must be defined with due reserve, for further discoveries may necessitate considerable modification of former ideas. Within the last two years Dr. L. F. Spath has recorded the occurrence of the ammonoid genus *Engonoceras* in the English Gault. This form belongs to a group marked by a pseudo-ceratitic suture line, and is typical of America rather than Europe. In assessing the significance of such records the relative abundance of the organism must be taken into account, but, like

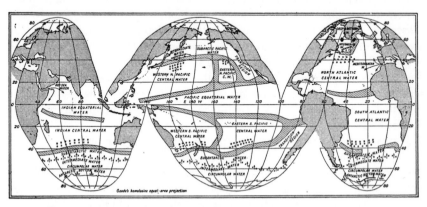

FIG. 3. THE UPPER WATER MASSES OF THE PRESENT OCEANS.
Reproduced, by permission, from 'The Oceans' by H. U. Sverdrup, M. W. Johnson, and R. H. Fleming, 1942.

the occasional presence of *Phylloceras* and rudistids in the English Cretaceous, they provide evidence of communication between the seas of different regions.

Now, H. U. Sverdrup, M. W. Johnson, and R. H. Fleming (1942) state that the ocean basins are occupied by a number of water-masses (Fig. 3), each of which has its own characteristics, especially of temperature and salinity. The mean annual temperature in different latitudes remains unchanged from one year to another, and is highest somewhat north of the equator, but the course of the isotherms is modified by warm ocean currents which transport a considerable amount of heat to higher latitudes. The surface salinity also varies with latitude; it is at a minimum near the equator, reaches a maximum at about 20° N. and S. lat., decreasing again in high latitudes. Since the density of sea-water depends on the temperature and salinity it is influenced by all processes that alter these conditions. At the surface the density is decreased by heating and the addition of fresh water by rainfall and streams; it is increased by cooling and by evaporation. In general, water of greatest density is formed in the cold seas of high latitudes, and because that water sinks and spreads to all the ocean-basins, the bottom water of all oceans is cold. Water of high density is also formed whenever converging currents are present, the sinking water spreading at inter-mediate depths according to its density. The most conspicuous example is the Antarctic Convergence which is traced all round the Antarctic Con-tinent at about 50° to 60° S. lat. The water that sinks here has low salinity but also low temperature and therefore its density is high; this Antarctic Intermediate Water spreads directly over the deep water and is present in all the southern oceans at depths between 400 and 600 fathoms. Farther north, about 40° S. lat., another rapid increase of temperature causes the Subtropical Convergence where the Subantarctic Water sinks.

The surface waters of the Southern Ocean, including those of the Sub-antarctic region, circulate from west to east around the Antarctic Continent, the circumpolar current being deflected locally by the distribution of land and by submarine topography. Water from the Antarctic region moves to the north near the surface and bottom while deep water from lower latitudes is drawn into the system to replace the loss. In the South Atlantic Ocean the Benguella Current flows north along the west coast of Africa up to about 18° S. lat.; then it gradually leaves the coast and continues westward across the ocean between 0° and 20° S. lat. as part of the South Equatorial Current. A branch of this current crosses the equator and continues into the North Atlantic; the other branch, having acquired high temperature and high salinity, flows south along the east coast of South America as the Brazil Current. These currents, together with the Antarctic Circumpolar current, form a conspicuous counter-clockwise gyral round the South Atlantic Central Water. The entire circulation is shallow and is probably limited to a depth of less than 100 fathoms lying above the Antarctic Intermediate Water. The water-masses in the equatorial region of the Atlantic Ocean are mainly of South Atlantic origin, but in the northern parts of the ocean there is evidence of admixture with large quantities of North Atlantic Central Water with high temperature and salinity. This admixture extends to about 10° N. lat. where an Equatorial Counter Current flows eastward between the Equatorial Currents of the two hemispheres. The water from the South Atlantic does not appear to have any great influence on the large body of North Atlantic Central Water. Greater influence is exercised by the exchange of highly saline warm water which flows under the surface through the Strait of Gibraltar from the Mediterranean basin. The outflowing Mediterranean water, with a salinity of 38 ‰ and a temperature of 13° C., is rapidly mixed with the Atlantic water, and can be traced at mid-depths over wide areas by a salinity maximum which decreases southwards; it is replaced by a flow of Atlantic water along the surface into the Mediterranean Sea. We need not discuss the complexities of the Mediterranean water with its admixture of less saline water from the Black Sea, for the present form of the Mediterranean Sea is a product of its later geological history.

The system of currents in the North Atlantic Ocean is dominated by the North Equatorial Current in the south and the Gulf Stream in the north.

The former flows from east to west, apart from a northward deflection over the Mid-Atlantic Ridge. In the west the North Equatorial Current joins the branch of the South Equatorial Current that has crossed the equator, mixes with its water of markedly different type and continues into the Caribbean Sea. A branch of the North Equatorial Current which flows along the northern side of the Greater Antilles carries water identical with that of the Sargasso Sea. The merging of these currents represents the beginning of the Gulf Stream which dominates the circulation of a great part of the North Atlantic Ocean. The Gulf Stream is misnamed, for the main current sweeps north from the Yucatan Channel through the Strait of Florida; only a small part of the water flows into the Gulf of Mexico, creating local eddies, and later, joins the Florida Current. At the Florida Strait the current flows at the rate of about three miles per hour; it leaves the continental slope off Cape Hatteras, and east of the Grand Banks (about 45° W. long.) it divides. The larger southerly branch goes eastward and turns south off the coast of north-west Africa as the Canaries Current which later rejoins the North Equatorial Current. The northerly branch flows northeastward as the North Atlantic Drift, and carries Atlantic water past the British Isles into the Norwegian and Barents Seas by several terminal branches.

Two water-masses exist at moderate depths in the Indian Ocean. The Indian Central Water is formed just north of the Subtropical Convergence in 40° S. lat., and extends northward to about 10° S. lat. The Indian Equatorial Water has a high temperature, 25° to 29° C., in the equatorial regions; its salinity shows the usual sub-tropical maximum (38‰) off western Australia, and elsewhere it is subject to seasonal variations due to precipitation. In the Arabian Sea this water is modified by admixture with highly saline water (40‰) from the Red Sea. Around these water-masses water is circulated by currents. Between South Africa and Australia (about 40° S. lat.) a current flows from west to east; during the northern summer it bends to the north before reaching Australia and is joined by a stream flowing from the Pacific to the Indian Ocean by the southern coast of Australia. To the north of 20° S. lat. the South Equatorial Current flows from east to west, reaching its greatest velocity during the south-west monsoon. In this season it is reinforced by water from the Pacific Ocean which enters the Indian Ocean to the north of Australia, but this current is reversed during the southern summer. In both seasons the South Equatorial Current turns southward along the east coast of Africa, feeding the strong Agulhas Current. To the south of 30° S. lat. the Agulhas stream is narrow and well-defined; south of Cape Province its greater part bends sharply to the south and then to the east, joining the flow from South Africa towards Australia. North of 10° S. lat. the surface currents of the Indian Ocean vary greatly from winter to summer owing to the variable character of the prevailing winds.

The water-masses of the Pacific Ocean are more complicated than those of the other oceans, for the circulation is more sluggish, and the development of a uniform body of water by mixing of different water-masses does not take place. In the southern part of the ocean there is the great Subantarctic Water-mass with low temperature, 4° to 8°, and salinity of about 34·3‰. Part of this water is deflected northward by the southern extension of South America, so that in the Pacific Ocean subantarctic water has an influence beyond the equator by the Peru or Humboldt Current. The temperature and salinity of this sluggish current gradually increase as it approaches its northern limit where it turns to the west and merges with the South Equatorial Current flowing west. This marks the northern limit of two water-masses which are separated by southward branches of the main circulation; they are (1) the Western South Pacific Central Water which is similar to the Central Water of the Indian Ocean, and (2) the Eastern South Pacific Central Water which has a lower salinity. The Equatorial region of the Pacific Ocean is occupied by an Equatorial Watermass of remarkably uniform character which extends entirely over the ocean from east to west. This equatorial water is probably formed off the west coast of South America by the gradual transformation of subantarctic water, involving an increase in temperature and salinity. It is widest along the South American coast from 18° S. to 20° N. lat., but tapers to the west near New Guinea; it is limited to the north by the westward-flowing North Equatorial Current, and a strong counter current north of the equator. In the North Pacific Ocean three distinct water-masses are recognized. In the western part a well-defined Central Water-mass of low salinity covers an area nearly equal to the North Atlantic Ocean. Another, but smaller, body of Central Water occupies the eastern area between the Hawaiian Islands and the American coast. In the extreme north there is a large Subarctic Watermass, with low temperature and low salinity, which is carried to the east and south along the coast of North America. In its journey through different climates the Subarctic Water becomes warmer and more saline, and at about 25° N. lat. it converges with the Equatorial Water. The two Central Water-masses increase the volume-transport of the North Equatorial Current as it flows westward across the ocean. Before it reaches the western limit this current divides. One branch turns south by the coast of Mindanao and merges with the Equatorial Counter Current. The larger branch turns to the north-east by the northern Philippines and, as the Japan Current or Kuro Siwo, flows past Formosa and the Japanese islands. At about 35° N. lat. warm water, representing the extension of this current, flows east to 160° E. long. and there divides. One branch, the North Pacific Current, continues east to the longitude of the Hawaiian Islands, then turns south to rejoin the North Equatorial Current. The northern branch extends to the Gulf of Alaska where it is deflected northwards to form an anti-clockwise gyral.

Intermediate waters of distinctive type are found below the Central Water-masses in all oceans, the most widespread being the Antarctic

Intermediate Water, with low temperature and low salinity. In the Atlantic Ocean the low salinity of the Antarctic Intermediate Water extends across the equator to about 20° N. lat., but in the Indian and Pacific Oceans it reaches only to about 10° S. lat. The corresponding Arctic Intermediate Water is more restricted. In the Atlantic Ocean it is formed to the east of the Grand Banks, Newfoundland, and is limited to the north-western part of the ocean. Similarly in the north-west Pacific it is present between 20° N. and 43° N. lat. but does not reach the American coast. Two other Intermediate Water-masses should be noted. The highly saline Mediterranean water, that flows out along the bottom of the Strait of Gibraltar, spreads over wide areas below the Antarctic Intermediate Water in the Atlantic Ocean. A similar stream, but not so well defined, flows from the Red Sea and occupies mid-depths in the north-western part of the Indian Ocean.

Below the Intermediate Waters the deep basins of the oceans are filled with Deep and Bottom Waters. These water-masses are formed in high southerly latitudes close to the Antarctic Continent, and in high northerly latitudes in the Atlantic Ocean. By reason of their high density these cold waters sink and spread into all the deeper parts of the oceans. The Antarctic Bottom Water flows northward and has been traced beyond the equator to 35° N. lat. in the Atlantic Ocean. The North Atlantic Deep Water flowing southward also crosses the equator below the Antarctic Intermediate Water and above the Antarctic Bottom Water both of which have lower salinity. In the Indian and Pacific Oceans there is apparently a slow exchange of Deep and Bottom Waters between the two hemispheres.

This complex system of oceanic circulation, of which we have noted only the outstanding features, depends primarily on the distribution of density within the several water-masses. This, in its turn, is controlled by processes of heating and cooling connected with the atmospheric circulation which is a direct consequence of the earth's form and relations to the sun. Hence it seems reasonable to suppose that the tracks of the ocean currents, which are influenced by the earth's rotation and deflected by the land-masses on the western sides of the oceans, have been generally constant through the ages, allowing for certain changes in the continental margins that are indicated in the biostratigraphical record. This thesis cannot be proved directly, but it is reasonably consistent with palaeontological evidence of migration as shown by the distribution of certain groups of marine fossils. We may cite here a few examples of such relationships in anticipation of discussion on later pages. The Neozoic deposits along the coast of East Africa contain large foraminifera which point to a current of warm water flowing southward; such foraminifera are absent from corresponding deposits in West Africa, south of Nigeria, that is, in the track of the present cold Benguella Current. The close relations between the Jurassic ammonites of Kachh and those of East Africa and Madagascar may also be explained by the existence of the warm current in the western part of the Indian Ocean. The well-known similarity of early Neozoic reef-corals in the Mediterranean and Caribbean regions may be due to the westward flow of the Equatorial Current, as also the close relations of Mesozoic ammonites in South Europe and Mexico. The similarity of Carboniferous and Devonian goniatites in Europe and eastern North America is explicable in the same way, also the relationship of the Cambrian trilobites in these regions. The distribution of olenellid trilobites between mid-continental North America, north-west Newfoundland and north-west Scotland, on the other hand, seems to indicate the operation of a northward current analogous to the present Gulf Stream. The distribution of the peculiar austral Devonian faunas seems to reflect the present anti-clockwise gyral round the South Atlantic Central Water. While the similarity of Cambrian trilobites in east Asia and western North America may be related to the clockwise gyral around the two water-masses of the North Pacific, the casual relationships of most faunas of South America and south-east Asia seem to show that the ocean currents of the South Pacific have always been as complicated as they are today. Some limitation in the presentation of the evidence is set, partly by incomplete knowledge of certain phyla which are not discussed in this volume, partly by the space available in a book of reasonable size, and again by the time which can be given to compilation from the records published in the vast literature. Some selection is inevitable, and in making it as representative as possible, attention is given to fossil-groups with contrasting habits of life; sedentary as well as free-moving forms are discussed. In this way the significance of regional distribution can be assessed apart from the wide margin of adaptability shown by some groups of marine animals. One point must be borne in mind throughout our discussions. We are not concerned with details of coast-lines as shown on many so-called palaeogeographical maps. Our aim is to take a broad and relative view of life-assemblages and to indicate, as far as possible, the general relations between the several life-provinces of past ages.

The distribution of terrestrial mammals and birds is similarly grouped in climatic belts, and is further influenced by the isolation of the several continental areas.

The **Holarctic Province** occupies the vast region comprising the whole of Europe, Africa north of the Sahara Desert, and Asia north of the Himalayan mountain system, besides that part of America which lies north of the Mexican plateau. The mammalian fauna includes a great variety of deer and oxen, besides rabbits, hares, rats, beavers, foxes, weasels, and bears. The Eurasian part of this area is often separated, as the Palaearctic Province, from the American or Nearctic portion, since the latter is especially marked by the occurrence of opossums among mammals and of certain ganoid fishes (e.g. *Amia*), reptiles, and amphibians. The chief Holarctic birds are the thrushes, wrens, tits, and finches.

The **Ethiopian Province** is the home of many apes, monkeys, and lemurs, of the hippopotamus and rhinoceros, the African elephant, antelopes, and many edentates, but deer and oxen are sparsely represented in the wild state. The chief carnivores are lions and leopards, but there are no bears. Among birds the ostrich is peculiar to this region, which extends through central and south Africa. Madagascar is noteworthy for the abundance of lemurs and for the absence of monkeys, antelopes, and lions.

The **Oriental Province,** extending through India, Malaya, and China, agrees with the Ethiopian Province in the occurrence of elephants and apes, but has also deer, oxen, and bears. The tapir lives in Malaya, and the chevrotain is also restricted to the Province. The most characteristic carnivore is the tiger. Peacocks and pheasants are typically Oriental birds.

The **Australian Province,** comprising Australia, Papua, and the Polynesian islands, is well known as the home of the marsupial and the monotreme mammals, typified by the kangaroo and the duckbill respectively. Many peculiar birds are restricted to this Province, including emus, cassowaries, and mound-builders.

The isolated **Novozealandian Province** is unique in having no indigenous mammals, no snakes, crocodiles, or tortoises, and only one frog. It is, however, the home of many flightless birds such as the kiwi and the moa. Of special interest is the Hatteria (*Sphenodon*), the only surviving rhynchocephalian reptile. The archaic aspect of the fauna in this and the Australian Province is ascribed to isolation of these areas since the end of Mesozoic time.

The **Neotropical Province** includes the Antilles and Central America, Colombia, Brazil, and Chile. The most characteristic faunal elements are prehensile-tailed monkeys, marmosets, peccaries, llamas, tapirs, and many edentates, while the carnivores are represented by jaguars and opossums. The toucans and humming-birds are typical of this Province. The general absence of oxen, sheep, antelopes, pigs, and ravens is also a noteworthy feature.

In connexion with the regional distribution of these animals it must be remembered that the geographical range of herbivorous mammals depends largely upon the distribution of the vegetation on which they feed. Consequently their horizontal range is a more significant index of climatal conditions than is the range of carnivorous animals. The latter may occur, irrespective of climate, wherever they can prey upon the herbivores. Thus the tiger, a characteristic 'southern' animal, is said to prey upon the reindeer in Siberia. Moreover, the range of herbivorous forms is liable to considerable variation, since their seasonal migrations may extend through many degrees of latitude. These factors may have determined in some measure certain peculiarities in the distribution of Pleistocene mammals in Britain; the curious mixture of northern and southern forms in some deposits has not yet been satisfactorily explained.

The above considerations make it necessary to discuss the various factors which control the movements of animals and plants. Probably the most important in the case of animals is the organic factor—the question of food-supply and of contending species, which determines whether or not a new area can be permanently occupied. Of inorganic factors temperature has perhaps the greatest influence after topographical barriers, while ocean currents, nature of substratum, and other circumstances also play their part. The several influences are, however, so intimately interwoven that the problems presented by the geographical distribution of life, difficult in the case of modern faunas, well nigh defy solution in the case of fossil faunas as we know them at present.

As regards the organisms themselves, two modes of distribution may conveniently be distinguished—the voluntary and the involuntary. The former may be called **migration,** the latter, **dispersal.** The separate consideration of these phenomena demonstrates well the dependence of organisms on their environment and exposes certain limitations of distribution which are often overlooked.

Dispersal may be defined as the distribution of animals and plants by causes not primarily invoking the activities of these organisms. Thus, seeds and spores of plants are dispersed by the wind, and many seeds possess mechanisms which materially aid dispersal by this means. Many marine organisms, known collectively as the **plankton,** spend the period of their existence floating in the sea. They drift about from place to place, having no power to direct their own course, and are at the mercy of ocean currents which largely determine their distribution. Such organisms as the pelagic Foraminifera and Radiolaria and jelly-fishes will serve as examples. These (the **holoplankton**) are to be distinguished from forms (**pseudoplankton**) which only become planktonic after death. In the latter group may be included shells which float and drift away after the death of the animal, drifted leaves and trunks of trees—indeed, any floating organic material that may be transported in this manner from its natural environment. Thus shells of the existing cephalopod *Spirula* are widely distributed on Australian shores where the organism never lived. This circumstance has been cited to support the suggestion that drifting accounts for the wide distribution of many Mesozoic ammonites. It may be so in some cases, but the preservation of the most delicate ornament and the fragile mouth-borders in many ammonites shows that these have not travelled far from their original habitat. Drifting of these shells, moreover, would not affect their value in stratigraphy, since they would be buried in contemporaneous sediments. Erroneous ideas concerning their geographical range, however, might arise if the pseudoplanktonic nature of certain fossils were not recognized.

The term **epiplankton** has been proposed for those organisms which habitually live upon a floating object to which they are attached or on which they move freely. Perhaps the best modern example is the 'floating menagerie' of the Sargasso Sea, where algae, hydroids, and polyzoa are attached to the floating seaweed, while crustacea, mollusca, and other animals live among its branches. Large seaweeds cast up on our own shores furnish similar examples on a smaller scale. The wide distribution of the Lower Palaeozoic graptolites is ascribed to similar conditions. These organisms are considered to have lived, after the manner of hydroids, attached to floating seaweeds, and their wide distribution is thus primarily dependent upon the movements of marine currents; but it has already been stated that the preservation of such delicate organisms needs 'quiet' conditions of deposition.

The larval stages of many animals which spend most of their lives on the sea bottom lead a planktonic existence, and are often distinguished as the **meroplankton.** These larvae suffer the same vicissitudes as the holoplankton, but sooner or later they sink to the bottom, where, if the conditions be suitable, they develop into the benthonic adult. The meroplankton is thus exceedingly important from a stratigraphical standpoint, since it determines the distribution of benthonic animals, which, of all organisms, afford the most reliable information concerning the physical conditions of the sea bottom. Dispersal of the meroplankton, effected by ocean currents, is limited by several factors, of which temperature and the duration of the larval stage may be briefly considered. The influence of temperature varies greatly in different instances. In some cases the larvae or eggs are able to resist changes of temperature which would destroy the adult animal. It is well known that the winter eggs of some crustacea (and of insects among the land fauna) survive, while the full-grown animals perish in the autumn. In other cases the adult is able to withstand changes of temperature which destroy the larvae; for instance, a difference of 2° or 3° F. in the temperature of the water is said to be sufficient to kill oyster larvae.

The agency of warm currents has been suggested to explain the distribution of certain fossil-groups. It is well known that ocean currents vary much in velocity. Thus the Gulf Stream issues from the Florida Straits at an average rate of eighty or ninety miles a day, but the drifts of the North Atlantic slow down to ten (or fewer) miles a day. It follows that planktonic organisms from the Florida coast would have to travel several months to reach the European coast. As the meroplanktonic larval stage of many benthonic animals is passed through very quickly, the larva will sink to the bottom before it has been carried very far, and in all probability the habitat, into which it settles after a few days, is likely to prove unsuitable, and therefore destructive, to the organism. This limitation to dispersal is well seen in the case of brachiopods whose larval stage passes quickly; as the adults are gregarious and sedentary forms, their restricted and sporadic distribution is doubly explained. The occurrence of apparently similar fossil brachiopods in widely distant areas in the same geological period is probably due to parallel development of distinct races. In any case, it is safer, though not always practicable in the present state of our knowledge, to separate under distinct appellations the British Carboniferous productids from similar North American species, or the British Jurassic rhynchonellids from those of Burma, than to assume a simultaneous world-wide distribution for such sedentary forms. To revert to the question of larval periods, it is possible that the organism may be favourably situated at the end of its pelagic stage, and such dispersal may result in exotic forms mingling with a previously established or endemic fauna. The presence of certain species, apparently from the Indo-Pacific province, in the modern gastropod fauna of eastern South America may be thus explained.

Migration, or distribution by means of active movements on the part of the organism, is, of course, confined to animals. It is convenient, in the present connexion, to consider the active aquatic animals with reference to their relation to the substratum as (1) swimming types and (2) bottom-living forms.

Swimming animals (the **nekton**) may be subdivided into three groups. The **holonekton,** typified by fishes, usually have a torpedo-like form with perfect bilateral symmetry, while the appendages of the body are modified for balancing and steering. The tadpole provides an example of the **mero-nekton,** since it is the swimming larval stage of an otherwise benthonic animal. Organisms attached parasitically to swimming animals are distinguished as the **epinekton**; examples are seen in the larvae of *Unio* attached to the gills of fishes. The more familiar barnacles fixed to the keels of ships and other floating objects are bottom-living forms which make use of convenient artificial support.

Only the holonekton, comprising the fishes and marine mammalia, demands discussion here. At first sight it would seem reasonable to suppose that these pelagic animals possess unlimited powers of movement, apart from the obvious restriction due to topographical barriers. Actually, however, the movements of fishes in the sea are limited by many factors, of which the available food-supply and temperature changes (including seasonal variations) have probably the greatest influence.

The nature of the food required by various species differs, since some are carnivorous, while others feed upon plankton, but ultimately the supply depends upon the distribution of planktonic organisms. Recent research has shown how largely the distribution of certain fishes in particular areas depends upon the availability of suitable food. Moreover, the hatching of the young fishes must coincide approximately with the profuse development of the right kind of plankton or the brood is practically a failure. Thus variations in the seasonal temperature-changes have been known to exert far-reaching influences on the plankton, and therefore on the abundance of certain fishes in a number of seasons. It will be obvious from these remarks that the questions of food-supply and distribution are intimately connected —at least in the case of young fishes.

Perhaps temperature, *per se*, has more influence in determining the general limits of distribution in terms of latitude. Thus in the case of fishes occurring around the British coasts, many authors distinguish northern species from southern species. The northern species occur mainly in and north of the North Sea, and include the haddock, whiting, plaice, sole, halibut, and cod. The proportions of these fishes in the fauna diminishes to the south-west of Britain, and they are not usually found in the Atlantic. The southern species, such as the dog-fish, sea-bream, pollack, hake, and conger-eel, are chiefly derived from the Atlantic and practically do not occur north of the North Sea. The coast-banks of North America show similar groups of northern and southern forms, the change occurring about the latitude of the New England States. Again, the common eel of north Europe undertakes vast migrations to the Middle Atlantic for the purpose of spawning, but apparently does not leave the warm waters of the Gulf Stream and its northern drift. It is well known that a sudden change of temperature has often a disastrous effect on fishes. An oft-quoted instance occurred in the months of March and April 1882 off the eastern coasts of the United States. A vast area, estimated at '5,000 to 7,500 square miles was so thickly covered with dead or dying fish that their numbers must have exceeded the enormous total of one billion'. There were no signs of disease, and after investigation it was concluded that an unusual lowering of the temperature in a belt of warm water on the border of the Gulf Stream killed many of its inhabitants. In 1884 numerous dead octopods were observed in the same region. Similar destruction of marine animals on a large scale has also been recorded in the Barents Sea, which is subject to very sudden changes of temperature.

Other organisms, known collectively as the **benthos,** live essentially upon a substratum, the sea bottom in the case of marine forms, the land surface for terrestrial forms. As already stated, marine benthonic animals are dispersed by their meroplanktonic larvae, and in the case of sedentary (or fixed) forms this is the only means of dispersal. The vagrant types, with power to walk, crawl, or creep over the sea bottom, are also able to migrate in search of food or to escape from contending species. The occurrence of these vagrant forms is dependent, to a much greater extent than in the groups already discussed, upon the nature of the sea bottom. Their distribution is consequently often local and sporadic in character. For instance, echinoderms are seldom found in clays, and where they do occur in these deposits they are usually small and stunted, thus reflecting growth in unfavourable surroundings. Lamellibranchs and gastropods vary locally in their occurrence, the assemblage found on a rocky coast, for example, differing from that on a sandy or muddy shore. The work of Peterson, discussed earlier (p. 28) in connexion with conditions of deposition, emphasises the possible variations in a fauna consequent upon small differences in habitat. As an example of 'facies-faunas' the molluscan assemblage from the muddy Gault and the sandy Upper Greensand may be compared; these formations are perhaps not strictly contemporaneous, but they are near enough in point of time to justify a comparison between the respective assemblages of gastropods and lamellibranchs. Again, the Corallian sands and limestones of southern England pass laterally into the Ampthill Clay of the Midlands, with corresponding modifications in the fauna. As an example of the sporadic distribution of a bivalve shell, the occurrence of the Lower Carboniferous species *Allorisma maxima* (Portlock) may be mentioned. This form is only recorded from two localities in north Wales, namely, Llangollen and Anglesey, and is unknown from the other Carboniferous Limestone outcrops. Now, in geology the absence of a particular species from any locality may be due to (1) limitations of geographical distribution; (2) absence of strata containing the fossil: that is, a portion of the sequence may be missing; (3) collectors may have failed to secure a specimen though the form may be present. In the case under discussion the last alternative can hardly be urged, since the richly fossiliferous Carboniferous Limestone has been assiduously searched for many decades; there is also no evidence for postulating a break in the sequence of strata. Consequently for the present the sporadic occurrence of this fossil must be ascribed to the limitations of geographical distribution. Similarly *Panopaea mandibula* (J. Sow.) is found in the Upper Greensand of Devizes, but is apparently absent from equivalent strata near Warminster and in Devon, where its associates flourish. Ammonites are rare in the Lincolnshire Limestone and corresponding part of the Inferior Oolite farther south, and in the Great Oolite generally where coral-reefs are developed. This antipathy between cephalopods and reef-corals is also noticeable in other systems besides the Jurassic. It may be that the surf and strong currents in the neighbourhood of coral-reefs furnished a habitat unfavourable to ammonites. In any case the recurrent distribution of these organisms provides an instance of local migration towards favourable conditions of life. The absence of ammonites from the 'Estuarine Beds' of Yorkshire is probably due to low salinity of the water.

Migration of the vagrant benthos is probably more restricted than is often realized. The fauna of the sea bottom chiefly inhabits the shallow waters of the continental shelf, and a channel of deep water is just as effective in restricting the migration of benthonic animals as a land barrier. In other words the shallow-water benthos requires continuity of coast for active migration. While modern examples could be given, an instance from the older rocks may be quoted. The Cambrian rocks of northern Scotland contain a fauna that appears to be more closely related to the Cambrian fauna of Newfoundland and western North America than to that of North Wales; the latter, on the other hand, is comparable with the Cambrian fauna of the Atlantic States of North America, which differs from that of the Pacific States. This distribution is usually explained by supposing that a long stretch of sea extended from America to Scandinavia, and that the western American and the north Scottish faunas existed on the northern shore, while the eastern American and Welsh faunas inhabited the southern coast of this sea. Deeper water between the coasts restricted migration and consequent mingling of the faunas.

The above remarks suffice to emphasize the necessity for considering the possible effect of various physical factors on the distribution of marine organisms, though the influence of these factors in the case of fossil faunas may not always be capable of direct proof.

One aspect of the problem of geographical distribution—the gradual invasion of a newly available area—is perhaps more familiar to the geologist than to the biologist, on account of the time factor involved. The most striking instance in modern times is probably to be found in the development of a new flora on the island of Krakatoa after it had been devastated by the eruption of 1883.

Students of geology will readily recall instances of invasions of the British area by marine faunas at the several periods when continental conditions were followed by submergence. Thus the Old Red Sandstone (a continental deposit) is succeeded in south-west England by shallow-water basal deposits of the Carboniferous Limestone. The fauna in these beds consists chiefly of lamellibranchs (*Modiola*, &c.) and brachiopods (chiefly rhynchonellids and athyrids). The presence of brachiopods testifies to the marine character of the fauna, and *Modiola* is closely related to the mussels, whose living representatives are known to have a wide range of adaptability with regard to salinity of the water. Another noteworthy point is that the fauna consists mainly of sedentary benthonic animals which have presumably been dispersed during their planktonic larval stage. In some localities these basal argillaceous limestones may be traced upwards into more purely calcareous strata that show the gradual incoming of the 'standard fauna' of the Carboniferous Limestone—an assemblage of brachiopods, crinoids, corals, and other forms.

Similar characters are seen in the fauna of the Rhaetic Beds which succeed the continental Triassic strata of Britain. Impersistent bone-beds at the base of the Rhaetic Series afford evidence of the periodic drying up of pools, consequent destruction of the fish fauna and concentration of bones by current-action in the initial stages of submergence. Later beds of marls, shales, and fine-grained limestones contain such shells as *Pecten valoniensis* Defr., *Pteria contorta* (Portlock), *Protocardia rhaetica* (Mérian), *Modiola minima* (J. Sow.), and *Ostrea liassica* Strickland. Here again the chief members of the new marine fauna are sedentary benthonic lamellibranchs. The episodes of accumulation are often separated by small unconformities of local significance. Later still, a typical and abundant marine fauna became established in the muddy waters of the main Liassic sea and in the exceptional calcareous facies of the Radstock area. Similar phenomena are witnessed in the marine beds which follow various estuarine phases in the Jurassic and Cretaceous systems. The Lower Pliocene, succeeding the continental Miocene period of subaerial erosion, is another instance. In this case the molluscan shells of the lower beds are related to their contemporaries in the Mediterranean region. Later these give place to invaders from the north in progressively increasing proportion until finally the molluscan assemblage is entirely northern in its affinities.

Other notable examples of migration and dispersal are shown, in the midst of marine deposits, by the comparatively sudden appearance of new forms. Asaphid trilobites first appear in Britain in early Ordovician strata, where such species as *Ogygia selwyni* Salter are typical and are later replaced by *O. buchi* (Brongniart), *Asaphus tyrannus* Murchison, &c. But *Ogygiopsis klotzi* (Röminger), which is very similar to the British ogygids, was already abundant in the Middle Cambrian rocks of British Columbia, and the large-tailed genera *Kootenia* and *Bonnia* were established at Lower Cambrian horizons in the Appalachian area. Migration of the asaphid stock from America to Europe is the only explanation at present advanced to account for this distribution. The sudden appearance of pentamerids in large numbers at the base of the Silurian deposits is also ascribed to migration from a distant area, for no likely ancestors are known in the older deposits of Britain. In the Carboniferous rocks of Britain an abrupt change in the flora without any corresponding difference in lithology occurs at a definite horizon in the 'Millstone Grit' and provides a line of division between Lower and Upper Carboniferous strata. In the equivalent succession of Belgium and Silesia there is floral continuity, the earlier plants being gradually replaced by later types. E. B. Bailey explains this by supposing the British area to be isolated during early Carboniferous time by open sea. Later the silting up of the marine area gave rise to deltaic conditions which permitted migration of the southern plants. A similar break occurs at the same horizon in the estuarine fish assemblages of Scotland, while the fauna of the marine deposits is continuous. Among vertebrate animals a most impressive instance of wholesale migration is indicated in the Karroo system of South Africa. The system begins with the Dwyka tillite, a product of glaciation in which no fossils are known, and the succeeding Ecca Beds have yielded only plant remains. The Beaufort Beds, next in succession, contain a great variety of tetrapod genera which have no ancestors in the African rocks. Twelve years ago, D. M. S. Watson (1942) drew attention to discoveries by Russian geologists of a series of reptiles from which the South African forms could be derived. It is therefore likely that the famous tetrapod faunas of the Beaufort Beds resulted from the southward migration of the Russian forms (see pp. 369-73).

The occasional migration of the ammonoid families Phylloceratidae and Lytoceratidae during Mesozoic time from the Mediterranean area to north-west Europe has already been mentioned, and also the similarly sporadic appearance of rudist lamellibranchs in British Cretaceous deposits. The English Pliocene fauna, which has a marked 'Mediterranean aspect' in its early assemblages, also contains certain elements unknown at that period in southern Europe. An important group of sea-urchins has affinities with West Indian forms, but no link in the geographical distribution is known. Furthermore, some of the mollusca are held to have originated in the North Pacific region. Such are the lamellibranch *Acila* (a nuculid genus with divaricate ornament) and the gasteropod *Liomesus*. The presence of these forms has been explained by supposed migration along the coasts of Siberia, whence they entered the British area from the north.

The original centre of dispersal cannot, however, always be fixed, and this circumstance was responsible for Neumayr's term 'cryptogenetic types'. Many of these forms have since been traced to their original home, and doubtless other instances will be elucidated by the extension of research. The dominant trilobites of Middle Cambrian strata belong to the genus *Paradoxides*, which, though related to the Lower Cambrian Mesonacids, has no direct connexion with them. In Britain the Lower Cambrian rocks are separated from Middle Cambrian strata by an unconformity and the Paradoxidian trilobites must therefore have migrated into this country. The area from which they came has still to be found.

The converse case of relict faunas is also of considerable interest and significance, and that of the inland Aralo-Caspian seas may be taken as an example. The meagre fauna includes a seal (*Phoca caspica*, Kerr), about sixteen species of mollusca, including members of the genera *Cardium*, *Adacna*, and *Venus*, two crustaceans and four sponges. The waters are brackish, but the fauna is of marine aspect. Another instance is that of Lake Baikal in western Asia. Its impoverished fauna also includes a seal (*Phoca baikalensis* B. Dyb.), a fish (*Salmo migratorius* Pallas), and about twenty-five molluscan species, of which only three are known elsewhere, and those are restricted to Siberia. There are also certain sponges of marine type, one of which (*Lubomerskia baikalensis* W. Dyb.) occurs also in the Behring Sea. Such 'relict seas' may arise in several ways. Parts of a sea may become isolated by the elevation of enclosing deposits; thus coastal lagoons are formed by the growth of sand-bars or coral-reefs. Basin-like depressions may be cut off from the marine area by negative changes of sea level as in the marginal lakes of fiord type in Norway. The Aralo-Caspian seas are due to the shrinking of the former Mediterranean Sea. In general the fauna of such isolated areas becomes modified as a consequence of different environmental conditions, though it retains some characters by which its marine origin can be traced. The fauna of the Permian Magnesian Limestone of Durham is a relict fauna isolated by the shrinkage of the Carboniferous seas. As the salinity of the waters gradually increased, the whole fauna became dwarfed and otherwise modified, and finally died out altogether when the conditions approached those of the existing Dead Sea.

Analogous modifications may occur in terrestrial faunas which have become isolated by the formation of islands. The Pleistocene deposits of Malta and Cyprus have yielded remains of dwarf races of elephants, and a relict assemblage of reptiles has been described from the Cretaceous rocks of Hungary. The existing life-assemblage of the Australian region may also be regarded as a relict fauna, for that area has been isolated from the rest of the world since Mesozoic time.

It is evident that many problems of geographical distribution are encountered in biostratigraphical studies, and it is necessary to interpret them by means of the principles which govern the movements of existing faunas. On the evidence thus obtained depends the correct reconstruction of past geographical conditions which is an important branch of stratigraphical research.

LITERATURE

While the facts concerning preservation and occurrence of fossils are widely scattered in geological literature, the following papers may be cited as discussing in detail some of the subjects mentioned in this chapter.

The Inorganic Constituents of Marine Invertebrates, by F. W. Clarke and W. C. Wheeler. Prof. Paper No. 124, U.S. Geol. Surv., 1922.

The Atoll of Funafuti: Report of the Coral Reef Committee of the Royal Society, pp. 1–428, 4to. London, 1904.

'The Present Distribution and Origin of the Calcareous Concretions in Coal Seams, known as "Coal-balls"', by M. C. Stopes and D. M. S. Watson, *Phil. Trans. Roy. Soc.*, ser. B, vol. cc, pp. 167–218, 1908.

'The Origin of certain Concretions in the Lower Coal Measures', by H. B. Stocks, *Q.J.G.S.*, vol. lviii, pp. 46–58, 1902.

'Beekite, or Cycloidal Chalcedony', by J. Strachan, *Proc. Belfast Nat. Field Club*, vol. vi, pp. 536–47, 1912.

'Beekite', by W. H. Wickes, *Proc. Bristol Nat. Soc.*, vol. ii, pt. 3, pp. 9–21, 1910.

'On the Important Part played by Calcareous Algae at certain Geological Horizons, with special reference to the Palaeozoic Rocks', by E. J. Garwood, *Rep. Brit. Assoc. for* 1913, pp. 453–72, 1914; also *Geol. Mag.*, vol. l, pp. 440–6, 490–8, 545–53, 1913.

'Some new Rockbuilding Organisms from the Lower Carboniferous Beds of Westmorland', by E. J. Garwood, *Geol. Mag.*, vol. li, pp. 265–71, 1914.

'A Freshwater Shale with Viviparus, and Associated Beds from the Base of the Carboniferous Rocks in Ribblesdale', by E. J. Garwood, *Geol. Mag.*, vol. lix, pp. 289–93, 1922.

Conditions of Life in the Sea, by J. Johnstone. Cambridge, 1908.

The Depths of the Ocean, by J. Murray and J. Hjort. London, 1912.

'The Animal Communities of the Seabottom and their Importance for Marine Zoogeography', by C. G. H. Petersen, *Rep. Danish Biol. Station*, No. xxi, 1913.

The Oceans: Their Physics, Chemistry and General Biology, by H. U. Sverdrup, M. W. Johnson, and R. H. Fleming. New York, 1942.

'Fossils and Life', by F. Bather, *Rep. Brit. Assoc. for 1920*, pp. 61–86, 1921.

'Evolutional Palaeontology in relation to the Lower Palaeozoic Rocks', by G. L. Elles, *Rep. Brit. Assoc. for 1923*, pp. 81–107, 1924.

'Organic Evolution', by C. T. Regan, *Rep. Brit. Assoc. for 1925*, pp. 75–86, 1926.

'Conditions of Deposition of the Stockdale Shales of the Lake District', by J. E. Marr, *Q.J.G.S.*, vol. lxxxi, pp. 113–36, 1925.

'Ecology of Modern Marine Organisms with Reference to Palaeogeography', by T. W. Vaughan, *Bull. Geol. Soc. Amer.*, vol. li, pp. 433–68, 1940.

II

FOSSILS AS GUIDES TO HORIZON

THE use of fossils in stratigraphy depends upon the ascertained fact that organisms show progressive changes in structure as they are traced through successive series of strata. The changes are apparently gradual, and generally in a definite direction, so that if the sequence of changes be correlated with geological position in a given district, the grades of development thus 'dated' can be applied to the investigation of outcrops at distant localities. Even a newly described species from a single locality when compared with the development of previously known forms may give information concerning its stratigraphical position.

The early recognition and investigation of this sequence of gradual changes ultimately led to the conclusion, first formulated by E. Haeckel and afterwards applied by A. Hyatt, S. S. Buckman, and other authors, that every organism, during the course of its individual development, tends to reproduce stages similar to those passed through in the history of its race. This 'theory of recapitulation', applied to those groups of organisms which have shells that grow by successive accretions and retain the earlier stages unaltered, seems to afford strong circumstantial evidence of genetic affinity in various stocks. But certain safeguards are necessary if false conclusions are to be avoided. The tendency towards diversity that is inherent in all organisms leads to an acceleration of development by which adult characters of an ancestor appear in earlier stages of later generations. Hence the older part of (say) a molluscan shell should afford some clue to its immediate progenitors. It is held, too, by the exponents of the recapitulation theory that extreme acceleration of development may result in the omission of some stages in the regular sequence. Thus, all young ammonites, immediately after the embryonic shell, have depressed whorls which remain smooth to a diameter of several millimetres. After this stage ornamentation may appear, sometimes as ribs, sometimes as tubercles. Now, tubercles are regarded as a later development than ribs; consequently if tubercles develop directly (as they sometimes do), it is assumed that acceleration of development has caused the ribbed stage to be omitted. It is significant, however, that the 'acceleration' never causes the development of ornament on the depressed earlier whorls. This explanation of the absence of certain features which might be expected in the presumed descendant of a given stock is not always convincing, and other possible interpretations should be fully explored. One cannot deny the possibility, but

F

there is seldom any proof, or even indication, that certain selected stages of development have been omitted.

L. F. Spath, however, has denied the validity of the recapitulation theory in its application to ammonite development. He points out that new characters may appear quite suddenly in the young, that is, on the inner instead of the outer whorls of an ammonite, and suggests that the widely accepted sequence of developmental stages should be reversed. The question is complicated by the development, in some young organisms, of characters which seem to be adaptations to some special mode of life during the larval period. These are not known in any adult ancestor, and are not considered to be of phyletic significance.

The recapitulation theory demands that changes should always take place in the same order, for instance in the case of ornament-development in ammonites, from the smooth, through striate and costate stages to the tuberculate condition, or vice versa in 'degenerate' forms. The rigid application of this 'rule' to the ornamentation, degree of coiling, and other features of ammonite development, has sometimes led to the conclusion that the presumed biological stage is not in agreement with geological position. Thus S. S. Buckman cites: '*Xipheroceras* above *Microderoceras*, *Paltopleuroceras* later than *Amaltheus*, *Hildoceras* after *Harpoceras* in geological position, when they should respectively precede biologically.' Obviously something is wrong, for biological development must be in accord with geological position; and since, in the above instances, the chronological succession is known, the biological development cannot have been correctly interpreted. These genera are nowadays regarded as belonging to different lineages derived successively from independent offshoots of the fundamental ammonite-stocks, *Phylloceras* and *Lytoceras*. Certainly the precise horizon and locality of every fossil must be known and taken into account before any pronouncement can be made concerning biological affinity. In short the succession must be established before affinity can be proved.

The co-ordination of numerous observations has led to the conclusion that evolution in various groups of plants and animals has taken place in definite directions—the Doctrine of Trends (W. D. Lang) or Programme Evolution (F. L. Kitchin). After the stages of morphological development attained by any particular group of organisms have been worked out through successive horizons in one area, they may be used to correlate the sequence of beds occurring in another district. Examples of such trends in various groups of fossils are cited on later pages. It must be noted, however, that the same trend may affect different stocks of the same group, and if these evolve at approximately the same rate, they give rise to similar forms within a comparatively short period of time. Thus the prevailing 'fashion' impresses upon an element of the fauna a characteristic appearance which may be used for purposes of correlation. As it is not always possible to name fossils precisely in the field, this tendency to synchronous parallelism in development (isochronous homoeomorphy of Buckman) is extremely useful in mapping. If, however, the stocks evolve at different rates, similar forms will appear at various periods of time. These heterochronous homoeomorphs have given rise to much confusion in stratigraphy, as they have often been grouped under the same specific name and have given the impression that certain 'species' have too long a range to be of value as guides to horizon.

The evidence afforded at the present time by the chief groups of Invertebrate, Vertebrate, and Plant fossils may now be briefly reviewed.

I. INVERTEBRATE ANIMALS

PROTOZOA are generally so small, the majority being less than a millimetre in diameter, that they can only exceptionally be identified in the field. Some Foraminifera, however, attain a much greater size, and, occurring in rock-forming abundance, are of value as guides to horizon. Thus the abundance of spherical tests of the arenaceous genus *Saccammina* gives a distinctive spotted appearance to certain of the Lower Carboniferous limestones in the north of England. The contemporary calcareous genus *Endothyra* and its allies seems to have given rise to larger forms which are now grouped in the family Fusulinidae. C. O. Dunbar and his collaborators have shown that the fusiform shell *Fusulina* is succeeded by the spherical *Schwagerina*, and *Pseudoschwagerina*, and these by *Paraschwagerina* evolved from the true *Schwagerina*. These genera lend their names to foraminiferal zones in the Upper Carboniferous and Permian rocks of Russia, southern Asia, and North America; they are further discussed on pp. 298–9 and 388–9.

Of similar stratigraphical importance are the large discoid Foraminifera grouped in the families Nummulitidae and Orbitoidae which bulk largely in massive limestones of early Neozoic age extending over large areas in southern Eurasia and corresponding latitudes in America. These large specialized shells have a complex internal structure which is subject to rapid evolutional changes, and various genera and species form valuable guides to stratigraphical position within the range of the families. The typical genus of the first-named group, *Nummulites* (Lamarck, 1801), is an involute form in which the whorls successively envelop the earlier ones by means of alar prolongations extending inwards to the centre (Pl. I). Traces of the septa are often seen on the outer surface of the spiral lamina; they are generally approximately radial in direction, but later irregularity often produces a reticulate pattern. The septal filaments are sometimes thickened at intervals by solid rods or pillars perpendicular to the surface, and continuous through several laminae and interlamellar spaces; the external ends of these pillars form granulations on the surface of the lamina. Thus successive groups may be recognized by the external ornamentation,

Table showing general succession of Large Foraminifera in early Neozoic Rocks of Southern Europe and Asia

MIOCENE	BURDIGALIAN	*Miogypsina* and small *Lepidocyclina* *Nummulites* rare or absent
	AQUITANIAN	Large forms of *Lepidocyclina* Reticulate *Nummulites* persist
OLIGOCENE	STAMPIAN SANNOISIAN	Reticulate *Nummulites* associated with small radiate forms *Lepidocyclina*
EOCENE	BARTONIAN	Appearance of reticulate *Nummulites* Extinction of *Discocyclina*
	LEDIAN	Pilate and small radiate *Nummulites* Large smooth species of *Assilina* Fusiform species of *Alveolina*
	LUTETIAN	Appearance of pilate *Nummulites* and abundance of radiate forms Medium-sized *Assilina* Large *Discocyclina* and *Dictyoconoides* Large elliptical *Alveolina*
	YPRESIAN LANDENIAN	Radiate group of *Nummulites* Small granulose species of *Assilina* Small thin species of *Discocyclina* Elliptical *Alveolina*
CRETACEOUS	UPPER	Species of *Orbitoides*
	LOWER	Species of *Orbitolina*

e.g. radiate, granulate, and reticulate groups, and these, as well as completely identified species, serve as zonal guides in the Eocene and Oligocene rocks. *Assilina*, confined to Eocene horizons, is related to *Nummulites*, but the alar prolongations are so thin that the outlines of the inner whorls are visible externally. The genera *Heterostegina*, *Spiroclypeus* (Pl. I), and *Cycloclypeus* have a spiral development like the nummulitids, but the later chambers are subdivided by secondary septa, and thus show some resemblance to those of the orbitoids. In the latter group the spiral mode of growth is sooner or later replaced by a cyclical development in which a layer of equatorial chambers is overlaid on both sides by several layers of flattened secondary chamberlets with a similar concentric arrangement. The genera may best be distinguished by the form of the principal chambers as seen in median section, rectangular in the Eocene genus *Discocyclina* (often cited as *Orthophragmina*), and its stellate variant *Asterocyclina*, hexagonal or lozenge-shaped in the Oligocene *Lepidocyclina* (Pl. I) and its subgeneric divisions. The most useful distinction of the Miocene *Miogypsina* is the pronounced spiral development of the inner whorls on which lateral layers of irregular segments are superposed. Several large porcellanous Foraminifera also show a structural complexity comparable with that of the orbitoids. The fusiform genera *Alveolina*, *Alveolinella*, *Borelis*, and *Trillina* are characteristic of Neozoic horizons. *Dictyoconus* is a large conical arenaceous form with subdivided chambers, and another arenaceous form, *Loftusia*, with fusiform test and labyrinthic chambers is one of the largest Foraminifera known, and is characteristic of basal Eocene rocks in Persia. The general succession of the large Foraminifera in early Neozoic rocks is tabulated on p. 68, and their distribution is discussed in Chapter XV.

The PORIFERA are of slight importance as stratigraphical guides. Apart from some siliceous sponges in the Upper Cretaceous, such as the long-stalked *Siphonia* and *Jerea* with pear-shaped body, the short-stemmed or sessile, bowl-shaped *Verruculina*, the funnel-shaped *Ventriculites* with intricately folded walls, and *Doryderma* with cylindrical branches, which serve as guide-fossils in the absence of better evidence, the majority are not of great use to the field-worker. Calcareous sponges also are too rare to be important in this connexion, though they may be locally abundant as are *Raphidonema* and *Barroisia* in the famous Lower Cretaceous sponge-bed of Faringdon in Berkshire.

That the GRAPTOLITES have proved of great value in stratigraphical investigation is shown by the classical work of Charles Lapworth in the southern Uplands of Scotland, and more recently by the work of many geologists along the lines initiated by Lapworth. The earliest graptolite at present known, *Dictyonema*, occurs in the Tremadoc Beds of North Wales, which are usually placed by British geologists at the top of the Cambrian system, though from a palaeontological point of view they might well be considered as basal Ordovician. *Dictyonema* consists of a large number of branches springing from a base of attachment; the branches are connected by numerous horizontal processes and so give the appearance of a network. Each branch extends by a succession of buds which produce cells or thecae of two kinds: the ordinary thecae or hydrothecae forming a series on the inner side of the branch, and the bithecae situated alternately to right and left of the hydrothecae. This form seems to have given rise to two quite distinct stocks. One, retaining the dendroid habit and thecal characters of *Dictyonema* persists through a long range of strata (Ordovician to Carboniferous) with little apparent change, and so is not reliable for purposes of correlation; this series is grouped in the order Dendroidea. In the other series, to which the name Graptolites is usually restricted, the branches bear thecae of only one type; it passed through a sequence of rapid developmental changes before the end of the Silurian period when it became extinct. It is this sequence of changes which forms the basis for the use of graptolites in the correlation of strata. The main developmental trends are: (1) a change in the direction of growth, (2) progressive simplification of branching, (3) elaboration of the thecae. The first of these trends 'brings about a change from the primitive pendent or hanging form to the scandent or climbing position' (G. L. Elles, 1922), as shown in Fig. 4. The second development consists in rapid reduction of the number of branches, as exemplified by *Clonograptus* with 32 branches, *Loganograptus* with 16, *Dichograptus* with 8, *Tetragraptus* with 4, *Didymograptus* with 2, and *Monograptus* with 1. These two trends appear to have developed almost simultaneously in the successful types; and forms in which the tendency to reduction proceeds more rapidly than the change in direction of growth soon die out, as for instance, *Azygograptus*, restricted to the top of the Arenig Series. Thus, *Dictyonema*, a pendent form, is followed on the one hand by pendent forms of which *Bryograptus*, *Tetragraptus fruticosus* (Hall) and *Didymograptus murchisoni* (Beck) form a series, and on the other hand by a horizontal or extensiform series exemplified by *Clonograptus*, *Loganograptus*, *Tetragraptus quadribrachiatus* (Hall) and *Didymograptus extensus* (Hall). Development was more rapid in the horizontal forms, so there is commonly an association of (say) pendent four-branched graptolites with horizontal two-branched forms. The graptolites so far mentioned are characteristic of Lower Ordovician strata. Upper Ordovician horizons are marked by widespread attainment of the scandent mode of growth in two-branched graptolites resulting in the prevalence of biserial forms. Afterwards a further decline in branching capacity led to the prolific monograptid type which is restricted to the Silurian system.

In mid-Ordovician time development on the lines just described was temporarily arrested, while the third trend became manifest. So far the thecae were of simple cylindrical type. But in rocks of Llandeilo age the majority of graptolites have thecae whose walls show a progressive degree of torsion, with the result that the obverse and reverse of the graptolites

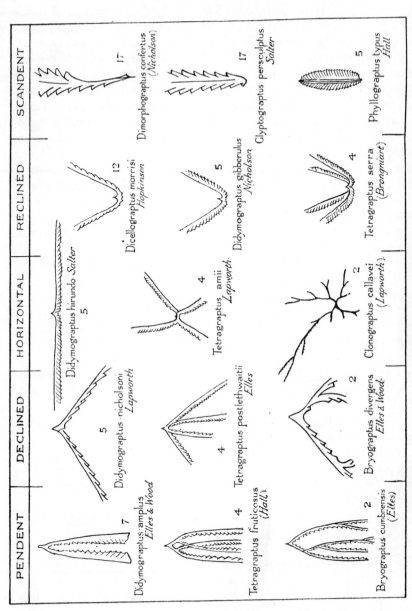

| PENDENT | DECLINED | HORIZONTAL | RECLINED | SCANDENT |

Didymograptus amplus *Elles & Wood* 7

Didymograptus nicholsoni *Lapworth* 5

Didymograptus hirundo *Salter* 5

Dicellograptus morrisi *Hopkinson* 12

Dimorphograptus confertus (*Nicholson*) 17

Tetragraptus fruticosus (*Hall*) 4

Tetragraptus postlethwaitii *Elles* 4

Tetragraptus amii *Lapworth* 4

Didymograptus gibberulus *Nicholson* 5

Glyptograptus persculptus *Salter* 17

Bryograptus cumbrensis (*Elles*) 2

Bryograptus divergens *Elles & Wood* 2

Clonograptus callavei (*Lapworth*) 2

Tetragraptus serra (*Brongniart*) 4

Phyllograptus typus *Hall* 5

FIG. 4. GRAPTOLITES, *showing direction of branching (after Elles and Wood). Figures all about three times the natural size. Numbers refer to zones enumerated in Tables on pp. 164 and 196*

present a very different appearance. This trend—the elaboration of thecae (Fig. 5)—is also well seen in the scandent *Climacograptus* and *Glyptograptus* groups of Upper Ordovician age, of which the most specialized types are not only introverted (turned inwards) but also introtorted (twisted inwards). Thecal elaboration of another type is seen in certain of the Silurian mono-graptids and develops along two lines: (1) in the direction of isolation, and (2) in the direction of lobation. Extreme lobation would most likely restrict the thecal aperture, and this type, along with the isolate forms, does not survive later than the Valentian Series. A moderate degree of lobation, however, persists in the hooked thecae of early Salopian horizons and later passes gradually into the 'old-fashioned' straight thecae similar to those of the earliest Silurian zones. Various thecal types are illustrated in Fig. 5. As numerous lineages attain the same stage of development within a re-stricted vertical range, the prevailing 'fashion' affecting graptolite society as a whole is invaluable as a guide to the correlation of Lower Palaeozoic strata.

The graptolite zones of the Ordovician and Silurian systems are dis-cussed in later chapters, but the broad outline of graptolite-history as sumarized by G. L. Elles (1922) may be given here:

1. General simplification of branching coupled with change in direction of growth. Attainment of two-branched pendent and horizontal forms with straight cylindrical thecae. Characteristic of the Arenig Series in the Ordo-vician system.

2. First conspicuous elaboration of thecae in the prevalent reclined grap-tolites. Development of biserial scandent types. Characteristic of Llandeilo Beds, Ordovician.

3. Widespread attainment of scandent position in two-branched, biserial types. Characteristic of Bala Series, Ordovician.

4. Reduction to one branch in scandent types which undergo conspicuous elaboration of thecae. Characteristic of Silurian system: isolate and lobate types in Valentian Series, hooked forms in Wenlock Series, straight thecae in Ludlow Series.

Thus the graptolite faunas may be recognized in a general way without special knowledge of the genera and species on which the above stages are further subdivided (Chap. IV and V).

The CORALS constitute a group of the phylum Anthozoa, distinguished from their allies the sea-anemones in secreting a hard calcareous structure known as the corallum. This encloses the lower part of the body, and may be regarded as an external skeleton. In a typical simple coral the corallum is more or less conical, but is usually bent into a cornute form; in some cases, however, the corallum is discoid, the sides of the cone being practic-ally horizontal. The cone is fixed to the substratum by its apex and grows larger upwards, forming a cup or calyx in which the polyp is fixed. The polyps multiply by budding in various ways, and in simple corals the

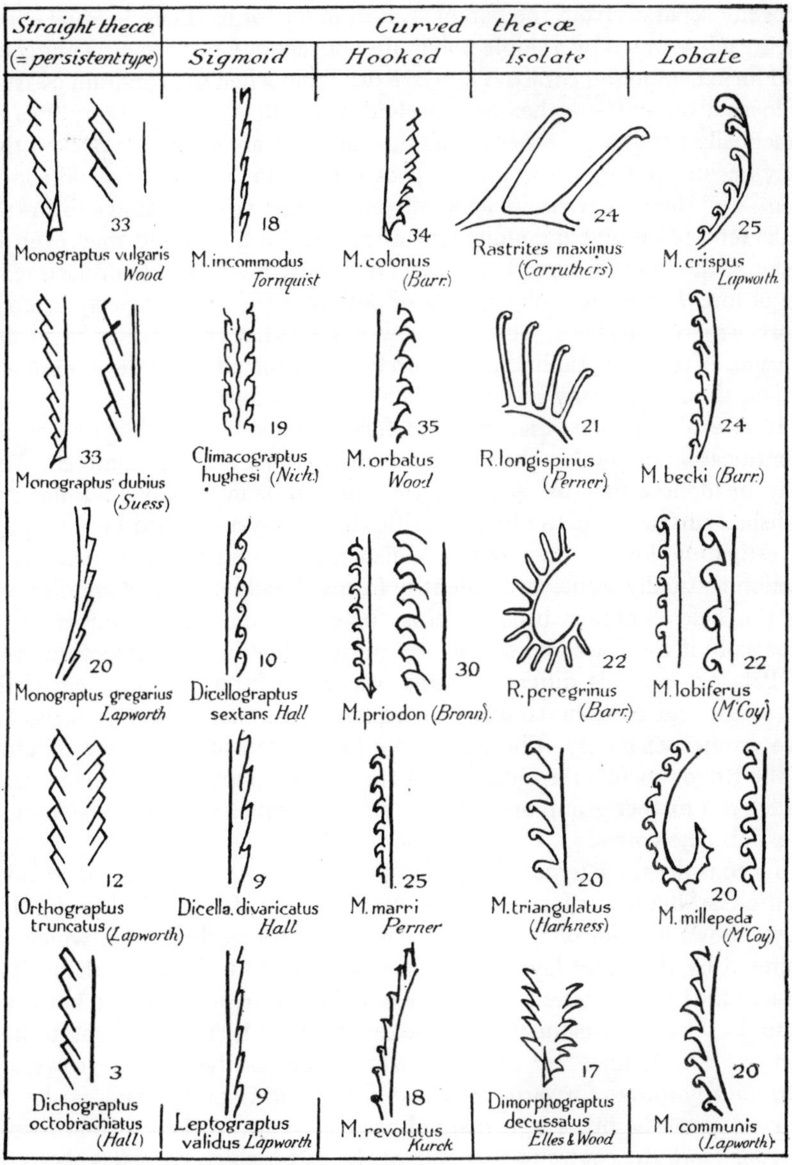

Straight thecæ	Curved thecæ			
(= persistent type)	Sigmoid	Hooked	Isolate	Lobate

Monograptus vulgaris *Wood* 33	M. incommodus *Tornquist* 18	M. colonus *(Barr.)* 34	Rastrites maximus *(Carruthers)* 24	M. crispus *Lapworth* 25
Monograptus dubius *(Suess)* 33	Climacograptus hughesi *(Nich.)* 19	M. orbatus *Wood* 35	R. longispinus *(Perner)* 21	M. becki *(Barr.)* 24
Monograptus gregarius *Lapworth* 20	Dicellograptus sextans *Hall* 10	M. priodon *(Bronn).* 30	R. peregrinus *(Barr.)* 22	M. lobiferus *(M'Coy)* 22
Orthograptus truncatus *(Lapworth)* 12	Dicella. divaricatus *Hall* 9	M. marri *Perner* 25	M. triangulatus *(Harkness)* 20	M. millepeda *(M'Coy)* 20
Dichograptus octobrachiatus *(Hall)* 3	Leptograptus validus *Lapworth* 9	M. revolutus *Kurck* 18	Dimorphograptus decussatus *Elles & Wood* 17	M. communis *(Lapworth)* 20

FIG. 5. GRAPTOLITES: *types of thecae (after Elles and Wood). Figures all about three times the natural size. Numbers refer to zones enumerated in Tables on pp. 164 and 196*

progeny separate from the parent. But in many forms the individual coral-lites, each secreted by a single polyp, do not separate but remain connected and form compound corals. These are dendroid when the corallum consists of loose divergent branches, or phaceloid (fasciculate) when the corallites are practically parallel. In other forms the corallites are so closely packed that they become polygonal by mutual pressure—the massive or cerioid condi-tion—and then the walls are generally coherent. In some massive forms the walls tend to become indefinite (the astraeoid condition) and may even be lacking, the internal septa becoming confluent; this is the thamnastraeoid condition. These successive grades of development were formerly taken to mark generic divisions, but it is now known that they can arise in any lineage. A true genetic line may therefore include all these developmental stages, though in many lineages only a few are known.

It is evident, then, that external form cannot be relied upon for the identification of corals—the internal features must also be examined. This may be done either by grinding the corallite transversely to a flat and polished surface, or better by preparing thin transverse slices. For complete investigation longitudinal sections also are necessary, but a transverse section is usually sufficient to identify forms already described and figured. In the field corallites broken across may give the desired information, especially if the fractured surface be wetted. The internal structural plan of Palaeozoic corals differs in some important features from that of the Mesozoic and Neozoic corals. Consequently it is desirable to discuss the two groups separately. The Palaeozoic forms are usually classed together as the Rugosa, while the more recent corals are grouped as the Hexacoralla. There is a further group of uncertain affinities which may be considered as the Tabulate corals.

To consider the **Rugosa** first. The simplest structural plan is illustrated in the Carboniferous forms referred to the genus *Zaphrentis* (Fig. 6). The calyx shows a series of radiating vertical partitions called septa which are secreted by the outer layers of body tissue folded in between them. The base of the body secretes a horizontal plate of calcareous material, known as a tabula, which forms the floor of the calyx; this is best seen in longitudinal section. The tabulae are built up successively as the animal grows and periodically moves forward in the extending calyx. Each tabula is slightly convex upwards, but a well-marked groove known as the cardinal fossula extends from the centre to that side of the calyx which corresponds to the convex curve of the corallite. Sometimes three other fossulae, dividing the tabulae into quadrants, may be recognized but they are never conspicuous. The median line of the cardinal fossula is occupied by the cardinal septum, and as this is shorter and less prominent than the other septa the fossula forms a conspicuous septal gap, which also marks a line of symmetry. Opposite to the cardinal septum is the counter-septum on each side of which is a counter-lateral septum. No new septa are formed between these, and therefore another break in septal arrangement is displayed here in transverse sections of the corallite. Further septal breaks occur next to the two alar septa which occupy positions on each side about midway between the cardinal and counter-septa. New septa are formed in pairs on the cardinal sides of the last-formed septa, starting from the counter-lateral and alar septa. Thus, although there are six primary septa, the septal breaks divide the corallite into four quadrants, and it is only in these quadrants that secondary septa appear. This feature, which led E. Haeckel to name

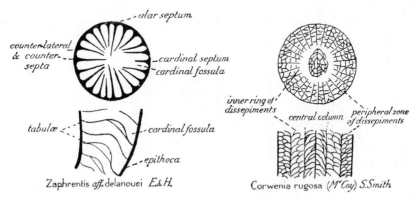

FIG. 6. STRUCTURAL PLANS OF RUGOSE CORALS

these corals the Tetracoralla, is characteristic of the Rugosa as a whole, though it is often obscured by other structural modifications.

More specialized corals like *Caninia* (Fig. 7), *Cystiphyllum*, and *Palaeosmilia* (Fig. 7) show an important modification in the horizontal structural elements. At the outer edges of the tabulae they form small plates known as dissepiments, which differ from the tabulae only in having a more vertical disposition. Their full development gives the outer part of the corallite a vesicular appearance which is conspicuous in transverse sections owing to the almost vertical trend of the plates. They are, however, regarded as horizontal elements because they appear to be secreted by the basal part of the body which has moved forward 'in instalments' instead of 'wholesale'. In some corals, *Lonsdaleia* (Fig. 7) for instance, the septa become obsolete in the dissepimental zone. Early in development the six primary septa meet at the centre and are joined by the major secondary septa. Later this central fusion is broken, leaving either an empty space, as in *Amplexus*, or a central structural unit; the latter is called a columella when it is solid as in *Lithostrotion* (Fig. 7), or a central column when (as in *Aulophyllum*) it has a spongy texture. The structure of the central column is of considerable classificatory importance. It consists of radial vertical elements known as septal lamellae, and horizontal elements called tabellae. When these are

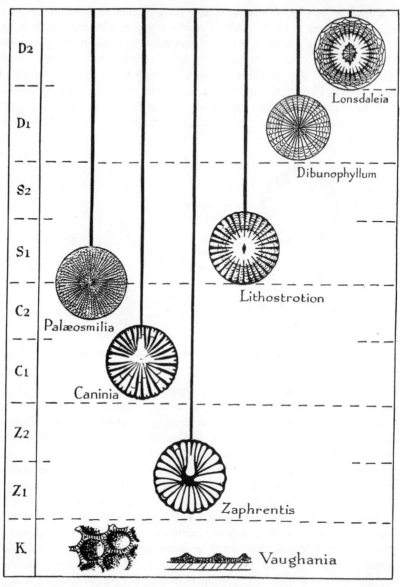

FIG. 7. STRUCTURAL TYPES OF RUGOSE CORALS DOMINANT AT VARIOUS
HORIZONS IN THE LOWER CARBONIFEROUS (*adapted mainly from W. D. Lang*)

regularly arranged as in *Corwenia, Dibunophyllum*, and *Lonsdaleia* (Fig. 7) they give the characteristic appearance of a spider's web. *Rhodophyllum* and *Aspidiophyllum*, now included by D. Hill (1938) in the variable genus *Dibunophyllum*, show some disturbance in the regularity of the pattern, while the central column of *Aulophyllum* is extremely irregular. This in crease in complexity of the structural plan is in general consonant with chronological succession in Lower Carboniferous strata (Fig. 7), and was utilized along with other series of fossils in the zonal scheme of A. Vaughan (1905) which is still the standard of reference for the Carboniferous Lime- stone throughout the British Isles. Slow evolution within a species group has been demonstrated by R. G. Carruthers (1910) who shows that pro- gressive changes in the group of *Zaphrentis delanouei* are consistent with stratigraphical position in the Carboniferous Limestone of Scotland. Rugose corals of other Palaeozoic systems have not been investigated in the same detail; some examples are mentioned in the appropriate chapters.

The **Hexacoralla** are essentially a post-Palaeozoic group. They differ from the Rugosa chiefly in the fact that the secondary septa arise in cycles, a secondary septum appearing between each pair of previously formed septa. The first cycle contains six septa, the second cycle twelve, the third cycle twenty-four and so on. The symmetry is therefore apparently radial, and in typical corals of this group there are no septal breaks. The simplest expression in hexacorallan structure (Fig. 8) is found in the genus *Mont- livaltia*, which may be regarded as a radical stock from which other types have been derived. A *Montlivaltia* whose corallites remain in contact gives rise to a dendroid form known as *Thecosmilia*; *Isastraea* is simply a massive *Thecosmilia*, while *Thamnastraea* is apparently derived from *Isastraea* by disappearance of the corallite-walls. Thus the generic terms mark grades of development which may occur over and over again in various lineages. In- deed, associations of *Montlivaltia, Thecosmilia, Isastraea*, and *Thamnastraea* occur at several Jurassic horizons, each association, which is probably a lineage, being marked throughout the branching-trend by a particular type of internal structure. Unfortunately these associations have not yet been adequately described. The hexacorallan forms just mentioned are usually grouped together as the Aporosa, because the calcareous material is solid. Some other forms show a tendency to become porous, and are grouped separately as the Perforata. This feature is well seen in the Cretaceous *Parasmilia* and the Pliocene *Balanophyllia* (Fig. 8) as well as in many other simple corals; it also occurs in many compound corals like *Litharaea* and *Porites*, especially in Neozoic reef-building forms. Opinion seems to be divided concerning the significance of porosity in the classification of corals, but the term 'Perforate' is a useful group name if applied without taxonomic significance.

The **Tabulate** corals comprise a number of genera which are marked by the feeble development or absence of septa, while tabulae are conspicuous.

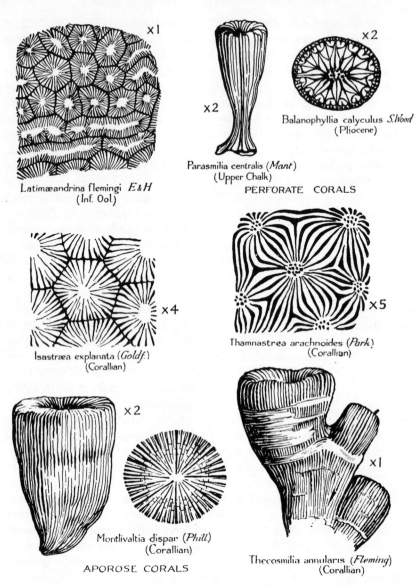

Latimæandrina flemingi *E&H*
(Inf. Ool.)

×2

Parasmilia centralis (*Mant*)
(Upper Chalk)

×2

Balanophyllia calyculus *S.Wood*
(Pliocene)

PERFORATE CORALS

×4

Isastræa explanata (*Goldf.*)
(Corallian)

×5

Thamnastrea arachnoides (*Park*)
(Corallian)

×2

Montlivaltia dispar (*Phill.*)
(Corallian)

×1

Thecosmilia annularis (*Fleming*)
(Corallian)

APOROSE CORALS

FIG. 8. SOME STRUCTURAL TYPES OF HEXACORALLA (*after Milne Edwards and Haime*)

They are all compound forms, and are the chief reef-building forms of the Silurian and Devonian systems; they first appear at late Ordovician horizons and persist into Carboniferous strata. The corallites of *Syringopora* consist of narrow irregular tubes which are connected at intervals by short transverse tubules; numerous species range from Silurian to Carboniferous horizons. *Favosites*, abundant in Silurian and Devonian strata, might be described as a massive development of *Syringopora*, for its corallites are polygonal from mutual crowding and communicate with one another by mural pores which suggest a limiting form of connecting-tubes. *Pachypora*, of Devonian age, is similar to *Favosites*, but its walls are thicker and the colonies grow out into feather-shaped masses. In the Ordovician and Silurian *Halysites* the narrow tubular corallites are arranged in anastomosing linear series, and form the well-known 'chain-coral'. *Heliolites*, ranging through the Silurian and Devonian systems, has two kinds of corallites; the smaller, more numerous, tubes are similar to those of *Favosites* and form a 'matrix' in which the larger, feebly septate corallites are embedded. The discoid or hemispherical corallum cited as *Michelinia* is often of considerable size; the large polygonal corallites are feebly septate, and the walls are pierced by irregularly distributed mural pores, while the numerous tabulae, often incompletely developed, give the appearance of loose vesicular tissue. The corallum named *Pleurodictyum*, so abundant at certain Devonian horizons, has essentially the same structure but is preserved in the form of internal moulds the centre of which is usually occupied by a foreign vermiform body. These two are now regarded as congeneric forms, and as the term *Pleurodictyum* has priority it should include the coralla formerly known as *Michelinia*. These tabulate genera are illustrated in Fig. 9.

ECHINODERMATA. This phylum comprises a series of marine animals whose vital organs are enclosed in a shell or test consisting of a large number of calcareous plates. There is considerable structural variation within the phylum according generally with differences in habits of life. The majority of the Palaeozoic echinoderms were of stationary habits, being fixed to the sea floor, generally by means of a flexible jointed stem, for at least part of their life. These fixed forms are often grouped together as the Pelmatozoa. Of this group only the crinoids (sea-lilies) have survived to the present day; the cystids are essentially Lower Palaeozoic forms, and the blastoids are found mainly in Upper Palaeozoic rocks. Other echinoderms, with a free habit of life, existed in these early periods, but it was not until the Mesozoic era that they became abundant. Thus on a general view it may be said that pelmatozoic echinoderms are characteristic of Palaeozoic rocks, and that free-moving or eleutherozoic echinoderms predominate in the Mesozoic and Neozoic systems. It is also worthy of note that most modern crinoids have lost the fixed habit and that some free-swimming crinoids are known from Mesozoic deposits; thus the gradual tendency to adopt eleutherozoic habits is further illustrated.

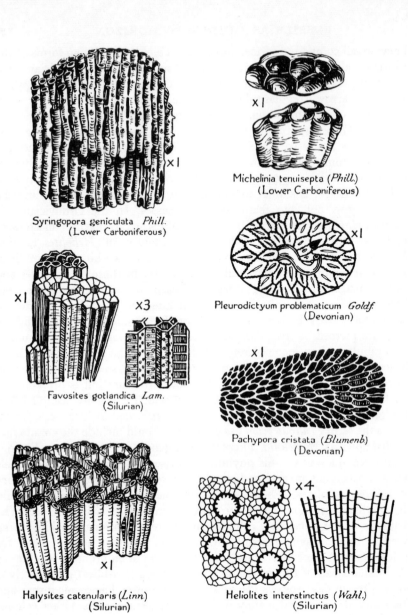

Syringopora geniculata *Phill.*
(Lower Carboniferous)

Michelinia tenuisepta (*Phill.*)
(Lower Carboniferous)

Favosites gotlandica *Lam.*
(Silurian)

Pleurodictyum problematicum *Goldf.*
(Devonian)

Pachypora cristata (*Blumenb*)
(Devonian)

Halysites catenularis (*Linn*)
(Silurian)

Heliolites interstinctus (*Wahl.*)
(Silurian)

FIG. 9. SOME GENERA OF TABULATE CORALS

The primitive **cystids**, of Ordovician age, are irregular sac-like forms with little approach to radial symmetry, e.g. *Aristocystis* (Fig. 10). From this unspecialized amphoridean condition later forms gradually developed regularity of plating and finally a pentamerous symmetry. Two orders are recognized, the distinction being based on peculiarities in the structure of the plates. In the Rhombifera, exemplified in Fig. 10 by the Ordovician genus *Echinosphaera*, the plates are folded in such a manner that rhombic striated areas are produced, half of each rhomb occupying part of one plate, the

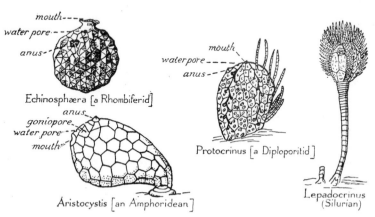

FIG. 10. CYSTIDS: *the chief morphological types* (after Brit. Mus. Guide)

other half part of the adjoining plate. Some members of the order, such as the Silurian *Lepadocrinus* have much fewer plates and show a distinctly radial symmetry. From the summit of the cup four food-grooves extend towards the base on specially developed plates, and numerous brachioles are borne at each side of the grooves. Furthermore, there are only three rhombs of a specialized type known as pectinirhombs. The general appearance of this cystid is that of a crinoid with arms recumbent on the cup, but the resemblance is only superficial. In the Diploporita the food-grooves are radially disposed and extend over the surface of the cup; they may be prolonged into branches connected with brachioles, as in *Protocrinus* (Fig. 10). The plates of the cup are perforated by canals normal to the surface; these are arranged in pairs and the external openings of each pair are enclosed in a well-defined oval area. The Diploporita are believed to have given rise by divergent development to the blastoids on the one hand, and to the crinoids on the other. The rarity of cystids and the allied edrioasteroids, however, prevents their use for zonal purposes; they are occasionally found in Britain in Ordovician and Silurian rocks, and *Echinosphaera* is locally abundant at Ordovician horizons in north Russia.

The **blastoids**, which probably arose from diploporitid cystids, have some resemblance to crinoids, but the food-grooves are recumbent instead of

being raised on flexible arms. True blastoids appear first in Silurian rocks but
are pre-eminently Devonian and Carboniferous fossils. They are rare in the
British Devonian and are locally common in the Carboniferous Limestone
of Clitheroe, Lancashire. Some genera, e.g. *Pentremites*, are exceedingly
prolific in the Lower Carboniferous Limestones of North America, but
are very rare in Europe (p. 30).

Remains of **crinoids** are rarely found in Cambrian rocks, but many types
were differentiated in the Ordovician. The class is distinguished by the
regular disposition of the plates and by the prolongation of the food-grooves
in the form of arms. It may be recalled that in simple Inadunate crinoids,
like the Silurian *Botryocrinus* (Fig. 11), the calyx is built up of two alternating rows of plates, the radials carrying the arms and the basals forming the
floor of the cup. In others, e.g. the Silurian *Cyathocrinus* (Fig. 11), the floor
is formed of two rows of plates, infra-basals being present as well as basals.
The two sub-classes thus distinguished, the Monocyclica and the Dicyclica,
follow practically parallel and synchronous courses, but while the monocyclic forms are now almost extinct, the modern crinoid fauna contains
many modified Dicyclica.

Development during early Palaeozoic times followed, in both sub-
classes, two main trends: (1) a tendency to incorporate the proximal portions of the arms in the cup; (2) the gradual formation of a rigid dome
covering the food-grooves on the oral surface of the cup. The two trends
develop simultaneously and give rise to the Camerate crinoids, which
appeared in the Silurian and reached their acme in early Carboniferous
time, but did not survive the Carboniferous period. The maximum
development along these lines is seen in the exclusively Carboniferous
monocyclic genera *Actinocrinus* and *Amphoracrinus* (Fig. 11), both found in
Britain and sometimes attaining rock-forming abundance. The Inadunata
also have numerous representatives (e.g. *Cyathocrinus*) in the Carboniferous
fauna, but, as already mentioned, the most specialized forms provide the
most reliable guide fossils.

No Palaeozoic genus of crinoids survived the end of that era, though
most Mesozoic forms are probably derived from simple dicyclic Inadunates
of earlier times. The Mesozoic crinoids show great diversity of structure
along different lines. Perhaps the most significant trend is the tendency,
repeated in various stocks, to adopt free-swimming habits by atrophy of
the stem. Well-known examples are the dicyclic Inadunates *Marsupites* and
Uintacrinus (Fig. 11) which by reason of their wide geographical distribution and restricted vertical range serve to distinguish definite horizons in
the Upper Cretaceous (p. 503). Both genera increase in size of the calyx;
but, while *Marsupites* enlarged the plates of the usual cycles, the increased
size in *Uintacrinus* is accomplished by incorporation of numerous small
brachial plates (analogous to the camerate trend). A free-swimming type of
monocyclic Indunata is *Saccocoma*, a genus known from the Solenhofen

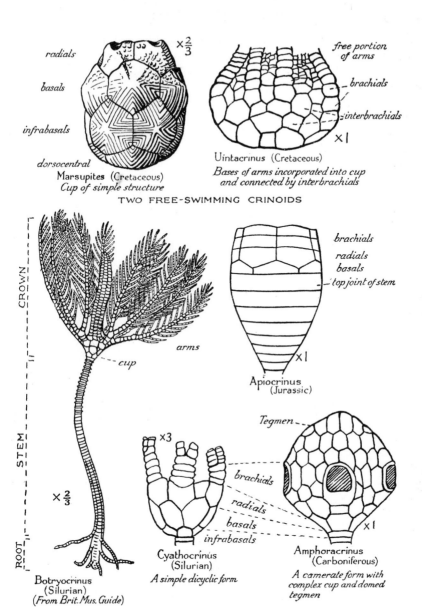

radials

basals

infrabasals

dorsocentral

Marsupites (Cretaceous)
Cup of simple structure

×⅔

free portion
of arms

brachials

interbrachials

×1

Uintacrinus (Cretaceous)
Bases of arms incorporated into cup
and connected by interbrachials

TWO FREE-SWIMMING CRINOIDS

CROWN

STEM

ROOT

×⅔

arms

cup

Botryocrinus
(Silurian)
(From Brit. Mus. Guide)

brachials
radials
basals
top joint of stem

×1

Apiocrinus
(Jurassic)

×3

brachials

radials

basals

infrabasals

Cyathocrinus
(Silurian)

A simple dicyclic form

Tegmen

×1

Amphoracrinus
(Carboniferous)

A camerate form with
complex cup and domed
tegmen

FIG. II. VARIOUS TYPES OF CRINOIDS

Stone of Bavaria and from the Kimmeridge Oilshale in Britain. It has been used with success as an index of horizon in the latter deposit during boring operations.

The **Echinoidea**, so abundantly represented in Mesozoic and Recent faunas, are rare in Palaeozoic strata, and early forms differ in a marked degree from the more familiar later types. The flattened Silurian *Palaeodiscus* has large, thin imbricating plates, and the earliest recorded echinoid,

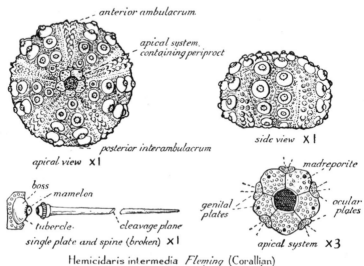

anterior ambulacrum

apical system, containing periproct

posterior interambulacrum

apical view ✕ 1

side view ✕ 1

madreporite

genital plates

ocular plates

apical system ✕ 3

boss

mamelon

tubercle·

cleavage plane

single plate and spine (broken) ✕ 1

Hemicidaris intermedia *Fleming* (Corallian)

FIG. 12. A TYPICAL REGULAR ECHINOID

Bothriocidaris from the Ordovician system is a small subglobular form with single columns of interambulacral plates and a few high hexagonal ambulacral plates. Upper Palaeozoic sea-urchins differ from all later types in possessing more than two columns of interambulacral plates; these were often imbricate, thus giving flexibility to the ellipsoid test. They appear to have developed along two distinct lines. One series specialized in the multiplication of ambulacral columns (e.g. *Melonechinus*), giving rise to a type which did not survive the Palaeozoic era. In the other line the ambulacra retained two columns, while the interambulacra had several columns of plates. The latter trend is exemplified by *Lepidocentrus* (Devonian) *Palaechinus* and *Archaeocidaris* (Carboniferous).

The Mesozoic echinoids are regarded as having developed from archaeocidaroid forms through the Permian *Miocidaris*, which, however, possesses characters that seem to connect it also with *Bothriocidaris*. The development of these later forms is characterized by loss of flexibility and reduction in the number of interambulacral columns to two, resulting in the cidaroid form which still exists (Fig. 12). Great diversity in form is shown by

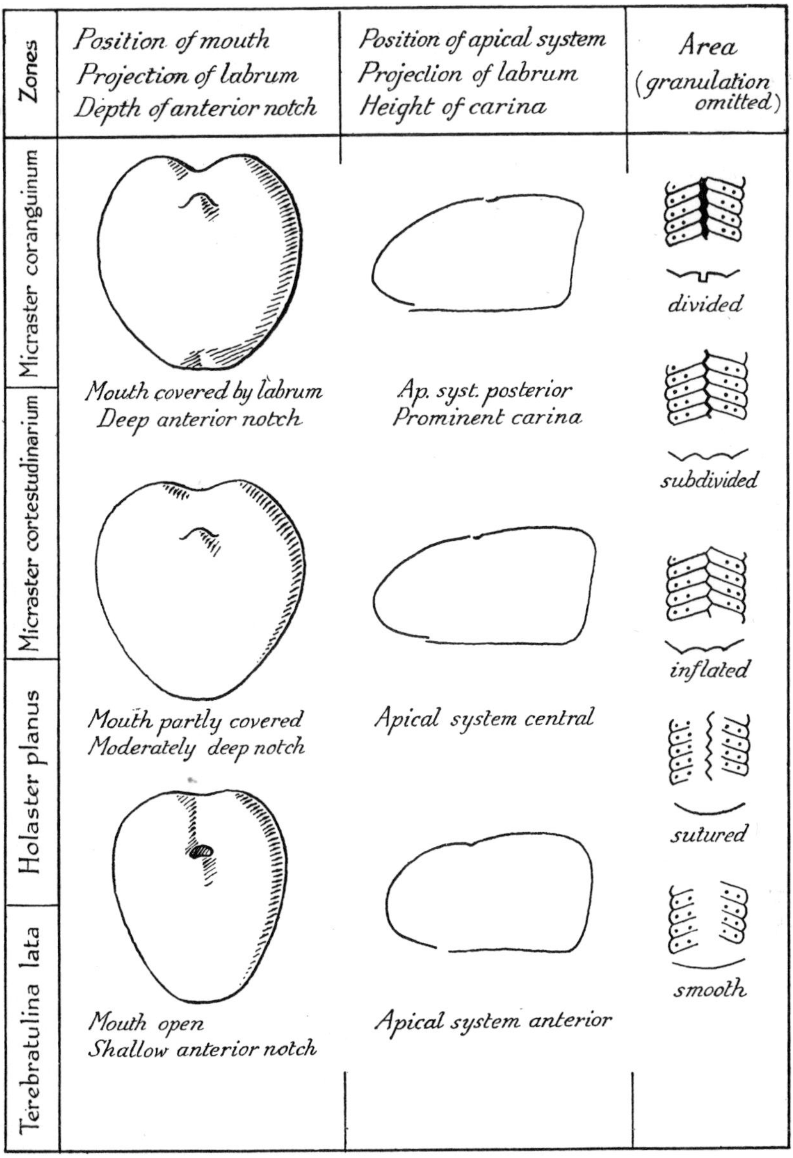

FIG. 13. THE EVOLUTION OF MICRASTER. *Areas in right-hand column are enlarged*

Mesozoic types, one of the most important advances being the early development of the Irregular types. Some of these are considered in later chapters. Owing to their preference for clear waters the record of echinoid history in British deposits is decidedly imperfect, and it is only in the Upper Cretaceous that these fossils have been extensively used for correlative purposes. Investigation of the evolution of the genus *Micraster* by A. W. Rowe (1899) has provided a basis for zoning the Upper Chalk; some of the developmental stages are illustrated diagrammatically in Fig. 13, and the zones are discussed in Chapter XIII.

Stelleroids (star-fishes) occur locally at various horizons in Palaeozoic strata, but, on account of their usually imperfect preservation, are seldom used as guides to horizon. Mesozoic rocks rarely yield entire specimens, but isolated ossicles are abundant in some formations. Study of a large series from successive horizons of the Chalk has indicated a general tendency to increase the depth of the body by increasing the height of the individual marginal ossicles. These isolated joints, therefore, are capable of yielding stratigraphical information of definite value, as shown by W. K. Spencer (1913).

The BRACHIOPODA are exclusively marine animals, and the majority are fixed to a rock or other convenient surface, usually by an organ termed the pedicle. The animal is enclosed in a bivalve shell, one valve being perforated, except in the most primitive forms, for the passage of the pedicle. The shell is symmetrical about a plane bisecting both valves. The pedicle valve is usually larger than the other, which is called the brachial valve because it carries internal structures (the brachidia) that support a pair of spiral appendages known as brachia. The nature of the pedicle-opening provides a basis for classification of brachiopods into four orders: the Atremata, Neotremata, Protremata, and Telotremata. The external features of a telotrematous form are shown in Fig. 14.

The **Atremata** are distinguished in having no special provision for the protrusion of the pedicle. The shell is horny or phosphatic, and the pedicle usually emerges freely between the two valves. In some genera the pedicle valve is notched, and tends to enclose the pedicle and to restrict it to this one valve. The early forms have a very simple hinge-line not furnished with interlocking teeth, but rudimentary articulation can be distinguished in later genera. The shape of the shell varies from the biconvex, circular outline of *Obolus* and its allies to the elongated and roughly rectangular form of the burrowing *Lingula*. The Atremata contain the most abundant brachiopods of the Cambrian and early Ordovician rocks; later they become a subordinate element in the faunas. *Lingula* survives from the Silurian to the present day.

The **Neotremata** comprise a small group of inarticulate brachiopods whose pedicle emerges through a perforation or sheath in the more or less cone-shaped pedicle valve. The pedicle-aperture may be restricted in size by the additional development of small plates. The shell is usually horny or phosphatic, but *Crania* and allied genera have thick calcareous shells without any pedicle-opening at maturity; they are then fixed to extraneous objects by cementation. Neotrematous forms arose in the Cambrian and are represented in most Palaeozoic faunas, but only a few genera survived the faunal changes of late Carboniferous and Permian time.

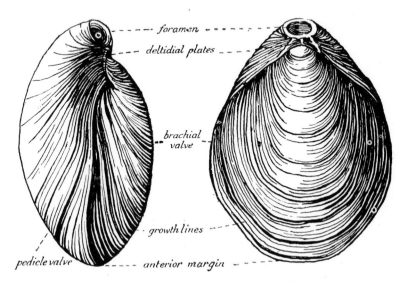

Terebratula grandis *Blum.* (Pliocene) X I

FIG. 14. A TYPICAL BRACHIOPOD: *external features*

The order **Protremata** includes more specialized brachiopods in which the size of the pedicle-aperture or delthyrium is restricted by a calcareous plate, known as the deltidium, secreted by the pedicle. The order is believed to have arisen from an atrematous form like the Cambrian *Kutorgina* which has a small deltidium and rudimentary hinge-teeth. The acquisition of hinge-teeth and consequent articulation of the valves seems to have led to the prolific development of the Orthidae (Pl. II) in early Ordovician strata. Members of the family continue in abundance through the Ordovician and Silurian systems, then rapidly decline in importance towards the close of the Palaeozoic era; they are represented in Mesozoic and Neozoic rocks only by the existing Thecidiidae. The Strophomenidae may be a terminal group derived from primitive orthids, from which they differ in general form and in details of organization (Fig. 36). They appear first in mid-Ordovician horizons and attain their maximum development in Silurian strata, finally disappearing at the end of Palaeozoic time. Their place is taken in the late Palaeozoic systems by the Productidae which have a similar concavo-convex shell with long, straight hinge-line. The pedicle-aperture is usually lacking in the productids; the shell was presumably anchored by the numerous hollow spines which projected from the external surface, but which are seldom preserved in the position of life. The old and familiar genus *Productus*, mainly of Carboniferous age, is nowadays divided into several subgenera, e.g. *Avonia, Buxtonia, Dictyoclostus, Overtonia, Gigantoproductus*, some of which are illustrated in Pl. IV. The associated *Daviesiella*, a chonetid for long wrongly assigned to the wide genus *Productus*, is distinguished by the possession of a well-marked cardinal area, hinge-teeth and, internally, by a pair of accessory adductor muscle-impressions in the pedicle-valve. Another family, the Pentameridae, is also apparently derived from an early group of orthids, but it develops on lines totally different from those of the foregoing families and becomes the most highly organized group of protrematous brachiopods. The shells are biconvex and usually much inflated, with highly incurved beaks. The umbonal region of the shell is divided internally into three chambers by five calcareous plates, but the chambers unite towards the anterior end. A pair of plates (the dental plates), situated under the hinge-teeth, converge and are supported on the edge of median supports which arise on the inner surface of the pedicle valve. This structure is duplicated in the brachial valve, but the median supports there are never developed to the same degree and may be altogether absent. When the fossil is represented as an internal mould (a frequent occurrence in decalcified limestones), the median septum and the margins of the valves together form a ⋀ which gives an unmistakable appearance to the rock containing them. Since pentamerids are, in this country, practically confined to Silurian rocks, this structural peculiarity is extremely useful in stratigraphical work. The external surface of the shell may be smooth or provided with radial ornament. Some genera and species of pentamerids are shown in Fig. 35.

The order **Telotremata**, like the preceding, is regarded as having evolved independently from an atrematous stock, since in the earliest stages of the shell the pedicle-opening is shared by both valves. The aperture is afterwards confined to one valve and usually becomes modified by the development of a pair of deltidial plates. These are secreted by the posterior part of the mantle, and therefore must be considered apart from the deltidium of the Protremata. A further distinction from the last-named order is the development internally of calcareous supports for the brachia. The order is divided into three suborders according to the nature of these brachial supports or brachidia.

The rhynchonellids (suborder **Rhynchonellacea**) usually have crura which support the bases of the brachia, and the earliest forms may have arisen from certain orthids which show the same feature. This internal structure is not always accessible in fossil forms, but certain external characters are generally reliable for identification of the shells. The shape may be briefly described as rostrate, the brachial valve having a median projection anteriorly, while the pedicle valve has a corresponding hollow. The general effect is a rough threefold division of the shell cavity, which, it has been suggested, is connected with the necessity for dividing the current of water entering by the anterior margin into two parts which pass through the brachia and out at the sides of the shell. In addition to the shape the general plication of the shell is distinctive; rarely the shell is spinose or smooth. The pedicle opening is nearly always situated below the beak, which is consequently acute in typical forms. Members of this suborder were first classified as species of the one genus *Rhynchonella*. This gradually became restricted, first by the transference of the Palaeozoic species to new genera, and more recently by the separation of most Mesozoic species. At the present time the old name *Rhynchonella* is restricted to a very few forms which occur in Upper Jurassic strata. The group arose in Ordovician strata with such genera as *Rhynchotrema* and *Orthorhynchula*. They were followed by such familiar Silurian forms as *Camarotoechia*, *Rhynchotreta*, and *Wilsonia*, illustrated in Fig. 41. In the Devonian system these are joined by *Hypothyridina*, *Leiorhynchus*, *Eatonia*, and other genera. *Camarotoechia* and *Pugnax* are among the forms represented at Carboniferous horizons. The Mesozoic forms are now classified on the basis of differences in arrangement of the internal muscle-scars and the dental plates. The disposition of the muscles would seem to depend in a great measure on mechanical requirements, which would vary according to the shape of the shell and other factors. In short, classification on this basis may not be phyletic. The classification of rhynchonellids is still incomplete, as the Cretaceous forms have still to be investigated. These are therefore named below (Fig. 75) as '*Rhynchonella*' spp., while the Jurassic forms are given their new names subject to the above reservation (Figs. 64 and 68).

The **Spiriferacea** include those brachiopods whose brachia are supported in the adult by spiral calcareous lamellae known as spiralia. In certain primitive forms, e.g. *Zygospira*, the spiralia are known to begin with a simple loop, spirals being formed later by elongation and coiling of lamellar projections from the sides of the loop. Typically the spires follow the course of the brachia and so form a pair of cones which are connected near the base by a transverse process known as the jugum. The disposition of the spiralia and the form of the jugum furnish a basis for dividing the suborder into three families, the Atrypidae, the Spiriferidae, and the Athyridae.

The Atrypidae include some of the simplest spire-bearing brachiopods. The apices of the spiralia are usually directed towards each other, the bases being connected by a simple jugum. Externally the shells show great variation, the general shape apparently being connected with the form of the spiralia. For instance, mature individuals of *Atrypa*, with spirals directed dorsally, have extremely convex brachial valves, while the pedicle valve is flattened. On the other hand, *Dayia*, in which the spirals are disposed laterally, has a flat brachial valve and convex pedicle valve. The surface ornament usually consists of fine radial ribs as in *Atrypa* and *Catazyga*, but some forms, as *Dayia*, are smooth. The internal features are of course seldom seen except in specimens dissected for the purpose; the external characters of some of these shells are shown in Plate III. The family begins in North America with the genera *Zygospira* and *Catazyga*. In Silurian strata *Atrypa* is widely and abundantly distributed, and *Dayia* is more restricted in range. *Atrypa* survives into the Devonian system, and the shells attain a large size in many regions.

Members of the family Spiriferidae have laterally directed spiralia connected by a simple transverse jugum. The shell of the most familiar genus, *Spirifer*, has radial ribs crossed by subcentric lines of growth, the hinge-line is long and straight, the pedicle valve has a cardinal area, while distinction is given especially by a median ridge on the brachial valve corresponding to a furrow in the pedicle valve (Pl. III). It should be noted that the modern practice of prodigal subdivision has affected the former comprehensive interpretation of *Spirifer*. For instance various smooth developments like *Martinia* are now separated from ribbed forms like *Brachythyris*, and all three genera are associated in the Carboniferous rocks where the family attains its maximum development. The contemporary *Syringothyris* is similar to *Spirifer* in many characters, but the cardinal area is exaggerated and the pedicle is provided with an internal tube or syrinx. Species of *Spirifer* are also abundant in Devonian strata where they are often used as guide fossils; some authors have instituted subgenera for various types. The Silurian species of *Eospirifer* and *Delthyris* mark the beginning of the family. It is interesting to note that the fine-ribbed *Eospirifer* is accompanied by the similarly ornamented *Cyrtia*, which also differs externally in the extreme development of the cardinal area (Pl. III); in this instance the delthyrium of *Cyrtia* is almost closed by a perforated calcareous plate known as the deltarium. These spiriferids combine with other spire-bearing forms and the pentamerids to give a special character to Silurian faunas. The family survives into Mesozoic time with the genus *Spiriferina*; this is like *Spirifer* in general form, but the shell-substance is punctate, and a prominent median septum is developed in the pedicle valve.

The athyrids also have their spiralia more or less laterally directed, but the jugum is V-shaped, with the apex produced and sometimes bifurcated or otherwise modified even in the early members of the family. The genera differ widely in their external features. The Silurian *Nucleospira* and *Meristina* (Pl. III) have smooth biconvex shells, as also do such Carboniferous genera as *Composita* and *Athyris*. The smooth appearance of *Athyris*, however, is sometimes due to accidental causes, for the shells of some species, when complete, possess thin, lamelliform outgrowths which are readily broken away before or during burial and so are rarely preserved.

Other athyrids, the Devonian *Ptychospira* and the Triassic *Tetractinella*, for example, simulate the rhynchonellids in external form. Some of the Triassic genera, like *Diplospirella* and *Koninckina*, have their internal spiralia duplicated by extensions of the jugum. These excessively specialized forms are among the last representatives of the Spiriferacea.

The suborder **Terebratulacea** includes those Telotremata whose brachia are supported by a calcareous loop. In external form the majority of terebratuloids contrast sharply with the rhynchonellids. The shell is often regularly biconvex, but sometimes broad folds are developed anteriorly. Moreover, surface ornament, apart from the usual growth lines, is rarely present, and the beak is often truncated by the foramen (Fig. 14). Fragments may often be distinguished as terebratuloid in character by the punctate structure of the shell visible under magnification. It is convenient to regard the suborder as containing two families, the Terebratulidae with a short loop, and the Terebratellidae with a long loop. The latter is formed of two parts, the descending branches being prolongations of the crura, the ascending portion being developed from a median septum which persists on the inner surface of the brachial valve. The presence of the median septum is sometimes indicated on the outer surface by a dark line showing through the translucent shell. There are also differences in the umbonal region; the terebratellids usually have sharp ridges on the sides of the beak, while the terebratulids are uniformly rounded. Moreover, the last-named group have no dental plates, while the delthyrium of terebratellids is supported by these structures. The suborder begins in the Devonian system with *Centronella* and its allies whose loops are composed of two lamellae from the crura which unite in the median line to form a broad arched plate. The widespread *Stringocephalus*, in which the centronellid loop develops into a long loop following the valve margin, is utilized as a guide fossil for a mid-Devonian stage. Another of these long-looped genera, *Cryptonella*, is said to persist into Carboniferous strata. These unusual forms are followed by short-looped terebratulids, such as the Carboniferous and Permian *Dielasma* and a large number of Mesozoic genera, some of which are illustrated in Figs. 65 and 66. The long-looped terebratellids (Fig. 67) of the Jurassic and Cretaceous systems are equally diverse and distinctive, and some of them are useful guide fossils at certain horizons and localities. The genus *Terebratula*, to which many of the genera were originally ascribed, is nowadays restricted to a Pliocene group typified by *T. grandis* (Fig. 14). It is evident that too much reliance should not be placed on the external features of brachiopods, for shells of similar shape and ornamentation may conceal very different internal structures.

Shells of MOLLUSCA are the most abundant of all fossil remains, and are usually well preserved, though the majority are formed of aragonite. They are subordinate to Brachiopoda in Palaeozoic deposits, but are dominant in later systems. Fossil mollusca are unsatisfactory from a biological standpoint, since the shell is usually external and shows few features related to internal structure. Also, in consequence of their varied habits of life,

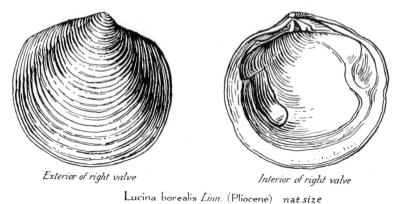

Exterior of right valve   *Interior of right valve*

Lucina borealis *Linn.* (Pliocene)   *nat. size*

FIG. 15. A LAMELLIBRANCH SHELL: *external and internal features*

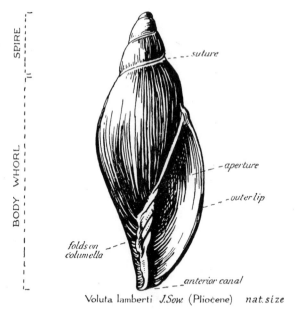

Voluta lamberti *J.Sow.* (Pliocene)   *nat. size*

FIG. 16. A GASTROPOD SHELL: *external features*

morphological modifications are abundant; and as these have appeared in many different stocks at various periods, few general trends of development can be traced among the larger groups. Indeed, of the three orders Lamellibranchiata (Fig. 15), Gastropoda (Fig. 16), and Cephalopoda (Fig. 17), only the last-mentioned has been used extensively for the detailed correlation of strata. Nevertheless peculiar assemblages of gastropods and lamellibranchs appear at various horizons (pp. 388–90), and evolutionary development has been traced in some restricted groups such as the oysters, *Inoceramus* (p. 501 and Fig. 74), and the rudistids (pp. 541–7, which may be used for purposes of correlation.

It must, however, be remembered that while such forms as oysters are very common bivalves in nearly all Mesozoic deposits, their investigation is beset with great difficulties, owing to the extraordinary variation in the form of the shell. As Woods says in his study of the Cretaceous lamellibranchs: 'The variation has been brought about by changes in the physical conditions of habitat, and particularly by differences in the character of the surface to which the left valve is fixed; it is found that the mode of growth and ultimate shape of the shell are determined mainly by the size, shape, and position of the attached surface, so that commonly any one species shows an amazing variety of forms which can, however, be linked together by large series of specimens.' The ostreid group has been subdivided into numerous 'genera', of which *Ostrea*, *Alectryonia*, *Exogyra*, and *Gryphaea* are most commonly cited. The characters on which these series are based have probably arisen several times independently during the history of the group. Exogyriform oysters are marked by a tendency for the shell to bend laterally and thus to show a twisting of the umbonal region. Grypheate oysters tend to thicken the left (attached) valve and to reduce the area of attachment. Some forms, usually classed as *Alectryonia*, have radial folds whose presence gives similarity of appearance but does not necessarily indicate close relationship. Some Mesozoic oysters are sketched in Fig. 69, but the number of illustrations that can be given (even in a monograph) is entirely insufficient to convey an adequate idea of the capacity for variation within the group.

The plane-coiled chambered shells of the **Cephalopoda** (Fig. 17) show variation in the general shape of the shell, its degree of coiling, and the development of ornament and septal sutures. Members of the class fall naturally into three orders, Nautiloidea, Ammonoidea, and Belemnoidea. The Nautiloidea is essentially a Palaeozoic order, though it is represented by a few genera in Mesozoic and Neozoic strata, and by *Nautilus* in modern seas. The oldest known assemblage of nautiloids, from late Cambrian rocks (Ozark Series) in North America, is described by E. O. Ulrich, A. F. Foerste, and A. K. Miller (1942–4). Many of the forms are sufficiently short and rapidly expanded to be called brevicones; these include species of *Burenoceras*, *Dakeoceras*, and *Ectenoceras*, arcuate shells with the siphuncle situated on the concave side. Higher strata in the Ozark Series contain these and the allied brevicones *Clarkoceras* and *Eremoceras*, associated with long, slender, slightly curved nautiloids (longicones) referred to *Ellesmereoceras*. Some of these nautiloids persist into the overlying Beekmantown Series which corresponds roughly with the Tremadoc and Arenig Beds of

Britain, but their associates in the Beekmantown Beds are distinctive. Among them are the brevicones *Piloceras* and *Cassinoceras* in which the annulated siphuncle is relatively large and, towards the apex, is almost filled with overlapping calcareous endocones; in many cases only the siphuncles are preserved in silicified internal moulds. The longicones *Endocycloceras* and *Bassleroceras* have arcuate shells with transverse annular ornament and marginal siphuncle. Some other annulated longicones, like the widespread *Protocycloceras* and *Catoraphiceras* have straight shells with small siphuncles. In addition, the upper beds of the Beekmantown Series are marked by the appearance of coiled nautiloids in some variety. The genera *Tarphyceras*, *Campbelloceras*, *Eurystomites*, *Centrotarphyceras*, and *Pionoceras* represent the Tarphyceratidae, *Curtoceras* and *Trocholitoceras* the Trocholitidae, externally similar but with the siphuncle placed dorsally. Some of these nautiloids have been recorded from Scandinavia, Scotland, east Asia, &c., but though some of the horizons can be recognized as contemporary, more data are needed before they can be correlated in detail. From the biological standpoint the American succession of early Palaeozoic nautiloids supports the view of L. F. Spath (1933) and other authors that 'the ancestral cephalopod was a bilaterally symmetrical cyrtocone or capulicone with wide marginal siphuncle'. From such primitive cyrtocones there developed independently orthocones on the one hand, ophiocones and nautilicones on the other, but the stages of coiling do not represent a progressive evolutionary series.

Many nautiloids in the Ordovician system show the development of calcareous structures within the siphuncular cavity. This tendency, already noted in *Piloceras* and *Cassinoceras*, is accentuated in *Endoceras*, *Cameroceras*, *Vaginoceras*, and allied genera, which have an elaborate series of invaginated endocones. Along with these distinctive Ordovician forms other straight and arcuate nautiloids show accretion of calcareous material around the siphuncular tube between the septa. Many of these shells have been included in *Actinoceras* from which other genera have now been separated. Unlike the endoceratids, which are restricted to Ordovician horizons, the actinoceratids have a long range and may have arisen from the persistent orthoceratid stocks at more than one period of time. In some of the coiled nautiloids, such as the oft-quoted *Lituites*, the early part of the shell is closely coiled but the later part is straight; this tendency to uncoil, perhaps an adaptation to change in the habits of life, was foreshadowed in earlier strata, and persists into the succeeding system.

Among the varied assemblage of nautiloids known from Silurian rocks there are the closely coiled shells of *Ophidioceras* and *Lituites* which both present a stage of uncoiling in their later growth, and loosely coiled forms like *Sphyradoceras*. Some of the straight and arcuate forms, like the true *Orthoceras* which now appears, are secondarily uncoiled offshoots of coiled nautiloids. Such actinosiphonate shells as the ovoid *Gomphoceras* and the cyrtoconic *Phragmoceras*, with laterally constricted apertures, are further illustrations of morphic diversity among Silurian nautiloids. Some of the Devonian and Carboniferous shells are the most highly ornamented forms within the order. The ornament takes the form of longitudinal ribbing as in the Carboniferous *Vestinautilus*, and it may be broken up into lines of tubercles as in the Devonian *Hercoceras*. Other genera in these systems show considerable variation in degree of coiling, but the straight shells of *Orthoceras* are still most abundant. These persist into the Triassic system where they are replaced by the first belemnoids, forerunners of the host of Jurassic and Cretaceous genera that continue the straight development. Some Triassic nautilicones, e.g. *Clydonautilus*, are noteworthy because the septal sutures are folded into lobes and saddles like those of early ammonoids. Otherwise the Mesozoic and Neozoic nautiloids, mostly referable to the genus *Nautilus*, have been affected only by very slight changes and are without significance as guide fossils, except perhaps the Cretaceous *Cymatoceras* with transverse ribbing, and the Eocene *Aturia* with lobed suture-line.

Ammonoids in general may be distinguished from nautiloids by the development (in the later members of the order) of elaborately frilled septal sutures, by the ventral position of the siphuncle, and by the common occurrence of transverse ribs and tubercles on the exterior of the shell (Fig. 17). The development of the septal sutures provides the best means of ascertaining geological age in a general way.

The earliest ammonoid known is *Agoniatites* from the Silurian, which is an occlusal form closely approaching certain nautiloids. The septal suture of this and early Devonian forms presents a smooth-flowing curve differing but little from that of many nautiloids. In later ammonoids the smooth curve becomes crumpled, and a number of folds, termed saddles (forwardly directed) and lobes (backwardly directed), are formed. The more or less angular character of this type of septal suture suggested the collective name 'goniatites' for these shells, which are characteristic of Devonian and Carboniferous strata (Pl. V). Permian ammonoids show a tendency to further subdivision of the lobes and saddles, a tendency which is continued in Triassic forms—indeed, one Triassic genus, *Pinacoceras*, attained the maximum of sutural frilling in known ammonoids. Along with shells bearing this 'ammonitic' type of septal suture are others in which the saddles of the suture are smooth, while the lobes are denticulate; this type, the ceratitic suture-line, is eminently characteristic of Triassic ammonoids, though it is imitated by certain Cretaceous forms. Owing to palaeo-geographical causes ammonoids of Permian and Triassic age are not found in this country, and in the rest of the world most of the old stocks became extinct at the end of Triassic time. Of the Triassic ammonoids that flourished in the Mediterranean area, only one family, the Monophyllitidae, produced forms which range into the Jurassic. These, the Phylloceratidae and the

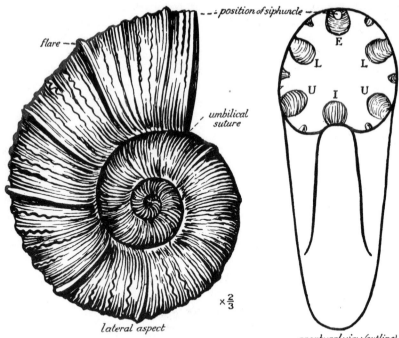

flare

position of siphuncle

umbilical suture

E

L L

U I U

×⅔

lateral aspect

apertural view (outline)

Lytoceras postfimbriatum *Vadasz* (Domerian)

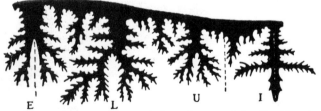

E   L   U   I

Suture-line of Lytoceras liebigi (*Oppel*)   [after Zittel] *enlarged*

guard or rostrum   apical line   protoconch siphuncle   alveolus
                                                        phragmocone

Section of a typical Belemnoid (pro-ostracum not preserved) *nat. size*

FIG. 17. STRUCTURAL FEATURES OF FOSSIL CEPHALOPODS

Lytoceratidae, persist through the Jurassic to the Upper Cretaceous and are characteristic, in general, of the Mediterranean region (the 'Tethys' of Suess). According to the attractive theory of L. F. Spath, these two stocks gave rise to successive short-lived offshoots, which radiated from the central (Mediterranean) area and specialized (presumably in response to environmental stimuli) in the direction of comparatively thick ornamented shells. Representatives of the stocks themselves, in the genera *Phylloceras* and *Lytoceras*, are occasionally found in certain British Mesozoic deposits, but, together with forms intermediate between the radicles and their trachyostracous derivatives, are more commonly present in areas nearer the Mediterranean 'cradle'. Thus the ammonites of British deposits are, for the most part, end-forms of numerous lines of evolution not directly connected with one another, and, for the full story of ammonite-history the sequence in southern Europe needs to be adequately studied.

Uncoiled forms appear at various horizons in Triassic and Jurassic rocks, but are most numerous in Cretaceous strata. The migration of new ammonite types into the British area and the dying out of old lineages enables the Mesozoic epoch to be divided into a number of 'ages', each characterized by the dominance of one or more families and corresponding, in a general way, with the stratigraphical stages. More detailed work has resulted in the ages being divided into 'hemerae', or periods during which one genus attained its acme of development and distribution. The corresponding stratigraphical division (representing the strata deposited during a hemera) is the zone. In this matter of minute correlation of Mesozoic deposits the ammonites have assumed an importance equal to that of the graptolites in Palaeozoic strata.

In this connexion may be noticed the successive modification of characters in given stocks which affects many forms at particular horizons. Thus as regards ornament, the liparoceratid type (Pl. VII) is characteristic of the Pliensbachian stage of the Lower Lias, the amaltheid type (Pl. VIII) of the Middle Lias, and the hildoceratid (Pl. IX) type of the Upper Lias. The Parkinsonian type (Pl. X) is restricted to the Bajocian stage of the Upper Jurassic, the kosmoceratid type (Pl. XI) to the Callovian, while the higher Jurassic strata are dominated by the perisphinctoid type (Pl. XIV). The hoplitid types are characteristic of late Albian deposits which also contain various keeled forms (Pl. XVI). These broad types are regarded as end-forms of various lineages which arose successively from the Mediterranean root-stocks, and they may be used in a general way for the identification of stages, though the determination of genera and species is necessary for the differentiation of zonal subdivisions.

Belemnoids have a straight chambered shell which, in most forms, is enclosed in a conical hollow at the anterior end of a solid, calcareous, more or less cigar-shaped rostrum or 'guard'. The shell, when found alone, resembles that of *Orthoceras*, but may be distinguished at once by the marginal position of the siphuncle. Belemnoids, *Aulacoceras* and *Atractites*, first appear in the marine Trias, and are abundant in Jurassic and Cretaceous rocks, while in younger strata their remains are very rare. Some Neozoic forms are, at least morphologically, transitional between the Mesozoic belemnoids and the living squids. Most Mesozoic belemnoids are difficult to classify, since there are so few features on the guard (often the only part preserved) that permit of ready and accurate identification. On this account, members of the group are not extensively employed as guide fossils, though a few easily recognizable forms, e.g. *Belemnitella* and *Actinocamax* from the Chalk, are so used (p. 503).

To the field-worker the most important group of ARTHROPODA is the order **Trilobita**, which ranges through the Palaeozoic systems. Though apparently complex in structure, trilobites are built up on an essentially simple plan, since they consist of a single series of similar segments (Fig. 18). Some of the segments at the ends of the body are modified by fusion and so exhibit the trends of cephalization and caudalization. In the former phenomenon five segments fuse to form the head. This number must have been fixed in Pre-Cambrian time, and there is no evidence for supposing that more have been absorbed since early Cambrian time. The central axis of the head (glabella) retains traces of segmentation and shows a progressive tendency towards a smooth condition. The general outline of the glabella changes in shape from a form with apex tapering in front to an anteriorly swollen form. These changes, however, appear in various stocks at different periods. Studies of the cephalic sutures and their bearing on the classification of trilobites have revealed wide differences of opinion in the interpretation of these structures, perhaps because there are no homologous sutures in living arthropods; a summary of these studies is given by C. J. Stubblefield (1936). Most trilobite genera fall into one of two categories; opisthoparian where the hind portion of the facial suture ends at the posterior margin of the head-shield, proparian where it diverges at the eyes and cuts the lateral margins of the cephalon. These two groups appear, as the Asaphini and the Phacopini respectively, in a classification by J. W. Salter (1864). Later C. E. Beecher (1897) renamed them as the orders Opisthoparia and Proparia, and added a third order, the Hypoparia, for trilobites with no apparent facial suture which he regarded as the most primitive forms. While the first two orders have been generally accepted, the validity of the Hypoparia has been questioned by many authors, and finality has not been reached concerning the relations of these trilobites to members of the Opisthoparia and Proparia. Caudalization is the tendency towards incorporation of body-segments into the tail (or pygidium). In some early forms the hind region is occupied only by a tail-spine (telson), and the fusion of two or three segments with the telson results in the formation of a small pygidium—the micropygous condition. Later forms may show fusion of more and more segments giving rise to the heteropygous

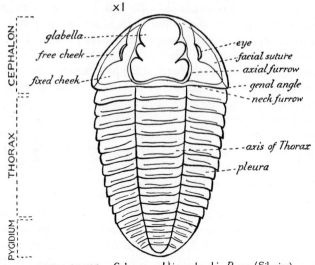

×1

CEPHALON

THORAX

PYGIDIUM

glabella

free cheek

fixed cheek

eye

facial suture

axial furrow

genal angle

neck furrow

axis of Thorax

pleura

A TRILOBITE – Calymene blumenbachi *Brong.* (Silurian)

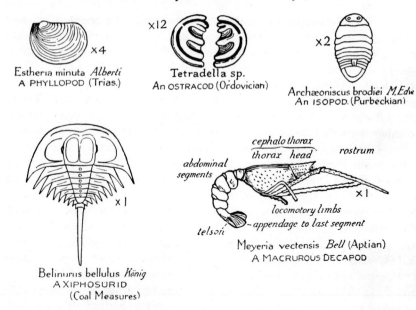

Estheria minuta *Alberti*
A PHYLLOPOD (Trias.)

×4

×12

Tetradella sp.
An OSTRACOD (Ordovician)

×2

Archæoniscus brodiei *M.Edw*
An ISOPOD. (Purbeckian)

cephalo thorax

thorax   head

rostrum

abdominal
segments

×1

locomotory limbs

appendage to last segment

telson

Meyeria vectensis *Bell* (Aptian)
A MACRUROUS DECAPOD

×1

Belinurus bellulus *König*
A XIPHOSURID
(Coal Measures)

FIG. 18. VARIOUS TYPES OF ARTHROPODA

condition when the head is larger than the tail, and finally the isopygous condition when the tail approaches the head in size. This trend, like the former, is progressive in several lineages at various periods of time. Thus in using trilobites as guides to horizon, it is necessary to differentiate between various lines of descent and to trace the progressive tendencies within each series of forms. At this stage only a summary of the families of trilobites dominant at the broad horizons need be given, as the subject is further considered in later chapters.

The Olenellidae, formerly Mesonacidae (Fig. 22), the dominant trilobite family in Lower Cambrian strata, has given rise to much discussion. Certain features of the head-shield seem to show that cephalization is less advanced than in most other families, and the pygidium of only one segment is taken as a primitive state of caudalization. It may be that the lack of a facial suture is also a primitive feature, but there is some uncertainty, for opisthoparian sutures are already developed in certain associated families such as the Ellipsocephalidae, Ptychopariidae, and Solenopleuridae. F. Raw (1925), however, claims that the cephalon of the ancestral trilobites bore seven spines of segmental origin, of which all but one were paired, and that as evolution proceeded the lateral spine-pairs successively attained dominance and produced in turn proparian, opisthoparian, and olenellid trilobites, the last group being the most specialized in having fused facial sutures. Raw's views have been criticized by several authors, e.g. C. J. Stubblefield (1936), on the ground that larval spines are not proved necessarily to have phylogenetic significance—they may be connected largely with a floating habit of life. Pending further investigation we may take the prevalent view that these early trilobites are primitive forms of the class.

In the Middle Cambrian rocks of Europe the dominant trilobites belong to the family Paradoxididae, which is usually regarded as an opisthoparian offshoot of the Olenellidae. In south and east Asia and Australia their place is taken by the closely allied family Redlichiidae. In both regions these families are accompanied by members of the Ptychopariidae, and by blind trilobites grouped in the Conocoryphidae, some of which may have originated in Ptychopariidae. There are also many species of the problematical Agnostidae and Eodiscidae (Fig. 23) which have no eyes or facial sutures and only two or three thoracic segments. Stubblefield (1936) follows O. Jaeckel (1909) in suggesting that these forms are proparians which became mature while development of the body was permanently arrested, and C. Poulsen (1927) believes that they are derived from early members of the olenellid stock.

The dominant Olenidae of Upper Cambrian horizons in Europe are often said to be derived (though E. Warburg, 1925 is doubtful) through the genus *Protolenus* from the Lower Cambrian Ellipsocephalidae, a short-lived family which appears to be closely related to the Ptychopariidae. But F. W. Whitehouse (1939) believes the olenids to be derived from the

ptychopariid genus *Lyriaspis* which developed into the subfamily Papyri-
aspinae in the Pacific region, and then evolved into other subfamilies in
South American and Atlantic waters. A. H. Westergaard (1922) has described the relations of the chief European genera within the family. Meanwhile in the Cambrian rocks of North America a series of large-tailed
(heteropygous) trilobites is associated with the ubiquitous ptychopariids.
They begin in the Lower Cambrian with *Bonnia* and *Bonniella* and continue
with such genera as *Kootenia*, *Dorypyge*, *Neolenus*, and *Olenoides*, all having
spinose segments and grouped in the family Dorypygidae. In Middle
Cambrian strata of British Columbia are such genera as *Bathyuriscus* and
Ogygopsis with entire pygidial margins, while farther east *Crepicephalus* and
Dikelocephalus, with two divergent pygidial spines, are characteristic of
Middle and Upper Cambrian horizons respectively. These genera (Fig. 27)
are largely restricted to American and Pacific localities, and their relations
are still undecided, though a ptychopariid origin has been suggested.

   The European Ordovician trilobite assemblages are dominated by members of the Asaphidae and Trinucleidae. The former appear abruptly, presumably by migration, in the Tremadoc Beds of Britain where *Niobella*,
Asaphellus, and *Symphysurus* are typical genera (p. 136). Later the large
species of *Asaphus* and *Ogygiocaris* (Fig. 30) are well-known Ordovician
forms. The origin of the asaphids is difficult to trace, but E. Warburg
(1925) does not admit any close relationship between asaphids and dikelocephalids. P. E. Raymond (1911) and H. H. Swinnerton (1915) trace the main
lines of asaphid development to the mid-Cambrian *Ogygopsis*, *Bathyuriscus*,
and the Bathyuridae and thence to an ancestral ptychopariid stock, but
there seem to be no connecting forms in the long intervening period. The
Trinucleidae comprises eyeless forms with no facial suture, and the cephalon is fringed by a wide pitted rim; three successive genera are generally
recognized, namely *Trinucleus*, *Cryptolithus*, and *Tretaspis*, and these are
divided by some authors into a number of subgenera. The late Cambrian
Orometopus (Fig. 24), which possesses eyes and facial suture, may represent
the ancestral type from which the trinucleids and *Ampyx* have developed
along different lines. The cephalon of the trinucleids shares certain features,
especially the pitted fringe, with the family Harpidae, and the two groups
are often said to be closely related. But differences in the glabella, thorax,
and pygidium lead E. Warburg (1925) and H. B. Whittington (1950) to
believe that the resemblance is an example of homoeomorphy, perhaps indicating similarity of habitat, and not the expression of a close relationship.
Certain other opisthoparian trilobites persist through the Ordovician system
with little change, and continue into younger strata. The Illaenidae, for
instance, in spite of certain differences, are perhaps related to the Asaphidae.
Species of *Goldius* show similarities with the illaenids in the hypostomes,
rostra, and pygidia, and many authors have considered a close relationship
probable, but again ptychopariid ancestry seems possible. The Calymenidae,

too, in which the facial sutures cut the genal angle, is usually regarded as an opisthoparian family derived ultimately from a ptychopariid ancestor, and the allied Homalonotidae, also persisting to Silurian and Devonian horizons, probably came from the same stock. The Lichadidae and Odontopleuridae, of uncertain origin, both show a tendency to develop separate lobes in the glabella by the union of the inner ends of the furrows. The Otarionidae and Proetidae, both appearing in Upper Ordovician strata are usually derived from the Olenidae despite the long interval between them. Both survive the Silurian and Devonian periods, the Otarionidae finally vanishing in Carboniferous, and the Proetidae in Permian time.

The Silurian trilobite assemblages are specially marked by the dominance of proparian forms (Fig. 37) distributed in three families. The Cheiruridae begin with *Anacheirurus* in the latest Cambrian horizons; the allied genera *Pliomera* and *Placoparia* follow closely. The family continues along orthodox lines with *Cheirurus* in Ordovician and Silurian strata, but in genera like *Sphaerocoryphe* and *Deiphon* the cheeks are reduced and the glabella becomes swollen to a globular form which projects beyond the anterior margin of the cephalon. The allied Encrinuridae are represented by *Dindymene* at early Ordovician horizons, *Cybele* at later stages, and *Encrinurus* in Silurian strata. *Staurocephalus* shows modifications similar to those in the more specialized cheirurids. The large and varied family Phacopidae has much the same history. It is represented by *Dalmanitina*, *Pterygometopus*, and *Chasmops* in Ordovician strata, *Dalmanites*, *Phacops*, and other genera in the Silurian system. Apart from these three proparian families the assemblage shows a decline in the number of opisthoparian families which survive, namely, Proetidae, Otarionidae, Illaenidae, Calymenidae, Homalonotidae, Lichidae, Odontopleuridae, and no new families appear. A further decline in number of genera is seen in Devonian assemblages; the dominant Phacopidae show several peculiar modifications while the other Silurian families are impoverished. Later, only the Otarionidae and Proetidae are left in the Carboniferous rocks and the whole group has vanished by the end of Permian time.

The **Entomostraca** is a convenient division in which to place several groups of primitive crustaceans whose chief point of resemblance is the presence of an unsegmented larval stage with three pairs of appendages.

The Phyllopoda are so called from the leaf-like form of their limbs. This is almost the only feature which the adults of the several genera possess in common, though they pass through nearly uniform developmental stages. The phyllopods are mostly non-marine, but inhabit salt-marshes and salt desert-pools as well as fresh water. The only form which needs consideration here is *Estheria* (Fig. 18) which, ranging from Devonian onwards, is abundant in certain Carboniferous, Permian, and Triassic strata. The shell is composed of two thin rounded valves united by a straight margin. The external surface has sub-concentric ridges closely resembling the growth-lines of a bivalved molluscan shell, such as *Posidonomya* (Fig. 47). The valves of *Estheria* may, however, be distinguished by the presence of a network of striae between the ridges, and by the absence of hinge structures; moreover, the shell is formed of chitinous, not calcareous material.

The Ostracoda include small, indistinctly segmented crustaceans which are completely enclosed by a horny or calcareous bivalve shell. This shell is the only part known in the fossil state, and but for the absence of growth-lines it may easily be confused with small lamellibranchs. The largest form is the Silurian *Leperditia*, which attains a length of some 20 mm. It has a straight hinge-line without teeth, and each valve bears a tubercle or 'eye-spot' on the antero-dorsal region. In *Tetradella* (Fig. 18) the valves have three lobes of which the central one is the smallest; this genus is often extremely abundant in Ordovician rocks. The minute valves of *Cytheridea*, *Cypridea*, and allied genera are often present in conspicuous abundance in Purbeck and Wealden strata, while the reniform shells of *Entomis* are profuse at some Devonian horizons.

The Cirripedia are unique among arthropods in adopting a sessile mode of life. The most familiar form is the common sea-acorn or barnacle, which secretes a solid calcareous pyramidal shell after becoming fixed to a convenient support. The cirripedes are all marine organisms, and while fossil forms occasionally occur in the older rocks, they do not become abundant until the later Neozoic stages.

Living forms grouped as **Malacostraca** have a constant number of segments; the cephalothorax is composed of thirteen, and the abdomen of seven segments besides the telson or terminal joint. The most primitive order is the Phyllocarida, mostly confined to Palaeozoic strata, but with one living genus, *Nebalia*. Members of this order connect the Malacostraca with the Entomostraca, since they combine characters of phyllopods and decapods with features peculiar to themselves. Fossil species have yielded only obscure traces of cephalic appendages. The head and thorax, composed of five and eight segments respectively, are covered by a thin carapace of one or two valves, while the abdomen has from two to eight annular segments. One of the earliest genera is *Hymenocaris*, which occurs in the Cambrian rocks of North Wales; it has a smooth, broad carapace, eight or nine segments in the thoracic and abdominal region, and six caudal spines disposed in three pairs. *Ceratiocaris*, an Ordovician genus, has a longer carapace and a long, spiny telson.

The Schizopoda bear a superficial likeness to the macrurous Decapoda, and a few fossil genera such as *Pygocephalus* and *Anthrapalaemon* from the British Coal Measures have been assigned to this order.

The Decapoda are not certainly known in rocks older than the Trias, though they appear to have arisen from Palaeozoic schizopods. The cephalothorax, bearing five pairs of walking limbs, is covered by a single carapace. A division into the two suborders Macrura and Brachyura, based primarily on characters of the abdomen, is convenient though not strictly natural. In the Macrura the abdominal region is free and strongly developed, being at least as long as the cephalothorax; this suborder includes the lobsters, shrimps, and prawns (e.g. *Meyeria*, Fig. 18). The abdominal region in the Brachyura (crabs) is short and curved round against the ventral surface of the cephalothorax. Both suborders occur sporadically at various horizons in Mesozoic and Neozoic strata, often being abundant at certain restricted localities.

The Isopoda include the terrestrial wood-lice, and also many freshwater and marine forms. They have a depressed body with seven free thoracic segments, and the carapace is but feebly developed. Fossil remains are somewhat rare, but one British species, *Archaeoniscus brodiei* M. Edw. (Fig. 18), occurs in enormous numbers in the freshwater Purbeck Beds of the south of England.

In the class **Acerata** the branchial folds function as gills or as lungs, or they may become metamorphosed into air-tubes known as tracheae, which penetrate the body tissues. Two regions of the body are distinguished, the cephalothorax and the abdomen, the limit being drawn behind the sixth pair of appendages. The segments of the cephalothorax are usually fused; those of the abdomen may be free. A fundamental distinction from the crustacea is the absence of antennae. The class is divided into two subclasses, the **Merostomata** and the **Arachnida**.

The sole surviving Merostome genus is *Limulus* (Fig. 2), the King crab, which inhabits the eastern coastal waters of America and Asia. The cephalothorax is semicircular and bears six pairs of locomotor appendages. The abdomen is composed of six segments consolidated into a triangular shield, and a long slender telson. There are six pairs of abdominal appendages which are modified into gill-books and function as respiratory organs. *Limulus* is placed in the order Xiphosura, which includes several fossil forms of similar aspect. Among these may be mentioned *Belinurus* (Fig. 18) and *Prestwichia*, occurring in the Coal Measures of Europe and North America. The genus *Cyclus*, also occurring in the Coal Measures of Europe and North America, has a small discoid cephalothorax with imperfectly preserved appendages apparently similar to those of embryonic *Limulus*. Some species of *Cyclus* may be larval forms of *Prestwichia* and allied genera.

The wholly Palaeozoic order **Eurypterida** (see Fig. 2) includes the largest arthropods known, some of them reaching a length of two metres. The cephalothorax usually bears two large faceted eyes and a pair of median ocelli on the dorsal surface. On the ventral side are six pairs of limbs, the hindmost being modified into paddles or claws, while the foremost may also be chelate. The abdomen consists of thirteen segments, the last being the telson, which varies in shape from a long slender spine to an expanded swimming organ. The anterior six abdominal segments (sometimes known as the mesosoma) bear broad leaf-like appendages similar to the gill-books of *Limulus*. The posterior six segments (the metasoma) bear no appendages. The presence of gills indicate aquatic habits for the eurypterids, but these animals are not usually associated with marine fossils; they are discussed in more detail with the Silurian faunas in Chapter V.

The **Arachnida**, which include scorpions, spiders, and mites, are comparatively rare as fossils, and little need be written concerning them. The scorpions show much resemblance to the eurypterids, but are adapted for terrestrial habits. They are known from Silurian rocks onwards, and a notable British occurrence is that in the Triassic rocks of Bromsgrove. The Araneae (spiders) are represented in the Carboniferous rocks of Silesia but are rare until the Oligocene; by far the greater number of known fossil species are preserved in amber from the Baltic area. A curious spider-like genus, *Eophrynus*, occurring in the English Coal Measures, is assigned to an order which appears to be restricted to the Carboniferous.

The **Myriapoda** (millepedes and centipedes) have a wormlike body with numerous similar segments, each bearing one or two pairs of limbs. They occur as early as the Devonian, but are very rare as fossils. Two genera, *Archidesmus* and *Kampecaris*, are recorded from the Old Red Sandstone of Scotland, while *Euphoberia* is found in the English Coal Measures.

The **Insecta** are occasionally abundant from the Coal Measures onwards, but the known total of fossil forms (upwards of 10,000 species) is very small in comparison with the multitude of species now living, and represents a mere fragment of the past insect faunas. The winged character of many forms, together with their fragile nature, militates against their abundant preservation as fossils. The lacustrine beds of Purbeckian and Oligocene age in the south of England are said to be rich in insect remains.

II. VERTEBRATE ANIMALS

The use of vertebrate fossils in stratigraphy presents special difficulties that do not arise in such classes as the corals, brachiopods, or the mollusca. The vertebrate skeleton consists of a large number of bones, held together by organic tissues. In the majority of cases the bones become more or less scattered after the death of the animal, so that isolated bones and teeth are more often found than complete skeletons. Also, the determination of the various bones and the identification of the animal to which they belonged demand a thorough training in comparative anatomy, which is rarely attained by field-geologists. At the same time the geologist should possess such knowledge of vertebrate fossils as will enable him to recognize their main characters and to decide if their importance demands the aid of a specialist. The following notes, therefore, deal with the general stratigraphical value of vertebrate remains, and with such easily recognized fossils as commonly occur in the various rock-formations.

FISHES, or fish-like organisms, must have passed through several stages of evolution before they acquired any skeletal structures capable of fossilization.

Consequently they are of no stratigraphical value below the uppermost beds of the Silurian system, when they appear in many parts of the world with a more or less extensive dermal armour. From the Silurian onwards there appear, in successive formations, certain dominant groups, each 'sharply distinguished from its immediate predecessor by some fundamental character, marking an advance towards the extreme adaptation for locomotion in water which was ultimately attained in the Cretaceous period' (A. S. Woodward 1915).

Within each of these progressive groups there are other structural trends which bear a close relation to habitat and mode of life as distinguished from the general conception of environment. Thus, while the ordinary fusiform shape of a typical fish is eminently adapted for swimming in the open water, other types of body-form correspond to more local conditions or habits of life. Fishes which habitually remain stationary near the surface of the water tend to develop a compressed, deep-bodied shape. The depressed and laterally expanded body of the flat fishes is correlated with a more or less sedentary life on the seafloor; the eyes of these forms are situated on the dorsal side of the head. A long body-form, with the median fins placed near the tail, is characteristic of rapacious fishes which suddenly dart upon their prey.

All fish groups seem to begin with fusiform types, the other adaptive forms appearing later. In many groups the latest members are eel-shaped, a condition that usually heralds extinction, though it also may be an adaptation to special habits of life. Spines and bony plates, as well as large size, always indicate a late development in any group.

The dominant Silurian fishes seem to represent a stage before the jaws had become completely differentiated, and before paired fins had been developed. The internal skeleton is entirely cartilaginous, and the body is stiffened by a hard dermal covering (hence the name **Ostracodermi**). In the majority of Silurian types the dermal armour has the form of hard, calcified granules. In Devonian types, the granules have fused into plates that correspond with the distribution of the underlying muscles in Lower Devonian ostracoderms, but in later forms are correlated with the course of slime canals which traverse the skin. These forms are discussed more fully in the chapter on Devonian faunas (p. 237–8), since a widespread facies of that system is classified by means of its fish faunas.

The acquisition of lower jaws and paired fins characterizes certain fishes as early as Lower Devonian time. They include the **Acanthodei** in which some of the skin-granules fused together at the front edge of the fins producing strong spines. These fishes are accompanied in Devonian strata by two other groups, the **Arthrodeira** and the **Antiarchi**, which, according to D. M. S. Watson (1925), 'possibly stand in some close relationship to the acanthodians'. The acanthodians did not survive the Palaeozoic era but gave place to forms more nearly approaching the modern sharks or

Elasmobranchii. Complete skeletons are rarely found, but the teeth of elasmobranchs are often sufficient to indicate the approximate age of strata in which they are found.

The typical **Dipnoi** (double breathers) are so named because, in their living representatives, the air-bladder assumes the function of a lung and thus provides a second means of respiration. These attained their maximum development and distribution during Devonian time, but afterwards rapidly declined in importance and are of no stratigraphical value in post-Palaeozoic rocks. The group is now nearly extinct, being represented at the present day only by *Protopterus* (Africa), *Lepidosiren* (South America), and *Ceratodus* (Australia).

The remaining fishes include the majority of modern forms and are often classed together as the **Teleostomi**, this name reflecting the regular development of membrane-bones on the margins of the jaws. The internal skeleton is always more or less ossified, and the body is usually covered with delicate overlapping calcified scales. It is convenient in the present connexion to consider separately two orders of the group based upon the structure of the paired fins. The earlier order have paddle-shaped paired fins, which consist of a scaly axis fringed on both sides by dermal rays; hence they are named the **Crossopterygii** (fringe-finned). Appearing in the Devonian period, these fishes were dominant in late Devonian and Carboniferous faunas, when they approached more nearly to land animals than any other group before or since. Thereafter they gradually declined and are now almost extinct, *Polypterus* and *Calamoichthys*, which live in the fresh waters of Africa, being the only existing genera.

The crossopterygians were gradually replaced in the dominant position by the ray-finned fishes or **Actinopterygii.** In these the scaly lobe of the paired fins is lacking, enlarged dermal rays forming the support of the fin-membranes. In the earliest members of this order (those of the Upper Devonian and Carboniferous) the fin-rays are more numerous than the corresponding skeletal supports, but the fins of later forms (in the Jurassic and Cretaceous) show correlation in the number of the rays with the internal supports. Moreover, the internal skeleton of early actinopterygians is imperfectly ossified, but later families show rapid progress towards complete ossification and become the dominant element of Mesozoic and later fish faunas.

The replacement of the cartilaginous internal skeleton by bony tissue, complete by the end of Mesozoic times, was accompanied by other evolutional changes. Gradual abbreviation of the tapering end of the body, and enlargement of the ventral lobe of the tail-fin, caused this appendage to change from the early heterocercal condition to the modern homocercal pattern, the latter becoming stereotyped at the end of the Mesozoic era. No bony fishes, however, developed large heads and short bodies until the Upper Cretaceous, and no sedentary types are known before the Eocene.

The Neozoic fishes are of interest to the geologist mainly from the standpoint of varying geographical distribution.

The following table correlates the chief structural changes in fishes, with the geological systems of which they are characteristic.

SILURIAN . .		Ostracoderms with granular armour.
DEVONIAN	Lower	Armour-plated ostracoderms (plates follow muscles). Appearance of fishes with paired fins.
	Middle and Upper	Armour-plated ostracoderms (plates follow slime-canals). Dominance of paddle-finned fishes. Beginning of ray-finned fishes.
CARBONIFEROUS and PERMIAN		Dominance of ray-finned fishes of early type (heterocercal tail, fin-rays more numerous than supports, slight ossification of skeleton).
MESOZOIC . .		Dominance of higher types of ray-finned fishes (completion of effective fins, homocercal tail, ossification of skeleton).
NEOZOIC . .		Numerous adaptive types of bony fishes.

The Devonian and Carboniferous fishes are described in some detail in Chapter VI, since they are of special stratigraphical value. The later fish faunas may here be reviewed in brief outline.

The fishes found in Permian rocks are closely similar to those of the underlying Coal Measures, but the rarity of sharks is a noticeable feature. Still, the remarkable pleuracanths attain their maximum development and are associated with a few acanthodians and cochliodonts and the dominant ray-finned palaeoniscids.

The marked faunal change which occurs at the end of the Palaeozoic system is noticeable in the fishes as in most other animal groups, though the Triassic fish fauna resembles that of the Permian in many respects. Thus pleuracanth and cochliodont sharks are wanting, though a few heterocercal scaly palaeoniscids and crossopterygians survive. Teeth of the Dipnoan *Ceratodus* are abundant in the Rhaetic of England, Germany, and India; this is the last important occurrence of the genus among marine fishes. The most characteristic of the early Mesozoic fishes are, however, the Cestraciont sharks and the homocercal ganoids. The former group, represented at the present day only by *Cestracion* (the Port Jackson shark), which has small prehensile teeth in the front of the jaw and crushing teeth at the sides, is represented by numerous teeth and fin-spines in Jurassic strata. The majority of Jurassic fishes, however, differ in that the anterior teeth are not small and adapted for prehension; they have a few, blunt front teeth. The chief genera are *Hybodus*, *Notidanus*, *Acrodus*, and *Strophodus*, the teeth of which have shallow undivided roots. When in contact their bases are merely deepened a little obliquely, but not fused, to produce firm fixation (Fig. 19). The fin-spines of all these genera are longitudinally ribbed, and differ from similar spines of the Carboniferous genera *Ctenacanthus, Sphena-canthus*, &c., in transverse section and other characters.

The homocercal ganoid fishes, which attained their maximum development in Jurassic time, are most numerously represented by the ray-finned, enamel-scaled Lepidostei, a group allied to the Palaeoniscids, and foreshadowed in the Permian *Acentrophorus*. Their blunt, rounded teeth, for-

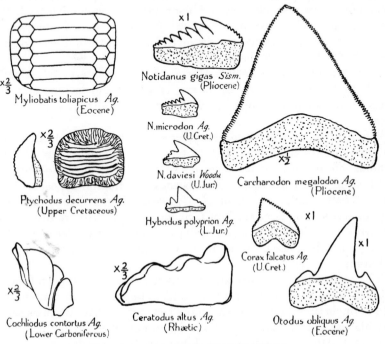

$x\frac{2}{3}$
Myliobatis toliapicus *Ag.*
(Eocene)

$x1$
Notidanus gigas *Sism.*
(Pliocene)

N. microdon *Ag.*
(U. Cret.)

N. daviesi *Woodw.*
(U. Jur.)

$x\frac{2}{3}$
Ptychodus decurrens *Ag.*
(Upper Cretaceous)

Hybodus polyprion *Ag.*
(L. Jur.)

$x\frac{1}{2}$
Carcharodon megalodon *Ag.*
(Pliocene)

Corax falcatus *Ag.*
(U. Cret.)

$x1$

$x1$

$x\frac{2}{3}$
Cochliodus contortus *Ag.*
(Lower Carboniferous)

$x\frac{2}{3}$
Ceratodus altus *Ag.*
(Rhætic)

Otodus obliquus *Ag.*
(Eocene)

FIG. 19. SOME TYPES OF FISH-TEETH

merly known as *Sphaerodus*, commonly occur in strata between the Trias and Wealden. *Semionotus*, a Triassic form, and *Dapedius*, restricted to the Lias, are allied genera. They show an advancement on earlier forms in the partial ossification of their internal head-bones and vertebrae. The pycnodonts, too, are deep-bodied fishes with powerful grinding teeth; their thin rhombic scales are often only partially preserved, but their hard jaws are characteristic and easily recognized.

In the higher fishes the lower jaw is simplified, consisting of only two pieces (instead of four or five) on each side. The earliest of these appear in the Lower Jurassic and may be exemplified by *Pholidophorus*, a form much like the herring in general aspect, but with ganoid scales and only ring-vertebrae. The practical absence of vertebral bodies is, indeed, a useful distinction between Jurassic and Lower Cretaceous fishes on the one hand and Upper Cretaceous and Neozoic forms on the other.

The Upper Cretaceous fish fauna is very different from that which immediately precedes it, and shows an increased resemblance with the modern assemblage. One distinction, the rarity of Cestraciont sharks and the abundance of typically predaceous forms, may, however, be due to differences in habitat. The teeth of many Upper Cretaceous and Neozoic sharks have deep roots, usually divided into two portions (Fig. 19), and are hardly distinguishable from modern forms. The tooth of *Corax* (Fig. 19) is, however, solid, not hollow as in Neozoic and living sharks. The familiar teeth of the skate *Ptychodus* (Fig. 19) are only known from the Upper Cretaceous, and minute differences are said to be distinctive of forms from the several zones through which they are distributed.

A few ganoids survive, notably *Macropoma*, a crossopterygian coelacanth. But bony fishes of modern aspect are dominant, and include even some spiny forms which are comparable with certain specialized fishes of modern seas.

The fish fauna of the Neozoic systems is of little value from a purely stratigraphical standpoint. Modern types are dominant, but occasional ganoids survive, as, for instance, *Pycnodus*, which ranges to the top of the Eocene. Small sharks occur in Eocene and Miocene deposits, and the characteristic dental pavement of *Myliobatis* (Fig. 19) is typical of the former series. The large teeth of *Carcharodon* (Fig. 19) are distinctive of late Miocene and Pliocene strata in all parts of the world. The chief interest of Neozoic fishes, however, lies in the variations of their geographical distribution.

The AMPHIBIA, intermediate in habit and structure between fishes and reptiles, attained their chief stratigraphical importance in Carboniferous and Permian times, that is, between the Devonian period, when fishes were the highest kind of life, and the Triassic period when reptiles became dominant. After the Triassic period there are few records of the class, and the relation of existing frogs, newts, and their allies to their Carboniferous predecessors is unknown. The early Amphibia, known as the **Stegocephalia,** are generally regarded as descendants of the Devonian paddle-finned fishes (Crossopterygii). They resemble these fishes in the arrangement of their external head-bones, the complexity of their teeth, the common occurrence of bony plates round the eye, and other characters of the skull. There is little evidence at present concerning the origin of the limbs. Small Stegocephalia, like newts in size and shape, are found in Upper Carboniferous and Permian rocks. *Branchiosaurus* and similar genera with barrel-shaped vertebrae are known from various places in continental Europe, while Microsauria such as *Lepterpeton, Keraterpeton, Urocordylus,* and *Dolichosoma*, with constricted cylindrical vertebrae, are recorded from the Coal Measures of Kilkenny and from the Permian of Bohemia. These small forms have comparatively simple tooth structure. Of the larger stegocephalians, *Mastodonsaurus* and *Labyrinthodon* occur in the British Trias.

These are distinguished especially by the complexity of their powerful conical teeth, the enamel covering of which is folded into the underlying dentine, forming a labyrinthine pattern. Numerous adaptive variations are known, but remains of these animals are too rare for general stratigraphical use. Their geological history is discussed in Chapter IX.

The REPTILES are linked with the labyrinthodonts on the one hand and the Mammals on the other, by a remarkable group of primitive land animals known as the **Anomodontia.** Collectively these reptiles approach the organization of warm-blooded mammals as no other cold-blooded group has done, while still possessing definitely reptilian characters. They are restricted to the Permian and Triassic rocks, and on this account are of stratigraphical importance; their known geographical distribution is also of interest. The massive Pareiasauria show in their skeletal characters a very close relationship with the labyrinthodont amphibians. The chief genus, *Pareiasaurus*, is known by nearly complete skeletons (8–10 feet long) from South Africa and Russia. The skull in another South African group, the **Theriodontia,** is remarkably like that of carnivorous mammals. Especially noteworthy is the dentition, which is differentiated into incisors, canines, and molars, a most unusual feature among reptiles. The **Dicynodontia** are large terrestrial reptiles of Triassic age, known mainly from South Africa and Europe. They resemble the turtles in having a horn-covered beak, but many have also a pair of tusks growing at the sides of the upper jaw. *Dicynodon* and *Ptychognathus* (*Lystrosaurus*) are South African genera, and similar forms, *Gordonia* and *Geikia*, are known from the Trias of Elgin. Concerning the relationship of anomodont reptiles with mammals, it may be said that the African, Asiatic, and European forms are closely similar, and make a near approach to mammalian organization. The American forms, however, develop into several groups that are almost or quite unknown in the Old World.

While the anomodonts appear to have originated in a group of labyrinthodont amphibians, the Microsauria seem to have given rise to another reptilian group, the **Rhynchocephalia.** These first appear in the Permian, are widely distributed in the Trias, and are almost wanting in rocks later than the Mesozoic. Their sole living representative is *Sphenodon,* the lizard-like Tuatera of New Zealand.

The trend towards complete adaptation to terrestrial conditions may be traced through the Rhynchocephalia to the **Deinosauria,** a varied reptilian group that dominated the land during Mesozoic times.

The deinosaurs all possess well-formed limb-bones adapted for habitual support of the body. Most of these animals were bipedal in gait, but some were quadrupedal, and all have a comparatively large tail, which suggests amphibious habits. They probably had a common ancestry with the crocodiles in such forms as *Aetosaurus* found in the Trias of Germany, while some of the Triassic forms may have been the ancestors of birds.

The Theropoda is a group of carnivorous deinosaurs with a lightly constructed skeleton (the limb-bones being hollow), and laterally compressed cutting-teeth in sockets along the margin of the jaws. The group of herbivorous quadrupedal deinosaurs known as the Sauropoda includes the largest-known four-footed animals, some of them, like the American *Brontosaurus* and *Diplodocus*, attaining a length of 80 to 100 feet. They are remarkable for the light construction of their vertebrae, some having a complex platy structure, others, as in the modern whales, attaining lightness by the spongy nature of the bone tissue. The herbivorous Ornithopoda have no relationship with birds although the pelvis and leg are bird-like in form. Their teeth are thick and leaf-shaped, and more coarsely serrated than those of the carnivorous Theropoda. They are typified by the bipedal *Iguanodon*, but also include quadrupedal armoured forms. *Iguanodon* is known by complete skeletons from the Wealden of Belgium, and by more fragmentary remains from the English Lower Cretaceous rocks. *Hypsilophodon* is an allied genus, known by complete skeletons from the Wealden of the Isle of Wight. These European forms have corresponding, but not identical, representatives in North American Cretaceous strata. The armoured forms, which are mostly quadrupedal, include the British genera *Scelidosaurus* (Lias), *Echinodon* (Purbeck), *Polacanthus* (Wealden), and the North American *Stegosaurus* (Upper Jurassic), all showing a strong development of bony dermal plates. *Triceratops*, and allied quadrupedal forms from the Cretaceous of North America, have bony horns on the skull. These forms are discussed more fully in Chapter XIV.

A distinct adaptive modification, which appears to have arisen in some early deinosaurs, is seen in the **Pterosauria** or flying reptiles. These are bird-like in general appearance, and their whole organization is modified to allow of flight through the air. Their bones are hollow and well articulated; the bird-like head is fixed at right angles to the neck; the breast-bone is keeled in front; and the fifth digit is much elongated, serving for the support of the large expanse of wing-membrane. They differ from birds most conspicuously in the presence of teeth, in the structure of the wings, and in the absence of feathers. They appear suddenly, but completely differentiated, in early Jurassic, and continue until the end of Cretaceous time. The Jurassic forms are mostly small, and are represented in the English Lias by incomplete skeletons of *Dimorphodon* and *Scapognathus*. Cretaceous pterosaurs are larger, and, like their Jurassic forerunners, English forms from the Chalk and Cambridge Greensand are furnished with large teeth in sockets along the margin of the jaws. The large American *Pteranodon* from the Chalk of Kansas is, however, toothless. On the whole, pterosaurian remains are too rare to be of general stratigraphical importance.

While land forms were evolving, other reptiles became adapted for an aquatic mode of life. Thus the extinct ichthyosaurs and sauropterygians, as well as the existing crocodiles and chelonians, form very distinct groups.

The **Crocodilia** were apparently differentiated in the Lias, and their subsequent evolution is more or less clear, but their Triassic predecessors are only with difficulty distinguished from the contemporary Rhynchocephalia and deinosaurs. The general form of existing crocodiles is lizard-like, but their internal organization is the most specialized known among reptiles. The phytosaurs of the Trias resemble the longirostrate crocodiles in several features, such as their considerable size, armoured trunk, elongate rostrum, coarsely sculptured head-bones, socketed teeth, and other characters of the skull. But the bones supporting the limbs are unlike those of typical crocodiles and suggest close relationship with early deinosaurs and rhynchocephalians. Another feature which distinguishes phytosaurs from crocodiles is the situation of the nostrils behind the rostrum in the former group. Phytosaurian remains are limited to the Trias, but the best-known genus, *Belodon*, has yet to be found in Britain. *Stagonolepis*, a form with tumid-rooted teeth, and ventral armour of rectangular scutes, is recorded from the Trias of Elgin.

The further evolution of the crocodiles is distinguished especially by the elongation of the rostrum behind the nostrils, the gradual development of a secondary palate, and the change from the amphicoelous to the procoelous type of vertebrae. The Jurassic and Lower Cretaceous crocodiles show an intermediate condition in these respects between the phytosaurs and the modern crocodiles; they are therefore classed together as the Mesosuchia. *Goniopholis*, a broad-headed form with powerful teeth, occurs in the Purbeck and Wealden Beds, while *Theriosuchus* and *Nannosuchus* are dwarf forms from the Purbeck Series. These are marsh-dwellers, and are covered with the thick, pitted, bony scutes characteristic of crocodiles. Certain Jurassic genera are marine, and possess paddle-like limbs adapted for swimming; their backbone turns sharply downwards at the end of the tail, as in the unrelated *Ichthyosaurus*, and probably bore a tail-fin during life. The Lower Jurassic forms *Teleosaurus*, *Mystriosaurus*, and *Pelagosaurus* resemble one another in their long, slender jaws and well-developed armour. Certain Upper Jurassic marine genera, such as the slender-jawed *Steneosaurus* and the massive *Dakosaurus*, are also armoured, but *Metriorhynchus* from the Oxford Clay has no external bony plates and its head-bones are only feebly sculptured.

Typical modern crocodiles (Eusuchia), with well-developed secondary palate and procoelus (concavo-convex) vertebrae, appear in the Upper Cretaceous. Characteristic vertebrae occur in the Cambridge Greensand. Several genera of alligators and crocodiles in the Eocene deposits of southern England demonstrate a wide distribution in early Neozoic time as compared with their present restriction to tropical and sub-tropical areas.

The **Chelonia** (turtles and tortoises) are easily recognized by their peculiar organization, especially by the investment of the body in a rigid, horny carapace or shield. Their origin is obscure, but the skull with its toothless

horn-covered jaws bears some resemblance to that of the Triassic dicynodonts, while certain features of the palate and pectoral girdle are suggestive
of the rhynchocephalians and labyrinthodonts. The earliest-known fossil
turtles, from the Trias of Germany, show that the typical Chelonian features
were already established. Certain Jurassic genera, including *Pleurosternum*
and *Platychelys* from the English Purbeck Beds, form a series of generalized
turtles, uniting characters of both the modern groups Cryptodira and
Pleurodira. Typical turtles occur in the British Cretaceous and Eocene deposits, while tortoises, which arose in early Neozoic time, are known from
the Eocene and Pleistocene of East Anglia. In general the only important
marks of evolution affecting the order are fenestration of the carapace and
elongation of the phalanges in truly marine types.

The **Ichthyosauria,** an extinct Mesozoic order, differ conspicuously
from all living reptiles in their fish-like body-form, paddle-shaped limbs
formed of numerous oval or polygonal phalanges, and the large elongated
head with sclerotic plates round the orbits. Their general form is that of a
porpoise, but the large tail-fin is vertical instead of horizontal. The occasional presence of young in the body of adults manifests a viviparous development and marks the complete adaptation of these reptiles to a marine
environment. The earliest ichthyosaurs (from the German Trias) are small,
and the elongated character of the limb-bones suggests derivation from
terrestrial animals, while, in some respects, the skull and teeth resemble
those of labyrinthodont amphibians. The genus *Ichthyosaurus* is occasionally represented in the English Lias by nearly complete skeletons and more
abundantly by isolated bones and teeth. The vertebrae are always very
short and deeply biconcave, and the precaudal ones have two pairs of
tubercles for articulation of the double-headed ribs; the neural arches are
never fused with their centra. The teeth are easily recognized; they are
acutely conical, the smooth or vertically striated crown is covered with
enamel, the somewhat tumid root is grooved at intervals, and a cross-
section shows a structure similar to that in labyrinthodont amphibians and
crossopterygian fishes. *Ophthalmosaurus*, an Upper Jurassic genus, is
practically toothless, and has broad paddles in which the phalanges are
reduced to rounded disks held together by cartilage. The ichthyosaurs
range upwards to the Chalk, but are wanting in later strata; the teeth of
Cretaceous genera usually possess a more tumid root than Jurassic forms.

The **Sauropterygia** are associated with the Ichthyosauria in marine
Mesozoic strata. They are lizard-like in form, with usually a small head and
long inflexible neck. The limbs are typically large and paddle-shaped, and,
since the tail is short with only a feeble fin, must have furnished the chief
means of progression. Early representatives of the group, like *Nothosaurus*
and *Lariosaurus*, are known from the marine Trias of central and southern
Europe. The limbs of these genera are less completely adapted for swimming than later forms and suggest derivation from land animals. *Plesiosaurus*,

the best-known genus from British Jurassic rocks, is a typical form with small head and long neck. Its vertebrae are flat-ended or only slightly concave, and the neural arches, being united by suture to their centra, are usually found attached. *Pliosaurus*, with a large head and short neck, is a gigantic form often associated with *Plesiosaurus*. The teeth of these reptiles are acutely conical and longitudinally grooved; those of *Pliosaurus* are carinated. *Cryptocleidus*, from the Oxford Clay, differs from *Plesiosaurus* in the organization of the pectoral arch, and its ribs are all single-headed. *Peloneustes*, also from the Oxford Clay, is a slender-jawed form allied to *Pliosaurus*. Teeth known as *Polyptychodon* occur in the Cambridge Greensand; they resemble those of *Pliosaurus*, but have more prominent ridges. This group of reptiles is not known in Neozoic rocks.

The order **Squamata** comprises the lizards and snakes, besides two extinct groups of aquatic reptiles which appear to be restricted to Cretaceous strata. The dolichosauria are small reptiles intermediate between lizards and snakes; they are distributed among a few genera restricted to the Cretaceous, but are of little geological importance. The mosasauria are large marine reptiles with lizard-like skull, greatly elongated body, and paddle-shaped limbs. The teeth are large and conical with swollen bases, but are not grooved like those of Cretaceous ichthyosaurs; the lower jaws are loose like those of snakes. The numerous vertebrae are more or less triangular and procoelous, the convex surface being posterior. The ribs are single-headed and slightly concavo-convex in section. Fragments of *Mosasaurus* are found in the English Chalk. Snakes and lizards are not definitely known before the Neozoic, and their remains are too fragmentary to be of geological value.

The BIRDS, which are undoubtedly derived from reptilian ancestors, are sometimes classed with the reptiles. Such fundamental characters as the warm-blooded condition and the covering of feathers, besides certain skeletal features, however, furnish ample justification for their separation into a distinct class. Fossil remains of birds are too rare to be of general geological utility. *Archaeopteryx*, the earliest bird, is known by two specimens from the Upper Jurassic Lithographic Stone of Bavaria. *Ichthyornis* and *Hesperornis*, from the American Cretaceous, have often been used for illustrative purposes in various textbooks; *Enaliornis*, an allied genus occurs in the Cambridge Greensand of this country. These Mesozoic birds demonstrate their reptilian ancestry especially in the possession of teeth. Fragmentary remains of birds recorded from British and other Neozoic deposits are interesting chiefly in connexion with questions of geographical distribution.

The MAMMALS represent the highest phase of development attained by the vertebrate animals. The acquisition of warm blood by presumed reptilian ancestors seems to have rendered possible (or made essential) numerous anatomical modifications that are necessarily accompanied by adjustments in the skeleton. Apart from these fundamental changes, various lines of divergence have been determined by differences in the habits of life.

The earliest mammals are represented in certain Mesozoic rocks by the lower jaws and teeth of small animals that are regarded as primitive allies of the pouched Marsupials whose specialized representatives are now restricted to the southern hemisphere. The most notable occurrences in British rocks are those of *Plagiaulax* from the Purbeck and Wealden Beds of the southern counties, *Amphilestes* and *Phascolotherium* from the Great Oolite of Stonesfield in Oxfordshire. *Amphitherium* from the latter horizon and locality, together with *Amblotherium* from the Purbeck Beds, belong to a group of early Placentals from which the later creodonts and Insectivores probably descended. Speaking generally, however, these Mesozoic mammals are too rare and too imperfectly known to have much stratigraphical utility.

It was not until Eocene time that the Placental Mammals rapidly evolved and rose to their present dominant position. The oldest Eocene Placentals all belong to one type. They are small animals with primitive pentadactyl limbs which were capable of rotation. They possess a continuous series of forty-four low-crowned (bunodont) teeth. The neck, having flat-ended vertebrae, is not flexible, and the tail is stout and long, not sharply differentiated from the body. From these primitive mammals various adaptive modifications rapidly developed in certain definite directions. The developmental trends are most easily traced by means of the limbs and teeth which readily become modified in accordance with changes in habitat and food. The grades of organization thus attained by various groups of mammals have been utilized in constructing a time-scale which serves as a reference for the correlation of Neozoic land and freshwater deposits.

In some of the early forms the teeth become sharp, and claws are developed on the digits. In more specialized forms, besides other modifications of the skull, one tooth above and below in the sides of each jaw is specially adapted for cutting purposes and is known as the carnassial. This feature is characteristic of carnivorous animals, and though the position of the carnassial teeth is not constant in these early Eocene **Creodonts**, this group is regarded as ancestral to the true carnivores or Fissepedia.

The true **Carnivora** appear in the Upper Eocene, being linked with the creodonts by forms like *Miacis*, which has a creodont organization, but the dentition approaches that of modern carnivores. *Cynodictis* is another early genus whose dentition is very similar to that of modern dogs and wolves, the least specialized of carnivorous mammals. In this group the skeleton appears to have undergone no important change since Upper Eocene time; their claws are not retractile, and their dentition comprises the full number of forty-four teeth. From some such general type as *Cynodictis* modification proceeds in two main directions.

In one line of descent the carnassial or cutting molars increase in size and importance, while the crushing teeth (both molars and premolars) are reduced. *Proaelurus*, from the European Upper Oligocene, is an ancestral type of this development which reaches its acme in the cats, lions, and tigers. In connexion with these changes the jaws gradually shorten and result in the broad skull characteristic of the group. The claws become sharper, more strongly hooked and capable of retraction. The widely distributed *Machaerodus* (sabre-tooth) may be specially mentioned as showing an extraordinary increase in size of the upper canine teeth; the genus ranges from the Lower Miocene to the Pleistocene.

In the second line of development the crushing molars increase in size and become larger than the carnassials. *Amphicyon*, ranging from Upper Oligocene to Lower Pliocene, is an early genus intermediate between dogs and bears. In the bears further reduction of the molars occurs, but the canines remain powerful.

Another group of early Eocene animals, collectively known as the **Condylarthra,** probably gave rise to the Ungulata or hoofed mammals, though some can hardly be distinguished from the Creodonta already mentioned. The Condylarthra are most abundantly represented in the oldest Neozoic strata of western North America; in Europe only a few scattered remains have been found. Typical ungulates rapidly become differentiated, and by the close of the Eocene period the main lines of divergence had been determined.

The general course of evolution is most conspicuously shown by modifications of the limbs and teeth, and it has been claimed that no other animal group has so far furnished such convincing evidence of its development. The early forms appear to have lived upon the succulent vegetation of marshes and forests and possess sturdy limbs with primitive five-toed feet. The molar teeth are low-crowned with well-developed roots. Later, some ungulates became adapted for life on grassy plains; their limbs and feet became progressively specialized for speedy movement, and their grinding teeth with crowns of increasing height are more fitted for masticating coarse dry herbage (see Fig. 20).

The changes just outlined have been traced in great detail in the **Perissodactyla** or odd-toed ungulates. This suborder includes a large number of extinct genera and species, but is represented at the present day only by the tapirs, horses, and rhinoceroses. In these the axis or middle-line of the limb passes along the central digit which, in the most specialized forms, persists as a single hoof, while the side digits are atrophied. This gradual modification is strikingly illustrated in the well-known series of equine remains from the Neozoic beds of North America, which leave no doubt that the modern horse is ultimately derived from a small four-toed ancestor of Eocene age. Concurrently with the modification of the limbs the molar teeth gradually change from the original low-crowned, many-rooted form to the high-crowned, prismatic, rootless type seen in the living horse.

Various genera have been instituted to mark the grades of development attained at definite horizons, and since these have often been described, a tabular summary will be sufficient to indicate the geological importance of these North American fossils.

PLEISTOCENE . . *Equus*—lateral digits represented by splint bones; deep prismatic molar teeth with cement filling the valleys in the crown.

PLIOCENE . . *Pliohippus*—much like *Equus,* but molar teeth less deep.

MIOCENE . . *Protohippus*—small, complete lateral digits; molar teeth little deepened.

OLIGOCENE . . *Mesohippus*—three digits on each foot, the laterals (II and IV) shorter and more slender than the median (III); comparatively low molars with no cement.

EOCENE . . *Orohippus*—four digits on fore-foot and three on hind-foot; molars low-crowned without any cement in the hollows of the crown.

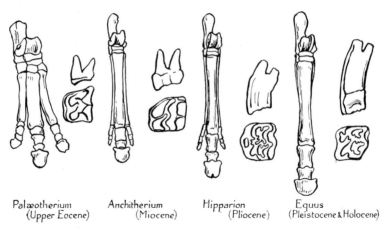

Palæotherium   Anchitherium   Hipparion   Equus
(Upper Eocene)   (Miocene)   (Pliocene)   (Pleistocene & Holocene)

FIG. 20. EQUINE MAMMALS: *right hind-limbs and upper molar teeth (much reduced)*

Among European forms (Fig. 20) *Hipparion* is equivalent in grade of development to *Protohippus, Anchitherium* to *Mesohippus,* and *Palaeotherium* is slightly more advanced than *Orohippus.* Thus a parallel development of equine mammals occurred in the Old and New Worlds.

The tapirs are comparatively unspecialized and show a practically complete dentition with short-crowned molars; they have four digits on the fore-limb and three on the hind-limb. Though found in the Miocene and Pliocene deposits of Europe and North America, tapirs are now restricted to the Indo-Malayan region and tropical America.

The well-marked family of Rhinoceroses seem to have arisen in the early Eocene from small perissodactyl animals which had a slender snout and a complete dentition of forty-four teeth. During their racial development the animals increased in average size, the nasal bones became enlarged and thickened, and the characteristic dermal horn was developed; the lips became more prehensile and the front teeth concurrently tended to disappear. At the same time the premolars, which were comparatively simple at first, gradually approached the molars in complexity. In early American rhinoceroses the foremost premolar is most like a molar, and the complication of the premolars proceeded successively from front to back. While the Middle Eocene *Prohyracodon* of Transylvania and *Epiceratherium* from the Lower Oligocene of Italy agree in this respect with North American forms, in all the known rhinoceroses from later European strata the complication proceeded forwards from the hind premolar. It is claimed, therefore, that two progressive series of these animals independently acquired the same characteristic feature. The former widespread distribution of the family in the Old World is shown by the presence of the large-horned woolly rhinoceros in North-west Europe and the Arctic regions.

In the **Artiodactyla,** or even-toed ungulates, the middle line of the limb passes between the third and fourth digits which become enlarged and form the characteristic cloven hoof. The existing pigs and hippopotami, camels and llamas, deer, sheep, and cattle all exhibit this feature in varying degree of development. The pigs are the least-altered descendants of primitive Artiodactyla. Their teeth are low-crowned and the dentition is complete. Their limb-bones are not fused together as in the more specialized cattle, and there are four digits on each foot, the middle pair (III and IV) being larger than the lateral digits (II and V). In the highest developed group, comprising deer, sheep, and cattle, there are only two digits (III and IV) on each foot, and the limb-bones are fused together to form the 'cannon bone'. The dentition is reduced, continuity being broken by a gap in front of the molars. The early camels had feet with pointed toes like those of deer, and this feature persists in the two groups into which the Lower Miocene genera are differentiated. The later Miocene forms of both groups, however, have irregularly nodular ungual phalanges which indicate the development of the characteristic cushioned foot. The same tendency towards the independent acquisition of one and the same structure is seen in the development of antlers by various races of deer. These structures are present only in the males, except that the female reindeer possess them. They are developed gradually in the individual: beginning with a single prong or tine in the first year, they become bifurcated in the second year, and one new tine is added during each succeeding year. Phylogenetic development proceeds in a similar manner. The oldest Miocene forms have no antlers. Late Miocene species of *Palaeomeryx* and *Dicroceros* possess a beam (or main stem) with one or two tines, and early Pliocene deer have two or three accessory tines. Antlers from Upper Pliocene and Pleistocene strata are conspicuous in size and development of branching, which is most elaborate in the extinct Irish deer *Megaceros hibernicus* Owen. In this Pleistocene and Neolithic form the antlers are palmated (flattened and expanded) and measure upwards of 3 metres from tip to tip; the females are hornless. Stags, elk, and reindeer provide living examples of this development in different lineages. The gradual acquisition of complex antlers seems to be broadly synchronous in various races of deer, and the several stages of development are therefore of certain stratigraphical importance.

The **Proboscidea,** represented at the present day by the elephants, are rendered conspicuous by the possession of a prehensile trunk or proboscis. The structure of their teeth also shows a degree of specialization not reached in any other group of animals. At the same time they retain certain primitive characters, such as the presence of five digits on each foot, which distinguish them from the true ungulates.

The dentition of the elephant consists only of incisors and cheek-teeth or molars; of the former only one pair in the upper jaw remain and these are modified to form enormous ivory tusks. The molars are distinguished by their large size and numerous compressed transverse ridges interspaced by thick deposits of cement in the valleys (see Fig. 21). There are rarely more than two molars functioning in each half of the jaw at the same time. The dental succession continues during the whole life of the animal, newly formed teeth gradually pressing forward and displacing their worn predecessors. Teeth of elephants are far from uncommon in British Pliocene and Pleistocene deposits, but since the teeth of any one species may show considerable variation, due care is needed in using them as guide-fossils.

The earliest-known proboscidean is *Moeritherium*, a tapir-like animal from the Upper Eocene of Egypt. This form has the second incisors in both jaws enlarged, the upper pair forming strong tusks; the nasal openings are situated far forward, indicating a short proboscis; the molar teeth have two transverse ridges (each composed of two cusps) and a small hind-lobe or talon. In the Lower Oligocene of Egypt, *Moeritherium* is associated with *Palaeomastodon*. This genus differs from the first-named in its greater size, in the absence of canine teeth and all incisors except the second pair in both jaws, in its three-ridged molar teeth, and in some minor characters which more nearly approach those of the later elephants.

No proboscidean remains have yet been found in the Upper Oligocene, but bones and teeth occur in the Miocene, not only of Egypt, but also in Europe, Asia, and North America. The skull of the typical Miocene genus, *Tetrabelodon*, is still more elephant-like than that of *Palaeomastodon*. It is especially distinguished by the presence of two pairs of tusks in which the dentine has acquired the peculiar structure of ivory; these tusks presumably supported the much-elongated snout. The molars are large and may have

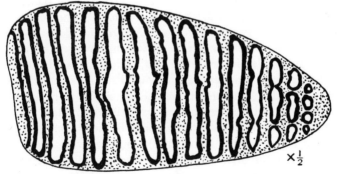

Elephas primigenius *Blum.* (Pleistocene)

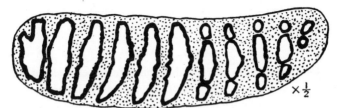

Elephas antiquus *Falconer* (Upper Pliocene)

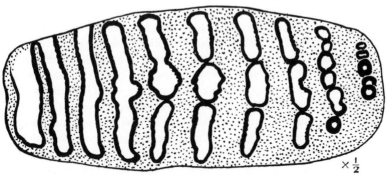

Elephas meridionalis *Nesti* (Upper Pliocene)

FIG. 21. BRITISH FOSSIL ELEPHANTS: *plans of grinding surfaces of molar teeth (enamel black, dentine white, cement stippled). Based on figures by Leith Adams*

five transverse ridges. In later species of *Tetrabelodon* the lower jaw is shortened and the lower incisors are much reduced. This tendency is continued in the Pliocene genus *Mastodon*; this also shows great increase in the size and complexity of the molar teeth, which, however, have no cement between the ridges. In the genus *Elephas*, which appears later in the Pliocene, the lower incisors are entirely absent, the chin is very short, and the valleys between the transverse ridges of the molar teeth are filled with cement. The greatest degree of complexity in the molars occurs in the Pleistocene Mammoth (*Elephas primigenius* Blum., which sometimes has twenty-seven ridges in the third molar), and the living Indian elephant. Thus, even from this brief summary, it is evident that the stages in the general evolution of the Proboscidea are of considerable stratigraphical utility.

Other mammalian groups are less perfectly known, and since their fossil remains are comparatively rare they are of little value in general stratigraphical work. They are discussed in Chapter XVII.

III. PLANTS

The geological record with regard to the succession of floras is decidedly imperfect, chiefly because land and freshwater deposits are specially liable to destruction. The majority of known deposits, being of marine origin, contain only drifted relics of the land flora. Some deposits of freshwater and terrestrial origin, however, have escaped denudation and afford valuable information concerning the evolution of plants.

Viewed broadly, successive groups of plants give evidence of evolution in two directions: (1) the development of the arborescent habit; and (2) a tendency to reproduce by means of seeds. Both trends are probably due to the necessity for adaptation to land conditions. While the general evolutional trends in the plant world may be used as guides to horizon in a general way, the imperfection of the record and the usual fragmentary preservation offer difficulties to the field worker. Certain broad horizons in the Coal Measures, however, may be distinguished by the general aspect of their floras. The calcareous algae, so abundant at certain geological horizons, cannot yet be considered from an evolutional standpoint, while the study of angiospermous seeds found in Neozoic deposits needs microscopic work in the laboratory. Pending a more detailed discussion in Chapter VIII the evolutional features of fossil land-plants may be summarized thus:

3. Neozoic floras

   Dominant angiosperms, many arborescent, all seed-bearing; subordinate gymnosperms and vascular cryptograms.

2. Mesozoic floras

   Dominant cycadophytes, mostly arborescent and seed-bearing. Many ferns and conifers.

1. Palaeozoic floras

> Dominant pteridosperms all seed-bearing; some true ferns; arborescent lycopods and horsetails.

LITERATURE

While the idea of evolution permeates all modern palaeontological work, the following papers are selected as providing useful summaries concerning various fossil groups.

'The Graptolite Faunas of the British Isles', by G. L. Elles, *Proc. Geol. Assoc.*, vol. xxxiii, pp. 168–200, 1922.

'Graptolithina', by O. M. B. Bulman, *Handbuch der Palaeozoologie*, Bd. 2D, Berlin, 1938.

'Trends in British Carboniferous Corals', by W. D. Lang, *Proc. Geol. Assoc.*, vol. xxxiv, pp. 120–36, 1923.

'Homoeomorphy in Fossil Corals', by W. D. Lang, *Proc. Geol. Assoc.*, vol. xxviii, pp. 85–94, 1917.

'Growth Stages in Parasmilia', by W. D. Lang, *Proc. Zool. Soc.*, *London*, pp. 285–307, 1909.

'The Evolution of Zaphrentis delanouei in Lower Carboniferous Times', by R. G. Carruthers, *Q.J.G.S.*, vol. lxvi, pp. 523–37, 1910.

'Evolution and Habit among the Echinoidea', by H. L. Hawkins, *Q.J.G.S.*, vol. xcix, 1943.

'The Morphology and Evolution of the Ambulacrum in the Echinoidea Holectypoida', by H. L. Hawkins, *Phil. Trans. Roy. Soc.*, ser. B, vol. 209, pp. 377–480, 1920.

'An Analysis of the genus Micraster', by A. W. Rowe, *Q.J.G.S.*, vol. lv, pp. 494–547, 1899.

'The Evolution of the Cretaceous Asteroidea', by W. K. Spencer, *Phil. Trans. Roy. Soc.*, ser. B, vol. 204, pp. 99–177, 1913.

'The Evolution of the genus Inoceramus in the Cretaceous Period', by H. Woods, *Q.J.G.S.*, vol. lxviii, pp. 1–20, 1912.

'The Evolution of certain Liassic Gasteropods with special reference to their Use in Stratigraphy', by A. I. McDonald and A. E. Trueman, *Q.J.G.S.*, vol. lxxvii, pp. 297–344, 1921.

'The Ammonites of the Gault', by L. F. Spath, *Mon. Pal. Soc.*, 1921–43.

'The Evolution of the Cephalopoda', by L. F. Spath, *Biol. Reviews*, vol. viii, No. 4, 1933.

'The Ammonites of the Liassic Family Liparoceratidae', by L. F. Spath, *Brit. Mus. Cat.*, 1938.

'The Development of Leptoplastus salteri (Callaway) and of Other Trilobites', by F. Raw, *Q.J.G.S.*, vol. lxxxi, pp. 223–324, 1925.

'Cephalic Sutures and their Bearing on Current Classifications of Trilobites', by C. J. Stubblefield, *Biol. Reviews*, vol. xi, pp. 407—40, 1936.

'Studies on Trilobite Morphology', by L. Stormer, *Norsk. geol. Tidskr.*, vols. xix and xxi, 1940 and 1942.

'The Use of Fossil Fishes in Stratigraphical Geology', by A. S. Woodward, *Q.J.G.S.*, vol. lxxi, pp. lxii–lxxv (Presid. Address), 1915.

'The Use of the Higher Vertebrates in Stratigraphical Geology', by A. S. Woodward, *Q.J.G.S.*, vol. lxxii, pp. lxv–lxxv (Presid. Address), 1916.

'The Marine Reptiles of the Oxford Clay', by C. W. Andrews, *Brit. Mus. Cat.*, Part I 1910; Part II 1913.

'The Tertiary Vertebrata of the Fayûm, Egypt', by C. W. Andrews, *Brit. Mus. Cat.*, 1906.

'The Evolution of Bony Fishes during the Triassic Period', by J. Brough, *Biol. Reviews*, vol. xi, pp. 385–404, 1936.

'The Acanthodian Fishes', by D. M. S. Watson, *Phil. Trans. Roy. Soc.*, Ser. B, No. 549, pp. 49–146, 1937.

'The Structure and Evolution of the Holostean Fishes', by D. H. Rayner, *Biol. Reviews*, vol. xvi, pp. 218–37, 1941.

'The Beginning of the Age of Mammals', by G. G. Simpson, *Biol. Reviews*, vol. xii, pp. 1–47, 1937.

Plant Life through the Ages, by A. C. Seward. Cambridge, 1931.

The general course of evolution in the vertebrate groups is discussed in 'Archaeopteryx and Evolution' by G. R. de Beer, *The Advancement of Science*, vol. xi, No. 42, pp. 160–170, 1954.

III

CAMBRIAN FAUNAS

THE oldest-known fossils of correlative value occur in strata collectively termed the Cambrian system from its typical occurrence in Wales. That some forms of life existed before Cambrian time is suggested by the presence of limestones and deposits of graphite in the Precambrian formations, and is adduced from the consideration that the comparatively highly organized animals of the Cambrian fauna must have evolved from an important series of ancestors. The virtual absence of Precambrian fossils may be explained by their probable destruction during later movements and metamorphism of the rocks. It has also been suggested that the oceans of those remote ages contained little lime in solution and consequently the organisms could not develop hard skeletons capable of preservation. However this may be, in the present state of our knowledge, consideration of fossils from a stratigraphical standpoint must begin with the Cambrian fauna.

The deposits of the Cambrian so far known are all marine, and yield representatives of most of the great groups of the Invertebrata. The dominant forms are trilobites and brachiopods, while two groups of the mollusca, namely the Cephalopoda and the Gastropoda, must also be considered as forming an appreciable element in the fauna of, at least, the later Cambrian strata. The other invertebrate animals do not commonly occur in British Cambrian rocks, and their relationships are not known to the same extent as are those of the dominant groups. This is the case with the Archaeocyathids, which are present, sometimes abundantly, in many countries where limestones are prevalent in the Cambrian succession (p. 156).

The most important index-fossils of the Cambrian are the trilobites. As a group they are easily recognized, though their remains are often fragmentary, consisting, it may be, of the head-shield (cephalon), of one or more segments of the thorax, or of the tail (pygidium). Generic and specific determination is often difficult on account of this fragmentary preservation, which is largely due to the destructive action of moving water on the moulted exoskeletons.

A. PALAEOCAMBRIAN FAUNAS

The oldest-known trilobite, *Nevadia*, has not yet been found in Britain, being recorded only from early Cambrian rocks of North America. Its general structure is primitive compared with that of later trilobites. Its glabella narrows towards the front and is divided transversely by five unbroken furrows. From the foremost (also the largest) of these divisions, eye-ridges project on either side, ending in crescentic eyes that lie close to the glabella. The fixed cheeks are therefore very narrow, most of the head-shield being occupied by the free-cheek areas, and there is apparently no facial suture. The rest of the body consists of 28 free segments, of which the anterior 17 have strong pleurae ending in long spines. The pleurae decrease in size posteriorly and in the last 11 segments the pleural spines are attached directly to the axis. None of the posterior segments are fused to form a pygidium.

According to C. D. Walcott, two lineages diverged from this primitive type; both show progressive specialization of the glabella and eyes, together with a reduction in the number of segments without pleurae. All the members of these two lineages, however, are classified with *Nevadia* in the family Olenellidae, since they possess many of the general characters of that genus. The family includes the trilobites formerly grouped under the name *Olenellus*, and is confined to the Lower Cambrian, which is therefore often called the Olenellidian Series.

F. Raw (1936), however, subdivides the family Olenellidae into three groups: (1) the Olenellus group, consisting of the genera *Olenellus, Wan-neria, Paedumias, Elliptocephala, Olenelloides*; (2) the Holmia group, con-taining the genera *Holmia, Kjerulfia, Schmidtiellus,* and *Callavia*; (3) the Nevadia group with *Nevadia, Nevadella,* and possibly *Esmeraldina*. These groups appear to be restricted respectively to more or less definite areas of distribution: of the genera present in British deposits, *Callavia* and *Kjerulfia* are common, though fragmentary, in Shropshire, and *Olenellus* is recorded from the north-west Highlands of Scotland.

The Cambrian rocks have been studied in minute detail around Church Stretton in Shropshire, by E. S. Cobbold, who has distinguished the fol-lowing eight faunal horizons in the Olenellidian Series.

8. Lapworthella Limestone.
7. Protolenus Limestone.
6. Strenuella Limestone.
5. Microdiscus bellimarginatus Limestone.
4. Olenellus Limestone.
3. Callavia Sandstone.
2. Holmia Sandstone.
1. *Obolella-groomi* Beds, resting on Wrekin Quartzite, which is practic-ally unfossiliferous.

The *Obolella-groomi* Beds contain, besides the index-fossil, species of the atrematous brachiopods *Paterina* and *Walcottina*. These two genera have the pedicle-valve more or less elevated, and the pedicle-opening is an orifice between the valves. *Paterina* is ornamented by crenulated concentric lines, while in *Walcottina* concentric striae are interspaced by flat bands. The index-fossil, *Obolella groomi* Matley, is an oval shell possessing a definite pedicle tube, and the edges of its concentric growth lines are very sharp, 'almost undercut in their sculpture'. Tubular, tapering shells, *Hyolithus strettonensis* Cobbold and *Hyolithellus sinuosus* Cobbold, which also occur, are usually classed as pteropodous gastropods.

The Holmia sandstones have yielded nothing but an obscure *Kjerulfia* and hyolithids.

The Callavia sandstone is more fossiliferous. The tribolites include two species of *Callavia, Microdiscus attleborensis* (Shaler and Foerste), and a doubtful *Wanneria*. The brachiopods *Paterina labradorica* (Billings) and *Obolella atlantica* Walcott occur, together with a few hyolithids. The *Microdiscus* is represented by isolated cranidia, quadrate in shape, with elevated triangular fixed cheeks.

The Olenellus Limestone was the first horizon in this area to yield recognizable Lower Cambrian fossils, and a much larger faunal list has been compiled from it. Its fauna is connected with that immediately below by the persistence of the brachiopods *Paterina labradorica* and *Obolella atlantica* and of the trilobites *Callavia callavei* Lapworth (Fig. 22) and *Microdiscus attleborensis*. Other forms, however, make their first appearance. Chief among these are five species of the trilobite genus *Micmacca*, 'with a large, rather prominent cylindrical glabella which extends almost to the front of the shield, and with continuous eye-lobes, and a short posterior extension of the dorsal suture' (Fig. 22). In Shropshire the genus seems to be restricted to the Olenellus Limestone.

The *Microdiscus bellimarginatus* Limestone is characterized especially by the occurrence of the index-fossil and of another trilobite *Strenuella pustulata* Cobbold. The head-shield of *Microdiscus bellimarginatus* Shaler and Foerste has a deep marginal rim beset with tubercles which become feeble or obsolete in front.

In the Strenuella Limestone three species of the index-genus occur, with two fresh species of *Microdiscus* and several brachiopods and hyolithids. *Strenuella* is a trilobite with narrow free-cheeks, small eyes, smooth glabella only faintly outlined, and a narrow rim round its head-shield. The genus appears to be restricted to this horizon and that immediately below. *Microdiscus lobatus* (Hall) is distinguished from all the other known British species by its cylindrical glabella and broad cephalic margin; the axis of the tail is marked by three conspicuous transverse furrows. *Microdiscus speciosus* Ford, a form with conical glabella and narrow margin, has also been found at this horizon (Fig. 23).

The Protolenus Limestone is especially interesting because it is the highest horizon at which Olenellid trilobites (fragments of *Callavia*) have so far been found. The index-genus *Protolenus* has a semi-circular head-shield with somewhat narrow free-cheeks provided with genal spines. The cylindro-conical glabella has three pairs of oblique furrows besides the occipital

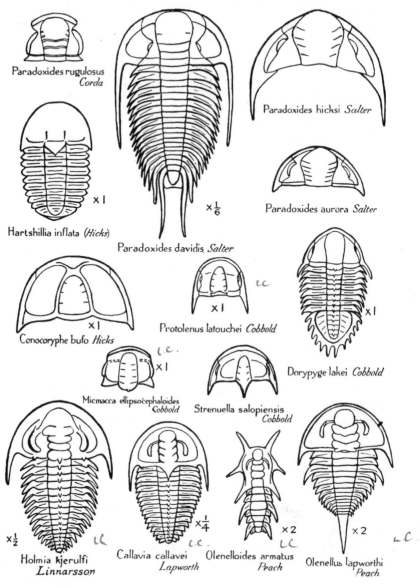

Paradoxides rugulosus *Corda*

Paradoxides hicksi *Salter*

Hartshillia inflata (*Hicks*) ×1

Paradoxides aurora *Salter*

Paradoxides davidis *Salter* ×1⁄6

Conocoryphe bufo *Hicks* ×1

Protolenus latouchei *Cobbold* ×1

Dorypyge lakei *Cobbold* ×1

Micmacca ellipsocephaloides *Cobbold* ×1

Strenuella salopiensis *Cobbold*

Holmia kjerulfi *Linnarsson* ×1⁄2

Callavia callavei *Lapworth* ×1⁄4

Olenelloides armatus *Peach* ×2

Olenellus lapworthi *Peach* ×2

FIG. 22. LOWER AND MIDDLE CAMBRIAN TRILOBITES

furrow. The pleurae of the thorax are prolonged backwards into pleural spines. Two species of *Protolenus* are associated with members of the genus *Mohicana* and with *Microdiscus comleyensis* Cobbold. The last-named species is intermediate between *M. speciosus* noted below and the later *M. punctatus* Salter; it differs from both in having seven annulations on the axis of the pygidium and a plain marginal rim to the head (Fig. 23). The genus *Strenuella* is absent, as also is the brachiopod *Obolella atlantica*. Certain hyolithids are restricted to this horizon.

The Lapworthella Limestone contains a fauna which 'seems to indicate the incoming of a change from Lower to Middle Cambrian' (Cobbold). Its reference to the lower series is determined by the presence of certain unnamed trilobite fragments with characteristic ornament, which are also found in the Protolenus Limestone, but not in the Paradoxides Beds of the Middle Cambrian. The fauna under discussion consists mainly of hyolithids, of which *Lapworthella* is confined to this horizon. This genus has the usual tapering tubular form and is ornamented by numerous transverse ridges. The upper surface of the Lapworthella Limestone is eroded, indicating a physical break in the sequence, while evidence of a palaeontological interruption is seen in the sudden appearance of *Paradoxides* in the beds above.

Correlation with the Lower Cambrian Beds of other areas is often attended with great difficulty, owing to the scarcity of fossils and the development of cleavage. Indeed, the whole of the Harlech Series of North Wales is only referable to the Lower Cambrian by reason of its stratigraphical position.

B. MESOCAMBRIAN FAUNAS

The Middle Cambrian of Britain contains a rich fauna, characterized especially by species of the trilobite-genus *Paradoxides*. Hence these rocks are often termed the Paradoxidian Series. *Paradoxides* has so many points of resemblance with the Olenellids that a common origin is probable, but the transitional stages are unknown. The sudden appearance of the genus in the British area is usually ascribed to migration from a region at present unknown. This postulates a palaeontological break in the sequence, and the evidence of physical unconformity at the top of the Lower Cambrian is significant in this connexion.

Paradoxides differs from the olenellids in:

(1) the presence of perfect facial sutures;
(2) the anterior widening of the glabella;
(3) greater concentration of the visual areas and the absence of eye-ridges;
(4) the presence of a true (though small) pygidium.

A detailed sequence, based mainly on species of *Paradoxides*, has been established for Scandinavia, and may be briefly tabulated as follows:

Zone of *Agnostus laevigatus* (not represented in Britain).
　„　　*Paradoxides forchammeri.*
　„　　*Paradoxides davidis.*

„　　*Paradoxides tessini*	⎧ Subzone of *Bailiella aequalis.* ⎨　　„　　*Agnostus parvifrons.* ⎩　　„　　*Ctenocephalus exsulans.*

　„　　*Paradoxides oelandicus.*

In Britain, the Paradoxidian Series has been studied in greatest detail around Nuneaton by V. C. Illing. This succession may be compared with that of Shropshire, which has been investigated by E. S. Cobbold. There are local faunal differences, as might be expected from different lithological facies, but both (though incomplete) agree broadly with the Scandinavian sequence detailed above.

NUNEATON (Illing)	SHROPSHIRE (Cobbold)
[Non-sequence] .	*Billingsella* Beds.
Upper *davidis* fauna	*Paradoxides davidis* Flags.
Lower *davidis fauna* .	*Paradoxides rugulosus* Sandstone.
Hartshillia fauna .	[Unexposed interval].
Upper *hicksi* fauna ⎫ Lower *hicksi* fauna ⎭	*Paradoxides intermedius* Grits.
P. aurora fauna . [Unexposed interval]	[Non-sequence with overlap on to Lower Cambrian].
P. sjogreni beds ⎧ (= upper part of ⎨ Purley Shales) ⎩	*Dorypyge lakei* Flags. *Paradoxides groomi* Grits resting uncomformably on eroded Lower Cambrian.

The Zone of *Paradoxides oelandicus*

The *Paradoxides groomi* Grits. The fauna consists of the index-fossil and other species of *Paradoxides, Dorypyge lakei* Cobbold, a variety of *Bailiaspis emarginata* (Linnarsson), the brachiopod *Acrothyra comleyensis* Cobbold, and some hyolithids. This assemblage is readily distinguished from Lower Cambrian faunas since no trilobite-genera are known to be common to both series. On the eroded surface of Lower Cambrian Beds is an impersistent layer of phosphatic gritty material overlaid by conglomeratic grits containing blocks of derived limestone and 'clots' of contemporaneous calcareous material. It is inferred that the fauna 'inhabited a shore among pebbles and boulders containing the previously fossilized Protolenus-Callavia fauna'. *Paraaoxides groomi* Lapworth is characterized by:

(1) the general flatness of the whole shield;
(2) the width and slight convexity of the margin of the free cheek;

(3) the pronounced smoothness of the upper surface;
(4) the presence of rugosities on the doublure;
(5) the comparatively narrow axial lobe.

It attains a length of 20 to 25 cm.

The family Conocoryphidae comprising blind trilobites, is represented by *Bailiella cobboldi* Resser, which is distinguished from other conocoryphids by a marginal rim round the head-shield. *Dorypyge lakei* Cobbold first appears at this horizon: it is somewhat semicircular in form, with a strongly convex axis, convex side lobes, and a flattened spinose border (Fig. 22).

Acrothyra comleyensis Cobbold, a neotrematous brachiopod with a very high and oblique pedicle-valve, is distinguished by its notched posterior margin and its ornament of delicate, close-set, concentric striae. The two last-mentioned forms persist into the *Dorypyge lakei* Flags, where they are associated with *Acrotreta socialis* Seebach, a shell which is typical of the zone of *Paradoxides oelandicus* in Sweden.

Equivalent strata in the Nuneaton district have not been fully investigated, but V. C. Illing records *Paradoxides sjogreni* from the uppermost part of the Purley Shales. This species is not known above the oelandicus zone in Scandinavia.

The Zone of *Paradoxides tessini*

Though the index-fossil of this zone has not been found in Britain, the faunal assemblage allows a general correlation with the Scandinavian classification in certain British localities. The zone is most completely shown in the Abbey Shales of Nuneaton, where Illing has established three faunal subdivisions based on the distribution of the trilobites.

The *Paradoxides aurora* beds occur above a series of comparatively barren strata and are broadly correlated with the upper part of the *exsulans* subzone of Scandinavia. The fauna includes *Paradoxides aurora* Salter, which is closely allied to *P. hicksi* Salter noted below. *Conocoryphe bufo* Hicks, nowadays referred to the genus *Bailiaspis* also restricted to this fauna, may be recognized by its large size, wide anterior margin, small and highly convex glabella, and wide cheeks; it is ascribed by Lake to *B. dalmani* Angelin from Sweden. Agnostids are rare, though several species are recorded. This fauna is not known in Shropshire, its probable position being marked by a non-sequence with strong overlap on to Lower Cambrian strata, but it is recorded from South Wales.

The succeeding *Paradoxides hicksi* beds of Nuneaton contain abundant remains of the index-trilobite whose main features may be gathered from the accompanying diagram (Fig. 22). *Liostracus elegans* Illing, a ptychoparid trilobite, is common in some beds, while the rarity of *Hartshillia inflata* (Hicks) is in striking contrast with its abundance in the succeeding fauna. A variety of the familiar *Microdiscus punctatus* Salter is also characteristic of this zone. The work of Illing on this and higher horizons is especially interesting for the application of the agnostids to zonal stratigraphy. Various species of these small trilobites have different vertical ranges, and the assemblage at any horizon appears to have definite stratigraphical significance. The accompanying table, compiled from Illing's work, shows the vertical distribution of certain agnostids whose characters are shown diagramatically in Fig. 23. The ranges of British species differ slightly from those in Scandinavia (probably an indication of depositional differences), and their application to zonal stratigraphy in other parts of Britain is awaited with interest.

Zone	Subzone	Fauna	Species ranges
Z. of *P. davidis*		Upper *davidis* fauna	*P. davidis*, *H. primordialis*, *A. glandiformis*, *A. rotundus*, *A. nathorsti*, *A. kjerulfi*
		Lower *davidis* fauna	*P. rugulosus*, *A. incertus*, *A. nudus var. ovalis*, *A. exaratus*, *A. altus*, *A. punctuosus*
Hartshillia Zone	Sz. of *Con. aequalis*	*Hartshillia*-fauna	*A. lens*, *A. fallax*, *A. parvifrons*, *A. barrandei*
Z. of *P. hicksi*	Sz. of *Agnostus parvifrons*	Upper *hicksi* fauna	*Paradoxides hicksi*, *A. nudus*, *A. fissus*, *A. cf. intermedius*, *A. rex*
		Lower *hicksi* fauna	
Z. of *P. aurora*	Sz. of *Cteno. exsulans*	*P. aurora* fauna	*P. aurora*, *B. bufo*
		Passage-beds	

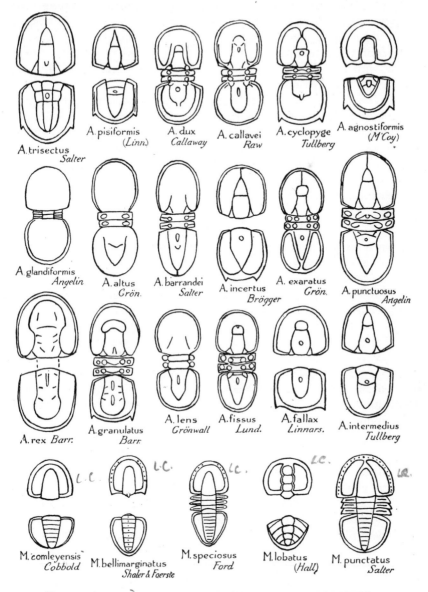

FIG. 23. BRITISH SPECIES OF *AGNOSTUS* AND *MICRODISCUS*
(*enlarged approximately five times*)

The *P. hicksi* beds of Nuneaton are regarded as equivalent to the subzone of *Agnostus parvifrons* of Scandinavia. Two faunal subdivisions are recognized: (1) a lower, characterized by rarity of *Paradoxides*, abundance of *Agnostus rex* Barrande, and occurrence of *Ag. granulatus* Barrande; (2) an upper, with abundant *P. hicksi* Salter and *Ag. fissus* Linnarsson, *Ag. tuberculatus* Illing occurring less commonly.

The *Hartshillia* beds of Nuneaton are distinguished from the preceding strata by the abundance of the trilobite *Hartshillia inflata* (Hicks), which is really the only common fossil. In contrast with the *P. hicksi* beds, agnostids are extremely scarce, but *Microdiscus scanicus* Linnarsson persists. This horizon is not at present known in Shropshire, the rocks where it might be expected being unexposed. The *Hartshillia* beds are probably equivalent to the subzone of *Bailiella aequalis* of Sweden.

The Zone of *Paradoxides davidis*

From a general standpoint the fauna of these rocks in the Nuneaton district is distinguished by a return of agnostids in abundance, but not the same species as those occurring in lower beds. *Paradoxides* is not common, but affords a basis for dividing the zone into two portions, *P. rugulosus* Corda being typical of the lower, and *P. davidis* Salter of the upper division. In the lower fauna, too, *Agnostus punctuosus* Angelin, *A. lens* Grönwall, and *A. granulatus* Barrande occur, while *A. punctuosus* Angelin, *A. kjerulfi* Brögger, *A. rotundus* Grönwall, and *A. bifurcatus* Illing are associated in the upper fauna. Other trilobites are not so plentiful. The equivalence of strata in Shropshire is determined by the presence of *Paradoxides rugulosus* Corda and *P. davidis* Salter respectively, but agnostids do not occur in the same abundance and variety.

The Zone of *Paradoxides forchammeri*

In Britain this zone is well represented only at Rushton, Shropshire. Here the *Par. davidis* beds are succeeded by grits containing *Par. forchammeri* Angelin, *Solenopleura brachymetopa* (Angelin), species of *Dorypyge* and *Agnostus*, associated with brachiopods and hyolithids. At Comley the equivalent Billingsella Beds contain only brachiopods, but these are closely related to forms in the *Par. forchammeri* zone of Sweden. At Nuneaton this horizon is cut out by a non-sequence at the top of the *Par. davidis* beds.

C. NEOCAMBRIAN FAUNAS

Upper Cambrian strata (the Olenidian Series) are distinguished by the presence of trilobites classed in the family Olenidae. These have no direct affinity with the trilobites of the Paradoxidian faunas, and, in this country at least, a widespread physical break is associated with this marked faunal change. The typical genus *Olenus* (Fig. 24) differs from the olenellids in—

1. The general quadragonal shape of the head shield.
2. The greater size of the free cheeks, which are about equal to the fixed cheeks.
3. The presence of a well-formed pygidium with large pleural portions.

At higher Olenidian horizons modifications of this typical form take two directions. In one trend the head-shield becomes very wide, the eyes are reduced in size, and the genal spines diverge abruptly from the sides of the free cheeks; *Sphaerophthalmus* and *Eurycare* illustrate this type. In the other trend, typified by *Peltura*, the chief features are the absence of spines and rounding of the genal angles. These forms are useful indexes for the determination of horizons within the Olenidian series.

The Upper Cambrian Beds so far described are generally grouped together as the Lingula Flags, so called from the frequency of *Lingulella davisii* M'Coy. In the neighbourhood of Dolgelley the following succession within the Lingula Flags was established long ago by T. Belt.

Dolgelley Beds	{	Soft black slates with *Peltura scarabaeoides* (Wahlenberg). Hard blue slates with *Parabolina spinulosa* (Wahlenberg).
Ffestiniog Beds	{	Bluish-grey flags with *Olenus micrurus* Salter. Grey micaceous flags with *Hymenocaris*.
Maentwrog Beds	{	Black slates and flags with *Olenus gibbosus* (Wahlenberg). Sandstone and slaty beds with *Olenus cataractes* Salter.

On account of the unfossiliferous nature of many Cambrian rocks this succession is often difficult to demonstrate, but it may be noted that typical olenids occur in the lower subdivisions, while the upper series contains more specialized forms. W. G. Fearnsides has instituted a further subdivision of the Dolgelley Beds thus:

Zone of *Peltura scarabaeoides* (Wahlenberg).
,,   *Agnostus trisectus* Salter.
,,   *Orusia lenticularis* (Wahlenberg).
,,   *Parabolina spinulosa* (Wahlenberg).

Strata containing *P. spinulosa* and *Orusia lenticularis* (Wahlenberg), a brachiopod formerly assigned to the comprehensive genus *Orthis*, are known in Shropshire, but their junctions with other beds are concealed.

In the Malvern area black shales containing *Peltura scarabaeoides* (Wahlenberg), *Ctenopyge bisulcata* (Philips), and *Sphaerophthalmus alatus* (Boeck) represent the Dolgelley Beds of North Wales, and a similar fauna occurs in the Oldbury Shales of the Nuneaton district. Upper Cambrian trilobites in shales of the Nuneaton type were obtained in a boring near Leicester. Among other characteristic Upper Cambrian fossils, *Agnostus reticulatus* Angelin and *A. pisiformis* (Linnaeus) from the Lower Lingula Flags, and *A. trisectus* Salter and *A. rudis* Salter from the upper subdivision may be mentioned.

D. THE TREMADOC SERIES

At still higher levels there occur strata, grouped together as the Tremadoc Beds, containing specialized trilobites of the Cambrian families Olenidae, Ptychoparidae, and Agnostidae, associated with primitive members of typically Ordovician families such as the Asaphidae and Trinucleidae. The olenids (Fig. 24) include the genera *Parabolinella, Leptoplastus, Pterocephalus*, and the well-known *Angelina*. The peculiar genus *Shumardia*, a long-ranged form, makes its first appearance in the Tremadoc Beds. The ptychoparids *Euloma* and *Neseuretus* seem to approach the Ordovician families Calymenidae and Homalonotidae in many structural features, while *Triarthrus* persists into Ordovician strata. The agnostids of this horizon are not known to occur below. They include *Agnostus calvus* Lake, *Ag. callavei* Raw, and *Ag. dux* Callaway (Fig. 23). The asaphids are represented by *Niobe, Asaphellus*, and *Symphysurus*; *Niobe homfrayi* Salter, *Asaphellus homfrayi* (Salter), and *Symphysurus croftii* (Callaway) being familiar species. *Orometopus*, the earliest known member of the Trinucleidae, is interesting as possessing eyes and facial sutures, which are absent in the typically Ordovician genus *Trinucleus. Lichapyge* is the first representative of the Lichidae in which there is a marked tendency to break up the glabella into separate lobes by coalescence of the furrows. The genus *Anacheirurus* foreshadows the important proparian family Cheiruridae; it has a parallel-sided glabella, small free cheeks confined to the anterolateral region of the head, eleven thoracic segments, and a small pygidium. Modification of these characters occurs in later members of the family.

The incoming of these Ordovician elements, together with the first appearance of the dendroid graptolite *Dictyonema* (Fig. 29), is a strong argument for following the Scandinavian practice in placing the Tremadoc Beds at the base of the Ordovician system. But in Britain the Tremadoc Series follows conformably on the Lingula Flags, and is separated from overlying beds by a widespread unconformity. The latter forms a more convenient boundary for mapping, and the Tremadoc Beds are therefore retained in the Cambrian system.

The detailed succession seems to be subject to local differences. W. G. Fearnsides records the following sequence in the type-area around Tremadoc (North Wales):

6. Garth Hill Beds with *Angelina*.
5. Penmorfa Beds with *Dikelocephalus, Asaphellus, Shumardia, Holometopus, Agnostus, Angelina, Symphysurus, Anacheirurus, Macrocystella* (a cystid).
4. Portmadoc Flags with few fossils. *Asaphellus*.
3. Moel-y-gêst Beds.
2. Dictyonema Band with *D. sociale, Psilocephalus, Hysterolenus*.
1. Niobe Beds—*Niobella, Psilocephalus, Hymenocaris, Lingulella*.

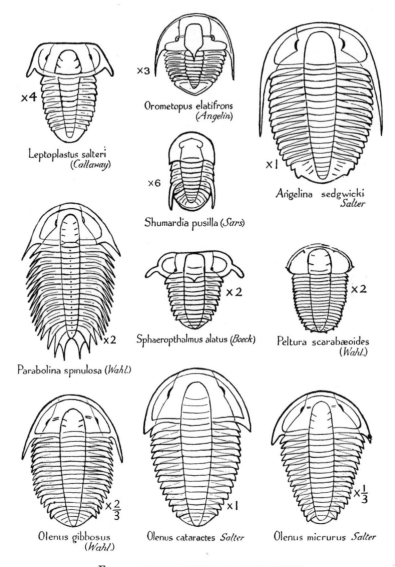

×4

Leptoplastus salteri
(*Callaway*)

×3

Orometopus elatifrons
(*Angelin*)

×6

Shumardia pusilla (*Sars*)

×1

Angelina sedgwicki
Salter

×2

Parabolina spinulosa (*Wahl.*)

Sphaeropthalmus alatus (*Boeck*) ×2

Peltura scarabæoides
(*Wahl.*) ×2

Olenus gibbosus
(*Wahl.*) ×$\frac{2}{3}$

Olenus cataractes *Salter* ×1

Olenus micrurus *Salter* ×$\frac{1}{3}$

FIG. 24. UPPER CAMBRIAN TRILOBITES

O. M. B. Bulman and C. J. Stubblefield have given the succession in the Shineton Shales of Shropshire thus:

Arenaceous Beds—*Acrotreta, Lingulella.*
Shumardia Beds—*Shumardia, Agnostus, Asaphellus, Symphysurus, Leptoplastus, Parabolinella, Triarthrus, Euloma, Orometopus, Dikellocephalina.*
Brachiopod Beds with *Obolus.*
Transition Beds with *Dictyonema, Euloma, Shumardia.*
Dictyonema Beds—*Dictyonema* and *Acrotreta.*

It will be noticed that *Niobella* and *Angelina*, both eminently characteristic in North Wales, are not recorded from Shropshire. Arenig Beds near Carmarthen (South Wales) carry a relict Tremadoc fauna which differs considerably from that of Shropshire and North Wales. The commonest trilobite is *Peltura punctata* Crosfield and Skeat, which is distinguished from *Peltura scarabaeoides* already mentioned by its parallel-sided glabella, its very narrow free cheeks, its entire pygidium, and by the presence of punctations in the marginal furrow in front of the glabella. This form is associated with *Ogygia marginata* Crosfield and Skeat, a fairly large trilobite which appears to be closely related to the Arenig species *Og. selwynii* Salter. Less commonly other trilobites of Cambrian affinities occur, namely, *Apatocephalus serratus* (Boeck), a variety of *Parabolinella rugosa* Brögger, and a species of *Erinnys*.

Mention must also be made of Tremadoc rocks in Buckinghamshire. At Calvert in that county a deep boring revealed cleaved mudstones enclosing *Clonograptus tenellus* var. *callavei* Lapworth and *Obolella salteri* Holl., lying immediately below beds of Lower Jurassic age. This discovery (in 1913) considerably extended the known horizontal range of Tremadoc rocks in this country. More recently (in 1933) an outcrop of Tremadoc Shales was described by S. Smith and C. J. Stubblefield from the Tortworth Inlier in Gloucestershire: the fossils recorded include *Dictyonema* and the trilobites *Beltella depressa, Niobella homfrayi,* and *Agnostus calvus*.

E. CAMBRIAN FAUNAS OF SCOTLAND

The Cambrian rocks of the north-west Highlands of Scotland do not conform to the Welsh palaeontological facies. The succession, attaining 2,000 feet in thickness, may be summarized thus:

3. Durness Limestone—Dolomites and limestones (in seven stages) with
   · fossiliferous horizons.
2. Serpulite Grit and Fucoid Beds yielding an *Olenellus* fauna.
1. Quartzites with worm casts in upper portion.

These strata were for long assigned to the Ordovician until, in 1891, the discovery of *Olenellus* proved their Cambrian age. Species of this genus (the true *Olenellus*) such as *O. lapworthi* Peach (Fig. 22), with a well-marked tail spine, have since been recorded from the Serpulite Grit and Fucoid Beds of several localities in the north-west Highlands. The peculiar trilobite *Olenelloides armatus* Peach (Fig. 22) and the annelid *Salterella* are also characteristic of these beds.

The lower part of the Durness Limestone is almost barren of fossils, but the upper beds have yielded a rich fauna, though trilobites are scarce and fragmentary. The most abundant fossils are gastropods which include euomphalids (*Maclurea* and *Ophileta*), murchisonids (*Hormotoma* and *Ectomaria*), and pleurotomarids (*Raphistoma* and *Euconia*). Cephalopods are represented chiefly by straight or slightly curved forms possessing wide, laterally placed siphuncles furnished with endocones; the genera *Piloceras*, *Endoceras*, and *Actinoceras* are typical. Lamellibranchs of the two genera *Euchasma* and *Eopteria*, the brachiopod-genus *Orthisina*, and the siliceous sponges *Archaeoscyphia* and *Calathium*, are also recorded. Another interesting genus is the widespread and problematical *Archaeocyathus*, which combines characters typical of sponges and corals. Thus there would appear to be very little relation between the Cambrian faunas of northern Scotland and those of Wales and the English Midlands.

The occurrence of the true *Olenellus* in the north-west Highlands, however, is a point of resemblance with the western province of North America. The higher molluscan assemblage of Scotland is closely similar to that of the Beekmantown Limestone of Newfoundland (possibly equivalent in age to the Tremadoc Series), many species being common to both areas (see pp. 184-5).

F. FAUNAL REGIONS

(a) EUROPE AND EASTERN AMERICA

Palaeocambrian faunas have been recorded at several localities on the margin of the Baltic Shield (Map, Fig. 25), where the Cambrian rocks often lie horizontally on the Precambrian foundation. In the Mjosen district of south Norway the Olenellidae are represented by *Holmia kjerulfi* (Linnarsson) and *Kjerulfia lata* (Kiaer) in association with *Strenuella primaeva* (Brögger). The first of these is also recorded from the province of Scania in south Sweden, and Opik (1929) reports its presence in Estonia, along with the closely related *Schmidtiellus mickwitzii* (Schmidt). This form also is associated with obolid brachiopods and the limpet-like gastropod *Scenella*. It may be noted that *Callavia* is not recorded from the Baltic region, its place apparently being taken by *Holmia*, but Cobbold (1934) states that *Holmia* has a long range, and the Estonian deposits may be older than the English Callavia Beds. The absence of *Protolenus* in Scandinavia, however, is due to a gap in the succession, for the Holmia Beds are followed directly by Mesocambrian strata.

Farther south, in central Poland, Samsonovicz (1920) and Czarnocki

(1927) have recorded *Holmia kjerulfi* associated with species of *Ellipso-cephalus*, *Strenuella*, and *Microdiscus*, closely resembling those from British and Scandinavian localities. Higher beds containing *E. nordenskjoldi* are correlated with the Holmia Beds of Sweden, and the species is recorded by Cobbold and Pocock (1934) from Rushton, Shropshire. Czarnocki further reports a Protolenus fauna in the highest beds of the Palaeocambrian Series. The species of *Protolenus*, *Strenuella*, and *Microdiscus* are mostly

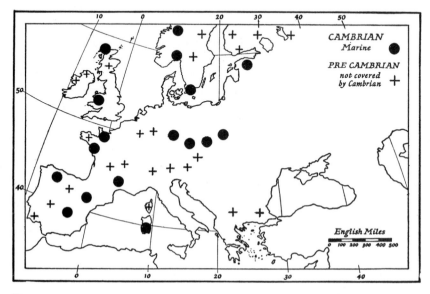

FIG. 25. SKETCH-MAP OF EUROPE SHOWING GENERAL DISTRIBUTION OF
CAMBRIAN ROCKS

new but they show close relationships with forms from equivalent beds in Shropshire. *Protolenus* and *Microdiscus* are also recorded by Schwartzbach (1933) from Silesia. Elsewhere in central and southern Europe the Holmia-Callavia fauna has not been found; the Przibram Sandstone of Bohemia is virtually barren of fossils, and in France, Spain, Sardinia, and Morocco the homotaxial strata are mainly Archaeocyathus Limestones with no trilo-bites.

Much farther east, Cambrian fossils from the shores of the Dead Sea have been described by W. B. R. King (1923). The fossils include trilobites re-ferred to *Anomocare campbelli* King, and compared with *Strenuella platy-cephala* Cobbold from the Protolenus beds of Shropshire. The associated brachiopods and hyolithids are consistent with reference to this horizon. No Palaeocambrian rocks are known elsewhere in Syria, and those of south-west Persia contain a fauna that differs considerably from the European assemblages.

It has already been noted that the British Mesocambrian sequence agrees broadly with its equivalent in Scandinavia. Many species of trilobites are common to the two areas, and there are allied or vicarious species in each; some of these are mentioned in pages 130 to 134. On this basis the Swedish zones marked by species of *Paradoxides* can be correlated with those in Shropshire and Warwickshire.

The Mesocambrian Series is absent from the Baltic States owing to a stratigraphical hiatus, but it is represented by a considerable thickness of clastic deposits in the mountains of Ste. Croix, central Poland. Here, Czarnocki (1927) describes an incomplete succession with species of *Paradoxides, Liostracus, Solenopleura,* and other genera comparable with British and Scandinavian forms from the zones of *Par. hicksi* and *Par. tessini.* The rarity of agnostids is noted, and is correlated with the prevalence of sandy deposits. Farther east in the same mountains, Samsonovicz (1920) records agnostids associated with *Par. tessini* without comment on the frequency of occurrence.

In Germany Mesocambrian rocks have been described from deep borings in the Niederlausitz, about 100 Km. south of Berlin, by Picard (1929), from the Oberlausitz by Schwarzbach (1932) and from the Frankenwald, Bavaria, by Wurm (1928). The trilobites indicate that part of the tessini zone is present, and most of the Bavarian forms are closely related to species that are characteristic of Bohemian localities.

The *Paradoxides* beds of Jince and Skrey in Bohemia are famed for well-preserved trilobites, many of which were first described by J. Barrande (1852). The species of *Paradoxides* are very similar to British and Scandinavian forms. P. Lake (1935), for instance, states that *Par. bohemicus* (Boecke) is close to the Scandinavian *Par. tessini* (Brongn.), and also to the British *Par. davidis* Salter. *Par. rotundatus* Barrande is comparable with *Par. hicksi* Salter, while *Par. rugulosus* Corda is listed by Cobbold (1911) from Shropshire, and doubtfully from Scandinavia by Gronwall (1902). *Conocoryphe sulzeri* Schlotheim, *Ellipsocephalus hoffi* Schlotheim, and *Sao hirsuta* Barrande are, however, all specially typical of the Bohemian deposits, the last-named species being present in such profusion that Barrande was able to describe a succession of growth-stages. Several species of *Agnostus* are listed, and most of them are reported from the hicksi and davidis horizons of Nuneaton (p. 134), but few of them are identical with Scandinavian species.

The Bohemian Paradoxides fauna is closely linked with assemblages described from various localities in southern Europe. Mesocambrian shales in the Montagne Noire, south of the Central Plateau of France have yielded to Blayac and Thoral (1931) *Par. mediterraneus* Pompeckj, closely allied to *Par. rugulosus* Corda, along with local species of *Conocoryphe, Ctenocephalus, Solenopleura,* and *Agnostus,* all closely related to Bohemian forms. A similar fauna is recorded by Hornemann (1891) from Sardinia and by R. Douville (1920) from the Vega Limestone of central Spain, which contains beds of archaeocyathids.

The southern limit of the Paradoxides faunas lies, as far as is known, in southern Morocco. Here, according to Russo (1927) archaeocyathid limestones rest directly on Precambrian rocks and are followed by shales containing *Par. rugulosus* and *Sao hirsuta*. This brings the Mesocambrian marine deposits within a short distance of the African Shield.

The eastern limit of *Paradoxides*, according to present knowledge, lies in Palestine, the genus being recorded from this area by Blanckenhorn (1910); the strata are horizontal and rest unconformably on Precambrian rocks.

The zonal sequence in the Neocambrian Series of Sweden has been defined by Westergaard (1922), and the Norwegian succession originally described by Brögger (1882) has been revised by Strand (1929). Though the deposits are not so thick as in Britain, the general succession of trilobites is the same, and many species are common to the two regions. At the same time the Scandinavian deposits have been subdivided in greater detail, possibly because they are more completely exposed than the soft shales of the British area. Overlying the typical Neocambrian horizons with *Peltura*, *Ctenopyge*, and *Sphaerophthalmus* are the widespread Dictyograptus Shales. Westergaard recognizes three zones based on graptolites, namely, (1) *Dictyonema flabelliforme*, (2) *Clonograptus tenellus*, and (3) *Bryograptus kjerulfi*. The succession in the Shineton Shales of Shropshire, described by Bulman and Stubblefield (1927) is very similar, as in more general terms is that of the Tremadoc Shales in North Wales. The Ceratopyge Limestone of Norway and Sweden, in places interstratified with *Dictyonema* Shales, contains species of *Parabolinella*, *Hysterolenus*, *Triarthrus*, *Symphysurus*, *Euloma*, *Dikelocephalina*, *Apatokephalus*, *Niobella*, *Orometopus*, and *Shumardia*. All these genera are represented in the Shineton Shales and Tremadoc Beds of Britain, but others, like the Scandinavian *Ceratopyge*, *Cyrtometopus*, *Bröggeria*, *Boeckia*, and the British *Lichapyge*, *Macropyge*, and *Angelina* seem to be more restricted in their distribution.

P. E. Raymond (1916) has shown that the character of these deposits in the Baltic regions is controlled by that of the underlying beds. In Scania, south Oeland, and south Norway, where the subjacent beds are Neocambrian shales and limestones, the Dictyonema Beds are developed mainly as shales, though local beds of limestone containing species of *Hysterolenus* are sometimes interstratified. In north Oeland a yellow sandstone, in which the brachiopod *Obolus apollonii* is abundant, overlies the *Paradoxides* Sandstone. In Estonia this Obolus Sandstone is interbedded with Dictyonema Shale, thus proving their contemporaneity, and in Dalecarlia the Obolus Sandstone overlaps on to crystalline Precambrian rocks.

In Poland Czarnocki (1926) states that Neocambrian horizons are well developed only in the southern parts of the Ste. Croix mountains. Early olenids are not yet known, but species of *Beltella*, *Eurycare*, *Ctenopyge*, *Protopeltura*, *Peltura*, and *Parabolina* are recorded in shales at Machocice, and at higher horizons the last two genera are associated with *Sphaeroph-thalmus*. The fauna of the Dictyonema horizon is not yet known in Poland, though Kloucek (1920) has recorded *Dictyonema* from Bohemia. The Euloma fauna is represented at Pilsen by the genera *Euloma*, *Asaphellus*, *Lichapyge*, *Megalaspides*, *Nileus*, and *Cyclopyge*. Near Hof in Bavaria, trilobites, which were known to Barrande (1868) and Pompeckj (1896), are also comparable with those of the Euloma fauna in Scandinavia and Britain, for the genera *Euloma*, *Dikelocephalina*, *Anacheirurus*, *Lichapyge*, and per-haps *Ceratopyge* are represented. Still farther west Malaise (1900) has reported *Dictyonema* from the Belgian Ardennes.

The highest known *Paradoxides* Beds in the Montagne Noire, according to Bergeron (1895) and Pompeckj (1902) are followed by grits and shales containing indeterminable fragments of trilobites. These are referred to the Neocambrian, and are succeeded by beds which correspond to the British Tremadoc horizon, for they have yielded species of *Agnostus*, *Euloma*, *Symphysurus*, *Dikelokephalina*, *Asaphellina*, *Niobella*, *Shumardia*, *Cyrto-metopus*, and *Anacheirurus*. Hence, as Brögger (1896) has shown, the Euloma fauna extends over a wide area in Europe, from Sweden in the north to Bavaria and Languedoc in the south, and to Shropshire and Wales in the west. No Neocambrian rocks appear to be known in Spain and other countries of southern Europe.

Cambrian faunas very similar to those of Europe are known from the Atlantic coastal region in North America, comprising a strip of country from south-east Newfoundland through New Brunswick and Nova Scotia to east Massachusetts. The rocks of this region are mainly dark shales and slates, but limestones, sandstones, and conglomerates occur locally.

The Palaeocambrian Series is well developed, as the Etcheminian Series of Matthew (1888), at Conception Bay and Trinity Bay in Newfoundland, where *Callavia bröggeri* (Walcott), *Microdiscus helena* (Walcott); *M. specio-sus* Ford, *Strenuella strenua* (Billings) are typical trilobites. The lowest Cambrian Beds of New Brunswick are barren of fossils, and those of Cape Breton, Nova Scotia have only yielded brachiopods and a few hyolithids. But in east Massachusetts species of *Callavia*, *Strenuella*, *Microdiscus*, and other trilobites are recorded. These assemblages are closely similar to the Callavia fauna of Shropshire (p. 127); some of the species are identical in the two regions, though others seem to be more restricted in distribution. At Hanford Brook, New Brunswick, a Protolenus fauna occurs just below beds containing *Paradoxides*; the chief trilobites are species of *Protolenus* and the allied genus *Bergeronia*, in association with species of *Micmacca*, *Avalonia*, and *Ellipsocephalus*. This fauna was first described by Matthew (1895), and similar, but not identical assemblages have since been found in south-east Newfoundland as well as in England and Poland.

The Mesocambrian Series of Manuel's Brook, Newfoundland, is sub-divided by B. F. Howell (1925) into the three zones of *Paradoxides bennetti*, *Par. hicksi*, and *Par. davidis*. In the lowest zone, *Par. bennetti* is associated with other species of *Paradoxides*, the concoryphids *Bailiaspis* and *Bailiella*, *Liostracus* and *Microdiscus*. This zone is represented also in New Bruns-wick (Hayes and Howell, 1937) and is correlated with the zone of *Par. oelandicus* of Scandinavia and Great Britain. The succeeding beds with *Par. abenacus* in both south-east Newfoundland and New Brunswick seem to correspond with the *Par. hicksi* zone of Great Britain, and the lower part of the *Par. tessini* zone of Scandinavia, for they contain several agnostids, such as *Ag. fissus*, *Ag. parvifrons*, *Ag. rex*, in common with the European faunas. *Par. davidis* is recorded from south-east Newfoundland in association with *Ag. punctuosus* and *Ag. sulcatus* as in Britain, and these agnostids occur in New Brunswick along with *Par. matthewi*. The fauna of the Scandinavian zone of *Par. forchammeri* is not yet recorded from Newfoundland or New Brunswick. But B. F. Howell (1937) has described a fauna from north-west Vermont containing rare specimens of *Paradoxides*, more frequent examples of the closely allied *Centropleura* and numerous agnostids, together with species of *Elyx*, *Solenopleura*, *Ptychoparia*, *Agrau-los*, *Dolichometopus*, and *Anomocare*. All these genera are represented in the Mesocambrian Beds of north-west Europe; in the Vermont fauna they are also associated with newly described forms mostly belonging to the old families Solenopleuridae and Ptychoparidae. This is perhaps the youngest *Paradoxides* fauna yet known, and it approaches nearest to the assemblage of the Scandinavian zone of *Par. forchammeri*. It also resembles a Centro-pleura fauna described by Holm and Westergaard (1930) from Bennett Island about 70 miles north of the New Siberian Islands (lat. 78° N., long 150° E.)

Succeeding the *Paradoxides* beds in south-east Newfoundland and New Brunswick are shales in which *Agnostus pisiformis* (Linnaeus) is the chief fossil. They correspond in stratigraphical position with the lowest Neo-cambrian Beds in Scandinavia, which contain the same trilobite. *Olenus* is represented in higher beds, both in Newfoundland and New Brunswick, and is followed by such species as *Parabolina spinulosa* (Wahlenberg), *Peltura scarabaeoides* (Wahlenberg), *Ctenopyge pecten* (Salter), *Sphaeroph-thalmus alatus* (Boeck), which are characteristic of the higher Neocambrian horizons in Britain and Scandinavia. These again are succeeded by shales containing the widespread dendroid graptolite *Dictyonema flabelliforme*.

Neocambrian trilobites of the family Olenidae are described from localities in South America. As long ago as 1876 E. Kayser recorded *Olenus argentinus* from Jujuy Province, north Argentina. Later (1912), H. Hoek described this species and *Parabolinella andina* from south Bolivia, and P. Lake (1906) figured *Peltura* from north Bolivia. In 1936, T. Kobayashi described from Argentina *Parabolinella argentinensis* and the new genus

Jujuyaspis which is said to combine characters of *Sphaerophthalmus* and *Leptoplastus*. According to this evidence, an Olenid fauna extended through Bolivia to north Argentina, but H. Gerth (1932) cites a Mesocambrian fauna of Pacific types and Kobayashi describes early Ordovician trilobites, also of Pacific type, from the same region.

(b) WEST AND INTERIOR OF NORTH AMERICA

A wide belt of Precambrian rocks separates the Cambrian strata of the Atlantic coastal region from the main outcrops of the system in the Interior and Western States of North America. These outcrops extend discontinuously across the continent, and are well developed in west Newfoundland and Quebec, in the Appalachian region, the Upper Mississippi Valley, and the Cordilleran region which extends from the Great Basin of Utah and Nevada through Montana and Colorado to British Columbia and Alberta. (Map, Fig. 26.) Farther north there are reports of Cambrian rocks in the Mackenzie Valley, Alaska, and Siberia, and a more extensive record for Greenland. The succession of faunas enclosed in these rocks differs greatly from that just described for the eastern States of North America, the distinction being so marked that the geographical limit between them can be defined with some approach to accuracy. The two types are about 100 miles apart in Newfoundland, and the belt of separation passes south-eastwards along the Green Mountains to the western slopes of the Appalachians, where the outcrops represent the edges of thrust masses.

The standard time-scale at present in use for the Cambrian rocks of North America is based on the stratigraphical succession in various parts of the continent. That of the southern Appalachians (Resser, 1938) is apparently the best available for the Palaeocambrian. A combination of several sections in the Cordillera furnishes a generalized Mesocambrian sequence, and the naturally complete succession in the Upper Mississippi Valley is used for the Neocambrian Series.

The most widely distributed Palaeocambrian trilobites belong to the family Olenellidae, the typical genus *Olenellus* being founded by J. Hall (1862) on material from Vermont. Subsequently the genus has been proved to range throughout the Appalachian region from Alabama to east Pennsylvania, and, farther north, to west Newfoundland and Labrador. Many trilobites that have formerly been referred to the type-species *Olenellus thompsoni* (Hall 1859) have lately been separated by C. E. Resser (1938) as distinct species, and the oft-quoted *Mesonacis vermontana* (Hall) is now regarded as congeneric with *Ol. thompsoni*. Other olenellids are included in the genera *Paedeumias*, *Wanneria*, and *Elliptocephala*, which commonly occur in association with *Olenellus* in the Appalachian region. The geographical distribution of certain species of *Olenellus* s.s. appears to have some significance. The type-species *Ol. thompsoni* (Hall) ranges from

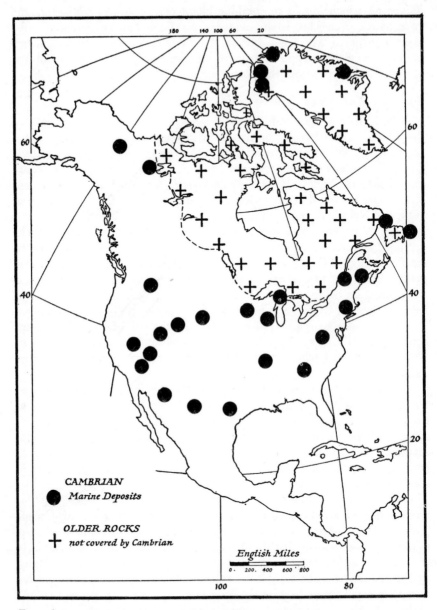

CAMBRIAN
Marine Deposits

OLDER ROCKS
not covered by Cambrian

English Miles

0   200   400   600   800

FIG. 26. SKETCH-MAP OF NORTH AMERICA SHOWING GENERAL DISTRIBUTION
OF CAMBRIAN ROCKS

Labrador and west Newfoundland south-westwards through the Hudson–Champlain valley to Alabama and east Tennessee; it is often associated in Vermont with *Ol. vermontana* (Hall), and with the closely related *Paedeumias transitans* Walcott, which occurs throughout the tract. An association of *Ol. canadensis* Walcott, *Ol. gilberti* Meek, and *Ol. fremonti* Walcott is characteristic in the north-eastern part of the Cordilleran region in British Columbia and Alberta; the last two species range south to Nevada and California (J. F. Mason 1938) where they are accompanied by *Paedeumias clarkei* Resser, *P. nevadensis* (Walcott), and *Peachella iddingsi* (Walcott). On the other hand *Ol. lapworthi* Peach and a few other species from the north-western Highlands of Scotland (Peach 1894) are the only known representatives in Europe. In view of these differences in specific association it may be well to recall that the distance between Scotland and Labrador is similar to that between Labrador and the Cordillera. The genus *Olenellus*, represented in the Mackenzie Valley by *Ol. mackenziensis* Kobayashi, also extends to Greenland where it is represented in the north-west by *Ol. arcticus*, *Ol. kentensis*, and *Ol. groenlandicus* Poulsen (1927), and in the east of the country by *Ol. simplex* and *Ol. curvicornis* (Poulsen, 1932).

Earlier olenellids were long ago described by Walcott (1910) from shales some 5,000 feet below the Olenellus Beds of Nevada. One of them is *Nevadia weeksi* which Walcott regarded as the most primitive member of the family. It is associated in Nevada with *Esmeraldina rowei* (Walcott) which is also recorded in a similar horizon from east California. The last genus has a considerable range, for *E. macer* (Walcott) is associated with species of *Olenellus*, *Paedeumias*, and *Wanneria* in Pennsylvania (Resser and Howell, 1938), and *E. occidens* is listed from west Alberta in association with *Ol. truemani*, '*Callavia*' *perfecta*, and '*C.*' *eucharis* of Walcott (1913). The last two species, however, have little in common with the true *Callavia* of the Atlantic borders, and F. Raw (1936) refers them to a separate genus, *Nevadella*, so named in allusion to their close relationship with the earlier *Nevadia*.

Above the Olenellus Beds in Alberta and British Columbia C. Deiss (1939) recognizes a *Plagiura* zone which contains many small trilobites belonging to the genera *Kochiella*, *Plagiura*, *Plagiurella*, and others of doubtful affinities. This is the highest stratigraphical horizon in the Palaeocambrian rocks of the Cordilleran region. It appears to be represented also in Nevada and California (J. F. Mason, 1938), and the Kochiella zone of the Appalachians occupies the same position, according to Resser and Howell (1938). Species of *Kochiella* are also associated with *Olenellus* in the Cape Kent formation of north-west Greenland (Poulsen, 1927).

The Mesocambrian succession in Alberta and British Columbia has been reviewed by C. Deiss (1940) who distinguishes seven horizons in the series, and most of them have been recognized by C. E. Resser (1938) in the south Appalachians. The lowest is the Kochiaspis zone where the ptychoparid genus *Kochiaspis* makes its first appearance. This horizon was formerly included in the Palaeocambrian Series, but as the genus ranges through the Mesocambrian, Deiss now takes it as the base of the higher series. Other species of *Kochiaspis* in the Highland Range of Nevada probably indicate the same horizon, but the genus is not recorded from north-west Montana or the Appalachians. The succeeding Albertella horizon of British Columbia contains species of the spinose *Albertella* which perhaps represents an offshoot from the olenellids; they are associated with *Kochina*, ptychoparids and oryctocephalids (*Vanuxemella*, *Poliella*, &c.). The entire fauna is not known elsewhere, but species of *Albertella*, *Kochina*, and *Vanuxemella* are reported from the lower part of the Gordon Shale in north-west Montana, and *Albertella* is present in the Comet Shale of Nevada. Some distance above the Albertella horizon in the Highland Range of Nevada is the Chisholm Shale marked by the presence of *Zacanthoides* in association with species of *Clavaspidella*, *Glyphaspis*, and *Amecephalus*. The upper part of the Gordon Shale in north-west Montana has *Anoria* in addition and this genus occurs also at the base of the Rutledge Limestone in West Virginia.

The Glossopleura zone which follows is widespread in the Mesocambrian sections of Virginia and Tennessee, Utah and north-west Montana, Alberta and British Columbia, the Mackenzie Valley of north-west Canada, and in north-west Greenland. The typical genus *Glossopleura* is usually accompanied by species of *Zacanthoides*, *Chancia*, *Kootenia* (Fig. 27), and other genera. After a considerable stratigraphical interval appears the Ehmania fauna which is recorded from the south Appalachians, north-west and central Montana, Wyoming, and Utah, but not from the Canadian Rockies. The index-genus *Ehmania* is often associated with species of *Bolaspis*, *Glyphaspis*, and the long-ranged *Kootenia*, besides, more rarely, by the Asiatic genus *Tonkinella*. Somewhat higher is the famous Ogygiopsis fauna of Mount Stephen, B.C., containing the oft-quoted association of *Ogygiopsis klotzi* (Rominger) (Fig. 27), *Neolenus serratus* (Rominger), *Bathyuriscus howelli* Walcott, *Agnostus montis* Matthew with species of *Elrathina*, *Zacanthoides*, and *Oryctocephalus*. Deiss states that this fauna is absent from other sections in Canada, but an association of *Oryctocephalus*, *Bathyurus*, and *Elrathina* is found in the Spence Shale of Idaho. The youngest Mesocambrian assemblage, known as the *Thomsonaspis* fauna, is described only from Montana and Castle Mountain, Alberta. In Montana the index-genus is accompanied by *Kochaspis upis* (Walcott) and species of *Coelaspis*, *Glossocoryphus*, and *Menairia*. In Alberta its associates are *Olenoides* and *Solenopleurella*, but the former is not recorded from Montana though it is present in the Majum Limestone of Utah. The zone may also be present in the Maryville Limestone of Georgia and Alabama, but trilobites are scarce and precise correlation is uncertain. A late Mesocambrian fauna of western type, described from west Newfoundland by C. Lochman in 1938, includes species of *Marjumia* and *Eldoradia*, genera that were previously known only from Utah and Nevada respectively.

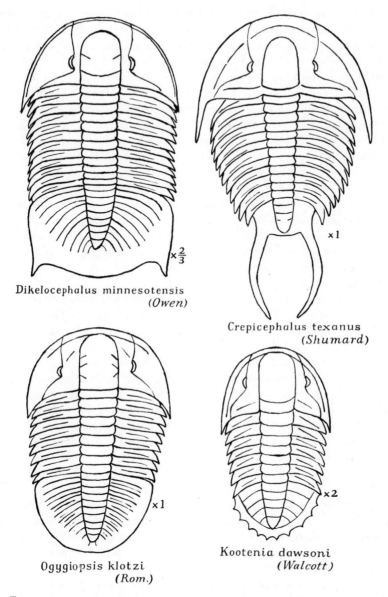

Dikelocephalus minnesotensis
(Owen)
×⅔

Crepicephalus texanus
(Shumard)
×1

Ogygiopsis klotzi
(Rom.)
×1

Kootenia dawsoni
(Walcott)
×2

FIG. 27. LARGE-TAILED CAMBRIAN TRILOBITES OF NORTH AMERICA

The best standard of reference for the Neocambrian faunas of North America is the succession in the Upper Mississippi Valley. In Wisconsin and Minnesota the Neocambrian strata rest unconformably on Precambrian crystalline rocks, and the sequence is interpreted by Twenhofel, Raasch, and Thwaites (1935) as practically continuous. This indeed is indicated by the overlapping ranges of numerous trilobite-genera recorded from the several horizons, which are conveniently grouped in the Dresbach Franconia and Trempealeau stages in ascending order.

The faunas of the Dresbach stage are linked together by the presence of *Crepicephalus* (Fig. 27) which is distinguished especially by its large pygidium with two broad postero-lateral spines. This genus and its allies range through the stage, but various associations of genera and species with more restricted ranges enable three zones to be recognized. The lowest beds known as the Cedaria zone are specially marked by the genera *Cedaria* and *Cedarina*, associated with early forms of *Crepicephalus*, the anomocarids *Coosia* and *Coosella*, various solenopleurids and plethopeltids, and the proparians *Menomonia*, *Millarda*, and *Norwoodia*. This fauna is widespread over the North American continent at intervals from west Newfoundland and the Appalachians, south-west and south-east Missouri to Texas, north-west into the Upper Mississippi Valley and across Dakota to the Cordilleran region. A few genera persist into the Crepicephalus zone where they are associated with typical species of *Crepicephalus*, various ptychoparids, and the proparian *Dresbachia*. The distribution of the fauna is much the same as that of the Cedaria zone. Higher beds in the Appalachians and the Rocky Mountains have yielded a fauna which, though many genera persist from below, is specially marked by the presence of *Aphelaspis*.

The Franconia stage in Wisconsin begins with the Ironton Sandstone in which species of *Elvinia*, *Irvingella*, *Camaraspis*, and *Housea* are typical trilobites. The assemblage differs essentially from that of the underlying beds, for the crepicephalids, so abundant in the Dresbach stage, are here absent. The index-genus *Elvinia* seems to be closely related to the ptychoparids, and *Camaraspis*, equally prominent in the Upper Mississippi Valley is perhaps an early member of the Plethopeltidae. Walcott's genus *Housea* is regarded by F. W. Whitehouse (1939) as synonymous with *Proceratopyge*, the type of which comes from Scandinavia. *Irvingella* is another genus with European connexions, for a rare species *I. nuneatonensis* (Sharman) is recorded by Stubblefield (1932) from the equivalent of the Maentwrog Beds at Nuneaton, England. On this evidence B. F. Howell and C. Lochman (1939) regard the Irvingella fauna as broadly corresponding to the Olenus fauna of Europe. The next zone, characterized by *Conaspis* and *Wilbernia*, has a wide distribution in the south Appalachians, Missouri, Wisconsin, and the Cordilleran region. *Conaspis*, with a large number of species, is allied to the Ptychoparidae, and *Wilbernia* seems to connect this family with the Asaphiscidae.

The next two zones are marked by *Ptychaspis* and *Prosaukia* respectively. The first genus is placed by Raymond (1924) in a separate family Ptychaspidae, but Ulrich and Resser (1933) believe this group to be related to the Dikelocephalidae through the sub-family Saukinae, of which the earliest genus is *Prosaukia*. The Ptychaspis fauna is recorded from Wisconsin and the Cordilleran region, the Prosaukia fauna is known in addition from Oklahoma and Texas.

The remaining Neocambrian horizons are dominated by different members of the Dikelocephalidae, their most distinctive feature being the large fan-like pygidium with the sides produced into a pair of short spines (Fig. 27). The lowest of these, yielding the Briscoia fauna, is widely distributed at various localities from Oklahoma and Texas in the south to Alaska in the north, and from Nevada, Montana, and south Dakota in the west to the Hoyt Limestone of New York State in the east. The pygidium from North Wales known as *Dikelocephalus celticus* (Salter) is referred to *Briscoia* by Kobayashi (1935) and provides evidence for correlating the Briscoia horizon of North America with the Upper Lingula Flags of Great Britain. The uppermost fauna of the Franconia stage is marked by the appearance of *Dikelocephalus*, *Saukiella*, and *Illaenurus*. B. F. Howell and C. Lochman (1939) state that the assemblage has been definitely recognized only in Wisconsin and a few localities in the Cordilleran region. The fauna has close relations with the early Trempealeau faunas of Wisconsin in which *Dikelocephalus* attains its maximum development, and is associated with *Saukia*, *Tellerina*, *Illaenurus*, *Eurekia*, and other genera.

Younger Trempealeau faunas have been recognized in Wisconsin and some of them are recorded at widely separated localities in the Western States. The genus *Eurekia* is used as the index of a zone reported from Nevada, Montana, and Wyoming. The succeeding Saukiella fauna contains species of the dikelocephalitid genera *Saukiella*, *Saukia*, *Calvinella*, and *Osceolia*, associated with ptychaspids and plethopeltids. This assemblage is known from Wisconsin, Missouri, Oklahoma, Texas, and the Appalachians, but is apparently doubtful or rare in the Western States, and several of the genera continue to the top of the Trempealeau stage. These trilobite faunas cannot at present be correlated satisfactorily with European assemblages. But the common occurrence of dendroid graptolites is a prominent feature in the Trempealeau rocks of Wisconsin and Montana. Hence Howell and Lochman suggest that this stage may possibly be broadly contemporaneous with the Tremadoc Beds of Britain and their equivalents in north-west Europe. A further link with the European *Ceratopyge* fauna is mentioned by P. E. Raymond (1937) who records the genus *Protapatokephalus* from late Neocambrian Beds in Vermont. He regards this form as ancestral to *Apatokephalus* which is characteristic of the Ceratopyge fauna of Scandinavia, and is described by P. Lake (1931) from the Tremadoc Beds of North Wales. Higher strata in Vermont have yielded asaphids that are referred to *Symphysurina*, *Symphysurinella*, and *Symphysuroides*. The first two genera are also known from the Western States, British Columbia, and Alberta, and with their associates are regarded by Raymond (1922) as indicative of the Ceratopyge fauna, though the characteristic *Euloma* and *Niobella* are both lacking in American records.

From the preceding review it is evident that the Cambrian faunas of Europe and North America are distributed in two Faunal Regions. The European strata carrying the successive *Callavia*, *Paradoxides*, and *Olenus* faunas were deposited in an eastern embayment of the Atlantic Ocean, and a western extension of the same ocean encroached on the eastern margin of the North American continent. This has long been termed the Atlantic Life-Province of Cambrian time. The equivalent deposits over the interior and western part of North America support successively the *Olenellus*, *Crepicephalus*, and *Dikelocephalus* faunas, and are regarded as having been formed in a vast extension of the Pacific Ocean to the northern part of Greenland, north-west Scotland, and Arctic Siberia. In North America the general limit between the two regions is well defined from east Newfoundland, along the Green Mountains to the Appalachians. But we have noted (p. 144) the presence of a Mesocambrian fauna of Atlantic type in northwest Vermont, preceded by Palaeocambrian and succeeded by Neocambrian faunas, both of Pacific type. Evidently the limit between the two regions was subject to some degree of fluctuation—even allowing for subsequent disturbance of the rocks by thrusting from the east. Moreover, apart from the Scottish Olenellus fauna, stragglers from the Pacific extension are occasionally present in European faunas at various horizons (pp. 150 and 151). Besides providing a means of correlating the several faunas of the two regions, this circumstance indicates some measure of communication across the Atlantic between the American interior and the European coast. Migration seems always to be from west to east, and one can only surmise the existence of an ocean current analogous to the Gulf Stream of the present day.

(c) EAST AND SOUTH ASIA; AUSTRALIA

The Cambrian system is well developed in east Asia, the strata in general representing marine transgression over the ancient rocks of the Precambrian floor. The deposits occupy two embayments separated by the Precambrian ridge of the Tsinling Range. In the north, trilobite faunas from the three main divisions of the system have been described from well-exposed sections in Manchuria, Korea, and the provinces of Chihli, Shansi, and Shantung in north China (Fig. 28). The southern area extends from the province of Anhwei to Yunnan and Tonking. Some 1,700 miles to the north-west, a succession of Cambrian rocks is involved in the Himalayan folds of the Spiti district and Kashmir in north India. Farther west, the Salt Range of the Punjab, and localities in south-west Persia have also yielded Cambrian faunas. In view of the scanty records from India and Persia, and of the great distances separating the several localities, any interpretation of relationship is bound to be tentative, but there is no doubt that a considerable degree of affinity links the Cambrian trilobite faunas of east and south Asia, an affinity that is shared to some extent by the equivalent Australian faunas.

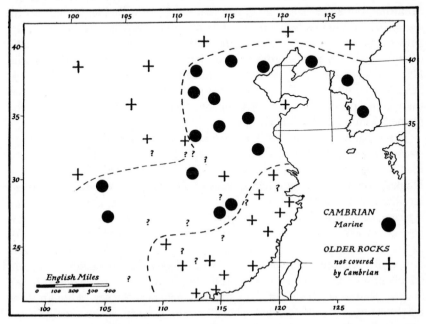

FIG. 28. SKETCH-MAP OF CHINA SHOWING GENERAL DISTRIBUTION OF CAMBRIAN ROCKS

The oldest Cambrian trilobites recorded in east Asia are examples of *Protolenus*, described by K. Saito (1936) from north-west Korea. The succeeding beds contain several species of *Redlichia*, notably *R. chinensis* Walcott. In the possession of long eyelobes and tapering glabella this genus appears to be related morphologically to the Olenellidae, but it differs from that group in the presence of definite facial sutures. The Redlichia Beds also contain species of *Bonnia*, a genus which is also represented in the Palaeocambrian Series of North America and Greenland. *Redlichia chinensis* is also the most distinctive trilobite in the Manto Shales of North China, where it is associated with species of *Ptychoparia* and other genera. In Yunnan *R. chinensis* is accompanied by the ellipsocephalid genus *Palaeolenus* established by Mansuy (1912). The Indian form *R. noetlingi* is associated with ptychoparids and peculiar local genera of brachiopods in the Neobolus Beds of the Salt Range, and F. R. C. Reed (1910) records an isolated example of the same trilobite from Spiti; this species differs from *R. chinensis* mainly in the shape of the glabella. The Chinese species is also described by W. B. R. King (1930) from south-west Persia where it is associated with other trilobites referred to the genus *Anomocare*. These, again, are brought into comparison with Chinese species, and the differences between the Indian and Persian faunas are attributed to slight differences in horizon within the range of *Redlichia*. This is usually taken as Palaeocambrian, but since Saito has shown that the Korean Redlichia Beds are all above the Protolenus horizon, it is possible that *Redlichia* extends into the Mesocambrian Series. According to F. W. Whitehouse (1936) *Redlichia* occupies a similar position in the Templeton Series of north-east Australia. Hence widely separated stations are linked by the presence of the Redlichia fauna, which C. D. Walcott (1914) considered to be 'so distinct that there is no probability of its having lived in the same province with the Olenellid fauna of N. America'.

Three Mesocambrian horizons are recognized in the Changhia Limestone and lower part of the Kushan Shale in north China. The lowest is readily distinguished by the widespread presence of *Dorypyge richthofeni* Dames, accompanied by other species of *Dorypyge*, *Ptychoparia*, and less familiar genera. Some of these persist into the next zone, that of *Amphoton typicum*, to which this trilobite is apparently restricted. The third horizon is specially marked by *Damesella blackwelderi* Walcott and other species of *Damesella*, all having a characteristic multispinose pygidium. Particularly noticeable are the abundant pygidia of *Drepanura premesnili* Bergeron, widely known as 'Stone swallows' from the shape of the large lateral spines, and adopted as the badge of the Chinese Geological Survey. Though these trilobites are distributed from Manchuria to Yunnan, a distance of some 1,500 miles, they are apparently peculiar to east Asia. Nothing like them is recorded from the Pacific States of North America, and such typically American forms as *Olenoides*, *Neolenus*, *Zacanthoides*, and *Ogygiopsis* are not known in the Chinese Mesocambrian deposits. Hence Walcott (1914) concludes that each of these assemblages 'belongs to a local fauna that did not obtain a distribution outside of the limited area in which it lived'. K. Saito (1934), however, describes a species of *Oryctocephalus* from north-west Korea, comparable with the *O. reynoldsi* of Mt. Stephen, British Columbia. F. R. C. Reed (1910) had previously recorded the same genus from a Mesocambrian horizon in Spiti, north India, accompanied by a species of *Zacanthoides*. There is also an abundance of ptychoparids which are said to be closely related to western American forms. But again it must be noted that many genera conspicuous in American Mesocambrian rocks are unknown from Spiti. From Kashmir, Reed (1934), and Kobayashi (1934) have independently reported the presence of *Tonkinella*, a genus related to *Oryctocephalus*, and also known from Indo-china, Korea, and British Columbia. In Kashmir it is associated with other trilobites that are referred to the dikelocephalitid genera *Saukia, Hundwarella*, and *Prosaukia* which also suggest American affinities. But species of *Anomocare* and *Chuangia*, named by Reed, are comparable with trilobites from China and Tonkin, though, as in Spiti, there is no indication of the peculiar Damesellidae of east Asia. Two trilobites from a high Mesocambrian horizon in south-west Persia are compared by W. B. R. King (1930) with east Asian forms of *Anomocare*, while two others are tentatively assigned to *Coosia asiatica* Mansuy and *Chuangia nais* Walcott, from Tonkin and China respectively.

The Mesocambrian Beds of north-east Australia are classified by F. W. Whitehouse (1939) in seven stages, from which a few typical trilobites should be noted. The corynexochid *Amphoton* and the ptychoparid *Nepea*, from the lowest stage, but persisting to higher beds, are comparable with east Asian and North American forms of early Mesocambrian age. A higher stage contains an abundance of *Xystridura*, which seems to have some relationship with the European *Paradoxides*; indeed a single fragment has been referred to a new species of this last genus. Later stages contain various agnostids and other trilobites which are said to have allies in the Asian, Cordilleran, Appalachian, and Scandinavian faunas. The record of *Oryctocephalus*, for instance, from the Templeton River Series, provides a link with western America, while *Papyriaspis* and *Rhodonaspis*, ascribed to the Olenidae, are said to be related to certain Korean ptychoparids. But again the absence of the peculiar Chinese genera is conspicuous.

In general, while the Australian and Indian Mesocambrian faunas have features in common with those of east Asia, each region has its own local characters. It seems that the Mesocambrian seas of Persia, India, and Australia were in communication with the general circulation of the Pacific Ocean, but that distance and probably other factors prevented the widespread migration of certain provincial races of trilobites.

In north China the Neocambrian Series begins with the Chaumitian Limestone of Willis and Blackwelder (1907), to which the Upper Kushan Shale has been added as a basal formation. Y. C. Sun (1935) has distinguished a number of palaeontological zones in north China and Kobayashi (1935) has determined a similar succession in Korea and Manchuria. A. Grabau (1937), however, states that the sequence is incomplete at most localities. The lowest zone is specially marked by species of *Chuangia*; this genus is placed in the Leiostegiidae, a well-defined family derived from the Oryctocephalidae, and distributed in south and east Asia and North America. The next zone has yielded an abundance of *Changshania*, a later member of the Asiatic family Emmrichellidae. Then follows the *Kaolishania* zone, the index-fossil being a late member of the indigenous Damesellidae. The entrance in abundance of ptychaspids and *Tsinania* gives character to the Ptychaspis zone. The appearance of the dikelocephalid genus *Prosaukia* precedes the establishment of *Saukia*, which with the ptychaspid *Quadraticephalus* provides a name for the next highest zone. Finally, representatives of the *Ceratopyge* fauna are recorded from south Korea, and calcareous mudstones in the Kaiping basin have yielded the dendroid graptolites, *Dictyonema*, *Callograptus*, and *Dendrograptus*.

The Neocambrian rocks bordering the Indian and Pacific Oceans thus show the same regional relationships as the earlier series of the system. It seems certain that the two oceans were in easy communication throughout Cambrian time. The Cambrian faunas of east Asia, India, Persia, and Australia are not identical but all have major features in common; the occurrence of local peculiarities is only to be expected in view of the vast distances involved. The northern limit of the Indian Ocean is indicated in the Himalayan region, and though the western and southern margins are not determinable, the Cambrian faunas of Australia are of the same general type, except that the Neocambrian faunas consist largely of cosmopolitan forms like the agnostids and so give little indication of provincial variation. It is probable that, apart from the extensive encroachments over the margins of the Asian and American continents the Cambrian Pacific Ocean had much the same extent as its modern suecessor.

THE ARCHAEOCYATHIDS

The Cambrian fossils grouped in the Archaeocyathidae constitute a family of somewhat doubtful systematic position. They have the general external form of sponges; sometimes the body assumes the shape of conical cups or bowls, other forms are almost cylindrical tubes, and most of them have a basal root-like projection for attachment to an external support. The central cavity is enclosed by two walls separated by a space known as the intervallum, and this space may be divided into loculi by perforate septa and tabulae, thereby simulating the structure of corals. There is considerable variety in structural details, and T. G. Taylor (1910) classifies the sixteen genera known to him in five subdivisions which may be considered as sub-families, namely Archaeocyathinae, Coscinocyathinae, Spirocyathinae, Dictyocyathinae, and Syringocneminae. There are other genera which have sometimes been referred to the Archaeocyathidae but are now transferred to other groups; we may note particularly *Archaeoscyphia* of Hinde (1889), which its author places with *Calathium* among the siliceous sponges.

According to W. T. Gordon (1920) the most complete and most extensive archaeocyathid fauna yet recorded is that of South Australia. The first Archaeocyathids described by R. Etheridge (1889) from this area are referred to the genera *Ethmophyllum*, *Coscinocyathus*, and *Protopharetra*. Later collections, described by T. G. Taylor (1910) from localities between 31° and 35° S. lat., comprise some thirty-five species representing fourteen genera. T. W. E. David (1932) states that the archaeocyathids of south and central Australia form immense reefs in the Flinders and

McDonnell ranges, and Taylor found few other organisms in association with them.

Eight of the Australian genera are represented in a block of limestone dredged from a depth of 1,775 fathoms in the Weddell Sea (lat. 62° 10' S.; long. 41° 21' W.) during the Scottish National Antarctic Expedition of 1902–4. W. T. Gordon (1920) describes fourteen species distributed among the genera *Archaeocyathus, Thalamocyathus, Spirocyathus, Syringocnema, Coscinocyathus, Protopharetra, Metaldetes,* and *Dictyocyathus,* but most of the species are distinct from the Australian forms. The Antarctic fossils are small in size and have thickened walls, conditions which seem to indicate growth under adverse circumstances. The same conditions are shared by specimens collected at a height of 2,758 feet on the Beardmore Glacier (lat. 82° 30' S.; long. 170° E.) during the British Antarctic Expedition of 1907–9 (T. G. Taylor, 1914). From a later collection, W. T. Gordon (1930) records species of *Archaeocyathus, Thalamocyathus, Dokidocyathus,* and the alga *Epiphyton.* All the Antarctic specimens are from drifted material but they indicate the development of Archaeocyathid limestones somewhere in Antarctica during Cambrian time.

Three of the Australian and four of the Antarctic archaeocyathids are referred to species first described by Bornemann (1886) from the south-western part of Sardinia (lat. 39° N.). The Cambrian rocks of this island include limestones which contain abundant archaeocyathids disposed in reefs that are said to rival the Australian examples. The fauna contains about thirty species belonging to the genera *Archaeocyathus, Anthomorpha, Coscinocyathus,* and *Protopharetra.* Several of the same species of *Archaeocyathus* and *Coscinocyathus* are also recorded by Toll (1899) from the reef-like Torgoschino Limestone in the banks of the River Yenesei opposite Krasnoyarsk (lat. 56° N.), Siberia, besides local species of these genera and of *Rhabdocyathus* and undertermined forms of *Spirocyathus* and *Protopharetra.* The Cambrian rocks of the south Urals (lat. 50° N.) also include some limestones containing species of *Archaeocyathus* and *Ethmophyllum* associated with the calcareous alga *Epiphyton* (Garan, 1937). At the northern end of the Urals, between the mainland and Novaia Zemlya, lies the island of Waigatch (lat. 70° N.) whence *Archaeocyathus* is cited by A. Geikie (1903). This seems to be the most northerly locality at which the group is recorded. In addition to the localities already mentioned there are records of archaeocyathids from intermediate places in Europe and Asia. A. G. Vologdin (1932) has described those of the Altai Mountains (lat. 50° N.). C. D. Walcott (1906) has named a single species, *Coscinocyathus elvira,* from Wutai (lat. 40° N.) in north China, and F. R. C. Reed (1908) records another, *C.* cf. *corbicula,* from Spiti (lat. 32° N.) in the Himalayan region. *Archaeocyathus* is reported by Vologdin (1934) from Laba River (lat. 44° N.) in the northern Caucasus. At a slightly higher latitude (50° N.) in the Cotentin, north France A. Bigot (1906) has described forms comparable with *Spirocyathus* and *Protopharetra*. Farther south, *Coscinocyathus* is recorded by Thoral (1934) from the Montaigne Noire (lat. 44° N.), *Archaeocyathus* from the Sierra Morena (lat. 38° N.) in Spain by F. Roemer (1880) and from certain localities in Morocco (lat. 33° N.), by Bourcart (1927) and Russo (1927).

In the western hemisphere the genus *Archaeocyathus* was originally founded by Billings (1861) on specimens from Belle Isle, Labrador (lat. 52° N.). On the adjacent coast of western Newfoundland reefs composed largely of *Archaeocyathus profundus* and *Spirocyathus atlanticus* are the most striking features of the Forteau formation. The reefs are lenses of limestone with a thickness of 10 to 20 feet and a width of many yards; according to Schuchert and Dunbar (1934), they grade laterally into bedded limestones. In the southern Appalachians Resser (1938) states that reefs of *Archaeocyathus* are beautifully developed in the vicinity of Austinville (lat. 38° N.), Virginia, and that such reefs, not yet fully explored, extend from Labrador to Alabama and Georgia. Like the Australian and European examples, they seem to be confined to a single horizon within the Palaeo-cambrian Series. Reefs at Silver Peak, Nevada (lat. 38° N.) have yielded species of *Archaeocyathus* and *Ethmophyllum* including the type of the latter genus established by Meek (1868). Farther north, the Mount Whyte Beds of British Columbia (lat. 52°) have furnished *Archaeocyathus atreus* to Walcott (1917). No archaeocyathids seem to be recorded from South America.

The development of archaeocyathid reefs is usually interpreted, by analogy with modern coral reefs, as indicating warm climatic conditions. But the Cambrian reefs are recorded from various latitudes between 30° and the Poles, whereas they are unknown from the climatic belt, roughly 30° on either side of the equator, in which modern coral reefs flourish. It may be that future exploration will diminish this gap, but meanwhile in-genious theories are being advanced to explain the apparent anomaly. W. T. Gordon (1930) explains the presence of Archaeocyathids in Antarctica 'on the assumption that the rocks of Cambrian age at present situated in South Polar regions were not accumulated in these latitudes, but had moved into that location since Cambrian times'. In this connexion it may be recalled that Wegener (1923) unites the continental blocks into a single 'Pangaea' which persists through Palaeozoic time: in this way Antarctica is brought to a position between the Tropic of Capricorn and the Antarctic Circle. Grabau (1935) brings all the continents together in the manner of Wegener's 'Pangaea', but places the Cambrian North Pole somewhere in the region of Egypt where Palaeozoic sediments are rare or absent. On this recon-struction the Siberian and Australian archaeocyathid reefs would be in the tropical belt, but, as Grabau himself realizes, the Sardinian locality would lie near 70° N. lat., too near the North Pole for reefs to flourish. None of these theories satisfies all the facts, and there is no positive evidence that a genial climate prevailed over high latitudes in Cambrian time. Solution of the problem must be left for the future; meantime it can be said that the identity of archaeocyathid genera (and even some species) at distant localities indicates easy communication between the oceans of Cambrian time despite the limitation of provincial trilobite faunas.

LITERATURE

Many Cambrian trilobites and other fossils were described and figured, chiefly by Callaway, Hicks, and Salter, by the middle of the nineteenth century. In recent years, however, palaeontological nomenclature has undergone considerable revision, which must be taken into account when interpreting the work of the earlier investigators. Consequently the plan followed in this chapter, and throughout the volume, is to make brief reference to a recent general work which contains an exhaustive list of literature, and to enumerate in some detail the chief works (generally of monographic scope) which are most useful for biostratigraphical investigation.

The detailed work of Mr. E. S. Cobbold on the Lower and Middle Cambrian of Shropshire is summarized in—

'The Stratigraphy and Geological Structure of the Cambrian Area of Comley (Shropshire)', *Q.J.G.S.*, vol. lxxxiii, pp. 551–73 (and map); 1927.

In earlier papers Mr. Cobbold has described and figured over 130 species of fossils from Lower and Middle Cambrian rocks, many of them being new to science and most of them new to England. These papers form a most important series indispensable to students of the British Cambrian rocks.

'Some Small Trilobites from the Cambrian Rocks of Comley (Shropshire)', *Q.J.G.S.*, vol. lxvi, pp. 19–51, 1910. Descriptions and figures of seventeen species of Lower Cambrian trilobites.

'Trilobites from the Paradoxides Beds of Comley (Shropshire)', *Q.J.G.S.*, vol. lxvii, pp. 282–311, 1911. Fifteen species of Middle Cambrian trilobites are described and illustrated. In an appendix Dr. C. A. Matley describes eleven species of brachiopods from the same beds.

'The Trilobite Fauna of the Comley Breccia-bed', *Q.J.G.S.*, vol. lxix, pp. 27–44, 1913. Descriptions of ten species of trilobites from Lower and Middle Cambrian horizons.

'The Cambrian Horizons of Comley (Shropshire) and their Brachiopoda, Gastropoda, &c.', *Q.J.G.S.*, vol. lxxvi, pp. 315–86, 1920. This paper contains descriptions and figures of sixty species, excluding trilobites, besides a list of all known Comley fossils, which are arranged in their respective horizons. References to earlier work are given throughout the series.

'Cambrian Hyolithidae, &c., from Hartshill in the Nuneaton District, Warwickshire', by E. S. Cobbold, *Geol. Mag.*, vol. lvi, pp. 149–58, 1919.

'The Cambrian Area of Rushton, Shropshire', by E. S. Cobbold and R. W. Pocock, *Phil. Trans. Roy. Soc.*, ser. B, vol. ccxxiii, pp. 305–409, 1934.

The Middle Cambrian rocks of the Nuneaton district are described by Prof. V. C. Illing in—'The Paradoxidian Fauna of a Part of the Stockingford Shales', *Q.J.G.S.*, vol. lxxxi (for 1915), pp. 386–450; 1916. This paper contains an extensive list of literature and many illustrations of Middle Cambrian trilobites. A feature of the work is the application of agnostid trilobites to detailed stratigraphical investigation.

'Notes on the Trilobite Fauna of the Middle Cambrian of St. Tudwal's Peninsula (N. Wales)', by T. C. Nicholas, *Q.J.G.S.*, vol. lxxi (for 1915), pp. 451–72, 1916.

Upper Cambrian rocks are described in—

'The Tremadoc Slates and Associated Rocks of South-east Carnarvonshire', by W. G. Fearnsides, *Q.J.G.S.*, vol. lxvi, pp. 142–88, 1910.

'The Shineton Shales of the Wrekin District', by C. J. Stubblefield and O. M. Bulman, *Q.J.G.S.*, vol. lxxxiii, pp. 96–146, 1927.

The latter paper contains descriptions and figures of new species of trilobites, brachiopods, and pteropods, together with a full faunal list and numerous references to literature.

'The Occurrence of Tremadoc Shales in the Tortworth Inlier (Gloucestershire)', by S. Smith, with notes on the fossils by C. J. Stubblefield, *Q.J.G.S.*, vol. lxxxix, pp. 357–78, 1933.

A monograph of *The Cambrian Trilobites*, by P. Lake, *Mon. Pal. Soc.*, 1906–46, contains revised descriptions of the species so far known from the British Cambrian rocks.

Another monograph of the Palaeontographical Society on *The British Dendroid Graptolites*, by O. M. Bulman, is also being issued. The first three parts, 1927–34, contain descriptions of certain species of *Dictyonema*.

With regard to the Scottish Cambrian rocks, figures and descriptions of the Lower Cambrian trilobites are given in 'Additions to the Fauna of the Olenellus-Zone of the North-West Highlands', by B. N. Peach, *Q.J.G.S.*, vol. i, pp. 661–76, 1894. Dr. Peach summarized the Cambrian succession of this area in 'The Relation between the Cambrian Faunas of Scotland and North America', *Rep. Brit. Assoc. for 1912*, pp. 448–59, 1913.

The Cambrian rocks and fossils of Scandinavia and the Baltic region are described by T. Strand in 'The Cambrian Beds of the Mjosen District, Norway', *Norsk. geol. Tidsskr.*, vol. x, pp. 308–65, 1929; by A. H. Westergaard in 'Sverigen Olenidskiffer', *Sver. geol. Undersök.*, ser. Ca, No. 18, 1922; and by A. Opik in 'Studien über dem estonischen Unterkambrium', *Publ. Geol. Univ. Tartu*, No. 15, 1929.

The Bohemian succession was first established by J. Barrande in his great work, *Système Silurien de la Bohème* (1852–83). The fundamental grouping of the strata remains much as he described it, but some of the stratigraphical details have been modified by later research, such as that by J. F. Pompeckj, 'Die Fauna des Cambriums von Tejrovic und Skrej, Böhmen', *Jahr. K. K. Geol. Reichsanst*, vol. xlv, pp. 495–614, 1896. J. Czarnocki has discussed the sequence in Poland in 'Le Cambrien et la Faune Cambrienne de la Partie Moyenne du Massif de Święty Krzyż (Ste. Croix)', *C.R. Internat. Congr. Geol.* (Madrid), vol. ii, pp. 735–50, 1927.

The following works give results of recent research on the Cambrian rocks and fossils of North America: 'Correlation of Middle Cambrian Faunas of North America', by B. F. Howell and J. F. Mason, *Journ. Palaeont.*, vol. xii, pp. 295–97, 1938; 'Succession of Later Cambrian Faunas in the Northern Hemisphere', by B. F. Howell and C. Lochman, ibid., vol. xiii, pp. 115–22, 1939; 'Cambrian Faunal Succession in Nevada and California', by J. F. Mason, ibid., vol. xii, pp. 287–94, 1938; 'The Cambrian, Ozarkian, and Canadian Faunas of North-west Greenland', by C. Poulsen, *Meddelelser om Grønland*, vol. lxx, pp. 233–343, 1927; and 'The Lower Cambrian Faunas of East Greenland', by C. Poulsen, *Medd. Groenl.*, vol. lxxxvii, pp. 1–66. All of them contain useful lists of references to earlier work.

In a noteworthy 'Revision of Croixian Dikelocephalids', *Illinois Acad. Sci. Trans.*, vol. xliv, pp. 85–128, 137–151, 1952, G. O. Raasch has shown that many species of these trilobites are based on inadequate material, and others on differences in successive growth-stages of a single species. On these grounds the number of species is reduced by two-thirds, to about 40. Raasch also separates the Saukidae, which arose through the Ptychaspidae from earlier Franconian conaspid trilobites, from the Dikelocephalidae which he derives through *Briscoia* from the early Franconian genus *Wilbernia*. The text on pp. 150–1 should be read in relation to this revision.

The pioneer work in eastern Asia by C. D. Walcott, *Cambrian Faunas of China*, Carnegie Inst. Washington, Publ. No. 54, 1913, and 'Cambrian Faunas of E. Asia', *Smithsonian Misc. Coll.*, vol. lxiv, pp. 1–75, 1914, has been followed by more detailed research by K. Saito; 'Older Cambrian Trilobita, &c. from Korea', *Jap. Journ. Geol. Geogr.*, vol. xi, pp. 211–37, 1934; by Y. C. Sun, 'Cambrian Faunas of North China', *Pal. Sinica*, ser. B, vol. i, No. 4, 1924; by R. Endo and C. E. Resser, 'The Sinian and Cambrian Formations and Fossils of Southern Manchukuo', *Manchurian Sci. Mus. Bull.* 1, pp. 1–474, 73 pls., 1937.

Collections of Cambrian fossils from southern Asia have been described by W. B. R. King in 'Cambrian Fauna of Persia', *Geol. Mag.*, vol. lxvii, pp. 316–27, 1930, and 'The Cambrian Fauna of the Salt Range of India', *Rec. Geol. Surv. India*, vol. lxxv, No. 9, pp. 1–15, 1941; by F. R. C. Reed in 'Cambrian Fossils of Spiti', *Pal. Indica*, ser, 15, vol. vii, mem. no. 1, pp. 1–70, 1910, and 'Cambrian and Ordovician Fossils from Kashmir', *Pal. Indica*, N.S., vol. xxi, No. 2, pp. 1–38, 1934; and by T. Kobayashi, 'Middle Cambrian Fossils from Kashmir', *Amer. Jour. Sci.*, ser. 5, vol. xxvii, pp. 295–302, 1934. The most recent work on the Australian fossils is contained in 'The Cambrian Faunas of N.E. Australia', by F. W. Whitehouse, *Mem. Queensland Mus.*, vol. xi, pp. 179–282, 1939.

Following the early work of G. J. Hinde, 'On Archaeocyathus, &c.', *Q.J.G.S.*, vol. xlv, pp. 125–48, 1889, and of J. Bornemann, *Verstein Sardinien*, 1887, numerous additions to genera, species, and their distribution have been made by T. G. Taylor in 'The Archaeocyathinae from the Cambrian of South Australia', *Mem. Roy. Soc. S. Austr.*, vol. ii, pp. 55–108, 1910; by W. T. Gordon in *Scottish National Expedition 1902–4*; 'Cambrian Organic Remains from a Dredging in the Weddell Sea', *Trans. Roy. Soc. Edin.*, vol. lii, pp. 681–714, 1920; and 'Some Limestone Erratics from the Beardmore Glacier', *Brit. Assoc., Rep. for 1929*, p. 324, 1930; by A. G. Vologdin in *The Archaeocyathinae of Siberia*, *1931*, Moscow.

IV

ORDOVICIAN FAUNAS

W HEN, in 1879, Charles Lapworth established the Ordovician system, he included in it the Arenig Series of Sedgwick (1852), the Llandeilo Series of Murchison (1833), and the Bala Series of Sedgwick (1838) in ascending order. At that time the mutual relations of the three series were imperfectly known, for the type-areas are widely separated geographically, It is now generally recognized that the three original divisions cover the entire system, so that subsequent modifications, like the addition of the Llanvirn Series by H. Hicks in 1875, and the nomenclature adopted by J. E. Marr (1905) seem only to introduce needless complexity. But while the three conventional series are consistent with the physical and strati-graphical relations of Ordovician strata in Britain, it is more convenient to follow other authors in using the terms Palaeordovician, Mesordovician, and Neordovician for the purposes of wider correlation; it should be noted that the prefix 'palaeo-' is preferred to the more usual 'eo-' in order to avoid confusion with 'neo-' in the spoken word.

The distribution of the British Ordovician rocks (exposed in north, cen-tral, and south Wales, Shropshire, the Lake District, the southern Uplands of Scotland, and eastern Ireland) suggests that they were laid down in a single basin of deposition bounded by land areas on the north-west (in-cluding the mountainous region of Scotland) and the south-east (including the Midlands and south of England). This idea is confirmed by the litho-logy, the rocks in the centre of the outcrop being mainly black shales and mudstones, those on the margins comprising a variable series of sandstones, shales, flags, grits, and limestones.

The fauna, also, presents two general types: (a) a graptolitic facies in which the principal fossils are graptolites, occurs in the mudstones of the central area; (b) a 'shelly' facies is present in the variable marginal deposits, where the most important fossils are benthic types such as trilobites and brachiopods. These have been regarded as representing in a general way a deep-water fauna and a shallow-water fauna, but it is now considered that the graptolitic facies does not depend upon depth *per se*, but essentially upon the prevalence of quiet conditions of deposition (see p. 33). It is con-venient to discuss the two facies separately, and to begin with—

A. THE GRAPTOLITIC FACIES

The use of graptolites as zonal guides has already been mentioned as hav-ing arisen mainly from the pioneer work of Lapworth. Later investigators working on the lines he initiated have elaborated Lapworth's original scheme of Ordovician zones, and the resulting classification has proved to be of immense value in detailed mapping. The accompanying table shows the zonal sequence at present in use, together with a summary of the main faunal characteristics, the whole being compiled from the more recent works of G. L. Elles.

The earliest known graptolites have already been noted as occurring in the Tremadoc rocks, which are classified in this country as the uppermost series of the Cambrian system. Those graptolites are dendroid forms, and some authors believe that the later 'true' graptolites evolved from some of the forms included in the genus *Dictyonema* (Fig. 29). In the Lower Tremadoc rocks this genus occurs alone, but in the higher zones it is associated with two main series which appear to have arisen from the dictyonemid stock. In one, *Bryograptus* (Fig. 29), the pendent form persists as in *B. cumbrensis* Elles and *B. divergens* Elles and Wood, while there is a progressive reduction in the branching capacity. The other, *Clonograptus* (Fig. 4), has a horizontal direction of growth and may be considered as a horizontally growing *Bryograptus*; *Cl. callavei* Lapworth is a typical form.

Lower Ordovician strata, comprising the rocks known as the Arenig (or Skiddaw) Series are characterized by the presence of some many-branched graptolites, such as *Clonograptus, Loganograptus,* and *Dichograptus,* of four-branched forms such as *Tetragraptus fruticosus* (Hall), and *T. postlethwaitii* Elles (Fig. 4), and of two-branched *Didymograptus*-types—the last two groups showing much variation in the direction of growth. The whole fauna comprising these members of the Dichograptidae is known as the DICHOGRAPTID FAUNA.

The Dichograptus zone is easily recognized (when present) without any specialized knowledge of graptolites by the occurrence of the many-branched forms cited above; *Dichograptus octobrachiatus* (Hall) (Fig. 29) is eminently characteristic. The upper part of the zone is specially marked by the presence of horizontal *Tetragraptus*-types, e.g. *Tetragraptus quadribriachiatus* (Hall), which are rare or absent in the lower beds. Possibly a subdivision of the Dichograptus zone will eventually be necessary.

The succeeding zones of the Arenig Series have two-branched types of *Didymograptus* as their index-fossils, the lower two being marked by the horizontal forms *D. extensus* (Hall) and *D. hirundo* Salter, the higher two by the pendent or 'tuning-fork' graptolites *D. bifidus* (Hall) and *D. murchisoni* (Beck) (Fig. 29). The more rapid evolution of the horizontal forms accounts for their early importance. *D. extensus* (Hall) may be recognized by its slender flexuous character, and by the circumstance that its first thecae grow away from the sicula, giving the proximal end an 'open' appearance; the thecae are inclined at a large angle and overlap considerably. Associated with the zone fossil, other horizontal Didymograpti are often found, including *D. sparsus* Hopkinson and *D. nitidus* (Hall), which differ from *D. extensus* in proportions and thecal characters. The reclined tetragraptids, *T. bigsbyi* (Hall), *T. serra* (Brongniart), and the horizontal *T. amii* Lapworth (Fig. 4), are also characteristic of this zone.

Ordovician Graptolite Zones

		Zones		Characters of Graptolite Faunas
Bala		15. *Dicellograptus anceps.* 14. *Dicellograptus complanatus.*	Diplograptid fauna	} Presence of Orthograpti with Dicellograpti and Climacograpti of simple thecal type.
		13. *Pleurograptus linearis.* 12. *Dicranograptus clingani.* 11. *Climacograptus wilsoni.*		} Acme of large Orthograpti. Persistence of Dicellograpti. Dicranograpti of complex thecal type.
Llandeilo		10. *Climacograptus peltifer* and *Mesograptus multidens.* 9. *Nemagraptus gracilis.* 8. *Glyptograptus teretiusculus.*	Leptograptid fauna	Scandent biserial forms abundant. Thecal type becoming more complex. Acme of simple sigmoid thecal type. Reclined branched forms and scandent biserial types.
Arenig		7. *Didymograptus murchisoni.* 6. *Didymograptus bifidus.*	Dichograptid fauna	} Pendent two-branched forms.
		5. *Didymograptus hirundo.* 4. *Didymograptus extensus.* 3. *Dichograptus.*		} Horizontal two-branched forms. Many-branched forms becoming simpler.
Tremadoc		2. *Bryograptus.* 1. *Dictyonema sociale.*		} Many-branched forms.

D. hirundo Salter (Fig. 29) is distinguished from *D. extensus* in that the stipes are straight except at the distal end of large specimens; moreover, the first thecae are closely appressed to the sicula, forming a 'closed' proximal end. *D. hirundo* often occurs to the exclusion of other forms, but a reclined species *D. gibberulus* Nicholson (Fig. 4), and the declined *D. nicholsoni* Lapw. (Fig. 4), may be found with it, and also *Azygograptus suecicus* Moberg. *Azygograptus* illustrates the development of a unilateral type from didymo-

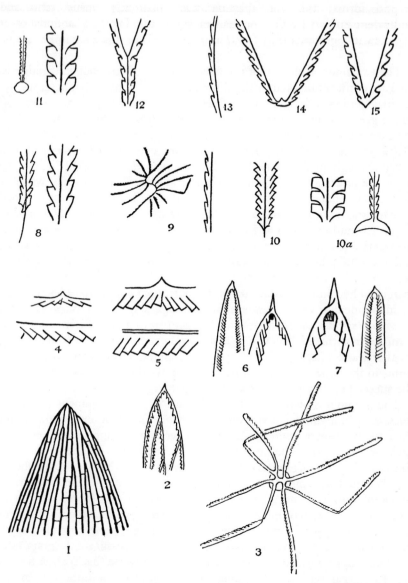

FIG. 29. ZONAL GRAPTOLITES OF THE ORDOVICIAN SYSTEM (*after Elles and Wood*). *Numbers refer to index-graptolites enumerated in Table opposite. About twice the natural size*

graptid forms; this specialization was apparently unsuccessful and underwent no further development of any kind. The local abundance of scandent tetragraptids (*Phyllograptus typus* Hall) in this zone must also be noted.

The two zones at the top of the Arenig Series (often grouped together as the Llanvirn), are marked by the abundance of pendent Didymograpti—the familiar 'tuning-fork' graptolites. These forms possess two branches (stipes) which grow downwards and become more or less parallel to one another; the thecae are obliquely inclined and overlap to a considerable extent. In *Didymograptus bifidus* (Hall) the stipes are continuously divergent and widen throughout their length, while in *D. murchisoni* (Beck) (Fig. 29) the stipes are practically parallel and widen gradually to a maximum which is reached at about 2 cm. of length. Associated with *D. bifidus* are declined Didymograpti with narrow stipes such as *D. affinis* Nicholson, *D. acutidens* Lapworth, and *D. nicholsoni* Lapworth; a horizontal form, *D. patulus* (Hall); the biserial, spinous *Glossograptus*, which appears in force for the first time; and the oldest known diplograptid *Glyptograptus dentatus* (Brongniart), which is, of course, biserial and scandent, and has an undulate apertural margin. The common associates of *D. murchisoni* (Beck) (besides its more rapidly widening variety *geminus*) are *D. amplus* Elles and Wood (Fig. 4), *Mesograptus foliaceus* (Murchison), a small (up to 3 cm.) biserial scandent form with a thread-like nema, and *Cryptograptus tricornis* (Carruthers), another scandent type with three proximal spines. The presence of scandent forms in the zone of *D. murchisoni* foreshadows their great development in the succeeding zones of the Llandeilo Series.

The graptolites of the Arenig Series thus show development in the reduction of branching capacity and in a change in direction of growth, but their thecae remain cylindrical, giving a rectangular appearance on compression. With the attainment of the reclined and scandent positions (illustrated by *Dicellograptus* and *Glyptograptus* respectively), thecal elaboration becomes general. This specialization is seen in the simple sigmoid thecae of Lower Llandeilo graptolites, and becomes progressively elaborated in the introverted (incurved) and introtorted (twisted) thecae of genera belonging to Upper Llandeilo, Caradoc, and Ashgill horizons. It is important to note that torsion of the thecae gives, on compression of the graptolite, a different appearance to the obverse (front) and reverse (back) aspects. The simpler thecal type is exemplified in *Leptograptus*, and the graptolite-assemblages of the Llandeilo Series are therefore collectively termed the LEPTOGRAPTID FAUNA. Members of the fauna include numerous bilateral types (*Leptograptus*, *Nemagraptus*, *Dicellograptus*, and *Dicranograptus*) and scandent forms of comparatively simple thecal type (*Climacograptus*, *Glyptograptus*, and *Mesograptus*), together with a few survivals of the dichograptid fauna.

The index fossil of the lowest Llandeilo zone is *Glyptograptus teretiusculus*

(Hisinger). This graptolite is a biserial scandent form with a straight thecal axis; the thecae are semicircular in section with undulate apertural margins, and open into wide excavations. Its commonest associates are *Mesograptus foliaceus* (Murchison), *Nemagraptus pertenuis* (Lapworth), and *Dicellograptus sextans* Hall (Fig. 5). The thecae of the last form have curved ventral walls and introverted and introtorted apertural portions; the direction of growth of the earliest thecae gives a diplograptid appearance to the proximal end of *D. sextans*, and brings the species into close relationship with the Dicranograptidae. *N. pertenuis*, a slender, bilateral, uniserial graptolite with long narrow thecae, has a few slightly curved branches diverging at a low angle from the sicula.

In the succeeding zone of *Nemagraptus gracilis* the Nemagrapti attain the acme of their development. The characteristic appearance of the genus is given by the growth of two main uniserial stipes from the central part of a well-defined sicula; from each of the main stipes, secondary branches may be given off. In *N. gracilis* (Hall) the main stipes are usually curved in a sigmoid fashion and give off numerous secondary branches. *N. explanatus* (Lapworth), also found in this zone, has almost straight stipes and few secondary branches. *Dicellograptus divaricatus* Hall has thecae which are only slightly sigmoid, and is associated with *D. sextans* Hall (see Fig. 5). *Leptograptus latus* Elles, by its general habit and the form of its thecae, seems to be allied to *Dicellograptus*; the rapid widening and great breadth of its stipes are characteristic features. *L. grandis* Lapworth is allied to *L. latus*, but its thecae are more crowded together. *L. validus* Lapworth (Fig. 5) typically has rigid stipes, and while the proximal thecae are slightly mucronate, the distal ones have straight outer walls and wide apertures. In the interesting *Hallograptus mucronatus* (Hall) the thecae are similar in form to those of a *Glossograptus*, since they bear conspicuous ventral spines; these, however, are always more or less flexed and may be connected by a membrane in *Hallograptus*. The distinctive *Orthograptus whitfieldi* (Hall) also bears resemblance to some species of *Glossograptus*; its thecae bear stiff slender spines which are directed obliquely upwards. *Didymograptus superstes* Lapworth, a horizontal graptolite with curved proximal portions, is a survival of the dichograptid type.

The zone of *Climacograptus peltifer* and *Mesograptus multidens* often contains many climacograptids, and their association and close similarity with dicranograptid and dicellograptid types leads to the conclusion that these 'genera' represent similar stages in several lines of descent. Thus *Climacograptus scharenbergi* Lapworth (Fig. 5), which ranges through the Llandeilo into the Caradoc, has an elaborate type of theca corresponding to that in *Dicranograptus nicholsoni* Hopkinson and *Dicellograptus sextans*, and may be regarded as the scandent end-form of a lineage comprising these three forms. *Cl. scharenbergi* is often associated with *Cl. bicornis* (Hall), whose characteristic pair of proximal spines at the base of the tapering polypary is familiar to most field-workers. *Cl. peltifer* Lapworth is a variety of *Cl. bicornis*, in which the membrane surrounding the basal spines has developed so as to envelop the entire proximal end of the graptolite in a triangular disk. *Dicellograptus patulosus* Lapworth is also common in the zone under discussion, and is easily recognized by its eminently characteristic thecae; these become narrow towards the aperture, which is oblique and directed inwards. *Mesograptus multidens* Elles has thecae of climacograptid character in the proximal part, but towards the distal end it acquires thecal characters approaching the orthograptid type; the thecae overlap to a great extent and the apertural margins are undulate. *M. multidens* is commonly associated with *Dicellograptus sextans* (which ranges through from the zone of *Nemagraptus gracilis*), the short-stemmed *Dicranograptus brevicaulis* Elles, and *Orthograptus acutus* Lapworth, which is a variety of *O. calcaratus* Lapworth, marked by the absence of basal spines and by the abrupt widening of the polypary. Another associate of *M. multidens* is *Amplexograptus perexcavatus* Lapworth, whose thecae in obverse aspect present a general climacograptid form with sigmoid curvature of the ventral margins and deep excavations, while in reverse aspect the thecae resemble the glyptograptid or orthograptid form, with less pronounced sigmoid curvature of the ventral margin, inconspicuous excavations, and somewhat oblique apertures.

The predominance of scandent biserial graptolites is so eminently characteristic of the Bala series that the higher Ordovician assemblages have been grouped together as the DIPLOGRAPTID FAUNA. Some elements of the previous fauna, such as *Dicellograptus* and *Dicranograptus*, with elaborate thecal characters, are often abundant, but the profusion of large orthograptids and climacograptids is sufficient to differentiate the Bala from the Llandeilo at first sight.

Climacograptus wilsoni Lapworth (Fig. 29), the zone-fossil of the lowest subdivision of the Caradoc stage differs from most members of the genus in the possession of a large sac at the proximal end of the polypary; the free end of the ventral wall is practically straight and vertical, and the apertural margin is horizontal. Associated members of the same genus are *Cl. bicornis* and *Cl. scharenbergi*, which persist from the Llandeilo beds. *Dicranograptus nicholsoni* Hopkinson, with its elaborate thecae, ornamented with stout spines in the biserial portion, also persists. Orthograptids are represented by abundant large individuals of *Orthograptus intermedius* Elles and *O. vulgatus* Lapworth. These, evolving from a *Glyptograptus* of the *teretiusculus* type, reach their acmaic development at about the same horizon, which is easily recognizable by their remarkable abundance. The parallel-sided polypary of *O. intermedius* Elles often attains a length of several inches and bears thecae somewhat intermediate between those of *Glossograptus* and *O. truncatus* of the succeeding zone. *O. vulgatus* Lapworth has inconspicuous basal spines which are similar in position to the large spines of *O. calcaratus*

Lapworth from the *clingani* zone; the polypary is relatively wide and the apertural margins are slightly everted.

Swarms of *Orthograptus calcaratus* Lapworth and *O. truncatus* Lapworth occur in the zone of *Dicranograptus clingani* Carruthers, which is also marked by the greatest profusion of the genera *Dicranograptus* and *Dicellograptus*. *O. calcaratus* is readily distinguished from all other Orthograpti by its long virgella and the long spines attached to its basal thecae; the apertural margins are strongly lobate. In *O. truncatus* (Fig. 5) the virgella is much shorter and may be absent altogether, and the apertural margins are only slightly lobate. The index-fossil has thecae of the general climacograptid type (approximately straight ventral walls and horizontal apertures), and the uniserial stipes diverge at 40°. *Climacograptus bicornis* is still in evidence, with *Mesograptus* of the type of *M. foliaceus*; the early thecae of the latter form resemble those of *Climacograptus*, but later thecae have the inclined free edge and marginal excavations of the diplograptid type. The species of *Dicellograptus* occurring in this zone, namely, *D. morrisi* Hopkinson (Fig. 5) and *D. caduceus* Lapw., are closely related forms with markedly curved thecal walls, and the apertures show conspicuous introversion and introtortion.

Pleurograptus linearis (Carruthers) (Fig. 29), which is confined to the succeeding zone, reaches an enormous length for a graptolite—one example is said to have been traced to a length of 3 feet. It is a slender form (maximum known width 1 mm.), having two main uniserial stipes which diverge from the sicula at an angle slightly greater than 180°; simple or compound secondary branches are given off in an irregular manner and the thecae are of leptograptid type. *P. linearis* is associated with *Leptograptus flaccidus* (Hall), a form with simple thecae and a graceful double curve in its narrow stipes. *Orthograptus pauperatus* Elles and *O. quadrimucronatus* (Hall) also occur at this horizon.

The Orthograpti are still the predominant graptolites in the zones of the succeeding Ashgill stage. The associated dicellograptids and climacograptids have thecae of a simple type, and this feature is almost the only difference between Caradoc and Ashgill graptolite-faunas.

The zone of *Dicellograptus complanatus* Lapworth is marked by the presence of the index-fossil associated with small diplograptids such as *O. socialis* Lapworth, which may be regarded as a dwarfed or starved variety of *Orthograptus truncatus*. *Dicellograptus complanatus* Lapworth (Fig. 29) is the type-form of a group whose thecae have straight ventral walls and horizontal apertures with only slight introtortion; the stipes diverge at about 270° from a strong sicula. *D. anceps* Nicholson (Fig. 29), which characterizes the succeeding zone, is of a similar type but differs in its narrow axil, the concealment of its sicula by the early thecae, and the presence of small spines on the proximal thecae. It is associated in south Scotland with small diplograptids such as *O. truncatus* var. *abbreviatus* Elles.

There is some uncertainty regarding the upper limit of the Ashgill Beds, and the zones of *Glyptograptus persculptus* and *Cephalograptus acuminatus* are often included in that stage. Though *Dicellograptus* is absent, the presence of various scandent biserial graptolites link these zones with the Ordovician, and from a purely palaeontological standpoint the lower limit of the Silurian should logically coincide with the important faunal change shown by the incoming of the monograptids. Stratigraphical considerations, however, favour the inclusion of the zones in question in the Silurian system.

B. THE SHELLY FAUNAS

Ordovician strata round the margin of the basin of deposition enclose faunas in which trilobites (Fig. 30) and brachiopods are the chief groups. For the typical areas of North Wales and the Welsh Borders the several faunas may be summarized thus:

Bala Series
- *Phacops mucronatus* fauna.
- *Phillipsinella parabola* fauna.
- *Chasmops* and *Nicolella actoniae* fauna.
- *Asaphus powisi* and *Heterorthis alternata* fauna.

Llandeilo Series *Ogygiocaris buchi* fauna.

Arenig Series
- *Placoparia* fauna.
- *Niobella selwyni* fauna.

The lowest Arenig fauna of the 'shelly' type has as its dominant forms the trilobites *Niobella selwyni* Salter, *Synhomalonotus tristani* Brongn., *S. parvifrons* Salter, *Ampyx salteri* Hicks, and *Trinucleus gibbsi* Salter. The first of these, which gives a name to the fauna, is distinguished among ogygids in: (i) the head and tail are equal in length; (ii) the genal spines are short and stout; (iii) the margin of the pygidium is broad and indistinctly marked off from the remainder of the tail, while the side-furrows do not extend to the pygidial margin. In *C. tristani* Brongn., the earliest calymenid known in Britain, and in the slightly later *C. parvifrons* Salter, the glabella segments are only two in number, and are short and oblique, with but little indication of lobe-formation. The blind trilobites of the family Trinucleidae show variations in structure which may be used as a general guide to horizon. The Arenig forms are exemplified by *T. gibbsi* and *T. murchisoni* Salter (Fig. 31), whose genal areas are divided by an oblique ridge, each portion having a different surface ornamentation. The ridge is regarded by some authors as the line of fusion between the free and fixed cheeks, i.e. the facial suture, which became obliterated after the loss of the compound eyes. The pitting of the head-fringe and the lobation of the glabella show minute differences which serve to distinguish species of *Trinucleus*. The commonest brachiopod is *Monobolina plumbea* (Salter), an atrematous phosphatic shell allied to *Obolus* but having the muscular attachments

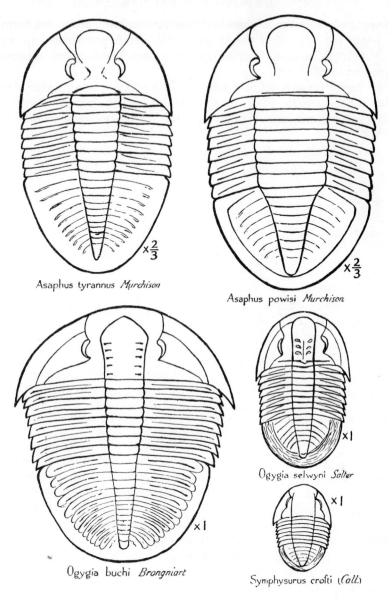

Asaphus tyrannus *Murchison* ×⅔

Asaphus powisi *Murchison* ×⅔

Ogygia buchi *Brongniart* ×1

Ogygia selwyni *Salter* ×1

Symphysurus crofti (*Call.*) ×1

FIG. 30. SOME ASAPHID TRILOBITES

concentrated along the median line. Various mollusca occur, but form a less important element of the fauna. It has already been noted (p. 138) that the Arenig rocks of Carmarthen carry a relict fauna closely related to Tremadoc assemblages.

The later Arenig rocks of Wales are distinguished by a peculiar fauna which is known as the PLACOPARIA FAUNA, from the occurrence therein of that genus of trilobites. The range of the fauna is approximately that of

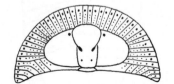

Trinucleus fimbriatus (Murchison)
Llandeilo stage

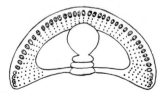

Tretaspis seticornis (Hisinger)
Ashgill stage

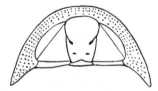

Trinucleus murchisoni (Salter)
Arenig stage

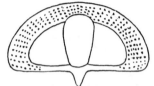

Cryptolithus nicholsoni (Reed)
Caradoc stage

FIG. 31. HEAD-SHIELDS OF SOME SPECIES OF *TRINUCLEUS* (after Reed). *About twice the natural size*

the 'tuning-fork' graptolites *Didymograptus bifidus* and *D. murchisoni*, and some authors have followed Hicks in referring these higher Arenig strata to a distinct stage, the Llanvirn. The chief trilobites are *Placoparia cambrensis* Hicks, *Calymene parvifrons* Salter, *Illaenus hughesi* Hicks, and species of *Trinucleus*, *Cyclopyge*, and *Ampyx*. The genus *Placoparia* is proparian, with narrow free cheeks, obsolete eyes, twelve thoracic segments, and a small pygidium. It seems to be allied to the more familiar genus *Encrinurus* that becomes important in later strata.

The Welsh Llandeilo fauna is composed chiefly of trilobites, the most familiar being the large species *Ogygiocaris buchi* (Brongniart) (Fig. 30) and *Basilicus tyrannus* (Fig. 30) Murchison, which are so abundant at Builth, and at Meadowtown and Middleton in Shropshire. Commonly associated with these are *Ampyx nudus* (Murchison) and *Trinucleus fimbriatus* Murchison (Fig. 31). The former may be recognized by its triangular head, the apex of which is prolonged into a median spine, its long genal spines and narrow free cheeks; it resembles *Trinucleus* in thorax and pygidium, but has no head-fringe. *Trinucleus fimbriatus* Murchison is distinguished by the deep radial grooves in which the pits of the head-fringe lie; there is no division of the genal areas, and the glabella is 'stalked' and obscurely lobed. *Cryptolithus favus* Salter has an unusual outline of the head-fringe. The genus *Barrandia* is also characteristically Llandeilan, and partakes of the features of ogygids and *Goldius*. It is ovate in shape; the head bears short spines and a clavate glabella; the tail is large and fan-shaped, with shortened axis and few lateral furrows. *Siphonotreta micula* M'Coy is the only common brachiopod.

Graptolites have been found at Builth associated with the characteristic trilobites, and the species *Dicellograptus sextans*, *Climacograptus scharenbergi*, and *Cl. brevis* enable the beds to be correlated with the Upper Glenkiln Shales of Scotland.

The Lower Bala (Caradoc) fauna is often rich in large brachiopods. *Heterorthis alternata* (J. de C. Sowerby) (Pl. II), distinguished among orthids by its strophomenoid outline, is sometimes present in rock-forming abundance, as in the Alternata Limestone of Shropshire. *Orthis (Platystrophia) biforata* (Schlotheim) (Pl. II), of spiriferoid aspect, and the familiar alate *Orthis (Harknessella) vespertilio* (J. de C. Sow.) (Pl. II), and *Sowerbyella sericea* (J. de C. Sow.) (Fig. 36), are also characteristic. These and other brachiopods are long-ranged though typically Caradoc forms, and are not sufficient for the recognition of small subdivisions. The trilobites are probably more reliable guides to age. While such forms as *Flexicalymene planimarginata* Reed, *Brongniartella bisulcata* (Salter), and *Cryptolithus caractaci* Murchison, seem to range through the Caradoc stage, others appear to be characteristic of the lower or the higher beds. Thus a division into two faunas may be made.

The lower fauna is marked by the abundance of the brachiopod *Heterorthis alternata* (J. de C. Sow.) and the large trilobite *Asaphus powisi* Salter. The latter is distinguished from the Llandeilo *B. tyrannus* by its unlobed glabella, its smooth tail, and broad axis. Associated with these two forms are *Flexicalymene planimarginata* (Reed), and the easily recognized brachiopods *Strophomena expansa* (J. de C. Sow.) (Fig. 36), *S. grandis* (J. de C. Sow.), *Orthis calligramma* Dalm., *Hebertella crispa* (M'Coy), and *Dinorthis flabellulum* (J. de C. Sow.) (Pl. II). Graptolites are sometimes found associated with the shelly faunas, and are then of special importance, since they enable some degree of correlation to be made between beds of the two facies. The graptolite *Orthograptus truncatus*, which appears to be characteristic of the zone of *Dicranograptus clingani*, has been found associated with the *Asaphus powisi–Heterorthis alternata* fauna in North Wales: hence the beds containing the latter fauna may be taken as the shallow-water equivalents of the zone of *D. clingani*.

The upper fauna contains species of *Chasmops* as characteristic trilobites, while a noteworthy brachiopod is *Orthis (Nicolella) actoniae* (J. de C. Sow.) (Pl. II). These may be combined to furnish a faunal appellation.

The genus *Chasmops* and its closely allied associate *Pterygometopus* (members of the proparian family Phacopidae) have the swollen anterior part of the glabella almost separated from the posterior portion, which is also deeply lobed (Fig. 37). *Illaenus bowmani* Salter, an opisthoparian trilobite with extremely wide glabella and large smooth tail, is also found in the upper Caradoc fauna. Other trilobites that are more abundant in the later fauna are *Flexicalymene caractaci* Salter, and the phacopid *Scotiella apiculata* (Salter).

Apart from the long-ranged brachiopods already mentioned, *Nicolella actoniae* (J. de C. Sow.) (Pl. II) and the strophomenid *Triplecia spiriferoides* (M'Coy) (Fig. 36) seem to be most characteristic. The greater abundance of cystid plates is sometimes a useful preliminary guide to the recognition of these higher beds. The common Monticuliporoids are not suitable as indexes of age, as similar forms range above and below the Caradoc, while the mollusca do not form an important element in the fauna.

The Upper Bala fauna differs widely from the preceding assemblages in several features, and though *Nicolella actoniae* (J. de C. Sow.), *Platystrophia biforata* (Schlotheim), and species of *Chasmops* do sometimes occur, these survivors of the earlier faunas are usually very rare. A conspicuous feature of the higher fauna is the virtual absence of the large brachiopods that are so typical of Caradoc strata. Several small brachiopods occur, especially varieties of *Dalmanella elegantula* (Dalman) and *Bilobites biloba* (Linnarsson), both long-ranged species that persist into the Silurian. The strophomenid *Christiania tenuicincta* (M'Coy), with its peculiar muscle markings (Fig. 36), is typical of late Bala faunas. The trilobites, however, form the most conspicuous element, and present a very different general aspect from that of the Caradoc assemblage. The most typical forms are species of *Cheirurus, Lichas, Cybele, Encrinurus, Staurocephalus*, and *Remopleurides*.

The lower Ashgill Beds are marked especially by the occurrence of the trilobite *Phillipsinella parabola* (Barrande) (Fig. 46), which has an elongated head-shield with an inconspicuous glabella whose front lobe is wide and inflated, six thoracic segments, and a moderately large, almost smooth tail. *Staurocephalus* (Fig. 37), another valuable guide fossil, is an extreme modification of the proparian family Encrinuridae, which is also represented in the fauna by species of *Cybele* and *Encrinurus*. These two genera are easily recognized by their tuberculate heads with narrow free cheeks, prominent glabella, and small eyes, also by their multisegmented tail, the pleural ribs being usually less in number than the rings on the axis. *Cybele* differs from *Encrinurus* in that the pleural ribs of the tail turn back sharply so as to be parallel with the axis.

The Ordovician species of *Encrinurus* apparently belong to two groups. The species-group of *Encrinurus sexcostatus* Salter has a distinctly lobed glabella with the lateral furrows clearly marked, and genal angles are pointed. The axial rings of the pygidium are complete and considerably more numerous than the pleurae. This group seems to lead to the Silurian group of *E. variolaris* Brongn. In the species-group of *E. multisegmentatus* Portlock the lateral glabellar lobes are nodular, and the glabella is coarsely tuberculated; the pygidium has numerous axial rings of which the anterior ones are complete, but the posterior rings are interrupted along the median line. This may be the ancestral group from which the Silurian *E. punctatus* Brunn. (Fig. 37) is derived.

Staurocephalus shows extreme development of the anterior glabellar lobe, which forms a rounded boss projecting beyond the anterior margin of the head-shield (Fig. 37). The glabella of the trinucleid *Tretaspis seticornis* Hisinger (Fig. 31) and its allies differs from that of earlier trinucleids; the swollen frontal lobe has small shallow pits at its sides representing the first pair of furrows; large isolated pits at the base of this lobe mark the second pair, while the crescentic third pair meet the fourth pair, forming a well-marked stalk. These features are modifications of the condition seen in the Llandeilo *Trinucleus fimbriatus*, and are very distinct from the unsegmented ovoid glabella of the Caradoc species of *Cryptolithus*. *Remopleurides*, another opisthoparian trilobite, has large crescentic eyes that extend round the sides of the almost circular glabella, eleven to thirteen thoracic segments, and a small tail. *Phacops (Dalmanites) mucronatus* Brongn. is very similar to the well-known *Dalmanites caudatus* of Silurian faunas. *Cheirurus bimucronatus* (Murchison) is the commonest of the Cheiruridae, a proparian family possessing small free cheeks and a small tail with stout pleural spines (Fig. 37). The genera *Sphaerexochus* and *Sphaerocoryphe*, with inflated glabellas, show a tendency among Cheiruridae similar to that already described for the Encrinuridae, and leading to the remarkable Silurian form *Deiphon*. Other features of the Ashgill faunas are the general abundance of Cystids (*Echinosphaera*, *Sphaeronites*, &c.), the local frequence of *Orthoceras vagans* Salter, and the occurrence of many ostracods.

J. E. Marr recognized two divisions of the Ashgill stage, the Phillipsinella Beds below, and the *Phacops mucronatus* beds above, but these are not always easy to separate.

The faunas described above seem to be typical in general of the Welsh and Cumbrian outcrops, representing the southern coastal belt of the basin of deposition. The assemblages in the Girvan district of Scotland, and at scattered localities in Ireland, situated in the northern coast belt, merit separate consideration. The Ordovician succession of Girvan has been studied in detail by F. R. C. Reed, whose works furnish the following summary. The strata, containing a shelly facies, interbedded with graptolite shales, are grouped thus:

Drummuck Beds	Ashgill
Whitehouse Beds	Caradoc
Balclatchie Beds . . . . }	Llandeilo
Stinchar Limestone Beds . . . }	
Radiolarian Cherts and Tetragraptus Shales	Arenig

The lowest beds were formerly supposed to represent marine deposition at a great depth and at a great distance from land. Nowadays it is widely accepted that the presence of Radiolaria alone does not justify this inference.

The STINCHAR LIMESTONE is rich in trilobites, twenty-six species classified in sixteen genera having been described. Species of *Illaenus* and *Goldius* (olim *Bronteus*) comprise more than one-third of the total number of species, and the first-named genus is most prolific in individuals. The occurrence of *Goldius* at this horizon is the earliest known for Britain, and the genus is otherwise extremely rare in this country until it attains its maximum development in Devonian strata. Other noteworthy genera are *Harpes*, *Bronteopsis*, and *Cybele*, while *Pliomerops*, a cheirurid whose tail-segments unite to form a hemispherical pygidium, is confined to this horizon at Girvan. Species of *Maclurea* are prominent gastropods; brachiopods are abundant in various genera of orthids and strophomenids, while *Parastrophia* and *Camarella* are forerunners of the later pentamerids. The occurrence of *Tetradium*, a sponge-like coral, is interesting in view of its geographical distribution. The Llandeilo age of the Stinchar Limestone is proved by the occurrence of *Didymograptus superstes* and *Dicellograptus sextans* in shales immediately above it.

The earliest Ordovician fauna known in Ireland is preserved in the Glensaul Limestone (overlying the D. extensus zone) and the Tourmakeady Beds (overlying the D. hirundo zone) in Galway and Mayo respectively. The trilobites include species of *Illaenus*, *Cybele*, *Bronteopsis*, *Pliomerops*, and other genera which show relations with the Stinchar fauna, while the presence of *Nileus* and *Chasmops* indicate affinities with Scandinavian assemblages. The fauna of the Tramore Limestone in south-east Ireland, with representatives of the Pliomeridae, Harpidae, Illaenidae, Enerinuridae, seems to show similar relationships. The records from the overlying Raheen Shales include *Nemagraptus* and the trilobites *Barrandia*, *Platycalymene*, and *Salteria*.

The BALCLATCHIE BEDS are marked by the abundance of the trilobites *Remopleurides*, *Acidaspis*, and *Ampyx*. Among the twenty-six trilobite-genera known from this horizon are *Bronteopsis*, allied to *Bronteus*; and *Teratorhynchus*, a bizarre spinose form with a peculiar pygidium—this genus is allied to *Remopleurides*. The genus *Aulacopleura* (olim *Arethusina*) of the Proetidae is rare elsewhere in Britain, though occurring in Bohemia at higher horizons. *Triarthrus*, also recorded from Tremadoc rocks of England and Wales, here occurs at a higher level than is usual for the genus. *Salteria* is confined to this horizon in Scotland, though it occurs in earlier strata in south Ireland. The cheirurid genera *Niezkowskia* and *Sphaerocoryphe* are represented by species that are closely allied to Scandinavian and Baltic forms.

The WHITEHOUSE BEDS contain several rare and peculiar trilobites among the sixteen genera recorded, but the trinucleid *Cryptolithus* is the dominant genus. F. R. C. Reed (1906) states that there is a distinct Bohemian element, represented by *Agnostus tardus*, *A. perrugatus*, *Telephus fractus*, *Cyclopyge armata*, *C. rediviva*, all originally named by Barrande, as well as *Bohemilla*. This is the earliest record of *Cyclopyge* in Scotland, though the genus is known from lower horizons in Wales and Bohemia. The species of *Bohemilla*, *Dionide*, and *Dindymene* are closely allied to Bohemian forms, and the last two genera are represented in Scandinavia. *Shumardia*, too is present in the Whitehouse Beds; it is apparently lacking in British Mesordovician rocks, but is present at Tremadoc and Arenig horizons in Wales and Shropshire. The Whitehouse Beds are associated with shales which contain graptolites of the zone of *Pleurograptus linearis*, that is, a late Caradoc horizon. A few elements of this trilobite assemblage are recorded by W. J. Pugh (1923, 1928) from central Wales where they are associated with members of the indigenous Bala fauna at some localities. Possibly the Portraine Limestone of Co. Dublin, Ireland, is related in the same way, for the fauna is of the same type, and C. J. Stubblefield (1939) states that it includes cyclopygids though these differ specifically from the Girvan forms.

The DRUMMUCK BEDS contain a fauna that approaches more nearly the typical Ashgill assemblage of northern England. It includes *Staurocephalus globiceps* (Portl.), *Phillipsinella parabola* (Barr.), *Tretaspis seticornis* (Hisinger), together with species of *Illaenus*, *Lichas*, *Remopleurides*, and *Cheirurus*. Several species are peculiar to the locality and many of the genera are only known at present by one species. Associated shales contain *Dicellograptus anceps*.

The individuality of the Girvan faunas is strongly marked by a large number of species unknown from other localities, suggesting a considerable degree of isolation, particularly in Lower Ordovician times. Its contrast with the Welsh faunas is well shown by the fact that of its eighty-three trilobite-species, only about twenty-five are known elsewhere in Britain, and many of these are rare or occur typically in Ireland. But there are many points of similarity with other faunas, notably those of Scandinavia, Bohemia, and North America which are considered in the succeeding paragraphs.

FAUNAL REGIONS

In view of the close relations between the Cambrian faunas of Britain and Scandinavia, a discussion of Ordovician faunas may appropriately begin with the latter region.

In the district of Scania, south Sweden, the Ordovician rocks are mainly shales and mudstones which contain few fossils except graptolites. Allowing for condensation of the deposits, the general succession is very similar to that of Britain. It begins with the Lower Didymograptus Shales in which extensiform didymograptids are dominant, and many species are identical with those present in the Skiddaw Slates of northern England. The Dichograptus zone has not been recognized, but there are unfossiliferous beds at the base of the sequence. The zone of *Didymograptus hirundo* also has not been separated, but G. L. Elles (1933) states that its fauna seems to be included in Tornquist's zone of *Isograptus gibberulus*, perhaps owing to condensation of the deposit. The assemblage in the lowest zone of the Upper Didymograptus Shales has the aspect of the British zone of *D. bifidus*, though it includes *Phyllograptus* which does not range so high in Britain. The next zone contains *D. geminus* Hisinger which is considered to be merely a variety of *D. murchisoni* (Beck), the name-fossil of the lowest horizon in the British Llandeilo Series. The Lower Dicellograptus Shales of Scania correspond closely with the graptolite shales of the Llandeilo sequence; the lower part contains *Glyptograptus teretiusculus* in abundance, while in the higher zone a variety of *Nemagraptus gracilis* is associated with *Hallograptus mucronatus* (Hall). The Middle Dicellograptus Shales comprise the two zones of *Dicranograptus clingani* and *Pleurograptus linearis* in which the zone-fossils are associated with *Climacograptus scharenbergi* and *Orthograptus quadrimucronatus* as in the Lower Hartfell Shales of Scotland. The Upper Dicellograptus Shales, containing *Dicellograptus anceps* and *Orthograptus truncatus* are obviously equivalent to the Upper Hartfell Shales of Scotland.

On the island of Bornholm, and in Jamtland, the place of the Didymograptus Shales is occupied by the shelly Orthoceras Limestone, but the Lower and Middle Dicellograptus Shales are represented up to the zone of *Dicranograptus clingani*. There is also a mixed sequence in the Oslo district of Norway. In Oeland, Vastergotland, and Dalarne, however, the Ordovician succession consists almost entirely of limestones containing an abundance of trilobites, brachiopods, and cephalopods; a similar development is present also in Estonia and north-west Russia.

This development of limestones is entirely different from the sequence of clastic sandy deposits which is prevalent in Wales and Shropshire. The difference also extends to the faunas, for the Scandinavian trilobite element consists largely of an association of thick-shelled asaphids, illaenids, and cheirurids. The conspicuous cephalopods of large size also have no parallel in Britain.

The lowest beds of the Orthoceras Limestone contain species of the trilobite genera *Ceratopyge, Euloma, Niobella, Symphysurus*, &c., which have already been mentioned (p. 136), for the assemblage is the equivalent of the Tremadoc fauna of Wales which in Britain is included in the Cambrian system. Palaeordovician horizons in the Orthoceras Limestone, corresponding to the Arenig Series of Britain, have yielded an important assemblage of trilobites. In the lower beds various asaphids are dominant and certain species of *Asaphus* (s.s.) and *Megalaspis* are used as zone-fossils. The associated illaenids become more abundant later with species such as *Illaenus esmarki* and *Ill. chiron*; the distinctive cheirurid genera of *Cyrtometopus* and *Pliomera*, together with the asaphid *Nileus* are restricted to this formation.

The characteristic genera of the British Arenig Series seem to be lacking entirely.

The Mesordovician rocks of Scandinavia, however, contain some genera which are represented in the Llandeilo Series of Wales. *Ogygiocaris*, typified by *O. dilatata*, is associated with species of *Cheirurus*, *Remopleurides*, *Ampyx*, and *Trinucleus*, but the relationship is not close. This association extends from the geminus to the gracilis zone.

The Neordovician rocks, corresponding approximately to the Bala Series of Britain, include the Cystidean Limestone, Chasmops Limestone, Trinucleus Shale, and Lower Leptaena Limestone. Equivalent horizons in the Baltic States, described by Raymond (1916) and Opik (1937), include the famous Kuckers Oil Shale. Besides distinctive species of asaphids and illaenids the trilobites include specialized dalmanitids such as *Chasmops* and *Pterygometopus*, cheirurids like *Nieszkowskia* and *Sphaerocoryphe*, and the encrinurid *Cybele*. The Trinucleus Shale contains *Tetraspis seticornis* (Hisinger), *Telephus fractus* Barrande, with species of *Remopleurides*, *Triarthrus*, *Ampyx*, and *Agnostus*. Many of these genera are represented at corresponding British horizons, especially in Scotland.

In central Europe the Ordovician system is best exemplified by the succession in Bohemia, made famous by the works of J. Barrande (1852). Here a prolific fauna of trilobites contains comparatively few species in common with Scandinavia, asaphids being rare while cyclopygid, cheirurid, placoparid, dalmanitid, odontopleurid, and other stocks are typical.

The lowest beds contain the oldest illaenids, including *Illaenus advena* Barrande, a typical form which, according to P. E. Raymond (1916), gives no indication of its ancestry. This author believes the nearest relative of the Illaenidae to be the Goldiidae, not the Asaphidae, but the goldiids do not appear until later, and are rare until the Silurian. The earliest trinucleid, now known as *Trinucleoides reussi* (Barr.), also appears here, together with agnostids, pliomerids, cyclopygids, dalmanitids, harpids, cheirurids, and other groups. Higher Palaeordovician-forms include species of *Cyclopyge*, *Placoparia*, and *Barrandia* which are represented in the contemporary Upper Arenig Beds of Wales.

The Mesordovician Series contains members of the same families together with homalonotids, calymenids, and asaphids. The dalmanitid *Dalmanitina socialis* (Barrande) is a notable form which is recorded from the later Caradoc Beds in South Wales.

Neordovician trilobites of Bohemian type have a wide distribution, some genera and even species having been recorded from the Whitehouse Beds of south Scotland (p. 177), and a few reaching Sweden. The trinucleid *Cryptolithus* is abundantly represented by the subgenus *Onnia* which is also characteristic of the Caradoc Beds in Shropshire. *Phillipsinella parabola* is another widespread trilobite, ranging from Bohemia to Portugal, Wales, Scotland, and Scandinavia.

The Bohemian fauna is distributed through much of central and southern Europe, e.g. Montagne Noire, Sardinia, Portugal, Brittany, Wales. A noteworthy Palaeordovician trilobite of western Europe is the calymenid genus *Synhomalonotus*, recorded from Portugal, north France, and Wales as far north as Anglesey. On a general view it appears that the Ordovician fauna of central and southern Europe differs widely from the contemporary Scandinavian assemblage, a fact that is probably connected in a considerable degree with the lithological differences in the deposits. C. J. Stubblefield (1939), however, points out that some British trilobites are not known in the Bohemian fauna, notably *Ogygiocaris* and *Platycalymene*; such important immigrants may have come from the west, but there is no real evidence as to the source.

NORTH AMERICA. Ordovician deposits in great variety are distributed around the Precambrian rocks of the Canadian Shield (Map, Fig. 32). They are best developed in the low lands bordering the St. Lawrence River, and extend south-eastward into the State of New York; sections exposed in this area form a standard for the correlation of Ordovician rocks in North America as a whole. The succession may be tabulated as follows:

		Shelly Facies	*Graptolitic Facies*
Neordovician		Richmond stage Lorraine Shale Trenton Limestone	Utica Shales
Meso-		Black River Limestone Chazy Limestone	Normanskill Shale
Palaeo-		Beekmantown Limestone	Deepkill Shale of New York Point Levis Shale of Quebec

Outliers between Lake Huron and James Bay, also on the western shores of Hudson Bay, represent temporary transgressions over parts of the Precambrian Shield. Similar deposits extend into the interior plains where flat-lying limestones occur as far west as Winnipeg.

On the northern margin of the Shield, the Trenton and Utica formations, with the typical shelly fossils, are represented at several places in the Arctic archipelago; according to summaries by C. Schuchert (1914) and A. Foerste (1929), no graptolites are known from these islands. Ordovician rocks have also been described from north-west and east Greenland by C. Poulsen (1927, 1930), and from north Greenland by G. T. Troedsson

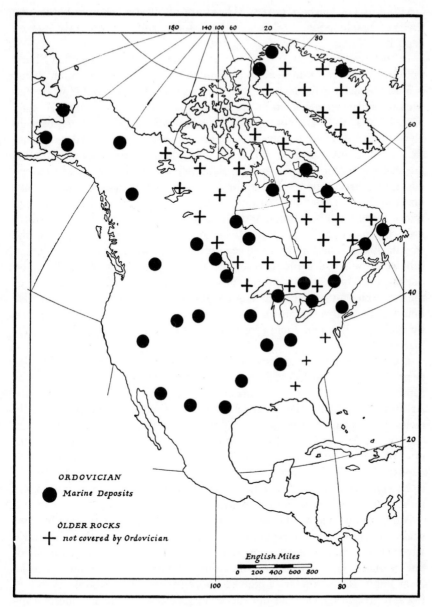

FIG. 32 SKETCH-MAP OF NORTH AMERICA SHOWING GENERAL DISTRIBUTION
OF ORDOVICIAN ROCKS

(1929) and C. Teichert (1937). These are all clastic deposits containing shells of brachiopods, molluscs, and trilobites, and are evidently inshore deposits.

In the Acadian region off the south-east margin of the Canadian Shield the Ordovician rocks in general are intensely folded, and are often thrust over the deposits of the inshore belt. In Cape Breton Island and New Brunswick the Palaeordovician rocks are mainly graptolite shales, but at Arisaig, Nova Scotia, they are coarse, clastic sediments. Equivalent deposits in Newfoundland form a mixed sequence of shelly rocks and graptolite shales. At Point Levis near Quebec a condensed succession of graptolite shales is thrust over flat-lying inshore deposits of Trenton and later age which rest directly on the Precambrian gneiss. This thrust-belt, first recognized by W. E. Logan in 1861, and often known as Logan's Line, has been traced from north Newfoundland, through the Acadian region, by Quebec, Lake Champlain, the Hudson River, and along the folded range of the Appalachians. The highly disturbed strata to the south-east of it differ, in lithology and fossil-content, from the flat-lying, undisturbed beds to the north-west which are probably equivalent in age. The close proximity of the two facies and the presence of conglomerates containing huge angular boulders of local rocks on the south-east side of the thrust are interpreted by Bailey, Collet, and Field (1928) as due to successive slips down a submarine slope.

A varied series of Ordovician rocks is exposed in the folds of the Appalachian Mountains, mainly calcareous and clastic deposits, close to the Precambrian core of the Range. Farther west, in Iowa, Wisconsin, Missouri, Arkansas, Oklahoma, Texas, south Dakota, Nevada, and Utah, the shelly facies is prevalent, but occasionally graptolite shales are intercalated in the succession. At many localities the system is incompletely represented, and often there are difficulties in precise correlation owing to variation of the deposits from place to place. The Richmond stage of Indiana is considered to be younger than the Lorraine of New York, and is taken as the uppermost member of the system in North America.

Along the course of the Rocky Mountains Ordovician limestones and shales occur at wide intervals through British Columbia to the Mackenzie River. The lowest division, some thousands of feet in thickness, consists of fine-grained, clastic sediments containing trilobites and other shelly fossils. Near Banff, B.C., they are followed by graptolite shales about 1,700 feet thick, representing a spread-out succession of Palaeordovician zones. Graptolite shales have also been recorded on the Dease River, Yukon Territory by T. H. Clarke (1926), and on Prince of Wales Island and Wrangel Island, south Alaska, by R. Ruedemann (1929).

It is now necessary to examine the two facies in more detail, beginning with the graptolite shales.

Ordovician graptolites were first noted in North America by Brongniart in 1829, and later described by J. Hall (1865), in the famous section at Point Levis on the south side of the St. Lawrence River opposite Quebec. The section has since been described by P. E. Raymond (1914), and interpreted from the British standpoint by G. L. Elles (1933). Above the Neocambrian Dictyonema Beds are much-disturbed (and often overfolded) shales which contain well-preserved graptolites in abundance. Raymond distinguishes four zones. The lowest (A) contains species of *Clonograptus* and *Tetragraptus*, some of which are also found in Britain. The next zone (B) is marked by abundance of *Dichograptus*, *Tetragraptus*, and *Phyllograptus*, some species again being identical with or closely related to British forms. The third zone (C) contains horizontal didymograptids, associated with two early pendent forms, *Didymograptus indentus* (Hall) and *D. protobifidus* Elles; this is probably equivalent to the zone of *D. extensus* in Britain. The upper part of zone D has numerous graptolites, notably *Glyptograptus dentatus* (Brongn.) and *Cryptograptus antennarius* (Hall); these two forms are found associated in the zones of *D. extensus* and *D. hirundo* in Britain. Elles mentions a locality in Levis town where the true *D. bifidus* (Hall) is abundant, and states that the whole succession agrees in general with that of the English Lake District, though the Levis fauna is far richer than that of the Skiddaw Slates.

Another well-known section, at Deepkill, New York State, is described by R. Ruedemann (1902). The Clonograptus and Dichograptus zones are not exposed, but the visible beds agree well with Raymond's zones C and D in the Point Levis section. Other localities for graptolites of this age are Cow Head Peninsula and Notre Dame Bay, Newfoundland. Again, at St. John, New Brunswick, F. H. McLean cites the extensiform *Didymograptus extensus* (Hall), *D. nitidus* (Hall), and *D. patulus* Hall associated with occasional *Tetragraptus*, *Phyllograptus* and, more rarely, *Loganograptus*. Apart from the last genus the assemblage is very similar to the fauna of the extensus zone in Britain. In western America Palaeordovician graptolites are recorded from Arkansas, Glenogle, B.C., Wrangel Island, and Prince of Wales Islands in south Alaska.

The zone of *Didymograptus murchisoni* has not yet been recognized in North America, but the zone of *Nemagraptus gracilis* (Hall) is well-known in the Normanskill Shale of New York State. It has yielded the index-fossil and species of *Dicellograptus* and *Climacograptus* characteristic of the Glenkiln Shales and Llandeilo Flags in Britain. The fauna has a wide distribution in North America. Besides numerous localities along the Hudson and St. Lawrence rivers it is known from Maine and New Brunswick, from the Athens Shale of west Virginia, north Carolina, north Alabama, and east Tennessee, from corresponding beds in Arkansas and the Ouachita Mountains of Oklahoma, and from south Nevada, Glenogle, B.C., Yukon Territory, and Alaska.

The Trenton Limestone of New York includes thick graptolite shales such as the Canajoharie Shale of the Mohawk and Hudson valleys. The graptolites recorded are mainly species of *Diplograptus*, *Corynoides*, *Lasiograptus*, *Climacograptus*, and *Glossograptus*, none of which are known in Britain. The shales are usually correlated with the British zone of *Dicranograptus clingani*, though the index-fossil is not known in America. The same fauna is well developed near Quebec and at the northern end of Lake Memphremagog.

The typical Utica Shales rest on the Trenton Limestone not far from Trenton Falls, N.Y. The graptolites cited by Raymond (1916) include *Dicranograptus nicholsoni* Hopk., *Pleurograptus linearis* (Carr.), and *Climacograptus typicalis* Hall, with species of *Leptograptus*, *Lasiograptus*, and *Mastograptus*. The reference of this assemblage to the zone of *P. linearis* is suggested by the record of the index-fossil, but only from a single locality. In Britain *D. nicholsoni* is typical of the clingani zone, so evidence for correlation seems not to be exclusive. The Utica fauna is recorded from localities in Vermont, Pennsylvania, Ohio, Wisconsin, Minnesota, and Winnipeg.

A variety of *Glossograptus quadrimucronatus* continues into the Frankfort Shale of central New York, which is regarded as the lower member of the Lorraine Series. Corresponding beds in Wisconsin and Minnesota have yielded local species of *Diplograptus*. In Oklahoma alone, the well-known Upper Hartfell species, *Dicellograptus complanatus*, is recorded from rocks that are tentatively correlated with the Richmond Stage.

It is evident that the succession of Ordovician graptolites in North America is closely comparable with that in the British Isles. The same sequence of dichograptid and leptograptid faunas can be readily recognized in the two areas, but comparison in the diplograptid zones is less certain. Many species of the lower horizons are common to both regions, but some American species are lacking in Europe, and certain European species are not known in America.

Ruedemann (1904) notes certain peculiarities in the graptolite faunas of New York and east Canada, especially the presence of *Goniograptus* in the Deepkill Shales. Later (1928) the same author cites *Oncograptus* and *Cardiograptus* associated with *Didymograptus* of the *bifidus* type in Palaeordovician deposits of Idaho, Texas, and Glenogle, B.C. These genera were first described from Australia, where they occur in the zone of *Glyptograptus dentatus* (p. 189). Hence Ruedemann postulates free communication across or around the Pacific Ocean between Australia and North America during at least the early part of Ordovician time.

Certain trilobite genera recorded from the Palaeordovician rocks of Scotland and Ireland are represented in equivalent strata in the eastern part of North America. The earliest example is *Petigurus nero* (Billings) which is recorded from the Durness Limestone of north-west Scotland, and is typical of the Beekmantown Limestone in Newfoundland; the trilobite is associated with several gastropod genera common to the two regions. Other species of *Petigurus* are known from Newfoundland and from equivalent strata in the province of Quebec and the states of New York and Vermont. The genus is separated by Raymond (1913) from *Bathyurus* (s.s.), which is represented by several species in the Beekmantown Limestone of the same area. The allied *Bathyurellus* seems to be restricted to Newfoundland and Quebec in deposits of Beekmantown age, but is more widely distributed in younger strata; outside America it is known only from the Glensaul Limestone of Ireland by a species related to *B. validus* of the Chazy Series. Some other trilobites formerly assigned to *Bathyurus* are now referred to distinct genera. Of these, *Goniurus* seems to be restricted to the eastern states, but *Leiostegium* extends to Colorado and British Columbia, and *Hystricurus* is reported from eastern North America, British Columbia, and Greenland. Besides these essentially American forms the Beekmantown Limestone has yielded genera like *Remopleurides*, *Eoharpes*, and *Pliomerops* which are represented in the younger strata of Scotland and Scandinavia. On the other hand *Shumardia*, which is represented in the shales of Point Levis, occurs already in the Tremadoc Beds of Wales and Shropshire, and persists to the Whitehouse Beds of Scotland. Stubblefield (1939) has noted that this genus is apparently restricted to the margins of the Atlantic Ocean.

As in Europe the families Illaenidae and Asaphidae attain considerable importance in the Ordovician rocks of North America. But while *Illaenus* is fairly abundant in the Beekmantown Series, asaphids seem to be more sparsely represented. The latter include *Isoteloides* from the Champlain Valley and Vermont, and certain forms from the south Appalachians which are assigned to *Hemigyraspis* by Raymond (1910). The type of this genus is *H. affinis* (M'Coy) from the Tremadoc Slates of North Wales, and, according to E. O. Ulrich (1930) the American forms are not congeneric with this species. *Nileus* is listed from typical Beekmantown strata and is also characteristic of early Ordovician faunas in Scandinavia and the Baltic States. But several asaphid genera, e.g. *Asaphus* (s.s.), *Niobe*, *Onchometopus*, *Pseudasaphus*, *Ptychopyge*, which with the cheirurid *Cyrtometopus* and the lichid *Platylichas* are typical of the Baltic region are unknown in America. Commenting on the faunal dissimilarities of the two regions Raymond (1916) regards the Scandinavian and American assemblages as autochthonous, mainly derived from late Cambrian faunas in their respective areas. It seems, however, that some measure of communication must be postulated in order to explain the relations of north European and North American forms. These relations seem to become closer in higher horizons, perhaps because the latter are better known on both sides of the Atlantic Ocean.

The Chazy stage of eastern North America is correlated (Ruedemann, 1929) with the Normanskill and Athens Shales, and is therefore of Mesordovician age. At many places there is disconformity at the base of the series, but some trilobite genera persist from Beekmantown horizons and are represented by distinctive species of *Bathyurus, Bathyurellus, Eoharpes, Illaenus, Pliomerops, Remopleurides*, for example. They are associated with such European genera as *Ceraurus, Nieszkowskia, Ampyx, Lonchodomas, Lichas, Pterygometopus, Robergia, Telephus, Dionide*, and *Bronteopsis*, which are unknown at lower horizons in North America. Raymond (1925) cites a fauna in west Newfoundland which is closely comparable with the Balclatchie assemblage of Scotland; most of the species are closely related and one, *Bronteopsis scotica*, is recorded from both regions. H. C. Stetson (1927) states that the Normanskill and Athens Shales have yielded two species of *Trinucleus* and one of *Tretaspis*; these genera are much more abundant and widespread in European Ordovician deposits. According to Ulrich (1930) *Telephus* and its associated genera are confined to the eastern part of the Appalachian Valley, and, farther north, to a few places in south-east Canada. The assemblage is absent from the western part of the valley which contains faunas similar to those of the Mississippi and Ohio valleys. None of the forms have been found in the Cordilleran faunas or in those of the Pacific and Arctic regions. Consequently, Ulrich regards the faunas containing *Telephus* and its associates as indigenous to the Atlantic Ocean. It is worthy of note that the faunal affinities lie with the Scottish and Scandinavivian rather than with the Welsh and Bohemian assemblages.

The thin Black River formation of eastern North America continues the transgressive deposits of the Chazy Series, and the fauna represents a transition between the Chazy and the succeeding Trenton faunas. From north Virginia Ulrich (1930) describes *Salteria oderi* as close to the Scottish *S. primaeva*, and states that all the associated trilobites are related to Balclatchie species. The Trenton Limestone is remarkable for the widespread abundance of the trinucleid *Cryptolithus tessellatus* Green which is reported from Quebec and Montreal, through the Champlain and Mohawk valleys and the States of New York, New Jersey, north-east Pennsylvania, Virginia, Tennessee, and Oklahoma (Stetson, 1927). Other trilobites recorded from the Trenton Limestone are *Calymene senaria* Hall, *Isotelus gigas* (Dekay) and species of *Ceraurinus, Bathyurus, Hemiarges, Eoharpes*. The Trenton Limestone, however, is not a constant stratigraphical unit, and G. M. Kay (1937) has shown that some of the species are restricted to part of its range. As a whole the limestone is the calcareous phase of a stage that is elsewhere represented partly or wholly by shales. The Utica Shale contains graptolites associated with such trilobites as *Cryptolithus tessellatus* and *Triarthrus eatoni* (Hall), the latter being distinct from *T. becki* Green which is characteristic of the underlying Canajoharie Shale. The genus *Triarthrus* seems to be restricted to shaly deposits, and its range extends up, with *T. spinosus* Billings, into the Gloucester Shale which succeeds the local Collingwood Beds with *Ogygites latimarginatus* (Hall) as the most prominent fossil. The long range of *Triarthrus* is paralleled on the eastern side of the Atlantic, where a species occurs in the Balclatchie Beds of Scotland. The Lorraine Shales of Ontario and New York are more calcareous in character, and the fossils are mainly lamellibranchs, but fragments of the asaphid *Isotelus maximus* Locke are often abundant. G. A. Cooper and C. H. Kindle (1936) have described a somewhat later fauna from Percé, Quebec. The assemblage of trilobite genera is said to be unique in North America, including *Tretaspis, Ampyx, Remopleurides, Cyclopyge, Encrinurus*, the cheirurids *Ceraurus* and *Sphaerexochus*, the lichids *Amphilichas* and *Platylichas*, and the asaphids *Brachyaspis, Gerasaphes*, and *Isotelus*. Many species are well known in the Keisley Limestone of England and the Leptaena Limestone of north Europe.

SOUTH AMERICA. Ordovician rocks are known from several localities on the Bolivian Plateau, and the eastern side of the Andean Cordillera between north-east Peru and north Argentina. Graptolite shales intercalated with sandstones are also reported in Columbia and Venezuela. A general map by H. Gerth (1932) shows that graptolite shales are predominant in east Peru as far as the latitude of Lake Titicaca, while coarser clastic sediments prevail from north Bolivia to north Argentina.

Palaeordovician graptolites recorded by J. V. Harrison (1930) from the Magdalena Valley, Colombia, include *Didymograptus extensus, D. hirundo, D. gibberulus*, and *D. nitidus*. The last-named species had previously been identified from the Tarijo district of Bolivia, and from north Argentina. Didymograptids of the *D. bifidus* type, with *Tetragraptus* and *Phyllograptus* are also reported from Bolivia. Several localities along the line of outcrop have yielded *D. murchisoni, D. geminus*, and *Glyptograptus dentatus* associated with species of *Glossograptus, Amplexograptus*, and trilobites. These faunas may be compared with those of the bifidus and murchisoni zones in Britain, but O. M. B. Bulman (1931) states that the murchisoni fauna is not fully developed, and that the assemblage bears closer relation to the highest faunule in the Deepkill section of New York.

Graptolite assemblages from Peru and north Argentina, reviewed by Bulman, may represent the Normanskill horizon of New York, and a record of *Dicranograptus* from Venezuela probably represents a later zone. Neordovician graptolites are better known in material from Hurchiyimi, Peru, where shales have yielded *D. nicholsoni* and *Orthograptus truncatus*, the latter being small like the variety *pauperata*. These graptolites suggest correlation with the Utica Shale of North America. No higher Ordovician forms appear to be known from South America.

Reviewing the graptolites as a whole, Bulman remarks on the unusual persistence of the multiramous dichograptids and the phyllograptids as compared with European standards, but such extension of range occurs also in North American sections. The presence of *Didymograptus murchisoni* and *D. geminus* is interesting in comparison with European faunules, for these species are not yet recorded from North America. The absence of *Corynoides* from the South American records is noteworthy, for the genus is an important element in the Canajoharie Shale of New York, and the clingani zone of North Europe: but the discrepancy may only mean that the South American equivalents of these horizons have not yet been explored.

Certain trilobites are recorded by Bulman in association with the graptolites. *Trinucleus nordenskjoldi* Bulman and *Triarthrus fischeri* Billings occur with the murchisoni graptolite fauna of Bolivia. The former species is said to be allied to the Swedish *T. coscinorrhinus* Angelin which Stetson (1927) takes as the type of his genus *Botryoides*. The latter is a typical fossil in Mesordovician rocks of Newfoundland which are correlated with the Normanskill Shale of New York. In Peru the Neordovician Shales yield another species of *Triarthrus* which Bulman brings into comparison with *T. eatoni* (Hall), a characteristic form in the Utica Shale of New York and Ontario.

AUSTRALASIA. On the margins of the Australian Shield rocks of Ordovician age are known only in central Australia, between the McDonnell and Musgrave Ranges. These rocks, some 6,000 feet in thickness, and consisting mainly of sandstones with thin bands of rubbly limestone, are of littoral character. They succeed the Cambrian rocks in apparent conformity, and are themselves only slightly deformed; Tate (1896) named them the Larapintine Series. Their possible extension to south and east is masked by the thick Mesozoic cover of the Great Artesian basin (David, 1932). In any case this development in central Australia probably represents deposition in an embayment of the Shield. Offshore deposits are present in Victoria, where there is a great development of graptolite shales, now highly folded and cleaved by earth-movement. Farther south, in Tasmania, the Ordovician strata are again mainly shelly deposits of littoral character, and are associated with areas of Precambrian rocks.

Knowledge of the graptolite succession in Australia is largely due to the work of T. S. Hall (1899, 1914), W. J. Harris (1916), and R. Keble (in David, 1932). Keble considers that the graptolite succession of Australia closely resembles that of North America, and Elles (in David, 1932) shows that the sequence of graptolite zones is practically the same as in Europe.

The oldest beds, known as the Lancefield stage, contain *Clonograptus rigidus* Hall, *Cl. flexilis* Hall, *Dichograptus octobrachiatus* Hall, *Tetragraptus approximatus* Nicholson, and other species; they clearly represent the Dichograptus zone of the English succession. The Bendigo and Castlemaine stages together represent the zone of *Didymograptus extensus*, which is more spread out than the British development and so has been divided into several horizons (see tables in David, 1932). There are many widespread species such as *Tetragraptus quadribrachiatus* Hall, *T. amii* Elles and Wood, *T. fruticosus* (Hall), *Phyllograptus ilicifolius* Hall, *P. typus* Hall, *Didymograptus extensus* Hall, *D. nitidus* Hall, *D. caduceus* Salter, *D. gibberulus* Nicholson, *D. protobifidus* Elles, together with the more restricted

Goniograptus. The overlying Darriwil stage includes the zones of *D. hirundo*, *D. bifidus*, and *D. murchisoni*. Besides the index species and numerous glossograptids the fauna has the genus *Oncograptus* T. S. Hall, which Bulman (1936) derives directly from a tetragraptid type, and its probable descendant *Cardiograptus* Harris and Keble. These peculiar genera have also been found in North America, and Ruedemann (1928) has cited this occurrence as proof that a Pacific Ocean already existed in Ordovician time. Elles (1933) regards the succession, thus far, as closely similar to the sequence in the English Skiddaw Slates, allowing for local differences and additions to the fauna.

The Gisborne Series contains the zones of *Nemagraptus gracilis* and *Climacograptus peltifer* with typical forms of the leptograptid fauna including the index species. In some Victorian localities higher horizons are recognized (Elles, in David, 1932), representing the zones of *Climacograptus wilsoni*, *Dicranograptus clingani*, *Pleurograptus linearis*, and *Dicellograptus complanatus*, with graptolites referred to many widely distributed species of the diplograptid fauna.

Benson and Keble (1936) have described a succession shown on the western side of South Island, New Zealand. This is so closely similar to that of Victoria that the same stratigraphical names are used. The Darriwil stage, however, is not known in New Zealand, and the Gisborne Stage is only reported at isolated localities. The sequence apparently ends with the zone of *Climacograptus peltifer*.

The Larapintine Series of the McDonnell Range has yielded a shelly fauna of about forty species, chiefly cephalopods and brachiopods with some trilobites, from several fossil beds. The original descriptions have been reviewed by T. Kobayashi (1940) who states that the cephalopods are related to east Asian forms. The trilobites are mainly asaphids; three species are compared with Korean species of *Basilicus* and *Basiliella*, one is tentatively referred to the Baltic genus *Ptychopyge* or *Pseudobasilicus*, and another is said to approach the American *Isoteloides*. It is probable that a better understanding would result from a new study of the actual specimens. Trilobites from Caroline Creek, Tasmania, include two asaphids which are tentatively ascribed to the genera *Isoteloides* and *Prosopiscus*, two peculiar endemic genera *Carolinites* and *Etheridgeaspis* which may be derived from solenopleurids, and *Tasmanocephalus* which is said to represent a terminal branch of the Asiatic Damesellidae. A Palaeordovician form from the Florentine River previously referred to Neocambrian *Dikelocephalus* is now placed in *Asaphopsis*, a genus of asaphids with a pair of lateral spines on the pygidium. This last genus is also represented in a small assemblage from Junee along with *Tasmanaspis*, an endemic genus which may be related to the Asaphiscidae. Two trilobites from South Island, New Zealand, named and described by F. R. C. Reed (1927), should be mentioned here. One, *Dionide hectori* is compared by Kobayashi with *Micquelina* from

Palaeordovician Beds in Languedoc, south France, and with *Taihung-shania* from a similar horizon in east Asia. The Mesordovician *Ogygites collingwoodensis* is ascribed to the Baltic genus *Pseudobasilicus*.

S. ASIA. F. R. C. Reed (1917) has described a Mesordovician assemblage from Yunnan which includes the trilobite genera *Harpes*, *Remopleurides*, *Asaphus*, *Ogygites*, *Illaenus*, *Nileus*, *Bathyurus*, *Metopolichas*, *Calymene*, and

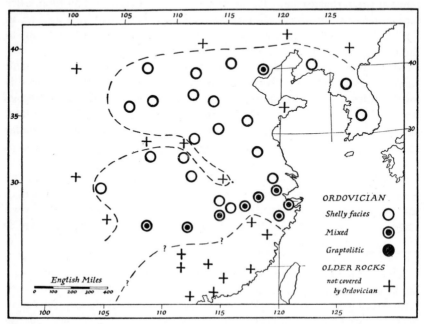

FIG. 33. SKETCH-MAP OF CHINA SHOWING GENERAL DISTRIBUTION OF ORDOVICIAN ROCKS

Pliomera, along with the graptolite *Didymograptus murchisoni*. The European affinities shown by this fauna are also seen in similar associations of trilobites described by Reed from the south Shan States of Burma in 1936, from the north Shan States in 1906, and from the central Himalayas in 1912.

Similar affinities are evident in the Ordovician faunas of southern and central China. The most conspicuous element is formed by large straight nautilids, locally known as 'pagoda stones'; they include species of *Ortho-ceras*, *Endoceras*, *Trocholites*, *Lituites*, and other genera. The associated trilobites of the genera *Ampyx*, *Asaphus*, *Ogygites*, *Taihungshania*, *Illaenus*, *Bathyurus*, *Goldius*, *Lichas*, *Acidaspis*, and *Calymene* are likewise compared by Y. C. Sun (1931) with European forms.

The Ordovician strata of south China are separated from those of north China by the narrow ridge of more ancient rocks now represented by the Tsingling Hills (Map, Fig. 33). In this northern embayment cephalopods again form the dominant fossil-group, but here *Actinoceras* is the most con-spicuous genus, associated with *Vaginoceras, Piloceras, Cameroceras*, &c. The whole assemblage is comparable with that of the Black River forma-tion in North America. The Mesordovician trilobites of south Korea, de-scribed by T. Kobayashi (1934), are largely asaphids showing affinities with North American forms, though some of the genera are also represented in the Baltic region. In places near the Pacific coast, especially in south Anhui, dark shales have yielded a long sequence of graptolites essentially similar to those in the European, North American, and Australian continents. Outside this somewhat restricted area the graptolite succession in China is far from complete.

The evidence of records so far available therefore indicates that the Ordovician faunas of the south Pacific border in Asia are related to their contemporaries in European waters, while those of north China and Korea show affinities with assemblages of similar age in North America.

LITERATURE

The majority of the known British graptolites are described and figured in 'British Graptolites', by G. L. Elles and E. M. R. Wood, *Mon. Pal. Soc.*, 1901–18. A useful summary of the graptolite assemblages characteristic of the various zones is given in 'The Characteristic Assemblages of the Graptolite Zones of the British Isles', by G. L. Elles, *Geol. Mag.*, vol. lxii, pp. 337–47, 1925. Evolutional trends within the group form the subject of 'The Graptolite Faunas of the British Isles', by G. L. Elles, *Proc. Geol. Assoc.*, vol. xxxiii, pp. 168–200, 1922. Comparison with North America is made in 'Lower Ordovician Faunas with Special Reference to the Skiddaw Slates', by G. L. Elles, *Sum. Prog. Geol. Surv. for 1932*, Part ii, pp. 94–111, 1933.

The circumstance that Ordovician rocks were first known by their varied shelly faunas accounts for the scattered nature of the literature dealing with the fossils of this system. A useful summary of the trilobite–brachiopod faunas is contained in a paper entitled: 'The Bala Country: Its Structure and Rock Succession', by G. L. Elles, *Q.J.G.S.*, vol. lxviii, pp. 132–75, 1922. It is supplemented by 'The Classifica-tion of the Ordovician Rocks', by the same author in *Geol. Mag.*, vol. lxxiv, pp. 481–95, 1937.

The Ordovician trilobites early attracted attention and many are described and illustrated in an unfinished monograph, 'British Trilobites', by J. W. Salter, *Mon. Pal. Soc.*, 1864–83. 'The Succession of the Ancient Rocks in the Vicinity of St. David's, Pembrokeshire, with Special Reference to those of the Arenig and Llandeilo Groups and their Fossil Contents', by H. Hicks, *Q.J.G.S.*, vol. xxxi, pp. 167–95, 1875, contains descriptions and illustrations of certain distinctive Trilo-bites which are not contained in the work previously cited. Another monograph is descriptive of the peculiar trilobite-fauna of Girvan, namely, 'The Lower Palaeozoic Trilobites of the Girvan District', by F. R. C. Reed. *Mon. Pal. Soc.*, 1903–6, with supplements in 1914, 1931, and 1935. Various groups of trilobites have been re-viewed and emended in recent years in the following works. 'Some New Species of Cryptolithus (s.l.) from the Upper Ordovician', by B. B. Bancroft *Mem. Manchester Lit. and Phil. Soc.*, vol. lxii, pp. 67–98, 1929; 'Some British Trilobites of the Family Calymenidae', by J. Shirley, *Q.J.G.S.*, vol. xcii, pp. 384–422, 1936; 'The Ordovi-cian Trilobite Fauna of the Shelve-Corndon District, West Shropshire', by W. F.

Whittard, *Ann. Mag. Nat. Hist.*, ser. 11, vol. v, pp. 153–72, and vol. vi, pp. 129–53, 1940; 'Trinucleidae in Eire', by A. Lamont, ibid., vol. viii, pp. 438–69, 1941; 'Revision of Certain Lower Ordovician Faunas from Ireland', by F. R. C. Reed, *Geol. Mag.*, vol. lxxxii, pp. 55–66, 1945; 'The Lower Ordovician Cryptolithids of the Llandeilo District', by A. Williams, ibid., vol. lxxxv, pp. 65–88, 1948. C. J. Stubblefield discusses 'Some Aspects of the Distribution and Migration of Trilobites in the British Lower Palaeozoic Faunas' in ibid., vol. lxxvi, pp. 49–72, 1939.

Many of the brachiopods are dealt with in T. Davidson's monograph on 'Fossil Brachiopoda', *Mon. Pal. Soc.*, 1866–71, with Supplement 1882–4. This work is in urgent need of revision, and, it may be noted, was written before the Ordovician was separated from the Silurian system. The Scottish brachiopods are described by F. R. C. Reed in 'The Ordovician and Silurian Brachiopoda of the Girvan District', *Trans. Roy. Soc. Edinburgh*, vol. li, pp. 795–998, 1917. 'Plectambonites and some Allied Genera' have been discussed and illustrated by O. T. Jones, *Mem. Geol. Surv., Palaeont.*, vol. i, part 3, pp. 367–527, 1928. Certain orthids and strophomenids are reviewed by B. B. Bancroft in 'The Harknessellidae', *Mem. Manchester Lit. and Phil. Soc.*, vol. lxxii, pp. 173–96, 1928; in 'Some New Genera and Species of Strophomenacea from the Upper Ordovician or Shropshire', ibid., vol. lxxiii, pp. 33–65, 1929; and in 'The Brachiopod Zonal Indices of the Stages Costonian to Onnian in Britain', *Journ. Palaeont.*, vol. xix, pp. 181–252, 1945, but revision is still incomplete.

Various gastropods are described in 'The British Ordovician and Silurian Bellerophontacea', by F. R. C. Reed, *Mon. Pal. Soc.*, 1920–1, and 'The Genera Omospira, Lophospira, and Turritoma', by J. Longstaff, *Q.J.G.S.*, vol. lxii, pp. 552–72, 1906. Many other Ordovician fossils are illustrated in a series of papers by F. R. C. Reed on 'New Fossils from the Haverfordwest District' in the *Geol. Mag.* for the years 1904 to 1908.

'Caradocian Cystidea from Girvan', by F. A. Bather, *Trans. Roy. Soc. Edinburgh*, vol. xlix, pp. 359–529, 1913, has figures of the peculiar cystids yielded by the Girvan rocks, and comments on the geographical distribution of some other fossil groups.

A typical succession of Ordovician rocks in Scandinavia is described by O. Holtedahl and others in 'The Geology of Parts of Southern Norway', *Proc. Geol. Assoc.*, vol. xlv, pp. 307–88, 1934. Among the recent works dealing with the fossils of this system are: 'The Trilobites of the Leptaena Limestone in Dalarne', by E. Warburg, *Bull. Upsala Geol. Inst.*, vol. xvii, pp. 1–446 and pls., 1925; 'Scandinavian Trinucleidae', by L. Størmer, *Skr. Norsk. Videns. Ak. Oslo*, vol. i, pp. 1–111, 1930; 'The Swedish Ordovician and Lower Silurian Lichidae', by E. Warburg, *Kungl. Sven. Vetensk. Handl.*, ser. 3, vol. xvii, pp. 1–162, 1939. The corresponding rocks of the Baltic States are reviewed by P. E. Raymond in 'Correlation of the Ordovician Strata of the Baltic Basin with those of Eastern North America', *Bull. Mus. Comp. Zool. Harvard*, vol. lvi, pp. 179–286, 1916. Following the great work of F. Schmidt, 'Revision der Ostbaltischen Silurischen Trilobiten', in *Mem. Acad. Imp. Sci. St. Petersburg*, 1881–1907, many groups of fossils from the Baltic region have been reviewed by A. Opik in a series of papers from Tartu University; among these we may mention 'Trilobiten aus Estland', *Publ. Geol. Inst. Univ. Tartu*, No. 52.

The Ordovician rocks and fossils of Bohemia, first described by J. Barrande in *Système silurien du Centre de la Bohème*, 1852, and Supplement 1872, have been reviewed by F. Heritsch in 'Das Silur von Böhmen', *Geol. Rundschau*, vol. xix, pp. 321–44, 1928. H. B. Whittington has discussed 'Some Trinucleidae described by Joachim Barrande', in *Amer. Journ. Sci.*, vol. ccxxxviii, pp. 241–59, 1940. The relations of the Bohemian with the Portuguese faunas are shown in *Système silurique du Portugal*, by J. F. N. Delgado, Comm. Serv. du Portugal, 1908, and with those of N. France in *Bretagne, Livret Guide* by C. Barrois, VIIIe Congr. géol. internat., Paris, 1900.

Correlation of the Ordovician Strata of the Baltic Basin with those of Eastern North America, by P. E. Raymond, 1916, has already been noted. Further discussion of this topic is contained in 'Ordovician Trilobites of the Family Telephidae and concerned Stratigraphic Correlations,' by E. O. Ulrich, *Proc. U.S. Nat. Mus.*, vol. lxxvii, art. 21, 1930; 'New Brachiopods and Trilobites from the Upper Ordovician of Percé, Quebec', by G. A. Cooper and C. H. Kindle in *Journ. Palaeont.*, vol. x, pp. 348–72, 1936; and 'The Trinucleidae, with Special Reference to North American Genera and Species', by H. B. Whittington, ibid., vol. xv, pp. 21–41, 1941. 'The Graptolites of North America', by R. Ruedemann, *Geol. Soc. Amer. Mem.*, xix, 1947 is an exhaustive monograph on this important group of fossils. Many other Ordovician fossils are figured in *Index Fossils of North America*, by H. W. Shimer and R. R. Shrock, New York, 1944. 'Ordovician Fossils from Northern Argentina', are described by H. J. Harrington in *Geol. Mag.*, vol. lxxiv, pp. 97–124, 1937, and O. M. B. Bulman discusses 'South American Graptolites', in *Arkiv. Zool. K. Svens. Vet. Ak.*, Bd. xxii A, No. 8, 1931.

A summary of the graptolite succession in Australia is given by G. L. Elles and R. A. Keble in T. W. E. David's *Explanatory Notes to Accompany a New Geological Map of Australia*, Sydney, 1932, and in 'Victorian Graptolites', by W. J. Harris and D. E. Thomas, *Proc. Roy. Soc. Vict.*, vol. xlvii, 1935. The similar sequence in New Zealand is recorded by W. N. Benson and R. A. Keble in 'The Ordovician Rocks of New Zealand', *Geol. Mag.*, vol. lxxiii, pp. 241–50, 1936. Other groups of Ordovician fossils from Australasia are discussed by T. Kobayashi in 'The Ordovician Shelly Faunas in the South-Western Pacific Province', *Jap. Journ. Geol. Geogr.*, vol. xvii, pp. 105–25, 1940.

Ordovician faunas from south-east Asia are described in several papers by F. R. C. Reed: 'Ordovician and Silurian Fossils from Yunnan', *Pal. Indica*, N.S., vol. vi, pt. 3, 1917; 'Lower Palaeozoic Fossils of the Southern Shan States', ibid., vol. xxi, no. 3, 1936; 'Lower Palaeozoic Fossils of the Northern Shan States', ibid., vol. ii, 1906, with supplement in 1915; 'Ordovician and Silurian Faunas of the Central Himalayas', ibid., ser. xv, vol. vii, no. 2, 1912.

In east Asia, Y. C. Sun has described the 'Ordovician Trilobites of Central and Southern China', in *Pal. Sinica*, ser. B, vol. vii, 1913; C. C. Yu discusses and illustrates 'The Ordovician Cephalopoda of Central China', ibid., vol. i, pt. 2, 1930; and A. W. Grabau describes some 'Ordovician Fossils from North China', ibid., vol. i, pt. i, 1922. *The Ordovician Formations and Faunas of S. Chosen*, are reviewed by T. Kobayashi in *Journ. Fac. Sci. Imp. Univ. Tokio*, sect. 2, vol. iii, pp. 329–519, 1934. All these works contain numerous references to other literature.

V

SILURIAN FAUNAS

THE Silurian rocks of Britain, as exposed at the surface, have a distribution similar to that of the Ordovician strata. The area of deposition, therefore, remained practically unchanged; and the comparison holds further, since a graptolitic and a shelly facies can be distinguished in the older Silurian rocks. Higher in the succession the two facies become less marked; graptolites are found in rocks of shallow-water type and are associated with other fossils. This 'mixed facies' in some areas is important as providing a means of correlating the graptolitic and shelly facies in other districts.

As with the Ordovician the Silurian graptolitic facies will be considered before discussing the shelly facies, and the accompanying table of the graptolite zones, with short summaries of the general characters of the faunas (again taken from the works of G. L. Elles), will serve as a basis for study. The zones are numbered consecutively with those of the Ordovician (p. 164).

A. THE GRAPTOLITIC FACIES

The tabulated classification shows that the several graptolite-zones of the Silurian system are identified mainly on the basis of thecal characters of the enclosed monograptids (see p. 196). Those of the **Valentian Series** may be divided into three groups. The lowest of these, comprising three zones, is marked by the appearance of monograptids with simple straight thecae, while survivals of Ordovician types are seen in species of *Orthograptus* and *Mesograptus*.

There is some uncertainty regarding the lower limit of the Silurian system, since some authors place the zone of *Cephalograptus acuminatus* and *Glyptograptus persculptus* in the Ordovician. Moreover, O. T. Jones divides this zone into two, using the graptolites just mentioned as the indexes of separate zones. But this separation is often difficult in North Wales and south Scotland where *Mesograptus modestus* Lapworth is by far the commonest graptolite, and it ranges into the succeeding zone of *Orthograptus vesiculosus*. *Cephalograptus acuminatus* (Nicholson) (Fig. 34) is straight or slightly curved, with a long and slender sicula, the proximal end approaching *Dimorphograptus* in appearance; the thecae are introverted with acuminate margins and show some resemblance to those of *Glyptograptus*. *Glyptograptus persculptus* Salter (Fig. 4) widens rapidly at the proximal end and has a conspicuous sicula; the thecae are strongly sigmoid especially in the proximal region.

The zone of *Orthograptus vesiculosus* and *Mesograptus modestus* witnesses the incoming of monograptids, associated with various species of *Dimorphograptus*. *D. swanstoni* Lapworth and *D. confertus* (Nicholson) (Fig. 4), forms with the orthograptid type of theca in the biserial portion are confined to this zone. *D. decussatus* Elles and Wood (Fig. 5) has only two thecae in the uniserial part. *Orthograptus vesiculosus* Nicholson is easily recognized by the presence of a fusiform vesicle prolonged beyond the extremity of its robust polypary; its broad thecae are slightly lobate, but of general orthograptid type (Fig. 34). Distal fragments of *Mesograptus modestus* Lapworth (Fig. 34) are somewhat like those of *O. vesiculosus*, but the proximal thecae of the former show climacograptid features—pronounced excavations and sharp sigmoid curvature of the ventral walls. *M. modestus* is a widespread species, even more abundant than *O. vesiculosus*, but is not confined to this zone. The thecae of *Climacograptus medius* Törnquist and the closely allied *Cl. rectangularis* (M'Coy) have straight vertical walls and horizontal apertural margins. O. T. Jones divides this zone into two, a zone of *M. atavus* Jones below, and a higher zone of *M. acinaces* Törnquist, but these are not always recognizable.

The zone of *Monograptus cyphus* contains an abundance of monograptids with thecae of simple type. The mature thecae of *M. cyphus* Lapworth (Fig. 34) are simple straight tubes with nearly parallel walls and even apertural margins; the thecae overlap to a considerable extent and the polypary is dorsally curved. The index-graptolite is associated with *M. atavus* Jones, a form with a long slender polypary bearing slightly curved thecae; this species, however, also occurs in the zone below. *M. incommodus* Törnquist (Fig. 5) is another long and slender species with general dorsal curvature, but its thecae are inclined at a low angle and the apertural margins are slightly introverted. *M. revolutus* Kurck (Fig. 5) has mature theca of *cyphus*-type and its proximal end is thread-like. *M. sandersoni* Lapworth has sigmoid thecae with oblique apertural margins, much like those of the Ordovician *Leptograptus*. *Dimorphograptus physophora* (Nicholson), a rigid form with thecae of orthograptid type, is the only member of its genus possessing a disk at the proximal end. *Climacograptus rectangularis* (M'Coy) persists from the underlying zone.

The next four zones are marked by the incoming and acme of monograptids with the lobate and isolate type of theca. The three lower zones are often united as the zone of *M. gregarius* since many species range throughout. A division, however, is often useful in field-work, and is justified by the recognition of three assemblages of graptolites.

The zone of *M. fimbriatus* (Nicholson) contains early lobate and isolate types associated with several survivals of the type of *M. incommodus*. The index-fossil (Fig. 34) has a dorsally curved polypary bearing triangular or conical thecae with reflexed apertural margins; there is a tendency towards isolation, but practically no lobation of the thecae. In *Rastrites approximatus*

Table of Silurian Graptolite Zones

	Zones	Character of graptolite fauna
LOWER LUDLOW	37. *Monograptus leintwardinensis* 36. ,, *tumescens* 35. ,, *scanicus* 34. ,, *nilssoni*	Prevalence of monograptids with simple thecae of dichograptid type.
WENLOCK SERIES	Band of *Monograptus vulgaris* 33. *Cyrtograptus lundgreni* 32. ,, *rigidus* 31. ,, *linnarssoni* 30. ,, *symmetricus* 29. *Monograptus riccartonensis* 28. *Cyrtograptus murchisoni*	Acme and waning of hooked monograptids. Acme of *Cyrtograptus*.
UPPER VALENTIAN	27. *Monograptus crenulatus* 26. ,, *griestonensis* 25. ,, *crispus* 24. ,, *turriculatus* Band of *Rastrites maximus* 23. *Monograptus sedgwicki*	Monograptids of hooked type. Acme and extinction of isolate type. Waning of lobate type.
LOWER VALENTIAN	22. *Monograptus convolutus* 21. ,, *argenteus* 20. ,, *triangulatus* 19. ,, *fimbriatus* 18. ,, *cyphus* 17. *Mesograptus modestus* and *Orthograptus vesiculosus* 16. *Cephalograptus acuminatus* and *Glyptograptus persculptus*	Monograptids of isolate and lobate types. Waning of diplograptids. Predominance of monograptids with simple thecae. Scandent biserial forms with simple thecae. Abundance of orthograptids, climacograptids, and large glyptograptids. Absence of *Dicellograptus*.

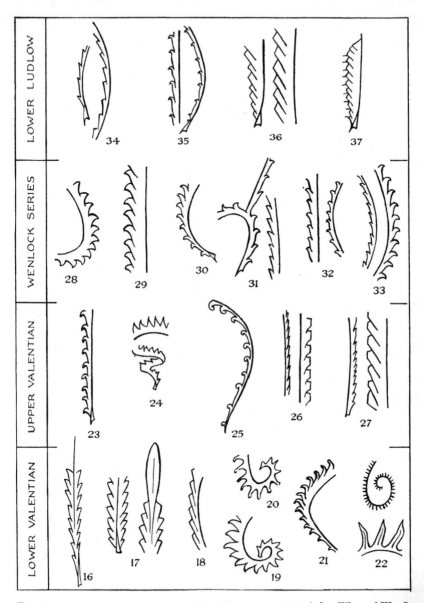

FIG. 34. ZONAL GRAPTOLITES OF THE SILURIAN SYSTEM (*after Elles and Wood*)
Numbers refer to index-graptolites enumerated in Table opposite. About twice the
natural size

(Perner), also restricted to this zone, the proximal end is typically convolute and the widely spaced thecae are on the convex margin. *M. gregarius* Lapworth, often occurring in swarms, has simple uniform thecae borne on a stiff, dorsally curved polypary, the robust proximal end being formed of the large sicula. Biserial scandent forms ranging through the Lower Valentian are *Glyptograptus tamariscus* Nicholson and *Climacograptus hughesi* (Nicholson) (Fig. 5).

A common species ranging through the gregarius-zone is *M. triangulatus* (Harkness), recognized by the circinate curvature of its polypary, and the linear triangulate form of its distal thecae which bear small, barbed apertural terminations (Fig. 34). This form attains its acmaic development in the middle portion of the gregarius zone, where it is associated with more distinctly lobed monograptids; this association determines the zone of *M. triangulatus*. The definitely lobed types include *M. millepeda* (M'Coy) (Fig. 5), whose polypary is strongly curved, the proximal portion being involute. Also typical of this horizon is *Mesograptus magnus* H. Lapworth, a biserial scandent form with a thick polypary and pronounced sigmoid curvature of the thecae.

In the zone of *M. argenteus* monograptids with hooked thecae appear for the first time, the isolate forms known as *Rastrites* become abundant, while other isolate and lobate types such as *M. gregarius* Lapworth, *M. triangulatus* (Harkness) and *M. communis* (Lapworth) persist. The index-graptolite *M. argenteus* (Nicholson) is easily recognized by the form of its polypary (Fig. 34); the proximal end is straight and slender, but after a sharp bend, the distal part becomes robust, and bears long, narrow, overlapping thecae with distinct and isolate apertural hooks. The associated *M. leptotheca* Lapworth has a straight polypary that bears long, slender, greatly overlapping thecae. *Rastrites longispinus* (Perner) (Fig. 5) also occurs here.

The zone of *M. convolutus* (Hisinger) witnesses the acme of the lobate type and the gradual evolution of hooked forms. The zonal-graptolite is spirally curved, but may be irregularly crushed in preservation; the early thecae are linear like those of *Rastrites*, but in maturity the cells are triangular with spined apertural terminations. The most characteristic of its associates are *M. lobiferus* (M'Coy) (Fig. 5) and *Rastrites peregrinus* (Barrande). The former is easily recognized by its uniform lobed thecae and the dorsiventral curvature of its polypary. *R. peregrinus* (Fig. 5) is a small form with short club-shaped thecae set at fairly close intervals. The biserial scandent *Cephalograptus cometa* (Geinitz) is abundant in a well-defined band near the top of the zone in south Scotland, the Lake District, and Ireland; its fusiform polypary bears long, narrow, straight thecae, whose apertural margins all lie close to the distal extremity.

The Upper Valentian zones are marked by the gradual predominance of hooked monograptids, the acme and extinction of the isolate type, and the waning in importance of lobate forms.

In the zone of *M. sedgwicki* the index-fossil is associated with *M. tenuis*, *Orthograptus bellulus*, and *Climacograptus scalaris*. *M. sedgwicki* (Portlock) (Fig. 34) has a straight polypary bearing small thecae with retroverted apertures; the apertural margin is often thickened and prolonged into a spiny projection. *M. tenuis* (Portlock) has a slightly arcuate polypary of great length; its thecae are long, slender, and sigmoid. Distal fragments of *O. bellulus* (Törnquist) closely resemble the earlier *Mesograptus modestus* in general characters. This form and its associate *Climacograptus scalaris* (Hisinger) are among the latest known biserial forms.

The zone of *M. turriculatus* has, at its base, a well-defined bed marked by the occurrence of *Rastrites maximus* (Carruthers). This graptolite, only known by fragments, has a thread-like polypary that bears very long thecae with triangular bases and retroflexed apertural margins; the thecae are twice or thrice the length of the interspaces (Fig. 5). The genus *Rastrites* attains its maximum development in this zone. *M. turriculatus* (Barrande) (Fig. 34) has the characteristic habit of a conical spiral, which, however, is often distorted during preservation; its thecae are of the type of *M. sedgwicki*. *M. marri* Perner (Fig. 5) is a hooked form connecting *M. sedgwicki* with *M. priodon* (Bronn), so characteristic of higher zones. *M. runcinatus* Lapworth, *M. becki* (Barrande) (Fig. 5), *M. nodifer* Törnquist, and *M. exiguus* (Nicholson) are lobate forms, distinguished from each other by the form and curvature of the polypary. *Climacograptus hughesi* (Nicholson) (Fig. 5) is a late scandent biserial form.

The most characteristic forms in the zone of *M. crispus* are the index-fossil, *M. discus*, and *Rastrites distans*. *M. crispus* Lapworth (Fig. 34) has a strongly recurved proximal portion, while the distal part of the polypary is broadly incurved; the thecae hardly overlap, since the greater part of each is involved in the strong lobe. *M. discus* Törnquist, which ranges up into the next zone, is coiled in a close plane spiral; it may be confused with *M. turriculatus* but is distinguished by the absence of spines. As its name implies, the thecae of *R. distans* Lapworth, are widely spaced, the length of the interspaces being about equal to that of the thecae; the apertural terminations are slightly reflected. Early mutations of *M. priodon* (Bronn) are associated with *M. marri* Perner (Fig. 5) in this zone, and a few lobate forms persist from lower horizons.

The index-graptolite of the zone of *M. griestonensis* (Nicol) has short thecae with abrupt sigmoid curvature, and some torsion of the axis (Fig. 34); in consequence of the torsion one aspect of the polypary resembles that of a later species *M. dubius* (Suess), while the other aspect is like a *Climacograptus*, since the apertural margins often appear in distinct excavations on the ventral margin. The chief associates are *M. discus*, *M. marri*, and early mutations of *M. priodon*. The first-named, though small, is a useful guide to horizon, being restricted to this and the preceding zone.

The zone of *M. crenulatus* contains, besides the index-fossil, *M. priodon*,

M. subconicus, and *Retiolites geinitzianus* var. *angustidens* (Elles and Wood). *M. crenulatus* (Törnquist) (Fig. 34) may be regarded as an early variety of *M. vomerinus* in which the thecae are more closely set and the apertural excavations are smaller. *M. vomerinus* (Nicholson) is characteristic of the overlying Wenlock zones and is described below along with *M. priodon*. *M. subconicus* Törnquist, has the spiral curvature of *M. convolutus*, but is more robust. The variety *angustidens* of *Retiolites geinitzianus* Barrande, differs conspicuously from the later typical form of the species in being more uniformly narrow throughout its length.

The graptolite zones of the **Wenlock Series** are marked by the maximum development of hooked monograptids, of which *M. priodon* (Bronn) and *M. flemingi* (Salter) are familiar examples. The former has a straight polypary bearing uniform thecae whose apertural margins are isolated and retroverted (Fig. 5). *M. flemingi* (Salter) is closely related, but has beak-like, rather than hooked thecae. The latter is common in the higher zones, while *M. priodon* belongs more to lower horizons. The broadly curved forms with secondary branches, usually grouped together as *Cyrtograptus*, are also characteristic of Wenlock horizons.

In the zone of *Cyrtograptus murchisoni* the branched and curved *Cyrtograptus* makes its first appearance. *C. murchisoni* Carruthers (Fig. 34) is a broadly curved form and its thecae have reflexed apertural margins. Its associates are *M. priodon*, *M. vomerinus*, and *Retiolites geinitzianus* Barrande. The latter is typical of the zone and may be recognized by the sword-like shape of its robust polypary. The appearance of *M. vomerinus* (Nicholson) differs with the direction in which it is compressed. It has a straight polypary bearing short thecae whose axes are twisted; the thecae may therefore appear in distinct excavations, they may be entirely concealed, or may show *priodon*-like curvature.

The zone of *M. riccartonensis* Lapworth, has for its index a narrow, limp graptolite with hooked thecae (Fig. 34); it is narrower than the associated *M. priodon* and its thecae are less markedly hooked; the absence of spines on the thecae is a distinction from *M. sedgwicki*. Early forms of the long-ranged type *M. dubius* (Suess) (Fig. 5) appear here. This species has a conspicuous sicula, and the proximal end of the polypary is slightly curved ventrally; the thecae are not retroverted. Another associate is *M. capillaceus* Tullberg, a slender curved form with lobed thecae like those of *M. lobiferus*, but only a small part of the cell is involved in the lobe. *Cyrtograptus flaccidus* Tullberg is also typical of this horizon.

In the zone of *Cyrtograptus symmetricus* the index-fossil is associated with *M. capillaceus*, *M. priodon*, and *M. dubius*, all of which occur in the preceding zone. *C. symmetricus* Elles (Fig. 34) is a small form, with a short recurved proximal end that rapidly widens; the thecae have reflexed apertural margins and, usually, the polypary bears only one branch.

The zone of *Cyrtograptus linnarssoni* is marked by the association of the name-fossil with both *M. priodon* and *M. flemingi*, in addition to *M. dubius*, *M. vomerinus*, and *M. flexilis* Elles. The latter species is like *M. flemingi* in thecal characters, but the polypary is flexed and possesses a long virgella. *C. linnarssoni* Lapworth (Fig. 34) is characterized by the short slender proximal portion and the graceful curvature of its polypary; moreover, the thecae, subtriangular with reflexed apertural margins at the proximal end, gradually become more tubular distally.

The association of *M. flemingi*, *M. dubius*, and *M. vomerinus* continues in succeeding zones of the Wenlock Series. They are accompanied, in the zone of *Cyrtograptus rigidus*, by the index-fossil and *M. retroflexus* Tullberg. The latter is like *M. capillaceus* (previously described), but widens more rapidly, though the average width is less; also the thecal lobes are more tightly coiled. *C. rigidus* Tullberg (Fig. 34) is long, slender, and straight proximally, but gradually widens and gives off a single branch; the subtriangular proximal thecae give place to more tubular cells that overlap to a greater extent distally.

In the zone of *Cyrtograptus lundgreni* Tullberg the persistent Wenlock forms are associated with the guide-fossil and a variety of *M. testis* (Barrande). The former (Fig. 34) has a slender polypary with several branches; the thecae have reflexed margins. There is possibility of confusion only with *C. murchisoni* which has a greater number of branches. The thecae of *M. testis* (Barrande), a small form with spirally curved polypary, show marked retroversion of the apertural margins.

The band of *M. vulgaris*, now included at the top of the lundgreni zone, is not always easy to differentiate. *M. vulgaris* Wood possesses a stiff, rigid polypary bearing short, broad thecae; its characteristic proximal end (Fig. 5) furnishes a ready means of distinction from its associates *M. dubius* and from the Ludlow form *M. tumescens*. *M. flemingi* also occurs here, possibly *M. nilssoni*, and rarely *Gothograptus nassa* (Holm) a small retiolitid with thecae of Glyptograptus type.

The graptolite-zones of the **Ludlow Series** are characterized by monograptids with simple, straight thecae—a return to the aspect of low zonal types. The late species may, however, be distinguished by curvature of the proximal thecae.

The most widespread and best-developed zone is that of *M. nilssoni* (Barrande) (Fig. 34), a slender form with a graceful doubly curved polypary; the thecae are simple tubes with slight sigmoid curvature. The zonal index is typically associated with a long form of *M. dubius* (Suess) (Fig. 5), *M. bohemicus* (Barrande), and *M. colonus* (Barrande). The polypary of the last species is ventrally curved at the proximal end, becoming straight distally; the proximal thecae are retroverted while those of the distal portion are straight (Fig. 5). *M. bohemicus* (Barrande) is distinguished by the broad ventral curvature of its polypary, and its simple, short, and broad thecae. *M. orbatus* (Wood) (Fig. 5) has thecae of the type of *M. flemingi* on the *colonus* form of polypary. *M. crinitis* Wood, a very slender, irregularly flexed form, is allied to other slender species of the *M. priodon* and *M. lobiferus* groups. *M. varians* Wood, whose short polypary has a slight ventral curvature, is also characteristic, the gregarious variety *pumilis* Wood often occurring to the exclusion of other graptolites. *M. salweyi* (Hopkinson), usually regarded as a variety of *M. chimaera* (Barrande), is sufficiently distinct in morphological characters and in geological occurrence to justify its separation as a definite species; its most conspicuous feature is the presence of long spines on the prismatic thecae.

The zone of *M. scanicus* contains *M. roemeri* (Barrande) and *M. dubius* (Suess) in association with the zonal index. *M. scanicus* Tullberg (Fig. 34) is a slender form with conspicuous ventral curvature at the proximal end, which is threadlike, but widens to a thickness of about 1 mm.; the thecae are of *M. flemingi* type, but with less of the tube involved in the claw-like hook. *M. roemeri* (Barrande), which occurs also in the preceding zone, has simple thecae (with the exception of the two retroverted proximal ones) borne on a wide polypary with slight double curvature.

The index-graptolite is the only common form in the zone of *M. tumescens* Wood. It has a straight wide polypary with ventral curvature at the proximal end (Fig. 34); the straight, overlapping thecae often have thickened apertural margins, giving, on compression, the appearance of distinct denticles. The typical species is sometimes associated with its variety *minor* (M'Coy), which differs only in its small size.

The zone of *M. leintwardinensis* Hopkinson is also monotypic. The index-graptolite (Fig. 34) has a short wide polypary that is straight distally, and only slightly curved proximally; the thecae are spined, those near the sicula being retroverted at the margin. No later graptolites are known in Britain with the exception of dendroid forms recorded from Lower Carboniferous rocks.

CORRELATION OF GRAPTOLITIC AND SHELLY FAUNAS

A comparison between the graptolitic faunas and shelly faunas of Valentian age may be based on the succession in the Llandovery district, where graptolitic shales are interbedded with shelly sandstones and mudstones. O. T. Jones has thereby determined the following limits for the three stages of the Llandovery Series.

The base of the lower stage includes the zone of *Cephalograptus acuminatus*, but, since the beds are often unfossiliferous, difficulty sometimes occurs in separating them from the Ordovician strata on which they lie.

The base of the Middle Llandovery is drawn between the zones of *Monograptus argenteus* and of *M. triangulatus*.

The base of the upper stage corresponds with that of the zone of *M. sedgwicki*.

The base of the Wenlock Series is formed by the zone of *Cyrtograptus murchisoni*.

In each case the limit is marked by a physical unconformity, besides the palaeontological break. This coincidence—if proved in other areas—will greatly facilitate the mapping of these rocks.

Similarly the 'mixed' succession at Girvan in southern Scotland may be grouped as in the accompanying table.

	Zones	Girvan succession	
Upper Llandovery	Crenulatus Griestonensis Crispus Turriculatus Maximus Sedgwicki	Drumyork group Bargany group with *M. priodon* and *M. acus* } Penkill group with *R. distans, M. becki*, &c. Camregan group of grits and limestones, with Maximus shales at the top Shales with *M. sedgwicki*	Gala Stage
Middle Llandovery	Convolutus Argenteus	Saugh Hill Sandstone (unfossiliferous)	[Craighead Inlier] } Glenshallock Shales	Birkhill Stage
Lower Llandovery	Triangulatus Fimbriatus Cyphus Vesiculosus Acuminatus	Woodlands Limestone and Shale Glenwells Shale Mulloch Hill Sandstone and Conglomerate	} Newlands Pentamerus Beds	

On evidence from various localities the later Silurian rocks may be broadly correlated as follows. The arrangement is largely that given by W. W. Watts for Shropshire.

	Graptolite zones	Shelly strata	
Ludlow Series	[No graptolites] . . . . Leintwardinensis . . . Tumescens . . . . Scanicus . . . . Nilssoni	Upper Ludlow stage Aymestry Limestone } Lower Ludlow Shales	
Wenlock Series	Lundgreni . . . . . Rigidus . . . . . Linnarssoni . . . . Riccartonensis . . . . Murchisoni	} Wenlock Limestone and Wenlock Shales Woolhope Limestone	

B. THE SHELLY FACIES

Bordering the Silurian graptolitic facies of central Wales, the equivalent rocks of eastern Wales, the Mendips, and south Wales show the lithological inconstancy usual in deposits formed in the shallow water of coastal areas. The faunas also show considerable variation, laterally as well as vertically, but some species can usually be found that enable the horizon to be determined.

In general, trilobites and brachiopods are most abundantly represented, but crinoids, cystids, reef-forming corals, polyzoa, and mollusca form important elements in these wonderfully varied Silurian assemblages.

Many trilobite-families that occur in Ordovician strata are represented also in Silurian rocks, but asaphids and trinucleids, so characteristic of the earlier system, no longer appear. The most abundant forms are phacopids and calymenids, commonly associated with encrinurids, illaenids, and proetids. The first-named group is typified by members of the genera *Phacops* and *Dalmanites* that are readily distinguished from other families by the size of their compound eyes. These range into Devonian strata where they are associated with modified forms of the same group. Species of the genus *Calymene*, familiar as the 'Dudley Locust' of Wenlock age, are much like the late Ordovician species in showing marked lobation of the glabella. Silurian species of *Encrinurus* are especially marked by extreme specialization, and the genus is not known from higher strata. The spiny character of *Acidaspis* and *Deiphon*, belonging to unrelated families, is probably adaptive, though it cannot be ascribed to any definite factor. *Proetus*, ranging from Ordovician to Permian, is also frequently found.

The brachiopod element is distinguished especially by the abundance of pentamerids, whose shells are partially divided into chambers by large internal plates. Indeed, the frequent appearance in weathered examples, of a ∧ formed by the mesial septum and the edges of the pedicle-valve, led Lapworth to the use of 'Government Rock' as a convenient field-term. Strophomenids and orthids abound, some forms, e.g. *Leptaena rhomboidalis*, *Orthis (Bilobites) biloba*, *Orthis (Dalmanella) elegantula* passing up from Ordovician rocks; Silurian varieties, however, appear to differ in minute details from the earlier forms. Rhynchonellids and spire-bearing brachiopods, such as *Atrypa*, *Meristina*, and early forms of *Spirifer*, are also common.

Notwithstanding the great profusion of Silurian fossils, it is only recently that the evolutional history of certain forms has been traced, giving reliable guides to the determination of horizons. Thus the numerous forms of the trilobite *Phacops elegans* (Sars and Boeck) have been found to show progressive modifications in upward sequence. The species-group of *Encrinurus punctatus* (Brünn.), which is probably derived from the Ordovician group of *E. multisegmentatus* Portlock, shows a progressive tendency in the interruption of the axial rings in the pygidium, this group culminates in the Wenlock variety *calcareus* whose tail possesses a definite mucro. Various species of the strophomenid genus *Plectambonites* are distinctive of definite horizons in the system. Many common British fossils, however, have yet to be investigated from the modern standpoint, and these at present are obviously of less value for purposes of correlation than forms whose evolutional history is known. For instance, the evolution of the British pentamerids still requires detailed investigation. The gradual increase in length of the median septum in pentamerids from successive horizons has been utilized by J. Kiaer for the correlation of Silurian rocks in the Christiania region. From general observations it would appear that a similar morphogenetic sequence could be established for British pentamerids, though, it may be noted, shells with short septa (e.g. species of *Barrandella*) persist into the Wenlock Series.

The Silurian shelly facies may conveniently be divided into (*a*) the Llandovery Series, (*b*) the Wenlock Series, and (*c*) the Ludlow Series, in ascending order.

The **Llandovery Series,** separated from the underlying Ordovician by a palaeontological break, has a wide distribution in Wales, the Welsh borders, the Lake District, southern Scotland, and Ireland, besides continental Europe. Although graptolitic assemblages alternate with shelly faunas in the Girvan area, the classification and correlation of the shelly deposits have always presented difficulties consequent upon the diversity of lithological and faunal characters and the lack of knowledge concerning the evolution of commonly occurring fossils.

Recent work by O. T. Jones and others in the type-area of Llandovery has shown the presence of 'three stages having unconformable relations one with another, and the series is overlain unconformably by the Wenlock deposits. Each stage is marked by a shelly fauna, and the local presence of graptolites makes possible a correlation of the shelly deposits with the graptolite zones of Wales, the Lake District and southern Scotland.' In other districts, such as Shropshire, south-east Wales, and the Mendips, the upper division alone is present, resting unconformably upon Ordovician or older rocks.

The chief brachiopod families present in the lower division of the Llandovery Series are the pentamerids and the strophomenids. One of the earliest pentamerids is *Barrandella undata* (J. de C. Sow.), a smooth, transversely oval shell with a wide fold in the brachial valve and a corresponding furrow in the pedicle valve; inside the pedicle valve the small converging dental lamellae are not supported by septal plates. It is often associated with *Stricklandinia lens* (J. de C. Sow.), a flattened lens-shaped form with a straight hinge-line; internally, the two small, converging dental plates in the pedicle valve are supported by a short median septum. The strophomenids are numerously represented by species of *Strophomena*,

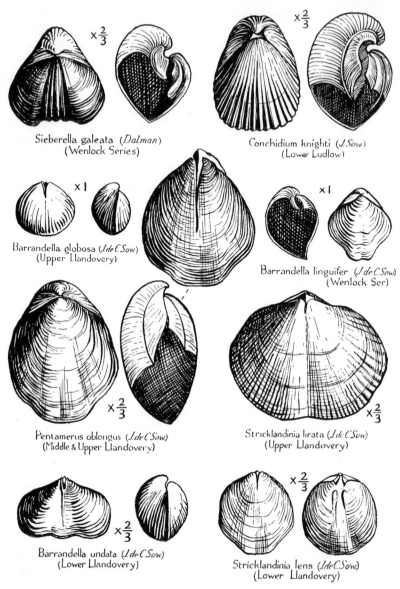

Sieberella galeata (*Dalman*)
(Wenlock Series)

$\times \frac{2}{3}$

Conchidium knighti (*J.Sow.*)
(Lower Ludlow)

$\times \frac{2}{3}$

Barrandella globosa (*J.deC.Sow.*)
(Upper Llandovery)

$\times 1$

Barrandella linguifer (*J.deC.Sow.*)
(Wenlock Ser)

$\times 1$

Pentamerus oblongus (*J.deC.Sow.*)
(Middle & Upper Llandovery)

$\times \frac{2}{3}$

Stricklandinia lirata (*J.deC.Sow.*)
(Upper Llandovery)

$\times \frac{2}{3}$

Barrandella undata (*J.deC.Sow.*)
(Lower Llandovery)

$\times \frac{2}{3}$

Stricklandinia lens (*J.deC.Sow.*)
(Lower Llandovery)

$\times \frac{2}{3}$

FIG. 35. SOME BRITISH PENTAMERIDS (*drawn from figures by Davidson*)

Stropheodonta, Schuchertella, Plectambonites, and the ubiquitous *Leptaena rhomboidalis* (Wilckens). Perhaps the most abundant and distinctive form is *Plectambonites duplicatus* (Murchison) (Fig. 36) and its variants, which usually occur as internal and external moulds. This form has often been confused with *Pl. transversalis* (Dalman) of Wenlock age, but is readily distinguished by its shape and ornament; it has recently been referred to the new genus *Sowerbyella* by O. T. Jones. *Pl. scissus* (Salter) and *Pl. undulatus* (Vanuxem) are often associated with *Pl. duplicatus,* but also range into higher beds. The spire-bearing brachiopods are represented by *Atrypa marginalis* (Dalman) *Meristina crassa* (J. de C. Sow.) and *M. subundata* (M'Coy).

Among trilobites *Phacops elegans* (Sars and Boeck) is a characteristic Lower Llandovery form, and is distinguished by its large eyes and the form of its glabella (Fig. 37). Higher forms show increased resemblance to the Wenlock species *P. stokesi* (M. Edwards). In the species-group of *Encrinurus punctatus* (Brünn.), the segments of the pygidial axis all tend to become obscure in the median line, an 'advance' as compared with Ordovician forms of the group of *E. multisegmentatus.*

The Middle Llandovery fauna contains some species that occur in the lower beds. *Stricklandia lens* (J. de C. Sow.) is often abundant, while *Barrandella undata* (J. de C. Sow.), *Leptaena rhomboidalis* (Wilckens), *Atrypa marginalis* (Dalman), and *Meristina subundata* (M'Coy) are commonly found. But it can be stated that these higher forms show certain differences from their predecessors, though the diagnostic value of the differences has yet to be fully defined. The most distinctive feature of this fauna is the presence of the well-known shell *Pentamerus oblongus* J. de C. Sow. (Fig. 35) which is not known in lower beds; it ranges, however, into the upper stage of the Llandovery Series.

Among trilobites, species of *Calymene, Lichas, Phacops,* and *Encrinurus* are prevalent.

The Upper Llandovery fauna is marked by the incoming of several species which either persist into the overlying Wenlock rocks or are represented therein by closely allied forms. Many of these are spire-bearing brachiopods, which may be taken as highly characteristic of Upper Llandovery and Wenlock strata. Thus *Eospirifer radiatus* (J. de C. Sow.), and *Cyrtia exporrecta* (Wahlenberg), unknown in lower beds, both range into the Wenlock Series. *Catazyga haswelli* (Reed) (Pl. III), an atrypid with a rhynchonelliform shell, is closely allied to the Wenlock species *C. pentlandica* (Haswell). *Atrypa reticularis* (Linn.) appears in abundance and ranges upwards. Many strophomenids approach very closely to their later allies; for instance, the Upper Llandovery varieties of *Leptaena rhomboidalis* (Wilckens) are nearer to the Wenlock forms than to the variants in Lower Llandovery strata. Towards the top of the Llandovery Series, forerunners of *Plectambonites transversalis* (Dalman) appear, but that species itself is not known to occur below the base of the Wenlock Series. On the other hand, the fauna under present consideration contains abundant forms of *Plectambonites* distinctive in size, shape, and internal characters. Also, certain pentamerids occur, which are not recorded in Wenlock faunas. Of these, the most familiar is *Pentamerus oblongus* J. de C. Sow., which is often abundant (especially in sandy beds) in Wales and the Borders, but is rare or absent in south-west England and South Wales. The transversely oval, ribbed shells of *Stricklandia lirata* (J. de C. Sow.) and its allies are also typical of this stage. A group of globose pentamerids, exemplified by *Barrandella globosa* (J. de C. Sow.), make their appearance here and range up into the lower beds of the Wenlock Series.

In striking contrast with the Ordovician 'shelly' faunas, the Silurian assemblages of the Girvan area are practically the same as in southern localities. The marked American types of Brachiopoda are absent, the brachiopod element being predominantly British. The Silurian trilobites recorded from Girvan number twenty-seven species, of which nineteen are known from other British localities. 'The proportion of the British element is therefore much larger than it was in Ordovician times, and seems to indicate a sudden inrush of species from the south at the beginning of the Llandovery period by the breaking down or removal of some intervening barrier' (Reed). Since the same general faunistic characters are found throughout northern Europe, Siberia, China, and North America, it has been suggested that a common Silurian ocean extended around the north polar regions.

In Britain, two more or less local faunules of shelly type have been detected in Upper Llandovery strata. The northern assemblage is typically developed in the Caradoc district of Shropshire and around Builth, extending southwards to the Malverns and northwards to Girvan. Its characteristic feature is the general abundance of *Pentamerus oblongus* Sow. usually associated with *Atrypa reticularis* (Linn.), *Coelospira hemispherica* (Sow.), *Schuchertella pecten* (Linn.), *Stricklandinia lens* (Sow.), *S. lirata* (Sow.), and species of *Plectambonites*. The southern faunule is typical of south-western England and South Wales, where *P. oblongus* is rare or absent, and the most characteristic fossil is *Stropheodonta compressa* (J. de C. Sow.). The latter is usually associated with *Coelospira hemispherica*, *Meristina furcata* (J. de C. Sow.), *Atrypa reticularis* (Linn.), and various rhynchonellids.

The boundary between the two faunules is sharply marked in Pembrokeshire, and extends in an east–west direction between Tortworth and May Hill. It is worthy of note that the extent of the southern faunule coincides with the only Silurian tract that contains volcanic rocks. Whether this has any significance is not known.

The **Wenlock Series**—more especially the limestone formations—has long been famed for the profusion of its fossils. Those of greatest

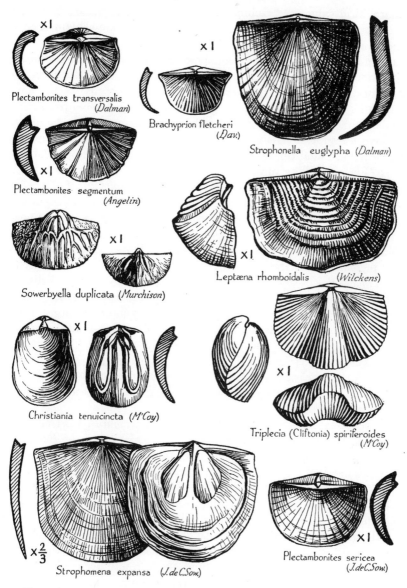

×I

Plectambonites transversalis
(Dalman)

×I

Brachyprion fletcheri
(Dav.)

Plectambonites segmentum
(Angelin)

×I

Strophonella euglypha *(Dalman)*

Sowerbyella duplicata *(Murchison)*

×I

Leptæna rhomboidalis   *(Wilckens)*

×I

Christiania tenuicincta *(M'Coy)*

×I

Triplecia (Cliftonia) spiriferoides
(M'Coy)

×I

×$\frac{2}{3}$

Strophomena expansa *(J.deC.Sow.)*

×I

Plectambonites sericea
(J.deC.Sow.)

FIG. 36. SOME BRITISH STROPHOMENIDS *(drawn mainly from figures by Davidson)*

stratigraphical value are brachiopods and trilobites; corals are also useful, but the commonly occurring mollusca and crinoids are seldom used for purposes of correlation.

Among brachiopods, the strophomenids and pentamerids are abundant and distinctive, while rhynchonellids and spire-bearers show increasing importance. The familiar *Leptaena rhomboidalis* (Wilckens) occurs abundantly in its typical form, which is said to be distinguishable from earlier forms of the species-group by details of ornament and geniculation. *Strophonella euglypha* (Hisinger) has a semicircular shell ornamented by numerous thin radial ribs; the pedicle valve is concave, the brachial valve convex (Fig. 36). The most distinctive species of *Plectambonites* is *Pl. transversalis* (Dalman), easily recognized by the convexity of its pedicle valve and its fine thread-like ribbing intercalated with striae. *Pl. segmentum* (Angelin) is less curved in section and has a few widely spaced principal ribs separated by striae. *Brachyprion fletcheri* (Davidson) is a characteristic Wenlock strophomenid, though it also occurs in Upper Llandovery Beds.

The pentamerids characteristic of Lower Silurian strata are replaced in the Wenlock Series by *Gypidula galeata* (Dalman), whose distinctive features will be recalled by reference to Fig. 35. *Clorinda linguifer* (J. de C. Sow.) is easily distinguished by the projection of its anterior margin. Rhynchonellids are often abundantly represented by the sharp-beaked *Rhynchotreta cuneata* (Dalman) and the transversely elongate *Camarotoechia borealis* (Schlotheim) (Fig. 41). The familiar *Atrypa reticularis* (Linn.) is the commonest spire-bearing brachiopod and needs no description, while other members of this group are species of *Meristina, Eospirifer, Delthyris* (a small coarse-ribbed spiriferid).

The trilobites include species of *Calymene, Encrinurus, Cheirurus,* and *Dalmanites,* besides other rarer forms. The species-group of *Encrinurus punctatus* (Brünnich) attains its highest degree of specialization in the variety *calcareus* Salter, whose tail-spine indicates the culmination of a progressive fusion of the pygidial segments. In this variety and also in var. *arenacea* Salter, the pygidium has numerous incomplete axial rings with a smooth median space bearing a row of tubercles fewer in number than the rings; the glabella is coarsely tuberculated and the lateral glabellar lobes are nodular. In the species-group of *Encrinurus variolaris* Brongn., the pygidium has complete axial rings which are about equal in number to the pleurae. The glabella is coarsely tuberculated, this ornament hiding the lateral glabellar furrows if such are present; the genal angles are rounded. This group may be connected with the Ordovician group of *E. sexcostatus* Salter.

The phacopids show considerable variety of form and structure. The well-known genus *Dalmanites* is represented by varieties of *D. caudatus* (Brünn.). Along with the earlier *Phacops elegans* (Sars and Boeck), *Ph. stokesi* M.-Edw., and *Ph. musheni* Salter, are often placed in the subgenus *Portlockia*; the peculiar basal ring of the glabella and the reduction of the basal lobes to mere tubercles are special features of the cephalon. The distinctive *Acastina downingae* (Murchison) has been described as having a *Dalmanites*-like head combined with a *Phacops*-like tail, but the genal angles are rounded. Some of these trilobites are illustrated in Fig. 37. *Proetus stokesi* (Murchison) and *Otarion megalops* (M'Coy), illustrated in Fig. 46 may be cited as representing the Proetidae.

The limestones contain an abundance of corals, especially compound tabulate forms such as *Favosites gothlandica* Linn., *Heliolites interstinctus* Wahlenberg, and *Halysites catenularis* Linn.—forms that are familiar to most students of Palaeontology. *Cyathophyllum* is a common representative of the rugose corals. Stromatoporoids, especially *Stromatopora typica* van Rosen, are sometimes abundant and are associated with the tabulate corals as important rock-builders.

The stems of crinoids are often sufficiently abundant to form the bulk of limestone beds, but complete crowns are rare, though a few localities, like Dudley, are noted for these fossils. The large and characteristic plates of *Crotalocrinus* are interesting in that they closely resemble those of the Cretaceous genus *Marsupites*, but the two genera differ greatly in organization. Some cystids also occur, notably *Lepadocrinus*, a specialized rhombiferid of 'crinoid' aspect (Fig. 10).

Mollusca are represented by numerous gasteropods and cephalopods, few of which are sufficiently known to be of precise stratigraphical value. Certain enomphalids with 'wrinkled' ornamentation, for instance *Horiostoma rugosa* (J. Sow.) (Fig. 47), are typical of Middle Silurian (Salopian) strata.

The **Ludlow Series.** Many brachiopods persist from the Wenlock strata, but they often show easily recognizable variations. Thus the Ludlow form of *Atrypa reticularis* (Linn.), besides being larger than the Wenlock variety, usually shows a greater convexity of the pedicle valve and a flattening of the brachial valve. These characters may be connected with the development of the internal ventrally directed spires, and are further accentuated in shells from Devonian strata. Late forms of *Gypidula galeata* (Dalman), on the other hand, seem to be smaller with less incurved beaks than Wenlock forms. Most characteristic of Ludlow rocks is *Conchidium knighti* (J. Sow.) (Fig. 35), a strongly ribbed pentamerid shell with markedly incurved beaks. This fossil attains rock-building importance in the Aymestry Limestone at some places (such as Weo Edge near Craven Arms), but at other localities it is hardly to be found in equivalent strata. *Dayia navicula* (J. de C. Sowerby) (Pl. III), a smooth, boat-shaped, spire-bearer, is abundant and typical; in decalcified rocks it may be recognized by the chevron form of its ventral muscle-markings. The genus *Wilsonia* provides the commonest rhynchonellids, which are in general more globose than earlier species.

Among mollusca *Cardiola* (*Slava*) *interrupta* (J. de C. Sow.) (Fig. 47) is

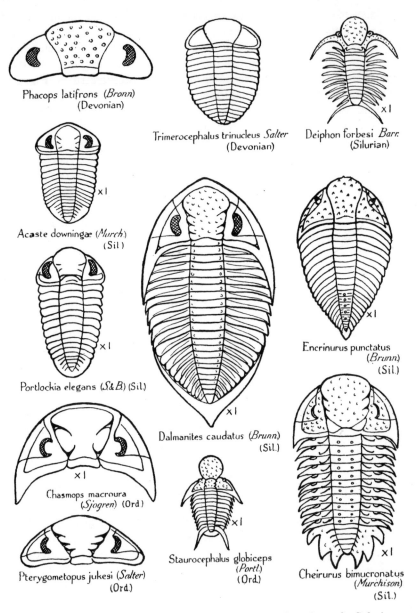

Phacops latifrons (*Bronn*)
(Devonian)

Trimerocephalus trinucleus *Salter*
(Devonian)

Deiphon forbesi *Barr.*
(Silurian)

×1

Acaste downingæ (*Murch*)
(Sil.)

×1

Encrinurus punctatus
(*Brunn*)
(Sil.)

×1

Portlockia elegans (*S&B*) (Sil.)

×1

Dalmanites caudatus (*Brunn*)
(Sil.)

×1

Chasmops macroura
(*Sjogren*) (Ord.)

×1

Staurocephalus globiceps
(*Portl.*)
(Ord.)

×1

Pterygometopus jukesi (*Salter*)
(Ord.)

Cheirurus bimucronatus
(*Murchison*)
(Sil.)

×1

FIG. 37. SOME PROPARIAN TRILOBITES (*drawn from figures by Salter*)

a typical lamellibranch, while species of *Orthonota* may possibly mark certain definite horizons. Cephalopods are often common, but need detailed investigation before they can be used for correlative purposes. The same must be said also of the Ludlow species of *Calymene* and *Dalmanites*, the only common trilobites.

In the higher beds, a frequent brachiopod-association is formed by *Orthis lunata* J. Sow., *Camarotoechia nucula* (J. de C. Sow.), and *Chonetes striatella* (Dalman), which often occur to the exclusion of other forms.

Towards the top of the Series, brachiopods become scarcer and ultimately disappear, *Lingula* being the last survivor. At the same time lamellibranchs—especially mytiloid forms—become more important, and thus the change from marine Silurian to estuarine or deltaic Old Red Sandstone is reflected in the fauna. These higher beds are also of interest in furnishing the remains of early fishes. These occur abundantly as isolated scales and teeth in the famous Ludlow Bone-bed, usually included in the Silurian system. But, since fishes comprise the bulk of the known Old Red Sandstone fauna, the Ludlow forms may be appropriately considered in the next chapter (p. 237).

FAUNAL REGIONS

It is evident that the classification of the Silurian rocks in Britain depends to a large extent on the facies of the deposits. The original Llandovery, Wenlock, and Ludlow Series, to which the Downton Series is added nowadays, are clastic and calcareous rocks which enclose a shelly fauna. The corresponding graptolite shales are grouped in two series, Valentian below and Salopian above, but the top of this succession corresponds with the Lower Ludlow Beds of the shelly facies, and no graptolites are known in this country above the Lower Ludlow Beds. Hence, to allow the comparison of distant faunas without extending the local facies-terms from one country or continent to another, it is convenient to modify the usual grouping as in the right-hand column of the table below.

Shelly facies	Graptolitic facies	Series
Downton Series		Neosilurian
Upper Ludlow Series		
Lower	Salopian	Mesosilurian
Wenlock Series		
Llandovery Series	Valentian	Palaeosilurian

The general succession of graptolite-zones, as demonstrated in the combined sections of various districts in Britain, is repeated in several areas of

Europe. One of the most complete sequences is that described by J. C. Moberg (1910) in Scania, south Sweden. Here the Silurian system begins with the Rastrites Shales, which show a succession from the zone of *Akidograptus acuminatus* up to that of *Monograptus runcinatus*, the latter being equivalent to the British zone of *M. turriculatus*. The lower zones of the overlying Cyrtograptus Shales must also be included in the Palaeosilurian Series, for in the Rostanga district the zones of *Cyrtograptus grayae*, *M. spiralis*, and *C. lapworthi* precede the horizon of *C. murchisoni* which is the lowest zone in the Salopian Series of Britain. Higher there seems to be a break in the succession, for the zone of *M. riccartonensis* is followed in Scania directly by the zones of *C. rigidus* and *C. carruthersi*. This graptolite sequence seems tolerably complete and is spread out through 300 metres of shales. It is followed by the widely distributed Cardiola Shale, some 800 metres in thickness, marked by the presence of *M. colonus*, *M. bohemicus*, *M. nilssoni*, *M. scanicus*, and therefore equivalent to the nilssoni and scanicus zones in the Upper Salopian beds of the British Isles.

Farther north, in Wastergotland and Dalarne, as recorded by C. Wiman (1910) and E. Warburg (1910) respectively, the Ordovician rocks are again followed by the Rastrites Shales the lower zones of which are not exposed, and the Retiolites Shales represent the lower Salopian zones, succeeded directly by Neosilurian sandstones. In Jamtland the Silurian rocks begin with sandstones containing trilobites; then follow shelly limestones covered by the Rastrites Shales. A similar mixed succession is described by C. F. Kolderup (1934) in the arcuate outcrops near Bergen, Norway, where the lower strata are mainly coral-limestones more or less metamorphosed, and higher phyllites yield the late Valentian graptolites *Rastrites peregrinus*, *R. maximus*, and *Monograptus jaculum*. On the other hand, graptolites are rare in the Oslo region of Norway (L. Stormer, 1934) where limestones, sandstones, and shales represent a long range of Silurian deposits corresponding to the British Llandovery, Wenlock, and Ludlow Series in a thickness of about 1,500 metres. Again, in the Baltic region H. Hederstroem, H. Munthe (1910), and W. H. Twenhofel (1916) have described the island of Gotland as occupied largely by non-stratified coral-limestones of reef-like type, bordered by stratified limestones and shales containing reef-detritus. The general age of this deposit is indicated by the presence of *Monograptus flemingi* and *M. dubius*, recorded by J. E. Hede (1921), about the middle of the sequence. In Estonia the equivalent of the Llandovery Series includes coral-limestones and shell-banks with myriads of *Pentamerus borealis*; limestones with corals and brachiopods also represent the Wenlock Series and continue upwards into horizons which probably correspond to the Ludlow Series of England. Thus in Scandinavia the disposition of the shelly and graptolitic facies in relation to the Baltic Shield is consistent with their interpretation as inshore and offshore deposits respectively.

The shelly fossils, especially the trilobites, brachiopods, and corals of the Silurian deposits also bear certain relations to those of contemporary British strata. Among trilobites there is a conspicuous absence of such Ordovician families as the agnostids, asaphids, styginids, telephids, and trinucleids. The most prominent Silurian forms are members of the Illaenidae, Proetidae, Odontopleuridae, Calymenidae, Encrinuridae, Cheiruridae, Lichidae, and Phacopidae, families which were already established in the previous system. Some genera of these surviving families have disappeared as, for example, *Chasmops* and *Cybele*, but others, like *Encrinurus, Illaenus, Otarion, Platylichas*, &c., persist and are joined by notable newcomers. In a review of the Silurian illaenids of the Oslo region, W. F. Whittard (1939) recognizes five species of *Illaenus* and four of the allied genus *Bumastus* which appear to be restricted to Scandinavia though both genera are represented at British Silurian localities. The genus *Goldius* which P. E. Raymond (1916) considers to be closely related to the Illaenidae is also represented in Britain and Scandinavia but again the species are different. Some trilobites, however, are identical in the two areas. For instance, the Scandinavian *Phacops elliptifrons* is cited from early Silurian horizons in Shropshire by C. J. Stubblefield (1939) and W. F. Whittard (1938). The latter author also recognizes the Scandinavian species *Otarion elegantula, Leonaspis marklini, Lichas marginatus*, and *Lichas norvegicus* in Upper Llandovery Beds in Shropshire. P. Lake (1896) had long before stated that two Swedish species of *Odontopleura* are closely related to British Wenlock forms. *Encrinurus punctatus* was first named from a Scandinavian specimen and has often been cited from the Wenlock Limestone of Britain. Likewise the cheirurid *Deiphon forbesi* is common to British and Baltic localities, though certain local variants in the two regions are recognized by W. F. Whittard (1934). *Calymene intermedia*, originally described from Gotland, is recorded by S. H. Straw (1937) from the Ludlow Series at Builth, central Wales, in association with *Dalmanites caudatus, Encrinurus punctatus*, and *Homalonotus knighti* which have also been cited from Scandinavian localities.

The Eurypterus Bed at Rutzikull on the island of Oesel, made famous by the works of J. Nieszkowski (1859), F. Schmidt (1883), G. Holm (1896), and others, should be noted here. The eurypterid fauna includes *Eurypterus fischeri* Eichwald, *Pterygotus oeseliensis* Schmidt, with the hemiaspid *Bunodes lunula* Eichwald and two other species described by Nieszkowski. The eurypterids are preserved in abundance, with the original chitin still unaltered; the fauna occupies only a limited area. A slightly later fauna, described by L. Størmer (1934) from Neosilurian rocks at Ringerikc, Norway, comprises species of *Hughmilleria, Pterygotus, Stylonurus, Mixopterus*, and *Bunodes*, those of the first-named genus being the most abundant. Similar eurypterids, but different species, are described and illustrated by H. Woodward (1866–78) and M. Laurie from a late Silurian horizon at

Lesmahagow, Scotland, including species of *Stylonurus*, *Slimonia*, and *Erettopterus*, the last being a sub-genus of *Pterygotus* with bilobed telson as in *P. oeseliensis*. A species of *Mixopterus* has more recently been recognized by L. Størmer (1936) among the Scottish material. Earlier strata in the Pentland Hills, usually referred to a Wenlock horizon, have yielded species of *Eurypterus*, *Slimonia*, *Carcinosoma*, *Stylonurus*, and the related genus or sub-genus *Drepanopterus*. The Scottish eurypterids are named from fragmentary specimens, often dismembered and water-worn, which appear suddenly in thin beds that are usually limited in areal extent; they are not directly associated with marine fossils, though such assemblages may be present in adjacent beds above and below. Remains of *Pterygotus* and *Eurypterus*, long ago recorded from a Downton horizon near Stoke Edith in Herefordshire, have been reviewed by E. N. Kjellesvig-Waering (1951). The full list from this locality now comprises species of *Hughmilleria*, *Salteropterus* (new genus), *Erettopterus*, *Carsinosoma*, *Mixopterus*, and a doubtful *Tarsopterus*. These eurypterids are stated to show most resemblance to the Pittsford assemblage of New York discussed later (p. 228). Eurypterids, such as *Stylonurus*, *Pterygotus*, and *Eurypterus* persist into the Old Red Sandstone of England where they are often accompanied by ostracoderm fishes; in Ireland *Eurypterus* is associated with the non-marine lamellibranch *Archanodon* and land-plants. But in Bohemia remains of several species of *Pterygotus* are mingled with typical and abundant elements of the Silurian marine fauna. While the marine shells are well-preserved the eurypterids are invariably broken and worn; no complete individual has been found, and the fragments have proved to be of uncertain value for precise identification. This question of habitat may be further discussed in regard to the American assemblages (pp. 228–9).

Among the Silurian brachiopods the pentamerids form the most widespread and conspicuous element, but though they are abundantly represented at several horizons only a few genera and species are associated in each. In his description of the Pentameracea of the Oslo region, J. K. St. Joseph (1938) shows that the Palaeosilurian species *Clorinda undata*, *Stricklandia lens*, and *S. lirata* are as prolific in Norway at their respective horizons as they are in the Llandovery Beds of the Welsh border. The earliest Scandinavian *Pentamerus* is *P. borealis*, first described from Estonia by C. E. Eichwald (1842) and afterwards recorded from Norway by J. Kiaer (1908); it is not known from British strata. At slightly later horizons the variable *P. laevis* of J. Sowerby forms shell-banks in some districts of southern Norway; it is the form which has for long been known in Britain as *P. oblongus*, though the former name has priority. The latest species in Norway is the large *P. gothlandicus* Lebedev which is distinguished specially by its long septum; this shell was first described from Gotland and does not appear in lists of British fossils. The lowest Silurian strata in Norway have yielded the earliest species of the ribbed *Conchidium*, namely, *C. munsteri*

Kiaer, which is not known elsewhere; but later species, such as the *C. knighti* so abundant in England, have been reported from Estonia. Among other brachiopod species common to the British and Scandinavian rocks are *Meristella crassa*, *Atrypa reticularis*, *Eospirifer radiatus*, *Dayia navicula*, *Strophonella euglypha*, *Leptaena rhomboidalis*, and *Chonetes striatella*.

The close relations between Scandinavian and British trilobites and brachiopods are maintained and even surpassed by the corals. The Silurian limestones of Gotland, Oesel, and Estonia contain abundant remains of reef-building corals, and definite reefs are reported at some localities; in southern Norway the figured specimens seem to be drifted fragments. Most of the corals belong to the Tabulata, but some representatives of the Rugosa are present, and species of both groups are identical in Britain and the Baltic region. W. H. Twenhofel (1916) cites such widespread species as *Favosites gothlandicus*, *Halysites catenularia*, *Heliolites interstinctus*, and the massive rugose form *Acervularia luxurians* from Baltic localities; species of *Syringopora*, *Alveolites*, and certain stromatoporoids also seem to be closely related in the two regions. The Silurian coral-reefs, reaching latitude 58° N., lie much farther north than the modern limit for these features; they indicate a warmer climate in Silurian time than that prevailing today in the same latitude. A. Hadding (1950) has recently called attention to the importance of calcareous algae as reef-builders in Gotland. In general the Scandinavian shelly deposits of Silurian age occupy the same position with regard to the graptolite shales as in Britain; the two facies represent the in-shore and offshore deposits on the margin of the Baltic Shield.

Silurian deposits in Poland are transgressive over Ordovician and earlier rocks, and both shelly deposits and graptolite shales are present. The graptolites listed by A. Born (in Salomon, 1926) show that the succession begins with Upper Valentian or early Salopian zones; some Upper Salopian horizons are also represented, and are followed by coarser clastic deposits with a shelly fauna. Graptolites are recorded also from a few detached areas in Germany. Shales which overlie a series of siliceous rocks in the Harz (F. Dahlgruen 1927) have yielded forms that belong to zones of the Upper Valentian and Salopian Series, and similar records are available from the Frankenwald. Representatives of several horizons of both the Valentian and Salopian Series are also recorded by E. Maillieux (1926) from the valleys of the Ardennes. The graptolites and shelly fossils from all these localities show close similarity with British and Scandinavian forms. L. Cayeux (1929) states that Neosilurian graptolitic deposits encountered in a deep boring at Danneville, Calvados, afford evidence of lagoon conditions. Near the margin of the Precambrian mass of Brittany a good succession of Palaeo- and Meso-silurian graptolite shales followed by shelly deposits as in Wales, has been described by A. Philippot (1950).

Proximity to a coast-line is also indicated by the mixed Silurian rocks of Bohemia which have been reviewed by J. Perner and O. Kodym (1922).

The lower beds of the system are chiefly black graptolite shales, beginning with the zone of *Orthograptus vesiculosus* which in places is transgressive over Ordovician rocks. The zone of *Rastrites peregrinus*, next in succession, apparently includes the remainder of the British Lower Valentian zones, and the Bohemian zones of *R. linnei, Monograptus turriculatus,* and *M. spiralis* are equivalent to the Upper Valentian sequence. Most of the Palaeo-silurian graptolites are common to Bohemia, Scandinavia, and Britain, and it is worth noting that several species were originally named by J. Barrande (1850) from Bohemian specimens. The zones of *Cyrtograptus murchisoni, M. riccartonensis,* and *M. testis* represent the lower Salopian horizons of Britain, and again many forms are common to the two countries; certain species of *Monograptus,* however, as well as the retiolitid *Stomagraptus* are not recorded from the British deposits. The next zone is marked by *M. colonus* associated with *M. bohemicus, M. nilssoni,* and *M. roemeri,* all familiar species in the Upper Salopian Beds of Great Britain. At about this level calcareous intercalations appear in the shales and become more numerous in higher beds where they pass up into thick-bedded limestones. Graptolites are not common in these calcareous beds, but are sometimes associated with the prevalent trilobites and other shelly fossils. In places the limestones are composed essentially of reef-corals, and then graptolites are rarely present. They have, however, been found at three horizons in the higher limestones marked successively by *M. transgrediens, M. ultimus,* and *M. hercynius* Perner. These forms, presumably of Upper Ludlow age, are not known in Britain, and the horizon of the last-named species may even be equivalent to the Downton Sandstone of Shropshire.

Several localities in the eastern Alps have yielded similar graptolite faunas, and the succession has been reviewed by F. Heritsch (1934). Lower Valentian forms have been found by G. Aiger (1930, 1931) at Fieberbrunn, Tyrol, in metamorphosed rocks of the so-called 'grauwacke zone' which follows the southern margin of the northern Calcareous Alps. Heritsch (1931) states that similar rocks near Eisenerz, Styria, enclose Valentian species ranging from the gregarius to the griestonensis zones, and other forms indicate the presence of the Salopian nilssoni zone. The record by F. Heritsch and A. Thurner (1932) of *Rastrites* and *Monograptus* from the neighbourhood of Graz together with the foregoing zones, suggests that Silurian graptolitic deposits may have a wide extension in the Palaeozoic region of the eastern Alps. Since G. Stache (1872) first recorded graptolites from the Carnic Alps, important Valentian and Salopian assemblages have been discovered by M. Cortani (1927) and E. Habnerfelner (1931). Most of the species, like *M. vomerinus, Cyrtograptus murchisoni,* and *C. carruthersi,* are identical with British forms, but the Bohemian *Stomatograptus* is present along with *M. sardous, M. tariccoi* Gortani, and *M. hemipristis* Meneghini which were first described from Sardinia. This island has provided well-preserved graptolites, first described by G. Meneghini (1857) and later by

M. Gortani (1922), which represent the Birkhill and Lower Salopian zones of Britain, but apparently no forms of the Gala Beds. The graptolites of the lower zones are species that are widely distributed in Palaeosilurian strata throughout Europe, but many in the higher zones are forms peculiar to the southern part of the continent. Some of these along with cosmopolitan species are recorded by F. Boncev (1931) from Lower Salopian horizons in Bulgaria, though Silurian deposits do not seem to be recorded from Yugoslavia, Albania, and Greece. Again, some of them range westward to the vicinity of Barcelona (Heritsch, 1934) and the district of Villarinho de Cima in Portugal (N. J. F. Delgado, 1908). As in Sardinia they are typical of late Valentian and early Salopian horizons, and they do not appear in the older zones of central and northern Spain. Later Salopian faunas again are similar throughout Europe; no special southern forms have been detected.

Silurian graptolites are also reported from several districts in North Africa. P. Russo (1922) gives a list which indicates the presence of several Valentian and early Salopian zones in Morocco, and these are extended to the Djebilet and High Atlas by E. Roch (1932). J. H. Sinclair (1928) reports the discovery of the riccartonensis zone in French Guinea, and C. Kilian (1933) records late Valentian species from the central Sahara. Many of these forms have a wide geographical distribution in north-west Europe and their presence in North Africa indicates easy marine communications between the Silurian seas of the two regions.

The Silurian shelly limestones of Bohemia contain a great variety of trilobites, cephalopods, brachiopods, and corals, along with representatives of other groups. The trilobites number over 400 species, which J. Barrande (1871) distributed in a score of genera, and very few of the species are recorded from Scandinavia and Britain. The Illaenidae, with fifteen species in Ordovician strata, are represented at Silurian horizons only by two local species of *Bumastus* which differ from the British and Scandinavian forms. Barrande named eight species of *Goldius* (= *Bronteus*) which foreshadow the unsurpassed development of the genus in the succeeding system. The twenty Silurian species of *Odontopleura* (formerly cited as *Acidaspis*) recorded by Barrande may be regarded as forming a typical Bohemian group, for P. Lake (1896) states that only two of them are related to the nine British and six Swedish species then known. The isolated family Harpidae, briefly reviewed by H. B. Whittington (1950), is strangely discontinuous in distribution. After the Palaeordovician *Eoharpes* there are no records until the six Neosilurian forms grouped under the comprehensive genus *Harpes* which persists into Devonian horizons; in contrast, no harpids are recorded from British Mesosilurian and Neosilurian rocks. The Otarionidae are represented in Bohemia by species of *Otarion* and the rare genus *Aulacopleura*; the former has species in the Wenlock Limestone of Britain, and J. E. Marr (1913) has compared a specimen of *Aulacopleura* (under its former name *Arethusina*) from the murchisoni zone of the English Lake District with

A. haueri described by F. Frech (1899) from the Carnic Alps. The allied Proetidae have about the same representation, but expand enormously in numbers at Devonian horizons. *Calymene* has declined to four species. Among proparian forms *Cheirurus* is prominent in local species along with *Ch. insignis* which is close to the British *Ch. bimucronatus*. More specialized forms of the Cheiruridae include *Sphaerexochus mirus* and *Deiphon forbesi* which are both widespread in the Silurian rocks of north-western Europe. *Encrinurus* is apparently a Silurian immigrant in Bohemia, for the family does not seem to be represented in older beds. *Phacops* also appears in Bohemia with four Silurian species and expands fourfold in the succeeding system; only a local species of *Dalmanites* is listed, and its usual English associate, *Homalonotus*, seems to be absent from the Bohemian assemblage. The Silurian trilobites of Bohemia, therefore, are markedly different from those of north Europe, for the two regions have only about four species in common, and few of the others are closely related. On the other hand the Silurian forms of south Europe, e.g. Spain, Portugal, Sardinia, are closely related to those of Bohemia. The eurypterid assemblage of the Bohemian rocks is reviewed by F. Prantl and A. Pribyl (1948); the fragmentary and waterworn remains are probably derived from non-marine habitats, and have been transported by streams to the area of marine deposition.

The Silurian brachiopods of Bohemia show the same general development as those of north-west Europe. Following the great expansion of Orthidae in Ordovician strata this family is well represented in Bohemian Silurian rocks, and though the majority of Barrande's species differ, some are identical with British and Scandinavian forms, e.g. *Dalmenella elegantula, Orthis lunata.* Some familar British strophomenids, as for instance *Leptaena rhomboidalis, Strophonella euglypha, St. pecten* are also listed from Bohemia among species of more local significance. Certain small brachiopods referred by O. T. Jones (1928) to the genera *Sowerbyella* and *Leptoidella* were formerly ascribed to *Leptaena* and later to *Plectambonites*; such species as *S. duplicata* and *S. transversalis* are present at Mesosilurian horizons in north-west Europe, and as Barrande (1879) cites '*Leptaena*' *transversalis* from Bohemia it seems that the genus ranged into central Europe. The distinctive pentamerids are well developed in Bohemia whence Barrande described about thirty-five Silurian species of which *Gypidula galeata* and *Clorinda undata* (= *P. linguifer*) appear in British and Scandinavian records. A. Pribyl (1943) has reviewed the five Bohemian species of *Conchidium* which include the common British form *C. knightii* (J. Sow.). The rhynchonellids include several species which, like *Camarotoechia tarda* and *C. famula*, seem to be restricted to the Bohemian facies, but also *Rhynchotreta cuneata, Camarotoechia deflexa*, and *Wilsonia wilsoni* which are northern species. Some of the spire-bearing forms also have a wide distribution, as for instance *Atrypa reticularis, Meristina tumida, Delthyris sulcatus, Cyrtia exporrecta*, which afford obvious links with north-west

European faunas. Others, like *Septatrypa megaera* (formerly ascribed to *Rhynchonella* auctt.), *S. sapho*, *S. zelia*, are distinctive members of the Bohemian assemblage, and restricted to southern Europe.

The Bohemian shelly fauna is also famous for the large number of nautiloid species named by Barrande (1877). They are referred to such genera as *Ascoceras*, *Cyrtoceras*, *Gomphoceras*, *Ophidioceras*, *Orthoceras*, and *Trochoceras* and are evidently in need of critical revision. Some of the limestones have yielded reef-corals among which some widespread species of the tabulate genera *Favosites* and *Halysites* are prominent.

We have noted above that the Silurian deposits of the Austrian Alps, as described by F. Heritsch (1934), are of graptolite facies. To the south-west the same author (1929) has described a shelly facies in the Carnic Alps which is closely similar to that of Bohemia. Silurian rocks in the Caucasus, described by M. Yanishewski (1918), also contain a shelly fauna of Bohemian type; the connexion can only have been by way of the Balkans and Alpine area, for the contemporary Podolian faunas are of northern type. L. S. Librovitch (1930) and B. Averianow (1931) have described graptolites from the south Urals which correlate with those of Upper Valentian and Lower Ludlow zones in Britain. At the northern end of the Urals M. Yermolaev (1937) has described a considerable succession on Novaya Zemlya. Graptolite assemblages indicate the presence of certain Valentian zones separated by thick beds of sandstone. Neosilurian horizons are proved by the presence of such brachiopods as *Chonetes striatella*, *Camarotoechia nucula*, *Crispella crispa*, and *Conchidium knighti*. The tabulate reef-corals *Favosites gothlandicus*, *Halysites catenularis*, *Heliolites interstinctus*, &c., are recorded by W. A. Obrutschev (1926) from various localities in Siberia, for example, Tunguska (64° N., 100° E.), Olenek (73° N., 120° E), Kotelny (75° N., 136° E.). Some of these corals are known from eastern Turkestan (*c.* 40° N.), and from the same region B. Averianoiv (1929) has produced evidence of graptolite faunas which correspond to certain Valentian and Salopian assemblages in Britain.

Silurian deposits are known from the mountainous region of northern India. In south-east Kashmir F. R. C. Reed (1912) has described a small, poorly preserved fauna of trilobites and brachiopods, among which the forms identified as *Acidaspis kashmirica*, *Encrinurus* cf. *punctatus*, *Leptaena rhomboidalis*, *Sowerbyella transversalis*, may be taken to indicate a high Palaeosilurian horizon. Among a collection of corals and brachiopods described by F. R. C. Reed (1912) from Spiti in the central Himalayas are *Stropheodonta compressa* and a group of weathered shells referred to *Pentamerus oblongus* (recte *laevis*); both species are restricted to Palaeosilurian horizons in Britain. Records by F. R. C. Reed (1906, 1915, 1936) from the Shan States of Burma are more definite. The earliest well-defined Silurian fauna here contains graptolites characteristic of the Palaeosilurian zones of *Orthograptus vesiculosus* and *Monograptus gregarius*; at a higher horizon the

Mesosilurian species *M. riccartonensis* is recorded. There are also forms of *Acidaspis, Dalmanites*, and brachiopods which show relations with certain Llandovery species in Britain. It is evident from these scanty records that the Silurian system in the Himalayan region is far from complete, despite the claim of D. N. Wadia (1939) and previous authors that the region 'has a continuous Palaeozoic record'.

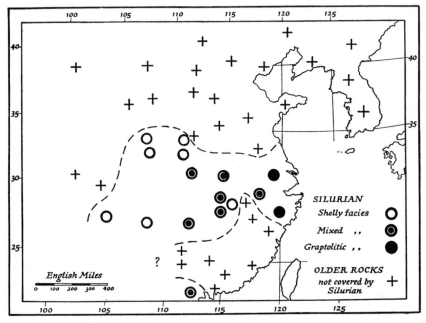

FIG. 38. SKETCH-MAP OF CHINA SHOWING GENERAL DISTRIBUTION OF
SILURIAN ROCKS

   F. R. C. Reed (1917) has also described two assemblages of Silurian graptolites from south-west Yunnan. The earlier fauna contains abundant climacograptids especially *Climacograptus rectangularis*, with occasional specimens of *Mesograptus modestus*, and is referred to the zone of *Orthograptus vesiculosus*. The later fauna has an abundance of *M. lobiferus*, associated with *M. sedgwicki* and other species which are characteristic of the zone of *M. sedgwicki* in Britain. J. S. Lee (1939) says that these Palaeosilurian rocks are unconformable on Mesordovician horizons in Yunnan and north-west Hupeh, where clastic rocks and limestones follow the graptolite-bearing shales (Map, Fig. 38). In the Tsinling Range similar deposits transgress on to the Precambrian foundation. To the south-east through Hupeh, north-west Kiangsi, Hunan, and south Anhui is an area of mixed deposits, a lower series of shales yielding graptolites typical of various Palaeosilurian horizons, higher strata having a shelly fauna mainly of trilobites and brachiopods. Only in the Nanking Hills and south-west Chekiang is the succession purely graptolitic, several Valentian zones being spread out through a thickness of 1,200 metres consisting mainly of shales. Some of the graptolites are local species, but others are familiar forms in the Valentian strata of Britain. No Meso- or Neosilurian rocks are known in China except in Yunnan; moreover, in the whole of northern China, that is north of the Tsinling range, Ordovician strata are overlaid comformably by sediments of Carboniferous age, and Lee (1939) suggests that probably no deposits were accumulated in Silurian time throughout that area. The early Silurian sea of south China therefore had no direct connexion with the Siberian transgressive waters, but a direct passage can be traced from the Indian Ocean near Moulmein by the graptolitic deposits of the Shan States and Yunnan north-eastwards to those of the Nanking area, which indicate an outlet to the Pacific Ocean.

In AUSTRALIA outcrops of Silurian rocks are almost restricted to the east of the continent, the States of Tasmania, Victoria, and New South Wales; thence they perhaps extend under the Mesozoic cover of Queensland to the small outcrops in the north of that State. Certain conglomerates in the Macdonnell range of central Australia though tentatively regarded as Silurian are excluded from our discussion because they are barren of fossils.

The earliest Silurian graptolites so far recorded from Australia are contained in an assemblage described by R. A. Keble (1925) from Loyola, Victoria. This includes *Monograptus leptotheca*, *M. mccoyi*, *M.* cf. *cutellus* and *M.* cf. *proteus*, the first-named being characteristic of the M. argenteus zone of Britain. T. W. E. David (1932) cites the Lower Valentian species *M. convolutus*, from the Walhalla district, and higher beds at Keilor Park, Melbourne have yielded *M. turriculatus* and *M. exiguus*. The early Salopian species *M. riccartonensis*, *M. priodon*, and *Retiolites australis* are recorded from the same locality. At Studley Park, Melbourne, O. A. Jones (1927) states that the highest beds include a thin band of mudstone containing the late Salopian forms *M. nilssoni*, *M. colonus*, *M. roemeri*, *M. chimaera*, all characteristic of the nilssoni zone of north-west Europe. A similar succession is recorded from New South Wales, and the Australian sequence, so far as it is known, is in accord with the standard succession in Britain.

While the Silurian graptolite faunas in Victoria and New South Wales, in the words of David and Brown (1950) 'appear to have fought a losing fight against uncongenial environment', the shelly faunas show great variety and abundance in the 300 genera so far recognized, and the Australian trilobites attained the acme of their development in Silurian strata. Most of the genera reviewed by R. Etheridge, jun. and J. Mitchell (1892–1917) are typical elsewhere, but the species are nearly all restricted to the Australian region though often showing relationship with European forms. The odontopleurid species, for instance, are said to be near certain Bohemian species described by Barrande. Five local species of *Goldius* again are comparable with Bohemian forms, as are species of *Otarion, Proetus, Lichas*, and *Harpes*. The typical *Calymene australis* was formerly cited as *C. blumenbachi*, and the encrinurids are now separated from *E. punctatus* with which they were at one time identified. The species of *Cheirurus* differ from the typical *Ch. insignis*, but *Sphaerexochus mirus* is still identified with European examples. The five species of *Phacops* and two of *Dalmanites* also differ in specific details from exotic forms. A fragment of a merostome referred to *Pterygotus australis* is stated by F. M'Coy (1899) to resemble the common Scottish form *Erettopterus bilobus*. The brachiopods include some cosmopolitan forms like *Dalmanella elegantula, Leptaena rhomboidalis, Rhynchotreta borealis, Atrypa reticularis, Eospirifer plicatellus, Delthyris sulcatus*, all known from Silurian strata in Europe. The distinctive pentamerids include *Pentamerus australis* which R. Etheridge, jun. (1892) regards as a representative of the European *P. oblongus* (recte *laevis*), a variety of *Clorinda linguifer*, and *Conchidium knighti*. This resemblance to European faunas is enhanced by the tabulate reef-corals which are abundantly preserved in the Silurian limestones of Victoria, New South Wales, and Queensland. A review by O. A. Jones (1937) of the massive species of *Favosites* shows the presence of the ubiquitous *F. gothlandicus* among a number of local species. The Heliolitidae are represented by three genera reviewed by O. A. Jones and D. Hill (1940); the widespread species include such forms as *Heliolites daintreei, H. interstinctus, Plasmopora heliolitoides, Propora conferta*. It is evident, therefore, that the Silurian faunas of Australia bear considerable relationship with those of Asia and Europe.

In NORTH AMERICA Silurian rocks are widely distributed around the margin of the Canadian Shield (Map, Fig. 39). A considerable development in Newfoundland, the Gaspé Peninsula, Anticosti Island, and Nova Scotia may be related with outcrops in Maine, eastern New York, New Jersey, Pennsylvania, and Maryland. The system also has an extensive development around the Great Lakes in Ontario, northern Illinois, Wisconsin, and Iowa. In more northerly latitudes Silurian strata occupy a large area on the south-west coast of Hudson Bay, and also around Lakes Winnipeg and Winnipegosis in Manitoba and Saskatchewan; a few limited outcrops in the Cordilleran region have yielded Silurian fossils. These strata are related to others around Great Bear Lake, the Mackenzie Valley, and southern Alaska, also to the extensive development of the system in the Arctic Archipelago, extending from Atpatok Island in Ungava Bay to Ellesmereland and northern Greenland. The subdivisions of the Silurian system in North America are named from typical localities, chiefly in the state of New York and the province of Ontario; they are tabulated on p. 226 along with the corresponding units in Great Britain.

Owing to the great development of arenaceous and calcareous rocks graptolites are not generally abundant in the Silurian deposits of North America. The combined evidence from graptolite shales at several notable

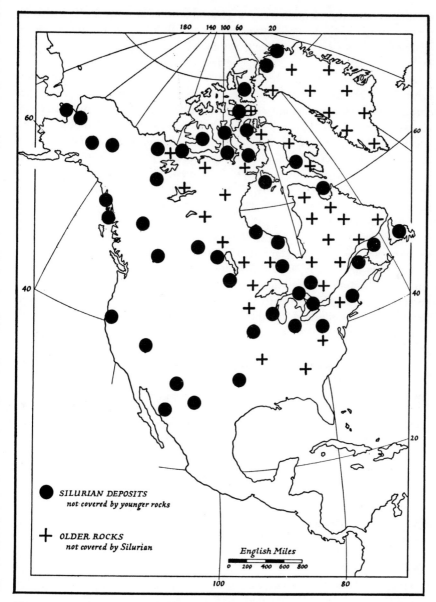

FIG. 39. SKETCH-MAP OF NORTH AMERICA SHOWING GENERAL DISTRIBUTION
OF SILURIAN ROCKS

localities, however, demonstrates a general similarity with the British succession, and further exploration may yet fill in some of the apparent lacunae. The earliest graptolite assemblage so far recorded seems to be that from the upper part of the Medina Series (Blaylock Sandstone) of Arkansas. From this horizon, C. E. Decker (1936) describes *Dimorphograptus decussatus*, *Monograptus argutus*, *M. communis*, and *M. gregarius* which are characteristic of various zones in the Birkhill Shales of Scotland. Likewise an assemblage from Idaho listed by R. Ruedemann (1947) includes such species as *M. communis*, *M. convolutus*, *M. delicatulus*, *M. intermedius*, and *M. urceolus* which are typical of the gregarius and convolutus zones in Scotland. *M. convolutus* along with *M. leptotheca*, *M. lobiferus*, and *Rastrites peregrinus*, is also recorded by C. Poulsen (1934) from northern Greenland. The presence of slightly later zones is indicated by the record of *M. spiralis*, *M. pandus*, *M.* cf. *priodon*, and *Retiolites geinitzianus* from the North-West Territory; *M. clintonensis* which also occurs here and at numerous localities between Nova Scotia and Quebec is closely similar to early forms of *M. priodon*. At Arisaig, Nova Scotia, *M. clintonensis*, and a variety of *Retiolites geinitzianus* are associated in black shales which are correlated by F. H. McLearn with the Gala Beds of Scotland. The same two species are recorded together in equivalent beds of Anticosti by W. H. Twenhofel (1928), New York State by R. Ruedemann (1908), and more distant localities.

North America	Great Britain	
Cayuga	Upper Ludlow	Neosilurian
Guelph	Lower Ludlow	Mesosilurian
Niagara	Wenlock	
Clinton	Upper Llandovery	Palaeosilurian
Medina		
Lower Llandovery not represented in North America		

Graptolites of the Niagara Series are remarkable for the number of dendroid forms. An assemblage of about fifty species is listed by R. Ruedemann (1947) from the Lockport dolomite at Hamilton, Ontario. Some of the genera, such as *Inocaulis*, *Calyptograptus*, and *Cyclograptus* are apparently restricted to North America; others, like *Ptilograptus*, *Desmograptus*, *Acanthograptus*, *Thamnograptus* are known also from Europe; while a few have a wider distribution, e.g. *Dictyonema* which is recorded from all six continents. The wide distribution of the last genus may be due to an epiplanktonic mode of life (p. 33) like that of the true graptolites, in contrast to the habit of most dendroid forms which, according to O. M. B. Bulman (1938) and R. Ruedemann (1947) were probably attached to the sea floor. Some of the genera just mentioned are recorded also from New York and Indiana, in the latter case associated with *Monograptus bohemicus*. C. E. Decker (1936) also describes an assemblage from Oklahoma in which the dendroid genera *Ascograptus*, *Mastiograptus*, and *Thallograptus* are associated with *M. bohemicus*, *M. crinitus*, *M. dubius*, *M. nilssoni*, *M. scanicus*, *M. tumescens*, and *M. vulgaris*, species which are typical of late Salopian zones in Britain. The cited species comprise about half the Oklahoma fauna, and R. Ruedemann (1947) states that no other assemblage of this age is known in America. It is worthy of note, however, that another late Salopian graptolite is recorded by F. H. McLearn (1924), namely, *M. wandalensis* the type of which was described by G. R. Watney and E. G. Welch (1911) from the nilssoni zone of Wandale Hill in the English Lake District.

The general succession of graptolites in North America conforms closely with that of Britain despite the development of local species, which is probably explained sufficiently by the distance separating the two continents. The general distribution of the graptolite-bearing strata in North America seems to be significant, for they are arranged in three belts roughly parallel to the margin of the Canadian Shield but at some distance from it. The eastern belt extends from Newfoundland through the eastern States to Alabama, the southern belt through Arkansas, Oklahoma, and north Texas, and the western belt along the Rocky Mountains to Alaska. This conforms with the view of G. L. Elles (1939) that the graptolite shales represent offshore deposits; in this case, they enclose the shallow-water limestones and sandstones which transgress the margin of the shield, and to which the sessile dendroids are largely restricted.

The shelly Silurian faunas of North America are contained in the shallow-water sandstones and limestones which occupy large areas in the eastern and central parts of the continent on the margin of the Canadian Shield. The trilobites belong mainly to genera which are prevalent in contemporary deposits of other continents, and several of the genera are already established at Ordovician horizons. The illaenid *Bumastus* is widely distributed in Mesordovician rocks of eastern and central North America, and other species are equally widespread in the Niagara Series of the Silurian system; the fifteen species in North America are in contrast with the three or four species in Great Britain and the two in Bohemia. *Goldius* (olim *Bronteus*) on the other hand is rare in North America, though common in European deposits of the same age. *Calymene* has widespread representation in North America, especially by *C. niagarensis*, but the species differ from most European forms; the homalonotid genus *Trimerus*, based on an American type, is also recorded from strata of Wenlock age in Britain. The North American species of *Otarion* again are restricted to that continent, and *O. christyi* is cited as diagnostic of the Niagara Series in Tennessee and Indiana. According to A. F. Foerste (1920) the number of lichid genera common to America and Europe increases in Silurian strata; they include the Bohemian genera *Dicranopeltis* and *Trochurus* which first appear in America in the St. Clair Limestone of Arkansas, giving rise to the view that they migrated to the western hemisphere by a southerly route, presumably the equatorial current. *Arctinurus*, a strictly American genus, appears at the same horizon. These genera later spread over eastern and central North America as far north as Ontario. F. B. Phleger (1936) says that the greatest evolution of this family took place in northern Europe. The family Odontopleuridae is represented by several species of the type-genus in the Niagara Series of Arkansas, Illinois, and Canada but the species differ from the European forms; the type of *Ceratocephala* is *C. goniata* from the Niagara Series of Wisconsin, Illinois, and Quebec, and the genus includes some Bohemian species. Several species of *Encrinurus*, including the old-established *E. ornatus*, are widespread through the eastern and central States, but all differ from European forms. Likewise the Cheiruriadae pursue a development similar to that in Europe; *Ch. niagarensis* and *Ch. welleri* are diagnostic species of the typical genus, while the specialized *Sphaerexochus romingeri* and *Deiphon americanus* are widespread in the Niagara Series. In a review of the Phacopidae D. M. Delo (1935) believes that the Ordovician genera of the family disappear completely in North America at the close of that period. He derives the Silurian *Dalmanites* of North America from European Ordovician forms and illustrates the markedly divergent evolution of the group during Silurian time. *Phacops* and its close allies are more conservative in North America, thus contrasting sharply with the distinctive radial divergence among the European genera.

The Silurian eurypterids of North America are best known from the Neosilurian Bertie Waterlime of New York State, but there are noteworthy assemblages in earlier strata. Indeed, the eurypterids seem to have had a longer history in North America than in Europe. J. M. Clarke and R. Ruedemann (1912) describe eurypterid remains from Ordovician strata as early as the Normanskill Shales; carapaces are referred to species of *Eurypterus, Eusarcus, Dolichopterus, Stylonurus, Pterygotus*, and their associates are graptolites and seaweeds. The Neordovician Schenectady Shale yields other species of the same genera and *Hughmilleria* associated with graptolites. Occasional remains of eurypterids are recorded from Palaeosilurian rocks at several localities, but they are usually fragments though they are accompanied by well-preserved marine fossils. In contrast, distinctive species of *Dolichopterus, Eurypterus, Eusarcus, Hughmilleria, Stylonurus,* and *Pterygotus* are commonly well preserved in shale-bands interbedded with the Shawangunk conglomerate of eastern New York; but other fossils, except *Ceratiocaris*, are absent. At a slightly higher horizon, the Pittsford Shale of New York has a comparable assemblage of different species, again associated only with crustaceans; marine fossils, including cephalopods and *Lingula*, are recorded from dolomite partings but not from the black shale with eurypterids. The Neosilurian Bertie Waterlime at the eastern end of Lake Erie has yielded a famous eurypterid fauna only comparable with that of the Baltic island of Oesel. Characteristic species of *Dolichopterus, Eurypterus, Eusarcus*, and *Pterygotus* are sometimes associated with dendroid graptolites, cephalopods, pulmonate gastropods, crustaceans, and *Lingula*. Similar eurypterids, but of local species, are recorded from Kokomo, Indiana, along with ceratiocarids; brachiopods are reported from limestones at a slightly higher level. The habitat of these eurypterid assemblages has been studied by M. O'Connell (1916) who concludes, (1) that well-preserved eurypterids are not typically associated with marine fossils, (2) that eurypterids which are associated with a well-preserved marine fauna are usually represented by fragments bearing signs of transportation, (3) that all known eurypterids are freshwater organisms which lived in rivers through their entire phylogenetic history. This extreme view is challenged by R. Ruedemann (1924) who stresses the association, in the Bertie Waterlime and certain other deposits, of eurypterids with dendroid graptolites, cephalopods, and other marine fossils in such an intimate manner that they all appear as members of a homogeneous fauna. He says, the assumption that the eurypterids flourished as euryhaline forms in shore lagoons or pools still accounts best for the peculiarities both of their distribution and of the strata in which they are found. L. Størmer (1934) agrees that the eurypterids never became a permanent element in marine faunas, and believes they were euryhaline forms adapted to live in lagoons of rather variable salinity, often behind coral-reefs.

The close similarity of North American and European brachiopods in the Silurian system is shown by the old records of such species as *Atrypa reticularis, Dalmanella elegantula, Plectambonites transversalis*, &c., in both regions. In most cases this is due to loose identification, and now that the interpretation of genera and species is more narrowly defined comparatively few of them are found to be common to both continents. Some genera already established at Ordovician horizons persist in Silurian strata, but in other cases the Silurian species possess distinctive features which justify their classification in separate genera. For instance, C. Schuchert and G. A. Cooper (1932) restrict the orthid genus *Dalmanella* to Ordovician species allied to the North American type *D. testudinaria* Hall and Clarke, while the familiar Silurian species identified with *D. elegantula* (Dalman) are now referred to the genus *Parmorthis* on account of the unusual crenulated teeth and sockets, and other internal features; the American species are regarded as distinct from the European ones. Another orthid, *Rhipidomella hybrida* (J. Sow.), a typical Wenlock fossil in Great Britain, is cited by Cooper (in H. W. Shimer and R. R. Shrock, 1944) from mid-Silurian rocks in New York, Ohio, Indiana, Wisconsin, Illinois, and Tennessee. The strophomenids include *Leptaena rhomboidalis* which is notorious for its long range and wide distribution; originally described from North Europe, it is said to be widespread throughout the Silurian rocks of North America. The group of smaller strophomenids formerly referred to *Plectambonites* is distributed by O. T. Jones (1928) in a number of genera, including *Sowerbyella*; the British species *S. sladensis* and a form near *S. undulata* are recorded on the island of Anticosti at horizons corresponding to Llandovery strata in Britain. The North European group of *S. transversalis*, afterwards transferred by R. Kozloswki (1929) to the separate genus *Plectodonta*, is cited from the Niagara series of New York, Indiana, Kentucky, and Alabama. Most of the American pentamerid species, and some of the genera, are restricted to that continent, but a few are more widespread. *Pentamerus oblongus* J. Sow., a typical species of the British Llandovery Series, is listed by Cooper (1944) from the Niagara Series of Canada, New York, Appalachians, and Alaska. The ribbed pentamerid *Conchidium knighti*, first described from English Neosilurian rocks, is cited also from Alaska, and other species of *Conchidium* are reported from eastern and central United States and Canada. *Stricklandia* and *Gypidula*, based on North American types are well represented in Silurian rocks of North Europe, while the European *Clorinda* and the American *Barrandella* are smooth forms separated by differences in internal structure. The rhynchonellid *Camarotoechia*, though typified by an American Devonian shell, and widespread in Silurian rocks of that continent, is widely represented in Europe by *C. borealis*. The genus *Rhynchotreta* established by J. Hall (1879) for the widespread European fossil *R. cuneata* (Dalman) is represented in all Silurian outcrops of North America by distinct species. Among the spire-bearing brachiopods, the type of *Atrypa reticularis* is a European Silurian species, but the name is loosely used for many unrecognized forms which answer to the generic definition; such shells are known from many Silurian and Devonian horizons in Europe and North America, and indeed are practically world-wide in those systems. Early spiriferids are also widespread in Silurian strata throughout North America. They include the typical British form *Eospirifer radiatus* (J. Sow.), which is recorded throughout eastern and central United States and Canada associated with purely American species. *Cyrtia exporrecta* (Wahl.), originally named in Scandinavia, is similar in distribution to the *Eospirifer* from which it differs chiefly in its exaggerated umbonal features. The coarsely costate *Delthyris sulcata* and *Crispella crispa* also range from north Europe to eastern North America.

The succession of coralliferous deposits in the Silurian rocks of North America has many points of resemblance with that of Britain. The alternation of clastic and calcareous rocks in the Medina and Clinton stages of New York and Ontario is roughly equivalent to the British Llandovery Series, and like the latter it contains few corals. These belong chiefly to the tabulate genera *Favosites* and *Syringopora*, along with the rugose *Streptelasma*. From

Anticosti Island W. H. Twenhofel (1928) has described small reefs mainly formed by species of *Favosites, Halysites, Propora* (usually recorded by American authors as *Lyellia*), and the stromatoporoid *Clathrodictyon*. The same fossils recorded by F. J. Alcock (1935) from the neighbourhood of Chaleur Bay are apparently drifted fragments, and corals are practically absent from the clastic deposits of Arisaig, Nova Scotia, described by F. H. McLearn (1924).

In the Niagara Series, the Lockport Dolomite, like its British counterpart the Wenlock Limestone, is largely composed of reef-corals and reef-detritus. The famous sections of Manitoulin Island, described by M. Y. Williams (1919) are specially remarkable for the variety and abundance of corals. The clastic rocks of Arisaig have only a few corals in the peculiar association of brachiopods and bivalved mollusca which F. H. McLearn (1924) interprets as adapted for life on a muddy sea floor. But the Lockport stage has a wide extension northwards and westwards; it is recognized along the western shore of James and Hudson Bays (C. Schuchert, 1908) resting unconformably on the Precambrian foundation, it is extensively developed in the Lake region of Manitoba (E. M. Kindle, 1914), and J. A. Allan records Halysites Beds at a number of limited areas in the Cordilleran region. Coral reefs containing *Favosites gotlandicus, Heliolites interstinctus,* and *Halysites catenularis* are described by D. D. Cairnes (1914) from the boundary of Yukon and Alaska near the latitude of the Arctic Circle. The same corals have been recorded from Southampton Island in Hudson Strait by C. Schuchert (1914), and others from Melville Island and other localities in the Arctic Archipelago by W. D. Lang (1926). In the United States a great development of coral-reefs in the Niagara Series extends from New York to Iowa; those of Indiana and adjacent States are well described by E. R. Cumings and R. R. Shrock (1928). At various places in this extensive area the stromatoporoids *Clathrodictyon, Stromatopora,* and *Actinostoma* form important reef-structures, while the tabulate corals *Favosites, Alveolites, Syringopora, Halysites,* and the Heliolitids are ubiquitous, including such cosmopolitan species as *Favosites gotlandicus, Halysites catenularis,* and *Heliolites interstinctus*. In view of this similarity with European faunas it is surprising that the records of rugose corals show considerable differences. This may be due in part to nomenclatural confusion, for it is evident from the index of genera compiled by W. D. Lang, S. Smith, and W. D. Thomas (1940) that most lists of Silurian rugose corals are in need of critical revision. It seems certain, however, that some genera, such as *Arachniophyllum* (sometimes confused with *Strombodes*), *Acervularia* (which apparently includes *Diplophyllum*), and *Ptychophyllum* are present on both sides of the Atlantic Ocean, but others, *Syringolites* and *Striatopora* for example, based on American types, seem to be absent from European faunas. It is probable that some differences in the records will disappear when further research has been carried out. For example, S. Smith (1930) reports the presence of

Calostylis in material from the Niagara Series of Ohio and Kentucky. Smith also states (in W. D. Lang, 1926) that many of the Silurian corals of Arctic America show closer relations to European species than to those from more southerly American regions. Thus the genus *Naos* of W. D. Lang (1926) from the Niagara Series of Melville Island is related to *Ptychophyllum* and *Chonophyllum* both of which are known in European strata, the type species of the latter being a common form in Gotland. According to available records the distribution of some forms is markedly discontinuous; S. Weller (1898) cites *Goniophyllum* from the Mesosilurian rocks of England, Gotland, and Iowa, and several crinoids (including *Petalocrinus*) show similar distribution, all these forms being unknown from the well-searched outcrops in eastern North America. Weller therefore suggests an Arctic migratory route, but A. G. Foerste (1929) states that 'recent investigations fail to find characteristic Racine or Gotland faunas in any part of the American Arctic region'. He also expresses the view that the Middle and Upper Silurian of that region is typically American and does not show marked affinities with the European Silurian. This appears to be in direct opposition to the opinion of Smith and Lang (1926), and the discrepancy emphasizes the need for further investigation of the Silurian faunas in the Arctic region.

A few reef-corals are recorded from the Guelph stage of New York and Ontario which is equivalent to the Lower Ludlow Beds of England. The corals comprise species of *Favosites*, *Halysites*, and *Pycnostylus*, the latter according to D. Hill (1937) probably representing the European *Tryplasma*. The stromatoporoids *Labechia*, *Clathrodictyon*, and *Stromatopora* also contribute to the reef-structures. The Guelph formation as such seems to be less widely distributed than the Lockport stage. The Racine Beds of Wisconsin and Illinois may, however, be equivalent to it, and species of *Pycnostylus* reported from James Bay and Lake Manitoba may indicate a wider extension than is known at present. The overlying Cayuga Series, including the peculiar gypsum-bearing Salina Beds, and the Bertie Waterlime with its eurypterid fauna represents special conditions of sedimentation in which corals have no place. On the whole it may be said that apart from a few special features of local significance, the succession of Silurian corals in North America is much the same as in Europe.

In SOUTH AMERICA Silurian faunas are reported from the lower part of the Amazon Valley, and from isolated localities in the Andean ranges of Peru, Bolivia, and Argentina. In the Amazon Valley the Silurian rocks rest directly on the Precambrian foundation of the Brazilian Shield. They consist of sandstones and shales which have yielded local species related to North American forms, together with *Climacograptus innotatus* var. *brasiliensis* which is closely similar to the type-species in the lowest zone of the Birkhill Shales in Scotland. Though another variety of the species is recorded from Idaho, R. Ruedemann (1947) believes that the presence of this graptolite indicates an open sea between Brazil and Britain, that is, the existence of the Atlantic Ocean, in Palaeosilurian time. *Monograptus priodon* is recorded from Argentina, along with *Pristiograptus frequens* which Ruedemann places in synonym with *M. tumescens*.

In 1910 F. R. C. Reed briefly summarized the views of older authors on the Silurian faunas preserved in the several continents. He remarked on the uniform character of the faunas from Europe through Asia to Australia, though local elements are developed from place to place, but his reference to 'American types' shows that some differentiation was recognized in that region. During the last forty years new discoveries have been made and many groups of fossils have been revised; it is now evident that the faunas of the Silurian seas that transgressed the margins of the eastern and western continents have few species, though many genera, in common. Greatest similarity is shown by the graptolites which, according to the view of R. Ruedemann (1934), were dispersed from 'Sargasso Seas' in the Atlantic and Pacific Oceans. The northerly extent of coral-reefs indicates an ice-free polar region which would facilitate migration and so promote a certain uniformity in the circumpolar shelly faunas of Eurasia and North America. Differentiation of certain American genera, however, is sufficient to imply some autochthonous development from Ordovician genera. It seems clear that the epicontinental seas of the western hemisphere were separated from those of the eastern hemisphere by a considerable distance presumably occupied by wide oceans corresponding to the Atlantic and Pacific Oceans of today.

LITERATURE

The general stratigraphy and palaeontology of British Silurian rocks are summarized in the following works, which contain numerous references to other literature. 'The Valentian Series', by O. T. Jones, *Q.J.G.S.*, vol. lxxvii, pp. 144–74, 1921, gives a general account of the graptolitic facies of the lowest Silurian series, its classification and correlation with the shelly Llandovery rocks. Higher strata are discussed in 'The Zonal Classification of the Wenlock Shales of the Welsh Borderland', by G. L. Elles, ibid., vol. lvi, pp. 370–414, 1900; 'The Aymestry Limestone of the Main Outcrop', by F. E. S. Alexander, ibid., vol. xcii, pp. 103–15, 1936; 'The Stratigraphy of the Wenlock Limestone of Dudley', ibid., vol. xcv, pp. 37–74, 1939. 'The Highest Silurian Rocks of the Ludlow District', by G. L. Elles and I. L. Slater, ibid., vol. lxii, pp. 195–222, 1906. An interesting ecological study is provided by 'The Conditions of Deposition of the Stockdale Shales of the Lake District', by J. E. Marr, ibid., vol. lxxxi, pp. 113–26, 1925. A description of some reef-like structures in Silurian strata is contained in 'A Study of Ballstone and the Associated Beds in the Wenlock Limestone of Shropshire', by M. C. Crosfield and M. S. Johnston, *Proc. Geol. Assoc.*, vol. xxv, pp. 193–228; 1914. Extra-British strata are described in 'Gotlands Silurstratigrafi', by J. E. Hede, *Sver. geol. Undersöken. Årsb.* 1920, No. 7, pp. 1–100, 1921; 'Das Silur von Böhmen', by F. Heritsch, *Geol. Rundschau*, vol. xix, pp. 320–44, 1928; 'The Ordovician and Silurian of the Carnic Alps', by F. Heritsch, *Geol. Mag.*, vol. lxvi, pp. 121–28, 1929; 'The Silurian Arisaig Series of Arisaig, Nova Scotia', by F. H. McLearn, *Amer. Journ. Sci.*, ser. 4, vol. xlv, pp. 126–40, 1918; 'Silurian Fossils from Northern Newfoundland', by R. R. Shrock and W. H. Twenhofel, *Journ. Palaeont.*, vol. xiii, pp. 241–66, 1939; 'The Geology of Parts of Southern Norway', by O. Holtedahl et alia. *Proc. Geol. Assoc.*, vol. xlv, pp. 307–88, 1934.

The indispensable work of reference for students of the graptolitic facies is that already mentioned in connexion with Ordovician graptolite-faunas, namely, 'British Graptolites', by G. L. Elles and E. M. R. Wood, *Mon. Pal. Soc.*, 1901–18. Two later papers on British graptolite-faunas, by G. L. Elles (see p. 191) summarize the monograph from the evolutional and stratigraphical aspects: 'The Graptolite Faunas of the British Isles', *Proc. Geol. Assoc.*, vol. xxxiii, pp. 168–200, 1922; 'The Characteristic Assemblages of the Graptolite Zones of the British Isles', *Geol. Mag.*, vol. lxii, pp. 337–47, 1925. Other useful works include 'Graptolithina', by O. M. B. Bulman, *Handb. der Palaeozoologie*, Lf. 2 Bd. 2D, Berlin, 1938; 'The Graptolite Faunas of the Gothlandian in the Eastern Alps', by F. Heritsch, *Geol. Mag.*, vol. lxxi, pp. 268–75, 1934; 'Graptolites of North America', by R. Ruedemann, *Geol. Soc. Amer. Mem.* No. 19, 1947; 'Bibliographic Index of Bohemian Silurian Graptolites', by A. Přibyl, *Czechoslovakia, Státní Geol. Ústav Kníhovna*, s.v. xxii, 1948. 'Silurian Graptolites from . . . Melbourne, Australia', by O. A. Jones, *Geol. Mag.*, vol. lxiv, pp. 101–5, 1927.

Many fossils of the shelly faunas are illustrated in monographs dealing with the various animal groups and revision of the older work proceeds gradually.

The pioneer work on 'British Fossil Corals', by Milne-Edwards and Haime: Part v, Silurian Corals, *Mon. Pal. Soc.* 1854, has now been supplemented by such works as 'Revision of the Corals described by Lonsdale in Murchison's Silurian System', by W. D. Lang and S. Smith, *Q.J.G.S.*, vol. lxxxiii, pp. 448–91, 1927; 'Some Valentian Corals from Shropshire and Montgomeryshire', by S. Smith, ibid., vol. lxxxvi, pp. 291–330, 1930; *Index of Palaeozoic Coral Genera*, by W. D. Lang, S. Smith, and H. D. Thomas, Brit. Mus., London, 1940. Among extra-British papers are: 'Niagaran Coral Reefs of Indiana and Adjacent States', by E. R. Cumings and R. R. Shrock, *Bull. Geol. Soc. Amer.*, vol. xxxix, pp. 579–620, 1928; 'The Australian Massive Species of the Coral Genus Favosites', by O. A. Jones, *Rec. Austral. Mus.*, vol. xx, pp. 79–102, 1937; 'The Heliolitidae of Australia', by O. A. Jones and D. Hill, *Proc. Roy. Soc. Queensland*, vol. li, pp. 183–215, 1940; 'Silurian Reefs of Gotland', by A. Hadding, *Journ. Geol.*, vol. lviii, pp. 402–9, 1950.

Some of the echinoderms are described in 'British Silurian Cystidea', by E. Forbes, *Mem. Geol. Surv.*, vol. ii, part 2, 1848, and 'The Occurrence, Structure and Affinities of Echinocystis and Palaeodiscus', by H. L. Hawkins and S. M. Hampton, *Q.J.G.S.*, vol. lxxxiii, pp. 574–603, 1927.

The monographs on 'British Fossil Brachiopoda' (Silurian Brachiopods), 1866–71, Supplement 1882–4, by T. Davidson, *Mon. Pal. Soc.*, and 'The Ordovician and Silurian Brachiopoda of the Girvan District', by F. R. C. Reed, *Trans. Roy. Soc. Edin.*, vol. li, part 4, pp. 795–998, 1917, are in need of revision from the modern standpoint. Some genera have already been reviewed by J. K. St. Joseph in 'A Description of Eospirifer radiatus', *Geol. Mag.*, vol. lxxii, pp. 316–27, 1935; 'Critical Examination of Stricklandinia lirata', ibid., pp. 401–24, 1935; 'Camarotoechia borealis', ibid., vol. lxxiv, pp. 33–48, 1937, and 'Rhynchotreta cuneata', ibid., pp. 161–76, 1937; also by F. E. S. Alexander, in 'A Revision of the Genus Pentamerus', *Q.J.G.S.*, vol. ciii, pp. 143–61, 1948; 'Plectambonites and Some Allied Genera', by O. T. Jones, *Mem. Geol. Surv. Palaeont.*, vol. i, part 8, pp. 367–527, 1928; 'Les Brachiopods Gotlandiens de la Podolie Polonaise', by R. Kozlowski, *Palaeont. Polon.*, vol. i, 1929; 'Brachiopoda of the Suborders Orthoidea and Pentameroidea', by C. Schuchert and G. A. Cooper, *Mem. Peabody Mus. Nat. Hist.*, vol. iv, part 1, 1932; 'Pentameracea of the Oslo Region', by J. K. S. St. Joseph, *Norsk. geol. Tidskr.*, vol. xvii, pp. 225–336, 1938; 'Die Gattung Conchidium aus dem böhmischen Silur', by A. Přibyl, *Mitt. Tschech. Akad. Wiss.*, No. 13, 1943; 'A Revision of the Brachiopod Species *Anomia reticularis* Linnaeus, Genolectotype of *Atrypa* Dalman', by F. E. S. Alexander, *Q.J.G.S.*, vol. civ, pp. 207–20, 1949.

Descriptions of certain mollusca found in British Silurian rocks are contained in 'The British Ordovician and Silurian Bellerophontacea', by F. R. C. Reed, *Mon. Pal. Soc.*, 1920–1; 'The Genus Loxonema, with Descriptions of New Proterozoic Species', by J. Longstaff, *Q.J.G.S.*, vol. lxv, pp. 210–28, 1909; 'The Upper Valentian Gastropod Fauna of Shropshire', by B. L. Pitcher, *Ann. Mag. Nat. Hist.*, ser. 11, vol. iv, pp. 82–132, 1939; *British Fossil Cephalopoda*, by J. F. Blake: Part i, Introduction and Silurian Species, 4to, London, 1882, but the last monograph is incomplete.

'British Trilobites', by J. W. Salter, *Mem. Pal. Soc.*, 1864–83 contains descriptions of many species from the Silurian deposits of Wales and the English Midlands. The Scottish faunas have been described at some length by F. R. C. Reed in 'The Lower Palaeozoic Trilobites of the Girvan District', ibid., 1903–6, Supplement, ibid., 1914. 'Recent Work on the Phacopidae', by F. R. C. Reed, *Geol. Mag.*, vol. lxiv, pp. 308–22, 337–52, 1927, gives a critical summary of the views on classification, with references to literature. 'Notes on the Family Encrinuridae', by F. R. C. Reed, ibid., vol. lxv, pp. 51–77, 1928, summarizes previous publications and contains notes on British members of the family. 'A Revision of the Trilobite Genera *Deiphon* and *Oncycopyge*', *Ann. Mag. Nat. Hist.*, ser. 10, vol. xiv, pp. 505–33, 1934; and, 'The Upper Valentian Trilobite Fauna of Shropshire', ibid., ser. 11, vol. i, pp. 85–140, 1938, both by W. F. Whittard, and 'Some British Trilobites of the Family Calymenidae', by J. Shirley, *Q.J.G.S.*, vol. xcii, pp. 384–422, 1936, carry the process of revision still further. The following papers published outside Britain are also useful: 'The Silurian Trilobites of New South Wales', by R. Etheridge jun. and J. Mitchell, a series of papers in *Proc. Linn. Soc. N.S.W.*, vols. vi–xliii, 1892–1917; 'A Revision of the Phacopid Trilobites', by D. M. Delo, *Journ. Palaeont.*, vol. ix, pp. 402–20, 1935; 'Lichadian Trilobites', by F. B. Phleger, *Journ. Palaeont.*, vol. x, pp. 593–615, 1936; 'The Silurian Illaenids of the Oslo Region', by W. F. Whittard, *Norsk. geol. Tidschr.*, vol. xix, pp. 275–95, 1939.

Since the pioneer work on Eurypterida by J. W. Salter (1859) and F. Schmidt (1883) the following are notable papers which have extended our knowledge of the group: 'The Eurypterida of New York', by J. M. Clarke, and R. Ruedemann, *New York State Mus. Mem.* xiv, 1912; 'The Habitat of the Eurypterida', by M. O'Connell, *Bull. Buffalo Soc. Nat. Sci.*, vol. xi, no. 3, pp. 1–277, 1916; 'The Origin and Habitat of the Eurypterida', by R. Ruedemann, *Amer. Journ. Sci.* Ser. 5, vol. vii, pp. 227–32, 1924; 'Eurypterids in Graptolite Shales', by R. Ruedemann, ibid., vol. xxvii, pp. 374–85, 1934; 'Merostomata from the Downtonian Sandstone of Ringerike, Norway', by L. Størmer, *Skrift. Norske Videns. Akad. Oslo* (1933), No. 10, pp. 1–125, 1934; '*Mixopterus dolichoschelus*, A Downtonian Eurypterid from Scotland', by L. Størmer, *Summ. Prog. Geol. Surv. for 1934*, Part ii, pp. 41–47, 1936; 'Downtonian (Silurian) Eurypterids from Perton near Stoke Edith, Hereforshire', by E. N. Kjellesvig-Waring, *Geol. Mag.*, vol. lxxxviii, pp. 1–24, 1951.

VI

DEVONIAN FAUNAS

IN the Welsh Borderland a thick rock-series dominated by red sandstones succeeds the marine Silurian strata, and is overlaid by marine deposits of Lower Carboniferous age. This series was originally termed the Old Red Sandstone in order to distinguish it from another formation (the New Red Sandstone) which occurs above the Carboniferous strata. The Old Red Sandstone is a peculiar facies which has been interpreted in various ways. Some regard it as a terrestrial deposit, the material having been laid down in rivers or lakes, and possibly also by wind-transport. Others favour the view of estuarine origin, or of deposition in shallow coastal lagoons. While the precise mode of deposition is conjectural on the available evidence, it is significant that many exclusively marine animal groups are not known to occur in the Old Red Sandstone.

Contemporaneous marine rocks were later discovered in Cornwall and Devon and were classified as the Devonian system, whose limits are necessarily those previously fixed for the Old Red Sandstone. As J. W. Evans has pointed out: 'The Devonian period is not a natural division of the history of marine sedimentation characterized by a gradual deepening and subsequently a gradual shallowing of the ocean waters, but was determined solely by the interval between the last marine beds of the Silurian and the earliest marine beds of the Carboniferous Limestone on the Welsh border, where these strata were first studied in the early days of stratigraphical research.' Nevertheless the establishment of the Devonian system is well justified palaeontologically.

Most of the Devonian strata of south Devon and Cornwall are indubitably marine, while in South Wales and the Welsh border country the Old Red Sandstone facies is prevalent. Between these two areas, namely, in north Devon, there is a repeated alternation of Old Red Sandstone and marine types of deposit, by means of which some degree of correlation can be made between the two facies. North of the Bristol Channel from South Wales to Scotland and the north of Ireland the Old Red Sandstone facies prevails to the exclusion of marine deposits. This great extension of the sandstone facies, and also the occurrence, in the marine Devonian Series, of beds containing the peculiar Old Red Sandstone fauna, renders it desirable to discuss the latter before describing the marine fossils.

The faunal history of the Old Red Sandstone is concerned chiefly with early stages in the evolution of fishes. Remains of these animals are the most characteristic fossils of that formation which, indeed, is subdivided on the basis of its fish faunas. Since the earliest known British fishes appear towards the summit of the Silurian—in the well-known Ludlow bone-bed—it is convenient to include them in the present account, though the line of demarcation between Silurian and Devonian is generally taken at a somewhat higher horizon.

The Ludlow bone-bed, containing the earliest known British fishes, abounds in calcified tubercles which are smooth or only slightly sculptured. These were long regarded as the skin-tubercles of a shark, but since the discovery of more complete remains in Lanarkshire they are known to belong to a small ostracoderm, *Thelodus*. This animal, 3 to 7 inches in length, had a large depressed head, a dorsal fin, and heterocercal tail. It is associated in the Scottish rocks with a similar form named *Lanarkia*, which differs from *Thelodus* in having spiny tubercles. Other forms, such as *Birkenia* and *Lasanius*, also from Lanarkshire, have the dermal tubercles partly fused into plates, but 'there is no doubt that the granular armour was the 'fashionable' fish-skeleton of Upper Silurian time' (A. S. Woodward).

A general tendency towards fusion of the skin-tubercles soon became manifest in the appearance of ostracoderms like *Pteraspis* and *Cephalaspis* in the uppermost Ludlow deposits and the passage-beds between them and the Old Red Sandstone. These were, indeed, foreshadowed by the less specialized *Cyathaspis* recorded from the Wenlock Limestone of the Baltic region, but so far unknown in Britain below the Upper Ludlow rocks of Herefordshire.

Typical fishes with lower jaws and paired fins also existed in Silurian times. These were formerly classed with the elasmobranchs, and were completely covered by hard skin-granules like those of the oldest ostracoderms. The paired fins seem to have arisen by the subdivision (and subsequent disappearance of intermediate parts) of continuous membranes which extended as a symmetrical pair along the lower side of the body. Some of the skin-granules fused together at the front edge of these fins, and also of the dorsal fins, forming strong spines. This character suggested the group-name Acanthodii for these fishes. The fusiform genus *Climatius*, typical of Upper Silurian and Lower Devonian deposits, possessed several pairs of ventral fin spines, these being remarkably broad and ornamented with coarse, beaded, longitudinal ridges representing fused rows of tubercles. The spines were scarcely at all inserted into the flesh.

The rocks known as the Old Red Sandstone contain three distinct and apparently successive fish faunas. But, as will be seen later, the upper two assemblages are closely related, while the lower fauna differs little from that of the Upper Silurian. This seems to indicate a prolonged period of time between the deposition of the Lower and Middle Old Red Sandstone respectively.

The fauna of the Lower Old Red Sandstone is distinguished especially by the abundance of the ostracoderm genera *Pteraspis* and *Cephalaspis*. The dorsal shield of *Pteraspis* is formed of seven separately calcified plates, namely, a large central disk with a triangular rostral plate anteriorly and a large median spine posteriorly, a pair of orbital plates, and a pair of postero-lateral cornua (Fig. 40). The ventral shield is a single plate, and the caudal region is invested with small rhomboid overlapping scales. Lines of fused tubercles run approximately parallel to the margins of pteraspid plates, and in Upper Silurian and basal Devonian forms these striae are crenulated, a character perhaps indicating a '*Thelodus* stage'.

In *Cephalaspis* the dorsal shield consists of one principal piece, in which the eyes are placed close together near the middle line. It is rounded in front and abruptly truncated behind. Two spaces, one between the eyes, the other just behind them, are closed by separately calcified small plates. Round the trunk the dermal armour takes the form of rings of scales corresponding with the underlying plates of muscles (Fig. 40). The approximate horizon is indicated by the length of the cornua in cephalaspid head-shields. Species without prolonged cornua do not occur higher than Downton horizons, while species with long cornua appear in the Lower Old Red Sandstone and persist to the Middle Series.

Acanthodians are of more importance than in the Upper Silurian fauna. *Climatus* is still the chief genus, but the fin-spines are thinner, and intermediate spines have mostly disappeared in these Lower Devonian forms.

A new element appears in the genus *Phlyctaenaspis*, which is a forerunner of the highly specialized armoured Arthrodeira so characteristic of later Devonian formations. The Lower Devonian forms of *Phlyctaenaspis* are relatively small with a well-tuberculated dermal armour.

The Middle Old Red Sandstone, best known in the Orcadian region of north Scotland, shows a remarkable change in the fish fauna. Nine families are represented, and only three of these pass up from lower strata. Of the simpler ostracoderms, only *Cephalaspis* survives, and it is extremely rare. A few small specialized acanthodians, such as *Mesacanthus* and *Diplacanthus*, also remain. The Arthrodeira alone of Lower Devonian groups attains greater importance in these higher strata.

The older ostracoderms are replaced by forms whose armour consists of a symmetrical series of overlapping plates on the top of the head and round the body. The plates are formed by fusion of skin-tubercles; the fusion, however, is not determined by the distribution of the muscles as in *Cephalaspis*, but by the course of slime-glands which traverse the skin. A pair of armour-plated flippers is appended to the forward part of the body. These animals, exemplified by *Pterichthys* (Fig. 40), bear a striking general resemblance to the contemporary eurypterids (compare Fig. 2).

The Middle Devonian Arthrodeira, typified by species of *Coccosteus* (Fig. 40) and *Homosteus*, are, in general, larger and more specialized than the Lower Devonian *Phlyctaenaspis*. Both head and trunk are armoured. The head-shield is formed of a few tuberculated plates, and is either notched

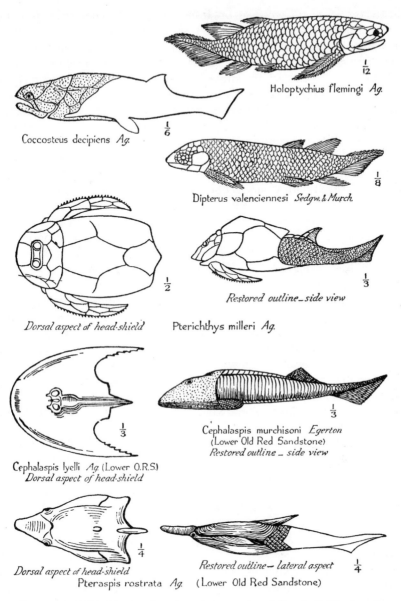

Holoptychius flemingi *Ag.*

Coccosteus decipiens *Ag.*

Dipterus valenciennesi *Sedgw. & Murch.*

Dorsal aspect of head-shield

Restored outline — side view

Pterichthys milleri *Ag.*

Cephalaspis lyelli *Ag.* (Lower O.R.S)
Dorsal aspect of head-shield

Cephalaspis murchisoni *Egerton*
(Lower Old Red Sandstone)
Restored outline — side view

Dorsal aspect of head-shield
Pteraspis rostrata *Ag.* (Lower Old Red Sandstone)

Restored outline — lateral aspect

FIG. 40. FISHES OF THE OLD RED SANDSTONE (*after A. S. Woodward*)

for the orbits, as in *Coccosteus*, or entirely surrounds them, as in *Homosteus*. Two pairs of bones on the palate bear conical teeth in *Coccosteus*, but *Homosteus* seems to be toothless. The armour of the body-region articulates with the head-shield by a pair of ball-and-socket joints which permit of free movement. This character is implied in the ordinal name Arthrodeira (joint-neck). The hinder parts of the body are destitute of armour and the paired fins are rudimentary. The systematic position of these fishes is somewhat doubtful, and they are best regarded at present as extremely specialized dipnoans. They are associated with typical Dipnoi in the genus *Dipterus* (Fig. 40). This is fusiform in shape and possesses two dorsal fins (hence its name), acutely lobate paired fins, and a heterocercal tail, while its scales are heavily invested with enamel. The mandible bears two dental plates each with tuberculated ridges radiating in a fan-like pattern.

The crossopterygians of Middle Devonian strata are slender fusiform fishes covered with rhombic scales, their paired fins possess short obtuse lobes, and their conical teeth are externally folded at the base. The typical genera, *Osteolepis*, *Diplopterus*, and *Thursius*, differ from each other mainly in the position of the dorsal fins with respect to the paired fins.

The earliest of the Actinopterygii, or ray-finned fishes, is *Cheirolepis* from the Middle Old Red Sandstone of Scotland, which has a fusiform body covered with small enamelled rhombic scales; its complete jaws were armed with an outer row of minute teeth and an inner row of stouter teeth. It thus foreshadows the rapacious palaeoniscids of Carboniferous time, but resembles the contemporary crossopterygians in the excessive harden-ing of the external skeleton, in the heterocercal condition of the tail, and in the structure of the median fins, whose rays were more numerous than their internal cartilaginous supports.

The Upper Devonian fish-fauna contains the same families as that just described, but evolutionary progress resulted in differences that are readily recognized. The ostracoderms are represented mainly by *Bothriolepis* and *Asterolepis*, genera which are very similar to the Middle Devonian *Pterich-thys* but differ in their larger size and in minor characters of the dermal armour; the tail in the later forms was probably destitute of scales. The tuberculated plates of *Psammosteus* probably belong to simpler ostraco-derms.

The acanthodians are relatively unimportant, but such genera as *Dipla-canthus*, with comparatively slender fin-spines, still persist. These Upper Devonian forms show little or no trace of the intermediate paired spines so characteristic of the earlier *Climatius*.

Arthrodeira, though represented by large forms in North America, are rare in British Upper Devonian rocks, but typical dipnoans are abundant. *Phaneropleuron* is fusiform, with a long dorsal fin continuous with the caudal, but with a separate anal fin; its thin rounded scales are marked with delicate radiating striae.

Fusiform crossopterygians with obtusely lobed paired fins, allied to the Middle Devonian *Osteolepis*, persist through the Upper Devonian; the genus *Glyptopomus* is distinguished by irregular reticulating ridges on its external bones and scales. More conspicuous, however, is *Holoptychius* (Fig. 40) a large-headed, depressed form whose paired fins (especially the pectoral pair) are acutely lobate, and whose large, rounded, overlapping scales have a wrinkled ornamentation. The acutely conical teeth have a complex, meandering, folded structure which bears a striking resemblance to that in the teeth of the slightly later Labyrinthodont amphibians, the earliest crawling land animals. These highly specialized holoptychiids do not survive the Devonian period, but the simpler osteolepids and rhizodonts still occur in rocks of Carboniferous age.

Another family of crossopterygians, the Coelacanthidae, are remarkable both for their long range in time (Upper Devonian to Upper Cretaceous), during which they hardly change, and for the structure of their dorsal spines, which are only superficially ossified, and so are hollow when preserved as fossils.

The chief fossils associated with the fishes of the Old Red Sandstone are eurypterids, such as *Pterygotus* and *Eurpyterus* (Fig. 2), and plant remains (see Chap. VIII). A lamellibranch shell, *Archanodon jukesi* Forbes, which closely resembles the modern freshwater mussel *Unio*, is also found in some localities. There is a virtual absence of typically marine animals. Brachiopods are certainly represented by occasional shells of *Lingula*, but this genus appears to be capable of living in brackish water. In this connexion the gradual disappearance of indubitable marine brachiopods in the upper beds of the Silurian may be recalled.

No rock-system other than the Old Red Sandstone is classified exclusively on the basis of fish faunas; but as the succeeding assemblage differs from those just described in several important features, it will be convenient for comparison to summarize here the main collective characters of the Carboniferous fishes.

In the first place, it should be mentioned that the heavily armoured fishes of the Devonian do not persist into higher strata; in other words, the ostracoderms and arthrodeirans are exclusively Devonian.

The spiny-finned Acanthodii are represented in Carboniferous faunas only by a few highly specialized forms which have no intermediate paired spines. Of these the last genus is *Acanthodes*, in which the pectoral fins are much larger than the pelvic pair, and the latter are situated much farther forward than in earlier forms. A group of sharks almost confined to Carboniferous strata is typified by *Pleuracanthus*, which has paddle-shaped paired fins resembling those of dipnoan and crossopterygian fishes. The spines of this fish are armed with a double row of recurved hooks, and the teeth (commonly known as *Diplodus*) have a divergent pair of conical cusps on an expanded base. Other Carboniferous elasmobranchs, such as *Cochliodus* and *Psephodus*, have only a few powerful crushing teeth more or less fused together into arches across the jaw. Large, flat, oblong teeth, with striate grinding surface, known as *Psammodus*, are also common in Carboniferous strata, but the fishes themselves are incompletely known.

The sharp-pointed teeth of sharks are also arranged in rows, and new series develop throughout life on the inside of the jaw, moving forward as the older teeth fall out. In Palaeozoic forms, the jaw being incompletely hardened, the teeth were fixed in the soft tissues by large expanded bases. Moreover the bases of successional teeth often became fused together and could not drop out in the usual manner, but remained as an arch or spiral outside the edge of the jaw. This condition has been noticed in the Devonian genus *Protodus*, which leads on to *Edestus* and *Helicoprion* of Carboniferous age.

Typical Dipnoi are abundantly represented by the genus *Ctenodus*, which differs from its Devonian predecessors in having large, rounded overlapping scales without a layer of enamel; moreover, its dental plates are more strongly crenulated. *Sagenodus* is similar, but its dental plates have fewer ridges.

Fusiform crossopterygians with thin, round, overlapping scales and obtusely lobed paired fins, attain their maximum size and development in Carboniferous rocks. These fishes are imperfectly known, but some large teeth and jaws from the Lower Carboniferous of Scotland indicate a probable length of 9 or 10 feet for the whole fish. In *Rhizodus* the teeth are conical and compressed to two sharp edges, while those of *Strepsodus* are slender and round in section. The rounded teeth of *Megalichthys*, a large fish with smooth rhombic enamelled scales, are common in the English Coal Measures.

The dominant fishes of Carboniferous times belong, however, to the ray-finned families Palaeoniscidae and Platysomidae. The former are fusiform types whose bodies are covered with enamelled rhombic scales, the inner faces of which show peg-and-socket articulation. The head-bones are also more or less enamelled, and the slender sharp-pointed teeth indicate rapacious habits. The Platysomidae are deep-bodied forms with small mouth and blunt crushing teeth. This family is confined to Carboniferous and Permian strata, while the Palaeoniscidae persist into Mesozoic formations, where they are gradually replaced by more advanced types (pp. 109–10).

MARINE FAUNAS

The Devonian rocks of Cornwall and Devon are intensely folded and shattered by subsequent earth movements, while the original bedding of the strata is almost obliterated by cleavage. Moreover the fossils are frequently distorted or entirely destroyed by the cleavage or by metamorphism consequent on the intrusion of igneous masses. The stratigraphical succession is therefore extremely difficult to follow, and the correlation of separated outcrops is at present somewhat uncertain. It seems best here to describe the faunal succession in an area like Belgium, where the rocks are less disturbed, and to indicate the evidence for the correlation of British strata summarized in the accompanying table.

Correlation of British Devonian Strata

Cornwall and south Devon	North Devon and west Somerset	Continental equivalents
Green and Purple Slates, &c.	Lower Pilton Beds Baggy and Marwood Beds (marine) Pickwell Down Sandstone with upper O.R.S. fishes *Holoptychius* and *Bothriolepis*	Famennian
Calcareous Slates Limestones of Torquay, Plymouth, &c.	Morte Slates Ilfracombe beds—upper part with *Sp. verneuili* Coombe Martin Beds	Frasnian
Hope's Nose Limestone	Hangman Grits { Upper (marine) with *Stringocephalus* Middle—with *Psilophyton* Lower—(?) fluviatile	Givetian
Limestone with *Calceola* Staddon Grits { Beds with *Sp. cultrijugatus* Beds with *Sp. arduennensis* Beds with *Sp. hercyniae*		Couvinian
	?	Emsian
Meadfoot Beds with fossiliferous Looe beds	Lynton Beds with *Pteraspis* Foreland Sandstone	Siegenian
Dartmouth Slates	..	Gedinnian

The **Gedinnian** fauna of Belgium is not well known, since it is often represented only by fragments of ostracoderm fishes. The chief form is a species of *Pteraspis*. The Dartmouth Slates of south Devon are regarded as representative of the Gedinnian stage; these purple and green slates contain a fish-fauna comparable with that of the Lower Old Red Sandstone. *Pteraspis cornubica* M'Coy and *Cephalaspis carteri* M'Coy are the best-known species, while the genera *Phlyctaenaspis*, *Climatius*, and *Parexus* are recorded from a few localities. The marine gastropods *Bellerophon trilobatus* Sowerby and *Loxonema* are confined to the southern outcrop.

The **Siegenian** fauna of Belgium comprises many species of Brachiopoda and mollusca, together with a few trilobites and corals. Many of them are still unknown in Britain, where the Siegenian stage is best represented by the Meadfoot Beds of south Devon. These comprise a fossiliferous horizon known as the Looe Beds, intercalated between two series of barren slates. The most characteristic fossils are three species of *Spirifer*. *Spirifer primaevus* Stein. is a convex shell with prominent fold and sinus, on each side of which are six or seven strong, simple ribs; the beak is incurved, and

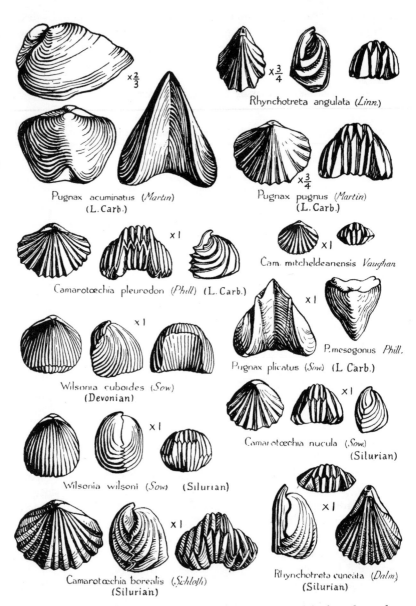

Rhynchotreta angulata (*Linn.*)

Pugnax acuminatus (*Martin*)
(L. Carb.)

Pugnax pugnus (*Martin*)
(L. Carb.)

Camarotœchia pleurodon (*Phill*) (L. Carb.)

Cam. mitcheldeanensis *Vaughan*

Wilsonia cuboides (*Sow*)
(Devonian)

Pugnax plicatus (*Sow*) (L Carb.)

P. mesogonus *Phill.*

Wilsonia wilsoni (*Sow*) (Silurian)

Camarotœchia nucula (*Sow.*)
(Silurian)

Camarotœchia borealis (*Schloth*)
(Silurian)

Rhynchotreta cuneata (*Dalm.*)
(Silurian)

FIG. 41. PALAEOZOIC RHYNCHONELLIDS (*drawn mainly from figures by Davidson*)

the triangular area has a large fissure. *Sp. hystericus* Schlotheim has a smooth fold and sinus with ten or twelve angular ribs on each side. *Sp. excavatus* Kayser is almost rhomboid in shape, and its smooth mesial fold is flanked by four or five angular ribs; lines of growth are conspicuous. In the abundance of strophomenids, such as *Stropheodonta gigas* (M'Coy), *S. sedgwicki* (Archiac and Verneuil), *S. murchisoni* (A. and V.), and *Leptaena rhomboidalis* (Wilckens), this fauna shows a certain similarity with Silurian assemblages. The orthid *Dalmanella circularis* (J. Sow.) belongs to a genus abundantly represented in Silurian strata, while *Proschizophoria personata* (Zeiller) and *P. provulvaria* (Maurer) foreshadow the later Devonian and Carboniferous development of the genus *Schizophoria*. Rhynchonellids are represented by *Camarotoechia daleidensis* (Roemer) and *C. papilio* (Krantz). The incoming of athyrids (*Athyris undata* Defr.) and terebratulids (e.g. *Rensslaeria strigiceps* Roemer) marks an important faunal change, since these groups are eminently characteristic of Upper Palaeozoic rocks. The commonest trilobite is *Phacops ferdinandi* Kayser, and the corals include the peculiar *Pleurodictyum problematicum* Goldfuss (Fig. 9), which is regarded as typical of Lower Devonian strata.

The Meadfoot Beds of south Devon are usually correlated with the Foreland Sandstone and the Lynton Beds of north Devon. The Foreland Sandstone is usually barren of fossils, but plant-remains ascribed to *Psilophyton*, a genus that occurs in the Lower Old Red Sandstone, have been recorded. The Lynton Beds contain remains of *Pteraspis*, along with marine lamellibranchs and brachiopods. Among the latter are *Spirifer primaevus* Stein. and *S. hystericus* Schlotheim, which afford evidence for referring the Lynton Beds to the Siegenian stage.

The lower horizons of the Staddon Grits which succeed the Meadfoot Beds in south Devon are now correlated with the **Emsian** stage of Belgium. The latter beds are marked by the presence at successive horizons of *Spirifer hercyniae* Giebel and *S. arduennensis* Schnr., both alate species which appear to be closely related. These fossils are not yet recorded from Devon. The occurrence there of the terebratellid *Tropidoleptus rhenanus* Frech (a planoconvex, plicated shell with a long, straight, and narrow cardinal area), which is associated in Belgium with *Spirifer hercyniae* Giebel, indicates the Lower Emsian age of these deposits.

The **Couvinian** stage of the Continent is marked by the occurrence of *Spirifer cultrijugatus* F. Roemer, a distinctive form with a carinated fold and coarse, rounded ribs. This species is said to occur in the highest part of the Staddon Grits. Two Couvinian spiriferids are undoubtedly present in south Devon, namely, *Spirifer speciosus* (Schloth.) and *S. ostiolatus* Schloth. The former is a coarse-ribbed, almost alate form with long hingeline, while *S. ostiolatus* is more equidimensional, with a short hinge-line and broad, smooth, mesial fold. Above the Staddon Grits is a series of slates and limestones containing the well-known slipper-coral *Calceola* *sandalina* Lamarck, which is typical of Upper Couvinian strata on the mainland of Europe. In north Devon the lower beds of the Hangman Grits may possibly be equivalent to the Staddon Grits, but they are of estuarine or lacustrine origin, and contain only obscure fossils besides the plant *Psilophyton*.

The **Givetian** stage of Belgium is represented in south Devon by dark slaty limestones, the Hope's Nose Limestone enclosing a fauna of corals and brachiopods. Among the corals the rugose form *Cyathophyllum heterophyllum* Frech and the alcyonarian *Heliolites porosa* Goldfuss are conspicuous, while the brachiopods include species of *Athyris, Atrypa, Pentamerus, Wilsonia, Orthotetes,* and *Spirifer*. Species of the latter genus appear to be especially useful in the classification of Devonian rocks, and *Spirifer mediotextus* Archiac and Verneuil and *S. undiferus* F. Roemer may be mentioned as typical of Givetian horizons. The former is a fine-ribbed species whose large cardinal area separates the umbo of the ventral from that of the dorsal valve; *S. undiferus* F. Roemer is of general oval shape and its flattened ribs tend to obscurity while concentric striae are conspicuous. In north Devon the upper horizon of the Hangman Grits is marked by the presence of the peculiar terebratulid *Stringocephalus burtini* Defr. which ranges up into the Coombe Martin Beds, where it is associated with lamellibranchs and gastropods. Though *S. burtini* ranges into Upper Devonian Beds, it is regarded as most typical of the Middle Series.

The well-known limestones of Torquay and Plymouth are referred to the **Frasnian** stage of the European classification and may be taken as the base of the Upper Devonian of this country. They are largely made of massive stromatoporoid and coral colonies which attain considerable size. Among the abundance of forms *Stromatopora concentrica* Goldfuss, *Acervularia goldfussi* de Verneuil, *Phillipsastraea hennahi* (Lonsdale), *Heliolites porosa* Goldfuss, and the feather-coral *Thamnopora cristata* Blumenb. (Fig. 9) may be mentioned. These rock-building organisms are accompanied by many brachiopods, mollusca, crinoids, and other fossils. *Spirifer verneuili* Murchison (Pl. III) is a typical Upper Devonian species distinguished by fine ribbing which encroaches on the mesial fold. *Sp. undiferus* Roemer ranges up from the Givetian stage. The most conspicuous rhynchonellid is *Hypothyridina cuboides* (Sow.) which is easily recognized by its inflated form. The orthid *Schizophoria striatula* (Schlotheim) has a circular outline and fine radiating ribs. *Productella subaculeata* (Murchison) is a forerunner of the productids which attain their maximum distribution in Carboniferous rocks. A notable terebratulid is *Stringocephalus burtini* Defr. Among trilobites the proparian *Phacops latifrons* (Bronn) frequently occurs, while *Trimerocephalus trinucleus* Salter (Fig. 37) is only known from Knowl Hill near Newton Abbott. The proetids *Cyphaspis ocellata* Whidborne and *Proetus batillus* Whidborne occur in some abundance at certain localities, but species of *Dechenella* (Fig. 46), *Bronteus*, and *Harpes* are less frequently found.

Other Devonian Beds which cannot be placed in continuous succession include mudstones with a goniatite-fauna similar to that of Budesheim in the Eifel district of Germany. These beds near Torquay have yielded species of *Tornoceras* and *Gephyroceras* as well as nautiloids (*Orthoceras*) and gastropods. Shaly limestones near Chudleigh appear to represent a higher horizon since they contain *Manticoceras intumescens* Beyrich and *Beloceras multilobatum* Beyrich, species characteristic of a high level in the Frasnian stage of Germany.

Green and purple slates containing the ostracod *Entomis serratostriata* Sandberger and the lamellibranch *Posidoniella venusta* Münster may probably be assigned to the **Famennian** stage. In Cornwall similar slates yielding these fossils enclose also various brachiopods, mollusca, and trilobites (species of *Phacops*).

CONDITIONS OF DEPOSITION

The uppermost Silurian rocks of the Welsh Borders give evidence of a gradual shallowing of the sea and the incoming of conditions that gave rise to the Old Red Sandstone type of sedimentation. North of the Bristol Channel this facies continued throughout the Devonian period. In south Devon and south Cornwall, however, the Devonian rocks are almost entirely of marine origin, except that (as also in Belgium) the lowest beds of the System are of Old Red Sandstone type. Between these two areas the strata of north Devon are marked by repeated alternations of undoubted marine Devonian rocks with deposits of the Old Red Sandstone type. Thus we may conclude with J. W. Evans that the coast-line, shelving gently from the foot of a mountainous region in Wales towards the sea in the south, seems to have shifted its position from time to time.

Three times the marine succession in north Devon is interrupted by a deposit of the Old Red Sandstone facies, each recurrence being marked by a distinctive flora and fauna. The first of these begins towards the top of the Silurian system and is represented by the Foreland Sandstone. The succeeding Lynton Beds represent a truly marine phase and are correlated with the Meadfort Beds of south Devon. The Hangman Grits, containing plants and fish remains, indicate a second sandy phase which is tentatively correlated with the marine Staddon Grits of south Devon. There follows a prolonged marine phase, extending through the Givetian and Frasnian stages, which is succeeded by a third arenaceous episode in the Pickwell Down Sandstone. Towards the close of the Famennian stage, the littoral Baggy and Marwood Beds mark the beginning of renewed marine deposition which continues through the Pilton Beds and reaches its maximum in the Lower Carboniferous, to the base of which the Upper Pilton Beds are now assigned. A considerable stratigraphical break then occurs, for the Lower Culm deposits are referred to a high horizon (D2) in the Lower

Carboniferous succession. This seems to indicate a period of elevation and erosion, followed by a further marine incursion.

At or towards the end of the Carboniferous period the area was disturbed by intense earth movements which, thrusting from the south, crumpled the strata into innumerable folds, induced a complex system of faulting, and imposed upon the softer beds a strong cleavage. To these circumstances are due the difficulties which are encountered in the stratigraphical investigation of the Devonian rocks of Cornwall and Devon.

The conditions under which the Old Red Sandstone was deposited have been the subject of considerable discussion, and general agreement has not yet been reached. Some authors would ascribe this sandstone formation to desert conditions. The prevailing red colour is attributed to oxidizing effects of the atmosphere in a comparatively warm climate. The conglomerates and much of the sandstone are regarded as probably of fluviatile origin, but wind-transport may have been an additional factor in the accumulation of fine-grained sandy material. According to J. W. Evans the conditions under which the Red Marls were deposited 'were probably similar to those that prevail in portions of the Bolivian plateau and the interior of south Australia, where a nearly level surface is covered after heavy rainfall with an expanse of shallow waters which, during periods of drought, dry up or contract to much smaller dimensions'. Wind-borne dust would be arrested by the water surface, and calcareous deposits, paralleled by the Devonian 'cornstones' would form in shallow depressions in arid areas.

It has been suggested, too, that Devonian plants were not perfectly adapted to land-conditions and therefore required an ample supply of moisture in the form of standing water or marshy ground through the greater part of the year. J. W. Evans suggests that 'desert conditions were consistent with ample rainfall, for wherever there is no vegetation to protect the surface from the action of sun and frost and wind a desert will come into existence'. But the evidence regarding Devonian vegetation is at present scanty and perhaps unreliable. There are few plant remains with structure preserved, the most notable being those from the silicified peat-bog at Rhynie, Aberdeenshire (p. 21). These are all marsh-plants and show the adaptive features of their ecological group; they are probably not truly representative of early Devonian floras as a whole. The Upper Devonian flora, however, includes the large fern-like *Archaeopteris* and its associates, some of which attained the stature of trees, and must have occupied somewhat drier situations. Their general habit suggests growth in a soil of some depth, and this seems inconsistent with the idea of universal desert conditions.

Still, some of the fossils of the Old Red Sandstone do give some support to these views. The ostracod *Estheria*, with representatives in the Old Red Sandstone, is characteristic of desert pools at the present day (see also p. 102). The mode of occurrence of fishes in shoals at certain levels in the sandstones of northern Scotland is consistent with the hypothesis of temporary shallow lakes. On the gradual drying up of pools at the present day some fresh-water fishes are known to bury themselves in the soft underlying mud, there to await replenishment of the water. The need for this habit is not expected in marine or estuarine habitats.

Such fishes as *Dipterus, Pterichthys*, and *Osteolepis*, however, occur in the marine Devonian rocks of the Eifel (Germany) as well as in the Old Red Sandstone of Britain. The exponents of the 'freshwater hypothesis' do not regard this as inconsistent with their views for some existing fishes are able to live in both fresh and salt water. Moreover, the upward range of several families of Old Red Sandstone fishes into the 'freshwater' deposits of the Carboniferous is also held to support that view. On the other hand, it has not been suggested that the Upper Silurian fishes were non-marine.

While there is no evidence of typical marine conditions north of the Bristol Channel, there are, in South Wales and north Devon, marine strata intercalated with arenaceous beds of Old Red Sandstone type, and the two facies are revealed in close proximity by borings in the London Basin. This certainly affords evidence of depositional variation near to a coast-line. Moreover, it suggests that the Old Red Sandstone was deposited in brackish-water coastal lagoons, since the formation of such features would require only slight change in the relative level of land and sea. Indeed, lagoons might arise merely by the accumulation of sandbanks such as often occur along existing coast-lines.

FAUNAL REGIONS

EUROPE. The Old Red Sandstone does not appear to be represented in Scandinavia, though Upper Silurian deposits of Downton type are re-corded from several places. On the west coast of Norway Reusch (1914) has reported fish remains from Hitteren and adjacent islands. J. Kiaer (1924) has described a number of small ostracoderm fishes from Ringerike, not far from Oslo. Two genera, *Aceraspis* and *Micraspis*, differ little from *Cephalaspis* except in having two dorsal fins instead of one. Certain other genera, such as *Rhyncholepis, Pterolepis, Pharyngolepis*, are remarkable in having the tapering end of the body turned downwards instead of upwards —the hypocercal condition. None of these genera are yet known from English deposits, and the Norwegian forms are associated with eurypterid remains ascribed to the American genus *Hughmilleria*.

In 1931 Kiaer reported a new fish-locality at Jeloen, Oslofjord, where, among a large number of indeterminate fragments, *Hemicyclaspis murchisoni* (Egerton) was identified. This species is an important index-fossil in the middle part of the English Downton stage.

In the Baltic area fishes of Downton age have long been known from the island of Oesel (Hoppe, 1931). The famous locality of Rutzikul has yielded the cephalaspid genera *Thyestes* and *Tremataspis* associated with the eurypterids *Bunodes, Eurypterus,* and *Pterygotus.* Fish-scales from other localities on the island have been placed in several new genera, but some of them may be synonymous with *Thelodus* and *Tremataspis.* Localities in Scania have furnished J. P. Lehman (1937) with scales of the ostracoderms *Thelodus* and *Tremataspis,* and the acanthodians *Diplacanthoides, Dendracanthus, Gomphodus, Onchus,* and *Proacanthodes*; the assemblage closely resembles those of Oesel and the English Midlands.

Off the northern limit of the Baltic Shield the Red Bay Series of Spitzbergen has provided abundant remains of numerous ostracoderm and acanthodian genera. They include several cephalaspids which E. Stensio (1927) has referred to the genera *Benneviaspis, Hoekaspis,* and *Kiaeraspis.* The first of these is represented later in the Palaeodevonian strata of the English Midlands, along with *Palaeaspis* and *Pteraspis.* Hence there is reason to infer continuity of water communication between Spitzbergen and England during the time represented by the Downton deposits. The Red Bay Series is succeeded conformably by the Wood Bay Series of Palaeodevonian age which has yielded to A. Heintz (1929), *Pteraspis, Gigantaspis,* and a number of acanthodians nearly related to *Phlyctaenaspis.* J. Kiaer (1931) correlates these rocks with the marine Coblenz stage of Germany. Holtedahl (1919) records scales of the Neodevonian genera *Holoptychius* and *Astrolepis* from Bear Island; they are said to be comparable with those of species which are widespread in Europe.

The only succession on the mainland of Europe (Map, Fig. 42) which is comparable with the Old Red Sandstone of Scotland is in the eastern Baltic States of Latvia (Livonia) and north-west Russia, but here the Palaeodevonian series is missing. The lowest fauna of this region (W. Gross, 1930) includes species of the ostracoderm genera *Psammosteus* and *Diptychosteus,* the antiarchian *Pterichthys,* the arthrodeirans *Coccosteus, Homosteus, Heterosteus,* and *Asterolepis,* the dipnoan *Dipterus,* the ganoids *Osteolepis, Diplopterus,* and *Gyroptychius.* Most of the genera are represented in the Middle Old Red Sandstone of North Scotland, particularly in the Achanarras Band and the Thurso Flagstones. A few species are identical with Scottish forms and others are closely related in the two areas. The Upper Sandstones of the Baltic States are interbedded with massive dolomitic limestones which are correlated with the Givetian, and perhaps the Frasnian, stage of central Europe on the evidence of their marine fossils. Among the fishes recorded from this stage, the ostracoderm *Psammosteus* and the arthrodeiran *Coccosteus* persist from earlier beds and are here associated with species of the antiarchian *Bothriolepis* and the ganoid *Holoptychius.* Again some of the species are identical with forms from the Upper Old Red Sandstone of north Scotland, notably the Nairn Sandstone and the Scaat Craig Beds. It seems probable that the highest Scottish horizon (the Rosebrae Beds) is not represented in the Baltic succession (T. S. Westoll, 1937).

South of these localities the facies of the Devonian rocks becomes increasingly marine. The approximate northern limit of wholly marine sequences is shown on the accompanying map; between this line and the Old Red Sandstone is a belt of mixed facies.

Neodevonian fishes are represented more widely than earlier forms at scattered localities throughout Europe. An exceptionally well-preserved

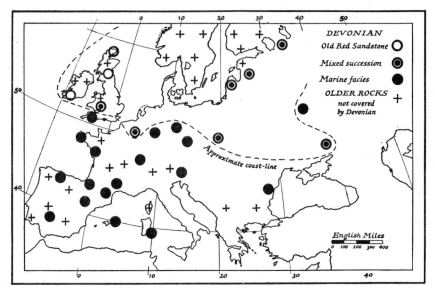

FIG. 42. SKETCH-MAP OF EUROPE SHOWING GENERAL DISTRIBUTION OF DEVONIAN ROCKS

assemblage of arthrodeiran species has been described by W. Goss (1932) from late Devonian strata at Wildungen, near Kassel, Germany. Notable forms include *Pholidotus*, related to the earlier *Phlyctaenaspis*, *Coccosteus*, and several allied genera, *Epipetalichthys* and the ptyctodonts *Rhynchodus* and *Rhynchodontus*. In addition, species of the coelacanth *Diploceroides* have been described by E. Stensio (1922). Many of these genera are, so far, unknown elsewhere, and may represent purely local developments. Occasional records of *Holoptychius*, *Bothriolepis*, *Dipterus*, *Osteolepis*, and other genera from marine Devonian rocks in Belgium, Germany, Bohemia, Russia, and Novaia Zemlya seem to indicate that some Devonian fishes could live in the sea as well as in fresh water. This affords an explanation of the presence of similar fishes in widely separated regions irrespective of facies.

The largest area of marine Devonian rocks in western Europe lies in the region embracing the Rhenish Schiefergebirge and the Ardennes. The existence of Devonian rocks here was first recognized by Murchison and Sedgwick in 1842, and their pioneer work was corrected and expanded by

F. Roemer in 1844. By later investigators the system has been subdivided into a number of stages which serves as a standard of reference for world-wide correlation. The rocks are almost exclusively marine sediments, and their thickness amounts to many thousands of feet. The deposits vary from place to place according to conditions of deposition, and there are many local gaps and transgressions, especially on the margins of the area. A useful summary of the Rhenish area has been compiled by N. Tilmann and collaborators (1938), and we have already noted (p. 247) the close palaeontological relations with the corresponding deposits in Devonshire. It seems desirable, however, that certain outstanding features of the fossil-assemblages should be emphasized.

Among the brachiopods which dominate the fauna of the sandy beds in the Rhenish area one conspicuous feature is the succession of spiriferids which has been utilized for purposes of correlation. The early Palaeodevonian Beds are marked by the predominant group of *Acrospirifer primaevus* which is almost restricted to the Siegenian stage. It is replaced in importance in the succeeding Emsian stage by strongly ribbed, alate species such as *Euryspirifer hercyniae*, and quadrate forms with smooth sinus, *Brachyspirifer carinatus*, for example. *Euryspirifer* continues in the Couvinian stage with the feebly ribbed *E. paradoxus* and *E. arduennensis*, while *Brachyspirifer* is represented by *B. ostiolatus*, but the most conspicuous Couvinian spiriferid is the large *Paraspirifer cultrijugatus* which is restricted to this stage. The group of *Trigonotreta subcuspidatus* also appears here and ends with *T. verneuili*, characteristic of the Frasnian and Famennian stages. The group of *Cyrtinopsis mucronatus* is typical of Mesodevonian horizons, but is also represented in higher strata by such species as *C. elegans*.

Only six families of trilobites are present in Devonian rocks and all of them are represented in earlier systems. The Devonian species are distributed in about fifty genera, only a few of which occur at Silurian horizons. One of these is *Goldius*, often cited as *Bronteus*, which is well represented in Silurian strata but is most abundant in the Palaeodevonian rocks of Bohemia; it is also recorded from Devonian horizons in other parts of Europe, in Asia, North America, and Australia. *Harpes* is another genus that survives from the earlier systems; and again the Devonian species are best known from Bohemia, though the genus is also represented in England and Germany. Devonian species of the proetid genera, *Proetus*, *Dechenella*, and *Otarion* are recorded from both Europe and North America. Among acidaspids, while *Primaspis*, *Leonaspis*, and *Ceratocephala* are widely distributed in Europe, North America, and Australia, records of *Pseudomonaspis* and *Radiaspis* seem to be restricted to European countries and those of *Ancropyge* and *Dicranurus* are likewise confined to North American localities. Five genera of Homalonotidae, originally regarded as subgenera of the Silurian genus *Homalonotus*, are recorded from the Devonian system in which the family reached the climax of its development. The European forms are distributed in *Digonus, Burmeisterella,* and *Parahomalonotus*; species of the first two genera are cited from Germany and south England, *Parahomalonotus* appears also in lists from France, Spain, and the Bosphorus. The genus *Dipleura,* to which certain American species are ascribed, is not recorded from European localities, nor is *Burmeisteria* which comprises species from the borders of the South Atlantic Ocean. The genera of phacopid-trilobites are nowadays distributed in two great families, Dalmanitidae and Phacopidae. In the former, *Odontochile* and *Prolobium* are recorded from both Europe and North America, but *Malladaia* is known only by one species from Spain and records of certain other genera are restricted to American localities. *Asteropyge* and other spinose genera are typically developed in Europe, while superficially similar American species are accommodated in the distinct genus *Greenops.* Likewise with regard to the true phacopids some genera are restricted to Europe or America, while others are represented in both continents. Delo (1935) remarks that these trilobites show great conservatism in America, sharply contrasting with the distinctive radial divergence among the European genera. This plainly suggests that the North Atlantic Ocean of Devonian time was of considerable width, though not sufficiently wide to prevent the migration of some genera. The records are certainly opposed to contiguity of the European and North American continents as Wegener suggests, and even to the modified position advocated by Dutoit (1937). On the contrary, the evidence favours the existence of a large North Atlantic Ocean with a wide embayment covering south Europe and North Africa, apart from certain islands.

The lithological character of these sandstones and decalcified limestones, combined with their fossil content, indicates that they were deposited in shallow water. The argillaceous rocks which are intercalated with them are almost certainly of similar origin, though their fauna shows variation in accord with the difference in habitat. The most conspicuous faunal element in the shales is a series of ammonoid cephalopods—the earliest members of the group loosely termed the goniatites. The earliest goniatite so far known is the close-coiled *Agoniatites* from the late Silurian rocks of the Kellerwald, which differs from contemporary nautiloids like *Barrandeoceras* only in the closer coiling of the innermost whorls. Species of *Agoniatites* and the allied *Anarcestes* persist at certain Palaeodevonian horizons, but specimens are rare and often indifferently preserved, so our knowledge of their stratigraphical and geographical distribution is still imperfect. *Agoniatites fidelis* is recorded from the Hunsruck Slates (Siegenian stage) of Germany, and the same form is present in the Mnenian Limestone of Bohemia associated with species of *Anarcestes* and the loosely coiled *Gyroceratites.* The last-named genus is often cited as ancestral to the goniatites, but L. F. Spath regards it and other loosely coiled forms as offshoots from the close-coiled *Anarcestes.*

Ammonoids are more abundant in the higher Devonian rocks of Central Europe, and a succession of goniatite assemblages has been established by Wedekind (1926) and Schindewolf (1934). The succession is best developed in the area east of the Rhine where argillaceous rocks are prevalent, and parts of the succession are known from other European localities and from other continents.

In the Couvinian stage species of *Anarcestes* are accompanied by various offshoots of the genus, notably the highly involute, compressed and acute-ventered shells of *Pinacites* and *Foordites*. Such forms are represented in the Wissenbach Slates of Germany, and the Hlubocep Limestone of Bohemia, which contain several species in common. The Wissenbach Slates also yield the loosely coiled *Gyroceratites gracilis* and straight shells usually placed in *Bactrites*. The type of Sandberger's (1843) *Bactrites*, however, is congeneric with the nautiloid *Orthoceratites* of Blumenbach (1803), and, according to Spath (1933) is 'merely an *Orthoceras* with a marginal siphuncle'. The group of '*Bactrites*' *carinatus* Sandberger, renamed *Lobobactrites* by Schindewolf, is closely allied to *Gyroceratites*. It is usually stated to be ancestral to the goniatites, though it appears long after the Agoniatitidae had become established. On the stratigraphical evidence so far available it seems more probable that *Lobobactrites* is a straight goniatite derived through *Gyroceratites* from *Anarcestes*. Outside central Europe Couvinian goniatites are little known; they occur, however, as far west as Brittany, for *Anarcestes subnautilinus* is recorded from the Porsgue Slates of that province.

At higher levels, corresponding approximately with the Givetian stage, species of the persisting Agoniatitidae are still useful as zonal guides, in conjunction with the genera *Parodoceras* and *Maeniceras*. These close-coiled shells with distinct lobes in the suture-line represent the family Tornoceratidae which becomes more conspicuous in the succeeding Neodevonian Series. The Maeniceras Beds are represented in Bohemia by the Hostin Shales which also contain the characteristic Givetian brachiopod *Stringocephalus burtini*. Beds near Istanbul, containing *Anarcestes*, *Agoniatites*, and *Paraphyllites*, are said to be at the same horizon (Sieverts, 1932).

The Tornoceratidae are specially characteristic of early Neodevonian strata, where numerous species are found in association with representatives of another offshoot of the Agoniatitidae, namely, the Gephuroceratidae. The typical genera *Gephuroceras* and *Manticoceras* are compressed serpental shells with variable umbilicus and angular suture-lines. Other genera, such as *Ponticeras*, *Koenenites*, and *Timanites* are distinguished on account of differences in coiling, whorl-shape, and suture-line. Three genera, *Beloceras*, *Eobeloceras*, and *Neomanticoceras* which A. K. Miller (1938) regards as derived from the Gephuroceratidae, are placed in a separate family Beloceratidae because they develop auxiliary lobes in the suture lines. Representatives of all these genera are characteristic of the lower part of the Frasnian stage, and the fauna is best-known from the famous Budesheim Shales of the Eifel district in Germany; we have already (p. 247) noted its presence in south England. The great variation in coiling, whorl-shape, and ornament displayed by the Gephuroceratidae is well shown by the prolific development of the family in the Domanik Beds of the Timan Mountains in north Russia. The upper part of the Frasnian stage is marked by the appearance of the Cheiloceratidae, a family closely related to the Tornoceratidae. Species of *Cheiloceras* are used as zonal indexes, and other genera *Dimeroceras* and *Sporadoceras* persist into the overlying Prolobites Beds of the Famennian stage. *Prolobites* also is related to the Tornoceratidae, and the stock persists into the basal beds of the Carboniferous system where it is represented by *Gattendorfia*.

These higher beds are further distinguished by a small group of goniatites in which the siphuncle is situated at the dorsal margin of the shell. Formerly they were all assigned to one genus, *Clymenia*, but as the number of known species increased, the genus was repeatedly subdivided until now about twenty genera are recognized in the family Clymenidae. The geological range of the clymeniids is short, for the entire family is confined to the Neodevonian Series. Most authors accept the view of Hyatt (1883) that the clymeniids must have arisen from some member of the close-coiled *Anarcestes* stock, and it is possible that the genus *Pseudoclymenia*, usually classified in Tornoceratidae may be a connecting link with the ancestral stock. No clymeniids are recorded from the Cheiloceras Beds, but ribbed forms with simple suture-lines appear in some variety in the Prolobites Beds, at the base of the Famennian stage. Thereafter the stage shows a succession in which first *Platyclymenia* and its allies, then *Clymenia*, with which *Laevigites* is probably synonymous, become dominant, and the last survivor of this group is *Oxyclymenia* which ranges up to the highest Devonian strata. Another group of clymeniids, with discoid, compressed, and widely umbilicate shells, but with angular suture-lines, is typified by the genus *Gonioclymenia*. This genus is important in the middle of the Famennian stage, and later gives place to such forms as *Wocklumeria* and *Kalloclymenia* which persist up to the basal strata of the Carboniferous system. This is the last record of the intrasiphonate goniatites; thereafter they vanish without leaving descendants.

With regard to geographical distribution there is sufficient evidence to show that a consistent succession of goniatite-assemblages can be traced through the Neodevonian rocks of Europe where the appropriate facies is present. None of the sections seems to be complete, but most of the zones are present in the Upper Harz, Sauerland, and Kellerwald in Germany, and Lysa Gora in Poland. At other places goniatite shales are replaced by, or intercalated with, limestones and sandstones without goniatites. West of Germany Clymenia Limestones of various horizons are known in Belgium,

Brittany, south England, the Central Plateau, and Languedoc in south France. C. Barrois long ago recorded Neodevonian goniatites from the Pyrenees, and Clymenia Limestones have since been reported from South Portugal and Sardinia, with a more complete sequence in the Carnic Alps. A similar succession, developed south of the Mediterranean Sea, in Morocco and Algeria, is said to equal, if it does not surpass in richness, the finest horizons in Europe. Hence we may tabulate the succession of Devonian goniatite assemblages in Europe for comparison with those of other continents.

Stratigraphical Stages	*Goniatite Faunas*
Lower Carboniferous (Horizon of Etroeungt)	Gattendorfia
Famennian	Wocklumeria Gonioclymenia Prolobites
Frasnian	Cheiloceras Manticoceras
Givetian	Maenoceras
Couvinian	Anarcestes

The European Devonian Limestones contain numerous reef-corals, some of which persist from the underlying Silurian system. These include certain tabulate corals, especially *Favosites*, *Syringopora*, *Pleurodictyum*, *Alveolites*, and *Aulopora*. The genus *Favosites* is well represented, and extends to Asia Minor, Australia, and North America. A few American and Australian forms are identified with European species indicating widespread migration, but the majority are distinct species which may be autochthonous developments. The same may be said of *Emmonsia* which differs from *Favosites* in that the tabulae are largely replaced by squamulae. *Thamnopora*, with a branching corallum composed of thick-walled corallites is also widely distributed; it includes the familiar feather-coral of Torquay, usually referred to the synonymous *Pachypora*, besides other species from Germany and Australia. Lists of Devonian corals usually include Koninck's genus *Michelina*, based on a species from the Lower Carboniferous rocks of Belgium, but this is now considered to be synonymous with the *Pleurodictyum* of Goldfuss (1829). *Pleurodictyum* usually occurs as decalcified moulds in the sandy Palaeodevonian rocks of the Eifel district, and the peculiar preservation is reflected in the specific name *P. problematicum*. The massive, ramose or encrusting *Alveolites*, and the slender adherent *Aulopora*, first described from Mesodevonian horizons in

Germany are widespread in equivalent beds in Belgium and France; the former genus is recorded as early as the Couvinian stage in the Carnic Alps.

Some members of the Heliolitidae also survive from the Silurian system, but are not known to occur above Mesodevonian horizons. Species of *Heliolites* are recorded from the coral-beds of west Germany, Belgium, south England, west France, Bohemia, and Austria. Though rare in Asia and North America, several species are described from Australian localities, including the European form *H. porosus.* Moreover, Jones and Hill (1941) state that the common Australian species *H. daintreei* is synonymous with the European *H. barrandei.* Species of *Plasmopora* also are recorded from Mesodevonian rocks in the Carnic Alps and Australia.

In contrast with the waning Tabulata the Rugosa increase in importance, and several new families appear in the Devonian rocks. Nomenclatural confusion which seems to have affected most coral genera has now been greatly reduced by the work of W. D. Lang, S. Smith, and W. D. Thomas who have jointly provided an invaluable *Index to the Genera of Palaeozoic Corals* (1940).

Many Devonian corals have long been referred to the genus *Cyathophyllum* and one of the most widely quoted is *C. caespitosum,* a phaceloid form whose internal structure has only recently been described by Lang and Smith (1935). Some twenty-five generic names are involved in a discussion of the synonymies, relationships, and structures of the corals formerly recorded under that name. These are reduced to five genera which form a cognate group, the family Disphyllidae. The phaceloid *Disphyllum* recognized as the ancestral form, persists through the Devonian succession. The usual trends of development have operated on the lineage, producing a number of derivatives that are given generic names. The trend towards compaction of the corallites gives rise to cerioid forms that are usually referred to *Prismatophyllum,* but Lang, Smith, and Thomas (1940) consider that this genus is synonymous with the *Hexagonaria* of Gurich (1896). The genus is very widespread in Mesodevonian and Neodevonian rocks of the Eifel, south England, and Poland; it is represented by different species in North America and Australia. Further operation of the same trend results in the loss of the wall between neighbouring corallites, and the confluence of their septa. Thus arises the plocoid *Phillipsastraea* which is highly characteristic of Neodevonian horizons in Europe, Asia, North America, and Australia. *Macgeeia,* with a similarly wide distribution is closely allied to *Phillipsastraea. Thamnophyllum,* a separate offshoot of *Disphyllum,* distinguished by the excessive thickening of its tissue, is typified by a Palaeodevonian species from Styria, and is also reported from French as well as Australian localities.

The family Spongophyllidae which persists from the Silurian system is not so clearly defined. Several species of *Spongophyllum* from the Mesodevonian rocks of south England, west Germany, France, and Australia seem to be closely similar to Neosilurian forms. The group is probably related to the Favistellidae, an ill-defined family of phaceloid corals which also ranges up from Silurian horizons; it is represented by *Favistella* from the east Alps and north Urals, and by *Fasciphyllum* from Germany and the east Alps, both being recorded also outside Europe.

Compared with Silurian reef-corals of Europe, the Devonian forms are restricted to more southerly areas by the development of the Old Red Sandstone around the Baltic Shield, otherwise there is little change in their distribution. Though not a reef-builder the distinctive 'slipper-coral' *Calceola sandalina* should be noted as an index-fossil in the Couvinian stage, widely distributed throughout Europe, and far beyond its boundaries.

A notable variation in facies is seen in Bohemia where Palaeodevonian strata, following conformably on Neosilurian rocks, are restricted to a small area between Prague and Beraun. The lowest beds are the pale limestones of Konieprus which are famed for well-preserved trilobites, brachiopods, and gastropods, with rare representatives of goniatites and fishes. Higher beds include nodular limestones, which, at Hlubocep and other localities, have yielded important goniatites (*Agoniatites* and *Anarcestes*), and the succession ends with black shales containing plant remains. The distinctive fossil assemblage of the Konieprus Limestone is also known from the lowest Devonian Beds of the Harz, but higher faunas in this area are more closely related to those of the Rhineland. Small outcrops of limestone near Marburg and Wildungen also enclose a number of Bohemian species, and the same facies is recorded by Frech (1887) as far south as the Carinthian Alps, and by Barrois (1886–9) from Brittany and the Pyrenees.

While the several Palaeodevonian facies are by no means continuously exposed each of them can be traced in a general east and west direction, the Old Red Sandstone in northern Europe, the sandy Rhenish facies farther south from Cornwall to Westphalia, the Hunsruck slates to the south of this line, and the calcareous Hercynian facies from Brittany and the Pyrenees to Bohemia and the Carinthian Alps. The sedimentary belts are therefore distributed more or less parallel to the Palaeodevonian coast-line as suggested by J. Shirley (1938). Their regularity, however, is disturbed by the intervention of ancient land masses which formed islands in the Devonian sea.

ASIA. On the eastern boundary of Europe a fairly complete succession of Devonian rocks in the Ural mountains appears to indicate submergence of this area during the entire Devonian period. Palaeodevonian Limestones contain trilobites, brachiopods, and other fossils which are comparable with those of the Hercynian facies in Bohemia. They are followed by Mesodevonian rocks of varied character with many distinctive fossils, including the Couvinian coral *Calceola sandalina*, the Givetian brachiopod *Stringocephalus burtini*, followed by *Hypothyridina cuboides* of Frasnian age. Higher come representatives of the Frasnian Manticoceras Beds, and Clymenia

Limestones of the Famennian stage. This succession may have connected with the Mediterranean development by way of the Kirghiz steppe, Turkestan, Asia Minor, the Bosporus, and Dobrudja.

On the northern border of the Angara Shield Neodevonian Limestones with brachiopods of European type are reported from the island of Kotelny: this is consistent with the more complete record of Mesodevonian and Neodevonian horizons in Novaia Zemlya. South-west of the Shield, near Tomsk, metamorphosed Palaeodevonian Limestones have yielded an assemblage of trilobites, brachiopods, and mollusca comparable with that of the Urals. The Mesodevonian rocks which follow are identified by the presence of *Stringocephalus burtini* and its associates, and Neodevonian horizons are recognized by a widely distributed limestone containing the characteristic spiriferid *Trigonotreta verneuili*. The goniatite *Beloceras multilobatum* typical of high Frasnian horizons in West Europe, also occurs here. Farther east the Palaeodevonian and Mesodevonian Series are over-laid by red sandstones with gypsum and rocksalt which mark the coast-line of the Irkutsk embayment. In the Altai mountains limestones with trilobites and brachiopods of European type represent Couvinian horizons, and are followed by beds of Givetian age. West of Kuznetsk the latter stage is over-laid by Carboniferous rocks, but between Bajaraiol and Karakalinsk rocks of Neodevonian age have yielded *Trigonotreta verneuili* and *Sporadoceras biferum*.

All three series of the Devonian system developed in the Kirghiz have affinities with the south Urals, but in the Tien Shan the system is trans-gressive, beginning with clastic sediments enclosing Givetian fossils. Ac-cording to F. R. C. Reed (1922) a Neodevonian assemblage in Chitral includes *Trigonotreta verneuili* and other brachiopods characteristic of the Frasnian stage in the Harz, but in the Pamirs the fossils are more closely related to those of the southern Urals. The lower part of the Plateau Lime-stone in the Northern Shan State of Burma had yielded *Calceola sandalina* and brachiopods characteristic of late Couvinian horizons in the Rhineland, but a series of shales at Wetwin contains a peculiar assemblage of lamelli-branchs which Reed (1921) considers to be more closely related to the Neodevonian Naples fauna of New York than to any known Asiatic or European assemblage. The Plateau Limestone extends into Yunnan (Reed, 1927) and south China with little faunal change; it is worthy of note that the Frasnian goniatite *Manticoceras* is recorded from Central Hunan (Y. C. Sun, 1935). In northern China, however, Carboniferous rocks rest on an eroded surface of Ordovician and older rocks (see Map, Fig. 43).

AUSTRALASIA. Rocks of Devonian age, exposed at intervals on the margins of the Australian Shield, exhibit at least three facies, namely, lime-stones with goniatites, limestones with reef-corals, red sandstones with fishes.

The presence of Neodevonian goniatites in western Australia has long been known, but the first detailed account is due to G. Delepine (1935) who described and figured several species of *Sporadoceras*, *Pseudoclymenia*, *Tornoceras*, and *Dimeroceras* from red limestones at Mt. Pierre in the Kimberley district. More recently C. Teichert (1941) has added *Beloceras*, *Cheiloceras*, *Imitoceras*, and *Platyclymenia* to the list of genera, and has shown that three horizons can be distinguished, representing the Manticoceras, Cheiloceras,

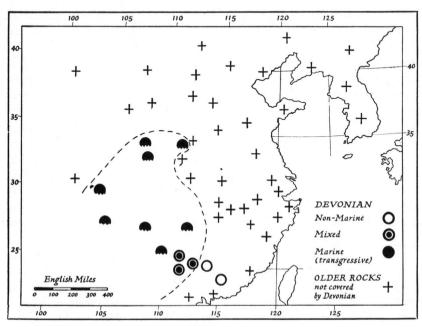

FIG. 43. SKETCH-MAP OF CHINA SHOWING GENERAL DISTRIBUTION OF
DEVONIAN ROCKS

and Prolobites Beds of Europe. The first of these horizons is known from central Hunan in China, but the other two have not yet been recorded anywhere else east of the Urals. The Australian goniatites therefore occupy an isolated position; and though Teichert holds that they must have arrived in the Australian area by way of the Devonian 'Tethys' along the line of the Himalayas, there is no evidence to substantiate his claim. At the same locality a white limestone without goniatites has yielded *Hypothyridina cuboides* and other brachiopods, together with certain corals, all of European affinities.

Mesodevonian rocks, chiefly limestones, are extensively developed in Queensland, Australia (Map, Fig. 44) whence many reef-corals and stromatoporoids are recorded; the Rugosa have been reviewed by D. Hill (1939–40) and the Tabulata by A. O. Jones (1941). The general aspect of the corals is similar to that of the European Couvinian stage, but all the species of

Tabulata and most of the Rugosa are purely Australian. Other assemblages of corals from New South Wales and Victoria are compared by D. Hill (1939–41) with the Couvinian and Palaeodevonian stages in Europe. These Australian fossils may therefore have developed autochthonously from Silurian ancestors which had a common origin with European forms. Many of the brachiopods from the associated clastic beds are also referred to European species. In places the succession ends with sandstones of

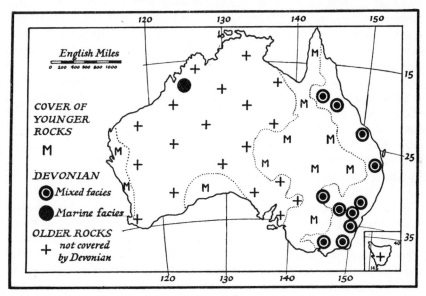

FIG. 44. SKETCH-MAP OF AUSTRALIA SHOWING GENERAL DISTRIBUTION OF
DEVONIAN ROCKS

freshwater origin which contain *Lepidodendron australe* and other plants, and rest unconformably on the Mesodevonian strata.

From a few localities in Victoria and New South Wales remains of Neo-devonian fishes have been described by E. S. Hills (1931–2). They comprise fragments of the antiarchian genera *Bothriolepis* and *Remigolepis*, the crossopterygian *Holoptychius*, and the heterostracid *Phyllolepis*. The aspect of the entire assemblage, as well as the lithology, is comparable with that of the Old Red Sandstone in north Scotland. It is remarkable, too, that *Remigolepis* is elsewhere known only from Greenland. This fauna is also present in the Beacon Sandstone of Antarctica, whence A. S. Woodward (1921) has described fragmentary remains of *Bothriolepis antarctica*, and species of *Byssacanthoides, Cheiracanthus, Holoptychius, Osteolepis,* and *Stegotrachelus*.

Passing over the doubtful Fingal Slates of Tasmania, rocks containing fossils of Palaeodevonian age are present at Reefton and Baton River in the north of South Island, New Zealand. An analysis of the fauna by J. Shirley

(1938) shows that the assemblage includes several brachiopods in common with the calcareous Palaeodevonian rocks of Bohemia, and a few species of Rhenish affinities; at least two forms are identical with species from corresponding rocks in North America. Hence the general relations of Devonian faunas through the vast area of marine transgressions on the continents of Asia and Australasia are overwhelmingly European.

In NORTH AMERICA the Old Red Sandstone facies and marine Devonian rocks are distributed much in the same manner as in Europe. The Old Red Sandstone is present on the margins of the Canadian Shield, in south-east Canada, and in east Greenland; marine Devonian deposits are exposed at intervals over a vast area to the south and west, in Canada and the United States (Map, Fig. 45).

A considerable number of fossil fishes has been obtained from localities in New Brunswick. Neosilurian rocks at Cunningham's Brook, Nerepis, in the south of the province, have furnished H. C. Stetson (1928) with the first American *Thelodus*, associated with *Cyathaspis*, *Ceratiocaris*, and *Bunodella*. Argillaceous beds near Campbellton on the southern shores of Chaleur Bay have yielded an assemblage of Palaeodevonian age, members of which have been described by J. F. Whiteaves (1881, 1893), R. H. Traquair (1890), A. S. Woodward (1892), and listed by F. J. Alcock (1935). There are several acanthodians of the genera *Acanthoessus*, *Cheiracanthus*, *Climatius*, *Doliodus*, *Gyracanthus*, and *Protodus*, the ostracoderm *Cephalaspis campbelltonensis* Whiteaves and three other species, and the arthrodeiran *Phlyctaenaspis acadicus* Whiteaves. A later, Neodevonian, fauna is enclosed in grey concretionary sandstones at Scaumenac Bay, a northern arm of Chaleur Bay. The most abundant fish here is *Bothriolepis canadensis* Whiteaves. The ostracoderms are represented by *Cephalaspis laticeps* Traquair and two other species reviewed by G. M. Robertson (1936). *Euphanerops longaevus* A. S. Woodward is a surviving member of the primitive anaspideans. Other groups include the arthrodeiran *Coccosteus canadensis* Whiteaves, the dipnoan *Scaumenacia curta* Whiteaves, the ganoids *Holoptychius quebecensis*, *Eusthenopteron foordi*, and *Cheirolepis canadensis* of Whiteaves, and the acanthodians *Acanthoessus* and *Diplacanthus*. The assemblage is clearly related to the Eday fauna of north Scotland, for, in addition to the presence of genera in common, *Eusthenopteron* is probably a descendant of *Tristichopterus*, and *Scaumenacia* is a derivative of *Pentlandia*. At the same time the specific differences reflect the influence of differing environment, and probably also separation of location by a considerable distance.

It may be noted here that the Mesodevonian and Neodevonian strata of Ohio, Wisconsin, and New York States have furnished remains of several large arthrodeirans described by J. S. Newberry (1889). Some of these, notably *Diplognathus*, *Dinichthys*, *Macropetalichthys*, *Titanichthys*, *Mylostoma* are better known in North America than elsewhere. They are, however, associated with such genera as *Coccosteus*, *Acanthaspis*,

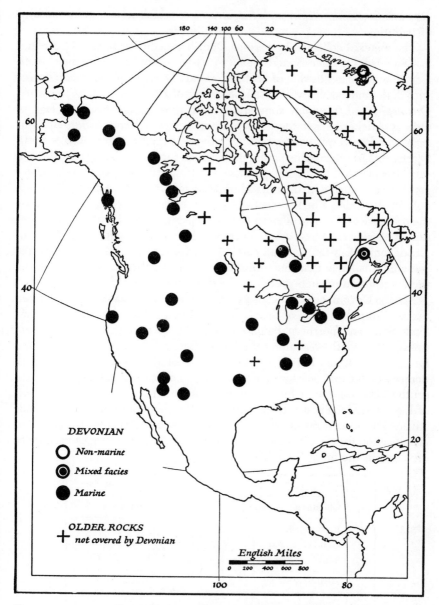

FIG. 45. SKETCH-MAP OF NORTH AMERICA SHOWING GENERAL DISTRIBUTION
OF DEVONIAN ROCKS

Rhynchodus, Bothriolepis, and *Stegotrachelus* which have a more uniform distribution.

The material collected by various Danish expeditions to east Greenland has enabled G. Save-Soderbergh (1934) to establish a sequence which amplifies and extends that of north Scotland. The known succession begins with dark sandy shales which enclose species of *Pterichthyodes, Diplopterax, Osteolepis,* and *Thursius,* comparable with those of the Rousay Flags of Orkney. Higher beds in the series contain species of *Holoptychius, Bothriolepis,* and *Phyllolepis* corresponding to those of the Rosebrae Beds of north Scotland. The intervening part of the Scottish succession is not yet known in east Greenland. The Phyllolepis stage is followed by beds containing *Holoptychius* associated with the antiarchian *Remigolepis,* a genus known elsewhere only in Australia. The highest fish-bearing beds in Greenland, marked by the presence of the arthrodeiran *Groenlandaspis,* are not known to be represented elsewhere. These assemblages emphasize the essential uniformity of Neodevonian fish-faunas in all parts of the world as far as they are known at present. It is likely that this uniformity will be further substantiated when the distribution of such genera as *Remigolepis* is better known.

Marine Devonian rocks occupy extensive areas in Canada and the United States. From the region of the Great Lakes they extend eastward into New York State and northern Pennsylvania. Thence narrow outcrops project towards the south-west along the line of the Appalachian Mountains, and farther west others border the older rocks of the Cincinnati and Ozark domes in Ohio and Missouri. To the north a considerable outcrop lies just south of Hudson Bay, while far to the west a further development lies west of Lake Winnipeg and extends at intervals to the mouth of the Mackenzie River. The succession in New York State is usually taken as the standard classification for the continent; it is correlated with the European sequence of stages in the following table.

	American Sequence		European Stages
Neodevonian	Chemung Sandstone		Famennian
	Portage Shales	Catskill Sandstone to East	Frasnian
	Genesee Shales		
	Tully Limestone		
Meso-	Hamilton Stage		Givetian
	Onondaga Stage		Couvinian
Palaeo-	Oriskany Stage		Siegenian
	Helderberg Stage		Gedinnian

The Helderberg stage is mainly restricted to the Atlantic border of North America, from the peninsula of Gaspe, through New Brunswick and

Nova Scotia, Maine, the eastern part of New York State and northern Pennsylvania. The stage has been placed by some authors in the Silurian system, but though the fossils are similar to Silurian forms, all the species are new except the long-ranged *Atrypa reticularis* and *Leptaena rhomboidalis*. Brachiopods form an important element in the fauna: the large orthid *Eatonia* is peculiarly American, the abundant strophomenids include *Strophonella punctulifera* (Conrad), a typical spiriferid is *Spirifer macropleurus*, and the loop-bearers are represented by *Rennslaeria aequiradiata* (Conrad), the genus being characteristic of Palaeodevonian horizons in Europe as well as in America. Gastropods are unusually prominent, especially in the great variety of capulids such as *Platyceras spirale*; this feature recalls in some degree the hercynian facies of Bohemia. Among the bivalved mollusca, a number of large-winged aviculids is conspicuous, as, for instance, *Actinopteria textilis* (Hall). Trilobites are fairly common and include *Phacops logani* Hall and the acidaspid *Dicranurus hamatus* (Conrad) which recalls certain Bohemian forms. Crinoids and corals are rare, probably on account of turbid waters indicated by the argillaceous character of the prevalent limestones.

The Oriskany stage extends farther into the interior of the continent, for it is transgressive at least as far as Lake Ontario and the Appalachians. The fauna shows a preponderance of large brachiopods mainly of the same genera as the Helderberg forms, but the species are new; *Acrospirifer murchisoni* (Castel), *Costispirifer arenosus* (Conrad), and species of *Hipparionyx*, *Rennslaeria*, and *Stropheodonta* are notable forms. Mollusca are abundantly represented by capulids, especially by the appearance of spinose species of *Platyceras*, and by unusually large and coarse lamellibranchs such as *Actinopteria textilis* var. *arenaria* Hall. Other fossil groups, including trilobites, are more sporadic in occurrence. The balance of the fauna seems to be influenced by the prevalent sandy character of the deposits.

The Onondaga stage consists largely of limestones which can be traced from New York State to the Mississippi basin and Nevada. It transgresses on to various horizons of the Silurian rocks, often with little evidence of unconformity. The fauna includes descendants or near relatives of Oriskany species along with other types which appear for the first time. Some of the limestones contain a profusion of corals including the reef-building genera *Disphyllum*, *Prismatophyllum*, *Phillipsastraea*, and *Spongophyllum*. In certain localities as, for example, the rapids in the Ohio River near Louisville, these corals are said to form true reefs. Brachiopods are abundant in the shelly limestones, especially spiriferids and stropheodonts; the former group includes *Paraspirifer acuminatus* (Conrad) nearly identical and probably contemporary with the European *P. cultrijugatus*. Other important brachiopoda are *Chonetes*, *Productella*, and the loop-bearing *Cryptonella*. Among mollusca the spinose capulids and large winged aviculids persist; nautiloid cephalopods are abundant and varied, and the goniatites are represented by a single species, *Tornoceras mithrax* (Hall) one of the oldest Devonian ammonoids known in America. About fifty species of trilobites are recognized including specialized acidaspids and lichads; *Odontocephalus aegeria* (Hall) is a dalmanitid with an ornate cephalic border. Another feature of the Onondaga stage is the presence at some localities of 'bone-beds' made up almost exclusively of dermal plates, teeth, and spines of fishes. These beds are due to the concentration of detritus by wave-action; the genera recorded are mentioned on p. 262.

The Hamilton stage, as developed between Lake Erie and New York, shows three distinct facies. At the base is the Marcellus Shale which encloses an assemblage of small, thin-shelled brachiopods and small lamellibranchs. The most characteristic brachiopod is *Leiorhynchus limitare* (Vanuxem), which is associated with *Chonetes coronatus* (Conrad), *Ch. scitulus* Hall, *Strophalosia*, and *Orbiculoidea*. The lamellibranchs are mainly species of *Leiopteria*, *Lunulicardium*, and *Nuculites*; the tubular gastropods *Tentaculites* and *Styliola* are often abundant in individuals. The only other fossil of note is the trilobite *Phacops rana* Green. Other shale-bands with much the same fauna are spaced at intervals in the succeeding argillaceous sandstones and limestones, which increase in importance eastward. The fauna of these latter deposits is dominated by the brachiopod element, among which various spiriferids are conspicuous, particularly *Mucrospirifer mucronatus* (Conrad) with allied species, and the smooth *Ambocoelia umbonata* (Conrad). Another notable form is the loop-bearing *Cryptonella rectirostra* (Hall). Many of these forms have possible ancestors in the underlying Onondaga stage, but three species lack such antecedents and must be regarded as immigrants. They are, *Tropidoleptus carinatus* (Conrad) which is utilized as the index-fossil of the assemblage, *Chonetes coronatus* (Conrad) which first appears in the Marcellus Shale, and the small spiriferid *Vitulina pustulosa* (Hall). These species are usually regarded as migrants from South America, for they are recorded from Bolivia in slightly earlier strata. The Hamilton lamellibranchs, especially the oblique aviculids, can be derived from Onondaga forms. Towards the east the sandstones thicken and merge into red and green sandstones which form the lower part of the non-marine Catskill Sandstone. Westwards, limestones become more prominent, and the balance of the fauna alters—corals which are rare in the east become abundant in the Appalachians and the Mississippi basin.

The Tully Limestone which overlies the Hamilton stage is usually taken as the base of the Neodevonian Series in New York and Pennsylvania. Its fauna consists mainly of Hamilton species and its separation from that stage depends almost entirely on the presence of two exotic species. One is the brachiopod *Hypothyridina venustula* (Hall) which has been confused with the widespread Frasnian species *H. cuboides* (J. de C. Sow.). Cooper and Williams (1935) as well as G. H. Chadwick (1935), however, find no more than generic resemblance, and the genus has several representatives in the

Mesodevonian rocks of Europe. The trilobite *Bronteus tullium* (Hall) also has no ancestors in the Mesodevonian faunas of New York, but the genus is well-known in the European development. In the absence of other elements of the widespread Frasnian fauna, it is possible that the Tully Limestone is earlier than the European stage.

The black bituminous shales of the Genesee section have a fauna of the same type as the shales lower in the succession, consisting of small brachiopods and lamellibranchs, with the addition in this case of numerous goniatites. Some fifty miles farther east, in the Naples–Canandague Valley, only a small part of the sequence has this fauna, and in the more sandy shales the goniatites become surprisingly varied and abundant. They include numerous species of *Manticoceras*, *Tornoceras*, *Probeloceras*, *Neomanticoceras*, and *Acanthoclymenia*. This is the celebrated Naples or Portage fauna first described by J. M. Clarke (1898), and later by A. K. Miller (1938), who correlate it with the Frasnian Manticoceras fauna of Europe and North Africa from which it is doubtless derived by the influence of oceanic circulation in the North Atlantic Ocean. The intervening sandstones of the Chemung stage carry a totally different fauna distinguished particularly by the predominance of brachiopods. These include *Cyrtospirifer disjunctus* (J. de C. Sow.) which is nearly allied to *C. verneuili* from the Neodevonian stages of Europe. There are several stropheodonts of the genera *Douvillina*, *Stropheodonta*, and *Strophonella*, besides species of the orthid genus *Dalmanella* and some persistent Hamilton forms. Lamellibranchs also are varied, and include species of *Pterinaea*, *Leiopteria*, *Leptodesma*, and *Buchiola*. The goniatites are clearly related to the Portage fauna, some species being common to both. Fishes are represented by species of *Coccosteus*, *Phyllolepis*, and *Holoptychius*. Above the true Chemung stage G. H. Chadwick (1935) distinguishes three other stages, Canadaway, Conneaut, and Conewango, presenting the same general facies, but showing slight differences in their faunal contents, and progressing gradually towards the Mississippian assemblage. Each stage has been traced eastward into the red beds of continental origin which were formerly grouped as a unit under the name Catskill Sandstone.

The Devonian rocks of the western Interior, comprising parts of Missouri, Iowa, Nevada, Manitoba, and northwards down the Mackenzie Valley to the Arctic Ocean, evolved in a different way. The vertical succession is considerable, for records of the widespread brachiopods *Stringocephalus burtini*, *Hypothyridina cuboides*, *Cyrtospirifer disjunctus*, and the goniatite *Tornoceras*, indicate that the beds correspond to the Givetian and Frasnian stages of Europe. Some of the brachiopods, e.g. *Str. burtini*, *H. cuboides*, and *Schizophoria striatula* are not recorded from the well-searched Hamilton stage of the eastern States, but are widespread in Europe and Asia. Likewise the goniatite *Timanites*, typical of the Manticoceras fauna in north Russia, is recorded from Alberta but not from New York. It is probable therefore that this western development of the Devonian system in North America was connected with its Eurasian equivalent by way of the Arctic Ocean, and was entirely separate, at least in its early stages, from the Atlantic embayment. This view is supported by the distribution of reef-corals in the limestones of the Mackenzie Valley which have lately been reviewed by S. Smith (1945). Collections from the neighbourhood of Great Slave Lake (lat. 61° N.) include species of the tabulate genus *Thamnopora*, and the rugose genera *Disphyllum, Prismatophyllum, Phillipsastraea, Spongophyllum*, and *Strombodes*. Smith states that the assemblage is very similar to that of the Frasnian stage of Europe, particularly that of north-east France. Comparable corals are also recorded from the lower part of the Mackenzie Valley and Alaska (*c.* lat. 70° N.), and from Ellesmereland (*c.* lat. 80° N.). These may be drifted fragments, but, even so, reefs must have been present at no great distance, and we may conclude that the temperature gradient from equator to poles was much more gradual than it is today, and the absence of ice-caps around the poles would greatly facilitate migration of marine organisms.

THE BORDERS OF THE SOUTH ATLANTIC OCEAN. The Icla Shales of Bolivia and the Maecuru Beds of Brazil contain Palaeodevonian fossils (J. M. Clarke, 1913), and many of the species are identical with those in corresponding beds of the Falkland Islands, and in the Bokkveld Beds of Cape Province, South Africa (F. R. C. Reed, 1907). These faunas bear a special impress which is characterized as austral, in contrast with the boreal aspect of homotaxial faunas north of the equator. This is particularly shown by the trilobites of which no less than thirteen genera are restricted to the southern hemisphere. In other words 25 per cent. of the Devonian trilobite genera are peculiar to the southern localities where the typical northern forms are unknown. The homalonotids are referred to the genus *Burmeisteria* which is distinguished from other members of the family by the presence of an epistomial projection from the cephalic margin. Among the phacopids several genera peculiar to the southern hemisphere are grouped in the sub-family Calmoninae; they include *Calmonia* recorded from Brazil, the Falkland Islands, and South Africa, *Pennaia* and *Anchiopella* represented in South America and South Africa, *Probolops, Proboloides*, and *Schizostylus* from South America alone, and the old-established *Typhloniscus*, records of which are still confined to South Africa. *Bouleia* and *Dereisma*, instituted by R. Kozlowski (1913) for two species from Bolivia belong to the Phacopinae. The spinose dalmanitid *Hadrorachis* is represented in both South America and South Africa, but the allied *Cryphaeoides* is only known from Bolivia. Another dalmanitid, of more usual aspect, is recorded only from Argentina.

The brachiopods tell the same story. Most of the spiriferids, for instance, belong to the 'radiate-fimbriate' group of *Spirifer antarcticus* Morris and Sharpe which is distinguished from all northern forms by the fimbriate ornament on the early stages of the shell. The athyrid *Leptocoelia flabellites* (Conrad) is abundantly represented in these southern localities, and is widespread in Palaeodevonian rocks elsewhere: its trivial name has been used for a supposed land-barrier, 'Flabellites Land', at the northern limit of these South Atlantic faunas—surely a choice example of terminological incompatibility. The genus *Chonetes* is abundant in species, including some with strong and rugged ornament quite unusual in other Devonian faunas. The rhynchonellid *Scaphiocoelia* and the terebratulids *Derbyina* and *Brazilia* are unknown outside these southern faunas. Some species of *Leptostrophia* have apparently the typical aspect of northern forms, but others, tentatively referred to the genus, show unusual characters of hinge and surface ornament. *Rennslaeria* is rare in South America, but more abundant in South Africa; all the species approach those of Europe and the Atlantic States of North America.

The outstanding features of the lamellibranchs is the overwhelming development of taxodont genera such as *Palaeoneilo* and *Nuculites*, while the aviculids so abundant in North America are sparsely represented in the southern continents. The gastropods have an impressive array of bellerophonts, but capulids are scarce. These contrasts with the northern faunas may, however, be due to differences of habitat.

The known distribution of the Austral fauna in South America and South Africa indicates that in early Devonian time the South Atlantic Ocean transgressed over the southern part of Cape Province and extended more widely over the margins of the Brazilian Shield. Certain southern elements mingled with European forms in the Saharan region, and point to a connexion with northern waters in this direction. Fossils of later Devonian rocks in the Amazon region (Erere Shales of Brazil) and the African Gold Coast (see A. E. Kitson and A. M. Davies, 1925) are more closely related to the Onondaga and Hamilton faunas of eastern North America.

LITERATURE

Neosilurian fish-faunas are described by R. H. Traquair in 'A Report on Fossil Fishes . . . in the Silurian Rocks of South Scotland', *Trans. Roy. Soc. Edin.*, vol. xxxix, pp. 591–4, 1899, with supplement, ibid., vol. xl, pp. 879–88, 1905. 'Rare and New Ostracoderm Fishes from the Downtownian of Shropshire' are described by L. J. Willis, ibid., vol. lviii, pp. 427–47, 1935. An admirable account of 'The Downtonian and Dittonian Strata of Great Britain and North Western Europe' is given by W. W. King in *Q.J.G.S.*, vol. xc, pp. 526–70, 1934, followed by a description of invertebrate 'Downtonian Fossils from the Anglo-Welsh Area', by F. R. C. Reed, ibid., pp. 571–84, 1934. Scandinavian fishes from equivalent horizons are recorded by J. Kiaer in 'The Downtonian Fauna of Norway', *Vidensk. selsk. Skrifter*, No. 6, 1924, and 'The Hemicyclaspis Murchisoni Fauna of the Downtonian Sandstone of Jeloen, Oslofjord', *Norsk geol. Tidsskrift*, vol. xii, pp. 419–31, 1931; by K. H. Hoppe in 'Die Coelolepiden des Obersilurs der Insel Oesel', *Palaeontographica*, Bd. lxxvi, 1931; and by J. P. Lehman in 'Les Poissons du Downtonien de la Scanie (Suède)', *Mem. Fac. Sci. Univ. Paris*, 1937.

'The Fishes of the Old Red Sandstone', by E. R. Lankester and R. H. Traquair, *Mon. Pal Soc.* 1867–1914, has been amplified by more recent work. A general account of 'The Fossil Fishes of the Orcadian Old Red Sandstone' is given by D. M. S. Watson in 'The Geology of the Orkneys', *Mem. Geol. Survey*, chap. xv, 1935, and another on 'The Old Red Sandstone Fishes of the North of Scotland' by T. S. Westoll in *Proc. Geol. Assoc.*, vol. xlviii, pp. 13–45, 1937. A. S. Woodward and E. I. White have described 'The Fossil Fishes of the Old Red Sandstone of the Shetland Islands' in *Trans. Roy. Soc. Edin.*, vol. liv, pp. 567–71, 1926, and E. A. Stensio has furnished an exhaustive memoir on 'The Cephalaspids of Great Britain', *Brit. Mus. Cat.* 1932. The latest work on The Middle Devonian Osteo-lepid Fishes of Scotland' is by B. E. Jarvik, in *Kungl. Svenska vet.-akad. Handl.*, ser. 3, Bd. xxv, pp. 301, 1948. These works contain extensive lists of literature.

For European material reference may be made to W. Gross, 'Die Arthrodeira Wildungens', *Geol. Palaeont.* Abh. Bd. xix, Heftl, 1932, and 'Die Fische des Balti-schen Devons', *Palaeontographica*, vol. lxxix, Abt. A, pp. 1–74, 1933; A. Heintz, 'Revision of the Estonian Arthrodeira', Part 1, *The Family Homosteidae*, Geol. Inst. Univ. Tartu, Publ. No. 38, 1934; E. Jarvik, 'The Species of Eusthenopteron found in Russia and the Baltic States', *Bull. Geol. Inst. Uppsala*, vol. xxvii, pp. 63–126, 1937.

'The Downtonian and Devonian Vertebrates of Spitzbergen' are described in *Skrifter om Svalbord og Ishavet*, by E. A. Stensio, No. 12 (Cephalaspida), 1927, A. Heintz, Nos. 22 and 23 (Acanthaspida), 1929, J. Kiaer, No. 40 (Cyathaspida), 1932, T. Nilsson, No. 82 (Antiarchi), 1941. 'The Placodermi of the Upper Devonian of East Greenland' are described by E. A. Stensio, Part I in *Meddelelser om Grøn-land*, Bd. 97, 1934, with supplements in 1936 and 1939, Part II by the same author, ibid., Bd. 139, 1948. The stratigraphical succession is given by G. Save-Söderbergh in 'Devonian Stratigraphy of East Greenland', *Medd. Grønl.* Bd. 96, pp. 1–40, 1934.

Devonian fishes from Canada are described by A. S. Woodward in 'The Lower Devonian Fish-Fauna of Campbellton, New Brunswick', *Geol. Mag.*, vol. xxix, pp. 1–6, 1892; by H. C. Stetson in 'A New American Thelodus', *Amer. Journ. Sci.* [5], vol. xvi, pp. 221–31, 1928; and by G. M. Robertson in 'New Cephalaspids from Canada', ibid. [5], vol. xxxi, pp. 288–95, 1936. Lists from the several localities and stratigraphical information are given by F. J. Alcock in *The Geology of Chaleur Bay Region*, Canada Geol. Surv. Mem. 183, 1935. 'Palaeozoic Fishes of North America', by J. S. Newberry in *U.S. Geol. Surv. Monog.* xvi, 1889, refers to specimens from the United States.

Australian forms are described by E. S. Hills in 'The Upper Devonian Fishes of Victoria, Australia', *Geol. Mag.*, vol. lxviii, pp. 206–31, 1931, and 'Upper Devonian Fishes from New South Wales', *Q.J.G.S.*, vol. lxxxviii, pp. 850–8, 1932. A. S. Woodward puts on record 'Fish Remains from the Upper Old Red Sandstone of Granite Harbour, Antarctica' in *Rep. Brit. Antarctic* ('*Terra Nova*') *Exped.* 1910, vol. i, 1921.

'The Devonian Fauna of the South of England', by G. F. Whidborne, *Mon. Pal. Soc.* 1889–1907, contains descriptions of many mollusca, crinoids, polyzoa, and some trilobites. Some species of Devonian trilobites are also included in 'British Trilobites', by J. W. Salter, ibid. 1864–83. The brachiopods have been described mainly by T. Davidson, the relevant part of his monograph being 'British Fossil Brachiopoda', Part VI, Devonian Brachiopoda, ibid. 1864–65, Supplement 1882–4. This work is in need of critical revision. More recently some marine fossils of Devonian age have been described by F. R. C. Reed in 'Notes on the Fauna of the Lower Devonian Beds of Torquay':—

Part I: Trilobites, *Geol. Mag.*, vol. lvii, pp. 299–306, 341–7, 1920.

Part II: Brachiopods, ibid., vol. lviii, pp. 313–24, 1921.

Part III: Mollusca, ibid., vol. lix, pp. 268–75, 303–9, 1922.

These papers contain numerous references to figures of foreign fossils.

Evidence for part of the correlation adopted in this chapter is given in 'Correlation between the Meadfoot Beds of Devonshire and the Siegenian of the Ardennes', by E. Asselberghs, *Geol. Mag.*, vol. lviii, pp. 165–9, 1921, and 'Contributions to the Geology of the Rhenish Schiefergebirge', by N. Tilmann and others in *Proc. Geol. Assoc.*, vol. xlix, pp. 1–48, 1938. Further biostratigraphical details are given by R. Wedekind in 'Die Devonische Formation', Band ii of Salomon's *Grundzüge der Geologie*, 1926. The corresponding goniatite succession in northern Russia is described by E. Holzapfel in 'Die Cephalopoden des Domaniks in Südlicher Timan', *Mem. comité geol.*, vol. xii, pp. 1–56, 1899, and that of south Europe and north Africa by H. Termier in *C.R. Soc. géol. France*, pp. 68–70, 1931.

Milne-Edwards and Haime describe several Devonian corals in their monograph on 'British Fossil Corals', Part iv, *Mon. Pal. Soc.* 1853. The genera therein described are gradually undergoing revision, and nomenclatural confusion has been reduced by the publication of an *Index of Palaeozoic Coral Genera*, by W. D. Lang, S. Smith, and H. D. Thomas, Brit. Mus. 1940. An important group of corals is described by W. D. Lang and S. Smith under the title 'Cyathophyllum caespitosum Goldfuss and other Devonian Corals', *Q.J.G.S.*, vol. xci, pp. 538–89, 1935. Other reef-building organisms form the subject of 'British Stromatoporoids', by H. A. Nicholson, *Mon. Pal. Soc.* 1886–92.

Papers on the Devonian strata in Asia include those by F. R. C. Reed on: 'Devonian Fossils from Chitral and the Pamirs', *Pal. Indica.*, N.S., vol. vi, pp. 1–134, 1922; 'Devonian Faunas of Northern Shan States', ibid., vol. ii, pp. 1–183, 1908. Devonian fossils from Yunnan are described by H. Mansuy in various papers in *Mem. Serv. géol. Indochinie*, 1908–20, and from south China by Y. C. Sun on 'The Occurrence of the Manticoceras Fauna in Central Hunan', *Geol. Soc. China, Bull.*, vol. xiv, pp. 249–54, 1935.

In Australia the Devonian corals have lately received considerable attention. D. Hill has written on 'Western Australian Devonian Corals', in *Journ. Roy. Soc. Western Austr.*, vol. xxv, pp. 141–51, 1939; on 'The Middle Devonian Rugose Corals of Queensland', *Proc. Roy. Soc. Queensland*, vol. l, pp. 55–65, and vol. li, pp. 150–68, 1939–40; on 'The Devonian Rugose Corals of Lilydale and Loyola, Victoria', *Proc. Roy. Soc. Vict.*, vol. li, pp. 219–56, 1939; on 'The Lower Middle Devonian Rugose Corals of the Murumbidgee and Goodrabidgee Rivers, N.S.W.', *Proc. Roy. Soc. N.S.W.*, vol. lxxiv, pp. 247–76, 1941; and, in collaboration with O. A. Jones, on 'The Heliolitidae of Australia', *Proc. Roy. Soc. Queensland*, vol. li, pp. 183–215, 1940. O. A. Jones has also described 'The Devonian Tabulata of Clermont, Queensland', ibid., vol. liii, pp. 41–60, 1941. G. Delepine's description of 'Upper Devonian Goniatites from Mount Pierre, Kimberley District, Western Australia', in *Q.J.G.S.*, vol. xci, pp. 208–15, 1935, has been amplified by C. Teichert in 'The Upper Devonian Goniatite Succession of Western Australia', *Amer. Journ. Sci.*, vol. ccxxxix, pp. 148–53, 1941. Many Devonian brachiopods are described by L. G. de Koninck, in *Palaeozoic Fossils of New South Wales*, Geol. Surv. N.S.W., Palaeont. Mem. No. 6, pp. 1–298, 1898. Lower Devonian faunas in New Zealand are described by R. S. Allan in *Fauna of the Reefton Beds (Devonian), New Zealand*, Geol. Surv. N.Z. Palaeont. Bull. No. 14, pp. 1–71, 1935; and by J. Shirley in 'The Fauna of the Baton River Beds (Devonian), New Zealand', *Q.J.G.S.*, vol. xciv, pp. 459–506, 1938.

Many Devonian species are among the *Index Fossils of North America* figured by H. W. Shimer and R. R. Shrock. This work may be supplemented by such papers as 'The Naples Fauna in Western New York', by J. M. Clarke, *N.Y. State Geol. Ann.*

Rep. xvi, pp. 29–161, 1898; *Devonian Ammonoids of America,* by A. K. Miller, Geol. Soc. Amer. Special Paper No. 14, 1938; *Upper Devonian Corals of the Mackenzie River Region, Canada,* by S. Smith, ibid., Special Paper No. 59, 1945; 'Faunal Differentiation in the Upper Devonian', by G. H. Chadwick in *Bull. Geol. Soc. America,* vol. xlvi, pp. 305–402, 1935.

The features of the Palaeodevonian faunas on the borders of the South Atlantic Ocean are described in 'The Fauna of the Bokkveld Beds', *Geol. Mag.,* vol. xliv, pp. 165–71, 222–32, 1907, by F. R. C. Reed, and 'Fosseis Devonianos do Parana', *Serv. Geol. Min. Brasil,* 1913, by J. M. Clarke. Both papers contain numerous references to the Falkland Islands.

VII

CARBONIFEROUS FAUNAS

STRATA of Carboniferous age in Britain present three distinct facies—(1) a lower series of marine origin, consisting mainly of limestones and known as the Carboniferous Limestone; (2) a middle series of variable and alternating shales, sandstones, and occasional limestones, termed the Millstone Grit; and (3) an upper series of shales and sandstones, mainly of freshwater origin, containing the chief coal-seams of the country, and termed the Coal Measures.

Though the fauna of the lower series, the Carboniferous Limestone, has long been familiar from the works of Phillips, Martin, M'Coy, and Davidson, it is only in the last fifty years that a satisfactory zonal classification has been devised. Most of the fossils characteristic of the Carboniferous Limestone are the remains of organisms that lived in a shallow sea, and the fauna shows the local variations consistent with peculiarities in physical conditions over limited areas. Nevertheless A. Vaughan (in 1905) was able to establish for the Bristol area a series of zones based upon the succession of certain corals and brachiopods. The pioneer work of Vaughan inspired investigations by Dixon, Garwood, Sibly, and others in various parts of the country, with the result that his zonal classification was found to apply (subject to slight local modifications) to the Carboniferous Limestone Series throughout Britain.

The zonal scheme on p. 274, established primarily for the Avon section near Bristol, also applies generally to the Mendips and South Wales; the area including these districts is conveniently designated the SOUTH-WESTERN PROVINCE. The Carboniferous Limestone of Derbyshire, Staffordshire, and North Wales forms the MIDLAND PROVINCE, which also extends to Lancashire, the Isle of Man, and eastern Ireland. The Lower Carboniferous of the Lake District and adjoining areas may likewise be considered collectively as the NORTH-WESTERN PROVINCE. NORTHUMBRIAN and SCOTTISH PROVINCES are also recognized. Each of these Provinces presents interesting features which may be discussed after a description of the zonal sequence in the typical area of the South-western Province.

The 'CLEISTOPORA' ZONE (K). The zonal index is an adherent coral whose precise relationships are obscure. It has a thick circular corallum composed of a few hexagonal corallites whose walls are built up of compact and fibrous calcareous material (Fig. 7). This structure distinguishes the form from *Michelinia* which, though generally of larger size, is somewhat

Zones of the Avonian Series

Upper Avonian	Dibunophyllum Zone (D)	D 2.	Subzone of *Lonsdaleia floriformis* (Flem.).
		D 1.	Subzone of *Dibunophyllum bourtonense* (G. and G.).
	[Lower limit defined by entrance of *Dibunophyllum*.]		
	'Seminula' Zone (S)	S 2.	Subzone of *Productus corrugato-hemisphericus* Vaughan.
		S 1.	Subzone of *Caninia bristolensis* Vaughan.
	[Lower limit defined by entrance of *Lithostrotion*].		
Lower Avonian	Syringothyris Zone (C)	C 2.	Subzone of *Palaeosmilia* φ Vaughan.
		C 1.	Subzone of *Caninia cylindrica* Scouler.
	γ. Entrance of *Caninia patula* Mich. or other large caniniid.		
	Zaphrentis Zone (Z)	Z 2.	Subzone of *Zaphrentis konincki* E. and H.
		Z 1.	Subzone of *Spirifer tornacensis* de Kon.
	β. Entrance of *Zaphrentis* and maximum of *Z. delanouei*.		
	'Cleistopora' Zone (K)	K 2.	Subzone of *Spiriferina octoplicata* (J. de C. Sow.).
		K 1.	Subzone of *Productus bassus* Vaughan.
	At base a shallow-water 'Modiola-phase' (Km.).		

NOTE: (1) The zones are generally named by the key letter shown in brackets.
(2) The horizons β and γ indicate 'faunal overlap', that is, a mixture of the faunas of contiguous zones.
(3) Since the Belgian names Tournaisian and Viséan do not correspond precisely with the English classification, the terms Lower Avonian and Upper Avonian are here substituted.

similar in appearance. In choosing this coral as the index of his K zone, Vaughan referred to it as *Cleistopora* aff. *geometrica* (Edw. and Haime). Later, L. B. Smyth (1927) rejected its reference to *Cleistopora* and assigned it to the genus *Vaughania* Garwood, with the specific name *Vaughania vetus* L. B. Smyth. This coral is confined to the K zone (but is somewhat rare in the lower portion) in the Bristol area: the upper limit of the zone is marked by the incoming of *Zaphrentis*.

The 'Modiola Phase' (Km.) constitutes the basal part of the zone, and marks a special phase of sedimentation intermediate between the Old Red Sandstone type of deposition and the standard marine conditions of the main portion of the K zone. The majority of the fossils are forms characteristic of coastal waters and include modioliform lamellibranchs, some gastropods and brachiopods, polyzoa, ostracods, and the worm *Spirorbis*. The brachiopods are shallow-water types such as *Lingula* and *Orbiculoidea*, together with a limited number of species such as *Athyris royssi* (l'Éveille) *Chonetes* cf. *hardrensis* Phil., *Eumetria* sp. which also occur in the overlying beds of ordinary marine type.

The subzone of *Productus bassus* Vaughan (K 1) contains representatives of the earlier Km. fauna, e.g. *Athyris royssi* (l'Éveille), as well as a characteristic fauna reflecting a change in physical conditions. The index-fossil, now assigned to the sub-genus *Avonia*, is a small *Productus* with abundant spines on the concentrically wrinkled and radially ribbed shell (Plate IV): it is a well-marked species, only resembling *Productus aculeatus* (Martin), which, however, belongs to a different line of descent and is characteristic of the top of the Avonian Series. Associated with *P. bassus* Vaughan, are small chonetids (*Chonetes failandensis* S. Smith and *Ch. stoddarti* Vaughan) which differ only in small details from those at higher horizons; they are only slightly convex and their ribs increase in number by forking and inter-calation. A small rhynchonellid shell, *Camarotoechia mitcheldeanensis* Vaughan (Fig. 41), is characteristic and generally abundant; spiriferids also occur, but are not prominent members of the fauna.

The subzone of *Spiriferina octoplicata* (K 2) contains few characteristic forms, but witnesses the maxima of '*Cleistopora*' and *Spiriferina octoplicata* (J. de C. Sow.). The diagnostic forms of K 1 are absent, and early repre-sentatives of the Zaphrentis fauna (next to be described) one by one make their first appearance and gradually become more abundant until at horizon β a characteristic Z facies is established.

The ZAPHRENTIS ZONE. The lower limit of this zone (known as horizon β) is marked by the first appearance of simple corals usually referred to the Devonian genus *Zaphrentis*. Some groups have already been separated under new generic names, but, pending full revision, the name *Zaphrentis* is here taken to include all the Carboniferous forms. These simple cornute corals exhibit bilateral symmetry which is rendered conspicuous by the presence of a radial depression (fossula) in each tabula. The cardinal fossula appears in cross-section as a radial gap which separates the two lateral septal groups. A lateral break in the septal sequence occurs on each side, but is usually less conspicuous. In the higher parts of zone Z the zaphrentids form the dominant faunal group, and at the upper limit of the zone they are replaced by the *Caninia* group which evolved from a zaphren-tid ancestor. Other important faunal features are the abundance of orthids, e.g. *Schizophoria resupinata* (Martin) and *Rhipidomella michelini* (l'Éveille) (Pl. II) and spiriferids (the group of *Spirifer tornacensis* de Koninck), the early evolution of the species-group usually referred to *Productus semireticu-latus* Martin, and the first appearance of *Syringothyris*.

In the subzone of *Spirifer tornacensis* (Z 1), *Zaphrentis* aff. *phillipsi* is the only zaphrentid coral; it is a form with a very deep calyx and only rudi-mentary secondary septa; the tabulae have the form of a dome with four grooves (the cardinal fossula being the deepest), down its sides. The index-fossil (*Spirifer tornacensis* de Kon.), a form with numerous fine separate ribs and a deep narrow sulcus, is usually abundant, as also are the characteristic shells *Orthotetes* (*Schellwienella*) *crenistria* and *Rhipidomella michelini* (l'Eveille). The earliest known examples of the papilionaceous *Chonetes* are associated with small forms of the *Ch. har-drensis* type.

The subzone of *Zaphrentis konincki* (Z 2) is marked by the association of *Z. konincki* (E. and H.) with *Z. phillipsi* E. and H., and by the gradual de-cline of the Z 1 brachiopod fauna. *Athyris glabristria* (Phil.) is often abun-dant in the lower part of the subzone. In the higher parts of Z 2 the zaphrentids are associated with early members of the incoming *Caninia* fauna—the coral *Caninia* and the brachiopod *Syringothyris*. The large papilionaceous *Chonetes* is now the dominant form of its group.

The SYRINGOTHYRIS ZONE (C). In this zone the characteristic coral-genus is *Caninia* (Fig. 7) which may be briefly described as a zaphrentid that has developed an outer zone of vesicular tissue, and an almost radial symmetry in place of the zaphrentid quadrantal grouping of the septa. As the vertical range of *Caninia* transgresses a marked faunal break, that coral is not taken as the zonal index. This distinction is given to the brachiopod *Syringothyris*, represented by the species *S. cuspidata* (Martin). A somewhat similar shell, formerly referred to *Syringothyris*, is *Tylothyris laminosa* (M'Coy). Both genera are recognized externally by the very large triangular cardinal area. They are associated with papilionaceous species of *Chonetes* and a mutation of *Schellwienella crenistria*, especially in the lower half of the zone (C 1). The upper subzone (C 2) has much the same fauna, but is specially indicated by the presence of *Palaeosmilia* φ (formerly *Cyathophyllum*) which is cited as the subzonal index. This coral appears to have evolved from *Caninia cylindrica* Scouler, a form which is especially abundant at the base of the zone. Certain fossils in the subzone C 2 herald the appearance of a distinct faunal assemblage. The assemblages so far described are closely related to one another and likewise the higher faunas are bound together by close relations; consequently the line of division between the Lower Avonian and the Upper Avonian is drawn between C 1 and C 2. The change in the coral-fauna comprises the replacement of *Caninia* by corals like the clisiophyllids (with a highly specialized structure in the central area) as the dominant forms. The entrance and establishment of the giganteid group of *Productus* (now the sub-genus *Gigantoproductus*), and the genera *Composita* and *Martinia* are distinguishing features of the Upper Avonian brachiopod faunas.

The 'SEMINULA' ZONE. The lower limit of this zone is marked by the entrance of the coral-genus *Lithostrotion*, which is easily distinguished by the presence of a solid rod-like columella in the central area. *Composita ficoidea* (Vaughan), formerly ascribed to the genus *Seminula*, is the dominant brachiopod. This shell is oval in shape, and has a smooth surface with strong concentric lines of growth; outwardly it resembles the terebratulid genus *Dielasma*, but may be distinguished by its non-punctate shell, while internally it possesses spiral brachial supports. *Composita ficoidea* sometimes attains rock-forming abundance in this zone.

The subzone of *Caninia bristoliensis* Vaughan (S 1) is characterized by the establishment of a dominant Upper Avonian fauna sufficiently exemplified by *Lithostrotion* among corals and *Composita* among brachiopods. Some survivors of the Lower Avonian fauna, such as species of *Caninia* and *Syringothyris*, however, still persist. A characteristic mutation of '*Orthotetes*' *crenistria* is also found, but this species-group has lost the predominance which it attained in the Lower Avonian fauna.

The index-fossil of the upper subzone (S 2) is *Productus (Linoproductus) corrugato-hemisphericus* Vaughan, a variant of the species often referred to *Productus cora* d'Orb. Papilionaceous *Chonetes, Composita, Lithostrotion martini,* and a distinctive species of *Syringopora* are characteristic, while *Spirifer, Schizophoria,* and *Syringothyris* are rare or absent. The higher parts of the subzone contain early representatives of clisiophyllid corals which attain the acme of their development in the succeeding zone. The limited nature of the S 2 fauna in the South-western Province points to the existence of special physical conditions, which caused either the immigration or the local extinction of many species. The peculiar lithology, exemplified by the dolomites, oolitic, and concretionary limestones, is consistent with this view.

The DIBUNOPHYLLUM ZONE is easily distinguished on account of its characteristic assemblage of corals. Not only do the highly specialized clisiophyllids become predominant, but the clisiophyllid character becomes impressed upon other elements of the coral-fauna. This character consists in the development of a specialized central column, formed of radial vertical elements (septal lamellae) and horizontal elements (tabellae), which becomes more complex and more irregular in members of the group with the progress of time. Among brachiopods, species and individuals of giganteid *Productus (Gigantoproductus)* are abundant, while the scabriculate and longispinous groups of the family rapidly become important. Mollusca (see Fig. 47) are abundant in some localities, especially in the reef-knoll phase of North Wales and north-east Lancashire. Species of *Bellerophon,* smooth euomphalids such as *Euomphalus pentagonalis* Phill., and *Naticopsis ampliata* (Phill.) are prominent among gastropods, while the lamellibranch *Conocardium aliforme* (J. de C. Sow.) is conspicuous by reason of the tubular prolongation of its posterior end. Trilobites are represented by the proetid genera *Phillipsia, Griffithides,* and *Brachymetopus,* and other forms, species of which are illustrated in Fig. 46.

The subzone of *Dibunophyllum bourtonense* Garwood and Goodyear (D 1) is diagnosed by the entrance in force of *Dibunophyllum* and the predominance of those members of the genus which possess a simple type of structure. It may be recalled that the central area of *Dibunophyllum* (Fig. 7) is bisected by a long mesial plate from which well-spaced lamellae radiate; in early forms this is not strongly marked, but in later forms the central area is cuspidate and strongly differentiated. The external area in D 1 forms is loosely vesicular and there is no well-defined inner wall; later species, characteristic of D 2, show a well-marked inner wall bounding the external area, which is crowded with vesicles. The horizon is also marked by the maximum development of the typical *Palaeosmilia murchisoni* E. and H., the zaphrentoid characters so noticeable in early forms from the C and S zones being almost entirely lost. Species of *Lithostrotion* and *Syringopora* are also abundant. A characteristic brachiopod at the base of the subzone is

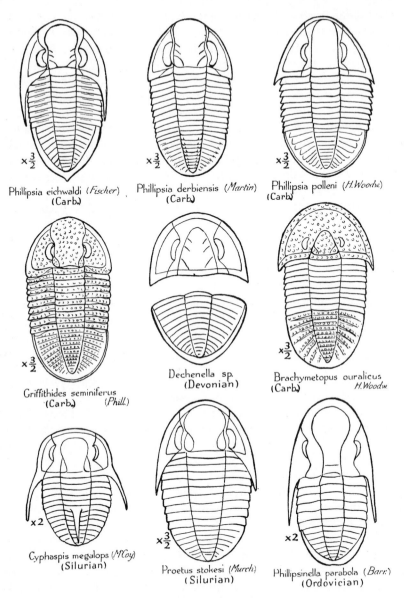

Phillipsia eichwaldi (*Fischer*) (Carb.)

Phillipsia derbiensis (*Martin*) (Carb.)

Phillipsia polleni (*H.Woodw.*) (Carb.)

Griffithides seminiferus (Carb.) (*Phill.*)

Dechenella sp. (Devonian)

Brachymetopus ouralicus (Carb.) *H.Woodw.*

Cyphaspis megalops (*M'Coy*) (Silurian)

Proetus stokesi (*Murch.*) (Silurian)

Phillipsinella parabola (*Barr.*) (Ordovician)

FIG. 46. SOME PROETID TRILOBITES (*drawn from figures by Salter and H. Woodward*)

Daviesiella llangollensis Davidson, which may be described as a productid with convergence towards *Chonetes*. It is easily recognized by the great thickness of the ventral valve, by the development of hinge-teeth, and by the presence of two pairs of adductor muscle-impressions on the interior of the valve (Pl. IV). Giganteid *Productus*—a large convex shell with fine flexuous longitudinal ribs and a broad, incurved beak—is often abundant.

In the subzone of *Lonsdaleia floriformis* (Fleming) (D 2), the highly specialized clissiophyllids are conspicuous, particularly species of *Dibuno-phyllum* and *Lonsdaleia*. The latter genus is distinguished by the fact that the septa are thickened in the middle and seldom extend through the outer vesicular zone (Fig. 7). Compound cyathophyllids such as *Palaeosmilia regia* (Phil.) show a tendency to develop clisiophyllid characters in that the original tabulae are replaced by vaulted layers of fine vesicles in the central space. Species of *Lithostrotion* frequently occur in masses and may be considered locally as rock-builders. *Zaphrentis enniskilleni* E. and H. appears to be characteristic of D 2. The productid *Gigantoproductus* is still common, and some forms show a tendency to develop a transverse shape—the latissimoid type. Spiriferids also are abundant, e.g. *Spirifer striatus* (Mart.) (Pl. III). *Athyris expansa* (Phill.) is locally common.

Higher beds (Horizon ϵ), marked particularly by a group of scabriculate and spinose productids, form the top of the Carboniferous Limestone in the Avon Section and are succeeded by the 'Millstone Grit'. In other parts of the South-western Province, e.g. in South Wales, the limestone facies extends higher and is more extensively developed in the Midland Province. Hence it seems probable that 'Millstone Grit conditions' did not begin at the same time over the whole country; otherwise the Grits must overstep the limestones uncomfortably in many districts. It is convenient to continue the account of the coral-brachiopod zones here, though it is necessary to refer particularly to the Midland Province.

The upper beds of the D 2 subzone are variable in lithological character. A shaly facies is marked by the occurrence of *Cyathaxonia*, a small coral whose septa retreat from the central area, but remain in contact laterally, and the space between their distal ends becomes filled with secondary calcareous tissue forming a columella. *Cyathaxonia* is known from the Midland Province (where this facies is characteristically developed), and from the highest limestone beds at Prestatyn in North Wales and Gower in South Wales. Scabriculate and spinose productids, bisulcate and smooth spiriferids, and late species of *Zaphrentis* and *Caninia* are also found here. A limestone facies, occurring in the north of England and the Vale of Clwyd, North Wales, contains numerous reef-building corals which include *Orionastraea phillipsi*, a development from a *Lithostrotion*, and *Corwenia*, a branching form whose corallites resemble those of *Dibunophyllum*.

The POSIDONOMYA ZONE (P). In some parts of the country, another shaly phase of the D 2 subzone, often termed the Posidonomya Zone, presents a striking change in the fauna. Many forms previously abundant become extinct, while others show excessive specialization. Thus the coral-genus *Carcinophyllum* shows a lonsdaleoid tendency, the brachiopod *Schizophoria* produces gigantic and spinous varieties. Also certain genera (e.g. *Camarophoria*) become abundant for the first time. Lamellibranchs become more important, and especially noteworthy is the occurrence of *Posidonomya becheri* Bronn (Fig. 47), the zonal index, since it appears to be eminently characteristic of a shale facies. The problematical *Conularia quadrisulcata* J. Sow. (Fig. 47), sometimes classed with the pteropodous gastropods, is occasionally abundant. Goniatites are common in some localities and, as they are more restricted in vertical range, are now used as zone-fossils for these upper beds; for the sake of uniformity they are discussed separately on pages 286–8. The lower part, at least, of the Posidonomya zone seems to indicate faunal overlap, marking a transitional phase between the coral-brachiopod fauna of the Avonian Series and the goniatite-lamellibranch assemblage of the variable strata above. The necessary adjustment of the zonal nomenclature is a task for the future.

PROVINCIAL VARIATIONS

The SOUTH-WESTERN PROVINCE extends from Pembroke to the Forest of Dean, the Clee Hills, and the Mendips, and is bounded on the north by the Midland ridge. Zoning of the Carboniferous Limestone Series was first effected in the Bristol area, and subsequent research has proved that local variations exist in Pembroke, the Gower Peninsula, and the Mendips. The faunal differences are in most cases correlated with variations in lithology. A Modiola-phase is usually, but not always, found immediately over the Old Red Sandstone; but Dixon and Vaughan have shown that Modiola-phases may occur at various horizons, giving evidence of changes in the relative level of land and sea and consequent variations in conditions of deposition. Thus in the northern part of the Forest of Dean the succession is:

$$\text{O.R.S.—K 1—K 2m—K 2.}$$

Shallow-water deposits are usually variable in character and are especially exemplified in the type-area (apart from Modiola phases) by the occurrence of contemporaneous dolomites (C and S) and oolites (in C 1, S 1, and S 2). In the Mendips C 2–S 1 consists of standard limestones with a fauna that is incompletely represented in the Bristol area; the Caninia Oolite (C 1) is represented by such limestones; and the D zone consists more completely of standard limestones, while 'Millstone Grit conditions' come on more abruptly. At Weston-super-Mare the Mid-Avonian deposits are intermediate between those of Bristol and the Mendips; two volcanic horizons occur at the base of C 1 and C 2 respectively with 'laminosa-dolomite' between

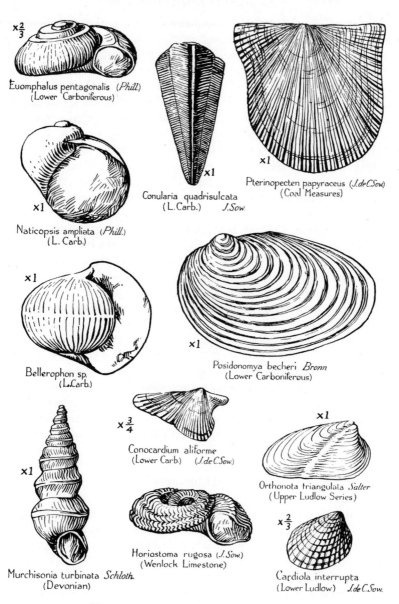

$\times\frac{2}{3}$

Euomphalus pentagonalis *(Phill.)*
(Lower Carboniferous)

$\times1$

Naticopsis ampliata *(Phill.)*
(L. Carb.)

Conularia quadrisulcata
(L. Carb.)   *J. Sow.*

$\times1$

$\times1$

Pterinopecten papyraceus *(J.de C.Sow.)*
(Coal Measures)

$\times1$

Bellerophon sp.
(L.Carb.)

$\times1$

Posidonomya becheri *Bronn*
(Lower Carboniferous)

$\times\frac{3}{4}$

Conocardium aliforme
(Lower Carb.)   *(J.de C.Sow.)*

$\times1$

Orthonota triangulata *Salter*
(Upper Ludlow Series)

$\times1$

Murchisonia turbinata *Schloth.*
(Devonian)

Horiostoma rugosa *(J.Sow.)*
(Wenlock Limestone)

$\times\frac{2}{3}$

Cardiola interrupta
(Lower Ludlow)   *J.de C.Sow.*

FIG. 47. SOME PALAEOZOIC MOLLUSCA

and are thus associated with shallowing due to earth-movements. This Mid-Avonian shallowing increases northwards, and in the north-west margin of the South Wales coalfield there is a marked unconformity of variable vertical extent; west of Pendine it is slight, at Pendine itself the C zone is cut out, while east of the Towy S 1 rests on K. In the Forest of Dean shallow-water deposits predominate all through the series, and there is contemporaneous dolomite in Z; the 'Millstone Grit' is apparently of S age and Upper Coal Measures rest unconformably upon it. In the Clee Hill, K, Z 1, and Z 2 are followed by thin shallow-water deposits, then conformable 'Millstone Grit', and finally unconformable Coal Measures. In Gower there is no typical 'Millstone Grit', the highest Avonian being succeeded by black shales with a characteristic molluscan fauna as in the Midland Province.

Only the highest Avonian is known in the MIDLAND PROVINCE, the lowest limestones in North Wales being formed by the band of *Daviesiella llangollensis* Dav. (Pl. IV) which marks the base of the D zone. The D 1 fauna is poorly developed as compared with the South-western Province, while that of the D 2 subzone in the Midlands is characterized not only by the abundance and variety of its brachiopods but also by the great development of large simple clisiophyllid corals. The Cyathaxonia phase is marked by the occurrence of small cornute corals (*Zaphrentis* and *Cyathaxonia*) and is said partly to succeed and partly to replace the D 2 subzone. The limestone *massif* in this province is succeeded by a series of black shales and limestones with a fauna consisting mainly of goniatites and lamellibranchs (P). The uppermost limestones in parts of the Midland Province also show the peculiar 'reef-knolls'—masses of pure, fine-grained, obscurely bedded limestones which give rise to abrupt and characteristically rounded topographical features. These knolls are not always rich in fossils but here and there throughout the mass they contain 'nests' or 'pockets' which have provided many museum-specimens of Carboniferous brachiopods. As a general rule corals are rare, with the possible exception of *Amplexus*. This genus is a cylindrical form with conspicuous tabulae but only a feeble development of septa; its characters are usually taken as indicating rapid growth in length. Among the abundant brachiopods are several forms that appear to be typical of the reef-knoll facies; species of *Pugnax* (Fig. 41), especially *P. acuminatus* (Martin), are generally profuse in individuals. *P. acuminatus* (Mart.) is typical of high D horizons, while plicated forms like *P. plicatus* (Sow.) occur in the C and S zones. It has been suggested that these plicated forms gave rise to *P. acuminatus* by disappearance of the lateral fold and increase in size of the central fold. *Leptaena analoga* Phillips, *Schizophoria resupinata* (Martin), *Rhynchotreta angulata* (Linn.) (Fig. 41), the peculiar *Productus striatus* Martin (Pl. IV), and species of *Pustula, Spirifer, Martinia, Dielasma* may also be cited. Another feature is the importance of mollusca, both lamellibranchs and gastropods, in the fauna of the reef-knolls. The stratigraphical relations of the knolls are obscure and the problem is complicated in many cases by faulting. It has become evident, however, that special conditions of deposition are involved, and that various knolls belong to different zones. While those of Derbyshire, North Wales, and the Isle of Man probably represent D 2 horizons (since they enclose certain species of goniatites to be mentioned later), the famous knolls of Lancashire belong to various horizons between C and D 2. Further, D. Parkinson has shown that the Clitheroe knolls change laterally into shale-deposits within a very short distance. This results in great irregularities in the level of the original sea floor which are apt to obscure the relations of overlying deposits.

The NORTH-WESTERN PROVINCE presents striking divergences from the typical Avonian area largely due to original differences in the conditions of deposition. Perhaps the most striking faunal feature is the importance of calcareous algae as rock-builders at certain horizons which can thereby be traced over considerable areas and used as datum-lines in mapping. In his investigation of this area E. J. Garwood found it necessary to use guide-fossils different from those utilized in the Bristol area. The fossil forms most useful in this connexion are given in the accompanying table, together with the corresponding zones of the Avon section.

Avonian Zones in the North-western Province

Zones	Subzones	Approximate equivalents in S.W. prov.
Dibunophyllum	Dibunophyllum muirheadi Thoms. and Nich.	
	Lonsdaleia floriformis (Fleming)	D 2
	Palaeosmilia murchisoni Edw. and Haime	D 1
Productus corrugato-hemisphericus Vaughan	Nematophyllum minus (M'Coy)	
	Cyrtina carbonaria (M'Coy)	S 2
	Gastropod Beds	S 1
Michelina grandis M'Coy	Chonetes carinata Garwood	
	Camarophoria isorhyncha (M'Coy)	C 2
Athyris glabristia (Phil.)	Seminula gregaria (M'Coy)	
	Solenopora	C 1

Calcareous algae are abundant at three horizons, namely, the *Solenopora* subzone (C 1), the base of the subzone of '*Seminula*' *gregaria* (top of C 1), and at the base of the upper *Dibunophyllum* zone (D 2). It is interesting to note that in the first two cases dolomitic limestones are closely associated with the development of calcareous algae.

The Carboniferous Limestone Series of the NORTHUMBRIAN PRO-VINCE is distinguished by its variable lithological characters, and on this basis has long been subdivided as follows:

BERNICIAN { Calcareous Division
            Carbonaceous   ,,

TUEDIAN { Fell Sandstone
          Cementstone Group

The Tuedian stage represents, in the main, lagoon phases, and its chief fossils are ostracods, *Spirorbis*, lamellibranchs, and gastropods suggestive of shallow-water habitats. The series is difficult to correlate with the Avonian of other areas, owing to this difference of facies. The highest beds of the Cementstone Group have, however, yielded *Syringothyris cuspidata* (Martin) and *Athyris glabristria* (Phil.), fossils which indicate the C zone of Bristol. The base of the Fell Sandstone locally contains *Camarophoria isorhyncha* (M'Coy), *Tylothyris laminosa*, and *Lithostrotion* which link it with S 1 of the North-western Province. The Carbonaceous Division of the Bernician stage consists mainly of shales and sandstones with thin impure limestones and beds of coal. In some districts this division has yielded species of *Lithostrotion* and other fossils of the S 2 fauna. In the upper division of the Bernician the limestones are thicker and more constant, and contain a rich marine fauna, representative of the two subdivisions of the Dibunophyllum zone. This development of shales, sandstones, and limestones is characteristic of a wide area in the northern counties where it has long been known as the Yoredale Series. It presents several interesting features which are probably due to depositional factors and its upper part is perhaps contemporaneous with the 'Millstone Grit' (so-called) of the South-western Province. The lower beds of the series contain faunas which can be correlated with D 1 and D 2 of the Midland and South-western Provinces. But with a continuation of the limestone facies and the consequent development of the same fauna, difficulties are encountered in comparing the Yoredale Series with the deposits of other areas where different conditions prevailed. The fauna of the Yoredale Series is marked especially by the development of large simple clisiophyllid corals, such as varieties of *Dibunophyllum bipartitum* (M'Coy) and *Koninckophyllum magnificum* Thoms., while the massive *Palaeosmilia regia* (Phillips) and *Lonsdaleia floriformis* (Fleming) accompany the dendroid *L. duplicata* (Martin) of lower horizons. *Orionastraea phillipsi* (M'Coy) represents an astraeoid development of the *Lithostrotion* stock and is highly characteristic of this zone. A further feature is the great development of the foraminifer *Saccamina carteri* which forms the bulk of certain limestone-bands. These bands or 'posts' are easily recognized by their spotted appearance and furnish a good index for correlation over a wide area. The productid *Gigantoproductus* is exceedingly abundant and is perhaps sufficiently exemplified by *Productus giganteus* Martin, and P. *latissimus* Sowerby (Pl. IV). *Composita ambigua* (J. de C. Sow.) (Pl. III) sometimes occurs in profusion.

The SCOTTISH PROVINCE. The Lower Carboniferous rocks in the Midland Valley of Scotland present much similarity with those in the north of England. They are readily divisible into the Calciferous Sandstone below, and the Carboniferous Limestone Series above. The Calciferous Sandstone begins with the Cementstone Beds, an alternation of grey or black shales and thin limestones or occasionally sandstones; in most places these beds pass up gradually from the Old Red Sandstone. The Cementstone Beds correspond to the lower part of the Tuedian Stage of Northumberland; and the Liddisdale Cementstone has yielded *Zaphrentis delanouei* E. and H., *Z. parallela* Carr., as well as *Camarotoechia proava* (Phillips), a species of *Vaughania*, and calcareous algae comparable with those from the C 1 beds of Cumberland. The succeeding Oil Shale Beds, interrupted in places by contemporaneous lavas, show an alternation of sandstones, shales, thin coals, ironstones, and thin limestones with shelly bands. The limestones of Lawston Linn have yielded *Zaphrentis lawstonensis* Carr. with species of *Clisiophyllum* and *Lithostrotion* which are referable to the D 1 subzone. A slightly lower horizon (S 2 D 1) is indicated at Arbigland Bay on the Solway Firth. Near the top of the Calciferous Sandstone reef-corals of the genera *Corwenia*, *Lithostrotion*, *Lonsdaleia*, and *Orionastraea* indicate a D 2 age. The overlying Carboniferous Limestone Series thus represents, at least in part, the Yoredale Beds of the north of England. It contains a considerable number of reef-corals, including species of *Lithostrotion* with derivative forms of *Aulina* and *Diphyphyllum*, *Lonsdaleia floriformis* (Martin), *Palaeosmilia regia* (Phill.), together with simple clisiophyllid forms. Above the limestones is the Coal Measures Series which is discussed on pages 288–92.

UPPER CARBONIFEROUS FAUNAS

The Carboniferous Limestone Series is succeeded by a variable series of shales and sandstones with subordinate limestones. The fauna of this series is very distinct from that enclosed by the strata below. Instead of the predominance of corals and brachiopods, the most abundant fossils are lamellibranchs and goniatites, while the abundance of well-preserved plant-impressions at some localities is not without significance. This change in fauna reflects the oncoming of the coarse detrital deposits of late Carboniferous horizons. The bivalves *Posidonomya becheri* Bronn. (Fig. 47) and species of *Pterinopecten* are characteristic forms, and while the former is accepted as a useful index-fossil, species of *Pterinopecten* have until recently been recorded by the comprehensive term *P. papyraceus* (J. de C. Sow.). This form is typical of the Coal Measures; but earlier species have now been separated by J. W. Jackson and promise to be useful for correlative purposes. Ammonoids have long been used as zone-fossils and the goniatites have not proved lacking in this quality. In 1924 W. S. Bisat proposed a series of zones based upon the succession of goniatites of which many species have a limited vertical range and apparently a wide geographical distribution. This classification, which is more detailed than the schemes suggested by E. Haug and by Wheelton Hind, has been verified by the Geological Survey in Lancashire, Yorkshire, and Derbyshire, and by other workers in Wales.

The lowest Carboniferous goniatites known in Great Britain occur in the Carboniferous Limestone (zone C) of South Wales, and are referred to species of *Muensteroceras* and *Pericyclus*. These genera are variable in degree of involution and inflation, and whereas *Muensteroceras* is ornamented only by growth-lines, *Pericyclus* has comparatively strong, rounded, transverse ribs which are embayed on the periphery. Owing to the scarcity of these cephalopods in the limestones, their full range in terms of the coral-brachiopod succession is not yet known.

The next well-authenticated record is in limestones of the D 2 subzone of the Isle of Man, North Wales, and Derbyshire, where compressed shells of *Beyrichoceras*, and globose species of *Goniatites* with angular suture-lines are associated with *Merocanites*, distinguished by its evolute shell with tongue-shaped septal sutures. Bisat has established the zone B for the rocks containing this assemblage, though it undoubtedly falls within the Dibunophyllum zone.

The younger zone P, with *Posidonomya becheri* as its most abundant fossil, consists mainly of shales, e.g. the Bowland Shales of Lancashire, and the lower part of the Holywell Shales in Flintshire. The characteristic goniatites belong to the genus *Goniatites* (s. str.), familiar under the name *Glyphioceras* which is now said to be a synonym. In this genus the shell is tightly coiled (occlusal) and extremely stout, while the septal sutures possess the acutely angular outlines which originally suggested the name *Goniatites*. The zone P carries two distinct faunas. The lower one contains *Goniatites crenistria* Phillips, a sphaeroid form ornamented by fine crenulated transverse striae. This shell is also found in limestone which contain a D 2 coral-brachiopod assemblage. As *P. becheri* has also been recorded from shales intercalated with D 2 limestones in Yorkshire and North Wales, it would appear that the lower P beds represent merely an argillaceous phase of the D 2 subzone. The upper fauna has the group of *Goniatites spiralis* Phillips (Pl. V) as its index. The trivial name recalls the typical spiral ornamentation which is the only diagnostic feature available when the shell is crushed flat in beds of shale. The top of this zone is taken as the line of division between Lower and Upper Carboniferous strata.

The next zone (E) is characterized by species of the genus *Eumorphoceras*. These forms are ornamented on the lateral area by elongated nodes which are bounded towards the periphery by two strong spiral furrows; outside the furrows the nodes are replaced by striae which are concave backwards, thus giving evidence of a hyponomic sinus. Species of *Eumorphoceras* occur in the upper part of the Bowland Shales, the Pendle Grit, and the lower part of the Sabden Shales in Lancashire. A typical form, *E. bisulcatum* (Girty), from the Holywell Shales of Flintshire is illustrated in Pl. V. The compressed shells of *Anthracoceras*, ornamented with delicate transverse striae, and the nautiloid *Tylonautilus nodiferus*, are valuable guide-fossils, having been recorded from localities in North Wales, Lancashire, Derbyshire, Yorkshire, Northumberland, Cumberland, and the Midland Valley of Scotland.

The genus *Homoceras* makes its appearance in overlying strata (zone H), the middle part of the Sabden Shales in Lancashire. *Homoceras* is recognized by its inflated whorl-section, its transverse non-crenulate ornament (spiral striae being generally absent), and the wide ventral lobe (with raised median saddle) of the septal sutures. A crushed specimen of *H. proteum* Brown, from Congleton (Cheshire) is shown in Pl. V; this form has spiral ornament intersecting the transverse striae. The same photograph shows fragments of *H. diadema* (Beyrich) with flexed transverse ornament. In the upper part of the zone, *Homoceras* is associated with *Homoceratoides prereticulatum* Bisat (Pl. V) whose ornament is similar to that of *H. diadema*, but the inner whorls (striate in *H. diadema*) bear fairly strong ribs as in the later genus *Reticuloceras*.

The upper part of the Sabden Shales, the Kinderscout Grit, and the so-called Middle Grits of Lancashire and Yorkshire constitute the zone R, and enclose species of *Reticuloceras*. This genus has crenulate transverse ornament crossed by feeble spiral striae, giving a reticulate pattern which is suggested in the generic name. The type-species, *R. reticulatum* (Phill.) shown in Plate V, has relatively strong ornament compared with later species. W. S. Bisat has distinguished 'mutations' which appear to be typical of definite horizons. Since, however, the term 'mutation' has been used in several connexions, specific names are here used instead of the usual Greek letters. *R. gracile* Bisat (Pl. V), often called 'mut. α', has extremely delicate ornament and a raised spiral ridge (the lingua) at the peripheral shoulder. In 'mut. β' or *R. bilingue* (Salter), there is a general lack of crenulation of the striae except in young individuals, and the lingua has a marked forward projection. The latter feature is strengthened in *R. superbilingue* Bisat ('mut. γ') so that a spiral groove is often seen on internal moulds and a superficial resemblance with species of *Eumorphoceras* is produced.

The genus *Reticuloceras* is succeeded by *Gastrioceras* which extends upwards into, and is especially characteristic of, the Lower Coal Measures. *Gastrioceras*, a robust form with tubercles on the umbilical margins, has been made familiar by the abundance of *G. listeri* (Martin) (Pl. V) and other species (preserved solid in the calcareous 'bullions') in the Lower Coal Measures of Lancashire and Yorkshire.

The COAL MEASURES comprise a thick series of shales and sandstones with intercalated seams of coal. These strata appear to have been deposited (for the most part in fresh water) on a low-lying land-surface, not far from the margin of the sea. Occasional bands, containing marine fossils, indicate temporary invasions of the sea over the area of deposition, and the widespread marine bands now furnish an important means of correlating the rocks of the coalfields. The zone of *Gastrioceras* (G) in the Lower Coal Measures is succeeded by the Middle Coal Measures with marine bands containing goniatites of the genus *Anthracoceras* associated with nautiloids such as *Metacoceras* and *Pleuronautilus*. This zone A shows three main horizons. The lowest is the Seven-foot Banbury Marine Band of north Staffordshire, and the Pennystone Ironstone of Coalbrookdale; the chief species here are *M. falcatum* (J. de C. Sow.) and *A. aegiranum* H. Schmidt. A middle horizon with *M. costatum* (Hind), and *A. hindi* Bisat is represented by the Gin Mine Marine Band of north Staffordshire, the Mansfield Marine Band in Nottinghamshire, the Dukinfield Band in south Lancashire, the Cefn Coed in South Wales, and Skipsey's Marine Band in Scotland. The highest horizon is seen in the Cwmgorse Marine Band at Cefn Coed in South Wales which yields *M. postcostatum* Bisat and *A. cambriense* Bisat.

The Coal Measures, comprising (in some areas) several thousands of feet of rock, were first classified on lithological features into Lower, Middle, and Upper Coal Measures. Correlation on this basis, however, is always uncertain, owing to the variable nature of the strata. Moreover, these divisions are too large for any but general purposes. Yet it is obviously desirable that a scheme should be devised, not only for correlating broad divisions of the Coal Measures of one coalfield with those of other coalfields, but also for the correlation and identification of individual coal-seams within smaller areas. The identification of coal-seams has necessarily been attempted by mining engineers, who rely chiefly upon the general characters of the strata, namely, thickness of the seam and its general appearance, the character of the roof, and the thickness of beds between the coal-seams. Such means of correlation, however, are not always sufficiently accurate owing to lateral variation of the rocks. In the case of thick seams correlation may be possible over a distance of a few miles, since continuous deposition of a thick bed would probably extend over a considerable area. But thin coals may have been formed in one area while sand or shale was being deposited elsewhere; thus the correlation of thin seams on the evidence of general characters is very uncertain.

Intensive work on the fossils of the Coal Measures during the last three decades has shown that palaeontological evidence is much more reliable. The fauna consists mainly of bivalved mollusca, long referred to the genera *Carbonicola*, *Naiadites*, and *Anthracomya*, which are believed to have lived under non-marine conditions. The first-named genus is much like the freshwater *Unio* of the present day, having a general oval shape with the umbones at some distance from either end (Fig. 48). Two distinct groups have recently been separated from *Carbonicola*. One comprises shells formerly ascribed to *C. aquilina* (J. de C. Sow.), compressed and ovate in form, with the anterior end small and rounded, the posterior end elongate and tumid; for these forms the old genus *Anthracosia* has been revived. The small tumid Carbonicolas of the *turgida* group (Fig. 48) have likewise been placed in the new genus *Anthracospherium*. *Naiadites* has the shape of a mussel, the umbones being situated at the extreme end of the shell, and *Anthracomya* is somewhat intermediate between *Naiadites* and *Carbonicola*. The familiar name *Anthracomya*, however, is a synonym, and *Anthraconaia* has been proposed in its place. Moreover, the group of *A. phillipsi* has been separated under the generic name *Anthraconauta*.

Species of these shells now provide a means for correlating broad zones in the Coal Measures, though former workers thought their vertical range too long for this purpose. W. Hind, however, drew up a chart of the north Staffordshire coalfield based on the distribution of these mollusca, while J. H. Davies and A. E. Trueman (1927) claim that 'at each horizon in the South Wales coalfield the various members of a single species-group show different degrees of advancement, but the proportions of different members of that species-group are constant everywhere at that horizon'. Accurate specific identification is essential, and this is rendered difficult because many of the present specific names apparently cover assemblages of several species-groups, each following a particular trend in evolution. Seams in a small area may be correlated by the assemblage of species-groups at each horizon, but this is uncertain for distant outcrops, since terrestrial assemblages are often dependent upon climatic or other physical conditions and thus may not be comparable with their contemporaries in widely separated localities. By means of these assemblages the Coal Measures succession is divided into the following zones:

The zone of *Anthraconaia lenisulcata* is the lowest zone marked by non-marine mollusca yet formulated in the Upper Carboniferous succession. The index-fossil *A. lenisulcata* Trueman has an elongate shell with small umbones, short anterior end, and straight lower border. It is associated with several species of *Carbonicola*. *C. recta* Trueman is an elongate form with strong growth-lines, blunt posterior end, and slightly hollowed anterior umbonal slope. *C. protea* Wright is a fairly large shell with small umbones and arched posterior slope. *C. fallax* Wright is broadly carinated and obliquely truncated at the posterior end. *C. limax* Wright is distinguished by a certain obliquity of the shell, and the conspicuous arch of the dorsal margin. In addition a few species persist into this zone from the underlying Millstone Grit, as, for example, the little *Anthraconaia bellula* (Bolton), and the large *C. pseudacuta* Trueman with straight ventral margin.

The zone of *Carbonicola communis*. The dominant shells in this zone are species of large Carbonicolas. *C. communis* Davies & Trueman is a

Anthraconauta phillipsi *(Will.)*   Anthraconauta tenuis *D.&T.*

Anthraconaia pulchra *Hind*   Anthraconaia wardi *Salter*

Anthraconauta adamsi *Salter*

Anthracosia similis *(Br.)*   Anthracosia aquilina *(Sow.)*

Naiadites carinata *I.deC.Sow*

Anthraconaia modiolaris *(Sow.)*   Anthraconaia williamsoni *(Brown)*   Anthracospherium turgida *Brown*

Carbonicola ovalis *(Martin)*   Carbonicola communis *D.&T.*   Carbonicola obtusa *Hind*

FIG. 48. LAMELLIBRANCHS FROM THE BRITISH COAL MEASURES (*drawn from figures by Hind and Trueman*). *All about two-thirds the natural size*

moderately tumid, ovate shell with bluntly rounded posterior end, and a practically straight lower border (Fig. 48). *C. martini* Trueman & Weir has a somewhat narrow posterior end with a straight dorsal margin. *C. obtusa* Hind has a thick, robust shell with small umbones and prominent growth-lines (Fig. 48). *C. crista-galli* Wright, which is restricted to the upper part of the zone, is a thick, coarsely ornamented shell with a short, oblique posterior margin. The large, tumid *C. pseudorobusta* Trueman, a derivative of *C. communis*, is also prominent in the upper part of the zone. The only species of *Anthraconaia* recorded from this zone is *A. minima* (Ludwig), a small elongate shell with almost parallel borders. *Naiadites triangularis* (J. de C. Sow.) is also present; it is with difficulty separated from apparently allied forms, like *N. carinata* (J. de C. Sow.) by the rounded character of its carina.

The **Zone of *Anthraconaia modiolaris*** is characterized by the appearance in abundance of distinctive species belonging to the group of *Anthraconaia modiolaris* (J. de C. Sow.). The index fossil is distinguished by its feeble carina and small umbones (Fig. 48); with the slightly more elongate *A. williamsoni* (Brown) it is dominant at the lowest horizons. These species are accompanied at higher horizons by *A. curtata* (Brown) and *A. insignis* (Davies & Trueman) in which the ridge or carina is more distinctly developed. The species of the *Carbonicola* group are generally small and often inflated forms which are now placed in the genus *Anthracospherium* (Fig. 48). *A. turgidum* (Brown) has stout, contiguous umbones and a straight lower border; *A. dawsoni* (Brown) is a nearly circular shell with almost central umbones; *A. exiguum* (Davies & Trueman) is more elongate and its hinge-line is nearly parallel with the long axis of the shell. Species of *Naiadites* range up from the preceding zone.

The former zones of *Anthracosia similis* and of *Anthraconaia pulchra* have been merged into one **similis-pulchra zone**, because they were distinguished from one another only with difficulty. The first index-fossil, *A. similis* (Brown), belongs to the old group of *Carbonicola aquilina*, which persists from the preceding zone. *A. aquilina* (J. de C. Sow.) comprises elongate shells with a small rounded and compressed anterior end, and a long tumid posterior end; the hinge-line is raised and is separated from the distant umbones by a longitudinal groove. *C. nitida* Davies and Trueman is similar in the form of the anterior end but the posterior is less tumid and the hinge-characters are less distinct. The rounded anterior end of *A. similis* passes uniformly into the slope of the umbones which do not project noticeably above the level of the hinge-region. These species mark the persistence of *Anthracosia* into the lower part of the similis-pulchra zone; the genus is extremely rare in the upper part of the zone. Here, *Anthraconaia pulchra* Hind represents a distinct series of *Anthraconaia* in which the posterior wing is less elevated than in the earlier groups of *A. modiolaris*, and the lower border is typically almost straight (Fig. 48). *A. wardi* Salter has only a feeble carina and the umbones do not project above the hinge-line which is almost parallel with the straight lower border of the shell. *A. adamsi* Salter has a more distinct carina than the last-named species and the lower border is obliquely convex. The assemblage also includes shells of *Naiadites* in some abundance, but the species are difficult to separate from one another.

In the **Zone of *Anthraconauta phillipsi*,** *Carbonicola Naiadites* and *Anthracosia* all seem to be absent. Shells are often abundant, but belong to a few types which are regarded as variants of *Anthraconauta phillipsi* (Williamson). Most specimens are crushed, but the hinge-line of this species appears to be straight and the posterior end curves round into the convex lower border, giving the shell an oval shape. The anterior end is short and rounded, and the umbones do not project above the hinge-line (Fig. 48).

The succeeding **Zone of *Anthraconauta tenuis*** is known in South Wales but has not been detected in Staffordshire. *A. tenuis* D. & T. is an elongate shell with a short, rounded, anterior end; the posterior end is expanded obliquely downwards and backwards (Fig. 48). Since *A. tenuis* is accompanied by *A. phillipsi* this zone is not sharply differentiated from the preceding one. No other shells are typically present.

The **Zone of *Anthraconauta prolifera*** is known only in the Radstock Series of the Bristol area. Here, shells of *Anthraconauta* are found sporadically in shales containing an abundance of plant remains. The shells are somewhat varied, but are all referred by A. E. Trueman to *A. prolifera* Waterlot.

FAUNAL REGIONS

WESTERN and CENTRAL EUROPE. Deposits of Carboniferous age are widely distributed in Europe, and the names Dinantian, Namurian, Westphalian, and Stephanian have long been used for successive divisions in ascending order. The limits of the series, however, remained uncertain until, at an international congress at Haarlem in 1927, they were defined by reference to goniatite horizons, the goniatites being regarded as the most reliable index-fossils. In the Westphalian Series, four successive floras, labelled A, B, C, and D were also defined at the same time, the limits between them being well-known and widespread marine bands containing goniatites. This classification of the Carboniferous system in western Europe with the addition of the non-marine lamellibranch zones is tabulated on p. 293.

Limestones of the Dinantian Series are well developed along the valley of the Meuse in Belgium and northern France. Near Avesnes, Dinant, and Liége the horizon known as the 'Zone d'Etroeungt' forms a transition between the marine Devonian and the Carboniferous Limestone. It shows a striking development of pale crinoid limestones which enclose early representatives of typical Carboniferous corals and brachiopods, together with a few Devonian survivors. This horizon is taken by the Belgian Geological Survey as the uppermost bed of the Neodevonian Famennian stage,

Carboniferous Zones of Western Europe

STEPHANIAN SERIES
    Zone of *Anthraconaia prolifera.*
    Conglomerat de Holz (Saar Basin).

WESTPHALIAN SERIES
    Maximum development of *Anthraconauta.*
    Zone of *A. tenuis.*   Flora D
    Zone of *A. Phillipsi.*   Flora C
    Marine horizon of Petit Buisson, Aegir, Mansfield, &c.
    Maximum development of *Anthracosia* and *Naiadites*
    (modiolaris and similis-pulchra zones)   Flora B
    Marine horizon of Katharina, Poissonière, Gin Mine, &c.
    Maximum development of *Carbonicola*
    (lenisulcata and communis zones).   Flora A
    Gastrioceras zone—horizon of *G. subcrenatum* at base.

NAMURIAN SERIES
    Reticuloceras zone.
    Homoceras zone.
    Eumorphoceras zone.

DINANTIAN SERIES
    Goniatites zone   } = Viséan stage.
    Beyrichoceras zone
    Pericyclus zone   = Tournaisian stage.
               Zone d'Etroeungt at base.

but A. Vaughan (1915) correlates it with the K 2 zone of the Avon succession. It will be remembered that the K zone follows deposits of the Old Red Sandstone type, and has an immigrant fauna which is essentially Avonian in character. Vaughan also states that the Upper Pilton Beds of Devonshire, which follow marine Devonian deposits, have a mixed fauna containing persistent Devonian forms. The base of the Carboniferous system in south-west England, therefore, lies at a level which, on the Continent of Europe, is included in the Devonian system. Hence the Dinantian Series of Belgium is not the exact equivalent of the Avonian Series of England, though many authors use the terms indiscriminately.

The Dinantian Series itself is subdivided into two stages, the Tournaisian below, and the Viséan above. The lower stage is correlated by Vaughan (1915) with zones Z 1, Z 2, and C 1 of the Avonian succession in south-west England. It begins with the Hastière Limestone and Shale which shows the first establishment of *Zaphrentis* and rare occurrence of *Caninia* which did not reach Britain until Z 2. The succeeding shales and limestones with an abundance of *Spiriferina octoplicata*, together with the basal beds of the Landelies Limestone, form the equivalent of Z 1. The main part of the Landelies Limestone, with the overlying Maredsous Shale, containing species of *Caninia, Zaphrentis konincki, Cyathaxonia cornu, Productus burlingtonensis,* and *Spirifer tornacensis,* is correlated with Z 2. A standard limestone with chert, known as Calcaire d'Yvoir, is marked by the appearance of *Caninia patula* and is placed with horizon γ of the Avon succession. The Belgian equivalent of zone C 1 begins with the 'Petit Granit', a peculiar limestone formed mainly of crinoid debris, with a rich fauna which includes an abundance of *Caninia patula*, the acme of *Spirifer konincki* and large-sized *Conocardium*. Much the same fauna is found in the Calcaire de Paire, a standard limestone with some early forms of typical Viséan genera, *Composita* for instance. A local phase around Waulsort shows the characters of the knoll limestones of Clitheroe with the special fauna of such deposits (p. 282).

Above the Tournaisian Beds just described is a group of brecciated oolite and black limestones, the so-called 'marbre noir'. These beds enclose a varied fauna in which new elements appear; for instance, the coral-genera *Lithostrotion* and *Diphyphyllum*, nucleate clisiophyllids, and early species of *Koninckophyllum* and *Carcinophyllum*, the punctate and fimbriate groups of *Productus*, and species of *Composita*. These beds, correlated with horizon δ of south-west England, are taken as transitional from Tournaisian to Viséan. The S zone of Bristol is represented in Belgium by massive limestones, often oolitic and sometimes cherty, containing *Lithostrotion martini* and *Composita ficoidea*; these are surmounted by a concretionary limestone known as the 'Grande Brêche' with a fauna that is matched in similar beds in south-west England. The D 1 zone includes coral beds containing early dibunophyllids, and the D 2 zone yields reef-building species of *Lithostrotion* and *Corwenia* in addition to such simple corals as *Dibunophyllum* and *Aulophyllum*. The limestone of Visé includes knoll limestones similar to those of Cracoe in England. While the faunas of these limestones are dominated by corals and brachiopods as in England, goniatites are occasionally found. G. Delepine (1930) cites a rich fauna, including species of *Pericyclus*, *Muensteroceras*, and *Protocanites*, in C 1 beds at Tournai and Dinant, and he shows that *Pericyclus* ranges up into C 2 S 1 horizons. The S 2 beds of Belgium have yielded no goniatites, but assemblages of *Beyrichoceras* and *Goniatites* are known within the Dibunophyllum zone of Visé. The same facies extends eastwards as far as Aix-la-Chapelle and Düsseldorf, but east of the Rhine the whole Dinantian consists of goniatite shales in which H. Schmidt (1925) has recognized a succession of zones and subzones comparable with the British sequence described above (p. 286).

The Namurian Series in Belgium is represented by the 'Houiller sans houille'. The famous horizon of Chokier, black shales with nodules containing *Homoceras beyrichianum* in abundance, obviously includes the Homoceras zone, and the record of *Eumorphoceras* may indicate the presence of the lower zone. The Grés d'Ardenne, with impure coals and plant remains, has some marine fossils; goniatites of the index-genus show that part, at least, of the Reticuloceras zone is present. The *Eumorphoceras* and *Homoceras* faunas appear in the Upper Alum Shales of Westphalia and the Rhineland, the *Reticuloceras* fauna in the Flozleere of Westphalia.

The Productive Coal Measures of the Westphalian Series present the usual alternation of plant-bearing shales and sandstones with coal-seams and marine bands at irregular intervals. We have already noted (p. 287) that the large inflated shells of *Gastrioceras* are abundantly preserved in successive marine bands intercalated in the Lower Coal Measures of England and Wales. Closely similar fossils are present in the highest part of the Epen Beds of Limburg, in the Assise de Vecoigne of north France, and in the Magerkohle of Westphalia. The succeeding *Anthracoceras* fauna, including some typical nautiloids, characteristic of well-known marine bands in the Middle Coal Measures of Britain, is also diagnostic of the famous Aegir horizon of Westphalia, the Petit buisson horizon of the Low Countries, and perhaps of the Poissonière of northern France. No marine bands with goniatites are known above the Aegir horizon in western Europe.

The dominance of *Gastrioceras* in early Westphalian horizons roughly coincides with the spread of non-marine lamellibranchs through the main depositional areas of western and central Europe. The genera concerned are *Carbonicola*, *Anthracosia*, *Naiadites*, *Anthracospherium*, *Anthraconaia*, and *Anthraconauta*. During the last three decades the recognition of a succession of distinct assemblages by J. H. Davies and A. E. Trueman (1927) has led to a new zonal classification which has been confirmed by many workers in England, Wales, Scotland, north France, Belgium, Holland, Saar and Lorraine, Westphalia, Saxony, Silesia, and the Donetz area of Russia. The maximum development of *Carbonicola* in the lenisulcata and communis zones where *Naiadites* is also becoming important, corresponds approximately with the range of the marine *Gastrioceras*. According to D. A. Wray (1932) *Carbonicola* finally disappears in Yorkshire at about the level of an important coal-seam known as the Middleton Main. In the modiolaris zone *Carbonicola* is replaced by *Anthracosia* which continues in the similis-pulchra zone, and is associated with abundance of *Naiadites* and *Anthracospherium*. About the horizon of the Mansfield Marine Band in England—the equivalent of the Aegir horizon in Westphalia—*Anthracosia* and *Anthracospherium* disappear, and there is a distinct change in the species of *Anthraconaia*. The later disappearance of *Naiadites* seems to correspond in Yorkshire with the level of the Shafton Marine band, and thereafter *Anthraconauta* becomes the dominant genus. A. E. Trueman and J. Weir (1946) suggest that the development of distinct assemblages of these non-marine lamellibranchs at successive levels was influenced by two factors. In the first place, the several marine incursions over areas where non-marine deposits were being accumulated must have led to the repeated disappearance of non-marine faunas in the submerged area. Secondly, the coal-seams appear to have been formed under conditions in which molluscan faunas did not flourish. Hence a change in the non-marine faunas, as shown in examples already cited, is often, though not always, found above a marine band or a coal-seam; it has been observed that zonal classification by means of non-marine mollusca is most readily accomplished in those parts of the succession where coal-seams are developed at short intervals. The wide distribution of the non-marine assemblages seems to indicate that several depositional areas in western and central Europe were not so completely isolated as was formerly supposed.

It is evident that the deposition of Coal Measures in western and central Europe indicates a regression of marine waters from a vast area, and the same phenomenon is repeated on a comparable scale in North America. This great change in sea-level is usually attributed to the folding movement of the Hercynian and Appalachian orogenies which began midway through the Carboniferous, and continued into the Permian period. It may be, however, that another event had an influence in the same direction. In the southern continents there is abundant evidence that extensive areas were subjected to extreme glaciation in late Carboniferous and early Permian time. The withdrawal of water from oceanic circulation to form the huge ice-sheets must have led to a general lowering of sea-level. This may well have accentuated the effect of earth-movements in producing the wide-spread geographical changes at this period of the earth's history. The question is discussed further in Chapter VIII, pp. 331 et seq.

The development of Carboniferous rocks in southern Europe shows certain similarity with that in central Europe but also some important differences. In the French Pyrenees G. Delepine (1937) records the Tournaisian goniatite genera *Muensteroceras*, *Merocanites*, and *Pericyclus*; from higher beds at Mondette, Ariège, species of the Viséan genus *Goniatites* are cited, and shales in the Lauriber Valley have yielded the early Namurian species *Eumorphoceras bisulcatum* Girty. In Asturia, north Spain, Delepine again describes the succession, beginning with the transgressive 'marbre griotte'; this is a variegated nodular limestone enclosing species of *Goniatites* which are typical of high Viséan Beds in Belgium and Britain. The 'marbre griotte' is overlain by shales and conglomerates with some limestone containing the foraminifer *Fusulina boeki* Moller. Above this are non-marine deposits containing plants of the Westphalian flora, and occasional marine bands yielding goniatites and foraminifera. The goniatites are species of *Anthracoceras* and *Homoceratoides*, associated with the nautilid *Metacoceras*, an assemblage characteristic of the Westphalian zone A. The record of *Anthraconauta phillipsi* and *A. wardi* in the adjacent non-marine deposits is consistent with this horizon. The foraminifera associated with the goniatites include *Fusulina cylindrica* Fischer and *Staffella sphaeroidea* (Moller) which are further discussed below. Here we may note that these foraminiferal shells constitute an element of the Neocarboniferous fauna which is not recorded from the corresponding marine bands of Central Europe and Britain. Farther south, around Belmez in the Sierra Morena, limestones of Dinantian age have yielded species of brachiopods which also occur in the British Carboniferous Limestones, and overlying coal-bearing beds contain typical Westphalian fossils. To the north-east of Belmez, at Puertollana, several species of Stephanian plants are recorded from transgressive beds which rest unconformably on marine Silurian rocks.

A considerable development of Carboniferous rocks exists in North Africa, though, as usual, no one locality shows the full succession. In western Morocco, between Rabat and Tiflet, Tournaisian sandstones and shales with typical brachiopods are overlaid by Viséan Limestones containing brachiopods and corals, but with *Goniatites striatus* and *Beyrichoceras truncatum* at some places. Neocarboniferous plants and non-marine lamellibranchs of the genus *Anthraconauta* are recorded from the High Atlas. Farther east, at Taouz to the south of the Tafilelt, late Tournaisian and early Viséan Limestones, resting unconformably on late Devonian Beds, have yielded to G. Delepine (1935) several brachiopods and corals comparable with British forms, together with the goniatites *Pericyclus* and *Muensteroceras*. North-north-east of Colomb Bechar, near the boundary between Morocco and Algeria, G. Delepine and N. Menchikoff (1937) have recorded the late Viséan *Goniatites striatus*, and a higher horizon with the Namurian *Cravenoceras*, *Proshumardites*, *Sagittoceras*, and *Dimorphoceras*. Later, Delepine (1939) announced the discovery at Kenadza, farther south, of the Namurian zone of *Reticuloceras* and the Westphalian zone of *Anthracoceras*: the fauna of the latter is similar to that of the Aegir, Petit Buisson, Gin Mine, and Cefn Coed marine bands in north-west Europe.

The Carboniferous rocks of the Carnic Alps and south-eastern Europe have been studied in detail by F. Heritsch (1939). The Dinantian stage in the Carnic Alps is represented chiefly by shales which contain corals and brachiopods, of Viséan type. The Westphalian stage is missing, for the succeeding deposits, clastic sediments with occasional limestones, contain brachiopods, corals, and fusuline foraminifera, which are closely comparable with those of the Uralian stage in Russia, still to be described. They are followed by the Troghofel Limestone which is referred to the Permian system. The Fusulina Limestones are widespread in the Neocarboniferous strata of Carniola and Dalmatia; they occupy considerable areas in Yugoslavia, Greece, islands in the Aegean Sea, and Asia Minor. Near Ankara E. Chaput (1933) has recognized limestones with Viséan productids, followed by limestones of Uralian age containing *Fusulina* and *Schwagerina princeps*, under Permian strata. Near the coast of the Black Sea the small coal-basins of Amassra and Zonguldak show Viséan strata with *Goniatites*, *Beyrichoceras*, and productids, followed by a thick series of coal-bearing beds enclosing a succession of Namurian, Westphalian, and Stephanian floras.

In Russia Carboniferous rocks appear in three large areas, namely, the Donetz, Moscow, and Ural regions. In the Donetz basin, north of the Sea of Azov, the system begins with thin limestones containing brachiopods which compare closely with members of Tournaisian assemblages in west Europe. These are succeeded by a series of thick sandstones and shales with some intercalated limestones in which productids of the *giganteus* group are conspicuous fossils. Higher in the succession this group of brachiopods is associated with goniatites of the genera *Reticuloceras* and *Gastrioceras*. The strata included in the 'Lower Carboniferous' of Russian geologists therefore represent the Namurian as well as the Dinantian Series of west Europe. This development of thick clastic rocks continues in the higher strata of the Donetz, together with coal-seams and some intercalated limestones containing brachiopods and fusuline foraminifera. The coal-bearing strata have yielded remains of land-plants such as are typical of the Westphalian and Stephanian floras of central and western Europe. Moreover, the non-marine lamellibranchs *Carbonicola*, *Naiadites*, and *Anthraconaia* exhibit a succession of assemblages which according to E. Dix and A. E. Trueman (1937) is closely comparable with that in the British Coal Measures. The marine fossils low in the series include the goniatite *Anthracoceras aegiranum* which has already been noted as a guide to a Westphalian horizon in Germany, France, and Britain.

In the Moscow region and the Urals the Carboniferous sequence is entirely marine, and correlation with the west European development is only indicated by the mixed facies of the Donetz basin. The early Carboniferous rocks in the eastern part of the Moscow district begin with limestones which contain such Tournaisian fossils as *Pericyclus*, *Spirifer tornacensis*, &c.; these are missing in the west of the region where older rocks are succeeded by limestones of Viséan age. These are marked, as in the Donetz, by the abundance of giganteid productids, with which *Goniatites striatus*, *Spirifer bisulcatus*, and dibunophyllid corals are associated. Limestones of the same age, investigated by V. N. Krestovnikoff (see M. K. Elias, 1937) in the area of the Saran River in the south Urals, are succeeded by limestones containing the Namurian goniatites *Eumorphoceras*, *Homoceras*, and *Reticuloceras*, which, as in the Donetz, are assigned to the 'Lower Carboniferous' by Russian geologists.

The beds just described are succeeded by a further series of limestones known as the Moscovian stage from its exposure in the Moscow area. The stage is specially marked by the sudden appearance of *Choristites*, a genus of spiriferid brachiopods with strongly developed dental plates, by early stages in the evolution of the fusuline foraminifera, and by goniatites of the genera *Gastrioceras* and its ally *Glaphirites*. The foraminifera of the earlier Carboniferous rocks are all microscopic forms of no particular stratigraphical significance. Among the numerous genera is *Endothyra* which with its allies seems to have given rise to larger forms now grouped in the family Fusulinidae. The type-genus *Fusulina* was first established by G. Fischer de Waldheim in 1829 for specimens from the Moscovian stage at Mjatschkowa near Moscow, but the typical species *Fusulina cylindrica* Fischer was not described until 1837. A later reviewer, V. Möller (1877), misinterpreted the genus, and subsequently the name *Fusulina* was used both in Europe and in North America for nearly all fusulinids with spindle-shaped shell, fluted septa, and thin walls of three distinct layers. In 1930 C. O. Dunbar and L. G. Henbest redefined Fischer's *Fusulina* and Möller's *Fusulinella*, and established a third allied genus *Wedekindellina*. Species of all three genera are prevalent in the Moscovian stage of Russia and equivalent strata in certain other parts of the world. These genera are often associated with *Staffella*, a genus which has been regarded as the ancestral form of all fusulinids, for it has an endothyral young stage; *S. antiqua* (Schellwein) appears early in the Moscovian stage and the genus continues in higher beds of the stage with *S. sphaeroidea* (Ehrenberg). According to S. V. Semichatov (1935) the Moscovian stage is incomplete in the Moscow district, for in the western Urals there are lower beds containing an association of *Choristites* with productids and spiriferids of Dinantian aspect. Moreover, the top of the stage in the Urals is marked by the abundance of *Wedekindellina*, small slender fusiform shells with plane septa, accompanied by *Staffella sphaeroidea*, *Fusulinella boeki* Moller, and other forms; this horizon again, according to Semichatov, has not been recognized in the Moscow district.

In 1904 G. H. Girty instituted the genus *Triticites* for small spindle-shaped or subglobose fusulinids with undivided chambers and alveolar walls. The type specimens were obtained from the Coal Measures of the Mississippi Valley in North America, but the genus is also recorded by V. E. Ruzencev (1936) from the Uralian stage of Russia. C. O. Dunbar (1937) states that two major divisions can be recognized in the Russian sequence, a lower one with small slender species of *Triticites*, and an upper one with larger, gibbous, and more advanced forms. The genus is regarded as broadly ancestral to the slightly later forms *Schwagerina* and *Pseudoschwagerina*. The genus *Schwagerina* was established by V. Moller (1877) for globose fusulinids from the Uralian 'Bergkalk' of the Pinega Valley in the province of Archangel, Russia, of which the *Borelis princeps* of C. G. Ehrenberg (1854) was taken as type. According to C. O. Dunbar and J. W. Skinner (1936), however, Moller's study of *Schwagerina* was based, not on the original types, but on material from the plateau of Timan, some 200 miles from the type-locality, and this material differs considerably from that described by Ehrenberg. After a study of Ehrenberg's types the true *Schwagerina* was redefined by Dunbar and Skinner; the species so long mistaken for *Schwagerina* fall naturally into two groups of independent origin, namely, *Pseudoschwagerina* developed from *Triticites*, and *Paraschwagerina* evolved from the true *Schwagerina*. These have nearly the same stratigraphical range and geographical distribution as the original genus, as shown by A. Vissarionova (1937) in Russia and F. G. Kahler (1938) in Austria. Another characteristic Uralian foraminifer is *Quasifusulina longissima* (Möller); some other genera are said to survive from Moscovian horizons, but these may belong to derived limestone blocks which are abundant in breccias of the Uralian stage. V. E. Ruzencev also records goniatites at certain Uralian horizons. Species of *Gastrioceras* and *Glaphirites* are cited from the lower divisions, and the upper beds at Iliinsk have yielded *Neodimorphoceras*, *Prouddenites*, *Uddenites*, *Vidrioceras*, *Prothalassoceras*, and other genera in addition. These ammonoids are not recorded from Westphalian localities and may represent the marine equivalent of the Stephanian stage of west Europe. The strata which overlie the Uralian stage in the type-area are assigned to the Permian system.

North of the Ural mountains Neocarboniferous strata, with some fusulines, extend northward into the Arctic regions, for H. Frebold (1935) cites localities in Novaia Zemlya, Bear Island, and Spitzbergen where such rocks are underlaid by limestones with *Choristites mosquensis* and other Moscovian brachiopods. In east Greenland L. Koch (1935) has described a considerable thickness of clastic sediments which contain land-plants of Dinantian, Namurian, and Westphalian aspect in succession. Later marine strata contain brachiopods typical of the Russian Uralian stage, but fusulinids do not appear in the record.

In ASIA the Russian sequence is continued into western Siberia where certain Dinantian horizons are overlaid by the limestones of Schartymka, from which Namurian goniatites and brachiopods were recorded over a century ago. The Moscovian stage, with *Choristites* and productids, is succeeded by thick detrital beds, including conglomerates, which have yielded typical Uralian fossils. In the Kirghiz steppes and the Kuznetsk basin Tournaisian limestones are succeeded by sandstones containing land-plants and non-marine lamellibranchs of Westphalian and Stephanian type. The three major divisions of the Carboniferous system have long been known in the Tian Shan Mountains of Turkestan. Representatives of the Dinantian and Moscovian stages are succeeded by Uralian limestones which have yielded *Schwagerina princeps* and many brachiopods identical with Russian species. Farther south, in the Pamirs and Chitral, F. R. C. Reed (1925) has described Neocarboniferous fossils, notably *Schwagerina* and brachiopods, which also bear considerable resemblance to Russian Uralian forms.

In the neighbouring province of Kashmir the unfossiliferous Muth Quartzite, perhaps of Silurian age, is directly overlaid by Carboniferous rocks. These are limestones of considerable thickness which contain an abundance of *Syringothyris cuspidata* auctt. associated with species of *Chonetes*, *Productus*, and other brachiopods, possibly indicating an early Viséan horizon. The fauna of the overlying Fenestella Shales exhibits special features of its own; many of the fossils are unknown elsewhere and precise correlation with other regions is difficult. The fan-shaped zoaria of *Fenestella* are most abundantly preserved, and are accompanied by many species and individuals of *Spirifer*, *Productus*, and other brachiopods. Some of the species range up into the so-called Slate Agglomerate, a fine-grained volcanic tuff of great thickness which contains angular pebbles of igneous and other rocks, and is possibly a product of submarine volcanic eruption. The fauna is regarded by H. S. Bion (1928) and F. R. C. Reed (1932) as late Carboniferous in age; it shows relationship, in the presence of *Eurydesma* and *Maeonia*, with the 'Speckled Sandstone' of the Salt Range, and the Eurydesma Beds of Australia discussed later (p. 388). In the Spiti district of the central Himalayas certain limestones in the upper part of the Lipak Series contain *Syringothyris cuspidata* associated with species of *Productus*, *Spirifer*, *Reticularia*, and other genera and are therefore assigned to the Lower Carboniferous Series. At some localities they are overlaid by shales from which fragments of Dinantian land plants, such as *Rhacopteris* and *Sphenopteridium* are recorded by H. H. Hayden (1904). Next in succession is the Fenestella Shale which has already been noted from Kashmir and referred to the Upper Carboniferous Series. The last two horizons are missing in central Spiti where the Lipak beds are directly overlaid by rocks of the Permian system.

Some 500 miles to the south-east, in the Umaria coalfield of Rewah State, Central India, thin bands of sandstone and clay intercalated among non-marine Gondwana deposits have yielded marine fossils which have been described by F. R. C. Reed (1928). This unique marine band overlies the Talchir Boulder Bed uncomformably, and appears to pass upward into the basal beds of the Baraker Series (p. 332). The chief fossils are species of *Productus*, *Spirifer*, and *Reticularia*, the first-named greatly predominating. The determinable species are all new or local forms, and their nearest relations are among Himalayan and Russian species. The Umaria marine bed is thought to occupy about the same horizon as the Speckled Sandstone of the Salt Range, and Reed (1928) suggests that it represents an ephemeral transgression from the north through Rajputana, or from the west coast. On the other hand, C. S. Fox (1931) recalls the presence of Gondwana deposits along the southern slopes of the eastern Himalayas in Bhutan and Assam, also the occurrence in the Abor country of a Carboniferous marine fauna described by C. Diener (1905), and suggests that 'the Umaria marine area had a freer outlet east-north-eastward than in any other direction'.

At localities west and north-west of Lhasa, Tibet, only the Uralian stage seems to be represented. The varied fauna from this area, described by F. R. C. Reed (1930), includes *Schwagerina princeps*, corals such as *Lonsdaleia salinaria* and species of *Syringopora*, brachiopods, including species of *Productus*, *Reticularia*, *Martinia*, *Camarophoria*, &c., closely allied to Russian forms. Reed comments on the wide extent of Uralian faunas of Russian type, especially those of the Schwagerina beds which range right across Asia from the Urals to China. But the Schwagerina Beds have not been recorded from the Himalayas, where the marine succession appears to be far from complete. No Carboniferous faunas are described from Burma; though the deposition of limestone is said to have been continuous from

Devonian to Permian horizons, there are serious gaps in the palaeontological record.

F. R. C. Reed (1927) has described a number of Carboniferous fossils from Yunnan which appear to indicate the presence of Dinantian horizons. H. Mansuy (1919–20) had previously noted a fauna remarkably like that of the Viséan in Europe from localities in Tonkin, Annam, and Laos. Later, J.

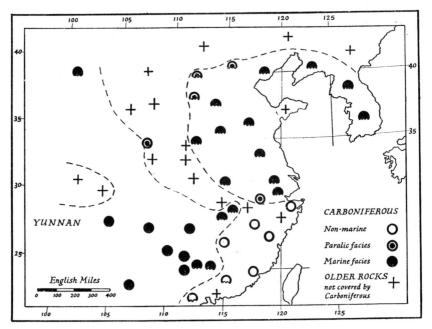

FIG. 49. SKETCH-MAP OF CHINA SHOWING GENERAL DISTRIBUTION OF
CARBONIFEROUS ROCKS

Fromaget (1931) recognized horizons of the Moscovian and Uralian stages in the same region. In the provinces of Kweichow and Kuangsi, south China, limestones and shales, resting unconformably on late Devonian strata, contain brachiopods of Carboniferous aspect, including species of *Productus*, *Eochoristites*, and *Schellwienella*; J. S. Lee (1939) assigns these to the Tournaisian stage. They are followed by limestones which enclose the first large productids of the *Gigantoproductus* type, indicating as in Europe horizons of Viséan age. These beds extend to central Hunan and north Kuangsi, but the series becomes reduced in thickness in a northeasterly direction (Map, Fig. 49). Farther east, in the province of Kiangsi on the western border of the old land of Fukien and Chekiang, a sequence of Carboniferous shales contains coal-seams and remains of land-plants, and is therefore of non-marine origin. This non-marine area extends to the north-west through Hupeh, Schzechuan, Kansu, and Shensi towards Manchuria, and throughout this extension Carboniferous rocks are missing from the succession, or older rocks occupy the surface. In the large area of north China, comprising the Nanking hills and the districts of Honan, Shansi, Shantung, and Kiangsu, mid-Carboniferous horizons are transgressive on Ordovician Limestones. The faunas closely resemble those of the Moscovian stage of Russia, especially in the abundance of *Choristites mosquensis* and of the foraminifera *Fusulina, Fusulinella,* and *Staffella.* The overlying beds, distinguished by local names, likewise resemble the Uralian stage of Russia, in the prevalence of the foraminifera *Triticites* and *Quasifusulina,* accompanied by forms which are usually identified as *Schwagerina princeps.* These beds in north-eastern China are separate from the equivalent strata in the south-west, and were evidently deposited during a transgression of the sea from the east, that is, from the Pacific Ocean. We shall continue the history of this area with the Permian system in Chapter X.

According to T. W. E. David and W. R. Browne (1950) most of AUSTRALIA, west of long. 142° E., appears to have been a land-area during Carboniferous time, but marine rocks of that period occupy considerable areas in Queensland, New South Wales, Victoria, and western Australia. Along the eastern coast of the continent the marine facies is restricted to the coastal tract, and in general the non-marine equivalents lie well inland. In east Queensland the earliest Carboniferous rocks are cherts and tuffs at the base of the Rockhampton Series; the fossils include the goniatite-genera *Protocanites* and *Pseudarietites* which enable the beds to be correlated with the Tournaisian stage of Europe. Higher in the series are mudstones, sandstones, and conglomerates associated with limestones containing corals (*Lithostrotion, Orionastraea, Aphrophyllum*) and brachiopods (*Spirifer, Chonetes,* &c.) comparable with Viséan forms in Europe. Farther inland, sandstones and shales have yielded the early Carboniferous plant *Lepidodendron veltheimianum.* In the Rockhampton district the Lithostrotion Limestone is followed by the Neerkol Series of mudstones and sandstones, some 4,500 feet in thickness. The lower beds have yielded numerous fossils, among which *Choristites* aff. *mosquensis* is conspicuous; they may represent an early Moscovian horizon. At another locality fossils of the *Eumorphoceras* type perhaps indicate the presence of Namurian Beds, and this is consistent with records of the *Rhacopteris* flora from other isolated outcrops.

In New South Wales the Lower Carboniferous marine deposits are grouped in the Burindi Series, which is restricted to the north-eastern part of the State. The prevalent mudstones and, more especially, the intercalated limestones contain numerous brachiopods, corals, and other fossils. The lower beds of the series near Tamworth have yielded the Tournaisian goniatites *Protocanites* and *Muensteroceras;* they are correlated by G. Delepine (1941) with the C 1 beds of the English succession. The fauna of limestones higher in the series includes reef-corals belonging to *Lithostrotion, Syringopora,* and other genera and is comparable with the

Viséan D 2 fauna of Britain. In places such limestones are interbedded with non-marine strata containing plant-remains, notably *Lepidodendron veltheimianum*, and belonging to the lower part of the Kuttung Series. The upper part of the Kuttung Series is composed largely of glacial deposits, but there is also a considerable proportion of non-glacial material which contains many land-plants, including species of *Rhacopteris*, *Clepsydropsis*, *Pitys*, and *Lepidodendron*. This assemblage is comparable with the Namurian flora of Silesia and Britain; it is important in that it proves the mid-Carboniferous age of the glacial deposits. The Kuttung Beds are said to pass up into shales and mudstones which are assigned to the Permian system but there is no record of a flora comparable with that of the Westphalian stage in Europe. Near the Queensland border a series of sandstones with typical Carboniferous brachiopods is considered to represent the Neerkol Beds farther north, but its stratigraphical relations are unknown.

In eastern Victoria the presumed Carboniferous sequence begins with sandstones and shales from which A. S. Woodward (1906) has described species of the fishes *Acanthodes*, *Elonichthys*, *Ctenodus*, &c. Higher beds are mainly unfossiliferous tillites which reach a thickness of 2,000 feet at the famous Bacchus Marsh localities west of Melbourne. They pass up into sandstones enclosing plants of the *Gangamopteris* flora, and these are referred to the Permian system. Evidence of glaciation extends southward into Tasmania, and westward into South Australia where tillites, presumably of Carboniferous age, rest on striated surfaces of much older rocks.

Lower Carboniferous, perhaps Viséan, brachiopods, including species of *Spirifer*, *Productus*, *Rhipidomella*, and *Orthotetes* are recorded from a massive limestone which overlies the uppermost Devonian sandstone in the extreme north-east of Western Australia. The presence of similar horizons south of the Kimberley area is suggested by the report of *Lithostrotion* and *Syringopora* from a borehole north of Christmas Creek. The remainder of the Carboniferous sequence is presumably represented by glacial deposits the age of which, in the absence of fossils, is assessed by analogy with those of New South Wales, and by their position beneath Permian strata.

Strata of Carboniferous age have not been clearly recognized in New Zealand, probably owing to the metamorphosed condition of the rocks. C. T. Trechmann (1917) has reviewed the earlier observations on the so-called Maitai Series of the Nelson district. He also records the presence of the Australian myalinid genus *Aphanaia*, brachiopods comparable with certain European species of *Spirifer*, *Martinia*, *Strophalosia*, and *Pugnax*, together with corals of zaphrentid aspect. The poor preservation of the known fossils, however, prevents precise correlation.

It is clear that marine deposits of Carboniferous age are transgressive at intervals over the more ancient rocks that border the Pacific Ocean from China to Australia, and that the general characters of the faunal assemblages show relations mainly with those of Asia and Europe. To

complete the review we have now to examine the corresponding palaeontological records from the eastern side of the Pacific, on the continents of
North and South America.

In NORTH AMERICA the rocks under discussion are usually classified in
two separate systems, the Mississippian (Map, Fig. 50) and the Pennsylvanian (Map, Fig. 51), corresponding respectively to the Lower and Upper
Carboniferous Series of Europe. The Mississippian rocks are strikingly
similar in lithology and general faunal characters to the Dinantian series of
Europe, but detailed analysis of the faunas, as that by R. C. Moore (1948),
demonstrates some strong divergences in the development of various phyla
on the two sides of the Atlantic Ocean. The American succession begins with
the Kinderhook stage which corresponds with the K and Z zones of England; the succeeding Osage stage is correlated with the C 1 zone, and the
two stages, sometimes combined in the Waverly stage, are together equivalent to the Tournaisian stage of Europe. The Meramec stage corresponds
broadly with the C 2 and S zones of England and the D zone is represented
by the lower part of the Chester stage in America. The upper part of the
last stage is equivalent to the Namurian zone E in England. The H and R
zones of the Namurian stage are apparently lacking in North America, and
the Pennsylvanian system begins with the Gastrioceras zone. The Mississippian rocks are mainly limestones, and the chief fossil groups, as in Europe,
are corals, crinoids, blastoids, brachiopods, and mollusca; the development
of these groups in the two continents must now be compared.

The corals, so widely used in zoning the Dinantian strata of western
Europe, appear to be comparatively scarce in the Mississippian rocks of
North America. Of the seventy genera reported in Europe only about
twenty are so far represented in the American records; most of these are
simple forms, and such genera as *Caninia* and *Dibunophyllum* have fewer
species in America than in Europe. The reef-corals *Lithostrotion, Diphyphyllum* and *Lonsdaleia* are also less prolific in North America than in Europe,
while *Aulina, Corwenia,* and *Orionastraea* have no American species in the
present records. It may be that these discrepancies are due merely to slight
differences in facies, and that the conditions of habitat induced more rapid
and more varied development in the European area.

Blastoid echinoderms are more conspicuous among American Mississippian fossils than in the corresponding Dinantian faunas of Europe. According to R. C. Moore (1948) a total of nineteen genera is distributed among
eight families. *Codaster,* the chief genus of the Codasteridae, has seven
species in the Waverly Series, while in Europe it has one Tournaisian and
two Viséan species. *Phaenoschisma,* the only genus of its family, has one
species in the Osage stage, another in the Tournaisian, and two in the
Viséan. Two other monotypic families are represented by *Nymphoblastus* and
Zygocrinus which are only known by two species of each genus in the Viséan
Beds of Europe. The family Troostocrinidae is represented throughout

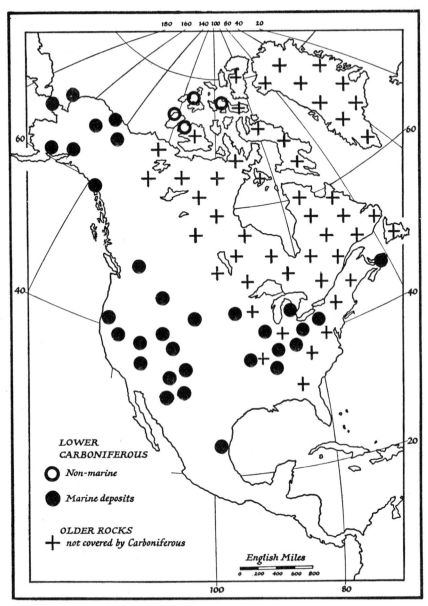

LOWER
CARBONIFEROUS

○ *Non-marine*

● *Marine deposits*

OLDER ROCKS
✛ *not covered by Carboniferous*

English Miles

0   200   400   600   800

FIG. 50. SKETCH-MAP OF NORTH AMERICA SHOWING GENERAL DISTRIBUTION
OF LOWER CARBONIFEROUS ROCKS

the Mississippian by three genera which are not known in Europe. *Schizoblastus*, the chief American representative of the Nucleocrinidae, has fifteen species in the Waverly Series and two in the Meramec stage, and the Irish form *Monoschizoblastus* has two species at Viséan horizons. The Orbitremitidae, sparsely represented in Europe by *Acentrotremites, Heteroblastus*, and *Mesoblastus*, is virtually an American family; many species of *Orbitotremites, Cryptoblastus*, and *Carpenteroblastus* are described from the Osage stage, but few from higher horizons. *Pentremites*, the only conspicuous genus of its family, begins with six Waverly species in North America and two Tournaisian species in Europe; it continues with sixty-seven species in the Meramec and Chester stages, but is apparently lacking in the Viséan Beds of Europe. It seems that the main evolution of the Carboniferous blastoids took place in the American region; the migration of the six common stocks across the Atlantic Ocean only resulted in the development of a few local genera in Europe.

The crinoids are present in the Mississippian rocks in even greater variety, and we shall discuss separately the distribution of important genera assigned to the subclasses Inadunata, Flexibilia, and Camerata. First we may note that many genera of stratigraphical importance are confined, or nearly so, to the Waverly Series, most particularly to the Osage stage, of North America. Among Inadunate forms R. C. Moore (1948) lists a round dozen of such genera, the most remarkable being the non-specialized *Barycrinus* with thirty-six Waverly species. This genus together with the more specialized *Halysiocrinus* is not known to occur in European strata. A few inadunate genera are virtually restricted to the Meramec and Chester stages; these include *Agassizocrinus* with eleven Chester species, *Eupachycrinus* with thirteen species, *Phacelocrinus* with ten species, none of which are recorded east of the Atlantic Ocean. Several inadunate genera, however, are represented in both continents. *Poteriocrinus* ranges through the Mississippian system with about 40 species, and in Europe has 8 Tournaisian and 5 Viséan species. *Cyathocrinus* also with 40 American species has about a dozen European forms; *Pachylocrinus* has 37 Mississippian species as against 4 Tournaisian and 5 Viséan forms: *Zeacrinus* with 23 American species, mostly in the Chester stage, has only 2 species in the Viséan Beds of Europe. On the other hand, *Woodocrinus, Hydreionocrinus, Aphelecrinus, Scotiacrinus*, and possibly a few others, from the Viséan strata of Scotland and northern England, are not yet known in North America. *Tribrachiocrinus* may also be mentioned here, for it is recorded from Europe and Australia but not from America.

Of the sixteen Mississippian genera of flexible crinoids listed by Moore five are restricted to the Osage stage of North America, and two, *Taxocrinus* and *Onychocrinus*, continue into the Chester stage. These two, together with *Forbesiocrinus, Euryocrinus, Wachsmuthicrinus*, and *Mespilocrinus* are also recorded from Dinantian rocks on the eastern side of the Atlantic Ocean.

Six European genera, mostly monotypic forms of rare occurrence, are unknown from Mississippian horizons, but two of them are recorded from Pennsylvanian rocks in the United States.

The Mississippian deposits enclose an astonishing profusion and variety of camerate crinoids, certain families of which are at present unknown outside North America. The Batocrinidae, with over 200 described species, is perhaps the most remarkable, for none of the seven genera, *Batocrinus*, *Alloprosalocrinus*, *Dizygocrinus*, *Eretmocrinus*, *Eutrochocrinus*, *Macrocrinus*, *Uperocrinus* are known in European strata. The Desmidocrinidae, including *Agaricocrinus* with forty species and *Dorycrinus* with seventeen species, are likewise almost confined to the Waverly Series of North America. These evidently indicate autochthonous development of purely American stocks, but some other families are represented on both sides of the Atlantic Ocean. For example, in the Actinocrinidae while *Cactocrinus* has thirty-two species in the Waverly stage, and, with four other genera, is not known in Europe, *Actinocrinus* has twenty species in Europe and fifty in North America. The dichocrinid genera *Camptocrinus* and *Dichocrinus* are represented in both continents, though North America has the greater profusion of species and three allied genera show a purely American distribution. The platycrinid genus *Platycrinus* again has nearly a hundred species in the Mississippian strata, but only thirty-six in the Dinantian Beds of Europe. The Amphoracrinidae are more equally distributed but the four American species of *Amphoracrinus* are confined to Waverly horizons, and there are five Viséan species in Europe. The rhodocrinid genera *Gilbertsocrinus* and *Rhodocrinus* are also wholly restricted to Waverly strata in the United States, but they continue in much smaller numbers at Viséan horizons in Europe. These examples are sufficient to show the striking contrast in crinoid development on the two sides of the Atlantic Ocean during Carboniferous time. It seems reasonable to suppose that the American stocks are autochthonous. Some of them seem to have travelled, probably by eastward-flowing ocean currents, into the eastern Atlantic embayment where some persisted almost unchanged while others ultimately gave rise to local genera.

Brachiopods are represented in the Mississippian rocks by the same general stocks as in the Dinantian stage of Europe. The most distinctive family, the Productidae, has members of the subgenera *Productus* s.s., *Avonia*, *Buxtonia*, *Dictyoclostus*, *Echinoconchus*, *Linoproductus*, and *Pustula* in both continents. Indeed some of the species are so similar in general appearance that in former days certain American shells were assigned to European species; more recently (1938) A. H. Sutton has stated that no American species is present in British strata. Various American members of the Chonetidae, Spiriferidae, Rhynchonellidae, as well as the old-established *Leptaena analoga* and *Schizophoria striatula* can hardly be distinguished from their European analogues. On the other hand, certain rhynchonellid genera, like *Tetracamera*, *Shumardella*, *Paraphorhynchus*, and

Pugnoides, which are widely distributed in Mississippian strata, do not appear in European records. Again, the large productid *Gigantoproductus* and the chonetid *Daviesiella*, so prolific at Viséan horizons in Europe, are only recorded in North America along the Pacific border of the continent. This distribution may perhaps indicate connexion with the Russian area by way of the Arctic Ocean.

Non-marine lamellibranchs in the Pennsylvanian Coal Measures of North America were formerly placed in the genera *Unio*, *Myalina*, &c., but in 1860 J. W. Dawson founded the genus *Naiadites* for such shells from the Coal Measures of Nova Scotia. Some of the species were transferred by J. W. Salter (1861) to *Anthracomya*, and these presumably fall into the modern genus *Anthraconaia*. Dawson later noted the genus *Anthracosia* from the same strata. Similar shells are recorded from the non-marine beds of the Pennsylvanian system in the states of Pennsylvania, Ohio, Alabama, and New Mexico by various authors, but in spite of this wide distribution the genera do not appear to be utilized as index-fossils to the same extent as in Europe. One marine lamellibranch should be mentioned, namely *Caneyella*, which was first described by G. H. Girty (1909) from the Caney Shale of Oklahoma, and afterwards recorded from the Moorefield Shale of Arkansas. It resembles the flat, concentrically corrugated shell of *Posidonia*, or *Posidonomya*, which is characteristic of the goniatite-shale facies in the upper D 2 zone of Britain, and is associated with comparable goniatites as noted below.

Cephalopods are not abundant in the Mississippian rocks of North America, but the same genera appear in the same order as in the Carboniferous Limestone of Europe. The Kinderhook stage of Indiana, Missouri, and Michigan has yielded the genera *Protocanites*, *Pericyclus*, and *Muensteroceras*, but the species are distinct from those in the Tournaisian stage of Europe. Some species of *Muensteroceras* are closely similar to *Beyrichoceras* which has an undefined range in the upper Dibunophyllum zone of Britain; only a single American representative of this genus has been reported by A. K. Miller (1947). The *Goniatites* fauna, which in Britain occurs in strata equivalent to the uppermost beds of the Dibunophyllum zone, seems to be represented in the Lower Caney Shale of Oklahoma and the Moorefield Shale of Arkansas whence G. H. Girty (1909, 1911) has described species of the genus, such as *G. newsomi*, *G. subcircularis*, and *G. granosum*, associated with the lamellibranch *Caneyella*. The goniatites cited have since been recorded by E. W. J. Moore (1936) from English localities where they are associated with *Posidonia becheri* which may be congeneric with the *Caneyella* of Oklahoma. The *Eumorphoceras* fauna, which in Europe marks the early horizons of the Namurian stage, is also represented in the Caney Shale of Oklahoma; indeed, the index-species *E. bisulcatum* was first described by G. H. Girty (1909) from these beds. In reference to the close relations of the *Goniatites* and *Eumorphoceras* faunas of North America and western Europe, W. S.

Bisat (1935) remarks, 'It can hardly be doubted that the two deposits were laid down in the same sea under the same physical conditions.' But the route of communication remains uncertain, for the Neocarboniferous strata of the eastern United States are entirely of non-marine character, and marine deposits, apart from ephemeral marine bands seem to be confined to Texas and the western States. Moreover, there are apparently no records of the *Homoceras* and *Reticuloceras* faunas from North America.

Low down in the Pennsylvanian system the Smithwick Shale of central Texas has yielded species of *Gastrioceras*, including the English form *G. listeri*, associated with species of *Nuculoceras*, *Eoasianites*, and *Pronorites*. According to F. B. Plummer (1937) the same assemblage is present in early Pennsylvanian strata of western Texas, Oklahoma, and east Kentucky. These records led to the remark of W. S. Bisat (1935) that the American deposits contain more than a trace of the Gastrioceras fauna of Europe. At a higher level in the system a fauna described by A. K. Miller and J. B. Owen (1939) from the Cherokee Shale of Missouri includes species of *Anthracoceras*, *Dimorphoceras*, *Gonioloboceras*, and smooth gastrioceratids of the genus *Eoasianites*; one species of this fauna had already been assigned by W. S. Bisat *et alii* (1931) to a Scottish species *Homoceratoides jacksoni*, but Miller and Owen suggest that it may be identical with *Dimorphoceras politum* (Shumard), this American name having priority. The nautiloid element in the Anthracoceras fauna, including the genera *Metacoceras* and *Cyclonautilus*, is closely allied to that described by G. H. Girty (1915) from the Wewoka Shale of Oklahoma, but W. S. Bisat (1930) does not admit precise correlation with the Aegir fauna of Europe though the relations are close.

Marine horizons in the Upper Pennsylvanian rocks of North America present a tolerably complete succession of goniatite genera, whose ranges often overlap one another, and in some instances extend into early Permian strata. The most important of these genera are grouped in the family Schistoceratidae which is derived from the Gastrioceratidae through the genus *Paralegoceras*. The earliest species of *Schistoceras* so far known comes from a low horizon in the Missouri stage of Oklahoma. There A. K. Miller and J. B. Owen (1937) have shown that it is associated with species of *Gastrioceras* and allied genera that persist from the underlying Des Moines stage, and with an early form of *Prothalassoceras*. The last-named genus connects the Dimorphoceratidae with their Permian successors, the Thalassoceratidae. Both *Schistoceras* and *Prothalassoceras* continue into higher Pennsylvanian horizons where they are accompanied by new forms of Schistoceratidae (*Shumardites*, *Pericleites*, &c.), by offshoots of the Pronoritidae (*Prouddenites*, *Uddenites*), leading to the Permian Medlicottidae, also by species of the persisting genera *Gastrioceras* and *Gonioloboceras*. This varied assemblage is described from the Nellie Bly Beds of Oklahoma by A. K. Miller and L. M. Cline (1934); F. B. Plummer (1937) cites it from the

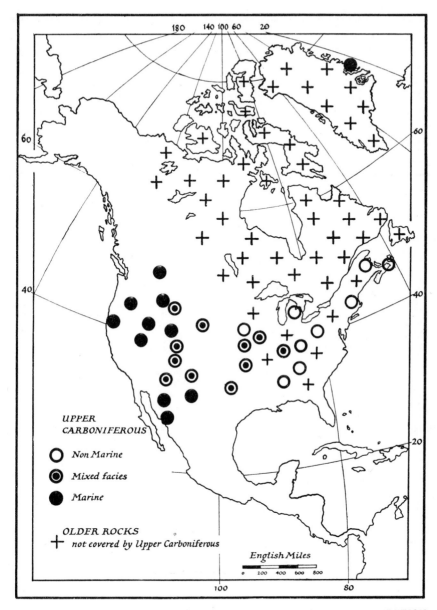

UPPER
CARBONIFEROUS

○ Non Marine

◉ Mixed facies

● Marine

OLDER ROCKS
✛ not covered by Upper Carboniferous

English Miles

FIG. 51. SKETCH-MAP OF NORTH AMERICA SHOWING GENERAL DISTRIBUTION
OF UPPER CARBONIFEROUS ROCKS

Conemaugh formation of Pennsylvania, the Drum Limestone of Kansas, and the Gaptank stage of Texas. The last formation is succeeded by the Wolfcamp stage which, judging by the ammonoid fauna, does not differ greatly in point of age though it is assigned to the Permian system.

These Upper Pennsylvanian faunas are entirely unknown in western Europe where, owing to a great regression of the sea, marine bands are not developed higher than the Aegir horizon of Westphalia. They are, however, represented in the southern Urals of Russia where such genera as *Prouddenites, Uddenites, Schistoceras, Shumardites,* and *Prothalassoceras* have been recorded by V. E. Ruzencev (1936). Observations by F. B. Plummer (1937) on the correlation of the Carboniferous goniatite zones in Russia and North America show clearly that the upper part of the Pennsylvanian Series is equivalent to the Uralian stage of south-eastern Europe.

The fusuline foraminifera in the Pennsylvanian Series of North America also conform in vertical range with those of Russia. At early horizons of the system, grouped in the Des Moines stage, species of the primitive genera *Staffella, Fusulina, Fusulinella,* and *Wedekindellina* are found at localities in the middle west and mid-continental regions of the United States. M. L. Thompson and H. W. Scott (1941) have recorded this association from Des Moines strata in Texas, New Mexico, Oklahoma, Kansas, Colorado, Wyoming, south-west Montana, Iowa, Illinois, and Missouri. The Des Moines stage, therefore, corresponds broadly with the Moscovian stage of Russia. F. B. Plummer (1937) states that the genus *Triticites* first appears in Texas and Kansas above the unconformity which separates the Des Moines from the Missouri stage, and continues to the top of the Gaptank formation which is taken as the upper limit of the Pennsylvanian system. The genus is also recorded from Oklahoma by N. D. Newell (1934), from Nebraska by C. O. Dunbar and G. E. Condra (1927), from Wyoming and Ohio by M. L. Thompson (1936). According to C. O. Dunbar (1937), primitive species of *Triticites* give character to the lower part of the Missouri stage; higher horizons of the Missouri and the Virgil stages are marked by more advanced members of the genus. A similar distinction is seen between the lower and upper beds of the Uralian stage in Russia. *Schwagerina* and its allies are reported occasionally in the Missouri Beds, but they are more abundant at early horizons of the Permian system.

Marine fossils of late Palaeozoic age have been known from SOUTH AMERICAN localities for more than a century. They were first described from exposures in Bolivia by A. d'Orbigny (1842) who named such species as *Productus cora, P. inca, Spirifer condor, Derbya buchi,* &c. Since Orbigny's time these have generally been referred to a Pennsylvanian age on the general aspect of the prevalent brachiopods. Other collections described by J. W. Salter (1861), R. Koslowski (1914), R. L. F. Meyer (1914), J. A. Douglas (1914, 1920), and others from Bolivia and Peru have also been assigned to the same system. The fusuline foraminifera are hardly mentioned in the older literature, but a study of these organisms by C. O. Dunbar and N. D. Newell (1946) has shown that most of the Bolivian and Peruvian rocks under discussion must be referred to early horizons of the Permian system (p. 386). Meyer, however, had described a fusulinid species from a particular horizon in the famous section at Tarma, central Peru, and this form is now referred by Dunbar and Newell to the genus *Fusulinella*. From this, and evidence provided by the abundant productids and *Neospirifer* cf. *cameratus*, the lower part of the Tarma section is correlated with the Des Moines stage of North America and the Moscovian stage of Russia; the succeeding red beds are tentatively regarded as Permian. From the Amotape Mountains in north-west Peru H. D. Thomas (1928–30) has described an assemblage of mollusca which includes local species of the *globulosum* group of *Gastrioceras* (now transferred to *Eoasianites*) which is widespread at early Pennsylvanian horizons in the United States, such as the Atoka and Smithwick formations of Texas discussed by A. K. Miller and W. M. Furnish (1940). Marine limestones of Mississippian age are reported by J. A. Douglas (1920) at a single locality north of Lake Titicaca. Again, J. Keidel and H. J. Harrington (1938) have described limestones containing brachiopods allied to North American species of *Syringothyris*, *Cyrtospirifer*, *Spiriferina*, and *Dielasma*, and associated with tillites, in the Precordillera of San Juan in western Argentina. Long ago, late Palaeozoic faunas from the basin of the Lower Amazon were described, and afterwards revised, by O. A. Derby (1874, 1894); later F. Katzer (1903) in a general account of the region figured most of the species, and F. R. C. Reed has added further records. Brachiopods are most prominent in these faunas and are comparable with those of Bolivia. Fusuline foraminifera, however, have apparently not been investigated, and it is possible that these reputed 'Upper Carboniferous' rocks, together with those of Colombia and western Venezuela reported by O. Stutzer (1927) and P. Christ (1927) respectively, may also belong to the Permian system.

Both Mississippian and Pennsylvanian rocks are represented in western CANADA, but there is the same uncertainty about the upper series as in South America. In western Alberta argillaceous limestones of the Banff formation have yielded to P. S. Warren (1927) fossils at two horizons. The lower one contains chiefly brachiopods with *Spirifer centronatus* as the dominant species. Most of the fauna is known in the United States from the Kinderhook Series of the Mississippi Valley and the Madison Limestone of Wyoming. A later assemblage, also mainly of brachiopods, is more like that of the Chouteau Limestone of Missouri and the equivalent beds of the Liard River (lat. 61° N.) described by G. S. Hume (1923). The massive grey limestones of the Rundle formation in Alberta have furnished numerous brachiopods and corals, including species of *Lithostrotion* which are said to form a reef near the top of the formation. This reef is now in lat. 51° N., much farther north than the limit of modern coral reefs. The

Rundle Limestone is correlated generally with the Chester group of the United States, but the upper beds may represent early Pennsylvanian horizons. The brachiopods and mollusca of the overlying Rocky Mountain Quartzite are referred to species that are recorded from Pennsylvanian strata in the United States, but beds near the top of the section have yielded the gastropod *Euphemus carbonarius* which seems to indicate a Permian age. A similar succession is described by J. A. Allan (1932) and his colleagues from Jasper Park, Alberta (lat. 53° N.).

Around Kamloops in British Columbia there is a great development of pale limestones, known as the Cache Creek Series, which contain numerous brachiopods and a few molluscan species. The brachiopods show a decided affinity with Russian species, but give little clue to the precise age of the beds. In recent years, however, ammonoids and fusuline foraminifera of Permian age have been described from the typical sections. M. B. B. Crockford and P. S. Warren (1935) state that the Cache Creek Series extends the whole length of British Columbia, from the Kamloops district in the south to the Yukon territory in the north. F. R. C. Reed (1950) writes of 'limestones formed almost entirely of *Fusulina*' in this area, but the only foraminifera which have been adequately described are Permian forms; moreover Permian ammonoids are recorded from the top of the series by A. K. Miller and M. B. B. Crockford (1936). In the Yukon Territory, near the Alaskan boundary, D. D. Cairns (1914, 1915) has recorded brachiopod assemblages which G. H. Girty compared with those of the Gschel Beds of the Uralian stage of Russia. It is therefore uncertain how far the Pennsylvanian system is represented in north-west America, for the palaeontological record is far from complete. The available evidence indicates some connexion between North Pacific waters and the Uralian sea, probably by way of the Arctic Ocean.

LITERATURE

The publication of Vaughan's work on the Lower Carboniferous succession in the Bristol Area was followed by other papers on the Avonian Series in various parts of the British Isles. Many of these works contain valuable notes on the fossils (especially corals and brachiopods) and their vertical distribution. The following list therefore contains the titles of selected papers dealing with the various provinces, and also those of more purely palaeontological works which describe the evolution of certain genera.

'The Palaeontological Sequence in the Carboniferous Limestone of the Bristol Area', by A. Vaughan, *Q.J.G.S.*, vol. lxi, pp. 181–307, 1905.

'The Faunal Succession in the Carboniferous Limestone (Upper Avonian) of the Midland Area (North Derbyshire and North Staffordshire)', by T. F. Sibly, *Q.J.G.S.*, vol. lxiv, pp. 34–82, 1908.

'The Faunal Succession of the Upper Bernician', by S. Smith, *Trans. Nat. Hist. Soc. Northumberland*, N.S., vol. iii, pp. 591–645, 1910.

'The Carboniferous Succession in Gower (Glamorganshire), with Notes on its Fauna and Conditions of Deposition', by E. E. L. Dixon and A. Vaughan, *Q.J.G.S.*, vol. lxvii, pp. 477–571, 1911.

'The Lower Carboniferous Succession in the North-west of England', by E. J. Garwood, *Q.J.G.S.*, vol. lxviii, pp. 449–586, 1912.

'The Lower Carboniferous Succession in the Settle District and along the Line of the Craven Faults', by E. J. Garwood and E. Goodyear, *Q.J.G.S.*, vol. lxxx, pp. 184–273, 1924.

'The Faunal Succession in the Carboniferous Limestone and Bowland Shales at Clitheroe and Pendle Hill (Lancashire)', by D. Parkinson, *Q.J.G.S.*, vol. lxxxii, pp. 188–249, 1926.

'Scottish Carboniferous Stratigraphy', by M. Macgregor, *Trans. Geol. Soc. Glasgow*, vol. xviii, part iii, 1929.

'The Carboniferous Geology of the Skipton Anticline', by R. G. S. Hudson and G. H. Mitchell, *Sum. Prog. Geol. Surv. for 1935*, Part 2, pp. 1–45, 1937.

'The Carboniferous Limestone Series of North Wales: Conditions of Deposition and Interpretation of its History', by E. Neaverson, *Proc. Liverpool Geol. Soc.*, vol. xix, pp. 113–44, 1946.

'The Stratigraphy of the Dovedale Area, Derbyshire and Staffordshire', by D. Parkinson, *Q.J.G.S.*, vol. cv, pp. 265–94, 1950.

'British Fossil Corals': Part III. 'Corals of the Permian and the Mountain Limestone', by H. Milne-Edwards and J. Haime, *Mon. Pal. Soc.* 1852.

'The Evolution of *Zaphrentis delanouei* in Lower Carboniferous Times', by R. G. Carruthers, *Q.J.G.S.*, vol. lxvi, pp. 523–38, 1910.

'Upper Viséan Corals of the Genus *Caninia*', by H. P. Lewis, *Q.J.G.S.*, vol. lxxx, pp. 389–407, 1924.

'*Caninia cylindrica* Scouler and other Large Caninias from the Carboniferous Limestone of Ireland', by H. P. Lewis, *Sci. Proc. Roy. Dublin Soc.*, vol. xviii, N.S., pp. 373–82, 1927.

'The Genus *Aulophyllum*', by S. Smith, *Q.J.G.S.*, vol. lxix, pp. 51–77, 1913.

'The Genus *Lonsdaleia* and *Dibunophyllum rugosum*', by S. Smith, *Q.J.G.S.*, vol. lxxi, pp. 218–72, 1916.

'*Aulina rotiformis, Phillipsastraea hennahi* and *Orionastraea*', by S. Smith, *Q.J.G.S.*, vol. lxxii, pp. 280–307, 1917.

'On the Index Fossil of the Cleistopora Zone', by L. B. Smyth, *Sci. Proc. Roy. Dublin Soc.*, vol. xviii, N.S., pp. 423–31, 1927.

'The Carboniferous Rugose Corals of Scotland', by D. Hill, *Mon. Pal. Soc.* 1938–41.

'The Lower Carboniferous Coral *Orionastraea* and its Distribution in the North of England', by R. G. S. Hudson, *Proc. Leeds. Phil. Soc.*, vol. i, pp. 440–57, 1929.

'The British Carboniferous Orthotetinae', by Ivor Thomas, *Mem. Geol. Surv., Palaeont.*, vol. i, part 2, 1910.

'The British Carboniferous *Producti*: 'The Genera *Pustula* and *Overtonia*', by Ivor Thomas, Mem. Geol. Surv. (Palaeont.), vol. i, part 4, 1914.

'The Small Species of *Chonetes* found in the Lower Carboniferous around Bristol', by S. Smith, *Geol. Mag.*, vol. lxii, pp. 85–88, 1925.

The British Carboniferous Producti, by H. M. Muir-Wood, Mem. Geol. Surv. (Palaeont.), vol. iii, part 1, 1938.

'The Classification of British Productids', by H. M. Muir-Wood, *Ann. Mag. Nat. Hist.*, ser. 10, vol. v, pp. 100–8, 1930.

'*Daviesiella llangollensis* (Davidson) and Related Forms', by F. W. Cope, *Journ. Manchester Geol. Assoc.*, vol. i, pp. 199–231, 1940.

'Studies in Avonian Brachiopoda', by T. N. George.

Part I: The Genera *Brachythyris* and *Martinia*, *Geol. Mag.*, vol. lxiv, pp. 106–19, 1927.

Part II: The Genus *Camarophoria*, ibid., pp. 193–201, 1927.

Part III: The Delthyrium of *Chonetes comoides*, ibid., vol. lxviii, pp. 554–57, 1930.

'*Ambocoelia* Hall and Certain Similar British Spiriferids', by T. N. George, *Q.J.G.S.*, vol. lxxxvii, pp. 30–61, 1931.

'The British Carboniferous Reticulate Spiriferidae', by T. N. George, *Q.J.G.S.*, vol. lxxxviii, pp. 516–75, 1932.

'On *Syringothyris* Winchell, and certain Carboniferous Brachiopoda referred to *Spiriferina* d'Orbigny', by F. J. North, *Q.J.G.S.*, vol. lxxvi (for 1920), pp. 162–227, 1921.

'The British Carboniferous Lamellibranchiata', by W. Hind, *Mon. Pal. Soc.* 1896–1905.

'New Carboniferous Lamellibranchs, and Notes on other Forms', by J. W. Jackson, *Mem. and Proc. Manchester Lit. and Phil. Soc.*, vol. lxxi, pp. 93–122, 1927. [Species of *Pterinopecten*, *Posidonomya*, and *Posidoniella* described and illustrated.]

'*Carbonicola, Anthracomya* and *Naiadites*', by W. Hind, *Mon. Pal. Soc.* 1894–6.

'A Revision of the Non-marine Lamellibranchs of the Coal Measures, and a Discussion of their Zonal Sequence', by J. H. Davies and A. E. Trueman, *Q.J.G.S.*, vol. lxxxiii, pp. 210–59, 1927.

'British Carboniferous Non-Marine Lamellibranchia', by A. E. Trueman and J. Weir, *Mon. Pal. Soc.* 1946 (in progress).

'A Revision of the British Carboniferous Murchisoniidae', by J. Longstaff, *Q.J.G.S.*, vol. lxxxii, pp. 526–55; 1926. Other papers by the same author on Carboniferous Gastropoda appear in the same Journal for 1889, 1892, 1895, 1898, 1912, 1917.

'The Marine Beds in the Coal Measures of North Staffordshire', by J. T. Stobbs, with Notes on their Palaeontology by W. Hind, *Q.J.G.S.*, vol. lxi, pp. 495–547, 1905.

'The Carboniferous Cephalopoda of Ireland', by A. H. Foord, *Mon. Pal. Soc.* 1897–1903.

'Fossil Cephalopoda', by A. H. Foord and G. C. Crick, 3 vols., *Brit. Mus. Cat.* 1888–97.

'The Carboniferous Goniatites of the North of England and their Zones', by W. S. Bisat, *Proc. Yorks. Geol. Soc.*, vol. xx, pp. 40–124, 1924.

'The Carboniferous Goniatite Zones of England, and their Continental Equivalents', by W. S. Bisat, *C.R. Congr. Stratigr. Carb.* (Heerlen, 1927), pp. 117–33, 1928.

'The Goniatite and Nautiloid Fauna of the Middle Coal Measures of England and Wales', by W. S. Bisat, *Sum. Prog. Geol. Surv. for 1929*, part 3, pp. 75–88, 1930.

'Goniatites of the Beyrichoceras Zone in the North of England', by W. S. Bisat, *Proc. Yorks. Geol. Soc.*, vol. xxii, pp. 280–309, 1934.

'The Lower Reticuloceras Goniatite Succession in the Namurian of the North of England', by W. S. Bisat and R. G. S. Hudson, *Proc. Yorks. Geol. Soc.*, vol. xxiv, pp. 383–440, 1943.

'The Goniatite Genus *Dimorphoceras* and its Development in the British Carboniferous', by E. W. J. Moore, *Proc. Yorks. Geol. Soc.*, vol. xxiv, pp. 103–28, 1939.

'The Carboniferous Goniatite Genera *Girtyoceras* and *Eumorphoceras*', by E. W. J. Moore, *Proc. Yorks. Geol. Soc.*, vol. xxv, pp. 387–445, 1945.

'Mid-Avonian Goniatites from Gower', by T. N. George and D. R. A. Ponsford, *Ann. Mag. Nat. Hist.*, ser. 10, vol. xvi, pp. 354–70, 1935.

The Higher Crustacea of the Carboniferous Rocks of Scotland, by B. N. Peach, Mem. Geol. Surv. (Palaeont.), vol. i, part 1, 1908.

'The Carboniferous Arachnida', by R. I. Pocock, *Mon. Pal. Soc.* 1911.

'The Fossil Insects of the British Coal Measures', by H. Bolton, *Mon. Pal. Soc.* 1921–2.

'The British Carboniferous Trilobites', by H. Woodward, *Mon. Pal. Soc.* 1883–4.

The principal features of the Carboniferous deposits in Europe are described in a series of papers in *C. R. Congr. Stratigr. Carb.* (Heerlen, 1927 and 1935). Those of eastern Europe are discussed by F. Heritsch in 'Karbon und Perm in den Südalpen und in Südosteuropa', *Geol. Rundschau*, Bd. xxx, pp. 528–88, 1939. The work of Russian geologists on 'The Carboniferous and Permian of the Southern Urals' is summarized by M. K. Elias in *Amer. Journ. Sci.*, ser. 5, vol. xxxiii, pp. 279–95, 1937, while 'The Middle Carboniferous of Russia' is described by S. V. Semichatov in *Geol Mag.*, vol. lxxii, pp. 433–41, 1935.

The review by C. O. Dunbar and L. G. Henbest of 'The Fusulinid Genera Fusulina, Fusulinella and Wedekindella', in *Amer. Journ. Sci.*, ser. 5, vol. xx, pp. 357–64, 1930, was followed by intensive study of late Palaeozoic Foraminifera, and a useful summary is given by M. L. Thompson in 'Studies of American Fusulinids', *Univ. Kansas Palaeont. Contrib.*, No. 4, 1948, which contains an extensive bibliography. Other fossils in the Carboniferous rocks of North America are discussed by R. C. Moore in 'Palaeontological Features of Mississippian Rocks in North America and Europe', *Journ. Geol.*, vol. lvi, pp. 373–402, 1948. 'Studies of Carboniferous Ammonoids', by A. K. Miller and W. M. Furnish in *Journ. Palaeont.*, vol. xiv, 1940, are followed by later papers by Miller and other collaborators in the same journal.

In Asia F. R. C. Reed has described 'Upper Carboniferous Fossils from Chitral and the Pamirs', *Pal. Indica*, N.S., vol. vi, Mem. 4, 1925, 'Upper Carboniferous Fossils from Tibet', ibid., vol. xvi, 1930, 'A Permo-Carboniferous Marine Fauna from the Umaria Coalfield', *Rec. Geol. Surv. India*, vol. lx, pp. 367–98, 1928, 'New Fossils from the Agglomerate Slate of Kashmir', *Pal. Indica*, N.S., vol. xx, Mem. 1, 1932, and 'Fossils from the Eurydesma and Conularia Beds of the Salt Range', ibid., vol. xxiii, Mem. 1, 1936. J. S. Lee summarizes the extensive Chinese records in *Geology of China*, London, 1939.

The most recent account of Carboniferous rocks in the Australian region is given by T. W. E. David and W. R. Browne in *Geology of the Commonwealth of Australia*, London, 1950.

VIII

FOSSIL LAND-FLORAS

I. PALAEOZOIC PLANTS

CAMBRIAN, Ordovician, and Silurian rocks, originally deposited under marine conditions, have furnished some evidence of the occurrence of seaweeds, but have provided no satisfactory records of land plants. It is in Devonian rocks of the Old Red Sandstone type that the oldest known representatives of land vegetation occur. The fact that the most important occurrence of Devonian plants so far discovered remained unknown until 1910 encourages the hope that further discoveries may be made; and it is by no means impossible that pre-Devonian rocks may yet yield satisfactory evidence of land vegetation.

The records of Devonian plants are generally external impressions in rocks that were originally formed at some distance from the habitat of the plants. But in 1910 Dr. W. Mackie discovered, in the Middle Devonian of Rhynie, Aberdeenshire, a bed of chert that contains silicified plants with their tissues admirably preserved. This flora, which has been described in detail by Kidston and Lang, is characteristic of a special habitat—a Devonian peat bog, and contains three genera of vascular plants: *Rhynia*, *Hornea*, and *Asteroxylon*.

Rhynia and *Hornea* were small leafless and rootless plants, having subterranean and aerial stems which ended in spore-capsules somewhat like those of the living *Sphagnum* (the bog-moss). The spores were adapted for dispersal on land, and the stems contained an axial strand of conducting-tissue. *Asteroxylon*, a somewhat larger plant, is distinguished from the other two genera by the presence of scale-like leaves on the aerial stems and a more elaborate arrangement of the conducting-tissue. These three genera are regarded as closely related to *Psilophyton*, a genus long known by external impressions from the Devonian rocks of Canada and Europe. They agree in general habit (but not in vascular structure and organization of the spore-capsules) with *Psilotum*, a living genus widely distributed in the southern hemisphere, belonging to the group Lycopodiales which includes the modern club-mosses. But Arber concluded that the similarity in habit with *Psilotum* is 'perfectly valueless', and that any affinity between these plants must be very remote. He regarded '*Psilophyton* as first and foremost a Thallophyte, which, while still Thallophytic in habit, may occupy anatomically a place halfway between the Thallophyta and Pteridophyta'.

More recently a new plant from the Lower Old Red Sandstone has been described by A. Heard under the name *Gosslingia breconensis* Heard. The aerial stems and rhizomes have a large central stele surrounded by a cortex and epidermis. Oval structures attached to a branch by a short stalk are regarded as fructifications. The affinities of this species are at present unknown.

The genus *Arthrostigma* from the Lower Old Red Sandstone of Scotland, Norway, Germany, Canada, and other countries has a stout stem, irregularly furrowed longitudinally, and bearing numerous large spine-like organs. The latter are probably of the nature of emergences such as are seen in some species of *Psilophyton*.

Other early Devonian plants are less completely known, but some serve to show that members of the Lycopodiales were relatively abundant in numbers and of widespread occurrence, while others seem to foreshadow the ferns of a later age. It is interesting to note also that certain specimens of these early vascular cryptogams indicate the stature of trees. The systematic position of other Devonian plants is still extremely obscure. *Parka decipiens*, abundant in the Lower Old Red Sandstone of Scotland and widely distributed in Great Britain, could only be described by Don and Hickling as a 'thallophyte with algal affinities'.

It is now established that Lower Devonian floras differ more from those of Upper Devonian age than do the latter from Lower Carboniferous assemblages. Arber distinguished two separate Devonian terrestrial floras—the **Psilophyton Flora** of the Lower Devonian and the **Archaeopteris Flora** ranging through the Upper Devonian Series.

Though some genera of the Psilophyton flora survive in the Upper Devonian, the plants of the Archaeopteris flora seem to have attained a higher degree of differentiation, and a greater variety of genera is known. The genus *Archaeopteris* is represented in the Old Red Sandstone of Caithness and southern Ireland by large, compound, fern-like fronds with cuneate leaflets and clusters of sporangia. Other species of *Archaeopteris* are recorded from equivalent deposits in Russia, Ellesmereland (North America), and Australia. The affinities of this genus are uncertain: it may be a true fern, or, on the other hand, it may belong to an extinct group of fern-like, seed-bearing plants, the pteridosperms, that attained a dominant position in Upper Carboniferous floras. Other fern-like fronds are *Sphenopteridum* and *Cephalopteris*, whose pinnules are divided into very narrow lobes, recorded from western Europe and the Arctic region.

Lycopods are represented by *Archaeosigillaria*, whose stem bears spirally arranged, contiguous, persistent leaf-bases, and small deltoid leaves, as well as by *Protolepidodendron* and *Cyclostigma*, which have been recorded from Ireland and Bear Island (within the Arctic Circle) with *Stigmaria*-like rhizomes. *Cyclostigma* is represented in the Devonian rocks of southern Ireland by *C. kiltorkense* (Haughton). The trunk bears leaf-bases which are arranged in whorls at first, but later become distant and quincuncially arranged, owing to the unequal extension of the surface. The decorticated stem may show a fluted appearance like the pith-casts of *Calamites*. The lower part of the trunk consists of a rhizophore which bears close resemblance to *Stigmaria* of the Coal Measures.

The large wedge-shaped leaves, with numerous spreading veins, shown by the genus *Psygmophyllum* recall, on a large scale, those of the living maidenhair tree (*Ginkgo*), but there is probably no close relationship, though the affinities of the Devonian plant are unknown. *Psygmophyllum* has been recorded from Devonian rocks in Ireland, Belgium, Norway, and Spitzbergen.

The extinct group Sphenophyllales, which persists into the Carboniferous, is represented in the Upper Devonian of the Arctic regions by *Pseudobornia* and *Sphenophyllum*. The group as a whole is distinguished by its slender stems with an axial strand of conducting-tissue, and the leaves spring in whorls from the stem-nodes. These characters suggest a general habit of growth similar to that of the scrambling *Galium* (cleavers) of modern hedgerows. The Devonian species of *Sphenophyllum* have small, narrow, finely divided leaves; this type persists into the Lower Carboniferous and contrasts strongly with Upper Carboniferous species, in which the leaves are wedge-shaped and entire. *Pseudobornia*, with stout stems bearing whorls of fimbriate leaves, combines characters shown by the later calamites and the sphenophylls.

The woody stems of certain Devonian trees, such as *Palaeopitys*, *Dadoxylon*, and *Callixylon*, are similar in structural details to some living conifers. Thus the various lines of development in plants were differentiated at a very early stage—much earlier in point of time than was formerly suspected. Indeed, A. H. Church believes that the differentiation was established 'in the Benthic epoch of the sea'; that is, before the plants became adapted for terrestrial life.

A few plants occurring in the Upper Old Red Sandstone of Scotland are regarded as survivals from the Psilophyton flora. *Thursophyton*, which is also known from the Middle Devonian of Norway and Bohemia, is a stem covered with crowded scale-like emergences, and bearing elliptical bodies which appear to be fructifications; the general aspect is remarkably like that of some club-mosses. *Ptilophyton* has a stout axis which gives off lateral shoots covered with scale-like emergences, and the ends of the shoots are circinately coiled like the young leaves of a fern; its relationships are entirely unknown.

In a brief summary, present knowledge of Lower Devonian floras is too meagre for generalization. Upper Devonian plants are better known but records are still imperfect and any general statement must be tentative. It is evident, however, that a flora containing most of the larger groups of plants had become established over wide areas of the globe before the end of the Devonian period. There is no indication of well-marked floral regions like those which are evident in the climatic belts of the present day; some local peculiarities are apparent, but they do not obscure the world-wide uniformity which is the most noticeable feature of the flora as a whole.

The Lower Carboniferous flora, often separated as the **Rhacopteris Flora**, has a general aspect similar to that of the Upper Devonian, but contains certain plants that are not known in the earlier assemblage. Also, some plant-groups give evidence of gradual change in passing from Lower Carboniferous to higher strata. The latter point may be illustrated by reference to the two genera *Asterocalamites* and *Calamites*, whose stems are longitudinally ribbed like those of *Equisetum*, the sole living genus of the same group. The pith-casts of the Lower Carboniferous species of *Asterocalamites* show that the ribs pass straight up the stems across the nodes or stem-joints, while in *Calamites*, from the Upper Carboniferous, the ribs almost invariably alternate at the nodes. Species of *Calamites* from the top of the Carboniferous Limestone Series show an intermediate arrangement, some ribs passing straight up the stem without alternation, others alternating at the nodes as in Upper Carboniferous species. These ribs are connected with the course of the vascular bundles within the stem, and the change in mode of ribbing reflects a change in the internal anatomy of the plants. The leaves of *Asterocalamites* are narrow and linear and are often divided into two portions, but the similar linear leaves of *Calamites* are never branched, thus giving a further distinction between the two genera. Among lycopods, *Archaeosigillaria*, persisting from the Devonian, is common at some localities in the Lower Carboniferous of North Wales and is recorded from the Lake District. *Lepidophloios*, with transversely elongated leaf-bases arranged spirally round the stem is a characteristic Scottish plant. *Sigillaria* and *Lepidodendron* occur rarely in the Lower Carboniferous, but are mainly characteristic of Coal Measure floras. The complex cone of *Cheirostrobus* and the 'seed' known as *Lepidocarpon* are interesting as showing the highly specialized nature of lycopodiaceous fructifications in these early times.

Numerous fern-like fronds occur in Lower Carboniferous rocks. It is necessary to remember that fossil plants are generally in a fragmentary state, the foliage being as a rule detached from branches, and the fructifications are rarely found in connexion with the leaves. The piecing together of the various organs is a matter of great difficulty, and is often impossible in the present state of our knowledge. The foliage is the most conspicuous, and most commonly preserved, among plant remains; the attention of geologists is therefore almost restricted to the general form of the leaves. The only method of grouping together plants which have certain similarities in the form of the leaves and the character of the nervation is to give them provisional names; consequently a number of 'form-genera' have been established, which are not genera in the usual definite sense, but which are useful for descriptive and recording purposes. Later discoveries may lead to a knowledge of the relationships between these 'form-genera', but much remains to be learned in this direction.

The foliage known as *Sphenopteris* has small, deeply divided leaflets with a central vein from which spring a number of branched lateral veins. Some sphenopterid fronds are now known to belong to fern-like plants of the seed-bearing pteridosperm group, but the affinites of many are still obscure. Sphenopterid foliage occurs in the Lower Carboniferous and persists into the Coal Measures. *Rhacopteris* (Fig. 52) is another 'form-genus', with large wedge-shaped leaflets, veins radiating from the base of each; though occurring rarely above and below, this form is mainly characteristic of Lower Carboniferous strata. *Rhodea*, a sphenopteroid frond whose leaflets are divided into very narrow segments, was formerly thought to be peculiar to Lower Carboniferous rocks, but is now known from higher horizons. *Sphenopteridium* and *Spathulopteris*, two closely allied genera confined to the Lower Carboniferous, have small leaflets with the veins arranged parallel with the margin; the leaflets of the former are wedge-shaped and divided into segments, those of the latter are lanceolate and entire. The name *Adiantites* is given to plants with wedge-shaped pinnules either attached to the rachis by a narrow base or by a more or less distinct footstalk; numerous fine veins of equal strength radiate from the base and frequently dichotomize. *A. antiquus* (Ett.) from the Lower Carboniferous of North Wales is illustrated in Fig. 52. The position of *Telangium affine* (L. and H.) as a pteridosperm is now established. The sterile leaves are divided into oblique narrow segments of sphenopterid type; a single vein enters the pinnules and by repeated dichotomy produces a radiating series of veinlets (Fig. 52). The fertile branches bear only synangia which comprise groups of microsporangia attached to the ends of branchlets of the frond. Only the cupules of the seeds are known.

These plants are mostly of undetermined affinity, and many may be pteridosperms. The occurrence of seeds—some as large as hazel-nuts—attest the presence of this group in the Lower Carboniferous of Europe and the Arctic regions. Indeed, Kidston expressed the opinion that 'as we pass downwards in geological time, pteridosperms and gymnospermous plants outnumber ferns so far as one can judge from the data available at present', and pointed out that were not true ferns found as petrifactions in South Scotland, there would have been no absolute proof of their occurrence in British Lower Carboniferous rocks.

The Scottish occurrence of petrifactions must be passed over briefly, since their discrimination (however important from the botanical aspect) is beyond the scope of the average field geologist. Their chief repository is the Calciferous Sandstone Series, from which some twenty plants have been described—six ferns, seven pteridosperms, and seven gymnospermous plants of uncertain affinities. The ferns occur in the upper part (Oil Shale group) of the series. One of the commonest is *Botryopteris antiqua* Kidston

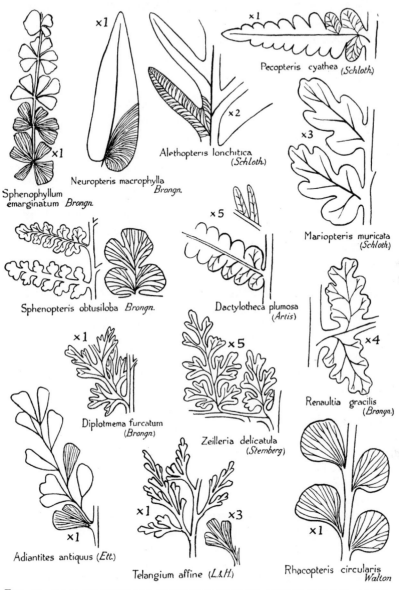

×1

Pecopteris cyathea *(Schloth.)*

×1

×2

Alethopteris lonchitica
(Schloth.)

Neuropteris macrophylla
Brongn.

Sphenophyllum
emarginatum *Brongn.*

×3

×1

Mariopteris muricata
(Schloth.)

×5

Sphenopteris obtusiloba *Brongn.*

Dactylotheca plumosa
(Artis)

×5

×4

Renaultia gracilis
(Brongn.)

×1

Diplotmema furcatum
(Brongn.)

Zeilleria delicatula
(Sternberg)

×1

×1

×3

×1

Adiantites antiquus *(Ett.)*

Telangium affine *(L.&H.)*

Rhacopteris circularis
Walton

FIG. 52. LEAF-IMPRESSIONS FROM THE BRITISH CARBONIFEROUS ROCKS
(drawn from figures by Kidston, Seward, and Walton)

with a simple, axial, vascular strand, while *Stauropteris* is little more complex. The stem-anatomy of pteridosperms exhibits distinct characters, especially the presence of transverse or reticulate bands of thick-walled tissue in the cortex. There is often evidence of this in fern-like plants preserved as incrustations, and thus pteridospermous affinities are suspected in many cases.

Lower Carboniferous plants have been recorded from many widely scattered localities—from Bear Island and Spitzbergen in the north, through European, Asian, and North American localities, to South Africa, South America, and Australia. The various records show striking similarity as regards both structure and habit of growth. There seems to have been no well-marked division into botanical provinces under varying climatic conditions as is the case with modern floras, since the Arctic plants apparently flourished quite as well as the southern floras. This world-wide uniformity has been regarded as proof of comparative uniformity of climate, but such a generalization does not seem to be justified by the available evidence. Some ferns, such as the common bracken, have an extremely wide distribution at the present day, and the Palaeozoic plants may well have shown a similar adaptability under diverse climatic conditions. As A. C. Seward has remarked: 'The knowledge that many recent plants can live and reproduce themselves in Arctic as in temperate lands, and our experience of the possibility of introducing tropical species to cooler regions, should warn us against hasty generalizations on the subject of fossil plants as tests of climate', especially (it may be added) in dealing with Palaeozoic floras about which so little is known.

Certain genera and some species are common to the Lower and Upper Carboniferous floras, but in general the two assemblages differ widely from one another. In Britain there is an abrupt change of flora at a horizon within the Millstone Grit, a fact for which Kidston could 'offer no satisfactory explanation'. Potonié, however, has more recently recorded a mixed assemblage in the corresponding position in Upper Silesia, and Renier records floral continuity in Belgium. E. B. Bailey has suggested that 'temporary marine isolation induced a difference in the Carboniferous floral history of the two regions, until the spreading deltas of the Millstone Grit provided a highway for plant migration', and that 'the plant-break of the Scottish Carboniferous is due to a replacement of the local flora by a southern competitor'. Incidentally it may be mentioned that Traquair in 1884 had recognized a similar change in the estuarine fish fauna of the Scottish Carboniferous rocks.

The records of plant life from the Upper Carboniferous rocks (the Coal Measures) show much greater variety than those from earlier formations. The plants occur in the coal-seams and associated shales, which were apparently accumulated in swamps and estuaries not far from the margin of the sea. While the flora is very abundant and is distributed through most of the vertical succession of the Coal Measures, plants are far more abundant at certain horizons than at others, and marine bands mark occasional incursions of the sea over the area of deposition.

The British Coal Measures were first classified on lithological grounds into Lower, Middle, and Upper Coal Measures. Later Kidston expressed the opinion that plants 'give the surest test of age' in Carboniferous rocks, and subdivided the Coal Measures on a palaeobotanical basis. The term Yorkian, proposed by W. W. Watts, was used for many years in preference to the continental term Westphalian. But discussions at the International Congress on Carboniferous Stratigraphy at Haarlem in 1927 and 1935 have resulted in a subdivision of the old Westphalian stage on the basis of successive plant-assemblages. These are shown in the table below in relation to the older classifications.

Upper Coal Measures . . .	Radstockian Stage.	Westphalian	D
Transition Measures . . .	Staffordian	,,	C
Middle Coal-Measures . . .	Yorkian	,,	B
Lower Coal Measures Millstone Grit (top) . . . . . }	Lanarkian	,,	A

The **Lanarkian Flora** occurs in the Lower Coal Measures and part of the underlying Millstone Grit, ceasing in North Staffordshire 'at a depth of about 50 feet below the Fifth Grit' (Kidston).

Lycopods are represented abundantly by several species of *Lepidodendron*. This genus is easily recognized by its numerous contiguous leaf-bases arranged spirally around the stem, presenting the appearance (on a gigantic scale) of the modern lowly club-moss *Lycopodium*. An allied genus, *Sigillaria*, whose leaf-bases are disposed in vertical rows, is not so common here as in later floras, but is represented by *S. tessellata* Brongniart, *S. elegans* Brongniart, and others. *Calamites*, identified by the vertical ribbing of the stem, is the most abundant genus of Upper Carboniferous equisetales, of which the living horsetails (*Equisetum*) represent a later development; *C. ramosus* Weiss and *C. communis* (Binney) occur in the Lower Coal Measures. The leaves of *Calamites*, known as *Annularia* and *Asterophyllites*, are given off in whorls at the stem-joints and are narrow and needle-like. The cones *Calamostachys* and *Palaeostachya*, known from petrifactions, also belong to *Calamites*. This genus, like the lycopods already mentioned, developed woody tissue and attained the stature of trees.

Prevalent fern-like fronds belong to the forms known as *Alethopteris* and *Sphenopteris*. These represent the foliage of pteridosperms, not true ferns, the stem corresponding to *Alethopteris* being known as *Medullosa*, while one species of *Sphenopteris* (*S. hoeninghausi* Brongniart) is the foliage of *Lyginopteris*, whose stem was called *Lyginodendron*, its 'male and female flowers' being known as *Crossotheca* and *Lagenostoma* respectively, before the connexion of the various organs was known. The leaves, however, besides being the most abundant fossils, are most easily recognized and so are the most useful to field-workers. *Alethopteris*, a compound frond, has long, narrow leaflets attached to the axis by their entire base; a median vein extends to the apex of the leaflet and lateral veins spring from the midrib almost at right angles to it. The commonest species is *A. lonchitica* (Schlotheim), which, however, is less profuse in the Lower than the Middle Coal Measures. Species of *Sphenopteris* in the Upper Carboniferous are characterized by entire wedge-shaped leaflets with branching venation, and are thus distinguished from Lower Carboniferous forms, in which the leaflets are narrow and much divided. *S. obtusiloba* Brongniart (Fig. 52) is found both in Lower and Middle Coal Measures.

The occurrence in Lancashire and Yorkshire of 'coal-balls' in certain coal-seams has already been mentioned (Chap. I). Stopes and Watson found differences between the flora of the 'coal-balls' and that of the shale forming the roof of the seam, though certain plants, such as *Stigmaria ficoides*, *Sigillaria tessellata* Brongn., and *Sigillaria elegans* Brongn., are common to both. Some of the differences are shown in the table below.

Genus	Flora of 'Coal-balls' (petrifactions)	Impressions and nodules in roof
Calamites	*C. communis* (Binney)	*C. ramosus* Weiss
Sphenophyllum	Several species	Unknown
Lepidodendron	Five species	Four species different from those in coal-balls
Mariopteris	Unknown	*M. muricata* (Schloth.)
Alethopteris	Unknown	*A. lonchitica* (Schloth.)
Lyginopteris	*L. oldhamium* (Binney) (common)	Foliage only.
Cordiates	Rare	Common

The plants in the roof are considered to represent a flora drifted from regions other than those which furnished the plants preserved in the coal-balls—it may be, an upland region. Thus the general question of correlation by means of a flora is complicated by ecological considerations.

The Yorkian flora. In this flora, *Sigillaria* is more abundant than *Lepidodendron*, common species being *S. elongata* Brongniart and *S. brardi* Brongniart. *Calamites* is abundant, as also is *Sphenophyllum*, though no species is restricted to the Yorkian flora. The latter genus has slender stems which produce four wedge-shaped leaves in a whorl at each node, the general aspect of the plant being similar to that of the scrambling *Galium* (cleavers), so abundant in modern hedgerows. *Sphenopteris* and *Neuropteris* are the commonest fern-like fronds, and reach their maximum abundance in the Middle Coal Measures. The latter form has larger leaflets than *Sphenopteris*, attached to the axis by a short stalk; the leaflets are oval in shape and the lateral nerves usually branch several times. *N. gigantea* Sternberg and *N. tenuifolia* (Schloth.) are characteristic of the Middle Coal Measures. *Sphenopteris delicatula* Sternberg, eminently characteristic of the Middle Coal Measures, is now referred to the genus *Zeilleria*, and *Sph. gracilis* Brongn. (Fig. 52) to *Renaultia* on the characters of its fructification. *Alethopteris lonchitica* (Schloth.) (Fig. 52), persisting from the Lanarkian flora, is common, but decreases in abundance later. *Mariopteris nervosa* (Brongn.) (Fig. 52), a widespread species, is of sphenopterid form but also approaches *Pecopteris* (characteristic of higher horizons) in some features. The widespread *Diplotmema furcatum* (Brongn.) (Fig. 52) is intermediate in form between *Sphenopteris* and *Mariopteris*, while *Dactylotheca plumosa* (Artis), with some pecopterid characters, is probably a pteridosperm. *Lonchopteris rugosa* Brongn. differs from most of these fern-like plants in having a reticulate venation.

The Staffordian flora. In certain coal-fields there are strata containing plant-remains that could not be placed definitely in the Middle or the Upper Coal Measures, and Kidston established a 'Transition Series' for their reception. This was afterwards called the Staffordian Series. These rocks contain typical Yorkian forms such as *Sphenophyllum cuneifolium* Sternberg. *Alethopteris lonchitica* (Schloth.), and *Annularia radiata* Brongniart (calamitean foliage), along with characteristic species of higher horizons, among which *Alethopteris serli* (Brongn.), *Neuropteris rarinervis* Bunbury, and *Sphenophyllum emarginatum* (Brongn.) (Fig. 52), may be mentioned. The relative abundance of the various species, important in all floras, is especially significant in the Staffordian Series. In north Staffordshire the series has been shown by Walcot Gibson to consist of three divisions, and the fossil floras of these groups have been described by Kidston. Their general characters may be summarized thus:

Newcastle-under-Lyme Group: Radstockian plants predominant; Yorkian plants few and rare.

Etruria Marl Group: Intermediate.

Blackband Group: Radstockian plants rare; Yorkian plants predominant.

The Radstockian flora. Above the Productive Measures of the north Staffordshire coalfield are certain barren strata, of which the topmost (Keele Group) was, until the year 1900, classified as Permian. After an examination of the plants Kidston came to the conclusion that the Keele Group should be correlated with the Upper Coal Measures (Stephanian) of the Continent. The Productive Measures of Staffordshire were recognized as Middle Coal Measures, and the intervening beds, the Newcastle, Etruria, and Blackband Groups, were assigned to the Transition Series. The topmost series of Coal Measures now takes its name from its development in the Radstock coalfield of Somerset.

The most characteristic plants of the Radstockian flora are fern-like

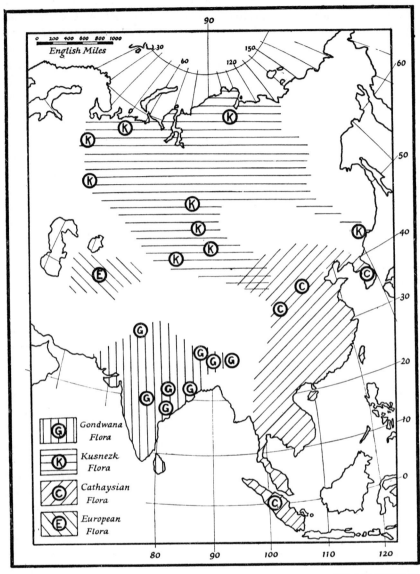

FIG. 53. SKETCH-MAP OF ASIA SHOWING DISTRIBUTION OF LATE PALAEOZOIC FLORAS (*after Halle*)

North American states of Oklahoma and Texas. According to D. White (1912) the paralic Wichita Series of this region contains such plants as *Odontopteris neuropteroides*, *Taeniopteris multinervis*, *Annularia spicata*, *Walchia piniformis* Schloth., and *Gigantopteris americana*. The last species has ribbon-like, forked fronds with parallel ribs giving off series of finer veins, and is closely related to the Chinese form *G. whitei*. The presence of plants that also occur in the Lower Permian of Europe and Asia testifies to the close resemblance of floras throughout the northern hemisphere at this period of time. A slightly later flora described by D. White (1929) from plant-beds in the Hermit Shale of Arizona enhances this resemblance. There the widespread pteridosperm *Callipteris* is well represented, including the characteristic European species *C. conferta*. There are also many fronds similar in habit to *Callipteris* and agreeing in venation with *Alethopteris* and *Neuropteris*, but others are usually assigned to such genera as *Thinnfeldia*, *Decroidium*, and *Danaeopsis* which are more typical of Mesozoic floras.

The striking resemblance between the floras of the Pennsylvanian system in NORTH AMERICA and the Westphalian Series in Europe has long been recognized. It is shown particularly well in the work of D. White (1899) on the flora of the Coal Measures in Missouri, in that of M. C. Stopes (1914) on the Carboniferous flora of New Brunswick, and, more recently, in a general review by Jongmans and Gothan (1937). A section in west Virginia, for example, extends through the entire Namurian into the Westphalian, the upper beds of which belong to stage C. A considerable part of the Dunkard formation of this area, mapped as Permian, is now said to belong to Westphalian D, from the presence of *Neuropteris ovata* and *N. scheuch-zeri*. This horizon has an enormous development in Pennsylvania also, and Westphalian E is recognized between it and the Lower Permian. The great similarity of the plants and the identical succession of floras on both sides of the Atlantic Ocean is extremely impressive, despite the apparent absence of some characteristic European forms (e.g. *Lonchopteris*) from the American floras. Many writers, indeed, consider that extensive land con-nexions are necessary to explain this uniformity, but the evidence of the tetrapod faunas must also be taken into account (Chap. IX). We may note, however, at this stage, that the development of Coal Measures over vast areas of the northern hemisphere formerly occupied by the sea is obviously the result of special circumstances. The succession of Coal Measures, as such, is interrupted by several marine bands, which indicate repeated submergence by the sea of low-lying land at or near sea level. In general, however, the sea-margin retreated over a great part of the northern hemi-sphere. This seems to be explained, at least in part, by an outstanding event in the southern hemisphere, where, in Africa, Australia, and South America, as well as in the Indian Peninsula, there is evidence of wide-spread glaciation during late Palaeozoic time. The formation of the ice-sheets would require enormous quantities of water withdrawn from the oceans, sea level would be lowered throughout the world, and the coastal margins correspondingly extended. In this way the conditions necessary for the development of the Coal Measures in the northern hemisphere may have arisen.

In contrast with the northern continents, the late Palaeozoic floras of India, Africa, Australia, and South America are dominated by *Glossopteris* and other genera which are not represented in the northern floras just discussed. The most abundant form, *Glossopteris*, has a tongue-shaped leaf, with a median rib and a network of lateral veins; several species are recognized, each with a wide horizontal range. It is often preceded by *Gangamopteris* of similar habit and form, but distinguished by the feeble development or absence of a midrib; this genus has a shorter vertical range than *Glossopteris*. The branched stem *Vertebraria* and the flanged seed-bodies known as *Samaropsis* are possibly parts of the same plants. Another widely distributed member of the flora is *Gondwanidium*, formerly called *Neuropteridium*, which has long fronds with two rows of large, deeply lobed leaflets, much like the Lower Carboniferous *Cardiopteris*. *Schizoneura* is somewhat like the northern *Calamites* but differs chiefly in having longer and broader leaves. The gymnospermous wood *Dadoxylon*, often with well-marked annual rings, may be related to the foliage formerly known as *Noeggerathiopsis* and nowadays ascribed to *Cordaites*. The general distribution of these plants is shown in the accompanying table (p. 333). It is worthy of note that the Glossopteris flora is a small assemblage of comparatively few genera, for this feature is probably related to other circumstances of its occurrence.

The Glossopteris flora was first described from the lower part of the Gondwana system in PENINSULAR INDIA. This consists of fluviatile or lacustrine deposits which, at intervals, rest directly on the Precambrian foundation over a territory between 36 degrees of longitude (64° E. to 100° E.) and 28 degrees of latitude (8° N. to 36° N.). The system begins with a series of olive-green clays (Talchir Series) which includes near the base a remarkable boulder-bed from 50 to 100 feet in thickness. Some of the boulders are striated and faceted, and the underlying rock is sometimes scored and polished. The glacial origin of the Talchir boulder-bed, first suggested by W. T. Blanford in 1856, gave rise to controversy for some thirty years, but is now generally admitted. The Talchir Series in places may be 800 to 1,000 feet thick, and the topmost beds contain remains of *Gangamopteris* and *Cordaites hislopi*. In the Umaria coalfield of Bengal the Talchir Series is overlaid by a marine band, less than 10 feet thick, which has yielded species of *Productus*, *Spirifer*, and *Reticularia*. F. R. C. Reed (1928) compares these shells with Himalayan and Russian species of Carboniferous and Permian age. Throughout the succeeding 5,000 feet of coal-bearing strata (the Baraker and Raniganj Series) the Glossopteris flora is abundantly represented by its typical species.

Table showing distribution of chief members of the Glossopteris Flora
in India and the southern continents

	India	S. Africa	Australia	Brazil	Falkland Is.
Gangamopteris					
cyclopteroides	×	×	×	×	×
kashmirensis	×	×			
Glossopteris					
ampla	×		×	×	
angustifolia	×	×			×
browniana	×	×	×	×	×
damudica	×	×			×
indica	×	×	×	×	×
retifera	×	×		×	
Gondwanidium					
validum	×	×		×	
Cordaites					
hislopi	×	×	×	×	
Phyllotheca spp.	×	×	×	×	×
Schizoneura spp.	×	×			
Vertebraria	×	×			
Dadoxylon spp.	×	×	×	×	×

In SOUTH AFRICA the equivalent strata are included in a vast sequence of nearly horizontal sandstones and shales appropriately termed the Karroo system, which extends at intervals over 200,000 square miles of territory. Like the Gondwana system of India, its lowest division (the Dwyka Series) is a tillite which contains a great variety of boulders derived from more ancient rocks. Many of the boulders are faceted and striated and the underlying rock-floor is often smoothed and scratched. It is generally agreed that the Dwyka tillite represents a huge ground moraine. The overlying Ecca Series is a group of shales and sandstones which has yielded an assemblage of plants generally identical with the Glossopteris flora of India. Details of the succession are well described by A. Dutoit in his *Geology of South Africa* (1926). It is interesting to note that a few genera of the northern flora have been recorded in association with *Glossopteris*. The lycopods *Sigillaria* and *Lepidodendron* are reported from Vereeniging in the Transvaal by

Seward and Leslie (1908). From the Ecca Series of the Wankie coalfield in Northern Rhodesia J. Walton (1929) has described species of *Pecopteris*, *Asterotheca*, and *Sphenophyllum*, preserved on the same bedding planes as leaves of *Glossopteris*. It is strange, therefore, that such plants do not appear in the lists given by A. C. Veatch (1935) from the Congo region where the succession of the Karroo system is again well developed.

The Santa Catherina system of south BRAZIL and the Paganzo system of ARGENTINA also begin with glacial boulder-beds which rest unconformably on Devonian or older rocks. In Brazil sediments intercalated between the boulder-beds have yielded plant remains among which are the cosmopolitan genera *Cardiopteris* and *Rhacopteris* of early Carboniferous age. Above the tillite in north Argentina, marine mudstones contain species of *Spirifer*, *Productus*, *Spiriferina*, and *Pseudamusium* and polyzoa which F. R. C. Reed (1927) ascribed without hesitation to the Upper Carboniferous. Plants between the boulder-beds, as in Brazil, include northern genera like *Lepidodendron*, *Adiantites*, and *Rhacopteris* referred to European species, besides typical members of the Glossopteris flora. Some doubt has been expressed as to the precise horizon of the two sets of plants, but Dutoit (1927) states that both occur within a short vertical range in a single series of beds. Likewise species of *Lepidodendron*, *Sigillaria*, *Sphenophyllum*, *Pecopteris*, and other northern forms are recorded with the dominant Glossopteris flora from the later Tuberao Series of Brazil. No northern plants are recorded, however, from Glossopteris beds which overlie a basal tillite in the Lafonian System of the Falkland Islands (Seward and Walton, 1923). Here may be mentioned the discovery in 1912 of *Glossopteris* from the Beardmore Glacier, only 300 miles from the South Pole (Seward, 1914).

In AUSTRALIA the sequence of rocks that carries the Glossopteris flora has been named the Kamilaroi System by T. W. E. David (1932). This begins with a marine series of fine-grained sandstones, with boulders (some of which are ice-scratched), and shells which include species of *Conularia*, *Eurydesma*, *Maeonia*, &c., closely resembling those from equivalent deposits in north India and south-west Africa. The Greta Coal Measures which follow contain two important coal-seams and a rich flora including well-known Indian species of *Gangamopteris*, *Glossopteris*, *Cordaites*, and *Dadoxylon*. An upper marine series contains more glacial boulders and a shell-fauna like that of the lower marine bed; it is followed by the Newcastle Coal Measures with abundance of *Glossopteris* and other plant remains, including foliage tentatively referred to *Sphenopteris*. The overlying Hawkesbury Series contains a flora of Mesozoic aspect.

The distribution and relations of the Glossopteris flora raise several important questions. Those which are pertinent at this stage concern the age of the glacial deposits and of the overlying sedimentary rocks containing the plant remains; the origin of the flora is also a matter for discussion.

The age of the glacial boulder-beds is not easy to fix, because of the enormous time-gap between them and the underlying rocks. The brachio-pods of the Umaria marine beds overlying the tillite in Bengal have their nearest affinities in faunas which are regarded as Permian, those in Brazil are ascribed to the Upper Carboniferous by F. R. C. Reed, and the marine series in Australia is usually referred to the Permian by Australian geolo-gists. The northern plants associated with the Glossopteris flora—Lower Carboniferous forms in South America, Upper Carboniferous species in the Transvaal, and early Permian species in Northern Rhodesia—indicate that the glaciation took place sometime during the Upper Carboniferous period or slightly earlier. The Glossopteris flora persisted through Permian time, and a new assemblage is associated with Triassic tetra-pods, though a few southern survivors remain in Triassic deposits in Tonkin.

The virtual identity of the Glossopteris flora throughout the late Palaeo-zoic deposits of India, Africa, South America, and Australia has long been considered to indicate continuity of a land-surface in explanation of its dis-tribution. Consequently most palaeogeographical maps (e.g. Seward, 1931) show these regions connected by land occupying the areas now covered by the Indian and South Atlantic Oceans: the whole forms a huge continent, which E. Suess (1888) called Gondwanaland, comprising about one-fifth of the total area of the globe. This idea was so widely accepted that in 1915 W. D. Matthew commented, 'This theory has, in its original form, gone so long uncontested that it is very generally regarded as incontestable. New discoveries have been interpreted in terms of it, the weakness of the original evidence, and the possibility that it might be otherwise interpreted, have been forgotten, and, like the Nebular Hypothesis, it has become almost im-possible to dislodge it from the affections of the average geologist.' Soon afterwards A. Wegener suggested that the problem of the glaciated areas would be simplified by grouping the southern continents and India around South Africa to form a compact land-area, with the South Pole in a central position occupying the point now 25° S., 25° E. So the hypothetical con-tinent of Gondwanaland became an indispensable part of the Theory of Continental Displacement.

But later discoveries have shown that the glaciated region extends far beyond the limits known to Wegener, and, while doubts have been expressed by P. Lake, Coleman, G. C. Simpson, H. Jeffreys, and others concerning the possibility of Continental Drift, the theory has been modified to suit the later evidence. A. Dutoit (1937), for instance, has a similar grouping of the continents, but a different position for the South Pole. The shifting of the Pole, however, creates difficulties with regard to the Glossopteris flora. Seward (1931) cites the discovery in 1912 of *Glossopteris* only 300 miles from the South Pole as indicating that Antarctica formerly had a different situation, on the grounds that the plant could not exist under glacial con-ditions. Yet the position of the Carboniferous and Permian South Pole shown by Wegener and Dutoit is within a similar distance of extensive *Glossopteris*-bearing rocks in South Africa and Madagascar. Other authors have noted the presence of the Glossopteris flora in close proximity to beds of glacial origin, and have held that the plants flourished in a cold climate. C. S. Fox (1931), however, emphasizes the fact that in India the plant remains are only found in the topmost beds of the Talchir Series, which are bedded sediments formed under water after the disappearance of the ice-sheet. Hence the flora might well be interpreted as indicating a temperate climate. It is well, however, to remember Seward's warning that it is not safe to infer climatic conditions from a study of extinct plants, and that in New Zealand at the present day tree-ferns of subtropical aspect cast their shadows on neighbouring glaciers.

Before the end of the nineteenth century the Glossopteris flora was not known from the northern hemisphere, apart from India, and the idea of a southern origin was quite naturally suggested. The subsequent discovery of *Glossopteris* in Antarctica (p. 335) led Seward (1914) to regard that continent as the original home of the flora. Meanwhile, members of the flora were discovered in Kashmir, north-west Afghanistan, north-east Persia, and north Russia, occurrences which are usually interpreted as migrants from the southern lands. Subsequently, however, Seward and Sahni (1920) formed the opinion that there is a closer resemblance between the Indian and European floras of Carboniferous and Permian age than has been generally realized. Moreover, as we have already noted (p. 334), northern genera are associated with the Glossopteris flora in South Africa and South America. Again, the tree-fern *Psaronius* is widespread, though not abundant, in the Permian strata of Brazil, North America, and Europe, while its apparent absence from South Africa is attributed by Dutoit (1930) to insufficient collecting. No genetic connexion between the two floras can be indicated at present, though the anastomosing venation of *Glossopteris* finds a parallel in the leaves of the European *Lonchopteris*. It seems likely, however, that the Glossopteris flora is a derivative of the cosmopolitan Rhacopteris flora, as D. White (1908) and A. Dutoit (1930) have already suggested. A noteworthy feature of the later northern elements associated with the Glossopteris flora in northern Rhodesia is the absence of such genera as *Alethopteris* and *Neuropteris* which are characteristic and abundant forms in the Coal Measures of Europe and North America. The seed-bodies of these genera are of the *Trigonocarpus* type, rather large nut-like bodies which appear to be ill adapted for rapid dispersal. On the other hand seeds of the *Samaropsis* type associated with *Glossopteris* are smaller and provided with flanges, a familiar device which aids dispersal by wind. That routes of dispersal were available is shown by the mixture of the two floras in Africa and South America, and by the distribution of the contemporary land faunas, discussed in Chapter IX.

II. MESOZOIC PLANTS

In their general aspect, Mesozoic floras contrast strongly with the Carboniferous floras outlined in earlier paragraphs. The vascular cryptogams, which developed the arborescent habit in Carboniferous time, are represented in Jurassic floras by smaller forms more nearly allied to their living successors. Thus the giant Carboniferous lycopods are replaced in Mesozoic floras by small herbaceous plants similar to modern club-mosses. The Jurassic *Equisetites*, though still large when compared with modern horsetails, agrees much more closely with these than with the arborescent Palaeozoic *Calamites*. The pteridosperms, so characteristic of the Carboniferous plant-world, are not represented in Mesozoic floras, and the true ferns show, at least in some forms, striking affinity with certain genera now living in tropical and subtropical countries. But the most remarkable feature in the general composition of Mesozoic floras is the abundance, variety, and widespread distribution of plants allied to the modern Cycads. The living Cycads, comprising only nine genera, are almost confined to the tropical regions, whereas the Jurassic cycadophytes were practically cosmopolitan, ranging from the tropics into the polar regions and from Europe through Africa and Asia into the American continent. The Mesozoic forms differ considerably from the existing Cycads in the structure of their reproductive organs, but their general habit is distinctly cycadean. The only great class of living plants not known in early Mesozoic floras is that of the flowering plants. This class, however, is now recorded from Jurassic rocks, and from Cretaceous times onwards it rapidly became the dominant element.

From what has already been written (p. 17) concerning the sporadic occurrence of terrestrial and freshwater deposits generally, it is not surprising that great gaps break the continuity of floral history. In the British area the Triassic rocks are of continental origin, but the conditions under which they were deposited precluded the development and preservation of a luxuriant flora. British Jurassic and Cretaceous rocks are mainly marine deposits, and contain only occasional fragments of drifted wood. At a few horizons, however, deltaic deposits were formed in some localities, the most famous being the 'Estuarine Series' (equivalent to the Inferior Oolite) of Yorkshire, which has yielded one of the richest of all Mesozoic floras. The 'Estuarine Series' of Scotland and the Stonesfield Slate of Oxfordshire (representing part of the Great Oolite Series) also contain fossil plants. The Purbeck Stage of Dorset and the Wealden Series of Kent and Sussex are largely estuarine or lacustrine in character, and have yielded many plant remains. Apart from these occurrences, widely separated in time and space, the marine character of the sediments effectually precludes the abundant preservation of land plants in the fossil state. Moreover, the Mesozoic floras are so closely related one to another, that their differences are not always apparent to the field-worker, and consequently they can be used only in a general way for purposes of correlation.

The British **Triassic** rocks furnish only scanty remains of plants, the prevailing desert conditions preventing the development of a luxuriant flora and affording little chance of fossilization to such plants as did exist. But the Lower Keuper at Bromsgrove has yielded a definite flora. In the equisetaceous genus *Schizoneura*, recorded from Bromsgrove, the leaf-sheaths were split into irregular leaf-like segments, thus differing from the continuous leaf-sheaths of living horsetails (*Equisetum*). *Schizoneura* occurs also in the Permian Glossopteris flora, and furnishes a link with Palaeozoic assemblages. One of the most characteristic Triassic plants is *Equisetites* which closely resembles the living *Equisetum* except in size. The stem of *Equisetites arenaceus* Bronn., only doubtfully recorded in Britain, though well known in continental Europe, attained a diameter of 8 inches and bore as many as 120 leaves in a whorl. In a Swedish species, *E. scanicus*, of Rhaetic age, the number of vascular strands is three times that of leaves in a whorl, attesting the complexity of vascular structure. In the modern *Equisetum* the numbers are equal, so that the Mesozoic *Equisetites* is transitional in this respect between Palaeozoic and modern forms. As petrified specimens are unknown, it is uncertain whether *Equisetites* possessed the power of secondary growth in thickness. Gymnosperms are represented by coniferous twigs and cones of *Voltzia*.

The late Triassic and Rhaetic deposits of Britain furnish only scanty remains of land plants, but rich assemblages occur in the Rhaetic Beds of Germany, Scandinavia, the Arctic regions, South Africa, Australia, and South America. The records show a remarkable world-wide uniformity, and include many genera that are found in British Jurassic rocks.

Drifted remains of plants are sometimes found in marine strata, but most British **Jurassic** plants have been obtained from the 'Estuarine Series' of Yorkshire, equivalent to the Inferior Oolite in the marine sequence. This flora may be regarded as typical of Mesozoic floras, and merits discussion in some detail.

The Horsetails are represented by *Equisetites columnaris* Brongniart and other species which closely resemble the living *Equisetum* in form; they have underground creeping rhizomes producing aerial shoots with whorls of leaves united at their base into sheaths. The lycopods are of little importance, except as attesting the continuous existence of the group. *Selaginellites*, a delicate branching plant with small curved leaves, has the habit of the living *Selaginella*.

The ferns form an important element in the Jurassic flora, and belong mainly to groups which are still living, though much restricted both numerically and geographically. The bulk of the ferns belong to the Osmundaceae, Cyatheaceae, Matonineae, and Dipteridineae, other families being subordinate. The Osmundaceae, a group including the living *Osmunda* (the Royal

Fern) and *Todea*, is represented by several common and widespread ferns, and probably attained its acme in Jurassic times. The large fronds of *Todites* exemplified by *T. williamsoni* (Brongn.) (Fig. 54), with fertile pinnules bearing large sporangia, closely resembles *Todea* now living in South Africa, Australia, and New Zealand. *Cladophlebis* is a form-genus designating sterile fronds of the same form and nervation as *Osmunda*; *C. denticulata* Brongn., a widespread species, is common in British Jurassic rocks (Fig. 54). The Cyatheaceae are represented especially by *Coniopteris*, whose finely divided fronds bear small cup-shaped fertile segments; *C. hymenophylloides* is found in both Jurassic and Wealden deposits. This genus closely compares with *Thyrsopteris*, a tree-fern now living in the island of Juan Fernandez in the South Pacific Ocean. The Matonineae are nowadays represented by a single genus *Matonia*, living in the Malayan region. The Jurassic *Matonidium* agrees in foliar characters but has a greater number of sporangia in each group on the back of some pinnules. *Matonidium goepperti* (Ettingshausen) (Fig. 54) is a common species of Jurassic and Wealden age; and *Laccopteris* (Fig. 54) is a similar form with the same range. The Dipterinidae, now containing only a few East Indian species, possess large fronds of a peculiar shape; the main stalk is divided into two equal parts which curve upwards into numerous spreading leaf-segments, each lobe having a main vein from which a network of small veins is given off. *Dictyophyllum* is a Jurassic genus which differs from the modern *Dipteris* in the crowding of the sporangia groups. Of the subordinate families, the Marattiaceae has only one English Jurassic form, *Marattiopsis*, which closely resembles the modern *Marattia*, with its large fronds composed of long, narrow leaf-segments bearing compound sporangia. This family appears to have been dominant in the Upper Trias, showing decline in the Jurassic period, and is now restricted to tropical countries.

Some fronds of uncertain affinities are placed, by reason of their shape and nervation, in the form genus *Sphenopteris*, but they probably have no genetic relation with Carboniferous fronds of similar appearance. *Taeniopteris* is another form whose relationship is obscure. It is a linear leaf with a prominent midrib, from which dichotomous secondary veins arise nearly at right angles. It is usually regarded as a fern, but it may belong to a cycadean plant. *T. vittata* Brongn. (Fig. 54) is a characteristic Jurassic species. *Sagenopteris phillipsi* Brongn. (Fig. 54) was formerly regarded as the leaf of a water fern resembling the living *Marsilia*. These fronds, of four small netveined leaflets, are now regarded as the foliage of *Caytonia* and *Gristhorpia*, two angiospermous genera whose fruits have been described by H. H. Thomas (1925).

The most characteristic element in Mesozoic floras is, however, the peculiar gymnospermous group Bennettitales, which is allied to the living Cycads but which did not survive after the Cretaceous period. The external habit and internal anatomy of these plants closely resemble that of existing

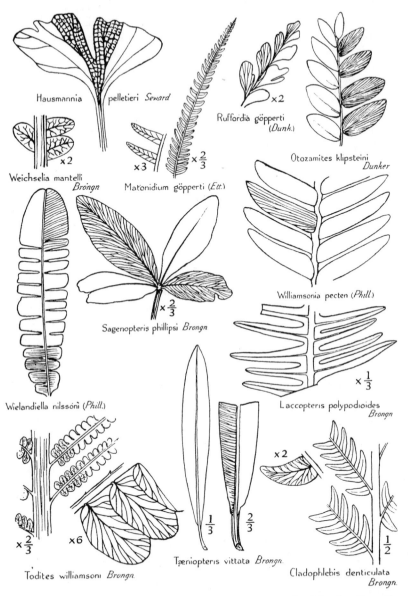

Hausmannia pelletieri *Seward*

×2

Weichselia mantelli
Brongn

×3 ×2/3

Matonidium göpperti (*Ett.*)

Ruffordia göpperti
(*Dunk.*)

×2

Otozamites klipsteini
Dunker

×2/3

Sagenopteris phillipsi *Brongn*

Williamsonia pecten (*Phill.*)

Wielandiella nilssoni (*Phill.*)

Laccopteris polypodioides
Brongn

×1/3

×2

×2/3 ×6

Todites williamsoni *Brongn.*

1/3 2/3

Tæniopteris vittata *Brongn.*

Cladophlebis denticulata
Brongn.

×1/2

FIG. 54. LEAF-IMPRESSIONS FROM MESOZOIC STRATA (*mainly after Seward*)

Cycads. Their reproductive structures, however, were very different, being built on a plan very like that of the angiospermous flower, though retaining certain features more typical of ferns and gymnosperms. The genera *Williamsonia* (with slender branched stems and freely exposed 'flowers') and *Bennettites* (with short stout stems bearing numerous 'flowers' embedded among the leaf-bases) illustrate the two chief structural types. Cycadean foliage found in association, though not in connexion, cannot always be certainly correlated with particular stems or 'flowers'. The leaf-genera *Zamites* and *Ptilophyllum* probably belong to species of *Williamsonia* (Fig. 54), while the familiar *Pterophyllum nilssoni* (Phill.) is now referred to the genus *Wielandiella* (Fig. 54). *Williamsonia* is typical of the 'Estuarine Beds' of Yorkshire, while *Bennettites* is known from the Purbeck Beds of Dorset and the Lower Cretaceous of the Isle of Wight. It may also be noted that large numbers of 'flowers' known as *Cycadeoidea* (very similar to *Bennettites*) have been obtained from Upper Jurassic and Lower Cretaceous strata in Dakota, Wyoming, and Maryland, U.S.A.

Another group of gymnosperms, abundant and widespread in Mesozoic strata, is represented today by one species, *Ginkgo biloba* Linn. (the maidenhair tree), which has been saved from probable extinction by cultivation as a sacred tree in China and Japan. The characteristic wedge-shaped and partially lobed leaves of *Ginkgo* are recorded fossil from the Arctic regions, Europe, North America, Central Asia, Indo-Malaysia, South Africa, and Australia. The Jurassic species *G. digitata* (Brongn.) shows considerable variation in form of the leaf and in the degree of its lobation. *Baiera*, an allied genus whose leaves are deeply dissected into narrow segments, is similarly widespread in Mesozoic strata.

The conifers also appear to have attained the acme of their development and distribution in Mesozoic times. Several of the Jurassic types probably belong to the Araucariaceae now restricted to the southern hemisphere. Indeed, the araucarian type of wood is found throughout Mesozoic deposits in many parts of the world. But though cones and twigs commonly occur, they are generally fragmentary, and their precise relationships are in many cases obscure. *Thuites* from the Stonesfield Slate resembles the modern *Thuja* and *Cupressus*, while *Taxites* from the Yorkshire 'Estuarine Series' is, as its name implies, much like the living *Taxus* (yew).

The **Wealden** flora is similar to that of Jurassic strata. Indeed, the resemblance is so close that difficulty is often experienced in separating the two assemblages. Equisetaceous plants (e.g. *Equisetites burkhardti* Dunker), closely related to living forms, are frequently found, and sometimes bear the characteristic underground tubers which were formerly described as fossil fruits under the name *Carpolithus*. Ferns are well represented, many genera persisting from the Jurassic, e.g. *Matonidium, Laccopteris, Taeniopteris, Dictyophyllum, Cladophlebis*. The graceful, finely divided fronds of *Ruffordia goepperti* Dunker (Fig. 54) attest the presence of Schizeaceae, and *Onychiopsis* is said to be an early representative of the Polypodiaceae, a group (probably polyphyletic) which nowadays is dominant among ferns. The stem *Protopteris* has the habit and vascular structure of the modern *Dicksonia*, while another stem, *Tempskya schimperi* Corda, is enveloped in a mass of interlacing roots. The genus *Hausmannia*, exemplified in the Wealden flora of Kent by *H. pelletieri* Seward (Fig. 54), is closely allied to the living *Dipteris* of the Malay Peninsula. The fronds of *Hausmannia* are deeply bilobed, or even more dissected, and some leaves are similar in shape to those of *Ginkgo*. The genus under discussion may be distinguished by its venation, which consists of a few strong ribs supporting an irregular network of finer veins. The occurrence together of *Hausmannia* and *Matonidium* is particularly interesting in view of the surviving association of *Dipteris* and *Matonia* on Mount Ophir in the Malay Peninsula. *Weichselia mantelli* (Brongn.) (Fig. 54), with bipinnate sterile fronds, has also been compared with the Matonineae, with the Marattiaceae, and even with Cycads.

The last-named group is abundantly represented in Wealden strata by fronds and reproductive structures. The fronds are usually found detached, and have been classified in 'form-genera' pending the discovery of actual connexion with fertile forms. The occurrence of such forms as *Cycadites*, *Nilssonia*, *Otozamites* (Fig. 54), *Anomozamites*, and *Zamites*, shows the close similarity with Jurassic floras. Fructifications are exemplified by *Bennettites saxbyanus* (Brown) and *Williamsonia carruthersi* Seward.

Gymnospermous plants are, in the main, imperfectly preserved, and special difficulties are encountered in the investigation of the fragmentary material. Certain fertile branches are referred to the genus *Araucarites*, which is a convenient name for cones that resemble those of the living *Araucaria*. Similarly, other cones are assigned to *Pinites*. Still other genera, such as *Elatides* and *Sphenolepidium*, have been instituted for cones with more or less definite characters but of uncertain relationships. Sterile vegetative shoots are still more difficult to place, since the general habit of coniferous plants is of doubtful value as evidence of affinity. The abundance in various strata of petrified wood with araucarian features suggests that much of the foliage belongs to plants allied to *Araucaria*. But other forms have the general habit of the living *Cupressus*, *Taxus*, and other genera, and are provisionally placed in alliance with them. For detailed discussion, reference should be made to the works cited at the end of this chapter.

Aptian deposits (Lower Greensand) contain an interesting assemblage of plants, known chiefly from petrifactions. In contrast with the earlier Cretaceous flora, ferns are rare, but include *Tempskya*, a tree-fern already noted among Wealden plants. Petrified specimens of cycadophytes and conifers have enabled the internal anatomy of several forms to be investigated. But the most interesting feature of Aptian floras is the occurrence of five species of dicotyledonous angiosperms, represented by pieces of petrified wood which show details of cellular structure. Though these trees are of well-developed types, present knowledge concerning the systematic anatomy of living dicotyledons is not sufficiently advanced to determine the precise affinities of the fossil forms. *Woburnia* and *Aptiana* are provisionally referred to the Dipterocarpaceae and the Theaceae respectively, both families being now restricted to subtropical and tropical regions. The relations of *Cantia*, *Hythia*, and *Sabulia* are still unknown (M. C. Stopes, 1912). Leaf-impressions are rare in Aptian deposits of this country, but early Cretaceous rocks of Portugal and North America contain them in abundance.

British strata of Upper Cretaceous age have yielded few plants of importance. Plant-bearing strata in the Upper Cretaceous of Europe and North America, however, manifest the rapid increase in importance of the angiosperms and a corresponding decline of the cycadophytes. The reason for this rapid rise to dominance has been abundantly discussed, and it has been suggested that the evolution of the higher insects concurrently with the development of honey-bearing flowers is significant. It is likely, however, that the elimination of the spermatozoic method of fertilization and increased efficiency of water-conducting elements, both tending to more complete adaptation to conditions of life on land, also contributed to the success of the angiosperms.

By the end of Cretaceous time the flora had assumed the general aspect that it has today. The cycadophytes had virtually disappeared, being replaced in the position of dominance by the angiosperms, but ferns and conifers still remained an important element in the flora.

In the southern continents the Permian Glossopteris flora is followed by the Thinnfeldia flora. This appears in the Upper Beaufort Beds of SOUTH AFRICA which are equivalent to the Lower Trias of the northern hemisphere. *Thinnfeldia* is a fern-like plant, possibly a pteridosperm, with thick, oval or linear leaflets springing from the stout axis of the frond. It is associated in the Upper Beaufort Beds with large fronds, bearing broad linear leaflets, referred to the genus *Glenopteris*, and some of the cycadophytes. The succeeding Molteno Beds also contain *Thinnfeldia* in association with species of *Ginkgo* and *Baiera*, the fern *Marattiopsis*, the cycadophytes *Zamites* and *Pterophyllum*, and the stem *Rhexoxylon* whose woody tissue is characteristically arranged in detached wedge-shaped masses. The plant-succession is then cut off by red sandstones overlaid by a thick development of basalt. In INDIA species of *Thinnfeldia* first appear in the Panchet Beds which are equivalent to the Upper Beaufort Beds of South Africa. The next higher series, the Rajmahal Beds, have yielded a rich flora in which the predominant cycadophytes are represented by the leaves *Pterophyllum*, *Ptilophyllum*, *Otozamites*, *Nilssonia*, &c., and by the 'flower' *Williamsonia*. The ferns *Gleichenites*, *Marattiopsis* and *Cladophlebis* are also important, accompanied by *Equisetites* and coniferous twigs such as *Elatocladus*, *Araucarites* and *Brachyphyllum*. The flora of the Jabalpur stage, next in succession, differs

from the preceding in containing a greater proportion of conifers and a reduced number of cycadophytes. The highest beds of the Indian sequence,
the Umia Beds of Kachh, have a similar floral assemblage. In Australia the
Upper Triassic Ipswich Beds of Queensland and corresponding horizons in
other States, have yielded several species of *Thinnfeldia, Ginkgo* and *Baiera,
Cladophlebis, Taeniopteris, Sagenopteris*, besides the cycadophytes *Nilssonia, Otozamites, Podozamites*, and *Pterophyllum*. Some of the genera persist into higher horizons, as for instance, *Cladophlebis, Elatocladus*, and
Taeniopteris. In certain Cretaceous beds they are associated with such
genera as *Hausmannia* and *Ruffordia*. The Thinnfeldia flora is well developed in the Paganzo system of Argentina in beds which are correlated
with the Triassic system of Europe. Farther south, on the borders of
Antarctica, Jurassic Beds in Grahamland have yielded a varied assemblage
of plants, astonishingly like the Yorkshire flora though including some
species very near to Australian and Indian forms. The Grahamland flora
includes species of *Equisetites*, the ferns *Cladophlebis*, '*Sphenopteris*', *Thinnfeldia*, the gymnosperm *Elatocladus* and the cycadean foliage *Nilssonia,
Zamites, Otozamites*, and *Pterophyllum*. It is evident that the Thinnfeldia
flora was almost co-extensive with its Permian forerunner, the Glossopteris
flora.

The Jurassic type of vegetation was gradually transformed by admixture
of angiosperms. The oldest Cretaceous rocks of Greenland have yielded a
flora in which ferns and gymnosperms like those of corresponding horizons
of Europe are associated with dicotyledonous leaves hardly distinguishable
from those of the living plane-tree (*Platanus*), *Cinnamonum, Artocarpus*,
&c. The oldest genera already noted from the Aptian stage of England are
likewise fully differentiated, and it is evident that the angiosperms had a
long ancestry which has still to be made known. The class rapidly became
dominant, for Cretaceous angiosperms in increasing abundance are known
from Portugal, Bohemia, Greenland, Dakota, Nebraska, and neighbouring
North American States. A striking feature in the composition of these
floras is the mingling of genera that nowadays are restricted either to temperate or tropical climates.

III. NEOZOIC PLANTS

The more obvious of Neozoic plant remains are leaf-impressions, which
often occur abundantly, and it is on the evidence of these fossils that the
commonly quoted lists were drawn up many years ago. The leaves are
almost entirely those of woody plants, many of which are deciduous, shed-
ding their leaves periodically as a consequence of seasonal changes in
climate. The leaves of herbaceous plants are more rarely preserved, since
they wither and die on the stems of the parent plant, and consequently have
not the same chance of reaching the waters of streams and mingling with
their deposited sediment. This limitation in the possibilities of preservation

must be taken into account when estimating the significance of the elements in a fossil flora, especially when it consists mainly of leaves.

In recent years much attention has been given to the seeds that occur in the plant-bearing strata, for it is now recognized that the minute characters of these organs afford a most reliable guide to generic and specific determination. While this method of work has been most fully applied to Pliocene and later floras, its application to Eocene assemblages has already yielded good results. In general, it is claimed that a study of the minute characters of fossil seeds affords a delicate and reliable guide to stratigraphical correlation. It has also been shown that European Neozoic floras contain a large number of species whose nearest living relatives grow in a region comprising Japan, China, the Himalaya, Further India, Malaya, Australia, and North America—a region which for convenience is often termed the Chinese-American region. The importance of these species has become manifest as a result of exploration in Eastern Asia during the last fifty years, and it is already evident that the classic work of the nineteenth-century investigators requires critical revision in the light of this advance in botanical knowledge.

The Chinese-American floral element is most conspicuous in the European Upper Eocene plant assemblages, while from Miocene time onwards it decreased in importance until it became extinct in Europe by the beginning of the Great Ice Age. Other exotic elements are apparently present, but much work must be done before generalizations can be made in respect of them.

The older Neozoic floras are preserved in Britain at several horizons where estuarine strata are intercalated with the marine sequence. In the lower part of the Eocene, the Thanet Sands and Reading Beds have yielded ferns, conifers, and leaves of many dicotyledonous flowering plants. Among genera identified by these leaf-impressions are *Populus* (poplar), *Platanus* (plane), *Laurus* (laurel) and *Acacia*, the whole flora having a temperate aspect. At a higher horizon, the London Clay in the Isle of Sheppey presents an estuarine phase which has yielded a rich flora and fauna suggesting warmer climatic conditions. Most of the plant remains are seeds or fruits preserved as pyritic casts. The most abundant are fruits of a palm, *Nipadites*, which can hardly be distinguished from those of a stemless palm, *Nipa*, now restricted to brackish estuaries in south-east Asia and Australia. *Nipadites* has a wide distribution in the Eocene rocks of Europe, and is also recorded from those of Egypt. The flora of the London Clay also has important links with the existing floras of the Himalayas, China, and Japan, besides some slight alliance with those of tropical North America, according to the investigations of E. M. Reid and M. E. J. Chandler (1933).

A flora of about the same age but preserved as leaf-impressions, is found in the pipeclay beds of Alum Bay in the Isle of Wight. The plants from this deposit are sometimes classified into three geographical groups. One group includes some of the commoner trees of the northern hemisphere, such as *Quercus* (oak), *Ulmus* (elm), *Salix* (willow), *Acer* (maple), *Juglans* (walnut). Other plants are referred to genera now living in tropical regions; among these, *Sabal* (a palm), *Ficus* (fig), *Artocarpus* (bread fruit), and *Aralia* may be mentioned. A third group, including the conifer *Podocarpus*, and leaves ascribed to *Eucalyptus* and various Proteaceae, is considered to be related to the South African and Australian floras. In view, however, of recent work on Neozoic plants, this grouping of the floral elements must be considered as subject to revision.

The slightly later Bournemouth Beds contain an extensive flora which has been studied by H. Bandulska (1923). The ferns, occurring in some variety, show general resemblance to modern genera and species living in warm regions. Thus *Gleichenia*, whose forking fronds have slender, hooked stalks, is now confined to the tropics. *Aneimia* and *Lygodium* represent the tree-ferns, and *Osmunda* is common in a species whose closest living ally (*O. banksiaefolia*) is now restricted to the coastal regions of eastern Asia. Another fern, *Acrostichum lanzeanum* (Visiani), is paralleled by *A. aureum* L., which lives in the *Nipa* swamps of Malaya. The most noteworthy coniferous genus is *Sequoia*, which has a wide distribution in Neozoic rocks but is now living only in the Rocky Mountains of California. Other conifers are related to *Taxodium* and *Cupressus*, the former being characteristically American. Monocotyledonous angiosperms include palms, such as *Nipadites* and other forms, but these together, with most of the dicotyledons, have yet to be worked out. Species of beech have lately been described, and one is assigned to *Nothofagus*, a genus now confined to subantarctic regions; tropical Lauraceae and Myrtaceae of East Asian type are also recorded.

An interesting flora is yielded by thin beds of freshwater origin, intercalated with sheets of lava (of early Neozoic age) in western Scotland. The fern *Onoclea hebridica* (Forbes) is almost indistinguishable from *O. sensibilis* L., now living only in East Asia and eastern North America. *Ginkgo* (the maidenhair tree) has leaves similar to those of the living Asiatic plant, and some leaves of a conifer are comparable with those of *Podocarpus*, a characteristic plant of south-east Asia. The numerous dicotyledonous leaves await critical examination.

The general characters of a flora from the Headon Beds (Upper Eocene or Lower Oligocene) of Hordle, Hampshire, can be given with more confidence, since the seeds form the subject of a recent monograph by M. E. J. Chandler (1926). Sixty-four plants are recorded, and most of these show close relationship with the living floras of south-east Asia and North America. In many cases, species of a widely distributed genus are closely allied to a living Asiatic species. Thus the Headon form of *Potamogeton* (a cosmopolitan genus) is nearest to *P. cristatus* Regel and Maack, a native of China and Japan. Again, *Rubus pungens* Cambess., living in the Himalaya and China, is the living species of the widely distributed brambles which most closely resembles the Headon fossil *Rubus*. Some fossil forms, however, are not so closely related to living species, but belong to genera now confined to the Chinese-American region. Such are, for instance, *Menispermum, Cinnamomum, Liquidamber, Phellodendron, Actinidia, Liriodendron, Sassafras, Gordonia, Nipa*, and *Sequoia*. The Eocene species are all extinct, and their living tropical relatives are chiefly mountain-plants, though a few occur at low altitudes.

Two plants with European affinities are recorded from the Headon Beds, namely, *Omphalodes* and *Stratiotes*. The former genus occurs in the Spanish sierras, but is truly characteristic of the eastern Asiatic and western North American mountains, while *Stratiotes* is an ancient genus, apparently always restricted to Europe and Western Asia, ending in *S. aloides* L. (the water soldier), its sole living representative. It must be noted that the living members of these genera are survivals from the Eocene flora, and are not typical of the modern European flora, which did not become established in this continent until a much later period.

The Chinese-American element is also pre-eminent in the flora of the Bembridge Limestone, which has been critically reviewed by E. M. Reid and M. E. J. Chandler (1926). The ferns are represented mainly by the widely distributed *Acrostichum lanzeanum* (Visiani), whose affinities with the living *A. aureum* L. of Malaya have already been mentioned. A species of *Azolla* (a genus of the Hydropterideae or water ferns) is interesting because it combines, in its reproductive organs, features that are separated in the two living groups of the genus. *Azolla* has a wide distribution in America, Australasia, Africa, and East Asia, and one species (reintroduced) is flourishing in parts of western Europe. Conifers are poorly represented, *Araucarites* being the chief genus. The monocotyledonous flowering-plants include species of *Typha, Sparganium, Potamogeton, Limnocarpus, Stratiotes*, and *Palaeothrinax*. The last named is a palm allied to *Thrinax*, which lives in Florida and the West Indies. The majority of the dicotyledons are species known only from Bembridge, but belong to genera typical of the Chinese-American region, and are often closely similar to species restricted to that area. Thus species of *Clematis* and *Ranunculus* from the Bembridge Limestone approach more closely to East Asian and North American species than to forms living in Europe at the present time. The genera *Engelhardtia, Brasenia, Cinnamomum, Neolitsia, Zanthoxylon, Zizyphus, Dipelta, Phyllanthera, Catalpa, Abelia*, and others represented in the Bembridge flora now live mainly in the Chinese-American area. A notable exception is *Papaver pictum* Reid and Chandler, whose nearest ally is *P. rupifragum* Boiss. and Reut., living in Spain and Morocco; the genus ranges through Europe and Asia. The general character of the flora indicates a warm temperature or subtropical climate.

The Upper Oligocene flora of Bovey Tracey in Devon shows the same general characteristics, and the rich Miocene floras of the European mainland also exhibit to a striking degree this distinctive association of plants. It is noteworthy that palms did not thrive in Europe after the Miocene period, and in general that Miocene floras present a warm, temperate aspect.

The Pliocene floras of Europe, reviewed by Mrs. E. M. Reid (1921) show a progressive decline in importance of the Chinese-American association and the establishment of other elements. The Pliocene plants may be classified into three categories: (1) species now living in those countries where they are also found fossil; (2) exotic species belonging to the Chinese-American association; (3) other exotics.

The exotics of Chinese-American affinities formed the whole flora in Middle Miocene time and then gradually decreased in importance. Thus in a flora from the base of the Pliocene of France, the Chinese-American element formed 64 per cent. of the total exotics, the proportion in a British flora from the top of the Pliocene (Cromerian) being 0·74 per cent. Floras of intermediate age, such as that from Castle Eden (Durham) with 31 per cent., give proportions which, plotted as a graph, give a smooth, regular curve.

Exotics other than those of the Chinese-American association gradually supplanted the latter element from the Middle Miocene onwards, and reached a maximum (35 per cent. of the total) in the Lower and Middle Pliocene. Thus 'although the West European flora was rather rapidly losing its Chinese-American character through Miocene and early Pliocene time, yet it was still almost entirely an exotic flora' (E. M. Reid). After the Middle Pliocene the exotic element gradually declined in importance, until, in the Cromer flora at the top of the Pliocene, its proportion is only 5 per cent. of the whole. Hence by calculation of the various elements in Pliocene floras a reliable comparison can be made, forming a means of estimating the age of the various plant-bearing deposits.

The Middle Pliocene flora of Castle Eden (Durham) has yielded some sixty determinable species of flowering plants, and differs from most of the known Pliocene assemblages in the relative scarcity of aquatic plants. It is essentially a dry-bank flora, which probably inhabited the sides of a deep upland valley cut in the Magnesian Limestone and drained by a rapid stream which received the fallen seeds and leaves and transported them to their present situation. The commonest plants are *Potentilla argentea* L., a species of *Erica*, two non-aquatic species of *Ranunculus*, and an extinct species of *Melissa*. Trees and shrubs are represented by species of *Liquidamber*, *Carpinus* (hornbeam), *Betula* (birch), *Alnus* (alder), *Crataegus*, *Rubus*, *Ilex*, *Solanum*, and other genera. About 30 per cent. of the plants belong to the Chinese-American association; of these the most interesting are 'a Japanese hornbeam, *Carpinus laxiflora* Blume; three species of *Crataegus* which belong to a North American section of the genus; three species of Chinese and Japanese *Rubi* related to the raspberry; *Pilea pumila*

A. Gray, the stingless nettle of North America, . . .; an extinct *Melissa* . . . whose nearest allies inhabit the Himalaya, the mountains of Khasia, and Java; two species of *Rhus*, an *Ilex*, and a gentian, all more nearly related to North American species than to European; also an *Aralia'*. Other species are exotic but do not belong to the association just mentioned. These include *Naias minor* Allioni, now widely distributed through central and southern Europe, central and eastern Asia, and tropical Africa; two species of *Cyperus* which cannot be assigned to any European species; *Alnus viridus* De Candolle, a mountain-species ranging through Europe, northern Asia, and northern America, but not found in the British Isles; and *Ranunculus nodiflorus* L., which lives in central and eastern Europe.

The Cromer 'Forest Bed' Series at the top of the Pliocene contains the remains of oak, birch, willow, maple, pine, and yew, as well as abundant marsh and water plants, over 130 species having been recorded. The conditions under which the Cromer Beds were laid down have been compared with those of the Norfolk Broads at the present time. Though the known flora is larger (owing to better conditions of exposure) than that of Castle Eden, it is significant that only seven exotic species are recorded. Of these, a variety of the nettle *Urtica dioica* L. is the only form assigned to the Chinese-American association. The other five exotics are still living in Europe, though extinct in Britain. They are *Picea excelsa* Link., living in the mountains of northern Europe; *Trapa natans* L. (water-chestnut), which occurs in central and southern Germany; *Naias minor* Allioni, widely distributed in central Europe, Asia, and Africa; and *Hypecoum procumbens* L., which flourishes in the Mediterranean region, China, and Japan. *Corema intermedia* Reid, an extinct species, is most nearly allied to the *Corema alba* Don of Spain, Portugal, and Azores. Thus the predominant exotic elements of earlier Neozoic floras had almost disappeared by the end of the Pliocene period.

An interesting theory has been formulated by Mrs. E. M. Reid to explain this destruction of genera and species. The whole Chinese-American element in the west European floras is regarded as derivative from a circumpolar source, and was driven southward by the ever-increasing cold of the Pliocene period. This retreat in Europe and west Asia was stopped by the east and west mountain-chains which extend from the Pyrenees to the Himalayas, and the flora became practically extinct. In North America and east Asia the southerly migration was not checked in this way and the flora survives in those regions.

Analysis of the Pliocene floras also led the same author to certain conclusions regarding those plants that survived to form part of the present flora of western Europe. Those species with a circumpolar distribution are mainly marsh or water plants, while the land plants in general range from the Himalayas westwards into Europe. This distribution suggests that the upland area of central Asia (including Tibet and the Himalayas) formed a subsidiary centre of dispersal from which the living flora of western Europe was derived during Pliocene time.

The earliest British Pleistocene flora is contained in the Arctic Fresh-water Bed which lies immediately below the Glacial Clays near Cromer on the coast of Norfolk. This flora includes some of the common marsh plants that occur in the Cromer Forest Bed and live at the present time in East Anglia. Along with them are leaves and twigs of *Salix polaris* Linn. and other species of Arctic willows and *Betula nana* Linn., all small-leaved dwarf shrubs now living in high latitudes or on lofty mountains. The presence of these species is always taken to indicate the cold climatic phase of the Pleistocene period. The possible occurrence of mild 'Interglacial' phases has long been a disputed question. Such plants as *Prunus avium* L., *Prunus padus* L., and *Crataegus oxyacantha* L. are sometimes regarded as 'Interglacial' types, but they occur in some localities associated with *Betula nana* and other 'Glacial' plants. Many difficulties are encountered in attempting to interpret the history of these Pleistocene deposits, for stratigraphical evidence is often obscure or even entirely lacking. Terrestrial deposition is notoriously spasmodic, with the result that deposits of considerably different ages may be brought into contiguity. This may explain the recorded association of *Betula nana* with *Hippopotamus* in a section at the Admiralty Offices, London. Landslips, too, have been invoked to account for such 'mixtures'. Again, the distribution of plants is influenced by many factors besides temperature. Previous writers have mentioned the influence of wind in preventing the growth of trees in the mild climate of the island of Tiree (Hebrides). In Saghalien a luxuriant flora occupies the deep sheltered valleys, while exposed uplands in the near vicinity can support only a steppe-flora. Moreover, the fronts of some glaciers in New Zealand are said to be hidden by groves of tree-ferns. On account of such apparent anomalies the botanical evidence for the occurrence of mild interglacial periods in Britain is not conclusive.

It remains to consider the post-glacial floras preserved in the peat beds and 'submerged forests' which lie on the undulating surface of the boulder clay at intervals round our coasts. The plant-assemblage of these deposits is a limited one, consisting of a few forest trees and a number of marsh and water plants. The forest trees most commonly found are *Betula alba* Linn. (birch), *Quercus robur* Linn. (oak), *Alnus glutinosa* Gaertner (alder), and *Pinus sylvestris* Linn. (Scots pine). Smaller trees and shrubs include *Corylus avellana* Linn. (hazel) and various species of *Salix* (willows). Among remains of herbaceous plants the seeds of *Menyanthes trifoliata* Linn. (bog-bean) and several species of *Potamogeton* (pond-weed) are often exceedingly abundant. Other seeds are generally less common, but the plants are mainly those of a swampy habitat. It is evident that the assemblage from these peat-beds cannot be regarded as representative of early post-glacial floras, since comparatively few plants could flourish in the special habitat.

F. J. Lewis has investigated the succession of post-glacial plant-bearing strata in Scotland and finds a marked constancy from the mountains of Galloway to the Shetlands, whether the peats are near sea level or on the mountains. The succession may be tabulated thus:

Recent Peat . . . . ⎫	
Forest Bed . . . . ⎬ Upper Forestian.	
Peat-bog with some Arctic plants . . . . ⎪	
Forest Bed . . . . ⎭	
Peat-bog plants.	Upper Peat-bog.
Arctic plant-bed	2nd Arctic bed.
Peat-bog plants.	Lower Peat-bog.
Forest Bed	Lower Forestian.
Arctic plant-bed	1st Arctic bed.

From this, Lewis makes some interesting deductions. The 1st Arctic bed, containing Arctic willows, brings the flora now confined to above 2,000 feet in Scotland down to 150 feet above sea level. The Lower Forestian carries the limit of trees (now 1,600 feet) up to 2,000 feet. The 2nd Arctic bed implies the descent of an Arctic flora to 150 feet, while the Upper Forestian carries the tree limit up to 3,400 feet. Thus the mountain-flora descended 1,850 feet during Arctic phases, while the tree-limit ascended 1,400 feet in the Upper Forestian, a total fluctuation of 3,250 feet. Allowing a change of 1° F. for 300 feet, the extreme Arctic phase implies a temperature of 6° F. colder than at present, and the Upper Forestian was 5° F. warmer than the present.

Clement Reid held that during the Ice Age 'any survival of our flowering-plants, except in the case of a few Arctic and Alpine species, was quite impossible', and that the earlier assemblage was swept away almost as completely and effectually as the celebrated volcanic eruption wiped out the plants of Krakatoa. It did not survive even in the unglaciated southern districts, since dwarf Arctic birch and Arctic mosses have been found in the sheltered valleys of south Devon. He regarded the post-glacial floras as due to a steady increase by occasional introduction, the oldest element being the Alpine association which occurs on nearly all our mountains. Other associations, including aquatic plants and the limestone flora, are of more recent introduction. The most striking floral elements have a marked coastal distribution, the plants corresponding to those of the opposite mainland. Thus the Cornish flora and that of south-western Ireland contain a Pyrenean element, the plants of Norfolk correspond to those on the opposite shore of the North Sea, and a few American plants are said to live on our western coasts.

LITERATURE

The foregoing description is necessarily brief, and much of the evidence on which taxonomic classification is based has been omitted. For such detail the reader should consult:

Fossil Plants, by A. C. Seward:

Vol. I: Algae, Fungi, Bryophyta, Equisetales, Sphenophyllales, 1898.

Vol. II: Lycopodiales and Filicales, 1910.

Vol. III: Pteridospermae, Cyadofilices, Cordaitales, Cyadophyta, 1917.

Vol. IV: Ginkgoales, Coniferales, Gnetales, 1919.

Plant Life through the Ages, by the same author (1931), is an invaluable discussion of past floras, with an extensive bibliography; certain geological interpretations, however, seem to be overdrawn.

An excellent account of early land-plants is given in *Devonian Floras* by E. A. N. Arber (8vo., Cambridge, 1921), which contains an extensive bibliography. It may be supplemented by the monographic treatment of 'Old Red Sandstone Plants Showing Structure from the Rhynie Chert Bed, Aberdeenshire', by R. Kidston and W. H. Lang:

Part I: *Rhynia gwynne-vaughani* K. and L., *Trans. Roy. Soc. Edin.* vol. li, part 3, pp. 761–84, 1917.

Part II: Additional notes on *R. gwynne-vaughani* and description of *R. major* K. and L. and *Hornea lignieri* K. and L.

Part III: On *Asteroxylon mackiei* K. and L., ibid., vol. lii, pp. 603–27, 643–50, 1920.

Part IV: Restorations and General Morphology.

Part V: Thallophyta. Conditions of Accumulation and Preservation of the Deposit, ibid., vol. lii, pp. 831–902, 1921.

A new genus and species, *Gosslingia breconensis* Heard, is described by A. Heard in 'Old Red Sandstone Plants showing Structure from Brecon (South Wales), *Q.J.G.S.*, vol. lxxxiii, pp. 195–209, 1927.

The latest monograph on Carboniferous floras is *Fossil Plants of the Carboniferous Rocks of Great Britain*, by R. Kidston, Mem. Geol. Surv. (Palaeont.), vol. ii, pp. 1–681, with 153 plates, 1922–6.

Additional information concerning some Lower Carboniferous forms is contained in 'Contributions to the Knowledge of Lower Carboniferous Plants', by J. Walton.

Part I: On the genus *Rhacopteris* Schimper.

Part II: On the Morphology of *Sphenopteris teiliana* Kidson, *Phil. Trans. Roy. Soc.*, ser. B, vol. ccxv, pp. 201–24, 1926.

Part III: On *Diplopteridium teilianum* Kidston, ibid., vol. ccxix, pp. 347–79, 1931.

Critical revision of familiar Coal Measures Plants is gradually being undertaken, as in the following 'Critical Studies of Coal Measure Plant Impressions', by E. A. N. Arber, *Journ. Linn. Soc. Bot.*, vol. xlvi, pp. 171–217, 1923.

Part I: A Revision of British Upper Carboniferous Species of the genus *Lepidostrobus* Brongniart, preserved as incrustations. Twelve species discussed and illustrated.

Part II: *Lepidodendron lycopodioides* Sternb., *L. ophiurus* Brongn., and *L. loricatum* Arber. Discussion and numerous illustrations.

Part III: *Neuropteris obliqua* Brongn. and *N. callosa* Lesq. reviewed and illustrated.

A detailed record of plant-distribution in various seams of part of the South Wales coalfield is given in 'The Ecology of the Westphalian and the Lower Part of the Staffordian Series of Clydach Vale and Gilfach Goch', by D. Davies, *Q.J.G.S.*, vol. lxxvii, pp. 30–74, 1921.

An interesting paper on local conditions of deposition is 'The Present Distribution and Origin of the Calcareous Concretions in Coal Seams known as "Coal-Balls" ', by M. C. Stopes and D. M. S. Watson, *Phil. Trans. Roy. Soc.*, ser. B, vol. cc., pp. 167–218, 1908.

The floras of several coalfields have been described from time to time. In 'The Fossil Flora of the Bristol and Somerset Coal Field', by R. Crookall, *Geol. Mag.*, vol. lxii, pp. 145–80, 385–410, 1925, numerous references are made to other coalfields and an extensive list of literature is given. The same author has provided a general summary of *Coal Measures Plants*, published in 1929, with illustrations of 240 species.

Recent views on the succession of Carboniferous floras are given by E. Dix in 'The Succession of Fossil Plants in the South Wales Coalfield', with special reference to the existence of the Stephanian, *C.R. Congr. Stratigr. Carb.* (Heerlen, 1935), vol. i, pp. 159–81, 1937, and by W. J. Jongmans in 'Contribution to a Comparison between the Carboniferous Floras of the United States and of Western Europe', ibid., vol. i, pp. 363–87, 1937.

The features and distribution of the Gigantopteris flora of E. Asia and North America are described in 'The Characters of the Fossil Plant *Gigantopteris*, and its Occurrence in North America', by D. White, *Proc. U.S. Nat. Mus.*, vol. xli, pp. 493–516, 1912, and 'The Relation between the Late Palaeozoic Floras of Eastern and Northern Asia', by T. G. Halle, *C.R. Congrés Stratigr. Carb.* (Heerlen, 1935), vol. i, pp. 237–45, 1937.

The Glossopteris flora is described by E. A. N. Arber in 'The Fossil Plants of the Glossopteris Flora', *Brit. Mus. Cat.* 1905. Additional information is given by A. L. Dutoit in 'A Short Review of the Karroo Fossil Flora', *C.R. Internat. Geol. Congr. (S. Africa)*, 1929, vol. ii, pp. 239–51; C. S. Fox in 'The Gondwana System and Related Formations', *Mem. Geol. Surv. India*, vol. lviii, pp. 1–241, 1931; A. C. Seward in 'The Association of Sigillaria and Glossopteris in South Africa', *Q.J.G.S.*, vol. liii, pp. 315–40, 1897; A. C. Seward and T. N. Leslie in 'Permo-Carboniferous Plants from Vereeniging (Transvaal)', ibid., vol. lxiv, pp. 190–26, 1908; and by J. Walton in 'The Fossil Flora of the Karroo System in the Wankie District, S. Rhodesia', *Southern Rhodesia Geol. Surv. Bull.*, vol. xv, pp. 62–75, 1929.

The Theory of Continental Displacement mentioned on p. 335 is propounded in detail by A. Wegener in *The Origin of Continents and Oceans*, English translation by J. G. A. Skerl, London, 1924, and in *Our Wandering Continents*, by A. L. Dutoit, Edinburgh, 1937.

The Mesozoic Floras are well described in a series of catalogues of the British Museum (Natural History), namely:

'The Jurassic Flora', by A. C. Seward.

Part I: The Yorkshire Coast, 1900.
Part II: Liassic and Oolitic Floras of England, 1904.

'The Wealden Flora', by A. C. Seward.

Part I: Thallophyta and Pteridophyta, 1894.
Part II: Gymnospermae, 1895.

'The Cretaceous Flora', by M. C. Stopes.

Part I: Bibliography, Algae, Fungi, 1913.
Part II: Lower Greensand (Aptian) Plants of Britain, 1915.

Several important publications serve to supplement the Catalogues, and contain numerous illustrations.

'The Flora of the Inferior Oolite of Brora, Sutherland', M. C. Stopes, *Q.J.G.S.*, vol. lxiii, pp. 375–81, 1907.

'The Jurassic Flora of Sutherland', A. C. Seward, *T.R.S.E.*, vol. xlvii, pp. 643–709, 1911.

'Jurassic Plants from Cromarty and Sutherland', A. C. Seward and N. Bancroft, *T.R.S.E.*, vol. xlviii, pp. 867–88, 1913.

'The Fossil Flora of the Cleveland District of Yorkshire:
    I. 'The Flora of the Marske Quarry', H. Hamshaw Thomas, *Q.J.G.S.*, vol. lxix, pp. 223–51, 1913.

'Williamsoniella: a new Type of Bennettitalean Flower', H. Hamshaw Thomas, *Phil. Trans. Roy. Soc.*, ser. B, vol. ccvii, pp. 113–48, 1915.

'New Bennettitean Cones from the British Cretaceous', by M. C. Stopes, *Phil. Trans. Roy. Soc.*, ser. B, vol. ccviii, pp. 389–440, 1918.

'The Caytoniales: a new Group of Angiospermous Plants from the Jurassic Rocks of Yorkshire', H. Hamshaw Thomas, *Phil. Trans. Roy. Soc.*, ser. B, vol. ccxiii, pp. 299–363, 1925.

'Petrifactions of the Earliest European Angiosperms, M. C. Stopes, *Phil. Trans. Roy. Soc.*, ser. B, vol. cciii, pp. 75–100, 1912.

Until a few decades ago the standard work of reference on British Neozoic plants was:

'The British Eocene Flora', *Mon. Pal. Soc.*
    Vol. I: By J. S. Gardner and Ettingshausen, 1879–82.
    Vol. II: By J. S. Gardner, 1883–86.

This monograph was left unfinished. During the last thirty years knowledge of plants obtained by various exploratory parties, especially in China, has shown the urgent need of revision of the earlier work. A beginning has been made with the publication of—

'The Upper Eocene Flora of Hordle', M. E. J. Chandler, *Mon. Pal. Soc.*, 1925–26.

'The Bembridge Flora', E. M. Reid and M. E. J. Chandler, *B.M. Cat.*, 1926.

These deal largely with the seeds (but also with leaves) of Upper Eocene and Oligiocene plants.

Further publications include:

'The Geological History of the Genus Stratiotes', M. E. J. Chandler, *Q.J.G.S.*, vol. lxxix, pp. 117–38, 1923.

Ten species of *Stratiotes* are discussed and illustrated. The evolutional sequence may possibly be of stratigraphical utility.

'The Cuticular Structure of certain Dicotyledonous and Coniferous Leaves from the Middle Eocene Flora of Bournemouth', by H. Bandulska, *Journ. Linn. Soc. Bot.*, vol. xlvi, pp. 241–69, 1923.

In the first of the two papers under this title three species of dicotyledonous leaves are referred to *Dicotylophyllum*, a new genus of uncertain affinity. Certain fossil gymnosperms are discussed, namely, *Araucarites goepperti* (Sternberg) Gardner, *Taxodium europaeum* (Brongn.), and *Sequoia tournalii* Brongn. In the second, one of the leaves, *Dicotylophyllum stopesae* Band., is transferred to the genus *Nothofagus*, and a fossil beech, *Fagus bouronensis* Band., is described from the Bournemouth Beds.

Two other papers by H. Bandulska deal with the cuticles of Lauraceae and Myrtaceae, *Journ. Linn. Soc. (Bot.)*, vol. xlvii, pp. 353–425, 1926, and ibid, vol. xlviii, pp. 657–71, 1931, respectively.

'The Charophyta of the Lower Headon Beds of Hordle Cliffs (South Hampshire)', by C. Reid and J. Groves, *Q.J.G.S.*, vol. lxxvii, pp. 175–92, 1921.

'The London Clay Flora', by E. M. Reid and M. E. J. Chandler, *B.M. Cat.*, 1933.

'A Comparative Review of Pliocene Floras based on the Study of Fossil Seeds', E. M. Reid, *Q.J.G.S.*, vol. lxxvi (for 1920), pp. 145–61, 1921.

'Two Pre-Glacial Floras from Castle Eden (County Durham)', E. M. Reid, *Q.J.G.S.*, vol. lxxvi, pp. 104–44, 1921.

The first of these papers summarizes the characters of Pliocene floras and gives useful lists of species. The second contains an account of the oldest British Pliocene Flora, with many illustrations of fossil seeds.

'The Pliocene Floras of the Dutch-Prussian Border', by C. and E. M. Reid, *Med. Rijksops Delstoffen*, No. 6, 1915.

'Recherches sur Quelques Grains du Pliocene du Pont de Gail, Cantal', by E. M. Reid, *Bull. Soc. Geol. France*, ser. 4, vol. xx, pp. 48–57, 1920.

'The Arctic Flora of the Cam Valley of Barnwell, Cambridge', by M. E. J. Chandler, *Q.J.G.S.*, vol. lxxvii, pp. 4–22, 1921.

Another line of inquiry developed during recent years should be mentioned here, while its application to British stratigraphy is in progress. Swedish geologists have paid considerable attention to the distribution of the pollen-grains of forest trees in peat and other plant-bearing deposits. An account dealing with certain British deposits together, with notes on technique, is given by G. Erdtman in 'Studies in the Post-Arctic History of the Forests of N.W. Europe'. I. British Isles, II. N.W. Germany and Holland, III. Belgium and N. France, *Geol. Foren. Forhandl.*, Bd. 50, 1928.

H. Godwin has reviewed 'Pollen Analysis and Quaternary Geology' in *Proc. Geol. Assoc.*, vol. lii, pp. 328–61, 1941. His 'Studies of the Postglacial History of British Vegetation' include papers on the deposits of the English Fenland in *Phil. Trans. Roy. Soc.*, ser. B, vols. ccxxix and ccxxx, 1938–9. Dr. Godwin has also edited a series of papers, giving 'Data for the Study of Postglacial History', in *New Phytologist*, vols. xxxvii to xli, 1938–42.

IX

TETRAPOD FAUNAS OF THE LATE PALAEOZOIC SYSTEMS

FOSSIL tetrapods from the Carboniferous system are of considerable interest because the distribution of their remains may eventually indicate the relations of the land areas during Carboniferous time. But so far tetrapods are only known from a few localities in Europe and North America. Until recently, none were recorded from earlier strata, but in 1932 certain primitive forms were described by G. Save-Soderbergh from Upper Devonian rocks of Ymer Island, east Greenland. These animals show features comparable with equivalent characters in certain primitive crossopterygian and dipnoan fishes (*Osteolepis* and *Dipterus*). Derivation of stegocephalian amphibians from the crossopterygian fishes has long been inferred from morphological characters, and Save-Soderbergh now claims that the Devonian ichthyostegids and the primitive crossopterygians must have had a common ancestor from which neither of the two groups has departed to any great extent.

We have already noted that owing to the nature of the vertebrate skeleton, composed of numerous separate bones, it rarely happens that fossil remains are completely preserved. For purposes of reference, however, incomplete skeletons, or even single bones, have to be named, though their relationships to better known forms may be uncertain. If and when additional material becomes available, some of the names may become unnecessary or invalid. For our discussion, therefore, it is necessary to refer to a list of genera which is generally accepted as reliable, and we shall use that of A. S. Woodward (1932) in his revision of the Zittel-Eastman textbook. This may be supplemented in certain instances, by references to later work.

Classification of the Palaeozoic Amphibia is based primarily on structural differences in the vertebral column. Four types are easily distinguished in fossil skeletons and there appear to be no transitional forms. The larger animals fall mainly into the order Labyrinthodontia, and the three grades of structure, Embolmeri (Carboniferous and Permian), Rhachitomi (Permian and Lower Trias), Stereospondyli (Trias) are said to represent an evolutional sequence (D. M. S. Watson, 1916, 1926). The smaller animals are usually distributed in the orders Lepospondyli (or Microsauria), Adelospondyli and Phyllospondyli (or Branchiosauria). The last-named group is nearest to the Labyrinthodontia and arose in early Carboniferous time from embolomerous forms. Many genera formerly included in the order Lepospondyli have been transferred to the Adelospondyli and the remainder are distributed in two groups, Nectridia and Aistopoda, easily distinguished by structure of the vertebrae, but the relationships of the groups are obscure. The Adelospondyli form a distinct group, not closely related to other amphibians, which shows a tendency to a reduction in the dermal bones of the skull.

The coal-bearing strata of Lower Carboniferous age in Scotland have yielded a small number of amphibians. Two embolomerous genera, *Otocratia* and *Crassigyrinus*, described by D. M. S. Watson (1929) from Midlothian, are referred (the latter doubtfully) to the family Anthracosauridae. Another Midlothian form *Spathicephalus* (Watson, 1929), together with *Loxomma* (T. Huxley, 1862) from the Gilmerton Ironstone near Edinburgh, belong to the family Loxommidae. A large form, *Pholidogaster* (T. Huxley, 1862) from the same locality, is more than a metre in length, and has a strong armour of ventral scutes; it is referred to a separate, monotypic family. Two small amphibians, *Adelogyrinus* and *Dolichopareias* (Watson, 1930) are placed among the Adelospondyli which differ from other early amphibians in features that approach the living urodelan type. Hence at this early stage the scanty remains so far known indicate considerable differentiation among the amphibians, and their early history must date back to Devonian time.

A greater variety of forms is known from the Upper Carboniferous Coal Measures in various parts of the world. From Lanarkshire, Scotland, there is the large *Anthracosaurus* (Huxley, 1863) with a skull nearly 40 cm. long, as well as a species of *Loxomma* (D. M. S. Watson, 1929). Another form from the English Coal Measures, usually referred to *Loxomma*, is considered by Watson to belong to another genus not yet named. *Palaeogyrinus* (Watson, 1926) is recorded from the Coal Measures of Fifeshire, while other anthracosaurians are *Pholiderpeton* (Huxley, 1869) from Yorkshire, *Pteroplax* (Hancock and Atthey, 1868) and *Eogyrinus* (Watson, 1921) from Northumberland, the last also recorded from Staffordshire. It may be noted here that the Anthracosauridae are almost confined to Europe as far as present records go; the family contains 11 genera (including 3 doubtfully assigned), of which 8 are known in Britain, 2 in Bohemia and only one, *Eobaphetes* from the Coal Measures of Kansas, in North America. The Coal Measures of Northumberland have also yielded remains of the nectridian *Batrachiderpeton* (Hancock and Atthey, 1871) referred to the family Diplocaulidae which is represented by other genera in the Upper Carboniferous and Permian of North America. The lizard-like branchiosaurians are only known in Great Britain by *Eugyrinus* (Watson, 1921) from the Lower Coal Measures of Lancashire, and *Ophiderpeton* from Newsham, Northumberland (Hancock and Atthey, 1869), though various genera occur in the Upper Carboniferous of Bohemia and North America and Lower Permian of central Europe.

Several tetrapod genera have long been known from the Coal Measures of Kilkenny, Ireland (Huxley, 1867). In contrast with the assemblage from Scotland and England only one form, *Ichthyerpeton*, is (doubtfully) referred to the Anthracosauridae. Three genera, *Urocordylus*, *Lepterpeton* and *Keraterpeton* belong to the Urocordylidae, a family of long-tailed nectridians which has representatives both in Europe and North America. The snake-like aistopods are represented by the genera *Dolichosoma* and *Ophiderpeton* both of which are recorded from Bohemia and North America as well as Ireland. It is noteworthy that only two of the Irish genera are known from Great Britain, namely, *Keraterpeton* which is recorded from Staffordshire (C. W. Andrews, 1895) and *Ophiderpeton* from Newsham, Northumberland (Hancock and Atthey, 1869).

Vertebrate fossils of Carboniferous age have long been known from the intermontane basins of central Europe, and certain localities are famous for the abundance and variety of tetrapod remains. The BOHEMIAN BASIN is one of these, and the 'Gaskohle' (cannel) of Nyrany, in particular, has yielded a large assemblage of specialized amphibians, first described by A. Fritsch (1879–94) and lately revised by M. C. Steen (1938). There is apparently a continuous succession of Upper Carboniferous and Lower Permian rocks which is difficult to subdivide because of similarity in facies. Consequently there is some confusion in the literature regarding the precise age of the tetrapod-bearing horizons. Thus, the appearance of animals which seem to foreshadow the typical Permian fauna led E. C. Case (1926) and A. S. Woodward (1932) to regard the 'Gaskohle' as early Permian in age, though F. Broili (1908) had already referred it to the Upper Carboniferous on account of the prevalent archaic types. Steen (1938) states that the Nyrany fauna belongs to the Westphalian stage, and T. S. Westoll (1944) compares it with a fauna of similar horizon in the Coal Measures of Linton, Ohio, U.S.A.

Among the large Labyrinthodontia there are members of both the major families of embolomerous forms. *Loxomma*, the typical genus of the Loxommidae, also present in the Coal Measures of England, is represented at Nyrany by a local species, and the anthracosaurians by the genus *Diplovertebron*. Jaws of *Gaudrya* from Nyrany, and vertebrae of *Nummulosaurus* from slightly higher strata at Tremosna, are also of embolomerid type. Rhachitomous forms include skulls of *Nyrania*, *Potamochoston*, and *Cochleosaurus*, the last including young specimens formerly assigned to *Dendrerpeton*, and they are succeeded in the early Permian strata of Olivetin and Ruprechtice by *Luxor* and *Chelydosaurus*; another skull from Ruprechtice is usually referred to *Sclerocephalus*, but Steen says it is generically distinct. The name *Macromerium* covers various fragments of vertebrae and ribs which appear to be of rhachitomous type, as also are certain vertebrae recorded as *Sparagmites*.

The Bohemian *Solenodonsaurus*, redescribed by H. S. Pearson (1924), is the oldest known form of the Seymouriamorpha, one of the many divergent branches which sprang from the Embolomeri. The group has usually been regarded as a primitive family of cotylosaurian reptiles (D. M. S. Watson, 1918; M. C. Steen, 1938), but R. Broom (1922) and P. Sushkin (1925) transferred it to the Labyrinthodontia; A. S. Woodward (1932) remarks that the teeth are labyrinthodont in structure and the mandible is typically stegocephalian in character, and Watson (1942) states that the Seymouria-morpha retained an amphibian life-history, though they developed certain reptilian characters in the skeleton.

The greatest variety among the Bohemian amphibians is seen in the small forms belonging to the Phyllospondyli, Adelospondyli, Nectridia, and Aistopoda. Indeed, the diversity among these small animals contrasts strongly with the structural uniformity shown by the labyrinthodont species. The Phyllospondyli is more closely related to the Labyrinthodontia than to any other amphibian order. The two genera already established with certainty in the Bohemian faunas are so distinct that they may repre-sent two separate families. *Branchiosaurus*, which has a skull of loxommid type, is present at the Nyrany horizon, and *Melanerpeton* with a skull of anthracosaur type, is cited from the higher beds of Olivetin, Mala Lhota and Ruprechtice. Outside Bohemia, several species of *Branchiosaurus* and allied genera have been described by O. M. B. Bulman and W. F. Whittard (1926) from the Lower Permian rocks of Odernheim in Rhenish Prussia. The same authors review other species recorded from the Stephanian rocks of Commentry, France (Thevenin, 1906), and from Lower Permian near Niederhasslich, Saxony (H. Credner 1881) and Autun, France (Gaudry, 1875). Species of *Melanerpeton* are described from Niederhass-lich (Credner, 1881) and from Moravia (A. Fritsch, 1883; M. C. Steen, 1938).

The nectridian genus *Urocordylus*, which we have already noted from the Kilkenny coalfield, Ireland, is also recorded from Nyrany and from the topmost Stephanian horizon at Kostalov. At Nyrany it is accompanied by another nectridian tentatively assigned to the Irish genus *Lepterpeton*, and by the broad-headed *Scincosaurus* which is not yet known elsewhere, though it seems to be related to the British *Keraterpeton*. Two genera of the limbless Aistopoda are listed in the Nyrany fauna. One of them, *Ophider-peton*, is known also from higher (Stephanian) strata at Kuonova, west of Prague, also from the Coal Measures of Jarrow, Ireland, and Newsham Northumberland. The other, *Dolichosoma*, is also represented in the Irish fauna, and a similar form, *Palaeosiren*, is cited from early Permian rocks at Olivetin, south of the Riesengebirge. The genus *Ricmodon*, with four species at Nyrany, is tentatively referred to the Aistopoda on the evidence of the vertebrae. The Adelospondyls comprise five species of *Microbrachis* and one of *Hyloplesion*. These genera are so far known only at Nyrany, but other members of the group are recorded from British and North American localities.

The Nyrany cannel also encloses remains of haplolepid fishes (T. S. Westoll, 1944) which are again associated with nectridians and aistopods at a few localities in Britain and North America. These animals seem to form an ecological group adapted to the special habitat of freshwater swamps supporting abundant vegetation—such is indicated by the carbonaceous character of the deposits.

Taken as a whole, the Coal Measures of NORTH AMERICA have furnished the greatest variety of Upper Carboniferous tetrapods. Among the earliest to be discovered (Lyell and Dawson, 1853) is a small assemblage of genera from the Coal Measures of South Joggins, Nova Scotia. Most of the remains are disarticulated and scattered fragments of amphibia enclosed in sandstone which filled the hollow trunks of erect Sigillarian trees. The plants in the associated strata indicate a mid-Westphalian horizon. The amphibian assemblage was one of the first to be described (Dawson, 1860–94; Owen, 1853, 1862), and several species from European localities have been referred to the Nova Scotian genera. Hence it is important that the latter should be exactly determined, and to this end the assemblage has been critically reviewed by M. C. Steen (1934). This author states that the greater part of the material is so fragmentary that several of Dawson's species are of doubtful validity. Most of the identifiable remains belong to *Dendrerpeton acadianum* (Owen, 1853) of which a nearly complete individual was later discovered (Owen, 1862). This small labyrinthrodont is specially interesting because it combines structural features of both embolomerous and rachitomous grades of the order, and may be interpreted as a morphological stage in the evolution of the Rachitomi from the Embolomeri. The other labyrinthodonts in the fauna, species of *Platystegos*, *Dendrysekos*, *Dendryazousa*, and *Calligenethon*, are known only by skulls and vertebrae. The lepospondyls, represented by species of *Fritschia*, *Leiocephalikon* and *Atopotera* are also incompletely known, but they agree with other lepospondyls in that the neural arch is fused with the centrum of the vertebra. The genus *Hylonomus*, for long placed in the Lepospondyli, has recently been transferred to the Adelospondyli on the evidence of vertebral structure (M. C. Steen, 1938). It is related to the Bohemian genera *Hyloplesion* and *Microbrachis*. The fauna as a whole seems to occupy an isolated position, for none of the genera are at present known outside Nova Scotia. Apparently the only other genus described from the Coal Measures of Nova Scotia is *Baphetes* (Owen, 1854) a member of the family Loxommidae which has other genera in the Coal Measures of the United States and Scotland.

A larger and more varied assemblage of amphibians has long been known from the Middle Coal Measures of Linton, Ohio. Nearly sixty species have been described by Newberry (1875), Cope (1868–97), and Moodie (1916) from an area about 100 yards in diameter in a layer of cannel coal only 4 to 6 inches in thickness. A. S. Romer (1930), in a critical review of the fauna, has shown that less than twenty of the species are valid, and M. C. Steen

(1931) has added to our knowledge of their morphological features by a study of the collection from Linton in the British Museum of Natural History. The labyrinthodonts are represented by the baphetid genus *Macrerpeton* Moodie, and a form comparable with the English *Orthosaurus*. These are placed in the family Loxommidae, while *Leptophractus* Cope is a cricotid genus related to the English *Eogyrinus*. Among the Lepospondyli, the lizard-like species of *Sauropleura* are most abundant at Linton, and the genus is represented also at Nurschan in Bohemia. *Ctenerpeton* Cope, a larger relative with better developed limbs may be compared with the Irish *Urocordylus*. The long-bodied, limbless *Ophiderpeton* has an elongate skull of peculiar structure; the Linton species is almost identical with European forms from Newsham (England), Jarrow (Ireland), and Nurschan (Bohemia). The rare *Phlegethontia* from Linton is related to the Irish *Dolichosoma*. The small, 'horned' *Diceratosaurus* with depressed body and long tail is comparable with the Irish *Keraterpeton*, which, however, is more primitive. Two genera are assigned to the Adelospondyli, namely, *Cocytinus* and *Pleuroptyx*, both instituted by Cope. The latter genus is referred to the order only on characters of the vertebral column. *Cocytinus* is better known and shows a very specialized type of skull-structure, also exemplified in *Adelogyrinus* and *Dolichopareias* from the Lower Carboniferous of Scotland, and later in *Lysorophus* from the topmost Carboniferous Beds of Texas. Of the Phyllospondyli or branchiosaurs, *Colosteus* Cope is the most abundant genus at Linton; it is a large form with elongate skull, and shows superficial resemblance to labyrinthodonts. *Erpetosaurus* is a much smaller ally with larger orbits. *Stegops* has a specialized spinescent skull, and *Platyrhinops* (Steen, 1931) is a related form with no spines. *Mytaras* (Steen, 1931) has a parallel-sided skull, much elongated in front of the orbits, but *Branchiosauravus* and *Pelion* are more primitive, tending to the short skull type. The last forms confirm the view that branchiosaurs and labyrinthodonts have a common ancestry. The Linton Phyllospondyli, however, already show a stage of morphological specialization that was reached by labyrinthodonts only at a much later geological period. Two primitive reptiles *Tuditanus* and *Eusauropleura*, sometimes placed in the Lepospondyli (A. S. Woodward, 1932), belong to the family Tuditanidae which has other genera in the Lower Permian of France and Silesia.

The slightly younger Coal Measures of Mazon Creek, Illinois, with a later Westphalian flora, have yielded a few amphibians (mostly small forms) which have been described at various times by E. D. Cope (1865), R. L. Moodie (1912, 1916) and D. M. S. Watson (1940). The fossils at this locality are enclosed in ironstone nodules, and the assemblage of amphibians is significantly different from that of the carbonaceous shales at Linton. Phyllospondyls, adelospondyls, and embolomeres are associated with fishes, among which are rare haplolepid forms (T. S. Westoll, 1944), but there is no trace of the nectridians and aistopods which form such a large proportion of the material collected at Linton. The phyllospondyl genera include *Amphibamus* and the closely related *Miobatrachus* (Watson, 1940), probably also *Micrerpeton* and *Eumicrerpeton* (Moodie, 1912). Watson has demonstrated the differences between *Miobatrachus* and the earlier branchiosaur *Eugyrinus*, and states that an extension of the changes would lead to the structure which exists in the primitive frog *Protobatrachus*, described by J. Piveteau (1937) from the basal Triassic rocks of Madagascar. *Miobatrachus* is, therefore, essentially an ancestor of the Anura (frogs). The genus *Cephalerpeton*, with a deep, triangular head is an adelospondyl but the relations of *Mazonerpeton*, *Erierpeton*, and *Erpetobrachium* are less certain. The embolomere *Spondylerpeton* shows structural characters which seem to link it with the Anthracosauridae. To this family also belongs *Eobaphetes* from the Coal Measures of Kansas (Moodie, 1911) and no other anthracosaurian forms seem to have been recorded from North America.

Several amphibian genera comparable with those just discussed are present in the late Palaeozoic 'Red Beds' of Texas. These strata by definition include the Cisco, Wichita, and Clear Fork formations in ascending order, the first being assigned to the Carboniferous, the remaining two to the Permian system (Cummins, 1890). A vertebrate fauna from the Wichita and Clear Fork Beds was considered by its discoverer (Cope, 1875) to be of Permian character, and most later authors have placed the Red Beds entirely in the Permian system. Later, however, A. S. Romer (1935) recorded certain of the genera as already established in the Upper Cisco Beds and suggested the inclusion of the Wichita in the Carboniferous system. It is convenient therefore to discuss the more conspicuous fossils of the Red Beds as a whole and so to review present information concerning the relationships of Permian tetrapods to their predecessors in Upper Carboniferous strata.

Among the labyrinthodonts, the embolomerous genus *Cricotus* ranges from Upper Cisco to the top of the Wichita, but is not known from the Clear Fork Beds. The rhachitome *Eryops*, which is the largest of the North American amphibians, is also recorded from Upper Cisco Beds, becoming more common in the Wichita and continuing through the Clear Fork formation. Fragments of a large rhachitome, *Edops*, with swollen muzzle and enormous labyrinthine teeth, are recorded from low horizons of the Wichita formation but are unknown in higher beds. Two other rhachitomes, *Zatrachys* and *Trimerorhachis* are apparently restricted to Wichita and Clear Fork horizons, and the latter are specially marked by the presence of armoured forms, *Broiliellus*, *Cacops*, *Dissorophus*, *Algeinosaurus* grouped in the Dissorophidae. The lepospondyl *Diplocaulus*, rare in the Wichita but common in the Clear Fork Beds, is stated by Romer (1935) to be as close morphologically to the Linton *Diceratosaurus* as to its later allies. Similarly the adelospondyl *Lysorophus* from the Clear Fork Beds of Texas, and a much earlier horizon in Illinois, shows structural relationship with the

Linton *Cocytinus*. Hence the amphibians of the Red Beds are regarded as direct derivatives of the Coal Measures stocks, or as Romer says, the vertebrates of the Red Beds are the last representatives of an essentially Pennsylvanian fauna.

Besides amphibians, the Red Beds at some horizons have yielded abundant remains of reptiles which are practically unknown in faunas of the Coal Measures, though *Eosauravus* from Linton is possibly a reptile. These animals gradually become more completely adapted for life on land, and Romer regards the lower part of the Red Beds as the dry-land equivalent of the Coal Measures. The most primitive order of reptiles, the Cotylosauria, is closely related to the embolomerous labyrinthodonts as shown by the continuous cranial roof and other details of structure. One of the earliest and best known of the cotylosaurs is the heavily built *Diadectes* whose recorded range begins in the Upper Cisco Beds and continues through the Wichita and Clear Fork formations. Case (1915) states that the powerful hind limbs, broad feet, short forelimbs, and depressed body of *Diadectes* suggest fossorial habits. Among its associates in the last-named beds is *Seymouria* which also has many resemblances with the cotylosaurs (Watson, 1918) and represents another divergent branch derived from the Embolomeri (Watson, 1942). A more advanced type of structure is shown by the lightly built *Captorhinus* and its larger relative *Labidosaurus* with the broad flat head of aquatic forms combined with the firm carpus and tarsus of terrestrial animals; these are not known below the Clear Fork Beds. The Pelycosauria, evolved from cotylosaurs, have been reviewed by A. S. Romer and L. W. Price (1940) who recognize three main evolutional lines. The earliest known pelycosaur is *Clepsydrops* from an Upper Carboniferous horizon at Danville, Illinois. This is allied to the large *Ophiacodon* which is recorded from Upper Cisco Beds; it shows steady increase in size and in depth of skull at various horizons of the Wichita, but is represented only by a small primitive form in the Clear Fork Beds. The small *Poliosaurus* from the Wichita Beds, and *Varanosaurus*, with low, flat skull, from the Clear Fork formation are also placed in the family Ophiacodontidae representing the first evolutional line. The second series is represented already in the Upper Cisco Beds by *Edaphosaurus* which is common at various horizons of the Wichita, but rare in the Clear Fork Beds. This is a highly specialized herbivorous form with long dorsal spines bearing cross-bars; in appearance it is the most bizarre of the Texan reptiles. A related genus, *Casea*, with shorter spines but divergent specialization in other respects, is apparently restricted to the Clear Fork Beds. This group, the Edaphosauria, is linked with the Ophiacodontidae by such primitive genera as *Glaucosaurus* and *Mycterosaurus* which, however, are incompletely known. The third line of descent is comprised in the Sphenacodontidae which shows the development of a carnivorous habit, culminating in the genus *Dimetrodon*. This family is apparently derived from such a type as *Varanops* which, in shape and dentition, resembles the primitive ophiacodont *Varanosaurus* and the edaphosaur *Mycterosaurus*. In other genera the dentition gradually becomes heterodont, a pair of teeth in each jaw becoming enlarged as canines. Only a trace of dental differentiation is shown by *Secodontosaurus* whose low and narrow skull is otherwise like that of the New Mexican *Sphenacodon*. This form is hardly to be distinguished from the Texan genus *Dimetrodon* which has developed large canine teeth with reduction of the maxillary teeth in front of them: the genus is often illustrated to show the long spines which form a crest along the back. *Dimetrodon*, along with sphenacodonts generally, is dominant in the Clear Fork Beds, but is already established at the base of the Wichita and perhaps at lower horizons. This is the culmination of the sphenacodonts and the end of Palaeozoic vertebrate history in North America, for the summit of the Red Beds has yielded no fossils. But these strata have revealed important data concerning the early history of the reptiles and it is possible to continue the history by means of information from other parts of the world. In particular we must examine the suggestion of Romer that the sphenacodonts alone among reptiles present the right type of carnivorous adaptation of skull and post-cranial skeleton from which to derive the later mammal-like reptiles that form such a striking element in the Permian faunas of South Africa and Russia.

Reverting to the faunas of the Carboniferous Coal Measures, many authors (e.g. Watson 1921) consider the resemblances of the European and North American tetrapods to prove that the two areas formed a single zoological province and demand a continuous land-bridge from Britain to Canada, during Carboniferous time. It is questionable, however, if the evidence justifies this conclusion, for the assemblages so far known from the Coal Measures are very restricted and are probably far from representative of the presumably varied tetrapod faunas of the period. This is indicated by the later work of A. S. Romer (1935) in which he traces certain early reptiles back into the lower portions of the Texan Red Beds that are probably of Carboniferous age. Moreover, if we compare the records of Coal Measures faunas on the two sides of the Atlantic Ocean, there are significant differences as well as similarities. The labyrinthodont family Anthracosauridae, for instance, according to present knowledge, is almost confined to Europe; of the eleven genera already known, only one, *Baphetes*, is known from American strata. On the other hand, present records of the Cricotidae are almost restricted to North America, and none of the amphibian genera of the Nova Scotian fauna appear to be known from European strata. Of the seventeen genera from the Coal Measures of Linton, Ohio, only two appear in the lists of European forms, namely, *Sauropleura* and *Ophiderpeton*. This is only about 12 per cent. of the total from Linton, a small proportion if there were direct land connexion. It is true that species of *Ophiderpeton* from Ohio and Bohemia are said to be almost identical, but it must be recalled that the distinct faunas of modern Canada and Patagonia, thousands of miles apart, contain some identical and related species. Hence it seems to us that the differences in the Coal Measures faunas of Europe and North America indicate a distant or restricted connexion between the two continents. Unfortunately, there is at present no information concerning Carboniferous tetrapods from Asia which might indicate an alternative route of migration.

THE PERMIAN TETRAPODS OF THE NORTHERN HEMISPHERE

We have already noted (pp. 362–4) that, according to a succession of remains found in the Red Beds of Texas and equivalent strata in New Mexico, Oklahoma, Kansas, and Illinois, Permian tetrapods have developed from their Carboniferous forerunners. Among labyrinthodonts the embolomerous types are replaced by rhachitomous forms, and the seymouriamorphs represent another and divergent side-line developed from the Embolomeri. The Lepospondyli and Phyllospondyli have dwindled almost to disappearance. On the other hand, three groups of reptiles are present, namely, the Cotylosauria, Pelycosauria, and the Araeoscelidia. The cotylosaurs, closely related to the embolomerous labyrinthodonts are represented chiefly by the Diadectidae and the Captorhinidae probably with aquatic habits of life. The pelycosaurs, evolved from cotylosaurs, are already differentiated into two herbivorous groups, Ophiacodontidae and Edaphosauridae, and the carnivorous Sphenacodontidae. These are rendered conspicuous by the extreme length of the neural spines of the vertebrae which form a crest on the back of the animal. A separate order is established for the Texan genus *Araeoscelis*, a lizard-shaped land-reptile with long, slender limb-bones and slender cervical vertebrae, features which probably indicate swift motion and agility. No later Permian tetrapods are known from American deposits, and it is now our task to examine the Permian rocks of Europe for evidence regarding the further course of reptilian evolution.

Permian deposits at scattered localities in the intermontane basins of CENTRAL EUROPE, extending through Germany into central France have yielded a variety of tetrapod remains. The assemblage as a whole shows a certain distinction from that of the Carboniferous System, consistent with its higher position in the stratigraphical scale. Thus the embolomerous labyrinthodonts, so conspicuous in European Carboniferous deposits are replaced by the rhachitomous family Archegosauridae. Remains of *Archegosaurus*, enclosed in ironstone nodules, are especially abundant in the Lower Permian deposits of Lebach near Saarbrucken; no less than 271 individuals of *A. decheni* are described by Meyer (1858) from this locality. Other species are known from the Rothliegende of Saxony and the Permian of Kashmir, India. The allied family Eryopidae, that includes the largest of the North American labyrinthodonts, is represented in the Lower Permian of Rhenish Prussia and Autun, France, by *Actinodon* (Gaudry, 1887) which has also been found in Kashmir (p. 373). *Onchiodon* from the

Rothliegende of Dresden shows close structural relationship to *Eryops*, but also certain similarities with the later *Rhinesuchus*. This last genus has a wide range of distribution; first described (Broom, 1908) from the Cape Province of South Africa, it is recorded from Permian deposits in Rhenish Prussia, Nyasaland, and south Madagascar, also from early Triassic Beds of Vologda, Russia. We may mention here the English form *Dasyceps* (Lloyd and Huene, 1910) from Kenilworth, Warwickshire, which is referred to the American family Zatrachysidae. The Phyllospondyl *Branchiosaurus* is particularly abundant and well-preserved near Dresden, as shown by Credner's elaborate study (1881–6) based on more than a thousand specimens from that locality. Several species have been recorded also from Oberhof and Fredericharoda in Thuringia, Odernheim in Rhenish Prussia, and Autun in France. Other members of the group (Bulman and Whittard, 1926) are *Pelosaurus* from Dresden, Odernheim, and Autun, *Leptorophus* and *Acanthostoma* from Saxony and *Micromelerpeton* from Odernheim. This abundance of branchiosaurs in the Lower Permian deposits of central Europe contrasts strongly with the absence of records from the Red Beds of Texas. The Lepospondyli are sparsely represented in these European rocks by *Hyloplesion* and *Petrobates* from Saxony. The '*Discosaurus*' described by Credner from the Rothliegende of Niederhasslich, Saxony, 'is a young Seymouriamorph, but probably not identical with *Seymouria* itself' (Watson, 1942).

The Permian strata of Germany, France, and England have also yielded remains of several reptilian genera. Only two Cotylosaurs are listed by Woodward (1932) from Germany, namely, *Stephanospondylus* from the Rothliegende of Dresden, and *Phanerosaurus* also from Saxony. They are both placed in the family Diadectidae which includes seven other genera, all from North America. No genera of the American family Captorhinidae are recorded from Europe. The long-tailed, lizard-shaped *Palaeohatteria* from Niederhasslich, Dresden (Credner, 1888; Nopcsa, 1928), is a primitive pelycosaur; according to Watson (1942) it is congeneric with *Haptodus* and *Callibrachion* from Autun, and *Pantelosaurus* from Dresden. Hence these should all be referred to *Haptodus* as the earliest name; the dentition is almost uniform but shows the beginning of a sphenacodont specialization. More advanced sphenacodonts are represented by the maxilla known as *Oxyodon* from Kenilworth, England, and vertebral spines of *Naosaurus* (= *Edaphosaurus*) from Dresden, Germany: these are important as proof that the group lived in Europe as well as in North America during early Permian time. A few imperfectly known genera are tentatively referred to the Araeoscelidia; these include *Protorosaurus* and *Gracilisaurus* from the Kupferschiefer of Germany, *Adelosaurus* from the corresponding Marl Slate of England, *Parasaurus* from the Zechstein of Thuringia, *Kadaliosaurus* from Niederhasslich, Dresden, and *Aphelosaurus* from Autun, France. Case (1926), however, places these genera in a separate family,

Protorosauridae, and suggests that they never penetrated into the true intermontane basins and never crossed to the American continent, but that they were littoral forms peculiar to the shores of the European Zechstein sea.

Compared with the Texan faunas, this Central European assemblage, mostly from Lower Permian horizons, is poor in genera though sometimes prolific in individuals. There are, however, some points of resemblance and also some differences that seem to be important. The assemblages agree in the dominance of rhachitome over embolomerous labyrinthodonts, but in Europe the most conspicuous form is the long-headed *Archegosaurus*, in America the broad-headed *Eryops*. The abundance of branchiosaurs in Europe contrasts strongly with their apparent absence from the Texan rocks. The scanty European records provide evidence that cotylosaurian and pelycosaurian reptiles attain the same grade of development in the two continents but the genera are distinct.

The story is continued farther east, for higher Permian deposits in RUSSIA, which occupy an immense area in that country, have provided an almost continuous series of tetrapods, though the succession is broken for short intervals at many places. The oldest beds to yield a vertebrate fauna are the copper-bearing sandstones of Kargalinsk in the southern Urals, the type-area of Murchison's Permian system. They are later than the Artinsk Series with which the Clear Fork Beds of Texas are correlated. The lowest horizon is linked with the Clear Fork Beds by the presence of the rhachitomous labyrinthodont *Zygosaurus* which is closely related to the American genera *Dissorophus* and *Cacops*. The reptiles of this horizon include heavily built animals with enlarged canine teeth and somewhat sprawling limbs. These Deinocephalia are of two types, the carnivorous Titanosuchidae with a comparatively large and elongated face, and the herbivorous Tapinocephalidae with a short and broad face. In the former family is placed *Brithopus* (Kutorga, 1838) which is usually cited under the later name *Rhopalodon* (Fischer, 1841); the shoulder girdle of this genus is intermediate in structure between that of *Dimetrodon* and that of the South African Deinocephalia (Watson, 1942). Two other titanosuchids, *Cliorhizodon* and *Titanophoneus*, have been described by Efremov (1940) and discussed by Watson (1942); it seems evident that both genera are very like pelycosaurs, are closely related to such carnivorous sphenacodonts as *Dimetrodon*, and are more primitive than the South African titanosuchids to be considered later (p. 371). *Deuterosaurus*, described by Nopcsa (1926) as 'intermediate between the mainly North American Pelycosaurians and the South African deinocephalians', is placed by Efremov (1940) in the Tapinocephalidae which he derives from carnivorous animals not unlike titanosuchids. A further development is shown by *Venjukovia*, a genus originally based on a fragmentary mandible (Amalitzky, 1922). On the new evidence of a complete lower jaw and the anterior half of a well-preserved skull, Efremov (1950 E) places the genus in the Tapinocephalidae. Watson (1942) goes further and shows that the mandible is essentially that of an anomodont reptile, and that the general character of the dentition and the structure of the palate might be derived from a primitive tapinocephalid type. He adds that the evolution of *Venjukovia* from a tapinocephalid, and the latter from a sphenacodont pelycosaur demands a considerable time-interval and therefore this Russian horizon is later than the Clear Fork Beds of Texas.

In a higher horizon of the Copper-bearing Sandstones *Venjukovia* and *Titanophoneus* are associated with *Phthinosaurus*, regarded by Efremov (1940) as a pelycosaur, but interpreted by Watson (1942) as intermediate between the sphenacodonts and the gorgonopsids. It shows features consistent with the general reduction of all parts of the skull lying below the brain which is one of the characteristic evolutional trends leading to the cynodonts and higher mammal-like reptiles generally and ultimately the mammals. The tapinocephalid *Deuterosaurus* is replaced by the more advanced *Ulemosaurus* in which the huge incisor teeth have developed into a crushing mechanism.

The next horizon is represented in the Kazan Beds of Mesen on the eastern shores of the White Sea. It is linked to earlier horizons by the persistence of the labyrinthodonts *Platyops* and *Melosaurus* which are referred to the family Eryopidae. There are two small cotylosaurs, *Nycteroleter* and *Nyctiphruretus*, which, in skull structure recall the common form of the smaller Texan cotylosaurs, but also resemble the later procolophonids of South Africa. *Mesenosaurus* (Efremov, 1940), a small reptile having a low triangular skull and uniform dentition, is apparently a pelycosaur, but according to Watson (1942) it is far removed from any other member of the group. As a whole, this fauna is peculiar in character, and represents a development quite different from those in other parts of Russia.

Numerous localities in Russia, including that on the northern Dwina made famous by Amalitzky (1900), have yielded an abundance of Pareiasauria, large heavily built cotylosaurs with short and stout limbs. The older Russian forms have been referred by Weinberg (1930) to the South African genera *Anthodon* and *Pareiasuchus* but Efremov (1940) considers that the only genus actually present differs from *Anthodon* though closely related to it. Another form from a higher horizon is named *Scutosaurus* (Weinberg, 1930) in allusion to the armour of exceptionally large scutes. The anomodont *Dicynodon* (Owen, 1845), the cynodont *Dvinia* (Amalitzky, 1900), the large gorgonopsid *Inotransevia* (Pravoslavlev, 1927), and the Therocephalian *Anna* (Amalitzky, 1927), all with heterodont dentition indicate the variety of this reptilian association. The labyrinthodonts are represented by the rhachitome *Dvinosaurus* (Amalitzky, 1924 A) and the Seymouriamorph *Kotlassia* (Amalitzky, 1924 B) which probably includes the *Karpinskiosaurus* of Sushkin (1925). The flora associated with these tetrapods (Zeiller 1899) is noteworthy because it includes such plants as *Gangamopteris major*, *G. cyclopteroides*, *Glossopteris angustifolia*, *Gl. stricta*, *Gl. indica*, and *Vertebraria*, the association being different from the contemporary *Walchia-Callipteris* association of central Europe, but very similar to the corresponding flora of India and the southern continents. Furthermore, species of the lamellibranch genera *Palaeomutela*, *Palaeodonta*, &c. (Amalitzky, 1895), may also be compared with their southern congeners. The relations of these floras and faunas must be considered in connexion with those of the southern continents (pp. 375–6).

Meanwhile we must refer to a similar but unique reptilian fauna described (E. T. Newton, 1893) from Upper Permian sandstone at Cutties Hillock, east of Elgin, Scotland. The species are *Gordonia juddiana* and four others of the same genus, *Geikia elginense*, and *Elginia mirabilis*. *Gordonia* is a close ally of *Dicynodon* and shows agreement in basic features with forms from the Upper Permian of north Russia and South Africa but has very small tusks. *Geikia* is derived from *Dicynodon* by the development of horns on the nasals: this tendency is seen to a less degree in the presence of slight thickenings or even distinct knobs on the nasal bones of South African dicynodonts. *Elginia* is similarly allied to *Pareiasaurus*, a South African cotylosaur with relatives in the Upper Permian deposits of north Russia; neither African nor Russian forms, however, are so highly ornamented as *Elginia* which represents the acme of spinosity in this group of reptiles.

The highest beds of the Permian sequence in Russia are marked by an abundance of labyrinthodonts. These are structurally intermediate between the typical Lower Permian Rhachitomi and the Lower Triassic Stereospondyli; hence Efrenov (1940) refers them to a new group, the Neorhachitomi. The best-known genus is *Benthosuchus*, which is extraordinarily abundant at some localities. Efremov believes this form to be essentially ancestral to *Mastodonsaurus*, and Watson (1942) states that other animals of the group 'have every appearance of being the immediate ancestors of *Capitosaurus* and *Trematosaurus* or *Trematosuchus*' which occur in Lower Triassic strata of Germany, Russia, and South Africa.

THE PERMIAN TETRAPOD FAUNAS OF THE SOUTHERN CONTINENTS AND INDIA

The late Palaeozoic deposits of SOUTH AFRICA are grouped in the Karroo system, and rest unconformably on an eroded surface of the Precambrian foundation (Map, Fig. 55). The lowest series, the Dwyka Beds, consist of a tillite of glacial origin, which is probably of late Carboniferous age (p. 335). The succeeding Ecca Series, of early Permian age, contains an important assemblage of plants, the Glossopteris flora, which is widely distributed in the southern continents and India (p. 332). It is only in the Beaufort Series, after the establishment of the Glossopteris flora, that tetrapod

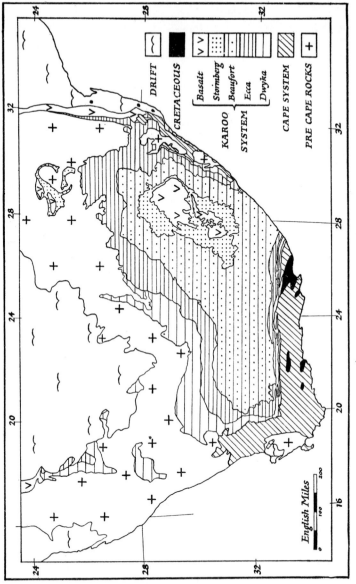

DRIFT

CRETACEOUS

KAROO
SYSTEM
{ Basalt
Stormberg
Beaufort
Ecca
Dwyka

CAPE SYSTEM

PRE CAPE ROCKS

English Miles
0   100   200

Fig. 55. Geological Sketch-Map of the Karroo System, South Africa

remains become abundant: they evidently represent migrants from an outside source.

The great mass of the Beaufort Beds, some 8,000 feet in thickness, is divisible into six palaeontological zones, each marked by a particular assemblage of tetrapods.

3 Upper Beaufort	— Cynognathus zone	
	Procolophon	,,
2 Middle Beaufort	— Lystrosaurus	,,
1 Lower Beaufort	— Cistecephalus	,,
	— Endothiodon	,,
	— Tapinocephalus	,,

The Tapinocephalus zone is named from the abundance of the deino-cephalian *Tapinocephalus*, which is associated with fifteen other genera of the group. It seems significant that all these genera are peculiar to South Africa, and that in certain characters of the skull they are more advanced than the Russian tapinocephalids already noted (p. 367). With them is *Anningia*, a small synapsid; the only known skull is imperfect, but Romer and Price (1940) compare it with the North American pelycosaur *Varanops*. Broom (1910, 1914), Haughton (1930), Watson (1930), Romer and Price (1940) all agree that the North American pelycosaurs are more primitive than, and hence structually ancestral to, the South African therapsids. Fifteen genera of therocephalians are recorded from the zone, and they also are restricted to South Africa, but *Scylacosaurus* is said to be related to the Russian genus *Anna* (Amalitsky, 1927). There are also three large, slightly armoured pareiasaurians which are not comparable with any of the Russian forms. The African zone is not easy to correlate with any of the Russian zones, but is probably equivalent to the pelycosaur zone of Russia.

The Endothiodon zone, around the town of Beaufort West, has yielded numerous remains of *Endothiodon* and other large forms of the same anomo-dont family. The index-genus has been recorded also from Tanganyika Territory (Haughton, 1932). In the upper part of the zone there are other endothiodont genera of smaller size, associated with dicynodonts of medium size. There are also several genera of peculiar gorgonopsids, and other forms of this group are known from Nyasaland (Haughton, 1926). The eight genera of therocephalians recorded from the zone are likewise re-stricted to Africa. The stegocephalian *Rhinesuchus* which persists from Lower to Middle Beaufort Beds has a wider distribution, for it is cited (Woodward, 1932) from Permian rocks of south Madagascar and Rhenish Prussia and even as high as Lower Triassic at Vologda, Russia. At present, however, the Endothiodon zone has not been recognized outside Africa.

The Cistecephalus zone is marked by the occurrence of four species of *Cistecephalus* with broad depressed skull and toothless jaws. The genus seems to be confined to the lower part of the zone, and, although it is usually referred to the Dicynodontidae, A. S. Woodward (1932) states that it may represent a distinct family. There are also the pareiasaurs *Anthodon* and *Pareiasuchus*; it may be noted that Russian forms originally referred to the second genus are now regarded as near to but distinct from *Anthodon* (Efremov, 1940). Higher beds of the Cistecephalus zone contain large species of *Dicynodon*, such as *D. tigriceps*, together with several genera of gorgonopsians and therocephalians. The genera of the last two groups and most of the dicynodonts are peculiar to South Africa, but *Dicynodon* is recorded also from Russia and an allied genus is known from Scotland (p. 369). The pareiasaur *Propappus*, with large, slightly sculptured, bony scutes on the back also occurs here, and it may be that the typical *Pareiasaurus serridens* (Owen, 1876) is not far removed stratigraphically. These armoured forms may be compared with the Russian *Scutosaurus*, and the African cynodont *Cynosuchus* with the Russian *Dvinia* and *Permocynodon*. Hence, as Watson (1942) concludes, the Cistecephalus zone may well correspond with the Pareiasaur zone of Russia.

In the Lystrosaurus zone, species of the index-genus are by far the commonest fossils. They are occasionally associated with other dicynodont genera, *Prolystrosaurus*, *Dicynodon*, and *Myosaurus*, for example. Six genera of cynodonts are also recorded, all of them rare and, so far, unknown outside South Africa. The presence of the thecodont *Chasmatosaurus* is worthy of note, because the genus has been discovered, associated with *Lystrosaurus*, at Sinkiang, China (C. C. Young, 1936). *Lystrosaurus* is also known in India (as *Dicynodon orientalis*) and Indochina (as *D. incisivum*). The labyrinthodonts are represented in the Lystrosaurus zone by occasional specimens of *Rhinesuchus* and *Lydekkerina* (Watson, 1919): the former has a wide distribution, having been recorded from Madagascar, Nyasaland, Cape Province, Rhenish Prussia, and Russia. The zone is correlated on stratigraphical grounds with the Benthosuchus zone of Russia which is marked by the abundance of labyrinthodonts (p. 369).

In the Procolophon zone the index-genus is the only common form. It is a little lizard-shaped reptile, about 18 inches long, with a broad triangular skull. This late cotylosaur is closely related to the Russian genera *Nyctiphuretus* and *Nycteroleter* (p. 368), which are more primitive in all respects and therefore indicative of procolophonid ancestry. Another close ally is *Telerpeton* from the Triassic rocks of Elgin, Scotland, and other genera of the family are cited from Switzerland, Germany and North America (Woodward, 1932). Of the two labyrinthodont genera recorded from the zone, *Micropholis* is so far restricted to South Africa, but *Capitosaurus* is widespread in the Lower Trias of Europe and Siberia (p. 550).

The Cynognathus zone is distinguished by the presence of cynodonts (including the index-genus), large dicynodonts of the genus *Kannemeyeria*, and the thecodont *Erythrosuchus*. The twenty genera of reptiles recorded from this zone are all peculiar to South Africa, but the cynodont *Gompho-*

gnathus is assigned to the same family as the genus *Gomphodontosuchus* from Brazil. It has been stated (Dutoit, 1926) that the African *Erythrosuchus* is closely allied to the Brazilian *Scaphonyx*, but according to Woodward (1932) and Romer (1945) the former is a thecodont while *Scaphonyx* is a rhynchosaurian, like the African genera *Howesia* and *Mesosuchus*. Eight labyrinthodont genera are recorded, two of which, namely, *Capitosaurus* and *Cyclotosaurus*, are typical of the Lower Trias of Europe (Watson, 1919); the last genus occurs in Spitzbergen and Australia also. There is little doubt that the Cynognathus zone of South Africa is the equivalent of the Capitosaurus zone of Russia.

The Beaufort Beds therefore represent the upper part of the European Permian and the lower part of the Triassic system: the later portion of the Trias is represented by the Stormberg Series in South Africa. The Beaufort tetrapods, which include the greatest variety of anomodont genera yet recorded from one region, are mostly unknown outside Africa. Formerly, the origin of the fauna was attributed to an unknown southern source, but in the last two decades earlier forms have been discovered in Russia, and some of them indicate a northern ancestry for the African animals. After migration southwards into virgin country, these tetrapods apparently evolved on lines of their own and so gave rise to the peculiar Beaufort fauna, the vast majority of the genera, certainly over 90 per cent., being unknown elsewhere.

Nevertheless, it has been repeatedly stated that the corresponding faunas of India, South America, and Australia are closely related to the African assemblage. Indeed, the supposed relationship has been considered to support the view that the southern continents and India were united into a single huge continent (known as Gondwanaland) during late Palaeozoic and early Mesozoic time. It is therefore necessary to examine the records of tetrapods from these regions.

INDIA. The scarcity of tetrapods in the Gondwana beds of India is in startling contrast with their abundance in the Karroo beds of Africa. This is probably due to unfavourable conditions for preservation of the remains.

The earliest Indian labyrinthodont is *Gondwanasaurus bijoriensis* (Lydekker, 1879) from the Raniganj Beds of the Damuda Series. It is a rhachitomous form of the family Rhinesuchidae, genera of which have a wide distribution in the Permian system of Europe and Africa (p. 371). The Gangamopteris Beds of Kashmir, not far distant in point of age, have yielded two other rhachitomes, *Archegosaurus ornatus* (A. S. Woodward, 1905) and *Actinodon risinensis* (Wadia and Swinton, 1928). Species of both genera are recorded from the Lower Permian of central Europe, and other genera of the same families are known from Permian strata in North America. A century ago, a stegocephalian skull, *Brachyops laticeps* (Owen, 1854) was obtained from the Mangli Beds at the base of the Panchet Series (Lower Trias), and other genera of the Brachyopidae have been described from Triassic strata in South Africa, Australia, and central Europe. At a higher horizon the Panchet Beds have yielded two species of *Gonioglyptus* (T. H. Huxley, 1865; Lydekker, 1885) and one of *Glyptognathus* (Lydekker, 1885). These genera are assigned to the Trematosauridae, a family with other genera in the Trias of Russia, Spitzbergen, Siberia, and Africa. Another form, *Pachygonia incurvata* (Huxley, 1865) belongs to the family Mastodonsauridae which is best known from the Trias of Europe, though fragmentary remains from South Africa are tentatively referred to it. Among reptiles, the so-called *Dicynodon orientalis* from Bengal (Huxley, 1865), and a similar form, *D. incisivum*, from Indo-China are either closely allied to, or congeneric with, *Lystrosaurus*, which is typical of the Middle Beaufort Beds of South Africa. Reptilian remains from higher beds, which show similar relationship with northern forms, are discussed in Chapter XIV.

The records of tetrapods from the Permian and Lower Trias of India are too few for a definite statement on affinities of the fauna. It may, however, be noted that relationship with Europe is at least as strong as with Africa. Moreover, all the Indian forms belong to families that are known to have had a widespread geographical distribution.

AUSTRALIA. The Kamilaroi system of Australia has yielded few tetrapod remains though the Glossopteris flora, and its successor the Thinnfeldia flora in the Hawkesbury Sandstone, are well represented (pp. 333–343).

The earliest Australian tetrapod so far recorded is the labyrinthodont *Bothriceps major* (A. S. Woodward, 1909) from an oil-shale in the Newcastle Series (Upper Permian). It differs in its more primitive structure from the early Triassic *Batrachosaurus* (Broom, 1903) of South Africa, but resembles the Indian *Brachyops* from the base of the Panchet Series. A smaller form called *Platyceps wilkinsoni* (Stephens, 1859) from the Narrabean stage of the Hawkesbury Sandstone has also been compared with the Indian *Brachyops* and, according to A. S. Woodward (1932) may be the young of *Bothriceps*. Another species *B. australis* from the Hawkesbury Sandstone is quite distinct from the South African rhachitome *Lydekkerina* (Broom, 1915) which was originally referred to the genus *Bothriceps*.

A skull obtained from the Hawkesbury Sandstone is provisionally referred to *Capitosaurus*, a labyrinthodont genus which is known from the Lower Trias of Europe, Siberia, and South Africa. The Wianamatta stage has yielded a complete skeleton of *Cyclotosaurus*, about 11 feet in length. D. M. S. Watson (1919) considers this form to be more primitive than *C. robustus* from the Lower Keuper of Wurtemburg: another species is described (Wiman, 1914) from the Triassic rocks of Spitzbergen.

Thus, the affinities of the Australian Permian tetrapods, so far as they can be judged from the scanty records, lie rather with genera of the northern hemisphere than with southern forms. The absence of anomodonts is particularly noteworthy, though it may be due to incomplete exploration. The presence of marine beds of late Palaeozoic and early Mesozoic age in New Zealand and the East Indies (pp. 387–8, 424–5) seems to indicate that Australia was already isolated from the other southern continents during the Permian period.

SOUTH AMERICA. In the Santa Catharina system of Brazil remains of tetrapods are scarce, and, so far, are only known from deposits of Triassic age.

The Botucatu Sandstone has long ago yielded the rhynchosaurian genus *Scaphonyx* (A. S. Woodward, 1908). More recently Huene (1929) has collected and described several additional forms from the Rio del Rasto red shales at Santa Maria, Rio Grande do Sul, namely, species of *Cephalastron, Cephalastronius, Cephalonia, Scaphonychimus,* and *Scaphonyx.* According to A. S. Woodward (1935) the discovery of these large rhynchosaurians, which have not yet been recorded from Africa, favours the supposition that the early Mesozoic faunas of the southern continents did not live on one continuous land area. It may be noted that typical representatives of the Rhynchosauridae are known from the Triassic rocks of Germany, Britain, and India, while the only two South African genera, *Howesia* and *Mesosuchus,* assigned to the Rhynchosauridae are regarded by Haughton (1925) and Huene (1929) as belonging to a distinct, though closely related family.

A cynodont reptile *Gomphodontosuchus braziliensis* (Huene, 1928) from the same Brazilian formation is said to be closely related to the South African *Gomphognathus.* These cynodonts, which were probably insectivorous or mixed feeders, are placed in the family Diademodontidae which is unknown outside Africa and South America. A giant dicynodont *Stahleckeria potens* (Huene, 1933), allied to *Kannemeyeria,* increases the resemblance to the South African fauna, but as typical dicynodonts resembling *Kannemeyeria* in skeletal features have also been found in Arizona (C. L. Camp, 1933) the Brazilian form may indicate an independent immigration from the north (A. S. Woodward, 1935).

In attempting an interpretation of the records of Permian tetrapods in the southern continents it is convenient to take the largest fauna as a standard of reference. The Beaufort Series of South Africa has yielded about 147 genera, of which only seven, that is, 5 per cent., are recorded outside Africa. The most conspicuous element is formed by the Therapsida, including the deinocephalian titanosuchids and tapinocephalids, the gorgonopsians, the dicynodonts, and lastly the cynodonts. All these show in their skeletal structure many resemblances to that of the mammals. They are associated with specialized cotylosaurs, particularly the pareiasaurians and procolophonids, besides smaller groups. Until late in the nineteenth century such animals, and the accompanying Glossopteris flora, were almost unknown in the Permian rocks of the northern hemisphere. It was perhaps natural to suppose that this fauna had a southern origin, though in South Africa it was clearly immigrant at the beginning of Beaufort time.

Then, in 1893-4, E. T. Newton described the Permian fauna of Elgin, Scotland, which includes pareiasaurians and dicynodonts closely related to South African forms. A similar discovery was made by Amalitzky (1900-27) on the banks of the northern Dwina near Archangel, Russia. These animals were regarded by many authors as migrants from the south. In 1926, F. Nopcsa pointed out that the genus *Deuterosaurus* from the Permian Kupferschiefer of Russia is intermediate in structure between the North American pelycosaurs and the South African Deinocephalia. From the same strata he described typical deinocephalians which are more primitive than the African forms. He therefore suggested that the South African fauna originated in the north. This view was supported by D. M. S. Watson (1930) who stated that the tetrapods provide no basis for a belief in a Gondwanaland. The more recent discoveries in Russia (Efremov, 1940; Watson, 1942) have amply confirmed these statements. In considering the route of migration between Russia and Africa it may be recalled that the tableland of Arabia is part of the African Shield, and that the Red Sea is of comparatively late origin.

The presence of a dicynodont in the Panchet Beds of India, reported in 1865, is a link with the African Permian tetrapods, and similar forms are known from Indo-China, and Sinkiang, China. The occurrence in the Indian strata of labyrinthodonts allied to contemporary European forms seems to indicate that migration was from Russia rather than Africa. Similarly, the few Australian records, which do not include dicynodonts, may be explained by migration from south-eastern Asia.

No Permian tetrapods are reported from South America, but Triassic Beds in Brazil have yielded a large dicynodont resembling a South African form. But A. S. Woodward (1935) has pointed out that typical dicynodonts are now known from Arizona (C. L. Camp, 1933) and provide the possibility of independent migration from the north. At the same time Woodward mentions the presence in the Trias of Brazil of large rhynchosaurians, a group which is unknown in the African strata: he infers that the African and Brazilian faunas did not live on a continuous land-area.

LITERATURE

The older genera mentioned above are listed by A. S. Woodward in the Zittel-Eastman *Text-book of Palaeontology*, vol. ii, 1932. Newer names are given in the text-book of *Vertebrate Palaeontology* by A. S. Romer, 2nd edition, Chicago, 1945, and in the *Catalogue of Fossil Vertebrates* cited on p. 575 below. Important papers mentioned above are: 'The Amphibian Fauna from South Joggins, Nova Scotia' by M. C. Steen, *Proc. Zool. Soc.*, pp. 465-504, 1934; 'The Fossil Amphibia from the Gas Coal of Nyrany . . . Czechoslovakia', by M. C. Steen, ibid., pp. 206-83, 1938; 'Review of the Pelycosauria' by A. S. Romer & L. W. Price, *Geol. Soc. Amer. Spec. Paper* No. 28, 1940; 'Permian and Triassic Tetrapods' by D. M. S. Watson, *Geol. Mag.* vol. lxxix, pp. 81-116, 1942.

X

PERMIAN FAUNAS

ON account of their general lithological features the strata lying between the Carboniferous and Jurassic systems in Britain were first grouped as the New Red Sandstone—the analogue of the Old Red Sandstone below the Carboniferous. The rocks are mainly of continental origin, and though marine limestones occur in some districts, they are of unusual type. Several distinct facies are presented by the New Red Sandstone, and, in consequence, the detailed correlation of isolated outcrops is often a matter of difficulty. In 1841 Murchison proposed a twofold division of the New Red strata, a lower series containing a fauna of Palaeozoic aspect, and an upper series which was placed as the lowermost system of the Mesozoic Group. The lower series was found to be especially well developed in the province of Perm (east Russia), and the name Permian was therefore applied to that rock-formation. This did not find favour in Germany, where the equivalent rocks, known to the old miners as Rothliegende and Zechstein, were grouped as the Dyassic system. The upper three divisions of the New Red Sandstone were similarly grouped as the Triassic system, but the middle division (Muschelkalk) of Germany is not recognizable in Britain. Thus the customary classification of the British New Red Sandstone becomes:

Trias	{ Keuper (including the Rhaetic Beds).
	{ Bunter.
Permian	{ Upper [= Zechstein].
	{ Lower [= Rothliegende]—missing in Britain.

For many years the Lower Permian was supposed to lie unconformably on the Coal Measures, but detailed mapping has shown that in many districts the two series are conformable. As a consequence, much of the British 'Lower Permian' is now referred to the Upper Coal Measures. The Upper Permian Beds, however, are always unconformable to the strata on which they rest (Map, Fig. 56). R. L. Sherlock (1926–8) has produced evidence which (he believes) tends to show that some of the strata generally referred to the Upper Permian are replaced laterally by the Bunter of other areas. Unfortunately, fossils are scarce in many districts and, so far, the discussion has been based entirely upon the persistence of certain lithological features at estimated distances below the base of the Rhaetic Beds. It may be recalled in passing that the marine Rhaetic Beds are transgressive, and therefore their base, however convenient as a datum-line in mapping, does not neces-

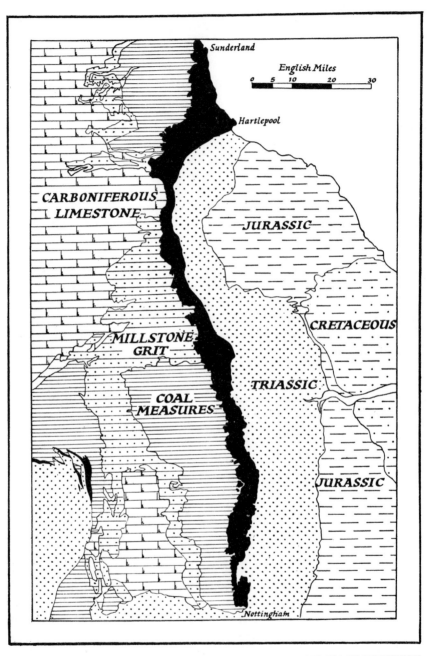

FIG. 56. SKETCH-MAP SHOWING RELATIONS OF PERMIAN STRATA IN NORTHERN
ENGLAND (based on maps of the Geological Survey by permission of the Director)

sarily represent a time-plane. Since Sherlock has revived old controversies in seeking to abolish the Permian system, analysis of the faunal evidence is, at the present time, of more than ordinary interest. It may be noted at once that the Magnesian Limestone encloses a characteristic fauna, while the Bunter of Nottinghamshire is almost barren of fossils. Consequently, if the two series are truly equivalent, it would seem more logical to assign the unfossiliferous Bunter to the Permian system.

The chief repository of marine fossils in British Permian rocks is the Magnesian Limestone Series of Durham. The succession in this area, consisting mainly of dolomitic limestones, may be briefly summarized thus:

Highest bedded Limestone Concretionary Limestone . }	Fauna limited to a few mollusca.
Upper Shell Limestone .	Highly fossiliferous, but with a restricted and dwarfed fauna.
Main Shell Limestone .	Profusely fossiliferous with a fully developed fauna. Masses of polyzoa.
Lower Limestones . .	Generally dolomitic, with few poorly preserved fossils.
Marl Slate . . .	Numerous fish remains, but few other fossils.
Yellow Sands . . .	Unfossiliferous. Resting on eroded surface of Coal Measures and older Carboniferous rocks.

The known fauna of the Marl Slate consists almost entirely of fishes, the genera *Platysomus*, *Palaeoniscus*, and *Pygopterus* being characteristic. *Lingula credneri* Gein. is the only recorded brachiopod, and other invertebrate remains are indeterminable.

The life-assemblage preserved in the Magnesian Limestone is often profuse in individuals, but shows significant limitations, when considered in conjunction with the peculiar lithology of the beds. The majority of the invertebrates belong to genera that were already established in the Carboniferous faunas. First consider the brachiopods, of which twenty species are recorded. The genus *Productus* is represented by *P. horridus* J. Sow., a quadrate species with a median furrow, prominent ears, and extreme development of spines. Various species of *Strophalosia*, spinose productoid shells, were cemented to various objects by their ventral umbones. *Spirifer alatus* (Schl.), a transversely elongate form, with rounded, striate ribs and an almost smooth median furrow, frequently occurs in the Main Shell Limestones. Species of *Camarophoria*, pentamerid shells with a rhynchonelliform shape, are also characteristic, though the genus ranges up from Carboniferous strata. The athyrid *Cleiothyris pectinifera* (J. de C. Sow.), distinguished by its spinose concentric lamellae, is another typical form, and the smooth terebratulid *Dielasma elongata* (Schl.) is one of the most abundant shells. Traced upwards, these brachiopods gradually become extinct, and are entirely unknown from the uppermost limestones. The larger forms,

Spirifer alatus (Schl.) and *Cleiothyris pectinifera* (J. de C. Sow.), are the first
to disappear, and are not long survived by *Productus horridus* J. Sow. and
the larger species of *Camarophoria*. The genera *Dielasma* and *Strophalosia*
persist longest, but are much dwarfed in the higher beds.

The same phenomenon is presented by the thirty recorded species of
lamellibranchs, but these, presumably more adaptable organisms, persisted
longer than the brachiopods. Indeed, *Pleurophorus costatus* (Brown), an
elongated, sparsely ribbed shell, occurs throughout the Magnesian Limestone Series along with species of *Mytilus* and *Schizodus*. The latter genus is
allied to the well-known Mesozoic *Trigonia*, being connected by the Triassic
Myophoria, but is smooth and the lateral hinge-teeth are not fluted. The
genus has a long vertical range, but is most abundantly represented in
Permian faunas. The genus *Bakewellia*, comprising small, obliquely elongate
shells with serial ligament-pits, appears to be restricted to Permian rocks;
several species are known from the Magnesian Limestone, and they partake,
along with species of *Byssoarca*, of the general dwarfing in the higher beds.
Certain gastropods, including some twenty-five species of shells assigned to
Turbo, Natica, Rissoa, Pleurotomaria, and other genera, occur in profusion
in the upper beds. Cephalopods are rare, only two nautiloid species being
known. A few corals are recorded, but their place as rock-formers seems to
be taken by the polyzoa, which often occur in large masses; *Fenestella* and
Synocladia are prominent genera. The Magnesian Limestone as a whole
seems to have been formed as reef-knolls, similar to those in the Lower
Carboniferous of Clitheroe. The sea in which they were deposited was
apparently cut off from the main ocean, and, gradually diminishing in area,
became increasingly saline with precipitation of sulphates. These unfavourable conditions are reflected in the gradual impoverishment of the fauna
and the general dwarfing of the persistent species. It is evident that the
characters of the British Permian faunas are no more representative of the
marine life of the period than the fauna of the modern Caspian Sea is typical
of present day marine assemblages. In order to obtain true perspective it
is necessary to look farther afield.

FAUNAL REGIONS

The German Rothliegende of terrestrial origin is typically developed in
the mining district of Mansfeld. It is composed chiefly of conglomerates,
sandstones, and shales, usually red in colour due to the prevalence of iron
oxide. The fossils are remains of land plants and tetrapod animals which
are discussed in Chapters VIII and IX respectively. Sometimes the Rothliegende lies conformably on the Productive Coal Measures, as in the
region of the Saar and Nahe, between the Devonian Schiefergebirge on the
north and the Trias of the Palatinate in the south. In some districts east of
the Schiefergebirge, to the north of the Thuringerwald, and again in
Saxony, the Rothliegende lies unconformably on steeply inclined Devonian

and Carboniferous strata. It probably extends northwards under the Neozoic rocks of the German Plain, for in the neighbourhood of Oslo A. Hoeg (1934, 1936) has discovered an early Permian flora associated with non-marine lamellibranchs which E. Dix and A. E. Trueman (1935) have provisionally assigned to the genus *Palaeodonta*.

The Zechstein deposits are best developed in Thuringia where four divisions are recognized. The series begins with a thin basal conglomerate which rarely contains fossils. Then follows the Kupferschiefer, bituminous shales containing copper pyrites for which they have long been mined. This bed is famous for the abundance of fishes, especially *Palaeoniscus* and *Platysomus*, and in this respect is like the equivalent Marl Slate in England. The succeeding Zechstein Limestone, with dolomitic beds of some thickness, has a fauna of few genera and species which are represented by great numbers of individuals. The most characteristic forms are brachiopods such as *Productus horridus*, *Spirifer alatus*, *Dielasma elongata*, and *Strophalosia goldfussi*, associated with mollusca, especially the bivalved genus *Schizodus*. Bryozoa are numerous in marginal reefs, but corals, echinoderms, and cephalopods are extremely rare. Hence there is considerable similarity with the Magnesian Limestone of north-east England. The final stage consists of red beds with dolomite, rock-salt, anhydrite, and carnallite which indicate saline concentration due to excess of evaporation over renewal of the sea water. This stage thickens in the north, as at Stassfurt in Saxony and in borings as far north as Memel, below the cover of Neozoic deposits. The eastern limit appears in Courland and farther south the Zechstein follows the margin of the Hercynian mountains, but apparently does not occur in France; it is recorded from borings in Holland and, as noted above, it is represented in north-eastern England. The general distribution of these rocks in Europe is shown in Fig. 57.

The marine Zechstein deposits of Germany are intercalated between formations of terrestrial origin, namely the Palaeopermian Rothliegende below, and the Palaeotriassic Bunter Series above. The Zechstein therefore represents a temporary transgression of the sea over a considerable land surface in central Europe. The lack of balance and variety in the Zechstein fauna, as well as the general dwarfing of the fossils show that the fauna must have existed under peculiar conditions—usually interpreted as excessive salinity of the sea water. We must now discuss the larger faunas, which are widely distributed in marine strata of southern Europe and other regions, and their relations with the restricted German assemblages. At the same time it is necessary to establish the full succession of marine Permian faunas as revealed by the ammonoids and the fusuline foraminifera.

Permian rocks have a considerable distribution in RUSSIA along the western slopes of the Ural Mountains between the Kirghiz steppe and the Arctic Ocean. After a summary of recent work by M. K. Elias (1937) it is evident that the record of late Palaeozoic rocks in this area is more complete than was formerly supposed. The strata to which the name Permian was originally given are underlaid by a series of sandstones which were named the Artinsk grits by Murchison and his associates (1841) who regarded them as equivalent to the English Millstone Grit. In 1874 A. Karpinsky showed that the fossils, especially the ammonoids, enclosed in these rocks, are distinct from typical Carboniferous forms, but similar to homotaxial faunas in parts of southern Europe. Karpinsky (1889) therefore added the

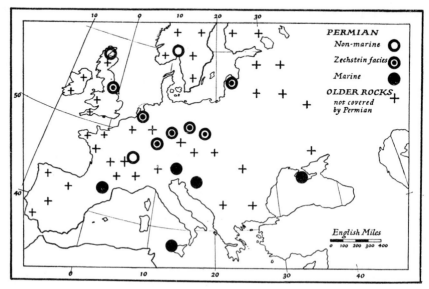

FIG. 57. SKETCH-MAP OF EUROPE SHOWING GENERAL DISTRIBUTION OF PERMIAN ROCKS

Artinsk stage to the Permian system. The lower beds are now placed in a separate Sakmara stage as a result of fresh analysis of the ammonoids by V. E. Ruzencev (1936); this is considered to be the basal stage of the Permian system.

The ammonoids have long been recognized as reliable guide-fossils for these rocks, but differences of opinion have existed concerning their relationships. Now there seems to be general agreement that the main groups of Permian ammonoids are derived from two Carboniferous stocks; the most conspicuous developmental feature in all of the genera is the gradual and progressive subdivision of the sutural lobes. One group is apparently derived from the great family Goniatitidae which, through *Dimorphoceras*, probably gave rise to the Permian family Thalassoceratidae, and through *Schistoceras* to the Perrinitidae, Popanoceratidae, and Cyclolobidae. From the same stock, the Gastrioceratidae, already established at Neocarboniferous horizons, persist through the Permian in the genera *Eoasianites*,

Paragastrioceras, and *Pseudogastrioceras.* The Adrianitidae and Agathi-ceratidae both resemble the Popanoceratidae but their precise relationship is still a matter for debate. The second group arose from the Carboniferous Prolecanitidae and its collateral the Pronoritidae. The main stock seems to lead through the smooth evolute Paralecanitidae to the Neopermian families Xenodiscidae and Paraceltitidae, members of which in their turn are ancestral to certain Palaeotriassic families (p. 405). The Carboniferous Pro-noritidae persist into Permian horizons and lead to the Medlicottidae on the one hand, and, through *Sicanites* and its allies, to the Sageceratidae on the other. Characteristic members of these families may be used, with the fusu-line foraminifera, in an attempt to piece together the fragmentary sections so far known into a chronological succession.

The ammonoids of the Sakmara stage include representatives of both groups just cited, as shown by the following list of genera:

> Thalassoceratidae: *Thalassoceras.*
> Popanoceratidae: *Popanoceras, Peritrochia.*
> Gastrioceratidae: *Eoasianites, Paragastrioceras.*
> Agathiceratidae: *Agathiceras.*
> Pronoritidae: *Pronorites.*
> Medlicottidae: *Propinacoceras, Artinskia.*

Fusuline foraminifera are mainly species of *Pseudoschwagerina, Schwagerina* and its derivative *Paraschwagerina.* Towards the close of the stage there is a striking reduction in generic representation, and only a few forms of *Schwagerina* persist.

The Artinsk stage has a fauna of about 300 species, in which the most distinctive element is the cephalopod assemblage. Many of the genera of the Sakmara Beds persist in different species. Other notable features are the greater abundance of the medlicottids *Artinskia* and *Medlicottia,* the appearance of *Stacheoceras* and *Adrianites,* and the rarity of *Agathiceras.* Fusuline foraminifera are rare, for only a single species of *Schwagerina* is recorded, and this is apparently restricted to the lower beds of the stage. To the west, on the Ufa Plateau these detrital beds are replaced by a great thickness of limestone with a varied fauna of brachiopods, fusulinids, corals, &c. The characters of the brachiopods led Murchison (1841) and Tscherny-schew (1902) to refer the limestones to the Carboniferous system, but they are now known to contain ammonoids and fusulinids in common with the Artinsk stage. Such changes of facies have caused much confusion in the study of the Permian strata.

The succeeding Kungur stage, south-east of Perm, is a series of dolomitic limestones which contain brachiopods and mollusca similar to the preced-ing forms, but ammonoids are entirely unknown. Higher beds around Kazan, to which the name Permian was originally restricted, also contain brachiopods and lamellibranchs, but the fauna becomes progressively impoverished, and the mollusca of the uppermost Tartary Beds are exclusively non-marine lamellibranchs: the important series of tetrapod remains is discussed in Chapter IX. A similar development is seen in the Donetz where the Permian sequence is said to reach a thickness of 2,000 metres.

C. O. Dunbar (1941) remarks that 'this is a poor standard of international correlation, just because so much of it is non-marine'. The same objection, however, could be made with regard to the German Triassic succession. R. L. Sherlock (1950) objects to the addition of the Artinsk stage to Murchison's original Permian system, and would relegate it to the Carboniferous. The remainder of the Permian strata he would add to the Trias to form a new 'Epiric' system. From the palaeontological standpoint, however, the Permian is in itself an important system, containing an important chapter in the history of fusulinids and ammonoids. The new classification advocated by Sherlock would arbitrarily cut across the continuous evolution of these organisms at points which provide no critical episodes in their history. Indeed the established stratigraphical classification is strongly supported by modern palaeontological investigation.

Some 1,800 km. east of the Artinsk region, Permian fossils are known in Darwas, Bokhara, in marly and sandy calcareous rocks. The beds are said to be concordant with the Upper Carboniferous and to be followed conformably by Triassic strata. The lower division contains numerous brachiopods, notably *Productus gratiosus* and *Leptodus nobilis* which have a wide distribution in the Permian rocks of Asia. The ammonoids, including species of *Pronorites*, *Propinacoceras*, *Agathiceras*, *Popanoceras*, *Thalassoceras*, enabled A. Karpinsky to correlate this horizon with the Artinsk stage of Russia. Later, G. A. Dutkiewiez (1937) recognized four zones in Darwas, and reported the fusulinids *Parafusulina* and *Polydiexodina* from the uppermost zone. This apparently indicates a higher horizon, equivalent to the Capitan Beds in the Texan sequence, next to be discussed. It is evident, however, that the Permian rocks of Darwaz represent only a fragment of the complete succession, and the apparent conformity with Carboniferous and Triassic strata must be deceptive.

A considerable sequence of Permian strata has been described by P. B. and R. E. King (1931, 1934, 1938) in western TEXAS, where the rocks are exposed for about 150 miles (see Map, Fig. 58). Here the oldest member of the system is the Wolfcamp formation of shales and limestones which rests with angular unconformity on Neocarboniferous rocks. The Wolfcamp Beds have yielded fusulinids, including species of *Schwagerina*, *Paraschwagerina*, and *Pseudoschwagenina*. Among the ammonoids are species of *Thalassoceras*, *Peritrochia*, *Eoasianites*, *Paragastrioceras*, *Uddenites*, *Properrinites*, *Propinacoceras*, and *Artinskia* which have been described and illustrated by A. K. Miller and W. M. Furnish (1940). Some of them are related to Pennsylvanian forms, but *Artinskia* and *Properrinites* are restricted to Permian horizons; the fauna is correlated by F. B. Plummer (1937) with the

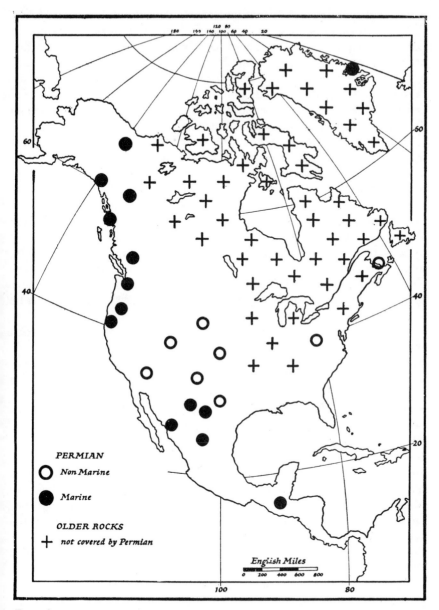

PERMIAN

◯ Non Marine

● Marine

OLDER ROCKS

+ not covered by Permian

English Miles

0   200   400   600   800

Fɪɢ. 58. sᴋᴇᴛᴄʜ-ᴍᴀᴘ ᴏꜰ ɴᴏʀᴛʜ ᴀᴍᴇʀɪᴄᴀ sʜᴏᴡɪɴɢ ɢᴇɴᴇʀᴀʟ ᴅɪsᴛʀɪʙᴜᴛɪᴏɴ
ᴏꜰ ᴘᴇʀᴍɪᴀɴ ʀᴏᴄᴋs

C C

Sakmara stage of Russia. The same genera of fusulinids are described by C. O. Dunbar and N. D. Newell (1946) from late Palaeozoic strata around Lake Titicaca in the central Andes of Bolivia and Peru. These rocks had been assigned to the Upper Carboniferous since the time of Orbigny (1842), but R. E. King (1931) recognized their Permian age while studying the Permian brachiopods of Texas. Dunbar and Newell confirm this observation in correlating the Bolivian strata with the Wolfcamp Beds of Texas on the evidence furnished by the fusulinids.

The Leonard stage, some 2,000 feet thick in western Texas, is separated from the underlying Wolfcamp Beds by a slight unconformity. The thickness decreases towards the east and the massive limestones grade laterally into the thinner bedded limestones formerly separated as the Hess formation. The Leonard Beds are marked by the abundance of *Perrinites hilli*, more rarely associated with *Medlicottia whitneyi*, *Adrianites defordi* and the aberrant brachiopod *Richthofenia*. The fusulinid assemblage is dominated by the large elongate *Parafusulina* which has evolved from *Schwagerina* by progressive specialization of the septa. The Leonard formation is commonly correlated with the Artinsk stage of Russia, but some authors believe that the Leonard is slightly younger than the Astinsk stage which may be assigned to the gap between the Wolfcamp and Leonard formations.

The Word stage of western Texas is 1,500 feet in thickness of which about half is limestone or dolomite, the remainder being shale and sandstone. The fauna is marked by large numbers of the genus *Parafusulina*, and, especially in the middle beds, by a rich assemblage of ammonoids. The large subglobular shells of *Waagenoceras*, with well-divided sutural lobes, make their appearance here, and are associated with species of *Stacheoceras*, *Medlicottia*, *Paraceltites*, *Adrianites*, *Agathiceras*, and *Paragastrioceras*. The brachiopods include species of the peculiar *Leptodus* and *Richthofenia*. In the Guadalupe Mountains the combined Leonard and Word formations are represented by the Delaware Mountain formation which, however, is not precisely equivalent to the formation of the same name in the Delaware Mountains. The Guadalupian fauna described by G. H. Girty (1908) contains a number of ammonoids which compare closely with those from the Word formation. A. K. Miller (1936) has recorded a few cephalopods from the upper part of the Cache Creek Series near Kamloops, British Columbia and C. O. Dunbar (1932) records *Neoschwagerina* from the same province. The ammonoid shells are not well preserved, but admit of reference to the genera *Propinacoceras*, *Agathiceras*, *Adrianites*, and probably *Paraceltites*. Miller regards the beds as the equivalent of part of the Word formation of Texas. Species of *Parafusulina*, allied to the Word forms are recorded by C. O. Dunbar (1939) from the reputed 'Carboniferous Limestone' of Guatemala, and the Permian age of this deposit is thereby established. A small ammonoid fauna, comprising species of *Peritrochia*, *Pseudogastrioceras*, and *Stacheoceras* from the Phosphoria Beds of western Wyoming has been described by A. K. Miller and L. M. Cline (1934) who suggest a relationship with the Word fauna.

Above the Delaware Mountain formation in the Guadalupe Mountains is a series of massive limestones, nearly 2,000 feet in thickness, known as the Capitan Limestone. Fossils occur sporadically, and many have apparently been destroyed by dolomitization. As described by G. H. Girty (1908), and summarized by P. B. King (1934), the fauna shows certain features which distinguish it from those lower in the succession. A large part of the fauna consists of brachiopods, many of which are unknown outside the Capitan Limestone. Sponges form a remarkable feature both in abundance and peculiar development. Bryozoa are moderately abundant but corals and echinoderms are rare. The ammonoid assemblage, cited by Miller and Furnish (1940), is related to that of the Word formation, and a few species, such as *Waagenoceras guadalupense*, are common to both horizons. In the Capitan stage, however, this genus is accompanied by its derivative *Timorites* which gives a special character to the fauna. Species of *Pseudogastrioceras* and *Medlicottia* are distinct from the Word forms, and the discoid evolute genera *Paraceltites*, *Cibolites*, and *Xenaspis* appear for the first time as an important element in the fauna. The Capitan fauna is also distinguished by a development of the large elongate fusulinids. *Parafusulina* continues from Word horizons but is gradually replaced by its derivative, the giant *Polydiexodina*, which develops a series of accessory tunnels. This specialized foraminifer has proved of value for purposes of correlation over a wide area outside America.

Fossiliferous Permian rocks on the island of TIMOR, East Indies, have yielded a great wealth of corals, bryozoa, echinoderms, brachiopods, cephalopods, &c., while limestones composed almost entirely of fusuline foraminifera are reported at some localities. The fossils are unusually well-preserved in limestone and marls which have a considerable admixture of fine-grained volcanic material. Apparently showers of volcanic dust buried the animals quite suddenly, so that the hard parts remain in perfect condition. Some 120 genera of echinoderms, including great numbers of the blastoid *Schizoblastus*, have been found, and as such remains are scanty in other Permian deposits it is hardly surprising that the great majority of the forms described by J. Wanner (1937) are unknown from the rest of the world. Brachiopods are numerous but have little stratigraphical value; spiriferids and productids are conspicuous, but *Leptodus* and *Richthofenia* are rare. The ammonoids, so far as they have been described by G. T. Haniel (1915) and J. P. Smith (1927) amount to about fifty species, the majority of which are new, distributed in twenty-three genera. Four distinct horizons or stages have been determined on the distribution of these shells; they are closely related by the overlapping ranges of the genera, but they have not yet been found superposed.

The ammonoid assemblages of the Somohole and Bitauni horizons include the genera *Marathonites* and *Vidrioceras*, which Miller and Furnish (1940) consider to be synonymous with *Peritrochia* and *Shumardites* respectively. The associated genera *Metalegoceras* and *Popanoceras* are also known to be widespread in early Permian deposits at distant localities. Hence the Somohole horizon is correlated with the Wolfcamp stage of Texas and the Sakmara stage of Russia; the presence of *Perrinites* in the Bitauni assemblage indicates equivalence with the Leonard stage of Texas. The most significant genus in the Basleo fauna is the cyclolobid *Waagenoceras* which, though rare in Timor, brings the horizon into comparison with the Sosio Beds of Sicily (p. 392), and the Word stage of Texas. The fusuline foraminifera described from the Basleo by M. L. Thompson (1949) include the genus *Parafusulina* which ranges from the upper part of the Leonard through the Word stage of Texas. The cyclolobid *Timorites* of the Amarassi horizon has been recognized outside Timor only in the Capitan stage of Texas. The four marine stages recognized in Texas are therefore represented in Timor, but as the stratigraphy is unknown they may be incomplete. Moreover, no younger Permian horizons are known in Timor, though such have been recognized in certain other sections.

Permian fossils are also reported from Letti, Savu, Rotti, and other islands in the East Indian Archipelago as well as from AUSTRALIA. C. Teichert (1942, 1944) has recorded ammonoids from three districts in Western Australia, namely *Metalegoceras* from the Irwin River, the same genus associated with *Thalassoceras* from the Kimberley district, *Paragastrioceras*, *Pseudogastrioceras*, and *Propinacocoeras* from the north-west district. These assemblages are correlated with the Sakmara and Artinsk stages of Russia. The equivalent deposits in New South Wales contain the peculiar molluscan genera *Eurydesma*, *Maeonia*, *Conularia*, &c., but no ammonoids; they are comparable with the Speckled Sandstone of the Salt Range, India (p. 301), and seem to indicate continuous marine connexion across or around the Indian Ocean between New South Wales and the Salt Range, but the assemblage is not known at intermediate localities. Many of the species occur again in the Upper Marine Series above an intercalated series of Coal Measures, but again no ammonoids are recorded.

Reverting to southern ASIA, the so-called 'Productus Limestone' of Sumatra has yielded to M. L. Thompson (1936) species of the fusulinid genera *Schwagerina* and *Pseudoschwagerina*, comparable with similar shells from China, Russia, and North America. Later forms from central and western Sumatra, and other places in southern and eastern Asia illustrate the development of other specialized fusulinids. The genera *Cancellina*, *Neoschwagerina*, *Yabeina*, and *Sumatrina* form a series which shows the progressive development of an elaborate system of pendent lamellae, called septula, by which the spiral chamber is subdivided into chamberlets. The most primitive genus, *Cancellina*, recorded from Indochina, China, and Japan, has a meridional series of septula crossing the true septa at right angles. In the subspherical *Neoschwagerina* the spiral chamber is subdivided by a network of septa and septula; this genus is widespread from China and Japan to Afghanistan and Sicily. *Yabeina*, from Japan, China, Tunisia, and Crimea, is a later specialized descendant of *Neoschwagerina* with modified wall-pendents. The elongate *Sumatrina* may be derived from a Neoschwagerine stock in which the alveolar texture of the wall and its pendents

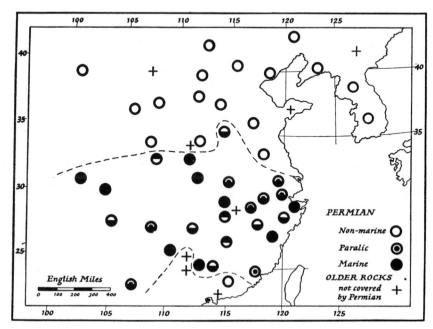

FIG. 59. SKETCH-MAP OF CHINA SHOWING GENERAL DISRIBUTION OF PERMIAN ROCKS

has been lost; this genus is known from Sumatra, south China, Japan, Afghanistan, and Sicily. In Afghanistan M. L. Thompson (1946) records *Neoschwagerina* in association with the giant *Polydiexodina*, and so apparently the Neoschwagerina–Sumatrina zone of Eurasia is to be correlated with the Polydiexodina horizon, that is, the Capitan stage of Texas. *Verbeekina*, originally described by H. Staff (1909) as a sub-genus of *Doliolina*, may belong to an independent line from *Staffella* to which it is connected by *Eoverbeekina*. The genus is associated with members of the *Neoschwagerina* lineage in Sumatra, Java, Indochina, China, Japan, Afghanistan, Turkestan, Turkey, Greece, and Sicily. C. O. Dunbar (1941) states that these fusulinids form a notable peculiarity in the later Permian faunas of southern Eurasia, though they are not recorded from the Salt Range, Russia, or the Alps. Certain contemporary groups of fossils, such as the brachiopods and ammonoids are not so restricted in geographical distribution. The isolation of the neoschwagerines cannot therefore be due to land-barriers alone, and their distribution may have been limited by the course of warm ocean-currents. This might also explain the presence of one species of *Yabeina* in British Columbia.

In the SALT RANGE of northern Punjab, India, Permian rocks show a fine development in the series known as the Productus Limestone. The fauna is extremely rich in brachiopods and these are associated with certain mollusca, corals, bryozoa, and echinoderms, but cephalopods are known only from the higher beds. Comparable strata exist in the central Himalayas, in Kashmir, and on the Tibetan frontier. The Productus Limestone rests on the Speckled Sandstone Series which contains a peculiar marine fauna, including the mollusca *Eurydesma, Conularia*, &c. comparable with Australian forms of early Permian age (p. 388): the Indian Geological Survey assign these beds to a late Carboniferous horizon. The Productus Limestone, referred to the Permian system has long been divided into three stages, and this arrangement is upheld in a review of the brachiopoda and mollusca by F. R. C. Reed (1944).

The lower Productus Limestone, or Amb stage, consists mainly of calcareous sandstone in which brachiopods are the most conspicuous fossils. Several of the species are identical or comparable with those in the Artinsk stage of Russia and in the Kamilaroi Series of Australia. Such species as the *Productus spiralis, Spirifer marcoui* and *Sp. niger* of W. Waagen (1882–5) are typical, and restricted to the Amb stage. The genus *Aulosteges* and the productid sub-genus *Taenitherus* are also confined to the stage, in which a species of *Dielasma* and *Marginifera* are specially abundant. On the evidence of the brachiopods H. D. Thomas (1929) believes that the Amb Beds correspond broadly with the Artinsk stage, but previous authors have held different opinions. Greater precision has resulted from a study of the oft-quoted '*Fusulina*' *kattaensis* by C. O. Dunbar (1933) who regards this foraminifer as a rather primitive representative of the genus *Parafusulina*. This determination brings the Lower Productus Limestone into correlation with the Leonard stage of Texas. Dunbar (1940) has described other species of *Parafusulina* from the Karakoram.

The Middle Productus Limestone, or Virgal stage, is distinguished by the presence of the orthotetid *Kiangsella*, the thecidiid *Leptodus* and the aberrant strophomenid *Richthofenia*. While the productid subgenera *Cancrinella* and *Haydenella*, with the spiriferid *Purdonella*, are confined to this and the lower stage, many other brachiopod species range into the next higher stage. Four ammonoids of different genera are cited by Reed (1944); *Palaeolecanites* is a new genus whose range is at present uncertain, *Paralegoceras* and *Paraceltites* are only provisionally identified, *Xenaspis carbonaria* Waagen is used as the index-fossil to this horizon which is taken as the lowest zone of the Neopermian Series. The last species is also recorded from the Zewan Beds of Kashmir, the Kuling Shales of the central Himalayas, and the Chitichun Limestone of Tibet. The discovery by H. Besaire (1936) of *Xenaspis* and *Cyclolobus* in Madagascar indicates direct marine communication across the Indian Ocean in mid-Permian time.

Ammonoids are more plentiful in the Upper Productus Limestone of the Salt Range, especially in the Chideru Beds at the top of the stage. Two of the species, namely, *Cyclolobus oldhami* and *Episageceras wynnei*, are used as indexes to successive zones; others, referred to the genera *Medlicottia*, *Xenodiscus*, *Stacheoceras*, and *Pseudogastrioceras* are of uncertain strati-graphical importance. Among the associated brachiopods are several forms of the productid sub-genus *Ruthenia* which resemble certain Arctic species; the characteristic genus *Cryptacanthia* is possibly a meganterid form. There is an abundance of bellerophontid gastropods, and the scaphopod *Plagioglypta* is limited to the stage. The Chideru Beds are overlaid with apparent conformity by strata of early Triassic age, which also rest on the Productus Shales in the Himalayas. The apparent conformity in both areas may be misleading, for study of Permian strata in Asia Minor and south Europe has led some authors to believe that higher Permian horizons exist in those regions.

The type of fauna contained in the Productus Limestone has a wide geographical distribution in many parts of Eurasia, from the Urals to Japan. Near Djulfa in Armenia marly limestones contain a brachiopod fauna which is related to that of the Upper Productus Limestone of India. The associated cephalopods, however, are distinct. Near the base of the section there are species of *Prototoceras*, a genus which foreshadows the Triassic *Otoceras*. Then comes a bed with species of *Productus* and *Reticularia*, followed by the horizon of *Pseudogastrioceras abichianum*. These beds are generally accepted as younger than the Productus Limestone of India, and L. F. Spath (1934) has provisionally grouped them in two ammonoid zones. The Djulfa beds are said to pass up into the Triassic system, but Spath recognizes a higher zone which is only represented in the south European succession next to be discussed.

In southern EUROPE the marine Permian strata so far known show only fragments of the complete succession, disconnected by the great orogenic movements of the Neozoic era by which the Alps of the present day were elevated. Our knowledge of the Permian rocks in this region has been summarized and amplified by F. Heritsch (1939). In the Carnic Alps the Permian succession begins with the Rattendorf Shales which contain the fusulinid *Pseudoschwagerina*; these beds are correlated with the Sakmara stage of Russia, and the Wolfcamp Beds of Texas. The succeeding Troghofel Limestone has yielded the fusulinids *Paraschwagerina* and *Parafusulina*, as well as the ammonoids *Medlicottia artiensis*, *Agathiceras*, and *Thalassoceras*, which indicate broad equivalence with the Leonard and Word formations of Texas. Above this marine sequence the non-marine Grodener Sandstone is widely developed in the eastern Alps; the Permian plant *Walchia* is recorded from it. The so-called Bellerophon Limestone of the Carnic Alps and the Karawanken is also largely of detrital origin, but intercalated calcareous beds carry a marine fauna of brachiopods, gastropods (*Bellerophon*), the fusulinid *Neoschwagerina*, and rarely the ammonoid *Paralecanites sextensis*. This is believed to be the youngest Permian unit so far known, and L. F. Spath (1934) places it at the top of the system in a zone named after the ammonoid just cited (p. 393).

In Sicily isolated masses of marine limestone are exposed in the valley of the Sosio River in the southern part of Palermo province. The stratigraphical relations are not clear, for these disturbed rocks lie among strata of Triassic, Jurassic, and Eocene age. The fauna is extremely rich and varied; the mollusca, brachiopods, and crustaceans have been described by G. G. Gemmellaro (1888–96), the species of *Richthofenia* by G. Stefano (1914), the corals and echinoderms by A. Gregorio (1930) and the fusulinids by A. Silvestri (1933). Among the last group is *Schwagerina* s.s. which is recorded from early Permian rocks of other localities. The ammonoids, recently reviewed by A. K. Miller (1933), are more varied than the Artinsk assemblage, and are surpassed in variety only by the faunas of Texas and Timor. *Medlicottia, Propinacoceras, Sicanites, Popanoceras, Thalassoceras, Agathiceras*, and *Hyattoceras* are notable genera, but *Waagenoceras* is probably the most significant, for it is also abundant in the Word stage of Texas. The Sosio Beds are therefore correlated with this horizon, which has six other ammonoid genera in common with them.

The Permian ammonoids described by O. Toumansky (1931) from localities in Crimea may also be assigned to the Waagenoceras zone, for, though the index-fossil is not recorded, other ammonoids referred to *Medlicottia, Propinacoceras, Sicanites, Paraprionites, Agathiceras*, and *Pseudagathiceras* seem to be closely related to Sicilian forms. Few details are available concerning the Mrzla Vodica Beds of Croatia described by V. Vogl (1913), but A. K. Miller (1933) states that the fauna does not differ greatly in age. The ammonoids, fragmentary and otherwise indifferently preserved, are referred to the genera *Agathiceras, Popanoceras, Sicanites, Propinacoceras*, and *Paraceltites*, and some of them are identified with Sicilian species. Likewise, the ammonoids described by J. Caralp (1903) and H. Schmidt (1931) from Permian shales at St. Girons, Ariège, in the central Pyrenees, and referred to the genera *Agathiceras, Daraelites, Paraceltites*, and *Thalassoceras*, probably belong to a horizon near that of the Sosio Beds. Marine beds dipping under Trias at Djebel Tabaga, Tunisia, have yielded the fusulinid *Neoschwagerina* together with brachiopods and mollusca. No precise correlation can be made in the absence of ammonoids but the fusulinid genus is characteristic of high horizons in the Permian system.

It is evident that the Permian succession is imperfectly represented at each of the known localities; this is shown in summary by the accompanying table below. At the same time the distribution of marine Permian strata raises doubts about the geography of the period as usually interpreted, especially in regard to the hypothetical southern continent known as Gondwanaland. This is supposed to have occupied more or less the sites of the present Indian and South Atlantic Oceans with the continents of India, Africa, South America, and Australia. But the close relations of the ammonoid faunas in Madagascar, north India, and Timor demand marine connexion across or around the Indian Ocean during at least a part of Permian time. The world-wide similarity of ammonoid faunas, when contemporaneous assemblages are compared, is consistent with the present relations of the main oceanic basins. The transgressive deposits on the present land surface, which form the subject of the foregoing review, indicate considerable fluctuations of the coastal margins during the period.

Provisional Ammonoid Zones of the Permian System, and their Distribution

Series	Faunas	Zones	E. Alps	Sicily	Croatia	Crimea	Urals	Djulfa	Darvaz	Salt Range	Madagascar	Timor	W. Australia	Texas	Brit. Columbia
NEOPERMIAN	PROTOTOCERATAN	Paralecanites sextensis	×												
		Pseudogastrioceras						×							
		Prototoceras trochoides						×							
	XENASPIDAN	Episageceras wynnei								×					
		Cyclolobus oldhami								×	×				
		Xenaspis carbonaria								×					
PALAEOPERMIAN	WAAGENOCERATAN	Timorites										×	×		
		Stacheoceras timoricum										×			
		Waagenoceras dieneri		×	×	×						×	×	×	×
	THALASSOCERATAN	Perrinites										×	×		
		Artinskia	×				×		×						
		Properrinites	×				×					×	×		

LITERATURE

The most recent account of the Permian faunas of England is contained in 'The Permian Formation in Durham', by C. T. Trechmann, *Proc. Geol. Assoc.*, vol. xxxvi, pp. 135–45, 1925.

Illustrations of most known Permian fossils of this country are given by W. King in 'The Permian Fossils of England', *Mon. Pal. Soc.*, 1850.

'Footprints from the Permian or Mansfield, Notts.', are described by G. Hickling in *Quart. Journ. Geol. Soc.*, vol. lxii, pp. 125–31, 1906.

A synopsis of *The Permo-Triassic Formations*, by R. L. Sherlock, 1950 is useful for the location and general characters of Permian and Triassic deposits throughout the world; it includes an extensive bibliography but many important palaeontological works are omitted. In 'Karbon und Perm in Den Sudalpen und in Sudosteuropa', *Geol. Rundschau*, pp. 529–88, 1939, F. Heritsch summarizes and amplifies knowledge of Permian rocks in south-east Europe. A. K. Miller in *Amer. Journ. Sci.*, vol. ccxxvi, pp. 408–27, 1933, discusses 'The Age of the Permian Limestones of Sicily', while J. Caralp had previously described 'Le Permien de L'Ariège, ses Divers Facies, sa Faune Marine' in *Bull. Soc. Geol. France*, ser. 4, vol. iii, pp. 635–50, 1903. A summary of the works of V. E. Ruzencev and other Russian geologists is given by M. K. Elias in 'Carboniferous and Permian of the Southern Urals', *Amer. Journ. Sci.*, vol. ccxxxiii, pp. 279–95, 1937, and G. A. Durkiewicz discusses 'L'Importance de la Microfaune Pour le Correlation du Permien de la Partie Meridionale de L'URSS' in *Abstracts of Papers*, pp. 95–96 Internat. Geol. Congr., Moscow, 1937. C.O. Dunbar contributes 'Permian Faunas: A Study in Facies' to *Bull. Geol. Soc. Amer.*, vol. lii, pp. 313–32, 1941, and mentions Russian instances. M. Solignac and E. Berkaloff have described 'Le Permian Marine de l'Extreme sud Tunisien' in *Mem. Serv. Carte Geol. Tunisie*, 1934.

The description by F. R. C. Reed of 'Brachiopoda and Mollusca from the Productus Limestones of the Salt Range', *Pal. Indica*, N.S., vol. xxiii, mem. 2, 1944, is illustrated by 65 plates, and contains an extensive bibliography of about 400 items. C. O. Dunbar has discussed the 'Stratigraphic Significance of the Fusulinids of the Lower Productus Limestone of the Salt Range' in *Rec. Geol. Surv. India*, vol. lxvi, pp. 405–13, 1933, and has also described 'Permian Fusulines from the Karakoram', ibid., vol. lxxv, Prof. Paper No. 5, 1940. 'Permian Fusulinids from Afghanistan' are described by M. L. Thompson in *Journ. Palaeont.*, vol. xx, pp. 140–57, 1946. Ammonoids recorded in 'Recherches Geologiques à Madagascar: La Geologie du Nordouest', by H. Besairie, *Mem. Acad. Malgache*, vol. xxi, pp. 1–259, 1936, are closely related to corresponding forms in the Salt Range. 'Die Cephalopoden der dyas von Timor' are described by C. A. Haniel, *Paleont. von Timor*, vol. iii, 1915, and supplemented by J. P. Smith in 'Permian Ammonoids of Timor', *Jaarb. Mijnwezen in Ned. Indie*, vol. i, pp. 1–158 with 16 plates, 1927. J. Wanner has described 'Permischen Echinodermen von Timor', in *Geol. Exped. Univ. Amsterdam, Sunda Is.*, vol. v, pp. 215–77, 1940, and previous works. 'The Permian Fusulinids of Timor' are discussed in *Journ. Palaeont.*, vol. xxiii, pp. 182–92, 1949, by M. L. Thompson, who had previously described 'Lower Permian Fusulinids from Sumatra' in ibid., vol. x, pp. 587–92, 1936. 'Permian Ammonoids from Western Australia' are recorded and illustrated by C. Teichert in ibid., vol. xvi, pp. 221–32, 1942, and vol. xviii, pp. 83–89, 1944.

In North America the work of G. H. Girty on *The Guadalupian Fauna*, U.S. Geol. Surv. Prof. Paper No. 58, 1908, has been supplemented by F. B. Plummer and G. Scott, *Upper Palaeozoic Ammonoids in Texas*, Univ. Texas Bull. No. 3701, 1937, and by A. K. Miller and W. M. Furnish, *Permian Ammonoids of the Guadalupe Mountain Region and Adjacent Areas*, Geol. Soc. Amer. Special Papers No. 26, 1940. A. K. Miller and L. M. Cline have described 'The Cephalopoda of the Phosphoria Formation of the Northwestern United States' in *Journ. Palaeont.*, vol. viii, pp. 281–302, 1934. Records of 'Permian Cephalopods from British Columbia' are given by A. K. Miller and M. B. Crockford in *Trans. Roy. Soc. Canada*, ser. 4, vol. xxx, sect. iv, pp. 23–28, 1936. 'Neoschwagerina in the Permian Fauna of British Columbia', is recorded by C. O. Dunbar in ibid., sect. 4, ser. 3, vol. xxvi, pp. 45–50, 1932. C. O. Dunbar and J. Skinner describe 'New Fusulinid Genera from the Permian of West Texas', *Amer. Journ. Sci.*, vol. ccxxii, pp. 252–68, 1931, and proceed to a revision of *The Permian Fusulinidae of Texas* in Univ. Texas Bull. No. 3701, part ii, with 40 plates, 1937. C. O. Dunbar records 'Permian Fusulines from Central America' in *Journ. Palaeont.*, vol. xiii, pp. 344–48, 1939, and in collaboration with

N. D. Newell, describes 'The Marine Early Permian of the Central Andes and its Fusuline Faunas', *Amer. Journ. Sci.*, vol. ccxliv, pp. 377–402 and 457–91, 1946.

The above works and others cited therein provide the evidence for the chronological succession in the Permian system which is given by L. F. Spath in the introduction to his *Catalogue of Fossil Cepalopoda in the British Museum*, Part IV: 'The Ammonoidea of the Trias', London, 1934. The succession is presented in slightly different tabular form on p. 393 of the present volume.

XI

TRIASSIC FAUNAS

ENGLISH Triassic rocks comprise a lower series termed the Bunter and an upper series known as the Keuper. These terms are taken from the threefold division of the Trias in Germany, but the middle division, the Muschelkalk, has not yet been recognized in Britain. That marine facies may never have reached this country, and its equivalent may be the middle part of the British Trias; moreover, an unconformity (though often slight) between the Bunter and Keuper may help to bridge the time-period involved.

In the type-district of the western Midlands the **Bunter** consists of a thick series of pebble beds (300 to 1,000 feet) between two 'Mottled Sandstones' each of which varies between 200 and 600 feet in thickness. The sandstones are generally false-bedded and their component quartz grains are highly rounded and polished, having the 'millet-seed' appearance of modern desert sands. It has therefore been concluded that these beds were accumulated largely by aeolian agency under desert conditions. The pebble beds in the central area form a mass of conglomerate consisting mainly of large, well-rounded pebbles; of these the majority are liver-coloured quartzite, but some are fragments of Carboniferous Limestone, sandstone, and grit, while others are volcanic rocks. These beds are often regarded as scree-deposits, brought down mountain slopes by the action of gravity or of torrential floods. All three divisions thin out towards the south-east in Staffordshire and are absent in Warwickshire, the upper beds overlapping the lower; moreover, the pebbles decrease in size and abundance towards Lancashire and Yorkshire in the northern part of the outcrop, though the sandy matrix persists. The St. Bees Sandstone represents the Bunter in the isolated Carlisle basin, while similar sandstones have been found by boring in the northern part of the Isle of Man and near Belfast in Ireland.

In Devonshire the pebble beds rest directly on red Permian Marl with no apparent break in conformity. Some of the quartzite pebbles here contain fossils and are regarded as derivative from the Ordovician Grés de May of Normandy. The southern origin thus suggested is confirmed by Dr. H. H. Thomas's study of the detrital minerals present in these sandstones. The fossils are mainly orthids and the commonest species is named *Orthis budleighensis* Dav., from the typical locality, Budleigh Salterton, in Devon. This form is very like *O. testudinaria* Dalm., but is more finely striated and more transverse in shape. Similar shells are recorded from the quartzite pebbles of the Midland Bunter, and, being referred to the same species, they suggest a southern origin for that deposit. An obscure orthid recorded from the pebble beds near Liverpool has also been cited as supporting the view of a southerly origin, but the specimen is too imperfect for specific identification. Moreover, orthids might well have been transported from northerly areas, whence came (according to the petrographers) the countless grains of sand that form the deposit.

Bearing in mind the mode of their deposition, it is hardly surprising that the Bunter rocks are practically devoid of contemporaneous fossils. This circumstance renders the correlation of distant outcrops a matter of some difficulty.

The **Keuper** has a much wider extension than the Bunter, which it oversteps in the southern Midlands. The Keuper of the Midland area is usually divided into—

| UPPER KEUPER | { Rhaetic Beds—mainly black shales and white marly limestones. Keuper Marls—red and grey marls with rock-salt. |
| LOWER KEUPER | { Waterstones—flaggy sandstones and shales. Basement Beds—false-bedded sandstones and basal breccias resting on an eroded surface of Bunter or older rocks. |

Much more is known concerning the flora and fauna of the Keuper than can be said for the preceding series. The known fossils consist of plants, a few mollusca, a crustacean, arachnids, together with several genera of fishes, amphibia, and reptiles. The most abundant, most widely distributed and most characteristic of these is the little phyllopod crustacean *Estheria minuta* Alberti, which is known from various horizons in the English Keuper and throughout the Trias of France and Germany. The genus has a wide distribution in fresh and brackish water at the present day, and is capable of living through great ranges of temperature and in regions subject to excessive drought. J. Lomas has described the occurrence of living species in the shallow hollows or 'vleys' in the sandy plains of South Africa. During the rainy season these are fed by temporary streams which carry down fragments of the scanty desert flora along with mud and dissolved salts. *Estheria* suddenly appears in the pools and, on evaporation of the water, its valves and the vegetable debris are entombed in the muds impregnated with salt residues. The Triassic species is usually associated with fragmentary (probably drifted) plant remains, and salt-pseudomorphs are often present in the rock; this mode of occurrence thus bears a close resemblance to that of the existing species in the South African desert-pools.

Several species of plants have from time to time been recorded from the British Trias, but the preservation is so poor and fragmentary that only vague ideas of the flora could be formed. In 1910, however, L. J. Wills published an account of fossiliferous Lower Keuper Beds at Bromsgrove which considerably extended our knowledge of the British Triassic flora and fauna. The plants include *Schizoneura paradoxa* Schimper and Mougeot, *Equisetites arenaceus* Jaeger, and *Equisetites keuperiana* Storeton, representing the Equisetales or horsetails, the coniferous species *Voltzia heterophylla* Brongn., together with *Yuccites vosgesiacus* Sch. and Moug., and *Strobilites* of uncertain affinities. The preservation of the leaves of *Schizoneura* and *Yuccites* suggests that they were thick and tough, probably of xerophytic habit. The abundance of arachnid fragments referred to the genus *Mesophonus* is interesting, since they suggest a general resemblance to the existing scorpion. Obscure impressions of a mytiloid shell testify the presence of bivalved mollusca, while bones and teeth of vertebrates are found in conglomeratic bone-beds which are probably lacustrine coastal deposits. The fishes include two fairly complete specimens of the rare *Dipteronotus cyphus* Egerton, and teeth of *Ceratodus*, *Acrodus*, and *Semionotus*. Remains of the amphibious labyrinthodonts are referred to the genera *Labyrinthodon*, *Capitosaurus*, *Diadetognathus*, and *Mastodonsaurus*. True reptiles include *Rhynchosaurus*, *Hyperodapedon*, and their allies; *Phytosaurus* is a forerunner of the crocodiles; *Thecodontosaurus* and *Teratosaurus* are early deinosaurs.

While bones, or hollow moulds formerly occupied by them, are preserved in some instances, other districts, notably Cheshire, have yielded only foot-prints of vertebrate animals. In many cases these cannot be referred to species whose osteology is known, and H. C. Beasley classified the foot-prints provisionally into three main types, each of which he subdivided on minor differences.

The largest foot-prints, apparently those of a hind foot, are known as the 'Cheirotheroid type', the name *Cheirotherium* having been proposed for the unknown perpetrator of these spoors as long ago as 1835. They have five digits and average 8 or 9 inches in length. The middle digit is the longest, the fifth is the shortest, and this is usually curved outwards. The palmar surface is about equal in area to that covered by the digits, and the whole print roughly simulates the form of a human hand. Much smaller prints, less heavily impressed, represent the fore-feet. The track is very narrow, the feet of the two sides being planted nearly on the same line, and the stride is usually about a yard long. Reasoning from these facts, D. M. S. Watson concludes that the *Cheirotherium* was a 'four-footed animal with relatively small forelegs, long, heavy tail, and narrow pelvis', and that 'there can be no doubt that *Cheirotherium* was a deinosaur or direct deinosaur ancestor'.

Associated with the large cheirotheroid spoors are innumerable small foot-prints which preserve no general direction, presumably those of a very active little animal. They have five digits, of which the fourth is the longest, and little or no palmar surface. These digitigrade prints most nearly correspond with the foot of *Rhynchosaurus*, and are therefore known as the 'Rhynchosauroid type', of which several variations are known.

Some other footprints are short and broad, with short digits and strong claws. The palmar surface occupies most of the impressed area, and the track is very wide. These prints were early ascribed to tortoises, and are therefore usually termed the 'Chelonoid type' without prejudice concerning their origin. It has been suggested that they are due to burrowing animals, and again they have been ascribed to anomodont reptiles.

Though other forms of foot-prints are recorded, none are intermediate between the three types described above, and apparently belong to a variety of animals. Thus, taken altogether, the tracks show the presence of a varied Triassic fauna of which little is so far known.

The whole assemblage of organic remains, then, indicates continental conditions, and 'although desert conditions cannot be proved to have existed here during the time of the deposition of the Waterstones, we have proof, in the nature of the deposit and of its contents, that a dry climate, verging on that of a true desert, prevailed' (Wills).

The question of the origin of the Trias is extremely difficult in itself, and the factors which govern the formation of terrestrial deposits at the present day are only imperfectly understood. Apparently, continuous deposition is the exception rather than the rule, and numerous non-sequences (exceedingly difficult, if not impossible, to detect) probably exist in the Trias. Incidentally, this factor is likely to render nugatory any attempt to correlate Permian and Triassic deposits by detailed lithological features.

The Upper Keuper consists of a thick series of red and variegated marls with layers of gypsum and rock-salt, which are usually ascribed to lacustrine conditions. Remains of life are scanty, and little can be said of them. The uppermost portion of the marls is consistently greyish-green in colour and is known as the 'Tea-green Marls'; these are overlain by black shales which are included in the Rhaetic Beds. The latter were formed as the result of marine transgression, and in the south-western countries sometimes rest directly on tilted beds of Carboniferous Limestone. Their base is usually well-defined, and forms a useful datum-line in mapping. Consequently the series is often placed at the base of the Jurassic, and has even been classified as a separate system. But the characters of the Alpine molluscan fauna are such that (palaeontologically) the Rhaetic Series is best classified with the Keuper.

In the Midland counties the Tea-green Marls are succeeded by black shales which are often named after a characteristic fossil, the *Pteria contorta* shales. The junction is very sharply defined, and sometimes there are signs of erosion on the surface of the marls. In the south-western counties the two horizons are separated by the Grey Marls, of which the uppermost portion (Sully Beds) contain certain fossils of the *P. contorta* shales. Even this sequence is probably incomplete, as the Sully Beds appear to have been eroded prior to the deposition of the black shales. The reptilian teeth referred to *Microlestes* (p. 657) were obtained from the Sully Beds, which also yield *Pecten valoniensis* Defr. and *Protocardia rhaetica* (Mérian).

The lower portion of the black shales is often rich in vertebrate remains, which occur in impersistent layers known as 'bone-beds'. The famous 'Rhaetic Bone-bed' of south-western England has yielded teeth of several fishes, including *Acrodus minimus* Ag., *Ceratodus latissimus* Ag., and *C. altus* Ag. (Fig. 19). The bone-beds probably represent the accumulation of verte-brate remains during a time of slow sedimentation. In this connexion, the occurrence near Frome of a thin conglomerate containing limestone pebbles bored by the worm *Polydora* is significant, since a living species of *Polydora* is abundant in inter-tidal areas throughout western Europe.

The upper portion of the black shales contains impure limestones which enclose numerous molluscan shells. The oblique shell of *Pteria contorta* (Portlock) (Fig. 70), with its prominent radiating ribs, is abundant in most localities where the shales are exposed. The globose and almost equilateral shell of *Protocardia rhaetica* (Mérian) is recognized by the depressed radial ribs at its posterior end; otherwise it is practically smooth. *Pleurophorus elongatus* Moore, an elongate shell with a ridge passing from the umbones to the posterior ventral margin, is particularly abundant just above the bone-beds in south-western England. The characteristic *Pecten valoniensis* Defr., *Anatina precursor* Qu., species of *Ostrea*, and small gastropods, are also abundant in many localities. In places the shales pass up into a series of yellowish marly limestones, which include the 'Cotham Marble', well known by its curious arborescent markings.

The White Lias, overlying the Black Shales in the south-western coun-ties, is a series of white or cream-coloured limestones some beds of which contain an abundance of a small mussel, *Volsella langportensis* Rich. and Tutcher, which is cited by J. W. Tutcher as a zonal guide. Above the White Lias are the Pleuromya beds marked by the abundance of *Pleuromya tatei* R. and T. In these beds a small oyster, *Ostrea liassica* Strickland, which occurs sparingly in the White Lias, becomes plentiful. In general form (see Fig. 69) it is more or less oval with a lamellose surface; the right valve is flat, the left valve convex: it is attached near the umbo; the surface of attachment is variable, though generally small in size. It attains its maxi-mum abundance in the succeeding beds, sometimes called the *Ostrea* zone, and persists into the planorbis zone of the Lower Lias. The surfaces of these limestone beds are often water-worn and bored by organisms, and some-times have oysters adherent to them; these features provide evidence of pauses in sedimentation and frequent oscillations of the submarine erosion level.

The New Red Sandstone of Moray in Scotland is of peculiar interest because of the occurrence therein of numerous reptilian remains of terres-trial type. The strata are exposed in three isolated areas, and their relative age cannot be determined by stratigraphy alone. Indeed, until the undisturbed equivalent strata of South Africa had been subdivided on a palaeontological basis, the Scottish deposits were generally referred to the Trias. It is now known that two of the three groups are of Permian age, the third being Triassic.

A small area east of Elgin is occupied by coarse, false-bedded sandstones composed of well-rounded quartz grains and containing wind-eroded pebbles of the type known as 'Dreikanter'. The deposit is therefore of desert origin. The reptilian remains consist largely of hollow moulds in the sandstone which were formerly occupied by bones of the animals. Casts made from the hollows revealed a unique series of anomodont reptiles comparable, but not identical, with forms from the Upper Permian of Russia, North America, and South Africa. They include five species of *Gordonia*, a genus closely allied to *Dicynodon* from the Upper Permian of South Africa and Russia. The genus *Geikia* is derived from *Gordonia* by development of horns on the nasal bones; this form is unknown elsewhere, but a slight tendency towards spinosity is seen in certain reptiles from the Upper Permian of South Africa. The remaining genus *Elginia* is a remarkable horned reptile allied to the massive *Pareiasaurus*, and foreshadowed by certain types from equivalent strata in Russia and South Africa. The Upper Permian age of these Scottish beds is therefore clearly established now that the general sequence in eastern Europe and South Africa is known.

A series of coarse, false-bedded sandstones around Cummingstone has yielded no fossils except foot-prints. There are several types of these which, however, agree in their general characters. They are short prints with five short digits provided with claws; the fore and hind foot-prints are about equal in size and in quality of impression. The tracks are broad, the right and left feet being widely separated when compared with the stride. D. M. S. Watson has suggested that these foot-prints, which are entirely different from all known Triassic prints, may be attributed to *Gordonia*. Similar tracks occur in the Permian of Mansfield and other British localities, and of Thuringia in Germany.

The New Red Sandstone around Lossiemouth yields a completely different fauna. The only reptile known elsewhere is *Hyperodapedon*, a rhynchocephalian, which is recorded from undoubted Trias near Warwick. This genus occurs, along with its allies *Stenometopon* and *Brachyrhinodon*, at Lossiemouth. *Telerpeton* is a small anomodont allied to *Procolophon* of the South African Trias. *Stagonolepis* and *Erpetosuchus* belong to the Parasuchia, which are regarded as ancestral to the longirostrate crocodiles; this group is exclusively Triassic and has a wide distribution, being well known in Germany and North America. *Ornithosuchus* and *Scleromochlus* are also Triassic genera, with some characters of both Parasuchia and deinosaurs. These forms all appear to be dry-land types, and the prevalence of desert conditions is held to explain the absence from the Scottish fauna of

D d

labyrinthodonts, which are often common in the Trias of other localities. The only genus approaching this group so far obtained in Scotland is *Dasygnathus*, whose precise affinities are uncertain.

Thus the evidence of the reptilian faunas renders inevitable a division into Permian on the west and Triassic on the east of the New Red Sandstone of Elgin. Other areas of New Red Sandstone in Scotland have so far yielded no fossils.

FAUNAL REGIONS

The German Trias, as we have already noted, consists of two series of terrestrial deposits, the Bunter and Keuper, separated by a middle marine series known as the Muschelkalk. The Bunter and Keuper consist mainly of red sandstones and argillaceous rocks which contain only sparsely distributed fossils, chiefly plant-remains and footprints, or more rarely bones, of tetrapod animals. These terrestrial fossils are discussed in Chapters VIII and XIV respectively. The calcareous Muschelkalk encloses a considerable variety of marine invertebrate fossils among which the mollusca are most prominent, the cephalopods in particular being most useful for purposes of correlation. The lower part of the Muschelkalk consists of wavy-bedded, yellow dolomitic beds, the so-called Wellen dolomite, containing species of *Beneckeia*, involute, smooth, oxynote ammonites with entire multilobate suture-lines. The main Wellenkalk follows with such fossils as *Natica gregaria*, *Chemnitzia socialis*, *Myophoria cardissioides*, *Coenothyris vulgaris*, &c. Besides *Beneckeia*, occasional ammonites are reported from some localities. For example, the evolute, highly ornamented *Balatonites* is probably related to the ceratitids which are represented at this horizon by *Paraceratites antecedens* Beyrich. This is one of the earliest members of the genus which is distinguished among ceratitids by the presence of a slight keel on the periphery. The Upper Wellenkalk is distinguished by intercalated beds of Schaumkalk, a yellowish-grey limestone which furnishes a durable stone. This division is one of the most fossiliferous horizons of the Muschelkalk, and contains many species of brachiopods and mollusca. Certain beds are characterized by the dominance of one or a few species, such as *Coenothyris vulgaris*, *Spiriferina fragilis*, *Myophoria orbicularis*, to the virtual exclusion of other forms. The ammonites *Beneckeia buchi* and *Paraceratites antecedens* seem to persist, and are accompanied by several other species, including the widely distributed *P. trinodosus* (Mojs.) which is an important index-fossil in the Alpine region. *Ptychites dux* (Beyrich) and species of *Judicarites* are also valuable in establishing a correlation with the Alpine region (see p. 416).

The Middle Muschelkalk consists of dolomite with beds of gypsum, anhydrite, and rock-salt; the total thickness is about 300 feet. Apart from bones and teeth of reptiles, this series is almost devoid of fossils.

The Upper Muschelkalk everywhere consists of two main divisions. At the base is the so-called Trochitenkalk, a very hard limestone consisting almost entirely of stems of the crinoid *Encrinus liliiformis* Miller, and often accompanied by glauconitic limestones. Above are 200 to 400 feet of thin-bedded limestones with argillaceous layers, which are noted for the abundance of the ammonite *Ceratites*. The numerous species of this variable form have been used by Riedel (1918) to demonstrate a succession of several horizons, and certain forms, separated as distinct genera on account of conspicuous differences from the true *Ceratites* (s.s.), are reviewed by L. F. Spath (1934). One of the earliest is *Progonoceratites* with compressed whorl-section and smooth body-chamber, but with ornamented inner whorls showing certain similarity with the earlier *Paraceratites*. Several species of *Progonoceratites* in these Lower Ceratite Beds are associated with early forms of *Ceratites*, such as *C. robustus* Riedel and *C. laevigatus* (Philippi) in which coarse tuberculation changes on the outer whorl into blunt lateral ribs. In the Middle Ceratite Beds only *Ceratites* is present in such species as *C. compressus* Philippi, *C. muensteri* Diener, *C. enodis* Qu. and *C. spinosus* Philippi. The genus continues into the Upper Ceratite Beds where *C. nodosus* (Brug.) (Pl. VI) and its near allies are the principal species. But these are accompanied by large, more or less smooth and involute forms with narrow venters, grouped under *Discoceratites*, which are closely connected with *C. nodosus* by transitional forms.

Above the Muschelkalk is the Lettenkohle or Kohlenkeuper, a series of grey sandstones, dark marls and clays, with abundant plants and some thin seams of impure coal. Near the top is a band of dolomite (Grenzdolomit) which contains shells of *Lingula*, marine lamellibranchs and an ammonite. This last fossil is *Alloceratites schmidti* (Zimmermann) and Spath (1934) regards it as a specialized offshoot of *Discoceratites* that develops prominent lateral tubercles and a subsulcate periphery bordered by clavi. Hence the Kohlenkeuper is closely connected with the Muschelkalk with which Quenstedt united it, though usually it is taken as the basal stage of the Keuper Series. The presence of this ammonite and other marine fossils indicates a temporary oscillation of the sea-margin during the widespread regression which preceded the formation of the Keuper deposits.

The northern limit of the German Muschelkalk is roughly defined by the Baltic Sea, for Lower and Middle Trias are unknown in Scania where the Upper Trias is transgressive. The Muschelkalk, however, is well developed at Rudersdorf near Berlin, and in the neighbourhood of Luneberg, but in Heligoland is only known in isolated blocks. The calcareous Muschelkalk has not been recognized in Britain where a slight unconformity exists between Bunter and Keuper. Deep borings in the eastern part of the Low Countries show that the Muschelkalk is represented largely by sandy deposits whose thickness decreases rapidly towards the west; a dolomitic sand at Gilsdorf near Dickurch, Luxemburg, has yielded *Ceratites nodosus*.

In the Saar and Moselle areas, the North Eifel, and Alsace Lorraine the

Lower Muschelkalk comprises grey dolomites and red marly sandstones containing *Coenothyris vulgaris* and mollusca; the higher beds are limestones with *Myophoria orbicularis*. The upper beds are particularly well developed in the Vosges; at Luneville large shells of *Ceratites evolutus* Philippi and *Discoceratites semipartitus* (Buch) have been recorded. In the north-east of the Central Plateau the Muschelkalk is missing, for the Grés Bigarré of the Bunter is succeeded by the Lettenkohle. Near Dijon the Keuper rests directly on granite, and farther west, at La Chatre, the Lias overlies the crystalline rocks. This condition extends to the north-east and centre of the Morvan.

The true Muschelkalk occurs again in the neighbourhood of Toulon and Montpellier. Here the Wellenkalk is not readily distinguished by fossils, but rocks below the recognized nodosus beds are referred to it. The fossil assemblage of the latter horizon is comparable with that of the Upper Ceratite Beds of Germany, and the Mollusca include species of *Ceratites* and *Discoceratites*. In the Pyrenees the Muschelkalk has the same lithology as in Lorraine, but has yielded only debris of crinoids. In the south of Aragon dolomitic limestone containing several lamellibranchs of the Muschelkalk and *Ceratites nodosus* is recorded from Soria. A similar assemblage occurs in the province of Jaen, Andalusia, but the Trias of the Betic region farther south is metamorphosed, and the stages cannot readily be distinguished. In general, however, the Muschelkalk of Spain nearly encircles the marine tract of Mora del Ebro and is limited in the west by the ancient Meseta. To the south the Muschelkalk sea evidently transgressed the northern margin of the African continent for J. Flandrin (1932) has recorded dolomitic limestones containing *Myophoria vulgaris* around Souk Aharas in Algeria. The distribution of Triassic rocks in Europe is shown in Fig. 60, p. 405.

The Muschelkalk consists of marine strata intercalated between deposits of terrestrial origin; it therefore represents a temporary transgression of the sea over a former land surface in central Europe. The fossils are not evenly distributed through the series but are usually restricted to certain beds in which they often occur in abundance though generally with only a few species. As a whole the fauna is poor in comparison with that of contemporary deposits in the eastern Alps and certain other parts of the world. This applies particularly to the ammonoids which are mostly ceratitids in the German Muschelkalk, but which exhibit a great variety of genera and species in other regions. We must now discuss these larger faunas and their relations with the German assemblages, and it is convenient to take the three divisions of the Triassic system separately.

The Himalayan region of northern INDIA has long been famous for a remarkable development of marine Triassic rocks. The sequence, about 3,700 feet in thickness, occupies a broad belt nearly a thousand miles in length from Kashmir by way of Spiti to north-west Nepal. The sections in

Spiti and Painkhanda are better known than those in Byans and Kashmir. A further development is present in the Salt Range. In general the Triassic rocks succeed Permian strata without apparent interruption, but the palae-ontological evidence at present available indicates a break which varies in extent at different places. North of the Himalayas an entirely different de-velopment, often termed the Tibetan facies, is seen in the region of exotic blocks in Malla Johar, &c. Here most horizons are of small thickness, and

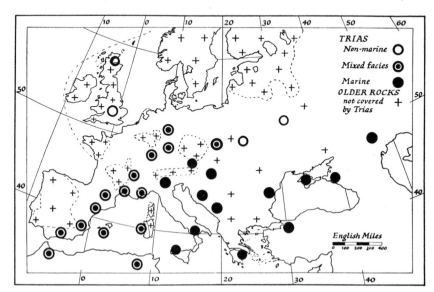

FIG. 60. SKETCH-MAP OF EUROPE SHOWING GENERAL DISTRIBUTION OF TRIASSIC ROCKS

consist of red marbles resulting from regional metamorphism. A develop-ment of igneous rocks furnishes another contrast with the Himalayan facies which is only 10 miles distant. By means of the fossil ammonoids each of the sections has been divided into a number of palaeontological zones (see table, p. 414).

The oldest known Triassic deposits are the famous Otoceras Beds of the Himalayas which are exposed to a thickness of only 3 feet in the Shalshal Cliff of Painkhanda. Though the fossils occur in thin bands separated by barren strata the three recognizable zones are closely related for, according to C. Diener (1912) and L. F. Spath (1934) *Otoceras* and *Ophiceras* are often present in the same rock-specimen. These two genera, both with ceratitic suture-lines, are closely connected genetically, both being derived through the Permian Xenodiscidae from the Carboniferous Prolecanitidae. Never-theless they differ considerably in external form. *Otoceras* (Pl. VI) is an involute, keeled shell, and its deep umbilicus has a sharp projecting rim. *Ophiceras* (Pl. VI) includes almost smooth compressed evolute shells with rounded venter and elliptical whorl-section. The family Ophiceratidae seems to have given rise to numerous derivative genera grouped for convenience in twelve families which become of greater importance at higher Palaeotriassic horizons. One early species of *Proptychites*, occurring in shales immediately above the main Otoceras layer, demonstrates the early divergence of the Proptychitidae from the ancestral Ophiceratidae. The genus *Episageceras* represents a different stock that is already established in Permian strata; it is a discoid, involute medlicottid form with a tabulate venter bordered by two sharp keels. The development of the Otoceras Beds in Spiti is very similar, but in Kashmir the lower beds with *Otoceras* are not recorded. Here too, the Ophiceras layer shows certain faunal differences which lead Spath to believe that it may be slightly later than the tibeticum zone of Spiti.

In Painkhanda the Otoceras Beds are followed by 18 feet of shales and limestone which have yielded no fossils. Above them is a dark concretionary limestone containing certain species of *Proptychites* and *Koninckites* as the most abundant fossils. The same shells are recorded from similar limestones in the Lilang section of Spiti, immediately above the Otoceras beds. These and other species of ammonoids were wrongly referred by W. Waagen (1895) to the American genus *Meekoceras* which belongs to a later horizon and has no direct affinity with the Indian forms. These are the only common ammonoids at this horizon in Painkhanda, but in Spiti and Byans they are associated with other derivatives of the earlier Ophiceratidae. The Gyronitidae are represented by such forms as the smooth, flat *Prionolobus*, and the Paranoritidae by the involute discoid *Clypeoceras* apparently related to *Koninickites* but with a simpler suture-line. These so-called 'Meekoceras Beds' containing the Gyronitan fauna would be more appropriately termed the Proptychites beds to avoid confusion with the American succession.

The Otoceras Beds are not known in the Salt Range where the basal Triassic beds of shale and sandstone have yielded no fossils. There follows a series of sandstones and calcareous beds with a total thickness of about 200 feet. These rocks, grouped by W. Waagen and C. Diener (1895) as the Scythian stage, are divided lithologically into (1) Lower Ceratite Limestone, (2) Ceratite Marls, (3) Ceratite Sandstone, and (4) Upper Ceratite Limestone, in ascending order. Used in this sense the word 'Ceratite' is a general term including ammonites with a ceratitic type of septal suture, but nowadays these are separated into a number of genera having no direct relation with the true Mesotriassic *Ceratites*. The Lower Ceratite Limestone has no species in common with the Himalayan Otoceras Beds, but the Gyronitan fauna is represented by species of *Prionolobus*, *Ambites*, *Koninckites*, and *Gyronites* in the zone of '*Celtites radiosus*' as distinguished by F. Frech (1901) and F. Noetling (1905). These authors subdivided the succeeding Ceratite Marls into three ammonite zones, the lower two carrying the Gyronitan fauna; the overlapping ranges of such species as *Gyronites frequens* and *Pseudosageceras multilobatum* indicate the essential continuity of the beds. The index-fossils of the upper zones, '*Celtites*' *fallax* and '*Koninckites*' *volutum* are examples of the costate, discoid forms that are probably derived from the Ophiceratidae. Other ophiceratid derivatives include species of *Proptychites* and *Prionolobus*. The succeeding Ceratite Sandstone is specially marked by species of *Flemingites*, evolute, round-ventered shells with strong costation, and often strigation on the outer whorls; they are associated with the compressed involute shells of *Anahedenstroemia* and *Clypeoceras*. Comparable assemblages are present in the Flemingites beds of Painkhanda, Spiti, and Byans, and a Flemingites fauna is recorded from Madagascar. A fauna described by C. Diener (1913) from the Guryul ravine in Kashmir is interesting for the association of *Pseudosageceras*, *Flemingites*, *Koninckites*, and *Paranorites* with ammonites not yet known from the central Himalayas. Among these are evolute shells, with quadrate whorls and strong ribbing, that Diener placed in a new genus *Kashmirites*, taking as the type a species from the Flemingites beds of the Salt Range. Another distinctive form is the tuberculate *Stephanites* which, along with *Prionites* and *Anasibirites*, is important for purposes of correlation. For *Stephanites* is present also in the Upper Ceratite Limestone of the Salt Range along with species of *Anasibirites*, and this genus is recorded from the Chocolate Limestone of Byans.

An eastern extension of the Himalayan marine development is seen in the Indonesian Archipelago, and a rich assemblage of ammonoids has been described, notably by O. A. Welter (1922), from the Palaeotrias of TIMOR representing several distinct horizons. The lowest, usually termed the 'Meekoceras Beds' consists of yellow limestones with admixture of tuffaceous material. This horizon has yielded some thirteen species of ammonoids, but L. F. Spath (1934) says there has been some confusion in the identification of various genera, and consequently in correlation of the strata. The association of *Pseudosageceras multilobatum* and large species of *Flemingites* with *Prionolobus* and *Paranorites*, however, indicates correlation with the Pseudosageceras beds of the Himalayas. In other localities in Timor limestones and marls, described as 'Ophiceras beds', have again furnished species of *Flemingites* together with shells that Welter placed in *Ophiceras* but referred by Spath (1930) to his new genera *Pseudoflemingites*, *Subflemingites*, and *Euflemingites*. The relations of these beds to the 'Meekoceras Limestone' are obscured by folding and thrusting, but they probably belong to the top of the Flemingitan substage. The Owenites Limestone also contains many ammonites, including species of *Flemingites* and its allies. The Proptychitidae are abundantly represented by large forms of *Owenites* and *Parowenites*. The compressed and involute *Anahedenstroemia* is represented by two species, one of which is also recorded from the Himalayan region. A further link with northern India is shown by the presence of

Kashmirites, and a species of *Prionites* has an analogue in the Salt Range. The white Anasibirites Limestone is probably equivalent to the Upper Ceratite Limestone of the Salt Range and the Chocolate Limestone of Byans. The chief ammonite is *Anasibirites multiformis*, a very variable species with ribbed early stage and smooth rounded outer whorls. It is associated with species of *Wasatchites*, *Hemiprionites*, and *Episageceras*. The highest Palaeotriassic Beds of Timor contain numerous fossils which are coated with a film of manganese dioxide, and Spath (1934) distinguishes two horizons in these beds. The lower one is specially marked by species of *Albanites*, a possible development of the Meekoceratidae which is typical of corresponding beds in Albania (p. 412). The genera *Procarnites*, *Dagnoceras*, and *Proptychitoides* are also common to Timor and Albania. Spath (1934) believes these beds to be later than the Columbites beds of Idaho (p. 410), and places them in the highest zone of the Columbitan substage. The second horizon under discussion is the Palaeophyllites bed in which the index-fossil is an evolute, rounded ammonite with flares on the otherwise smooth inner whorls, and pronounced ribs on the outer whorl. It is the earliest of the true Monophyllitidae, but the ribbed body-chamber seems to exclude the species as a direct ancestor of the Mesotriassic forms. Another characteristic genus is *Prohungarites* which is represented also in loose blocks near Pastannah, Kashmir. This Prohungaritan fauna is tentatively placed at the top of the Palaeotriassic Series.

In the USSURI district near Vladivostok (43° N., 132° E.) transgressive Palaeotriassic rocks, chiefly sandstones and clays, have furnished C. Diener (1895) with a considerable number of ammonoids and lamellibranchs. One of the most abundant ammonoids is *Proptychites hiemalis* which has a suture-line only slightly more complex than that of *P. markhami* from the Himalayan Gyronites beds. *P. hiemalis* is connected with the genus *Ussuriceras* separated by L. F. Spath (1930) from the typical *Proptychites* by reason of its distinctive suture-line. The ophiceratid *Protophiceras* and other genera, such as *Ussuria*, are regarded by Spath (1934) as offshoots from the common Palaeotriassic stock. These Ussuri beds are probably equivalent to the lower part of the Gyronites horizon. F. Frech (1901), however, suggested that more than one horizon is represented, and Spath (1934) states that the Ussuri species of *Xenoceltites* belong to a much higher horizon in the Palaeotrias, but its position is uncertain.

A Triassic fauna was discovered at the mouth of the OLENEK River (71°N., 124° E.), by Middendorf in 1884. Later collections made by Czekanowski were described by E. Mojsisovics (1886–8) who inferred that the association of ammonite genera indicates a Scythian age. These Siberian fossils have more recently been discussed by L. F. Spath (1934). The dominant forms are species of Hyatt's genus *Olenekites* which Spath regards as a simplified offshoot from the sibiritid stock that also produced the associated *Keyserlingites*. These shells and the allied *Sibirites* are regarded as ribbed and tuberculate developments of the great family Meekoceratidae. Several evolute, discoid forms with irregular ribbing are referred to the genus *Xenoceltites*, and another noteworthy form is the involute and greatly compressed fragment on which *Hedenstroemia* is based. Spath (1934) considers this last genus to differ from the Indian forms that have been identified with it, not only in shell-characters but also in age, for the two associations are very distinct. The presence of sibiritid derivatives in the Olenek fauna indicates a high horizon, and Spath places it in the highest Palaeotriassic substage, though he states that it may include some representative of the Columbitan fauna.

The Palaeotriassic Beds of SPITZBERGEN, summarized by H. Frebold (1935) have yielded ammonites at two horizons. Most abundant in the lower fauna are species of *Xenoceltites*, compressed shells with irregular ribbing on the outer whorls. There are also various sibiritids such as the highly sculptured *Wasatchites tridentinus*, the tuberculate *Arctoprionites nodosus* and the almost smooth *Gurleyites freboldi*. The presence of *Xenoceltites* and sibiritids leads to the correlation of this horizon with the Columbitan substage of other regions. The higher beds are characterized especially by species of *Arctoceras*, a genus of Meekoceratidae which ranges up from the foregoing horizon. They are apparently unknown outside Spitzbergen and are placed by Spath (1934) provisionally with the Olenek Beds of Siberia at the top of the Palaeotriassic Series.

Early Triassic deposits in east GREENLAND are of considerable importance for they have furnished ammonite faunas of Otoceratan age which have been described and illustrated by L. F. Spath (1930, 1935). The lowest strata, termed the Glyptophiceras beds, contain small species of the index genus, associated with fragments of *Otoceras* and derived Carboniferous fossils. The succeeding Ophiceras beds enclose an abundance of *Ophiceras*; the several species show considerable diversity comparable with the Himalayan development. In the upper beds the index genus is accompanied by the large *Otoceras boreale*, several species of *Glyptophiceras* and two of *Vishnuites*. The last genus becomes more prolific in the overlying Vishnuites beds where it is connected with *Ophiceras* by transitional forms. The young whorls of *O. dubium* acquire a tabulate periphery like the Meekoceratidae and later families. The only other ammonite genus in the Proptychites beds is the name-genus itself, which is represented by a great abundance of *P. rosenkrantzae* and simple forms of the genus which demonstrate relationship with the ancestral Ophiceratidae. Higher strata, named the Anadontophora Beds, have yielded no ammonites; they are shallow-water, detrital deposits with lamellibranchs and remains of stegocephalians, and are followed immediately by sandstones of Cretaceous (Aptian) age. The Triassic deposits of east Greenland, therefore, represent a temporary transgression of the Arctic Ocean over the continental margin at the beginning of the period.

The best-known localities for Palaeotriassic rocks in NORTH AMERICA extend over a range of 600 miles in Idaho, Utah, Nevada, and California (Map, Fig. 61). The thickness and character of the deposits vary from place to place, and nowhere is the succession complete. The most important fossils are the ammonoids which have been described by J. P. Smith (1932), A. L. Matthews (1929), and previous authors. The earliest Triassic Beds in the region rest directly on the mid-Permian Phosphoria Stage, and have yielded to N. D. Newell and B. Kummel (1941) the ammonoid *Discophiceras subkyoticum* which L. F. Spath describes as diagnostic of the Otoceras zone in east Greenland. A considerable palaeontological gap separates this zone from the Meekoceras beds which contain representatives of *Meekoceras*, *Submeekoceras*, and *Wyomingites*. These genera are late offshoots from a primitive flemingitid or gyronitid stock. They are at present almost unknown outside North America, but are associated with other ammonites which are more widespread. Among these are the involute lenticular shells of *Owenites* and *Aspenites* in the Inyo Range of California, which have near allies in the Owenites beds of Timor; *Anahedenstroemia* also appears to be represented in California, Idaho, Timor, and India. Hence the Meekoceras beds of North America are approximately equivalent to the Owenites beds of Timor, the lower half of the Palaeotriassic sequence being almost unknown in North America. Beds of slightly later date are described from Utah, from 40 to 100 feet above the Meekoceras beds. The ammonoids at this horizon are dominated by species of *Anasibirites* which are comparable with varieties of the Timor species *A. multiformis* Welter. These striate forms contrast sharply with the highly ornamented, but allied, shells which are assigned by Matthews (1929) to *Wasatchites*, a genus known from Spitzbergen as well as Utah and Timor. The higher Palaeotriassic Beds of south-east Idaho, which follow within 200 feet of the Meekoceras beds, are divided by J. P. Smith (1932) into Tirolites beds below and Columbites beds above. From the lower zone Smith cites a number of species identical or comparable with European species of *Tirolites*. But L. F. Spath (1934) questions the occurrence of the genus in Idaho though the Tirolites zone appears in his list of subdivisions for North America. The Columbites beds are marked particularly by the presence of evolute, feebly ornamented ammonoids with coronate inner whorls and narrow, arched venter; these comprise the genus *Columbites* which is regarded as a development from a primitive meekoceratid stock. Other forms recorded by Smith are included in *Submeekoceras* by Spath. These Columbites beds form the highest Palaeotriassic horizon definitely known in North America, though younger beds of the series occur in Timor, Kashmir, Siberia, and Spitzbergen. Hence the American sections represent a mere fragment of the complete Palaeotriassic sequence, and indicate a temporary transgression of the Pacific Ocean over the borders of the continental nucleus.

In southern EUROPE the Palaeotrias of the eastern Alps begins with the

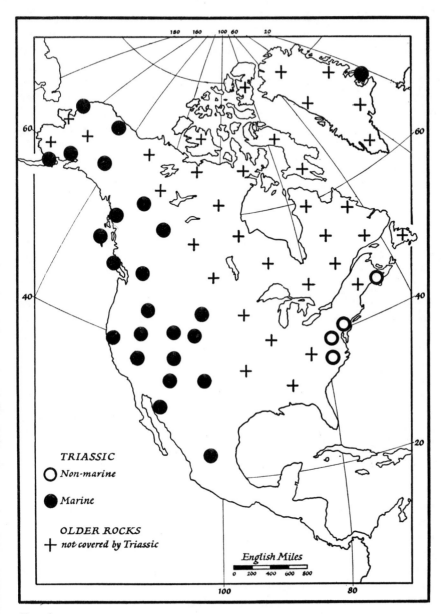

TRIASSIC
○ Non-marine
● Marine

OLDER ROCKS
+ not covered by Triassic

English Miles
0   200   400   600   800

FIG. 61. SKETCH-MAP OF NORTH AMERICA SHOWING GENERAL DISTRIBUTION
OF TRIASSIC ROCKS

Werfen Beds near Salzburg which have yielded a considerable molluscan assemblage but no ammonoids. The gastropod *Naticella costata* and the lamellibranchs *Myophoria ovata* and *M. costata* are typical forms; the last species is also found in the Roth Beds of the German Bunter, and is a useful guide in correlating the two facies. In Carinthia and south Tyrol two divisions of the Palaeotrias are distinguished. The Seis Beds form the base of the series where a conglomerate passes up into sandy shales and marls with interbedded limestone bands. The most abundant fossil is the widely distributed lamellibranch *Pseudomonotis clarai* which is associated with species of *Myophoria* and *Adontophora*. The succeeding Campil Beds are thick red and grey shales with interbedded ripple-marked sandstones. Again, lamellibranchs and gastropods are most abundant, but the ammonoid *Tirolites cassianus* is also recorded. This type of Werfen Beds is continued in the Dinaric Alps, and at localities in Croatia, Herzegovina, and Dalmatia. E. Kittl (1903) has described many ammonites from Muc in Dalmatia where the Campil Beds are richer in those fossils than most places in Europe. The assemblage is specially notable for the abundance of tirolitids; the typical evolute, tuberculate, and broad-ventered *Tirolites* is represented by several species, including the familiar *T. cassianus*. The genera *Tirolitoides*, *Diaplococeras*, *Svilagites*, and *Bittnerites* are closely related, but distinguished by style of ornamentation. Another group of genera with very simple suture-lines forms the family Dinaritidae which is typified by the smooth involute *Dinarites*. The genera *Pseudodinarites, Plococeras, Hololobus, Carniolites* are separated on account of morphological differences. These two families are believed to represent parallel offshoots from the same meekoceratid stock.

A different cephalopod assemblage has been described by G. Arthaber (1911) from red limestones in the Campil Beds of Kcira, about 25 miles east of Skutari in Albania. Here the most conspicuous ammonites are species of *Subcolumbites*, evolute, robust shells with reticulate ornament and narrow periphery. An extreme development of the genus is shown by the strongly keeled *Protropites*, and the associated *Prenkites* is a cadicone offshoot of the same stock. These columbitids are connected with the earlier Paranannitidae through such genera as *Paragoceras, Isculitoides*, and *Arnautoceltites*, smooth, inflated, involute shells with gradually widening umbilicus and simple suture-lines. The Proptychitidae and Meekoceratidae are still represented, but more important are early members of the Monophyllitidae, referred to several species of the genus *Eophyllites*. This family is probably derived independently from a persisting ophiceratid stock, and it becomes more prolific at Mesotriassic horizons. It is evident that the Albanian Subcolumbites fauna has little in common with the Tirolites assemblage of Dalmatia, and Spath (1934) is probably correct in regarding them as of different dates. The Albanian fauna shows close relationship with the *Albanites* association of Timor, and these two assemblages are thought to be slightly later than the Tirolites fauna, though referred to the same Columbitan substage. Possibly a later horizon is indicated by the presence in the Roth Beds of Thuringia, of the ammonoid *Beneckeia tenuis*. This is the only Palaeotriassic species of a genus that is better represented in the overlying Wellenkalk. It appears to indicate a northward extension from the Palaeotriassic sea which developed over a wider area during Muschelkalk time.

The South Alpine marine development has been traced at intervals through Hungary and the Balkans into Asia Minor. Along the Gulf of Ismid (41° N., 30° E.) at the eastern end of the Sea of Marmora, Triassic rocks lie unconformably on Palaeozoic strata. They begin with red conglomerates, sandstones and marls enclosing such mollusca as *Myophoria ovata* and *Naticella costata*. This horizon is therefore correlated with the Alpine Wer-fen Beds, and is succeeded by Mesotriassic strata (p. 412). In the Araxes Pass near Djulfa (40° N., 45° E.) in Armenia high Permian horizons are overlaid by red limestones containing ammonoids which have been de-scribed by A. Stoyanow (1910). These include a form of *Stephanites* similar to typical shells from the Salt Range of India, associated with species of *Paratirolites* which resemble those of the true *Tirolites* in many respects. There are also species of *Kashmirites* which were formerly confused with *Celtites*. Thus the Armenian deposits are probably equivalent to the Indian Stephanites beds of the Owenitan substage. Farther north at Mount Bogdo (45° N., 47° E.) in the Government of Astrakhan, south Russia, continental Permian deposits are followed by marine beds of Werfen age. They con-tain lamellibranchs and ammonoids among which species of *Tirolites* and the allied genus *Dorikranites* are conspicuous fossils. This northern exten-sion of the Tirolites beds is but another short-lived transgression of the sea in which the longer Palaeotriassic sequence of northern India was accumu-lated. The relations of the more important Palaeotriassic sections in Eurasia and elsewhere are shown in the accompanying table (p. 414).

The **Mesotriassic** rocks of EUROPE as developed in the Alpine region have long been divided into two stages. The lower, or Anisian, stage is so called from Anisus the latin name for the River Enns in the Austrian Tyrol, and the upper, or Ladinian stage is named after the Ladini people of Tyrol. It is generally agreed that the two stages together represent the Muschel-kalk of Germany. A number of palaeontological zones based on the am-monoids have been recognized in the Alpine Muschelkalk but the details of the succession are not always clear because of orogenic disturbance. It may be recalled that the eastern Alps consist of great thrust masses of imbricate type (schuppen) and translated sheets of rock (nappes) which have apparently been moved considerable distances northward from their place of origin. Hence the Alpine geologists recognize a number of tectonic belts arranged roughly east and west parallel to the general axis of the mountain chains. The rocks of each tectonic belt preserve the same general

Provisional Ammonoid Zones of the Palaeotriassic Series and their distribution (adapted from L. F. Spath, 1934)

Series	Faunas	Zones	Germany	Alps	Asia Minor	Salt Range	Himalayas	Madagascar	Timor	W. America	E. Greenland
PALAEOTRIASSIC	PROHUNGARITAN				×					×	
	COLUMBITAN	Columbites								×	
		Tirolites			×	×				×	
	OWENITAN	Anasibirites				×	×		×	×	
		Owenites	Only non-marine deposits						×	×	
		Pseudosageceras				×			×	×	
	FLEMINGITAN	Flemingites flemingianus				×	×	×			
		Koninckites volutus				×	×				
	GYRONITAN	Celtites fallax				×	×				
		Prionolobus rotundatus				×	×				
		Celtites radiosus				×	×				×
	OTOCERATAN	Ophiceras tibeticum					×				×
		Episageceras dalailemae					×				
		Otoceras woodwardi					×				×

facies in that direction, but striking changes of facies have been recorded from north to south, transverse to the Alpine axis. The tectonic belts are therefore regarded more or less as facies belts and, in some cases, the origin of certain nappes has been inferred from similarity of facies in the presumed root zone. Hence, if the nappes be smoothed out and referred back to their former locations, some idea of the original geographical conditions can theoretically be formed. But while each nappe and its roots might be correlated by the facies, it does not necessarily follow that rocks of similar facies belong to the same nappe. Facies may vary in all directions and their limits may not coincide with tectonic units. So prudence must restrain far-reaching generalizations based on differences of facies. A great deal remains to be done before the detailed stratigraphical problems can be solved, but agreement seems to have been reached in regard to the general succession of ammonite faunas.

Several of the early Mesotriassic ammonite genera are grouped in the family Beyrichitidae, and appear to have originated in Palaeotriassic types that were formerly grouped in the Meekoceratidae. These, according to L. F. Spath (1934), are connected by transitional forms with the Ceratitidae that are derived from the same ancestral group and therefore produce similar offshoots. It is still uncertain if the early beyrichitid genera are present in the Alpine region though *Nicodemites* is recorded from Thuringia, and the later *Beyrichites* is represented by the type *B. reuttensis* Mojs. in the Virgloria Limestone of Tyrol and its equivalent in Lombardy. The cephalopod assemblages in the higher beds of the Anisian stage are dominated by numerous species of *Paraceratites* (Pl. VI) from which the familiar *P. binodosus* (Hauer) and *P. trinodosus* (Mojs.) have been selected as successive zonal indexes. In the binodosus zone the index-fossil is accompanied by other species of *Paraceratites*, its offshoot *Balatonites*, and the beyrichitid *Philippites*. The genus *Acrochordiceras* makes its appearance in a species with strong costation extending continuously across the arched venter. Members of this fauna are recorded from localities in the Alps, Balkans, and Asia Minor (Map, Fig. 60, p. 405).

The trinodosus zone is marked especially by the association of *Paraceratites trinodosus* and other ceratitids with distinctive species of *Ptychites*, *Monophyllites*, arcestids, and cladiscitids. The ceratitids include certain forms with simple ornament which are sometimes grouped in the genus *Semiornites*; the allied beyrichitids are represented by occasional specimens of *Hollandites petersi* and *Beyrichites reuttensis*. The non-tuberculate *Acrochordiceras enodi* resembles the species in the binodosus zone, but certain later members of the genus develop a flattened periphery and outer spines, thereby acquiring a certain similarity with ceratitids. The evolute *Monophyllites sphaerophyllus* is often accompanied by *Leiophyllites suessi* and the involute *Megaphyllites sandalinus*, all showing monophyllic endings to the sutural saddles. The arcestids, robust, involute forms developed from Palaeotriassic paranannitids, are represented by species of *Pararcestes* and *Proarcestes*. The cladiscitid genus *Hypocladiscites* and the ptychitid *Sturia* are often conspicuous by reason of their strigate ornament. The robust *Ptychites flexuosus* and the oxynote *Pinacoceras damesi* are also noteworthy members of the fauna. These ammonoids are widely distributed in south Europe and have long been known from the red marmoritized limestones in the neighbourhood of Hallstadt; they are also recorded in similar facies from Hageghol in the Dobrudja, Kuna Gora in Croatia, the Volujak Mountains in Bosnia, and the Argolis region of Greece. In Austria, black nodular limestones forming the lower part of the Reifling Beds carry the same fauna. The black Prezzo Limestone of Judicaria was also referred to the trinodosus zone by E. Mojsisovics. In places the zone is represented by brachiopod beds and algal limestone without ammonoids.

The Buchenstein Beds of the Ladinian stage contain several ammonoid genera, like *Ptychites*, *Monophyllites*, *Proarcestes*, &c., which persist from the trinodosus zone but are represented by distinctive species. These are accompanied in the Buchenstein Beds by *Protrachyceras reitzi* which is used as the zonal index. The genus *Protrachyceras* is thought to be derived from the Anisian *Anolcites* which is recorded from the lower part of the Reifling Limestone in the Austrian Alps. The involute *Joannites*, and the discoid *Arpadites* are represented by distinctive species. The zone of *Aplococeras avisianum* was separated by E. Haug (1910) for part of the Marmolata Limestone which contains species of *Megaphyllites, Gymnites, Sturia* and *Sageceras* in addition to the zonal index. This and the comparable Esino Limestone of Lombardy are deposits of great thickness often formed largely of the calcareous algae *Diplopora* and *Gyroporella*, but sometimes of corals. *Aplococeras avisianum* is also recorded from the Wengen Beds along with other species of the Marmolata and Esino Limestones. The index-fossil of the Wengen Beds is *Protrachyceras archelaus*; there are other species of this genus which are closely similar to those of the Buchenstein Beds, and this applies also to species of *Arpadites*. The upper part of the Reifling Limestone carries a similar fauna, as also does the Fured Limestone in the Forest of Bakony which is specially marked by the presence of *Joannites tridentinus*. The Cassian Beds of the Tyrol next in succession enclose a fauna which is closely related to the Wengen assemblage, but the Cassian Beds are placed at the base of the Neotriassic Series.

We have already noted that the genus *Ceratites* of the German Muschelkalk seems to be derived from the Mediterranean or Alpine *Paraceratites* stock through the intermediate form *Progonoceratites*. Hence the Ceratite beds of Germany cannot be earlier than the Anisian stage; indeed the presence of *Ptychites dux* and species of *Judicarites* in the Upper Wellenkalk provides evidence for correlating this horizon with the trinodosus zone. The close relations of the ammonoid faunas in the Buchenstein, Wengen, and Cassian horizons, however, seem to imply continuous deposition which leaves no room for the Ceratites beds in the Ladinian stage. Yet species of *Protrachyceras* and other Ladinian genera are recorded from Mora d'Ebro and the island of Minorca in beds with the position and lithological characters of the Muschelkalk. Further, in Sardinia, a species of *Protrachyceras* is said to be associated with *Ceratites muensteri*. On these grounds L. F. Spath (1934) tentatively places the Ceratites Beds of central Europe in the reitzi zone of the Ladinian stage. It is possible, however, that the general absence of *Ceratites* from the Alpine Trias indicates a gap in the sequence.

From grey limestones on the shores of the Gulf of Ismid, Anatolia, F. Toula (1896) has described ammonoids indicative of four Mesotriassic horizons. The earliest assemblage is marked by species of *Nicodemites*, a beyrichitid genus with irregular subfalcate ornament. The species are local forms, but the genus is also known in Thuringia where it precedes the true *Beyrichites*. This Beyrichitan fauna is followed in the Ptychites beds by an assemblage which includes *Paraceratites binodosus* and local species of the same genus together with members of the genera *Acrochordiceras* and *Ptychites*; this is the binodosus fauna of the Alpine region. The fauna of the succeeding Proarcestes Beds, which includes *Paraceratites trinodosus* and species of *Acrochordiceras, Proarcestes,* and *Procladiscites,* is clearly that of the Alpine trinodosus zone. The highest beds in the sequence, which contain *Protrachyceras anatolicum* Toula and *Clionites* of the type of *C. dobrogensis* Kittl, form the base of the Ladinian stage.

Mesotriassic faunas are contained in about 400 feet of strata in the HIMALAYAN REGION of Spiti, Painkhanda, and Kashmir. The lower beds contain numerous brachiopods, including species of *Spiriferina, Spirigera,* and rhynchonellids comparable with Alpine forms. There are also some cephalopods, the most characteristic of which are species of *Durgaites,* a genus of the Sibiritidae which persists from Palaeotriassic horizons. The Beyrichitidae are represented by species of *Hollandites,* a development parallel with the semiornate ceratitids of the Alpine region. Species of *Gymnites* and its offshoot *Japonites,* as well as the monophyllitids *Leiophyllites* and *Ussurites* are also recorded. This assemblage is referred to the Beyrichitan substage of Spath's classification. The Durgaites Beds are succeeded by the Ptychites Beds in which cephalopods are again the most important fossils. *Paraceratites trinodosus* and the allied *P. thuillieri* are associated with species of *Hollandites, Beyrichites, Acrochordiceras, Gymnites, Ptychites, Sturia, Monophyllites,* &c., some of which are identical or comparable with Alpine forms of the trinodosus zone. L. F. Spath (1951) mentions the presence of Anisian cephalopods in Pahang state, Malaya. The assemblage, including such distinctive genera as *Paraceratites, Acrochordiceras, Ptychites,* and *Sturia,* resembles that of the Himalayan Muschelkalk especially in the numerical preponderance of *Paraceratites* and its allies.

Anisian cephalopods have been described by O. A. Welter (1915) from TIMOR, where they occur in loose blocks of red limestones containing tuffaceous material. The list of ammonoids includes species of *Paraceratites, Gymnites* and its derivative *Japonites, Ptychites, Acrochordiceras,* the monophyllitids *Ussurites, Leiophyllites,* megaphyllitids, the beyrichitid *Durgaites,* the cladiscitid *Sturia,* the sageceratid *Parasageceras* and forms of *Xenodiscus* transitional from the Palaeotriassic *Anakashmirites.* Many of the species are peculiar to Timor, but the generic assemblage is comparable with that of the Paraceratitan fauna of Europe. Several of the genera persist in a Ladinian fauna preserved in dark-red manganiferous limestones and calcareous tuffs. The significant genera here are *Protrachyceras, Proarcestes, Joannites, Hungarites, Pinacoceras,* associated with distinctive species of such persistent genera as *Ptychites, Monophyllites, Megaphyllites, Sageceras,* &c.

In NORTH AMERICA, strata which are apparently equivalent to the Anisian stage occur in the Inyo mountains of California, where a sequence of black limestones have yielded significant ammonoids. The zonal index is a species of *Parapopanoceras,* a genus which, according to L. F. Spath (1934) is close to *Megaphyllites* and other later developments. Among the other genera listed by A. Hyatt and J. P. Smith (1905) are *Xenodiscus, Acrochordiceras,* and *Durgaites* (as *Tirolites*), and the assemblage is regarded as equivalent to the Beyrichitan fauna of Asia Minor at the base of the Anisian stage. In Shasta county, California, siliceous shales containing occasional badly preserved ammonoids are correlated with thick fossiliferous limestones in the Humboldt Range, Nevada. The most abundant ammonites here are the robust beyrichitid *Gymnotoceras* and its descendant *Frechites* which is regarded as a development parallel with the associated *Paraceratites* (Pl. VI). Other genera in the assemblage include *Beyrichites*, *Nevadites*, *Arcestes*, *Tropigastrites*, *Anolcites* with species closely related to European forms. Moreover, the lamellibranch *Daonella dubia*, which is abundantly preserved in intercalated shales, is close to the Alpine species *D. paucicostata*. These Anolcites Beds of Nevada, however, may be slightly later than the European trinodosus zone; unfortunately the higher shales of possible Ladinian age in California and Nevada have not yielded determinable fossils.

Another fragment of the Mesotriassic succession survives in SPITZ-BERGEN whence L. F. Spath (1921) has described a few poorly preserved ammonoids. The association of *Monophyllites* cf. *sphaerophyllus* with species of *Ptychites* and *Gymnotoceras* indicates the presence of the Anisian stage, probably the trinodosus zone. Other crushed specimens associated with *Daonella* are doubtfully referred to the Ladinian stage.

The **Neotriassic rocks** of the eastern ALPS are classified in three stages, namely, Carnian, Norian, and Rhaetian, in ascending order. Each stage is divided into a number of palaeontological zones based chiefly on the ammonoid assemblages. In south Tyrol the Wengen Beds of the Ladinian stage are followed by the St. Cassian Beds which enclose a dwarfed fauna of extraordinary richness, more than 300 species according to M. O. Gordon (1893), including many gastropods, lamellibranchs, and brachiopods. The most significant ammonoid genus is *Trachyceras* (Pl. VI) which, with the persistent *Protrachyceras*, is derived through the Ladinian *Nevadites* from the ceratitid *Popinites*. The species *T. aon* and *T. aonoides* are cited by L. F. Spath (1934) and previous authors as the index-fossils of two successive zones in the St. Cassian Beds. These highly ornamented forms are accompanied by smooth globose arcestids and the peculiar *Paralobites pisum*, by the compressed *Lecanites* and its falcicostate ally *Badiotites* with simple goniatitic suture-line. Similar Trachyceratan faunas are cited in the literature from other localities in the Alpine region. *T. aonoides* is recorded by E. Haug (1911) from the lower part of the red marble at the Feuerkogel near Aussee together with members of other families including arcestids and the allied joannitids, monophyllitids and megaphyllitids, tropitids and haloritids. The first four of these families were already established at earlier horizons, but the last two are most typical in higher strata. It may be, therefore, that this record includes forms from the succeeding zone of *Carnites floridus*. *T. aonoides*, and *Joannites cymbiformis* are reported also from tuffa-

Ammonoid Zones of the Mesotriassic and Neotriassic Series and their Distribution (adapted from L. F. Spath 1934)

Series	Faunas	Zones	Germany	Alps	Asia Minor	Himalayas	Timor	N. America
NEOTRIASSIC	EOPSILOCERATAN	*Eopsiloceras planorboides*		×				
	CHORISTOCERATAN	*Choristoceras marshi*		×				
		Choristoceras haueri		×				
	PINACOCERATAN	*Sirenites argonautae*		×				
		Pinacoceras metternichi		×				
	HALORITAN	*Cyrtopleurites bicrenatus*		×		×	×	
		Sagenites giebeli		×				
		Heinrichites paulckei		×				
	TROPITAN	*Tropites subbullatus*		×		×		×
	CARNITAN	*Carnites floridus*		×		×		
	TRACHYCERATAN	*Trachyceras aonoides*		×				×
		Trachyceras aon		×				
MESO-	CERATITAN	*Protrachyceras archelaus*		×				
		Protrachyceras reitzi	×		×			
	PARACERATITAN	*Paraceratites trinodosus*		×	×	×		×
		Paraceratites binodosus	×		×	×		
	BEYRICHITAN		×		×	×		×

ceous beds in the Dolomite country, and the lower part of the Raibl Beds of the Julian Alps. Records of the aonoides zone in the Forest of Bakony and the Argolis Peninsula of Greece likewise probably include some forms of the floridus zone. The genus *Carnites* is regarded as one of the numerous derivatives of the Mesotriassic ceratitids. The typical *C. floridus* is present in the lenticular masses of fine-grained red limestone near Bleiburg in the Salzkammergut, also in the Reingraben Shales of the Austrian Alps, the upper Raibl Beds of the Julian Alps and the Bakony Wald in Hungary where it is frequently associated with *Trachyceras austriacum* and members of the families cited above.

The zone of *Tropites subbullatus* is known at the Vordere Sandling and the Raschberg near Aussee where the zone-fossil abounds. The same fauna has been found by G. Geyer (1900) near San Stefano in Cadore in black limestones containing cephalopods and brachiopods. The genus *Tropites* comprises cadicone shells with keeled venter and contracting body-whorl; it may be connected with the Anisian *Tropigastrites* but L. F. Spath (1951) says there is not a convincing series of passage forms. Variation in form and ornament is reflected in the associated genera *Paratropites, Paulotropites,* and *Hoplotropites.* Some persistent genera, such as *Arcestes, Megaphyllites,* and *Pinacoceras* are represented by distinctive species. *Anasirenites* is a late development of the Trachyceratidae, and *Mojsvarites* of the Monophyllitidae. The large family Haloritidae is more typical of Norian horizons, but several genera, including *Jovites, Juvavites, Sagenites* are already prominent in Carnian assemblages. Similar faunas have been described by G. G. Gemmellaro (1904) from Carnian and early Norian horizons in Sicily which, like those in the Alps, have been displaced by orogenic disturbance. In the provinces of Palermo and Gigenti the two stages are represented by limestones containing species of *Halobia, Daonella,* and *Monotis,* alternating with cephalopod-beds belonging to the zones of *Trachyceras aonoides* and *Tropites subbullatus.* The ammonoids are closely comparable with those of the Hallstatt Limestone already discussed, but some genera are special to Sicily; the haloritid *Gonionotites,* for instance, is unknown elsewhere in south Europe, though it is recorded from Asian and North American localities.

In the Norian stage near Hallstatt a sequence of ammonoid zones has been established by E. Mojsisovics (1893) and C. Diener (1920). The index-fossils of the lower three zones are the haloritids *Heinrichites paulckei* Diener, *Sagenites giebeli,* and *Cyrtopleurites bicrenatus* (Hauer); these horizons may be grouped in a Haloritan substage. The upper zones are likewise marked by the presence of *Pinacoceras metternichi* (Hauer) and *Sirenites argonautae* respectively; together they form the Pinacoceratan substage. Each of the index-fossils is accompanied by a varied assemblage of distinctive species belonging mainly to the families Arcestidae, Cladiscitidae, Haloritidae, Megaphyllitidae, Discophyllitidae, Pinacoceratidae. The lowest zone, that of *Heinrichites paulckei,* includes the *Discophyllites patens* beds of the Someraukogel near Hallstatt; *Discophyllites* is the typical genus of its family, which includes the ancestors of the Jurassic and Cretaceous *Phylloceras.* Another genus of Discophyllitidae is *Diphyllites* which appears in the Carnian stage and is represented in the Norian zones of *Sagenites giebeli* and *Cyrtopleurites bicrenatus* at Leislingwand and Someraukogel respectively. The Pinacoceratan fauna of the Steinbergkogel near Hallstatt is specially distinguished by the presence of *Pinacoceras metternichi,* a flat involute shell with an extremely elaborate suture-line. It is accompanied by the large *Cladiscites tornatus* which contrasts in size with the smaller species of earlier horizons, also by species of arcestids, haloritids, and the straight *Rhabdoceras.* The last genus belongs to the Choristoceratidae, a family established for a few genera which combine various degrees of uncoiling with a simple suture-line. The extremes are seen in *Choristoceras* which comprises discoid evolute shells that gradually become uncoiled, and *Rhabdoceras* in which the shell is straight. The family gives rise through the genus *Peripleurites* to the sinistral helicoid *Cochloceras*. These genera are conspicuous in certain grey marls, known as the Zlambach Beds in the Salzkammergut, where they are associated with the usual types of *Arcestes*, *Cladiscites*, *Megaphyllites*, and the lamellibranch *Monotis salinaria*. The un-coiled genera persist in the Choristoceratan faunas of the Rhaetian stage in the Alpine region where the lower zones of the stage are marked by *Choris-toceras haueri* and *C. marshii*. The uppermost Rhaetian Beds contain *Eopsilo-ceras planorboides*, a discophyllitid form which is known only in crushed specimens. North of the Alps ammonites are rare or unknown in the Rhaetian Beds and the stage is recognized by certain lamellibranchs such as *Pteria contorta* which is recorded from localities as widely separated as the Rhaetian Alps, Corsica, the Pyrénées, Portugal, Germany, England, and south Sweden. In western Europe generally, the Rhaetian Beds are trans-gressive on the continental Keuper Series, and at some places they over-step on to Carboniferous rocks.

In EASTERN EUROPE, Carnian and Norian horizons of Alpine type are known in the Carpathians, and at localities in the Balkans, notably in Bosnia and the Peninsula of Argolis. In Crete Triassic limestones contain brachio-pods and lamellibranchs, but no cephalopods are reported. A more varied assemblage in a similar facies at Balia Maden in the north-west of Asia Minor is said to show affinities with Rhaetian faunas. Some 800 miles to the south-east, at the north-eastern corner of the Dead Sea, L. R. Cox (1924) has recorded lamellibranchs and brachiopods which are identified with species of the Alpine Raibl Beds. The strata wedge out to the east and south-east, and were obviously formed close to a shore-line. No Triassic rocks are recorded from the eastern part of Asia Minor and Mesopotamia; more than a thousand miles must be traversed eastward from the Dead Sea to the next locality. This is in the district of Naiband and Houzikdan (32° N. 57° E.) in eastern PERSIA where Norian horizons have been described by J. A. Douglas (1929). The fauna consists almost entirely of lamellibranchs, the most abundant being large scallops of the *Pecten clignetti* group, for which Douglas established a new subgenus *Indopecten*. The nearest fauna which shows affinity with the Persian assemblage is that at Elphinstone Inlet, Oman, at the entrance to the Persian Gulf, described by G. M. Lees (1938), which also includes *Pecten clignetti*. None of the Persian fossils can be certainly referred to species typical of the Mediterranean area, and there seems to be no close similarity with Norian faunas of the Himalayan region. The fauna shows a close parallel, however, with a Triassic assemb-lage described by L. Krumbeck (1913) from the East Indian Archipelago which also has an abundance of *Pecten clignetti*. Douglas concludes that communication with the Mediterranean marine area was severed in Norian time and, as the Himalayan region was separated from the Persian sea by a Neotriassic continental facies in Afghanistan, communication with the Indonesian area was effected south of the Indian Peninsula.

He suggests that the probable habitat of the fauna was an archipelago of islands.

The Carnian stage in the HIMALAYAN REGION consists mainly of arenaceous rocks with intercalated clayey and calcareous sediments. In Spiti the stage begins with the Halobia Limestone, but in its meagre fauna *Halobia* cf. *comata* Bittner is the only fossil directly indicative of Carnian age. Almost immediately above, grey shales with concretions have yielded ammonoids among which C. Diener (1908) records *Carnites floridus* and *Joannites cymbiformis* with species of *Trachyceras* and *Monophyllites* comparable with Alpine forms from the Carnitan substage. A higher fossiliferous horizon is rich in brachiopods, some of the genera being peculiar to the Indian region, but others are represented in the eastern Alps. About 600 feet higher still is the Tropites Limestones of Lilang and Tikha with numerous ammonoids which include species of *Tropites* and its allies *Discotropites* and *Paratropites*, together with *Anatomites*, *Trachysagenites*, *Jovites*, *Sandlingites*, *Clionites*, and *Proarcestes*. Some species are local developments, but all the genera and a good proportion of the species are represented in the Alpine zone of *Tropites subbullatus*. The thick dolomitic limestone which follows has yielded only a few badly preserved brachiopods and lamellibranchs, but is included in the Carnian stage. In Painkhanda two Carnian horizons rich in cephalopods are recognized by C. Diener (1912) in the Shalshal and Bambanag cliffs. From the lower one, known as the Traumatocrinus Limestone, Diener (1909) has described species of fourteen ammonoid genera of which *Protrachyceras*, *Trachyceras*, *Sirenites*, *Carnites*, *Proarcestes*, *Lobites*, *Joannites*, *Monophyllites*, *Mojsvarites*, *Celtites*, *Isculites*, *Arpadites*, and *Dittmarites* are represented in the Carnitan fauna of the Alps. A local genus *Rimkinites* is considered by L. F. Spath (1951) to connect *Carnites* with the Mesotriassic ceratitids through the Hungaritidae. From a higher series of dark calcareous shales Diener has recorded species of the haloritids *Jovites*, *Juvavites*, *Anatomites*, and *Griesbachites*, with *Hypocladiscites*, *Placites*, *Mojsvarites*, and *Discophyllites*, but the fauna of the Tropites beds is not yet known in Painkhanda. The Neotriassic rocks of Byans are difficult to interpret because of intense orogenic disturbance, and the Carnian stage is said to be reduced to about 170 feet, in contrast with 800 feet in Painkhanda, and 1,600 feet in Spiti. The Tropites Limestone of Byans has yielded a fauna of 168 species of which no less than 155 are ammonoids. As described by C. Diener (1906) the assemblage shows considerable affinity with the Tropitan fauna of the Alps, though there are several elements peculiar to the Indian locality. Diener (1908) has also described ammonoids from an 'exotic block' of red marble on the Tibetan border. The assemblage agrees closely with that of the Carnian stage in the eastern Alps especially in the preponderance of *Arcestes* and *Cladiscites* (Pl. VI) which are rare in the main Himalayan sections. It also contains *Gonionotites italicus* and three other forms recorded from Sicily but not from the Alps.

The Norian strata of the Himalayas are mainly pure limestones and dolomites. In the Lilang section of Spiti the Carnian stage is followed by a sequence of brown limestones with interbedded shales and sandstones, the whole being about 500 feet in thickness. Numerous cephalopods are found in the upper beds, especially species of the haloritid *Juvavites*. This genus is accompanied by the allied *Anatomites*, by the arpaditid *Dittmarites*, and by genera of the Tibetitidae. This last family is an Indian development, parallel with the European Cyrtopleuritidae, derived from Mesotriassic ceratitids. This is the highest horizon in the Norian stage of Spiti to contain cephalopods. Succeeding strata have only yielded brachiopods and lamellibranchs, except one horizon at Lilang which is a true organic limestone abounding in corals and crinoids. In Painkhanda the development is somewhat different. The Carnian stage there is succeeded by a nodular limestone containing a small assemblage of cephalopods so poorly preserved that Diener (1912) could record only a single species of *Proclydonautilus* along with indeterminate forms of *Hauerites*, *Arcestes*, &c. As other forms, referred to *Parajuvavites* and *Pinacoceras*, seem to have Norian affinities, the nodular limestones are assigned to that stage. The richest Neotriassic fauna in Painkhanda is enclosed in the Halorites Limestone of the Bambanag section; it is pre-eminently a cephalopod horizon the proportion of brachiopods and lamellibranchs being very small. Among the sixty-seven species of cephalopods described by E. Mojsisovics (1899), species of *Halorites* and *Parajuvavites* predominate, though they are not known in Spiti, and the rare local element *Gümbelites* belongs to the same family. Three species of *Pinacoceras* (Pl. VI), including *P. metternichi*, are identified with European forms, but the allied *Bambanagites* is a rare local development. The Indian family Tibetitidae is represented, as well as several widespread genera, but only three species of the whole assemblage are present in the Juvavites Beds of Spiti. The differences may be due to variation of facies or to difference in age of the deposits.

Marine deposits of the Rhaetian stage are not certainly known in the Himalayan belt, but M. Healey (1908) has described a unique Rhaetian fauna from Upper Burma. At Napeng (22°, 30° N., 97° E.), intensely crushed grey shales rest directly on Palaeozoic limestones, and contain a fauna consisting mainly of lamellibranchs. The species *Pteria contorta* (Portlock), *Grammatodon lycetti* (Moore) and *Gervilleia praecursor* Quenstedt leave no doubt as to the age of the deposits. Species of *Palaeoneilo*, *Protocardia*, *Cardita*, and *Gervilleia* are nearly related to forms from the Rhaetian and Liassic rocks of Europe. New species of *Cassianella*, *Hoernesia*, and *Myophoria* resemble European Triassic forms. The genera *Burmesia*, *Prolaria*, and *Datta* are unique, and are placed in new families. Several species of the Napeng Beds have been recognized in material from the west coast of Sumatra.

The Neotriassic rocks of TIMOR, like those of the regions already discussed, exhibit various facies which are now often juxtaposed by reason of tectonic disturbance. Certain red and pale limestones, often inter-bedded with tuffs, contain an abundance of cephalopods, among which such leiostracous genera as *Arcestes* and *Cladiscites* are most prominent. The trachyostracous *Halorites* and its allies are also conspicuous, for among the fifty genera cited by H. A. Brouwer (1925) *Amarassites, Anatomites,*

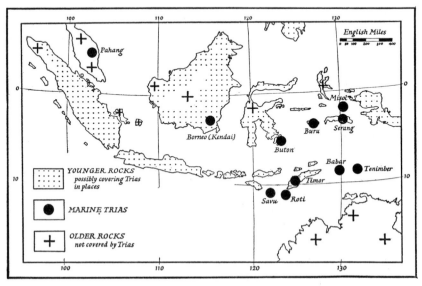

FIG. 62. SKETCH-MAP OF THE EAST INDIES SHOWING DISTRIBUTION OF MARINE TRIAS

Gonionotites, Griesbachites, Indonesites, Jovites, Juvavites, Malayites, Miltites, Molengraaffites, Sagenites, and *Trachysagenites* also belong to the Haloritidae. Apart from local elements like *Amarassites, Indonesites,* and *Malayites,* most of these genera are represented in the Halorites Limestone of the Himalayas and the Hallstatt Limestone of the Alps. The genera *Anatibetites, Metacarnites, Neotibetites* and *Paratibetites* represent the Indian Tibetitidae and replace the European Cyrtopleuridae. Other light-coloured limestones associated with marls and shales contain the lamellibranch *Halobia* as the most prominent fossil. This facies is recorded from other islands of the Timor arc (Map, Fig. 62) and on Buru has yielded *Pecten clignetti* which we have already cited from Persia (p. 421). Still other masses of pale limestone with indistinct stratification contain reef-corals such as *Thecosmilia* and *Isastraea,* associated with certain mollusca and brachiopods. These facies are all comparable with similar developments in the Himalayan and Alpine regions. Little is known of the Rhaetian stage in Timor though certain bituminous limestones and dark shales containing *Choristoceras* are

assigned to it. Neotriassic rocks are recorded from other islands of the
Malay Archipelago and from New Caledonia, and China (Map, Fig. 63).

Triassic rocks occur in NEW ZEALAND at localities in both the North
and South Islands whence numerous fossils have been described by C. T.
Trechmann (1917) and O. Wilckens (1927). The succession begins with a

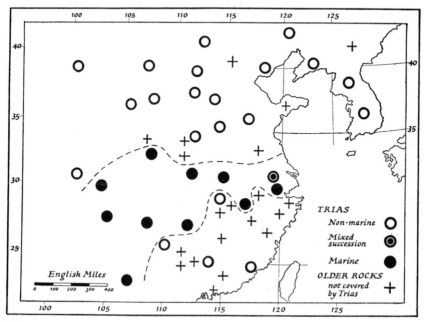

FIG. 63. SKETCH-MAP OF CHINA SHOWING GENERAL DISTRIBUTION OF
TRIASSIC ROCKS

late Ladinian or early Carnian horizon, and continues with representatives
of the Carnian and Norian stages. Cephalopods are rare in the prevalent
clastic rocks, but include poorly preserved specimens referred to *Arcestes*,
Cladiscites, *Pinacoceras*, and *Discophyllites*. Some of the lamellibranchs are
of value for general correlation; for instance *Daonella indica* is characteristic
of the base of the Neotrias in the Himalayas, several Carnian species of
Halobia are recorded, as well as an abundance of Norian *Pseudomonotis*. The
brachiopods include the rhynchonellid genus *Halorella*, the spiriferids
Mentzelia, *Retzia*, *Spiriferina*, and the local *Mentzeliopsis* and *Hectoria*.
Some of the spiriferids are related to Himalayan and Alpine forms, but
F. R. C. Reed (1951) states that the fauna is nearest to that of New Caledonia. Both Trechmann and Wilckens recognize the transgressive character
of the series.

In NORTH AMERICA the Carnian stage is represented in California by
the uppermost part of the Pit Shale and the lower part of the Hosselkus

Limestone. The earliest horizon consists of shales in which *Halobia rugosa* is the chief fossil, accompanied by other lamellibranchs. This *Halobia* was first described by C. W. Gümbel (1861) from early Carnian deposits in the Austrian Alps where it is abundant. Crushed ammonoids from the Pit Shale are referred to *Protrachyceras storrsi* Smith (1927) which is said to resemble the Alpine *Trachyceras gridleri* Mojs. The remainder of the Carnian stage comprises the zone of *Tropites subbullatus*. This begins with calcareous shales full of *Halobia superba* Mojs., a large shell which is typical of Carnian strata at many places in the Alpine and Himalayan regions. In the succeeding shaly limestones *Halobia superba* is associated with a large number of ammonoids, including *Tropites subbullatus* and other species of the genus together with species of *Discotropites*, *Paratropites*, *Sagenites*, *Trachyceras*, and *Clionites*. The abundance of *Trachyceras* at this horizon in America contrasts with its disappearance from the Alpine area before the advent of the Tropitan fauna. The species of *Tropites* persist into a higher limestone where several species of *Juvavites* give distinction to the fauna. Other prominent genera include *Gonionotites*, *Discotropites*, and *Sagenites*. Several species of *Juvavites*, *Pinacoceras* and other genera are identical or comparable with Alpine forms, but the American forms of *Tropites* are distinct and may be autochthonous. Marine Triassic fossils from black shales and sandstones alternating with volcanic rocks near Zacatecas, Mexico, are described by C. Burkhardt (1905). Badly preserved ammonoids are referred to the genera *Protrachyceras*, *Sirenites*, *Clionites*, and *Anatomites*, and the horizon is correlated with the Hosselkus Limestone of California.

Sixty years ago J. F. Whiteaves (1889) described an ammonoid assemblage, including species of *Dawsonites* and *Nathorstites*, from the Liard River in British Columbia. The fauna was presumed to occur below the zone of *Halobia superba* but the two horizons were not seen in sequence. Another species of *Nathorstites* in association with *Trachyceras* and *Cladiscites* is recorded near the mouth of the Nation River, a tributary of the Yukon River, again within a short distance of shales enclosing *Halobia superba*. Later F. H. McLearn (1939) described a Nathorstites fauna from the Schooler Creek, Western Peace River, British Columbia. Here species of *Nathorstites* are associated with *Protrachyceras*, *Paratrachyceras*, *Isculites*, *Lobites*, and *Silenticeras*; McLearn suggests a Ladinian or very early Carnian age for the fauna. Now L. F. Spath (1951) places *Nathorstites* in a family by itself, for it differs from *Megaphyllites* in having a keeled venter and simple suture-line; *Dawsonites* is interpreted as an independent offshoot of *Anolcites* distinct from *Protrachyceras*. Spath also says that the association in Spitzbergen of *Nathorstites* with *Monophyllites spetzbergense* and *Ptychites trochleaformis* indicates an age not later than the Ladinian stage. Comparable faunas are known from Alaska, Ellesmereland, Bear Island, and the New Siberian island of Kotelny.

According to J. P. Smith (1912) the Norian stage in California begins with the Coral Zone of the Hosselkus Limestone, which contains numerous reefs of *Isastraea, Stephanocoenia, Astrocoenia, Thecosmilia, Thamnastraea,* and other corals. Some species, like *Stephanocoenia juvavica* Frech, *Isastraea profunda* Reuss, *Thecosmilia fenestrata* Reuss., *Thamnastraea rectilamellosa* Winkles are common and typical species in the Zlambach Beds (Upper Norian) of the Alpine region. This regional similarity extends to certain lamellibranchs, for example, *Halobia halorica* Mojs. above the coral zone, and *H. superba* Mojs. below it. Similar reef-corals are recorded by Smith (1927) from the Blue Mountains, Oregon, from the island of Vancouver and the vicinity of Cook Inlet, Alaska. These coral faunas are very similar to another in Nevada which S. W. Muller (1936) has shown to be of Carnian age. Incidentally it may be noted that the discovery of Triassic reef-corals in Alaska extends their geographical range from the Alps and Oregon (lat. 45° N.) to lat. 60° N. This is much greater than the range of living reef-corals, and is proof of subtropical climatic conditions at high northerly latitudes during Triassic time. The consequent absence of a polar ice-cap would facilitate the migration of animals, both on land and in the sea. This goes far to explain the world-wide distribution of ammonite faunas which is evident when strictly contemporaneous faunas are compared. Furthermore it is consistent with the view that the ocean basins are permanent features of the earth's surface and that their margins are subject to oscillation by reason of local transgressions and regressions of the seas.

LITERATURE

'A Correlation of the British Permo-Triassic Rocks', by R. L. Sherlock: Part I. North England, Scotland, and Ireland, *Proc. Geol. Assoc.,* vol. xxxvii, pp. 1–72, 1926. Part II. England South of the Pennines and Wales, ibid., vol. xxxviii, pp. 49–95, 1928. Gives a general account of the strata and details of their lithology, and an extensive list of literature.

'The Fossiliferous Lower Keuper Rocks of Worcestershire', by L. J. Wills, *Proc. Geol. Assoc.,* vol. xxi, pp. 249–331, pls. x–xxvi, 1910, is the only complete account of a British Triassic life-assemblage so far published; it contains descriptions and illustrations of plants, arachnids, and fishes, besides an extensive list of literature.

'A New Catopterid Fish from the Keuper of Nottingham', by H. H. Swinnerton, *Q.J.G.S.,* vol. lxxxi, pp. 87–99, 1925. *Woodthorpea wilsoni* Swin. described and illustrated.

'An Investigation of the Fauna and Flora of the Trias of the British Isles', by several authors, including a classification of the footprints by H. C. Beasley, is given in *Reports of the British Association for the Advancement of Science,* 1903 to 1909.

The Scottish Permian and Triassic Reptiles are described in the following papers:

'Some New Reptiles from the Elgin Sandstone', by E. T. Newton, *Phil. Trans. Roy. Soc.,* ser. B, vol. 184, pp. 431–503, 1893; and vol. 185, pp. 573–607, 1894.

'A new Dinosaurian Reptile (*Scleromochlus taylori*) from the Trias of Lossiemouth, Elgin', by A. S. Woodward, *Q.J.G.S.,* vol. lxiii, pp. 140–4, 1907.

'Reptilian Remains from the Trias of Elgin by G. A. Boulenger, *Phil. Trans. Roy. Soc.,* ser. B, vol. 196, pp. 175–89, 1903; and *Proc. Zool. Soc.,* pp. 470–81, 1904. The second of these papers contains a list of the Elgin reptiles known in 1904, with an account of their distribution.

'The Triassic and Permian Rocks of Moray', by D. M. S. Watson and G. Hickling, *Geol. Mag.*, vol. li, pp. 399–402, 1914, summarizes the palaeontological evidence concerning the age of the Scottish rocks.

Faunas of the Rhaetic Beds in England are discussed in:

'The Zones of the Lias and the *Avicula contorta* Zone', by C. Moore, *Q.J.G.S.*, vol. xvii, pp. 483–516, 1861. Descriptions and figures of some forty species of Rhaetic fossils.

'On *Pteromya crowcombeia* Moore, and some species of *Pleuromya* and *Volsella* from the Rhaetic and Lower Lias', by L. Richardson and J. W. Tutcher, *Proc. Yorks. Geol. Soc.*, vol. xix, pp. 51–58, 1916.

The Triassic Cephalopoda, which afford the basis of a zonal classification of the marine deposits in the system, form the subject of an extensive literature. The most recent monograph is the *Catalogue of The Fossil Cephalopoda in the British Museum (N.H.)*, Parts IV (1934) and V (1951) on 'The Ammonoidea of the Trias' by L. F. Spath. Part IV deals with the majority of the families and genera dominant in the Lower and Middle Trias; these are completed in Part V along with the ammonoids of the Upper Trias. Unfortunately the illustrations to Part V are delayed indefinitely, and it seems desirable here to cite a few of·the important works in which Triassic ammonoids are figured.

Many European forms are described and illustrated by E. v. Mojsisovics in 'Die Cephalopoden der Mediterranen Triasprovinz', *Abh. geol. Reichsanst. Wien*, vol. x, pp. 1–322, 94 pls., 1882, and 'Die Cephalopoden der Halstatter Kalke', ibid., vol. vi, pt. ii, pp. 1–835, 130 pls., 1873–93. Mojsisovics and C. Diener separately described many Indian forms in a number of monographs published under the general title 'Himalayan Fossils' in *Pal. Indica*, ser. 15, 1895–1909, and W. Waagen described 'Fossils from the Ceratite Formation of The Salt Range', ibid., ser. 13, 1895. G. v. Arthaber made known the 'Ammonoidea Leiostraca aus der Oberen Trias von Timor' in *Jaarb. Mijnw. Nederl. Ind.*, vol. lv, pp. 1–174, 1926, while other ammonoids from the island are discussed by O. A. Welter in *Palaeont. Timor*, vols. v (1915) and xi (1922). *The Middle Triassic Invertebrate Faunas of North America* are described and illustrated by J. P. Smith in U.S. Geol. Surv. Prof. Paper No. 83, 1914, those of the Upper Trias in Prof. Paper No. 141, 1927, and the Lower Triassic ammonoids in Prof. Paper No. 167, 1932. 'The Eotriassic Invertebrate Fauna of East Greenland' is described with numerous illustrations by L. F. Spath in *Meddel. om Groenland*, vol. lxxxiii, pp. 1–90, 1930, and vol. xcviii, pp. 1–115, 1935. All these works contain extensive bibliographical lists.

We should also note the following papers on other fossil groups because of their important evidence on the geography and climate of the Triassic period. 'Coral Reefs in the Triassic of North America', by J. P. Smith, *Amer. Journ. Sci.*, ser. 4, vol. xxxiii, pp. 92–96, 1912; 'The Geology and Tectonics of Oman and of Parts of South-Eastern Arabia', by G. M. Lees, *Q.J.G.S.*, vol. lxxxiv, pp. 585–670, 1928, and 'A Marine Triassic Fauna from Eastern Persia', by J. A. Douglas, *Q.J.G.S.*, vol. lxxxv, pp. 624–50, 1929.

XII

JURASSIC FAUNAS

THE Jurassic rocks of Britain are mainly of marine origin, and, as a whole, they represent a long-continued transgression of the sea over the continental Trias. The main outcrop extends from the coast of Dorset in the south, across the Midland counties to the mouth of the River Tees in the north. There are also several outliers. Those of South Wales, Shropshire, Carlisle, and Antrim consist of early Jurassic rocks (Lias) only. In the western isles of Scotland (Skye, Raasay, Mull, Shiant) the Liassic rocks are followed by later members of the System. The distribution of the Scottish rocks and the relations of their faunas indicate open communication with the sea to the north, and show that the Hebridean area was already dissected in Jurassic time. They also connect with the main outcrop in England by way of the Carlisle and Shropshire outliers, but it is unlikely that the sea covered the high ground of the Lake District, the Pennines and Wales. On the north-eastern coast of Scotland the Triassic rocks of Moray are followed by deposits of early Liassic age, and these by non-marine beds equivalent to the Great Oolite of England (as at Brora in Sutherland). Later marine beds are represented along the same coast, and seem to indicate temporary encroachments of the North Sea over the margin of the ancient Caledonian land-mass.

Throughout the system the marine faunas are of shallow-water character; sometimes, as in Yorkshire and north-east Scotland, beds of deltaic origin are intercalated with the prevalent marine deposits, and often both contain bones of tetrapod animals transported or washed down from the adjacent land. Naturally, in strata of this episodal character, gaps in the succession are to be expected, but, taken as a whole, the marine faunas provide a series sufficiently continuous to serve as a standard of correlation throughout western Europe. The Lower Jurassic (or Liassic) series consists mainly of clays with only subordinate limestones, but the Upper Jurassic rocks are more diversified.

Subdivision of the Jurassic Series of Britain dates back to the early years of the nineteenth century, and stratal terms adopted by William Smith (1815–16) and Dean Buckland (1818) still appear on current maps of our Geological Survey. These terms, based largely on lithological characters, are not always applicable to deposits of equivalent age on the mainland of Europe. So, about 1850, the famous French geologist Alcide d'Orbigny attempted greater precision in correlation by a system of stages, based on the sections exposed at typical localities. His seven stages of the Upper

Jurassic (tabulated on p. 445), with the exception of the Bajocian (from Bayeux in Normandy), are founded on English localities, and, as a whole, they form a well-balanced scheme of classification. The scheme has been modified from time to time by authors who named stages to suit their own districts, and some of these have been added to the original list. But there is now a tendency to return to Orbigny's stages, with two modifications. The term Corallian, originally applied to a facies of the Oxfordian stage, has been abandoned as a stage-name by general consent, and the Purbeckian stage has been added because the Purbeck Beds have been transferred from the lowest Cretaceous to the highest Jurassic. It has been objected that the limits of the Callovian and Oxfordian stages do not correspond to the sections at Kellaways and Oxford respectively. But W. J. Arkell has lately explained that Orbigny took his type-localities for these stages from Yorkshire (as given in Phillips's *Geology of Yorkshire* of 1829). Similarly, the Kimmeridgian and Portlandian stages are based on Fitton's sections of 1836.

The zonal succession is based on that of Oppel (1856–63) for the lower part, and of Salfeld (1914) for the upper part of the series. It has become apparent, however, that zones are not of universal application, and that a zonal succession must have specific reference to a particular area. The accompanying table therefore shows the zones recognized in the several stages of the Upper Jurassic strata in Britain and north-west Europe; those for the Alpine-Mediterranean region, central Russia, the coasts of the Indian Ocean and of the Pacific Ocean, all differ in certain respects.

The Upper Jurassic deposits of Britain show local variations consistent with deposition in shallow water near a shore-line. So many are these variations that it is impossible to discuss them fully in this volume; only the more important can be outlined. Moreover, detailed palaeontological work has revealed the presence of numerous non-sequences in some districts, while the missing deposits are represented elsewhere. To such circumstances are due certain differences of opinion regarding the correlation of these deposits. From the lithological standpoint we may consider the Upper Jurassic Series as consisting of three main divisions, namely, a lower series composed mainly of limestones, a middle series of clays, with subordinate limestones, followed by another calcareous division.

The limestone series comprising the Inferior Oolite and the Great Oolite, or the Bajocian and Bathonian stages of Orbigny, varies in character when traced from Dorset north-eastwards along the outcrop. In the south-western counties the sequence is entirely marine, but broken by local non-sequences. In Oxfordshire the lower part of the Inferior Oolite is missing, and the upper part (sometimes referred to a separate Vesulian stage) rests on the Upper Lias. Farther north, in Northamptonshire and Lincolnshire, the lowest representatives of the Inferior Oolite (grouped as the Northampton Sands and Ironstone) rest non-sequentially on an eroded surface of the

Upper Lias. They are followed by a fissile limestone known as the Colly-weston Slate which forms the base of the massive Lincolnshire Limestone. This is usually considered to represent the main mass of the Bajocian stage but ammonites are rare (only *Hyperlioceras discites* being recorded) and the other faunal elements, which show certain peculiar features, have not yet been adequately investigated. The Upper Inferior Oolite of this district is deltaic in character, and is succeeded by the Great Oolite limestones. Most of this series in Yorkshire consists of deltaic deposits with some marine intercalations.

Strata of Bathonian age also occur on the east coast of Scotland where they consist of estuarine sands and clays with the Brora coal-seam at the top: the base is not exposed. In the Hebrides, Bajocian Limestones enclose numerous ammonites which invite comparison with equivalent rocks in the south-west of England. The Upper Bajocian and possibly higher strata of western Scotland are of non-marine origin.

The middle (argillaceous) series of the Upper Jurassic comprises the Oxford Clay, the Corallian, and the Kimmeridge Clay of the older classi-fication. The Oxford Clay succeeds the Upper Cornbrash which contains the familiar Macrocephalitan fauna, marking the base of the Callovian stage. The Cornbrash is very persistent in character all along its outcrop from Dorset to Yorkshire. Higher beds, known as the Kellaways Beds are calcareous and sandy from Dorset to Lincolnshire and pass up gradually into the Oxford Clay. In Yorkshire, however, the calcareous character per-sists through the Callovian stage, and only the Oxfordian (that is, the upper part of the Oxford Clay in other districts) is argillaceous. Certain peculiari-ties are also apparent in the ammonite faunas of these Yorkshire beds—perhaps due to the variation in physical conditions compared with those of Oxfordshire and Dorset.

Deposits of the Oxfordian stage—including the Corallian of former generations—are also episodal in character. In the south of England they consist of a variable series of sands and clays, but are calcareous in Wilt-shire and Oxfordshire where the typical Corallian facies is developed. In the north of the last-named county some of the upper Corallian Beds are replaced laterally by the Ampthill Clay which, except for a local develop-ment of limestone in Cambridgeshire, persists into Lincolnshire. Thus in the Midland counties there is a thick clay series extending through the Callovian, Oxfordian, and Kimmeridgian stages, whose differentiation depends almost entirely on palaeontological evidence. The calcareous facies is again fully developed in Upper Oxfordian strata of Yorkshire with cer-tain modifications of the fauna. The succeeding Kimmeridge Clay is more constant in lithological characters, but north of Cambridgeshire the higher beds are concealed by overstep of transgressive Cretaceous strata. On the east coast of Scotland, the Oxfordian and Kimmeridgian stages are largely of estuarine origin but include some marine beds.

The upper series of the present discussion is formed by the calcareous deposits known as the Portland Stone and the Purbeck Beds. These strata are so variable that little generalization can be made in respect of them. The fossils indicate some alternation of marine and estuarine or deltaic conditions. In the northern part of the Portlandian outcrop many of the marine beds are marked by the large amount of glauconite which gives them a green tinge. This development extends through Buckinghamshire and Oxfordshire into Wiltshire, but is not noticeable in Dorset. In the last-named county, and to a less extent in Wiltshire, the lower Portland Beds contain conspicuous cherty bands, but this siliceous development is absent farther to the north-east. There seems to be some lateral replacement of marine beds by deposits of estuarine character, but the absence of continuous exposures makes correlation difficult. The beds that yield mollusca typical of brackish water are marly in character and contain neither glauconite nor chert. The Purbeck Beds are also variable; some contain echinoids and are presumably marine, others are marked by *Viviparus, Unio,* and other freshwater genera. Where the Wealden Beds lie conformably on the Purbeck Beds some difficulty is encountered in attempting to fix a boundary line between the two stages.

It has already been noted that the zonal method has been applied to Jurassic rocks more extensively than to any other series. The zones of this system are based on the occurrence of various species of ammonites, the dominant group of marine invertebrates. The last forty years have seen the establishment of a theory which bids fair to revolutionize ideas on the evolution of these organisms. L. F. Spath in this country, and H. Salfeld in Germany, have independently arrived at the conclusion that the two Mediterranean genera *Lytoceras* and *Phylloceras* are the fundamental root-stocks of the Mesozoic ammonoids. These two stocks have repeatedly given rise to trachyostracous (thick-shelled) offshoots which have become specialized in various directions as they were dispersed in the north-western seas. Various intermediate forms have been detected in south European localities, but are practically unknown in Britain. Thus the British ammonites cannot be satisfactorily classified without a knowledge of southern forms, but the diversity of unconnected end-forms have furnished the means for a scheme of minute zonal divisions.

At the same time there is often a striking likeness between ammonites of widely differing ages. As Spath has pointed out, 'all the different types of ornamentation had already been tried from Devonian clymenids onwards'. In view of this heterochronous homoemorphy, which is held by Spath to support his theory of the common descent of Mesozoic ammonids from *Lytoceras* and *Phylloceras*, care must be taken to avoid confusion when using ammonites to determine the age of strata.

It is modern refinement in the discrimination of species that has made possible the great increase in the number of zonal divisions. These have become so numerous that usually the time-intervals represented by them (hemerae) have been grouped into a number of 'Ages'. The stratal equivalents (stages) correspond roughly to the limits of Oppel's zones, and, since these are small enough for general purposes, the detailed zonal scheme will not be considered in this work. The broad faunal features of the stages form a good basis for more detailed work; and, indeed, many of the smaller zones are probably recognizable only at localities where deposition took place fairly rapidly so that the faunas are distributed through a fair thickness of rock. In the present chapter the names proposed by Buckman for the 'Ages' are applied to the several faunas because they seem to indicate the characters of the ammonite faunas better than the trivial names of the zonal indexes.

The Jurassic of Britain may be held to begin with the strata containing the earliest ammonite fauna. This is denominated the **Psiloceratan Fauna,** because its characteristic ammonites are members of the genus *Psiloceras*, that is, allies of the smooth evolute species long known as *Ammonites planorbis* J. Sow. The form of the suture-line with its phylloid endings, shows that this genus is derived from the monophyllitid branch of the *Phylloceras* stock.

Some species of *Psiloceras* show costation on the inner whorls, and thus foreshadow the polygyral, coarsely ribbed ammonites of the genus *Caloceras* (Pl. VII) which retain this feature in the adult stage. *Psilophyllitse*, a reduced type of psiloceratid with almost ceratitic suture-lines, occurs in the succeeding fauna.

Associated with late members of the assemblage just described are species of *Waehneroceras*, involute, ribbed ammonites with rounded venters, marking the incoming of the **Schlotheimian Fauna.** The most typical members of this assemblage are ammonites formerly grouped with *Ammonites angulatus* Schlotheim, an oft-quoted form now placed in the genus *Scamnoceras*, and possessing coarse costation which is usually interrupted by a groove on the venter. *Schlotheimia* is now restricted to allied forms with unequal ribs that tend to disappear on the sides of the outer whorls. *Saxoceras* is an allied, finely costate genus which shows the schlotheimid groove in its early growth, while its outer whorls are rounded like *Psiloceras*. These genera are included with others in the family Schlotheimidae, which is (according to Spath), 'derived from Psiloceratidae by way of *Waehneroceras*'. The genus *Alsatites* (though probably polyphyletic), includes forms derived from *Psiloceras* through certain caloceratids, further emphasises the close relation of the two Hettangian faunas, and foreshadows the form of ornament typical of the succeeding assemblages.

Though they have not the same zonal significance as ammonites, a few Hettangian fossils belonging to other animal groups may be mentioned. Brachiopods exhibit their usual sporadic occurrence, but the little *Rhynchonella calcicosta* Dav. (now re-named *Calcirhynchia calcaria* S. Buckm.)

Classification of the Lower Jurassic

Stratigraphical stages		Faunas	Zones
UPPER LIAS	TOARCIAN	Grammoceratan	*Lyt. jurensis*
		Haugian	*H. variabilis*
		Hildoceratan	*Hild. bifrons*
		Harpoceratan	*Harp. serpentinum*
MIDDLE LIAS	DOMERIAN	Amalthean	*Pl. spinatum*
			Am. margaritatum
LOWER LIAS	PLIENSBACHIAN	Liparoceratan	*Pro. davoei*
		Polymorphitan	*Trag. ibex*
			U. jamesoni
		Eoderoceratan	*Eod. armatum*
			Ech. raricostatum
	SINEMURIAN	Oxynoticeratan	*Ox. oxynotum*
		Asteroceratan	*Ast. obtusum*
		Arietitan	*Ar. turneri*
		Agassiceratan	*Arn. semicostatum*
		Coroniceratan	*Cor. bucklandi*
		Vermiceratan	*M. conybeari*
	HETTANGIAN	Schlotheimian	*Sc. angulatum*
		Psiloceratan	*Ps. planorbis*

abounds at some localities. The long-looped *Ornithella sarthasensis* (d'Orb.) is probably the earliest of its genus, while the smooth *Spiriferina pinguis* Zieten (Fig. 64) is a link with the Palaeozoic spire-bearing brachiopods. At many Jurassic horizons, ostrean stocks produced offshoots marked by great curvature and thickness of the left (fixed) valve, and by much variation in the size of the area of fixation. The earliest of these offshoots is

Gryphaea arcuata Lam. (or *G. incurva* of many authors), which is a common and characteristic Hettangian lamellibranch (Fig. 69). A. E. Trueman has devised a statistical method for using these fossils for detailed correlation, but the commonly occurring *Plagiostoma gigantea* (J. Sow.) (Fig. 70), *Cardinia listeri* (J. Sow.) and other species, are not yet capable of such use.

Suess long ago classified the Jurassic ammonoids into *Phylloceras*, *Lytoceras*, and *Ammonites*, but the third group has since been divided into a multitude of genera. In 1922 L. F. Spath revived the genus *Ammonites* by restricting it to the allies of *Ammonites bisulcatus* Brug., and more recently adopted the group-name Ammonitida to include many allied Sinemurian genera with strong ribbing interrupted by a keel and furrows on the venter.

One of the earliest ammonitid genera, *Vermiceras*, a derivative of the alsatitids, supplies a name for the earliest of the Sinemurian assemblages—the **Vermiceratan Fauna**. *Vermiceras* is evolute, and the ribs are recurved laterally but are not definitely geniculate. The associated and similar, but more compressed, group of *Ammonites conybeari* (s.l.) is now separated generically as *Metophioceras*; this form has a high keel which persists to large diameters, and the ribs develop peripheral nodes.

The last-named genus probably gave rise to *Coroniceras*, which is the typical element in the **Coroniceratan Fauna,** and to other allied forms. These are all evolute ammonites with strong ribs, developing tubercles at an early stage; they also have a strong keel on the venter bordered on each side by a groove. *Paracoroniceras* (the group of Oppel's *Ammonites gmuendensis*) is a more involute ammonitid genus developing a trigonal whorl-shape. The absence of these large coronicerates in Yorkshire records may perhaps be explained by inadequate exposure of early Sinemurian horizons in the northern area. Associated with these are forms at present classed in *Arnioceras*, a long-ranged group still imperfectly known and therefore difficult to use for purposes of exact correlation. In this genus, ribs are developed late and are straight on the lateral area, becoming geniculate on the peripheral border. The arniocerates are in close affinity with *Epammonites*, an evolute ammonitid that has not acquired the stiff ribbing of *Arnioceras*. Besides these forms, *Charmasseiceras* may be mentioned as representing the persistence of the schlotheimid type.

Perhaps the most familiar Sinemurian brachiopod is the broad-plaited *Spiriferina walcotti* (J. de C. Sow.) (Fig. 64), which is associated with late members of the Coroniceratan fauna. Its short vertical range makes it a useful guide fossil in the south-west of England. The numerous species of *Cardinia*, *Pecten*, and other lamellibranch genera are not so restricted in their range.

The **Agassiceratan Fauna** takes its name from the typical *Agassiceras*. This shows its ammonitid origin in the development of bisulcation, but also exhibits a tendency to delay the appearance of this feature. The early arniocerates, characterized by simple suture-lines with shallow lateral lobes,

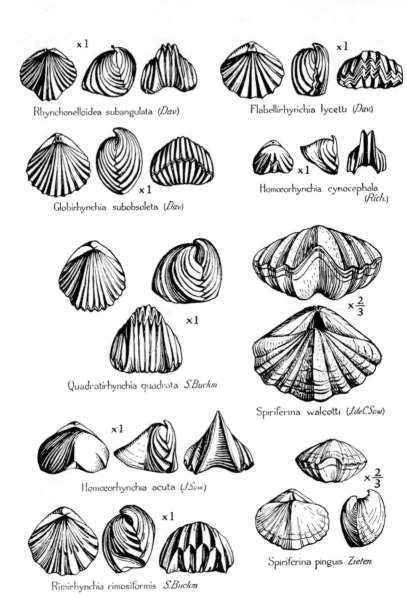

x 1

Rhynchonelloidea subangulata (Dav.)

x 1

Flabellirhynchia lycetti (Dav.)

x 1

Globirhynchia subobsoleta (Dav.)

x 1

Homœorhynchia cynocephala (Rich.)

x 1

Quadratirhynchia quadrata S.Buckm

$\times\frac{2}{3}$

Spiriferina walcotti (J.deC.Sow.)

x 1

Homœorhynchia acuta (J.Sow.)

$\times\frac{2}{3}$

Spiriferina pinguis Zieten

x 1

Rimirhynchia rimosiformis S.Buckm

FIG. 64. LOWER JURASSIC RHYNCHONELLIDS AND SPIRIFERIDS (drawn from figures by Davidson)

continue to form an important faunal element, and include *A. geometricum*, one of Oppel's original zone-fossils.

The **Arietitan Fauna** includes as its typical members some familiar ammonites such as *A. turneri* Sow. (Pl. VII) and *A. brooki* Sow., now placed in the restricted genus *Arietites*. They are markedly bisulcate, and possess strong ribs of the arietid type, geniculate at the peripheral shoulders. These have been regarded as originating in the arniocerates previously mentioned, and are associated with later members of this group. *Eparnioceras*, in which the development of bisulcation is delayed, leads to *Cymbites*, an interesting ammonite that is often abundant in the lower part of Oppel's original obtusus-zone. This fauna also contains, in the genus *Sulciferites*, an independent development of schlotheimid type which has a very restricted vertical range. Another important form, making a late appearance in the fauna, is *Microderoceras birchi* (J. Sow.). This evolute and planulate ammonite (Pl. VII) is an early forerunner of the superfamily Eoderoceratidae which attained its acmaic development in the Pliensbachian stage.

The **Asteroceratan Fauna** is closely connected with the preceding assemblage. The name is taken from the dominant arietid genus *Asteroceras*, exemplified by the well-known species *A. obtusum* (J. Sow.), probably a derivative of the group of *Arietites turneri*. This ammonite is easily recognized by its simple radial ribs which bend forward on the keeled and channelled periphery. The characteristic asterocerates of the *obtusum* and *stellare* groups are abundant in Dorset. Corresponding horizons in Yorkshire are marked by the presence of asterocerates in which the keel and furrows are practically obsolete; these are the so-called 'crippled' or 'degenerate' ammonites of the *sagittarium* type which are almost confined to Yorkshire. The commonest ammonite, however, is probably *Promicroceras planicosta* (J. Sow.), (Pl. VII) whose trivial name recalls this familiar little capricorn species with the well-marked flattening of the ribs on the venter. The somewhat similar, associated species of *Xipheroceras* are perhaps more closely connected with *Microderoceras*, and Spath regards them as independently derived from the fundamental *Lytoceras* stock, merging at a later stage into the Eoderoceratidae.

The succeeding **Oxynoticeratan Fauna** is marked especially by the compressed, sharp-keeled, involute ammonites included in the genus *Oxynoticeras*, generally regarded as derivatives of the arietids. Their typical shape, with its sharpened keel and feeble ornament (Pl. VII) is termed the oxycone, and Spath regards this as a specialized adaptive modification to be correlated with a free-swimming mode of life. *Gagaticeras*, a genus that is sometimes associated with the oxycones, especially in Yorkshire, may be a capricorn development of the arietid stock and is homoeomorphous with the xipheroceratid genus *Bifericeras*. The last of the schlotheimids are represented in this fauna by species of *Angulaticeras* such as *A. lacunatum* (J. Buckm.).

In the **Eoderoceratan Fauna** two ammonite-families alternate in the position of dominance, a circumstance that has caused some confusion with regard to the detailed subdivision of the strata. These families are sufficiently exemplified by the genera *Eoderoceras* and *Echioceras* (Pl. VIII) respectively. The series of ammonites conveniently grouped as the Eoderoceratidae are evolute forms with rounded whorl-section, tuberculate ornament and a highly ornate suture-line. They bear only one row of tubercles at the peripheral shoulders, thus contrasting with the earlier *Microderoceras*, which has two rows, one on the lateral area in addition to the peripheral row. According to Spath these ammonites represent an independent offshoot from the *Lytoceras* stock, through such forms as *Derolytoceras*, which are unknown outside the Alpine-Mediterranean area. The biological affinites of the Echioceratidae have been the subject of speculation. They may be briefly described as keeled capricorns and they possess simple suture-lines like those of some arietids. While they show some external resemblance to simple eoderoceratids they are, perhaps, best interpreted as arietids derived from an earlier Mediterranean stock. Oxycone ammonites of several genera, whose precise affinities are yet obscure, are frequently associated; many attain a large size, and their different sutural characters may indicate diverse origins.

The Eoderoceratan fauna, with its alternating dominance of *Eoderoceras* and *Echioceras*, is well developed in the northern areas (Yorkshire and Scotland). From the Midlands only early members of the fauna are known. Somerset, as shown by records from the Radstock district, is rich in species of the typical genera (though nearly all the echiocerates are derived), but some early forms seem to be missing. There are also lucunae in the records of the Dorset coast.

The Polymorphitidae, which dominate the **Polymorphitan Fauna**, have simple ribs in their early development, and later become bituberculate with an angular venter; some, however, are practically smooth in the adult stage. *Gemmellaroceras*, recorded from Dorset, but better known in the Alpine-Mediterranean area, demonstrates the probable derivation of polymorphitids from the ancestral lytoceratids. *Polymorphites* includes evolute species with small, annular ribs, more or less V-shaped on the periphery. *Uptonia*, including the zonal index *U. jamesoni* (J. de C. Sow.), develops tubercles, and later becomes heavily ribbed, somewhat like the capricorns. *Platypleuroceras* (the familiar *brevispina* group) is bituberculate in the adult stage, with usually a rounded venter; it resembles *Microderoceras* to some extent, but its simpler suture-line is different in plan. The genus *Dayiceras*, from the ibex zone of Dorset, is regarded as a late member of the family; it is perhaps a local development, for nothing like it is recorded from well-searched localities in Wurtemburg and the Mediterranean area. The polymorphitids are replaced in the upper horizons of the jamesoni zone by the genera *Tropidoceras* and *Acanthopleuroceras* for which the family Tropidoceratidae has been established. *Tropidoceras*, widely distributed in Britain (Dorset, Yorkshire, Pabay) and in south Europe, may be derived through *Polymorphites* or *Gemmellaroceras* from a derolytoceratid stock with rounded whorls. *Acanthopleuroceras* typified by *A. valdani* (Opp.) (Pl. VIII), is similar, but develops a keel. It is usually regarded as a descendant of the polymorphitid *Platypleuroceras*, but may have been produced by long-ranged forms of *Tropidoceras*. The heavily ribbed and tuberculate *Phricodoceras* is probably related to the Eoderoceratidae; they are associated in the ibex zone with species of *Tragophylloceras* (Pl. VIII), a development showing close affinity with the ancestral *Phylloceras*.

The Polymorphitan fauna of Yorkshire compares with that of the Midlands in the scarcity of the genus *Uptonia*; in particular, *U. jamesoni* (Sow.) has not yet been found in Yorkshire. This county also lacks *Acanthopleuroceras valdani* (d'Orb.) and its allies, though these are abundant in the Midlands, and are recorded from Scotland. *Tragophylloceras ibex* (Qu.) is another notable absentee from Yorkshire records, though other species are present. A feature of the Scottish fauna is the presence of large rhynchonellids of the *rimosa* type, showing the characteristic anterior coalescence of ribs at a later stage of growth than in southern species, which are also smaller in size.

The **Liparoceratan Fauna** is especially marked by the occurrence of the familiar capricorn ammonites, and of inflated, round-whorled shells with multituberculate ornament. These are all grouped in the family Liparoceratidae, lately revised by L. F. Spath (1938). The early liparoceratids are sphaerocones which seem to be connected with bituberculate serpental ammonites of the Eoderoceratidae, such as *Tetraspidoceras*. These sphaerocones are often referred to the familiar comprehensive genus *Liparoceras* (s.l.), but several distinct forms are separated as subgenera. Thus *Vicininodoceras* and *Parinodoceras* from the jamesoni zone of Somerset are early parinodate stocks, the first showing features that connect it with *Tetraspidoceras*, while the second is transitional to the more evolute *Platynoticeras* of the same zone. The later restricted *Liparoceras* (Pl. VIII) likewise has two lateral rows of nodes but the costation is stronger and the suture-line is complex; this genus ranges through the ibex and davoei zones. The finely ribbed *Becheiceras*, with spiral as well as transverse ornamentation, is characteristic of the davoei and margaritatus zones. Thus the sphaerocones persist through the Upper Pliensbachian to the Domerian stage. They give rise at various horizons to dwarf, smooth, and globose end-forms which Spath includes in his genus *Metacymbites*.

In the lower horizons of the davoei zone the inner whorls of some liparoceratids are evolute, but the adult whorls return to the ancestral sphaerocone form. Thus arise the so-called 'dimorph' forms of the family; they are placed in the genus *Androgynoceras*, though they represent a broad stream of development rather than a single line of descent. Closely related to this genus, but slightly earlier in appearance, are dwarf species of *Beaniceras* which form unituberculate and costate transitions between the dimorphs and the persisting sphaerocones. Finally in the upper davoei and the margaritatus zones there is another broad development, known as *Oistoceras*, in which the evolute capricorn stage persists to the adult, and the simple suture-line contrasts strongly with the complex one of the involute *Liparoceras* or *Becheiceras*. The main development of the Liparoceratidae, from sphaerocone to capricorn, is in north-west Europe, and the family may be autochthonous in this area, though rare examples have been recorded from south Europe and north Africa.

Lytoceras of the *fimbriatum* group (Fig. 17) indicates one of the sporadic migrations of Mediterranean stocks into the British area. The index-fossil *Prodactylioceras davoei* (J. Sow.) marks the first appearance of another Mediterranean stock in Britain, and is the earliest representative of the family Dactylioceratidae, a family which attains its maximum development in the Toarcian stage.

Pliensbachian brachiopods are most abundant in the limestone facies of Somerset. A striking feature is the large number of species and individuals of *Cincta*, a discoid, long-looped terebratellid (Fig. 67) occurring with the Polymorphitan ammonite fauna. Associated with them are such characteristic forms as *Zeilleria darwini* (Desl.), *Lobothyris radstockiensis* (Dav.) (Fig. 65), and the rhynchonellids *Rimirhynchia rimosiformis* S. Buckm. (Fig. 64) and *Cuneirhynchia dalmasi* (Dumortier). *Spiriferina verrucosa* (Buch) and *Aulacothyris waterhousei* (Dav.) are characteristically associated with the Eoderoceratan fauna.

Among lamellibranchs, *Gryphaea cymbium* Lam. is often abundant, and is sometimes accompanied by *Pteria inaequivalvis* (J. Sow.)

Two of Oppel's original zones, those of *Amm. margaritatus* and *spinatum*, which together are equivalent to the Domerian stage, contain ammonites with crenulate keels as their chief faunal element. These dominate the **Amalthean Fauna,** named after the involute, flat-whorled genus *Amaltheus* (Pl. VIII), one of its early constituents. Prominent among later forms is the genus *Pleuroceras* (Pl. VIII) with quadrangular whorls and massive ribs. The crenulate keel, due to the transgression of the ribbing, is very distinctive, and marks off this fauna from all other Liassic assemblages.

Amaltheus is connected with the liparoceratid genus *Oistoceras* by transitional forms, and in its turn gives rise to *Pleuroceras*, with quadrangular whorls and massive ribs (Pl. VIII). Large species of *Amaltheus* and massive forms of *Pleuroceras* (the *spinatum* type) are characteristic of Domerian faunas in the Midlands and south-west England. These types are rare in Yorkshire and Scotland where the thin-whorled *Pleuroceras hawskerense* (Young and Bird) is the prevailing type of its genus, and *Amauroceras*, a flat oxynote derivative of *Amaltheus* is peculiar. A dwarf species, *Amaltheus laevis* (Quen.) occurs in Scotland and Dorset but is not known elsewhere in

Britain. Occasional specimens of *Seguenziceras* and *Leptaleoceras* represent early hildoceratids which are more abundant in Domerian strata of south Europe.

The Domerian brachiopods form a distinctive assemblage. Among rhynchonellids, the group of *Rhynchonella acuta* J. Sow. (Fig. 64), now raised to generic rank with the name *Homoeorhynchia*, is recognized by its sparse ribbing, and the long anterior projection of the brachial valve. Another prominent group, that of *Rhynchonella tetraedra* J. Sow. is somewhat similar, but with more numerous ribs developing after a protracted smooth stage. This group is now distributed among three genera, *Grandirhynchia*, *Tetrarhynchia*, and *Quadratirhynchia*, based upon internal differences: the recorded distribution of these genera in Great Britain is interesting. Scotland has a remarkable development of the massive *Grandirhynchia*; *Tetrarhynchia* is characteristic of the English Midlands, while *Quadratirhynchia* appears to be typical of south-western England and Normandy. This distribution applies to forms of average size, but dwarfs of these genera are more widely dispersed. For instance, dwarf species of *Grandirhynchia* occur in western Scotland, Yorkshire and Gloucestershire; small forms of *Tetrarhynchia* range from the Midlands into southern England. Among terebratulids the group of *Terebratula punctata* J. Sow. (Fig. 65), now referred to the genus *Lobothyris*, is characteristic; *L. punctata* has a flat brachial valve and plain anterior margin. *Aulacothyris resupinata* (J. Sow.) and species of *Zeilleria*, especially *Z. cornuta* (J. de C. Sow.) and *Z. subquadrifida* Oppel, are representatives of the long-looped terebratellids. *Spiriferina oxygona* Dav. testifies to the continued persistence of the spire-bearing brachiopods. At high horizons of the Domerian stage these brachiopods are often associated with characteristic lamellibranchs, especially species of *Pecten*, such as *P. aequivalvis* (J. Sow.) (Fig. 76), and *P. liassianus* Nyst. Other lamellibranchs, including *Modiola scalprum* J. Sow., and *Protocardia truncata* (J. de C. Sow.), are hardly less typical.

The hildoceratids and their allies are predominant in several succeeding faunas, the lowest being named the **Harpoceratan Fauna,** from the abundance of species of *Harpoceras* (Pl. IX). This genus comprises flat-whorled ammonites with well-marked sickle-shaped ribs, and a hollow keel cut off from the shell-cavity by a calcareous partition. Various other genera of the same type are associated in this fauna. The occurrence of *Phylloceras* and *Lytoceras* is worthy of note in connexion with the varying geographical distribution of those genera at different periods of time.

The succeeding **Hildoceratan Fauna** is marked by the dominance of *Hildoceras*, typified by the familiar *H. bifrons* (Brug.) (Pl. IX). This differs from *Harpoceras* in that its whorls are quadrangular and the doubly curved radial ornament is less conspicuous. The allied genus *Frechiella*, being inflated and practically smooth, was ascribed to *Nautilus* by early investigators, but has a keeled periphery and ammonoid suture-line.

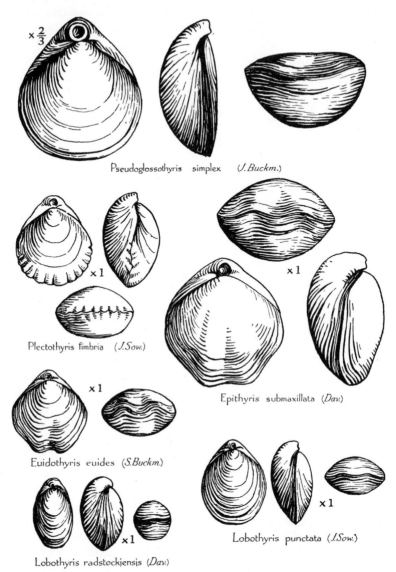

$\times \frac{2}{3}$

Pseudoglossothyris simplex   (*J.Buckm.*)

Plectothyris fimbria   (*J.Sow.*) $\times 1$

Epithyris submaxillata (*Dav.*) $\times 1$

Euidothyris euides (*S.Buckm.*) $\times 1$

Lobothyris punctata (*J.Sow.*) $\times 1$

Lobothyris radstockiensis (*Dav.*) $\times 1$

FIG. 65. LOWER JURASSIC TEREBRATULIDS (*drawn from figures by Davidson*)

In both of these Toarcian faunas the hildoceratids are nearly equalled in abundance and variety by planulate ammonites of the genus *Dactylioceras* (Pl. IX) and its allies. Many species were placed in *Ammonites communis* by early observers, and *D. tenuicostatum* is now utilized as a zonal index.

The succeeding **Haugian Fauna** is distinguished by species of the hildoceratan genera *Haugia*, *Lillia*, and *Denckmannia*, besides others. They are nodose forms whose ribs are almost straight on the lateral area. *Lillia*, one of the earliest of these genera, has one row of tubercles and a fairly simple suture-line. The slightly later *Denckmannia*, exemplified by *D. variabilis* (d'Orb.) is stouter, more involute, and more heavily ornamented. The ornament of *Haugia* is somewhat intermediate between these two, but the shell is more carinate than either.

The **Grammoceratan Fauna** is marked by hildoceratids with geniculate ribs. In *Grammoceras* (Pl. IX) the forward projection of the ribs on the peripheral border is not great, and the suture line may be described as simple. *Pseudogrammoceras* is similar, but has an elevated hollow keel, more crowded ribs and more elaborate suture-line. In *Phlyseogrammoceras* the ornament is coronate, the ribs originating in small tubercles on the inner margin. Species of these genera, e.g. *G. striatulum* (J. de C. Sow.) (Pl. IX) are used as guide-fossils for a succession of subzones in ascending order as mentioned.

The great family Hildoceratidae continues its development with the **Dumortierian Fauna.** Early species of *Dumortieria* are evolute, keeled shells, with close annular ribbing; later species are compressed and involute. Another genus of the same subfamily Grammoceratinae, namely, *Pleydellia*, furnishes a guide-fossil (*P. aalensis*) which marks the top of the Toarcian stage; it is a transitional form leading to the Leioceratinae which are conspicuous in Bajocian strata. Keeled ammonites of the genus *Hammatoceras*, with tuberculate ornament and complex suture-line, have been regarded by some authors as eoderoceratids that have acquired a hildoceratid aspect: Spath states, however, that they are closely related to *Haugia* and so belong to the Hildoceratidae.

The most noteworthy Toarcian brachiopods are the small species of *Cadomella* and *Koninckella* that occur in the so-called 'Leptaena-beds' of Somerset and Gloucestershire. The shells belong to the order Protremata, which is predominant in Palaeozoic faunas but unimportant in later assemblages except as providing interesting examples of 'relict' forms. The order has two living representatives in the genus *Thecidium* which ranges from the Cretaceous upwards.

Nuculana ovum (J. de C. Sow.) may be mentioned as a typical lamellibranch of Toarcian zones, especially in Yorkshire. *Inoceramus dubius* (J. de C. Sow.), occurring as pyritous films in the Whitby shales, is a useful guide fossil, while *Posidonia bronni* Goldf. (similarly crushed) was one of Oppel's zone-fossils.

It has been shown above that the later zones of the Liassic Series are marked by the dominance of hildoceratid ammonites. These develop a variety of new forms in the lower zones of the Bajocian stage; later they are associated with an abundance of 'coronate' ammonites so called from the development of tubercles on their depressed whorls, suggesting the shape of a crown. These and their allies were formerly classed together in the super-family Stephanoceratida, a heterogeneous group now subdivided on morphological grounds into a number of smaller 'families'. According to L. F. Spath these were repeatedly replenished by offshoots from the phyllocerates and lytocerates of the Mediterranean area.

Another polyphyletic group is the Oppelidae of older classifications. Spath considers this group to include, not only many forms intermediate between the trachyostracous families and the fundamental stocks, but also many end-forms of various lineages that have acquired the oxycone shape. Both the oppelids and the coronates persist through the Upper Jurassic stages, but their diversity is such that numerous forms can be used for purposes of correlation, because of their short vertical range and wide horizontal distribution. The main zones recognized on this basis within the stages are shown in the table on p. 445.

The lowest (opalinum) zone of the Bajocian stage contains the **Leiocera-tan Fauna,** a varied suite of compressed, sharp-ventered hildoceratids which resemble the Toarcian grammocerates in general form, but are distinguished by details of ornament, degree of coiling and carination. Conspicuous among them are species of *Leioceras*, which were formerly included under the name *Ammonites opalinus* Rein. and taken as the index of the zone. They are compressed shells ornamented with sigmoid striae, and are derived from the grammocerates by way of the Toarcian genera *Pleydellia* and *Cotteswoldia*. The top of the zone is marked by the occurrence of *Tmetoceras scissum* whose annular ribs end in tubercles on the borders of a peripheral groove; it is a derivative of the Leioceratinae which is placed in a separate sub-family on account of its distinctive characters.

Oppel's zone of *Ammonites murchisonae* is easily recognized by the occurrence of hildoceratids which are distinguished by the marked angularity of their radial ornament. These ammonites and their associates form the **Ludwigian Fauna.** The genus *Ludwigia*, typified by *L. murchisonae*, are fairly stout forms with moderately wide umbilicus (Pl. IX). *Brasilia* is less coarsely ornamented than *Ludwigia*, but less involute and less discoid than *Graphoceras* in which the broad V-shaped course of the radial ornament is a very noticeable feature. *Ludwigella*, exemplified by *L. concava* (J. Sow.) has a biarcuate type of ribbing and a small basin-shaped umbilicus formed by the close superposition of the concave margins of the inner whorls (Pl. IX). These genera, grouped in the Graphoceratinae, lead directly to the smooth, highly keeled *Hyperlioceras* of the sauzei zone. Other hildoceratids associated in the Ludwigian fauna include rare hammatocerates which are transitional to the sonninians of the succeeding fauna.

Classification of the Upper Jurassic

Stratigraphical stages		Faunas	Zones
PURBECK BEDS	PURBECKIAN	[No ammonites in Britain]	
PORTLAND STONE	PORTLANDIAN	Titanitan	*T. giganteus*
		Crendonitan	*C. gorei*
KIMMERIDGE CLAY	KIMMERIDGIAN	Pavlovian	*Pav. rotunda*
		Pectinatitan	*Pect. pectinatus*
		Subplanitan	*S. wheatleyensis*
		Gravesian	*G. gigas*
		Aulacostephanitan	*A. pseudomutabilis*
		Rasenian	*R. cymodoce*
		Pictonian	*Pict. baylei*
CORAL-LIAN	OXFORDIAN	Ringsteadian	*R. pseudocordata*
		Perisphinctean	*Per. plicatilis*
		Cardioceratan	*Card. cordatum*
OXFORD CLAY	CALLOVIAN	Quenstedtoceratan	*Q. lamberti*
		Kosmoceratan	*K. jason*
		Proplanulitan	*Prop. koenigi*
CORN-BRASH		Macrocephalitan	*M. macrocephalus*
GREAT OOLITE	BATHONIAN	Clydoniceratan	*C. discus*
		Tulitan	*T. subcontractus*
INFERIOR OOLITE	BAJOCIAN	Parkinsonian	*Park. parkinsoni*
		Stephanoceratan	*St. humphriesianum*
		Sonninian	*Ot. sauzei*
			Son. sowerbyi
		Ludwigian	*Lud. murchisonae*
		Leioceratan	*Leio. opalinum*

Among early Bajocian brachiopods the familiar rhynchonellid *Homoeorhynchia cynocephala* (Rich.) is easily recognized by the extreme anterior projection of its brachial valve, which gives the 'dog's head' outline suggested in its trivial name (Fig. 64). This shell is associated in the Leioceratan fauna with the terebratulid *Euidothyris euides* S. Buckm. (Fig. 65), with folded anterior margin, and the terebratellid *Zeilleria whaddonensis* S. Buckm. In the Ludwigian fauna, *Homoeorhynchia cynomorpha* S. Buckm. is closely allied to its predecessor *H. cynocephala*, and, perhaps in a lesser degree, to the small *H. ringens* (Dav.) of the Dorset-Somerset area. *Rhynchonelloidea subangulata* (Dav.) (Fig. 64) shows an approach to the cynocephalous shape, while *Flabellirhynchia lycetti* (Dav.), restricted to the Cotswolds, is biconvex and strongly ribbed. The genus *Globirhynchia*, comprising the group of *Rhynchonella subobsoleta* Dav. (Fig. 64), fully costate forms with rather large pedicle aperture, appears to be local to the Cotswolds. The terebratulids include the distinctive *Plectothyris fimbria* (J. Sow.) (Fig. 65) easily recognized by the many plications on its anterior margin. This form (indeed its genus) is apparently unknown in Britain outside the Cotswolds, as is *Epithyris submaxillata* (Dav.) (Fig. 65), which has fewer anterior plications and an incurved, truncated beak. *Pseudoglossothyris curvifrons* (Dav.) and *P. simplex* (J. Buckm.) (Fig. 65) are respectively dorsally sulcate and planiconvex terebratulids with large pedicle apertures; they often attain a large size in the Cotswold district. *Zeilleria leckenbyi* Walker and Dav., abundant in the Cotswold area, may be mentioned as a typical terebratellid. It will be realized that the brachiopods of the Cotswolds include many species that are wanting in equivalent strata of Dorset and Somerset; moreover, many shells found in the latter area and in France are unknown in the Cotswolds, while, between the two districts, early Bajocian strata are imperfectly developed. It is inferred that movements along the Mendip axis had effected a temporary separation of the northern from the southern region as far as submarine deposition is concerned.

Numerous gastropods and lamellibranchs occur in the same deposits, but are not so restricted in their vertical range. Some of the bivalved forms, such as *Gresslya abducta* (Phill.), *Pholadomya fidicula* J. Sow. (Fig. 70), *Trigonia striata* J. Sow., and *Modiola sowerbyana* d'Orb., show close relationship with shells of later horizons in the Inferior Oolite.

The most conspicuous ammonites in the **Sonninian Fauna** of the sowerbyi and sauzei zones are the keeled sonninines, which are connected with the Hammatoceratinae by passage forms. They bear some resemblance to the Domerian amaltheids, but the inner whorls are spinose, and the outer volutions ribbed or smooth; the suture-line is very complex, especially in the smooth forms. The early genus *Euhaploceras* comprises massive, strongly ribbed ammonites with quadrangular whorls, and *Haplopleuroceras* is remarkably like the Domerian *Pleuroceras*, but its tubercles develop long, sharp spines which are septate; it is very distinct among Bajocian ammonites, though apparently unknown in Britain outside Dorset. Later members of the Sonninian fauna include the typical genus *Sonninia* which acquires smooth, trigonal outer whorls, and its associate *Witchellia* which possesses compressed outer whorls with feeble ornament. Other hildoceratids in the fauna include members of the surviving graphoceratine genera *Graphoceras*, *Ludwigella*, and *Hyperlioceras*. Late members of the fauna are associated with the inflated coronate genus *Otoites*, a cadicone shell with lateral auricles on its mouth border, and ornamented with numerous fine ribs and feeble tubercles (Pl. X). Numerous sonninines are present in the Bajocian strata of western Scotland but the stepheoceratids are unknown there. This difference between Somerset and Scotland has been explained by supposing that the sonninines were able to migrate farther northward than the other group.

The cadicone shape just noted also appears in several members of the **Stephanoceratan Fauna,** such as the coarsely ornamented *Teloceras* which exhibits an extreme development of whorl-depression (Pl. X). *Stephanoceras* and *Stemmatoceras* are evolute and planulate, with tubercles at the junction of the primary and peripheral ribs; their mouth-border is a plain annular band preceded by a constriction, the absence of auricles being a distinction from the earlier *Otoites* and other genera. These fossils were for long grouped as *Ammonites humphriesianus* J. de C. Sow. (Pl. X), and are connected by transitional forms; their distinctive type of ornament gives an unmistakable aspect to the fauna as a whole. *Poecilomorphus cycloides* (d'Orb.), an involute, sphaeroid sonninine with laterally curved ribs, is often an associate of *Teloceras*. A sphaeroid ally of *Otoites* is seen in the genus *Chondroceras*, which may be exemplified by *C. delphinus* S. Buckm. (Pl. X).

The most conspicuous of the Bajocian rhynchonellids are species of the spinose genus *Acanthothyris* (Fig. 68) bearing short spines in rather irregular transverse lines. The strongly ribbed, irregularly shaped *Stolmorhynchia*, which is said to range up into Cretaceous strata, is represented by *S. stolidota* S. Buckm., and possibly other species. A group of terebratulids eminently characteristic of Bajocian faunas is that of *Terebratula perovalis* Dav., for which the generic name *Loboidothyris* has been instituted. The group includes massive biconvex shells, with large overhanging beaks, and showing a tendency towards folding on the anterior margin; they are among the largest of fossil terebratulids. The genus *Lobothyris*, comprising smooth, elongate terebratulids, is represented by such species as *L. buckmani* (Dav.) and *L. cortonensis* S. Buckm., both more strongly biconvex and plicate than Domerian members of the genus. The elongate and biplicate species *Terebratula buckmaniana* Walker, and *T. phillipsiana* Walker, are similar to species of *Lobothyris* in their elongation, but are placed in the genus *Heimia* on account of their internal features. Some of these brachiopods are shown in Fig. 66. Species of the terebratellid genus *Aulacothyris* are also typical, especially *A. carinatus* (Lam.) (Fig. 67).

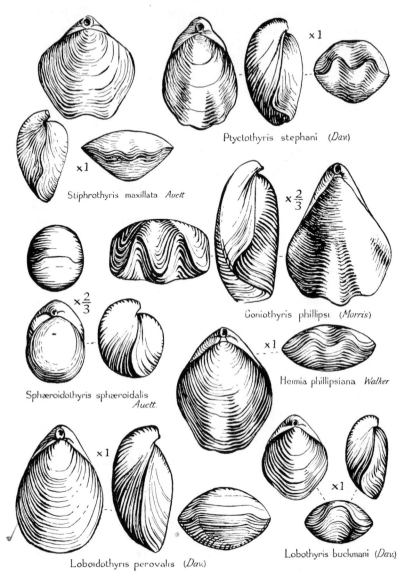

Ptyctothyris stephani (*Dav.*)

Stiphrothyris maxillata *Auctt*

Goniothyris phillipsı (*Morris*)

Heimia phillipsiana *Walker*

Sphæroidothyris sphæroidalis
Auctt.

Loboidothyris perovalis (*Dav.*)

Lobothyris buckmani (*Dav.*)

FIG. 66. TEREBRATULIDS FROM THE INFERIOR OOLITE (*drawn from figures by Davidson*)

Many molluscan forms occur; perhaps the most conspicuous are numerous species of the gastropod *Pleurotomaria* which often attain a considerable size. Among lamellibranchs, *Astarte elegans* J. Sow., *Pecten (Aequipecten) barbatus* J. Sow., and *Gresslya abducta* (Phil.) may be mentioned. The ammonites and brachiopods are so abundant and distinctive that other groups have received less attention with regard to their stratigraphical significance.

The distinctive ammonites of the **Parkinsonian Fauna** have simple ribs interrupted on the venter by a conspicuous groove which extends along the median line. An early form showing this character is *Strenoceras niortense* (d'Orb.); it is much like the earlier *Tmetoceras* in having spines on the borders of the ventral groove, but the inner whorls are coronate. The typical *Parkinsonia* (Pl. X) has lateral auricles on the apertural border, but *Garantiana*, with ribs ending in tubercles at the margins of the ventral groove, has a plain mouth border. *Spiroceras* is a loosely coiled offshoot of the same stock. The Parkinsonidae are developed through the Stephanoceratinae from one of the fundamental lytoceratid stocks, and, in the upper horizons of the zone, give rise to the Zigzagiceratinae so named from the distinctive form of the ornament. The genus *Zigzagiceras* sometimes shows a change from the coronate to a massive planulate without tubercles known as the perisphinctoid form; this becomes important in Bathonian and higher strata. Another development of the Stephanoceratid stock is *Morphoceras*, a sphaerocone in youth, but later developing compressed whorls with periodic constrictions. *Polyplectites*, a serpental form with rounded whorls, has lateral auricles on the mouth border. Certain oppelids are also associated with these genera. *Strigoceras* (Pl. X) is perhaps the most noticeable, as it is a large involute shell with compressed whorls, hollow keel and complex suture-line; unlike other Jurassic ammonites, it has linear, longitudinal ornament. *Lissoceras*, a smooth, compressed form with rounded periphery, has a simpler suture-line than most oppelids. *Oecotraustes* is also like *Oppelia* but tends to the scaphitoid condition owing to a progressive decrease in the degree of coiling.

Brachiopods associated with the Parkinsonian fauna include several species of the spinose rhynchonellid genera *Acanthothyris* and *Acanthorhynchia*. These two groups are separated mainly on account of differences in internal features, but the latter may also be distinguished by its more regular ornament and its narrow, sub-erect beak. The well-known group of '*Rhynchonella*' *obsoleta* Dav. (Fig. 68), now divided between the genera *Cymatorhynchia* and *Rhactorhynchia* is associated also with *Sphenorhynchia*, a genus comprising cuneiform, areolate forms typified by *S. plicatella* (J. de C. Sow.). The terebratulids are perhaps more easily recognized. The distinctive group is *Sphaeroidothyris*, a series of globose forms, with only faint waving of the anterior margin, more familiar under the name *Terebratula sphaeroidalis* (auctt.). Somewhat similar, but less tumid, and distinguished by a large incurved and truncated beak is *Stiphrothyris* which includes some species formerly grouped with *Terebratula maxillata* and *T. globata* by various authors. Another conspicuous form is *Terebratula phillipsi* Morris (Fig. 66), a long, narrow shell with short beak, apical foramen, and broad anterior folding; this fossil now belongs to the genus *Goniothryis*. Another typical genus, *Ptyctothyris*, including the group of *Terebratula stephani* Dav. is distinguished especially by the distinct and persistent carination of its pedicle valve (Fig. 66).

Of the many lamellibranchs present in the same assemblage, species of *Trigonia* are perhaps the most important; indeed, these shells have provided a name for the 'Trigonia Grits' of the Cotswolds. *T. costata* J. Sow., and *T. duplicata* J. Sow. are illustrated in Plate XIII. Several species of *Opis*, such as *O. cordiformis* Lycett and *O. similis* (J. Sow.) are easily recognized by the triangular shape of the shell. Among burrowing forms *Gresslya abducta* (Phill.) and *Pholadomya fidicula* are typical shells of the Inferior Oolite generally. Some beds are marked by the abundance of corals, and frequently, distinctive associations of *Montlivaltia*, *Thecosmilia*, *Isastraea*, and *Thamnastraea* may be observed. Thus, *M. smithi* (Edw. and Haime) and *Thecosmilia gregaria* (M'Coy) are probably closely related, and both occur in the Lower Trigonia Grit of the Cotswolds. Other series have been suggested but apparently require detailed investigation. Echinoids are often found in these limestones; the chief genera are *Stomechinus*, *Hemicidaris*, *Holectypus*, *Nucleolites*, and *Collyrites*, while the abundance of *Clypeus ploti* Klein at one horizon has provided the term 'Clypeus Grit'. The sporadic occurrence of some sea-urchins is illustrated by that of *Magnotia forbesi* Wright, which is recorded only from the Upper Bajocian of Dundry Hill, Somerset.

The Bathonian Stage begins with the Lower Fuller's Earth of Dorset and Somerset. Here ammonites are virtually absent, and the horizon is usually identified by the abundance of *Ostrea acuminata* J. Sow., a small oyster with a sharply pointed umbo (Fig. 69). The succeeding Fuller's Earth Rock of south-west England provides a variation to the prolonged scarcity of ammonites in the Bathonian stage of this country, in yielding the **Tulitan Fauna.** The Tulitidae are robust, coronate ammonites with feeble ornament and rather simple suture-lines. Formerly included in the genus *Teloceras*, they are now distributed among *Tulites* and a few other genera closely connected with the contemporary otoitids and also with the later macrocephalitids. Since these ammonites are not widespread, the horizon is usually determined by the brachiopods *Ornithella bathonica* and *Wattonithyris nunneyensis* in association with species of *Rhynchonelloidella* and *Acanthothyris*. There are also such lamellibranchs as *Lima duplicata* J. Sow., *Ostrea costata* J. Sow. and *Pseudomonotis echinata* (J. Sow.) which are equally characteristic at the top of the Bathonian stage.

The base of the Great Oolite Limestone in the Cotswolds and Oxfordshire is a fissile limestone known as the Stonesfield Slate. It has yielded rare ammonites, namely, the compressed, planulate *Gracilisphinctes*, and the oppelid-like *Micromphalites*. On account of imperfect knowledge of this assemblage it is not advisable to regard either of these forms as an index of a separate fauna, but other fossils of the Stonesfield Slate merit special mention. Besides brachiopods and lamellibranchs by which the horizon may be determined, the fauna contains some interesting but rare vertebrate remains, including mandibles of the small mammals *Phascolotherium* and *Amphitherium*, bones and teeth of reptiles and fishes, the latter including *Ceratodus*. The most abundant brachiopods are the rhynchonellids that have long been grouped under the names *Rhynchonella concinna* (J. Sow.) and *R. obsoleta* auctt. These forms, being but slightly folded anteriorly, and having close-set ribbing and acute, prominent beaks, are closely similar in external appearance. Differences in the arrangement of the internal muscle-scars, however, have led S. S. Buckman to distribute many species of these groups among several genera, including *Burmirhynchia* and *Kallirhynchia* (Fig. 68). These two genera range through Bathonian strata, and form a distinctive element in the faunas, while the numerous species may eventually provide a detailed sequence for local sections. Other distinctive fossils of the Stonesfield Slate are *Trigonia impressa* J. Sow., *Gervillia acuta* J. de C. Sow., *Pecten (Camptonectes) lens* J. Sow. and several species of *Lima*.

The Great Oolite Limestone of Minchinhampton long ago yielded a few ammonites, including the types of *Tulites subcontractus* (Mor. and Lyc.), and *Morrisiceras morrisi* (Oppel), besides that of the oppelid *Oxycerites water-housei* (Mor. and Lyc.), but the precise horizons from which they were obtained are not recorded. It seems certain, however, that the Tulitan fauna continues into this limestone, though its relations to the assemblage of the Stonesfield Slate remain uncertain.

Besides ammonites, brachiopods also are often scarce in these limestones. But the terebratulid genus *Epithyris* is typical, and easily recognized by its incurved and truncated beak, and by the broad folding of its anterior margin. Members of this genus fall under the old group of *Terebratula maxillata*; *E. bathonica* S. Buckm. and *E. oxonica* Arkell are distinctive species in the Great Oolite. Many gastropods occur; among them *Purpuroidea nodulata* (Young) (Fig. 70) and other species, *Patella rugosa* J. Sow. and *Nerinaea voltzi* Morris and Lycett (Fig. 70) may be cited as typical. The lamellibranchs include many shells which, like *Homomya gibbosa* (J. Sow.) and *Pholadomya murchisoni* Moesch, are indicative of physical conditions, but have no precise value in stratigraphy. *Trigonia clavulosa* Rig. and Sauv., and *T. signata* Ag., however, are typical of the Great Oolite. Echinoids, represented by species of *Nucleolites* and *Acrosalenia*, are usually in a fragmentary condition, but corals are often conspicuous in preservation and abundance. A suggestive coral-association in the Great Oolite consists of *Montlivaltia slatteri* (Tomes), *Thecosmilia obtusa* (d'Orb.), *Isastraea limitata* (Mich.) and *Thamnastraea lyelli* E. and H., along with other forms.

The great development of strata which includes the Bradford Clay, Forest Marble, and the lower part of the Cornbrash, contains few ammonites. The genus *Clydoniceras*, a smooth oxycone with simple suture-line, is characteristic of the Lower Cornbrash, and its name is taken as an index for the **Clydoniceratan Fauna**. It is convenient to include here the fossil assemblages of the Bradford Clay and Forest Marble which contain brachiopods of a similar aspect to those of the Lower Cornbrash, though future discoveries of ammonites in the lower strata may necessitate a different grouping. Since the lithological horizons are distinguishable by their brachiopod faunas, these may be described in some detail.

The Bradford Clay has long been famous for its distinctive suite of brachiopods. The rhynchonellids include the genus *Cryptorhynchia*, with prominent beak and imbricate ribbing, besides the more distinctly trilobed *Goniorhynchia*, comprising the group of *Rhynchonella boueti* Dav. Species of *Avonothyris*, a terebratulid genus characteristic of the horizon, are like *Epithyris* in their anterior folding, but have a smaller beak with a small circular foramen. The associated *Dictyothyris*, typified by *D. coarctata* (Park.), is probably unique among terbratulids in the beautifully reticulate ornament of its shell. The terebratellid *Ornithella digona* (J. Sow.) (Fig. 67) has long been used as a guide-fossil and is too well known to need description here. Also typical of the Bradford Clay are the familiar 'pear-encrinite' *Apiocrinus* (Fig. 11) and the lamellibranch *Oxytoma costata* (J. Sow.)

The Forest Marble may be recognized by the abundance of *Epithyris marmorea* (Oppel), but this large terebratulid appears to be rather limited in distribution. Though the shelly limestones are often crowded with fossils the fauna is relatively poor in species. One of the commonest forms is *Ostrea sowerbyi* Morris and Lycett, an oyster of moderate size which is recognized by its lunate shape and blunt apex (Fig. 69). *Gervillia crassicosta* Mor. and Lyc. is also characteristic, but seems to be somewhat sporadic in occurrence. Other common shells include *Pecten (Chlamys) obscura* J. Sow., *Modiola imbricata* J. Sow., and species of *Kallirhynchia* (the group of *Rhynchonella concinna* auctt.). The most abundant sea-urchin is *Acrosalenia hemicidaroides* Wright (Pl. XII). It may also be noted that the Forest Marble near Oxford has yielded the remains of a gigantic reptile, *Cetiosaurus oxoniensis* Phillips, which attained a length of 60 feet, and a height of 16 feet.

The commonest brachiopods associated with Clydoniceratan ammonites in the Lower Cornbrash are *Ornithella obovata* (J. Sow.) and *Cererithyris intermedia* (J. Sow.). The former is easily recognized by the two feeble plaits at the extremities of its anterior margin; the shell is gibbous and has a rounded beak with lateral ridges (Fig. 67). *C. intermedia* has a short, stout beak, and the anterior margin of the shell is almost straight, though two feeble folds are present. These are associated with species of *Kallirkynchia*.

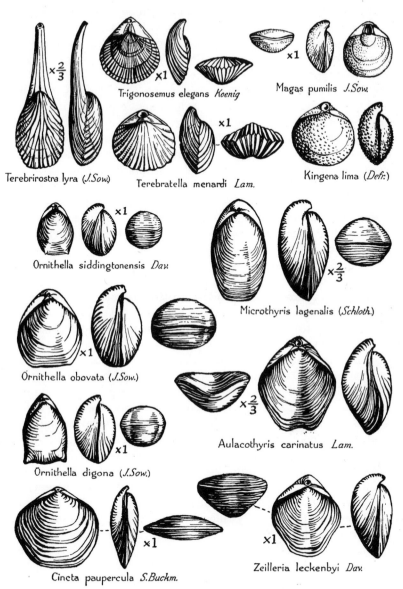

$\times\frac{2}{3}$

Trigonosemus elegans *Koenig*

$\times 1$

Magas pumilis *J.Sow.*

$\times 1$

Terebrirostra lyra *(J.Sow.)*

Terebratella menardi *Lam.*

Kingena lima *(Defr.)*

$\times 1$

Ornithella siddingtonensis *Dav.*

$\times\frac{2}{3}$

Microthyris lagenalis *(Schloth.)*

$\times 1$

Ornithella obovata *(J.Sow.)*

$\times\frac{2}{3}$

$\times 1$

Ornithella digona *(J.Sow.)*

Aulacothyris carinatus *Lam.*

$\times 1$

$\times 1$

Cincta paupercula *S.Buckm.*

Zeilleria leckenbyi *Dav.*

FIG. 67. SOME MESOZOIC TEREBRATELLIDS (*drawn from figures by Davidson*)

Among many lamellibranchs which have an extended vertical range, there are a few that are only known in association with the Clydoniceratan fauna. Such are, *Astarte robusta* Lyc., *Trigonia moretoni* Mor. and Lyc., *T. flecta* Lyc., and *Pecten (Eopecten) gradus* Bean. *Nautilus truncatus* J. Sow. also appears to be typical of this assemblage.

The **Macrocephalitan Fauna,** occupying the Upper Cornbrash, is marked by renewed abundance of ammonites, especially of numerous species formerly united as *Ammonites macrocephalus* Schlot. These include the robust, and more or less inflated, *Macrocephalites* and several allied genera separated on differences in ornament and suture-line: the family Macrocephalitidae includes direct developments from *Sphaeroceras* which are derivatives of the Bajocian Stephanoceratidae. The general type of ornament is that of regular, close-set ribbing which projects forwards on the periphery, forming an angle of varying degree. In the somewhat compressed and fine-ribbed *Macrocephalites*, however, the ribs extend straight across the venter without forward projection.

The faunal distinction between Upper and Lower Cornbrash is also evident in the brachiopod element, though perhaps to a lesser degree. The most typical brachiopods associated with the macrocephalitids are *Ornithella siddingtonensis* Walker and Dav., and *Microthyris lagenalis* (Schlot.) (Fig. 67). The latter is an elongate shell with incurved and truncated beak, convex gibbous valves with practically straight anterior margins. *O. siddingtonensis* is more elongate than the earlier *O. obovata*, and with *O. stiltonensis* Walker and Dav., has often been confused with *O. digona* from the Bradford Clay. By far the most abundant and typical lamellibranch is *Pseudomonotis echinata* (J. Sow.); the convex left valve has strong radiating, spiny ribs which give the shell its characteristic appearance; the right valve is flat and almost smooth, while both valves have small ears (Fig. 70). A further feature of the lamellibranch assemblage is the abundance of large species of *Pholadomya*, such as *P. phillipsi* Lycett, and *P. lyrata* J. Sow. Echinoids, too, are usually present in exposures of the Cornbrash, the commonest species being *Nucleolites clunicularis* (Wright), *N. orbicularis* (Phill.), *N. quadratus* (Wright), and the form usually called *Holectypus depressus* (Leske) (Pl. XII).

The **Proplanulitan Fauna** occurs in the variable series of sands and clays known as the Kellaways Beds from the village in Wiltshire where they attain their typical development. The distinctive ammonites are species of *Proplanulites* (Pl. XI), compressed, costate shells with smooth, rounded periphery and simple suture-lines. These proplanulitids are probably connected with such Bathonian derivatives of Parkinsonidae as *Procerites* and *Wagnericeras* but these are too rare for the ancestral forms to be traced at present. Another offshoot from the Bajocian Zigzagiceratidae is represented in the Callovian stage by *Reineckia* and allied genera, tuberculate ammonites with smooth venter; these are rare in England, and the record from Mull is now discredited. *Cadoceras*, a development from the macrocephalitid stock, with numerous rounded ribs in youth, and developed into stout sphaerocones (Pl. XI), is well known in the Kellaways Beds of Wiltshire. Here also occur early representatives of the Kosmoceratidae which, in the overlying Oxford Clay, develop forms with flattened venter bordered by tubercles. In *Kepplerites*, the adult is similar to *Macrocephalites*, but runcination of the periphery appears on the inner whorls. *Sigaloceras* is more compressed, more involute, and a more definitely flattened periphery persists to the end; thus the genus approaches certain members of the succeeding fauna.

Other mollusca in the Kellaways Beds form a distinctive and easily recognized group, which can be used for purposes of correlation in the frequent absence of ammonites. Especially characteristic is a suite of grypheate oysters, rather variable in character, but by their narrow form and posterior alar expansion of the left valve are mostly comparable with *Gryphaea bilobata* J. de C. Sow. (Fig. 69); small shells appearing in the lower beds are less incurved than the larger *G. bilobata* typical of higher horizons. These oysters often occur in great numbers, and more than one species may be represented. They are associated with *Pecten (Camptonectes) lens* J. Sow., *P. (Entolium) demissum* (Phill.), *Pleuromya recurva* Phil., and *Belemnites oweni* Pratt. This assemblage, therefore, is well contrasted with that of the underlying Cornbrash.

The lower part of the Oxford Clay in its typical development around Oxford, and in the English Midlands generally, contains the **Kosmoceratan Fauna.** Species of *Kosmoceras*, smooth-ventered ammonites, with feeble ribs that bear tubercles on the lateral area and end in spines on the peripheral shoulders, are extremely abundant. The 'early kosmocerates are usually preserved in a calcareous condition, and crushed flat in the shales (Pl. XI) but sometimes the shells are found 'solid' in concretions. They are associated with *Erymnoceras* a genus of massive coronate ammonites developed from a *Cadoceras* stock. Later kosmocerates are generally uncrushed and preserved as pyritic moulds, the shell having disappeared (Pl. XI). They are accompanied by species of *Peltoceras*, an offshoot of a perisphinctid stock; these are planulate in youth, becoming bituberculate and flat-ventered in the adult. Species occurring here are of the type of *P. athleta* (Phill.), their peripheral ribs uniting in groups of three at the tubercles on the peripheral shoulders. The brachiopods *Aulacothyris bernardina* (d'Orb.) usually preserved in shining black phosphate, and *Rhynchonelloidea socialis* (Phill.) (Fig. 68), are also associated with these ammonites. A nearly equilateral grypheate oyster, which often occurs in great numbers, is usually ascribed to *Gryphaea dilatata* auctt. (Fig. 69), but the shell is smaller and thinner than the typical Corallian form and may be specifically distinct. The belemnoid *Cylindroteuthis oweni* (Pratt) often occurs in enormous numbers and ranges through the Oxford Clay. The 'unguarded' *Belemnoteuthis* is comparatively rare, perhaps because of its fragility.

These Kosmoceras Beds are further characterized by a lamellibranch assemblage consisting of small species of *Astarte*, *Nucula*, and *Cucullaea*. Many of the species appear to be undescribed in British literature, but collectively they give a distinctive character to the fauna, especially in the lower beds. Other invertebrate fossils include the sea-urchin *Acrosalenia* and the small simple coral *Anabacia complanata* Defr., but these are comparatively rare. A curious annelid tube *Serpula vertebralis* J. de C. Sow., whose trivial name is sufficiently descriptive, is often abundant in the lower clays. It should be mentioned also that the lower beds of the Oxford Clay near Peterborough have yielded a large number of reptiles and fishes, many being represented by almost complete skeletons. The ichthyosaurid *Ophthalmosaurus*, the pliosaurids *Peloneustes* and *Simolestes*, the elasmosaurids *Muraenosaurus* and *Cryptocleidus*, and the marine crocodile *Metriorhynchus* are among the genera catalogued by C. W. Andrews (1910 and 1913).

Higher in the Oxford Clay the kosmocerates and their associates are gradually replaced by the **Quenstedtoceratan Fauna.** The commonest ammonites are usually referred to *Quenstedtoceras*; they vary in shape from oxycone to sphaerocone, and are ornamented by ribs which incline forwards to the median line of the venter where they tend to form a crenulate keel. They are transitional between the cadocerates of the Kellaways Beds, and the cardiocerates of the Oxfordian stage next to be discussed. There are intermediate forms in many directions, one of which (*Scarburgiceras*), from the highest beds of the stage, is illustrated in Plate XI. Associated with the quenstedtocerates are various oppelids, e.g. *Creniceras*, a smooth discoid genus whose discontinuous keel gives a crested appearance (Pl. XI), *Lunuloceras*, evolute, with sickle-shaped ribs, but without keel, *Taramelliceras*, involute and compressed, ornamented with fine striae. Bivalved mollusca are not abundant in this fauna, but *Grammatodon concinnus* (Lor.), *Nuculana roederi* (Lor.), and *Pinna mitis* Phill. are typical when found.

The Lower Oxfordian strata, containing the **Cardioceratan Fauna,** are determined by the abundance of *Cardioceras*, a genus in which the characters of *Quenstedtoceras* are accentuated, the ribs being more strongly projected forwards, and furrows developing on either side of the well-marked crenulate keel (Pl. XIV). The group of *Am. cordatum* J. Sow. is now distributed among several genera besides *Cardioceras*, and includes some large forms which assume an oxycone shape with little or no ornament. The genus *Peltoceras* is represented by a few species, as also is the similarly tuberculate *Euaspidoceras*, which persists in the succeeding fauna. Many planulate ammonites of the type of *Perisphinctes plicatilis* (J. Sow.) have also been recorded.

Among characteristic fossils belonging to other animal-groups may be mentioned a series of grypheate oysters of large and massive type, which are probably the true species-group of *Gryphaea dilatata* J. Sow. *Pecten fibrosus* J. Sow., a shell with concentric striations between the strong radial ribs, is also typical of this fauna. Echinoids are sometimes abundant, *Nucleolites scutatus* Lam., *N. dimidiatus* (Phill.), and *Holectypus oblongus* Wright being noteworthy forms.

The strata containing this fauna comprise the uppermost part of the Oxford Clay with the Lower Calcareous Grit, the latter being absent from the outcrop between the north of Oxfordshire and the south of Yorkshire. Near its margin in north Oxfordshire the Lower Calcareous Grit is locally represented by a peculiar impure cherty rock composed essentially of the globular spicules of a sponge, *Rhaxella perforata* Hinde; this rock contains species of *Cardioceras* and other fossils of the Cardioceratan fauna.

The **Perisphinctean Fauna** is characteristic of the Upper Oxfordian. The typical ammonites are forms which are usually referred to *Perisphinctes* —planulate shells bearing bifurcating ribs that pass uninterruptedly over the venter, and numerous constrictions that are usually oblique to the general course of the ribbing. Perisphinctoid ammonites occur in many faunas from the Bajocian upwards, but they represent homoeomorphic developments of many lineages, and much stratigraphical confusion has resulted from their general similarity. In dealing with these forms, there-fore, it is necessary to exercise great care in their determination. The asso-ciated *Euaspidoceras* (Pl. XIV) and various other fossils are, however, unmistakable. Like the ammonites, lamellibranchs are often abundant in the 'condensed' shell-beds which represent slow deposition in still, shallow water. These assemblages are dominated by species of *Trigonia* from which they take their names, the widespread *Trigonia hudlestoni* Lycett, and *T. clavellata* J. Sow. (Pl. XIII). The shells, unbroken and perfectly pre-served, also include species of *Lima, Pecten, Gervillia, Astarte, Cucullaea*, &c. They are often accompanied by gastropods, of which *Pseudomelania heddingtonensis* J. Sow., *Natica arguta* Phill., *Nerinaea fasciata* Voltz, *Pleurotomaria reticulata* and *Bourguetia striata* J. Sow., are characteristic. A more restricted assemblage is peculiar to the coral rags, in association with the typical reef-building corals *Thecosmilia annularis* (Flem.), *Isas-traea explanata* Goldf., *Thamnastraea arachnoides* (Park.) and *Tham. concinna* (Goldf.); this association of corals forms reefs of considerable size between Calne and Oxford. The lamellibranchs typical of the coral rag are *Chlamys nattheimensis* Lor., *Lima zonata* Arkell, *Ostrea gregaria* J. Sow., and *Lithophaga inclusa* (Phill.); the association also includes the gastropod *Littorina muricata* J. Sow., and the sea-urchin *Cidaris florigemma* Phill. Still another assemblage is typical of the Wheatley Limestones which were formed of the detritus from erosion of the reefs. Almost the only lamelli-branch in an unbroken condition is the small oyster *Exogyra nana* which occurs in enormous numbers. It is associated with the sea-urchins *Nucleo-lites scutatus* (Lam.), *Pygaster semisulcatus* Phill. and *Hemicidaris inter-media* Flem.; the perfect preservation of these echinoids indicates that they actually lived among the detrital material in which they are enclosed. In the

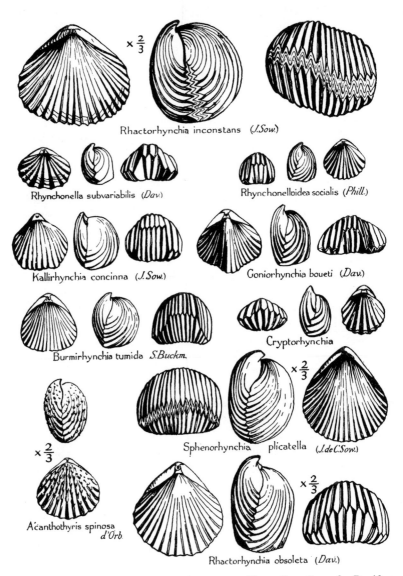

×⅔

Rhactorhynchia inconstans (*J.Sow.*)

Rhynchonella subvariabilis (*Dav.*)

Rhynchonelloidea socialis (*Phill.*)

Kallirhynchia concinna (*J.Sow.*)

Goniorhynchia boueti (*Dav.*)

Burmirhynchia tumida *S.Buckm.*

Cryptorhynchia

×⅔

Sphenorhynchia   plicatella (*J.de C.Sow.*)

×⅔

A'canthothyris spinosa
d'Orb

×⅔

Rhactorhynchia obsoleta (*Dav.*)

Fɪɢ. 68. ᴜᴘᴘᴇʀ ᴊᴜʀᴀssɪᴄ ʀʜʏɴᴄʜᴏɴᴇʟʟɪᴅs (*drawn from figures by Davidson and Buckman*)

Ampthill Clay there is an abundance of the massive oysters *Gryphaea dilatata* J. Sow. and *Ostrea discoidea* Seeley (Fig. 69) with occasional members of the cardioceratid genus *Prionodoceras*, long familiar under the name *Amoeboceras serratum* (J. Sow.). This form is most commonly found 'derived' in the Boulder Clay of the English Midlands, but is also recorded *in situ* in the upper beds of the Ampthill Clay. It shows a very pronounced forward projection of the ribs on the peripheral border, and the keel is crenulated by intersection with the ribs; the outer whorls are inflated at the umbilical margin, and are often devoid of ornament.

The name-genus of the **Ringsteadian Fauna** is *Ringsteadia* (after Ringstead Bay in Dorset), established by Salfeld for the group of *Ammonites pseudocordatus* Blake and Hudl. (Pl. XIV). These ammonites are compressed (approaching the oxycone shape) and bear strong, inflated ribs on the inner whorls, the outer volutions being usually smooth. Associated with these forms in some localities are compressed species of *Prionodoceras*, e.g. *P. superstes* (Phill.) (Pl. XIV), marked by feeble ribbing which projects some distance forwards to the sharp, almost keeled venter. The associated *Ostrea delta* W. Smith often forms 'oyster beds', and *Gervillia kimmeridgensis* d'Orb. and *Nucula menkei* F. Römer make their first appearance. These lamellibranchs range into higher beds and are usually quoted as characteristic of the Kimmeridge Clay. The Westbury Iron-ore, containing the Ringsteadian fauna, is an interesting lithological variation of local importance in Wiltshire.

Succeeding the Oxfordian rocks is a thick series of clays (with subordinate sands) known as the Kimmeridge Clay, from its typical development near Kimmeridge in Dorset. The series is limited above by the base of the Portland Stone Series. Considering the fossils of the Kimmeridge Clay as a whole, two faunas are readily distinguishable, marking a lower and an upper division. Long ago, continental geologists restricted the term Kimmeridgian to the lower subdivision and placed the upper clays in the lower part of their 'Portlandien'. As a compromise, Blake proposed the term Bolonian for the Upper Kimmeridge Clay, but the suggestion has not met with general acceptance. In these pages, therefore, the Kimmeridgian stage is retained in the original sense.

The **Pictonian Fauna** is named from the distinctive genus *Pictonia*, round-ventered ammonites with almost obsolete ornament. The genus, like *Ringsteadia* and *Rasenia* in the adjacent zones, represents an offshoot from the main perisphinctid stock, as also does the associated *Dichotomoceras*. *Pictonia* and *Ringsteadia* are both recorded from the Westbury Ironstone, and there is some doubt whether this should be regarded as a true succession of the two zones, or as a condensed deposit in which ammonites of the two zones are mingled.

Salfeld's genus *Rasenia*, which marks the **Rasenian Fauna,** includes many of the coronates of the Kimmeridge Clay, well known from the beautifully iridescent specimens so abundant at Market Rasen in Lincoln-shire. The coronate appearance is especially marked in immaturity, adults being either smooth or ornamented by strong, undivided ribs. These ammonites have yet to be investigated in detail; the form illustrated in Pl. XIV may be brought into comparison with *R. involuta* Salfeld. Asso-ciated with them are keeled, tuberculate ammonites ascribed to *Amoebo-ceras*, a genus closely related and very similar to *Prionodoceras* mentioned above; these are particularly abundant in the Lower Kimmeridgian beds of north-eastern Scotland, and of the Hebrides.

Aulacostephanus, the distinctive ammonite-genus of the **Aulacostephan-itan Fauna,** includes somewhat compressed forms in which the bifurcate ribbing is interrupted on the venter by a smooth band. They are inter-preted as a discoid development from the *Pictonia* group of perisphinctids. Species of the aspidocerate genus *Physodoceras* are recorded in association with *Aulacostephanus*. The fossil known as *Aptychus*, usually regarded as the operculum of ammonites, is often abundant.

The **Gravesian Fauna** is specially marked by large, inflated, coronate ammonites, grouped in the genus *Gravesia*. These, according to Spath, are derivatives of depressed species of *Rasenia*. They are sometimes accom-panied by perisphinctoid forms like '*Perisphinctes*' *bleicheri* (Lor.). Beds containing this fauna were first recognized in Dorset by Salfeld (1913), and have since been recorded tentatively from the Sutherland coast of Scotland.

Apart from cephalopods, the fossils of these four early Kimmeridgian faunas are closely related throughout, and may be discussed as a unit. The most typical brachiopod is *Rhynchonella inconstans* (J. Sow.), assigned nowadays to the genus *Rhactorhynchia*, and recognized most readily by the unsymmetrical fold of the anterior margin (Fig. 68). This fossil is typically associated with Rasenian ammonites. The lamellibranchs are of little value in narrow correlation, but in the absence of ammonites they are useful in distinguishing Kimmeridgian from later strata. The species-group of *Exogyra virgula* (Defr.) is most characteristic, and is said to show well-marked variation during the progress of its history. Small shells with fine longitudinal ornament are associated with the Rasenian ammonites, while later shells show an increase in size together with a coarsening of the sur-face-sculpture. *Ostrea delta* W. Smith., an oyster whose shape is described by its trivial name (Fig. 69), is a member of the Rasenian fauna and also of the earlier Ringsteadian assemblage. *Gervillia kimmeridgensis* (d'Orb.) and *Nucula menkei* F. Römer may also be regarded as typically Kimmeridgian though they also occur earlier; since they have been found in association with *Aulacostephanus* they must have a longer vertical range than the oyster just mentioned. *Astarte ingenua* Lor., a small shell with delicate and crowded concentric ornament, is often abundant in association with early members of the Aulacostephanitan fauna. A gasteropod regarded as typical

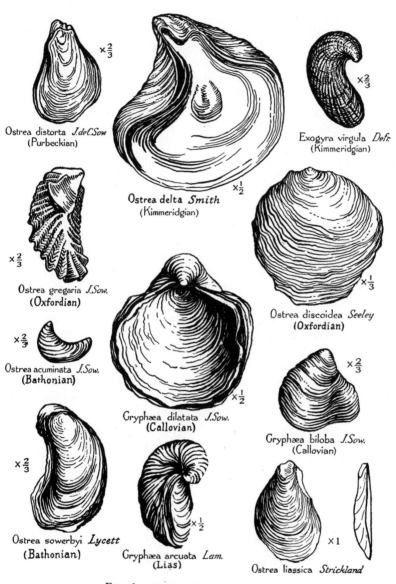

Ostrea distorta *J.deC.Sow.* ×⅔
(Purbeckian)

Ostrea delta *Smith* ×½
(Kimmeridgian)

Exogyra virgula *Defr.* ×⅔
(Kimmeridgian)

Ostrea gregaria *J.Sow.* ×⅔
(Oxfordian)

Ostrea discoidea *Seeley* ×⅓
(Oxfordian)

Ostrea acuminata *J.Sow.* ×⅔
(Bathonian)

Gryphæa dilatata *J.Sow.* ×½
(Callovian)

Gryphæa biloba *J.Sow.* ×⅔
(Callovian)

Ostrea sowerbyi *Lycett* ×⅔
(Bathonian)

Gryphæa arcuata *Lam.* ×½
(Lias)

Ostrea liassica *Strickland* ×1

FIG. 69. SOME JURASSIC OYSTERS

of the Gravesian faunas is *Harpogodes oceani* (Brongn.). It is a member of the family Strombidae, with a large outer whorl whose margin is produced into a number of tubular spinous processes; the latter are, however, often broken off either before fossilization or during extraction from the rock. It is interesting, in view of the northerly latitude, to note that large (presumably drifted) blocks of the reef-coral *Isastraea oblonga* (Flem.) are numerous in the Kimmeridge Clay of Sutherland. This is the most northerly occurrence of Mesozoic reef-corals yet recorded in Europe.

Later Kimmeridgian faunas are especially distinguished by the dominance of planulate ammonites whose ribs are mainly bifurcate; an irregular tendency to trifurcation, or even a higher degree of branching, provides a useful guide to their separation from some other perisphinctoid groups. The assemblages are chiefly mollusca, fossils of other groups being rare, and while three ammonite faunas can readily be distinguished, the same species of gastropods and lamellibranchs persist through the series.

The lowest of these ammonite assemblages is the **Subplanitan Fauna.** The index-genus *Subplanites* includes evolute ammonites with rounded whorl-section ornamented with fine biplicate ribs; the shell is constricted at intervals, and occasionally 'flares' are developed as in *Lytoceras*. Many species show a rapid change from fine, close ribbing on the inner whorls to a distant costation on later volutions. They are accompanied by other forms with coarse and irregular biplicate ribs; these are now referred to the long-ranged perisphinctid genus *Subdichotomoceras*.

The **Pectinatitan Fauna** contains various ammonites of the familiar *pectinatus* type, now classed in the genus *Pectinatites*. These are distinguished generally by their high whorl-section and fine-ribbed ornamentation. Some species, however, become inflated and possess strong biplicate ribs in the adult stage. Where the mouth-border is preserved, it takes the form of a peculiar horn-like projection from the venter.

In Dorset these ammonites are associated with the small radial plates of the free-swimming crinoid *Saccocoma*, which is abundant in the oil-shales of Kimmeridge, Dorset, and has been found in similar shales (revealed by borings) in Kent and Norfolk.

The **Pavlovian Fauna** includes ammonites which were formerly grouped under the comprehensive terms *Ammonites biplex* auctt., and *A. rotundus* J. Sow. In 1925 these were classified in a number of genera which Spath later considered to be synonymous with *Pavlovia* of Ilovaisky (1917). In general characters they often resemble species of the persistent genus *Subdichotomoceras*, but may be distinguished by their simpler suture-line. The fauna of the rotunda zone is well represented at Chapman's Pool, Dorset. The slightly later assemblage of the Hartwell Clay in Buckinghamshire, marked by species like *P. pallasioides* (Pl. XIV), is distinct and shows some resemblance to that of the overlying Portland Sands. The Hartwell Clay has also yielded fragmentary outer whorls with obsolescent ornament which possibly represent the genus *Dorsoplanites*, otherwise unknown in England.

Associated with the three ammonite-faunas just described are numerous species of lamellibranchs; the assemblage is very different from that of the Lower Kimmeridge Clay, and reliance may be placed upon it, in the absence of ammonites, for general correlation. Special mention may be made of *Hartwellia* (*Astarte*) *hartwellensis* (J. de C. Sow.) which is only abundant in the Pavlovian fauna. It is regarded as the end-form of an undetermined astartean lineage, and the genus *Astarte* has several associated species; *A. saemanni* Lor. (Fig. 84) is perhaps the most abundant. One of the commonest bivalves is *Modiola autissiodorensis* (Cott.), a small 'mussel' with well-marked radial ribbing. *Protocardia morinica* (Lor.) (Fig. 70) is abundant and characteristic, ranging up from the lower zones of the Kimmeridgian as here understood. *Pecten* (*Camptonectes*) *morini* Lor. a form very similar to the well-known *Pecten lens*, is restricted to Upper Kimmeridgian strata, while the smooth *P.* (*Syncyclonema*) *nitescens* Phill. is equally typical. Clavellate species of *Trigonia* are large and well developed. Occasionally, almost smooth shells of this genus, practically circular in shape, with no differentiation of the posterior ornament, are encountered; these appear to be allied to *Trigonia gibbosa* J. Sow., which is abundant in the overlying Portland Beds. Beds of oysters and *Isognomon* (*Perna*) are occasionally conspicuous. Gastropods are only of subordinate importance, but include the elegant *Pleurotomaria reticulata* J. Sow. (Fig. 70), while brachiopods are very rare. The last group includes *Orbiculoidea latissima* (J. Sow.), an undescribed terebratulid, and a rhynchonellid, '*Rhynchonella*' *subvariabilis* Dav. Spines of the sea-urchin *Rhabdocidaris* are also recorded.

In the lower part of the Portland Sands, species of *Pavlovia* are still dominant, and the assemblage apparently represents a late phase of the Pavlovian fauna (p. 462). But higher beds contain the first representatives of *Crendonites* which, in such later species as *C. gorei* (Salfeld), become more evolute, with distant biplicate and simple ribs, smooth constricted collar at the mouth border, and simple suture-line. Another form in the Portland Sands, but only recorded from Dorset, is *Progalbanites albani* (Arkell), also close to the inner whorls of *Crendonites*. These ammonites in the upper part of the Portland Sands may be taken as distinctive of the **Crendonitan Fauna**. Some large species of *Crendonites*, *C. polygyralis* (Buckm.) and *C. mikrolobus*, for example, were originally referred to other genera. The related *Behemoth* is also of pavlovid origin, but has variable inner whorls which foreshadow *Kerberites* of the overlying limestones.

Formerly the Portland Limestones were divided into the 'pseudogigas beds' below, and the 'giganteus beds' above, and both divisions contain huge perisphinctid ammonites, some of which reach a diameter of 700 millimetres. Those usually identified with *Perisphinctes pseudogigas* Blake are now placed in Buckman's genus *Kerberites*, typified by *K. kerberus*

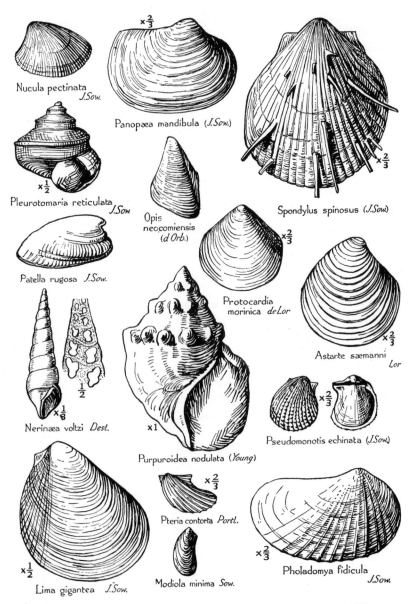

Nucula pectinata *J. Sow.*

$\times \frac{2}{3}$

Panopæa mandibula (*J. Sow.*)

$\times \frac{1}{2}$

Pleurotomaria reticulata *J. Sow.*

Opis neocomiensis (*d Orb.*)

Spondylus spinosus (*J. Sow.*)

$\times \frac{2}{3}$

Patella rugosa *J. Sow.*

$\times \frac{2}{3}$

Protocardia morinica *de Lor*

Astarte sæmanni *Lor*

$\times \frac{2}{3}$

$\frac{1}{2}$

$\times \frac{1}{8}$

Nerinæa voltzi *Dest.*

$\times 1$

Purpuroidea nodulata (*Young*)

$\times \frac{2}{3}$

Pseudomonotis echinata (*J. Sow.*)

$\times \frac{2}{3}$

Pteria contorta *Portl.*

$\times \frac{2}{3}$

$\times \frac{1}{2}$

Lima gigantea *J. Sow.*

Modiola minima *Sow.*

Pholadomya fidicula *J. Sow.*

FIG. 70. SOME MESOZOIC LAMELLIBRANCHS AND GASTROPODS

Buckm. They comprise evolute forms ornamented with blunt triplicate ribs which arise from thickened primary costae. Other species show variation in whorl-section and degree of coiling; *K. fasciger* (Buckm.) with multiplicate ribbing is compressed and almost occlusal, the form designated as the paratype of *Pleuromegalites forticosta* Buckm., with coarse triplicate ribs, is an inflated *Kerberites*, and these forms apparently persist to the top of the Portland Limestone. Ammonites of the group of *Perisphinctes giganteus* (J. Sow.) were distributed by Buckman in several genera which Spath considers to be synonymous with *Titanites*; hence this genus is taken as the index of the **Titanitan Fauna.** Species of *Titanites* attain gigantic proportions, and often only the outer whorls are visible, so that their relationships are imperfectly known. But Spath records from the highest *Titanites* beds in Dorset small examples of the genus that cannot be distinguished from the inner whorls of *T. okusensis* (Salfeld), so common in the lower limestones of Swindon, and formerly ascribed to *Kerberites*. Hence it seems that the former division of the Portland Stone cannot be maintained for the present. Indeed, the Portlandian ammonites of this country are in urgent need of revision, with more favourable material than is yet available.

The Portlandian fauna as a whole is essentially a molluscan assemblage, lamellibranchs and gastropods being especially abundant, while ammonites are more sporadic in occurrence. The large *Pecten lamellosus* J. Sow., in which the delicate radiating ornament of the *Camptonectes* group is restricted to early growth-stages, is characteristic and abundant. *Lima rustica* J. Sow., a form with strong radial ribs is perhaps most typical of the lower beds. The large *Protocardia dissimilis* (J. de C. Sow.) contrasts strongly with the smaller species from Kimmeridgian strata. While clavellate forms often occur, the characteristic species of *Trigonia* are of the *gibbosa* type (Pl. XIII), showing a strong tendency to smoothness and a loss of differentiation between the anterior and posterior areas; the shells are commonly dissolved away, leaving the internal moulds, 'horses' heads' of the quarrymen. The mussels are represented by the large *Modiola boloniensis* Lor., and by a small radially ribbed species that closely resembles the earlier *M. autissiodorensis* (Cott.). A common burrowing form is *Pleuromya tellina* Ag. Among gastropods, *Cerithium portlandicum* J. de C. Sow. is often abundant, the internal moulds being known to quarrymen as 'screws'. The little *Natica ceres* Lor., easily recognized by its acute spire, impressed sutures and linear transverse ornament, occurs abundantly at many localities, accompanied by larger species of *Natica*, *Alaria*, and other genera. The argillaceous character of many of the limestones accounts for the rarity of brachiopods, echinoids and corals, but four genera of sea-urchins (*Tetragramma, Trochotiara, Hemicidaris,* and *Clitopygus*) are represented in the basal beds of the Portland Stone in the Isle of Portland. The familiar star-coral *Isastraea oblonga* (Flem.), usually preserved in chert, is most abundant near Tisbury in Wiltshire.

The Purbeck Beds as developed in England are not readily subdivided on a palaeontological basis. They consist chiefly of freshwater deposits with intercalated marine beds, and the characters of the faunas are clearly determined more by fluctuations of local conditions than by evolutionary changes in series of organisms. The following summary of the type-section in the Isle of Purbeck illustrates the variation in conditions of deposition.

Upper Purbeck
- Grey and purple marls with *Viviparus*.
- Shales with beds of Paludina Limestone (Purbeck Marble). Abundant ostracods.
- *Unio*-beds and shelly limestones with *Viviparus*.

Middle Purbeck
- Alum Shales and thin limestones with layers of gypsum and estuarine shells.
- Hard shelly limestones with partings of shale, fossils of marine and estuarine species.
- Cinder-bed, a mass of *Ostrea distorta* J. de C. Sow.
- Thin limestones, marls and shales, with remains of insects, fishes, and freshwater shells.
- Black shale with mammalian remains.

Lower Purbeck
- Marly freshwater beds with *Physa* and *Planorbis*.
- Marls and soft limestones with *Cardium, Corbula, Cyrena*, &c.
- Beds of broken limestone.
- Brown bituminous limestones with a layer of dark earth (dirt-bed) resting on Portland Stone.

The freshwater fauna of the English Purbeck Beds is still imperfectly known. It includes species of the molluscan genera *Cyrena, Unio, Viviparus, Planorbis*, &c., and several ostracods, such as *Cypris purbeckensis* Forbes, *Candona boloniensis* Jones, and *Cypridea punctata* (Forbes). The isopod *Archaeoniscus brodiei* M.-Edw. (Fig. 18) occurs in profusion in Wiltshire, and has been recorded elsewhere. Fish remains—scales and teeth of *Lepidotus* and *Pleuropholis*—occur in many parts of the outcrop, and the type-locality has yielded carapaces of the turtle *Pleurosternum*, besides remains of crocodiles and deinosaurs. Of extreme interest are the remains of diminutive mammalia from a 'Dirt' layer at the base of Middle Purbeck Beds in Durlston Bay. These have been ascribed to several genera of insectivorous and herbivorous animals, the best-known being *Plagiaulax, Tricodon*, and *Sphalacotherium*, but the fossils are far from abundant. Plants, chiefly wood and fruits of *Cycadeoidea* and conifers, are commonly seen in the dirt beds, while the little fruit-bodies of the alga *Chara* are recorded from cherty layers.

The intercalated marine beds contain species of *Ostrea, Protocardia, Modiola*, and other bivalved mollusca. *Protocardia purbeckensis* Lor. is noteworthy for its wide distribution, and *Ostrea distorta* J. de C. Sow. (Fig. 69) often forms well-marked 'oyster beds' at various localities. The occurrence of an echinoid, *Hemicidaris purbeckensis* Forbes, should also be noted, though the Isle of Purbeck is still the only locality from which it is recorded; it occurs there in some abundance, associated with an undescribed form tentatively referred to *Pseudodiadema*.

FAUNAL REGIONS

In the foregoing summary of British Liassic faunas, reference is repeatedly made to relations with equivalent assemblages of the Mediterranean region. The great majority of the British ammonites are highly ornamented, thick shells which, in view of their abundance, are evidently characteristic of the shallow transgressive seas. The almost smooth shells of the Phylloceratidae and Lytoceratidae are sporadic in occurrence and never abundant. The paucity of these forms in British deposits contrasts strongly with their dominance in Alpine and Mediterranean areas where, sometimes, they occur almost to the exclusion of other groups. In these southern areas, too, there are ammonites unknown in Britain which are intermediate between the highly ornamented forms and the fundamental phyllocerates. The faunal change is gradual, but the northern limit of the Mediterranean type seems traceable along a line from Portugal across Spain and France, thence along the northern border of the Alpine arc to the Crimea and the Caucasus. The faunas from the last two areas, like those from Chanaz in Savoy, and Villanj in Hungary are essentially Mediterranean in character, though they contain some northern elements. The contrast is clearly marked already in the lowest Lias, and throughout the Series the ammonites of the northern areas represent merely an impoverished assortment of migrants from the rich assemblages of the Alpine region. Space will not allow a full discussion of these faunas—only a few outstanding examples can be cited, chiefly from the writings of L. F. Spath.

The Hettangian family Psiloceratidae is abundantly represented in Mediterranean localities, and is derived, through *Mojsvarites* (p. 420), from the Triassic Monophyllitidae. The family Alsalitidae (including such genera as *Paracaloceras*, *Tmaegoceras*, *Pseudotropites* and *Canavarites*) is probably polyphyletic; it may include offshoots of *Psiloceras*, through the *tortilis-subliassicum* group of *Caloceras*, as well as derivatives of *Parapsiloceras* and *Pleuracanthites*. The last two genera are not recorded from Britain, but both are known from Swabian and Italian localities, whence they have usually been grouped under the comprehensive name *Ectocentrites*. This genus, nowadays restricted to the Hettangian group of *E. petersi* (Hauer), together with allied Sinemurian genera, is placed in a separate family Ectocentritidae, and regarded by Spath as transitional between the fundamental discophyllitid stock and its trachyostracous offshoots. *Analytoceras*, the earliest known lytoceratid, is also related to the Psiloceratidae, and the true *Lytoceras* appears in the Pliensbachian stage.

It is generally agreed that the Discophyllitidae includes the ancestors of the Jurassic Phylloceratidae, though the course of development from the Triassic Monophyllitidae cannot yet be precisely defined. The phyllocerates are represented in the Hettangian stage by the constricted shell *Calliphylloceras togatum*; the genus persists through the Jurassic succession and, with other phyllocerates, gives rise at intervals to offshoots which connect with the thick-shelled, ornamented ammonites.

The Sinemurian family Arietidae, well represented in England by numerous genera, is still more varied in southern Europe. For instance, the evolute *Epophioceras* (group of *Amm. landrioti* d'Orb.) is rare in England but abundant in Italy, and the Portuguese forms for which Spath has instituted the genera *Ptycharietites* and *Pompeckjoceras* are probably related to *Eparietites*. These Mediterranean groups were probably replenished from lytoceratid stocks. The species of *Echioceras* all have suture-lines comparable with those of arietid genera, and Spath traces that genus back through the capricorn *Gagaticeras* to *Parechioceras* of the oxynotum zone which he regards as a lateral offshoot of one of the lytoceratid stocks that replenished the arietids.

The early Pliensbachian family Eoderoceratidae is most completely represented in south Europe where there are genera, such as *Epideroceras* and *Coeloderoceras*, unknown farther north. They are connected with the fundamental Lytoceratidae by the transitional Derolytoceratidae which again are largely confined to deposits of the Mediterranean region. Certain derolytoceratid forms appear to connect with *Gemmellaroceras*, the earliest of the Polymorphitidae, most typical of the Alpine and Mediterranean regions. The Tropidoceratidae, successors of the Polymorphitidae, are also widely distributed in the Alps, Apennines, and Sicily, but are scarce in Britain, France, and Germany.

The southern development of the Domerian stage, which takes its name from Monte Domero in the Lombardy Alps, is far richer in ammonites than the corresponding stage in northern areas. We have noted (p. 443) that the family Dactylioceratidae which attained its maximum development in the Toarcian stage, can be traced back to the late Pliensbachian zone-fossil *Prodactylioceras davoei*. The few British representatives of this genus stand in sharp contrast with the wealth of forms described from such localities as Monte di Cetona. Obviously it is in the Alpine and Mediterranean faunas that the detailed relationship of the family must be sought; unfortunately the stratigraphy of the region is not yet known in sufficient detail for the purpose. Members of the Domerian family Seguenziceratidae, forerunners of the great family Hildoceratidae, are again best represented in south Europe. In addition to *Seguenziceras*, other genera like *Protogrammoceras*, *Lioceratoides*, and *Fuciniceras*, are recorded chiefly from the Mediterranean region, including localities in Italy, Sicily, south France, Morocco, and Tunisia.

Many of these genera are represented in Liassic deposits farther east, at various places near the borders of the Indian Ocean. For instance, in late Domerian or early Toarcian deposits of Kelat, Baluchistan, there are forms of *Phylloceras*, *Rhacophyllites*, *Lytoceras*, *Dactylioceras*, *Porpoceras*, *Fuciniceras*, *Protogrammoceras*, *Polyplectus*, &c. which can be closely matched in corresponding faunas in the Apennines and Sicily. The Liassic faunas of Madagascar also include European types. We may therefore infer that the Mediterranean faunas of Liassic time extended through a widened Persian Gulf and Arabian Sea into the Indian Ocean. In addition to the Mediterranean types there are also peculiar oxynote developments of certain hildoceratan stocks which are unknown in Europe. One of them, *Bouleiceras*, was first described from Madagascar, and was afterwards recorded from Baluchistan; another, *Shenarpites*, named by L. F. Spath, is not known outside Baluchistan. Such genera give an individuality to the Liassic fauna of the Indian Ocean, and support the view that part of that ocean was more or less permanent in early Jurassic time.

In the FAR EAST, Liassic deposits are present on some of the eastern islands of the East Indian Archipelago. The ammonites from Rotti are noteworthy because they include species of *Liparoceras*, *Becheiceras*, *Parinodoceras*; since Spath states that the main development of the Liparoceratidae is in north-west Europe, these records provide a puzzling instance of discontinuous geographical distribution.

On the Australian continent, deposits of Jurassic age are mainly of fresh-water origin, and the chief fossils are land plants. But in NEW ZEALAND Liassic ammonites have been described by Spath from three horizons which are separated by conspicuous lacunae in the records. It may be that some of the gaps may be filled by plant-bearing sediments that are intercalated among the marine beds. The earliest Jurassic ammonites are species of *Psiloceras* from the Hokonui Hills on the south-east coast of South Island. These are of early Hettangian age and probably belong to the megastoma horizon of the planorbis zone. A later fauna, not precisely localized, comprises species of *Phylloceras*, *Rhacophyllites* and *Lytoceras* similar to the association in the Domerian Beds of Baluchistan and Sicily. Species of the Toarcian genus *Dactylioceras*, from the neighbourhood of Kawhia on North Island, resemble forms described from the island of Rotti, East Indies.

Liassic ammonites are reported from various localities on the vast continent of SOUTH AMERICA, chiefly in the south and west, but only general correlation of stages can be made at present, and further exploration will probably extend the records. The earliest ammonites, *Psiloceras* and *Schlotheimia* show the presence of Hettangian horizons in Peru. They are followed in that country by *Arietites*, *Microderoceras*, and *Echioceras* representing various Sinemurian zones. Chilean records include the late Sinemurian *Eoderoceras*, followed by the Pliensbachian *Polymorphites*. Argentine localities have yielded the Sinemurian *Oxynoticeras* and *Eoderoceras*, besides the Pliensbachian *Uptonia* and *Tropidoceras*. Toarcian hildoceratids are recorded from Neuquen and Mendoza provinces in Argentina, but the cited genera, *Hildoceras* and *Harpoceras* seem to have been given a wider interpretation than is customary in Europe nowadays.

A greater range of Liassic strata is recorded in Mexico. The Sinemurian and Pliensbachian stages seem to be almost complete, and most of Oppel's zones from bucklandi to jamesoni are recognized by the familiar European genera. The position of the Domerian and Toarcian stages is occupied by non-marine strata containing land-plants.

Farther north, on the Pacific coast between California and Alaska, the Liassic deposits are interpreted by Crickmay as an eastward extension of the Pacific Ocean. The ammonite genera are greatly in need of revision, and consequently the stages present can be named only with reserve. The earliest forms, apparently arniocerates of early Sinemurian age, are reported from western Nevada. Hyatt's genus *Arniotites*, of uncertain affinities, is said to be of later date; it is cited from north California, British Columbia, and south Alaska. From the Alaska Peninsula ammonites are doubtfully ascribed to *Aegoceras* and *Amaltheus*; though the generic names are uncertain, these ammonites probably indicate the presence of Pliensbachian and Domerian horizons. Some part of the Toarcian stage is indicated in the Queen Charlotte Islands by McLearn's citation of *Harpoceras* and *Dactylioceras*. Above this stage the marine succession is interrupted by volcanic tuffs which are said to enclose Bajocian fossils.

In Greenland, the Liassic deposits described by Rosenkrantz (1934) are interpreted as due to temporary transgressions from the Arctic Ocean. The earliest horizons, yielding *Uptonia jamesoni*, are of mid-Pliensbachian date. The Toarcian stage is indicated by *Dactylioceras* and the hildoceratan genus *Pseudolioceras*. This last stage is also reported by Bodolevski on the east coast of Spitzbergen as yielding *Dactylioceras*, *Harpoceras*, *Grammoceras* and *Haugia*.

These scattered records of Liassic deposits from various parts of the world are too disconnected to form the basis of so-called palaeogeographical maps. Nevertheless two broad conclusions can be drawn from them. In the first place, most marine successions on the present land-surface are incomplete, and evidently represent short-lived transgressions from seas of more permanent character. Secondly, when stratal units small enough to be contemporaneous are compared, the assemblages of highly ornamented ammonites are remarkably similar in all parts of the world, though there may be local modifications of some forms. This implies easy communication between the several ocean-basins, probably by means of currents which could assist the dispersal of ammonites during the free-swimming larval stage.

Our review of Upper Jurassic faunas in Britain shows that the general inferences drawn from the preceding Liassic faunas are largely applicable to later Jurassic assemblages. With regard to geographical conditions, the south-eastern half of England was still submerged under the sea, as were portions of the Hebridean area. The latter was no longer connected directly with the English sea, for no deposits younger than Lias are present in the outliers of Antrim, Carlisle, and Shropshire. The Upper Jurassic rocks of Sutherland, comprising a broken sequence from Bajocian to Kimmeridgian, with close relations to Yorkshire, indicate the existence of a 'North' Sea during Jurassic time. Temporary shrinkage is shown by the 'Estuarine Series' of both areas, and by the absence of strata above the Kimmeridge Clay. The sea was not far away, however, for the Lower Cretaceous deposits of Yorkshire and Lincolnshire are marine, in contrast with the freshwater deposits of the Wealden area farther south. On the western mainland of Europe the Mesozoic deposits occupy similar positions with regard to the Palaeozoic horsts in France, Germany, and Spain (Fig. 71).

A quarter-century ago the view was generally held that the British Jurassic succession is very incomplete. This was largely due to S. S. Buckman, who proved many non-sequences at different levels in various parts of the country. More recently, L. F. Spath has pointed out that the non-sequences are only of local extent, and are reasonably explained by small regressions such as those indicated by the so-called 'Estuarine Series' of Yorkshire and north-east Scotland, and by changes in the submarine erosion-level resulting in condensed deposits. Furthermore, the faunas of successive stages are closely related, indeed, the vertical ranges of many ammonite-genera overlap one another. It follows that, in spite of local interruptions, the British succession as a whole is tolerably complete, sufficiently continuous in fact to be taken as a standard of reference for northern Europe generally.

We have already noted that the great majority of British Jurassic ammonites are highly ornamented shells which are evidently characteristic of shallow epicontinental seas. Various stages at many localities in Europe admit of detailed correlation with the British succession, and some amplify the British records. But in south Europe the highly ornamented ammonites become subordinated to the dominant forms of *Phylloceras*, *Lytoceras*, and their immediate offshoots, the Oppelidae. Thus correlation becomes more difficult, and the difficulty is increased by the frequent occurrence of condensed deposits. Numerous instances are given in the works of Spath and others; here only a few outstanding examples can be cited.

In Dorset the five Bajocian zones containing the Ludwigian, Sonninian and Stephanoceratan faunas may be contained in less than 50 feet of strata, but in Hanover the opalinum zone alone (subdivided into three distinct horizons) has a thickness of 90 feet. At Cap San Vigilio in Italy the opalinum and murchisonae zones are condensed into a limestone only 1 metre in thickness, and the usual Bajocian hildoceratid and stephanoceratid genera are accompanied by numerous phyllocerates and lytocerates which are rare or unknown in Britain.

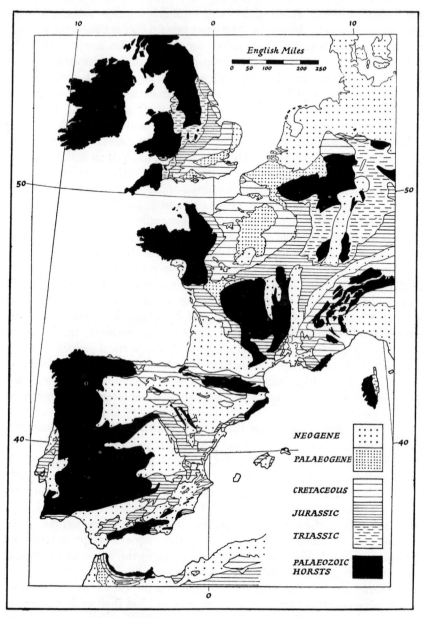

English Miles

0   50   100   200   250

NEOGENE

PALAEOGENE

CRETACEOUS

JURASSIC

TRIASSIC

PALAEOZOIC
HORSTS

FIG. 71. SKETCH-MAP SHOWING THE RELATIONS OF MESOZOIC DEPOSITS TO
THE PALAEOZOIC HORSTS IN WESTERN EUROPE

Bathonian assemblages are somewhat deficient in ammonites, but contain early representatives of two families that become widespread in later faunas. The Perisphinctidae, which developed from various parkinsonid stocks, are represented by such genera as *Procerites* and *Siemiradzkia*; these occur together in the Fuller's Earth Rock of England, and in equivalent strata of France and the Mediterranean area. They are associated with the latest stephanoceratids (e.g. *Polyplectites*) and the earliest Macrocephalitidae. This last family, also polyphyletic, can be traced back, through such genera as *Sphaeroceras* and *Tulites* respectively, to the Morphoceratidae and Tulitidae; it gave rise successively to the Callovian Kosmoceratidae and the Oxfordian Cardioceratidae.

At La Voulte in the Rhône Valley south of Lyons pyritized ammonites belonging to the genera *Kosmoceras* and *Cardioceras* suffice for correlation with the Callovian and Oxfordian zones of south England, though the dominant form is *Sowerbyceras*, a phyllocerate offshoot. A similar succession is present in Central Russia, where the Callovian stage is transgressive; here kosmocerates and cadocerates occur to the exclusion of phyllocerates. As far as is known, kosmocerates and cardiocerates were confined to the shallow seas north of the Tethys, and they are unknown beyond the eastern shore of the Caspian Sea (Mangyschlak and Kara-Bugaz). The younger cardiocerates, *Amoeboceras* and its allies, of the Kimmeridgian stage, occur in England, but are more abundant in northern localities, as can be seen on comparing records from Dorset with those of north-east Scotland and Russia. Amoebocerates are associated in Britain with the coronate perisphinctid derivative *Rasenia* which again is essentially a genus of northerly distribution, as also is the closely related, but younger, genus *Gravesia*. On the other hand, certain ammonites in the same stages are most abundant at southern stations. The Callovian *Reineckia*, for instance, cognate with the perisphinctids, is rare in Britain and altogether absent from Yorkshire, north Germany, Lithuania, and Russia, but is a characteristic element of Callovian faunas in south Europe and north Africa. The abundance and variety of perisphinctids associated with the cardiocerates in the English Midlands are paralleled at certain localities in west Germany, and the association is found as far south as Moravia. The modified derivatives of perisphinctid stocks, ascribed to the Callovian and Oxfordian *Peltoceras*, and the later *Aspidoceras*, are also widespread southern elements which do not appear at northern stations.

Above the Kimmeridgian stage faunal divergencies appear both in central Russia, and in the Mediterranean area. It may be significant that equivalent deposits in Germany are of freshwater origin, the highest marine beds containing the Gravesian fauna. The lower beds of the Russian Volgian stage contains species of *Pavlovia* and *Dorsoplanites*, and may be correlated with the Upper Kimmeridge Clay of England. They are succeeded by a unique assemblage of the multicostate *Virgatites*, quite unlike any forms yet known in England. The next zone contains giant ammonites which Pavlow considered to be the same as the English Portlandian forms; more recently Arkell has referred them to *Kerberites* and *Titanites*. If this be correct, the succeeding Upper Volgian zones with species of *Craspedites*, must represent the Purbeckian stage which has not yielded ammonites in England. The equivalent rocks in the Mediterranean area are massive limestones which constitute the Tithonian phase of Oppel, and which represent at least the Portlandian and Purbeckian stages. The ammonite-faunas are composed almost entirely of phyllocerates and such oppelids as *Streblites*, *Glochiceras*, and *Haploceras* which give no help in correlation with the British strata.

The faunal differences just described are often attributed, especially by continental authors, to bathymetrical conditions, the northern faunas occupying temporary and shallow epicontinental seas, the Mediterranean faunas a deep and permanent ocean. But the presence of non-sequences and condensed deposits shows that many of the Mediterranean sections are no more complete than those of north-west Europe, and Haug cites numerous local transgressions which, of course, indicate coastal conditions. The frequent occurrence of 'red beds', such as the so-called 'calcaire rosso ammonitico', seems to show the presence of detrital material due to atmospheric denudation of nearby land. Moreover, the presence of coral-reefs intercalated at various horizons throughout the European area testifies equally to the shallow-water character of the succession as a whole. It is worth while to note in this connexion the general features and distribution of Upper Jurassic coral-reefs.

Reefs of Bajocian and Bathonian age in the Cotswolds and Lincolnshire have already been mentioned (pp. 450–1). On the European mainland similar coral-limestones are recorded from Aquitaine off the ancient land of Brittany, from the margin of the Central Plateau of France, from the Ardennes and the Vosges, from the sedimentary cover of the Aar massif, from the Trentino, south Tyrol, from the margin of the crystalline massif of Maures and Esterel in south-east France, and from the western border of the Iberian meseta. Coral growth also extends over a wide area in the Oxfordian stage; the great spread of reefs from Wiltshire to Yorkshire is responsible for the term Corallian being given to British deposits of Oxfordian age. The reefs near Oxford have been investigated in detail by W. J. Arkell (1935), who has made a comparison with reefs of similar age extending from Normandy and Poitou to the Ardennes, Erzgebirge, and the Jura chain; also in south Europe from Sardinia, Sicily, Italy, the Carpathians to Galicia, and the Donetz. Arkell has noted the fact that these southern reefs contain a far greater variety of corals than the British examples. He suggests that south Europe was the dispersal centre of Jurassic corals, and that the small British assemblages consist of those species that could migrate and colonize most rapidly before they were overwhelmed by the recurring floods of clastic sediment. In this way he explains the close similarity of the coral assemblages at separate horizons throughout the Jurassic rocks of England. The limited association has a modern parallel in the reefs of Bermuda which lie at the margin of reef-formation in the present Atlantic Ocean. It may be that Britain occupied a similar situation in Jurassic time, for Sutherland is the most northerly locality in Europe at which Mesozoic reef-corals are known.

Ammonite assemblages of various ages within the Arctic Circle prove to be closely related to equivalent faunas of north-west Europe. From Spitzbergen is known a Kimmeridgian assemblage which includes species of *Amoeboceras* so close to Scottish forms that Spath postulates direct marine communication between the two areas. In east Greenland, a considerable succession, from Callovian to Portlandian, has been described by Spath. The earliest Callovian ammonites of Jameson Land are mainly species of *Arctocephalites* and *Cranocephalites*, both derivatives of an early macrocephalitid stock. They are followed, first by *Arcticoceras*, a cadocerate development from *Arctocephalites*, and then by *Cadoceras* and *Kepplerites*. These also are local races, probably developed from European immigrants. The poverty in genera shown by these boreal faunas is maintained in younger assemblages from the transgressive deposits of Milne Land. The genus *Cardioceras* is only represented by one species, probably because the Oxfordian stage is incomplete. The Lower Kimmeridgian Beds contain several amoebocerates some of which are referred to Scottish and Russian species. The perisphinctid genera *Ringsteadia*, *Pictonia*, and *Rasenia* are also represented in the order named. The higher strata are characterized mainly by a succession of *Subdichotomoceras*, *Subplanites*, *Pectinatites*, *Pavlovia*, *Crendonites*, and *Dorsoplanites*. Many of these are comparable with forms in the Kimmeridgian and Portlandian stages of north-west Europe, but *Dorsoplanites* is extremely rare in England, and *Kerberites* is not yet recorded from Greenland. In spite of these discrepancies, one is forced to conclude that a broad channel of communication from east Greenland to Scotland existed between the Arctic and Atlantic Oceans during Jurassic time—the absence of marine Jurassic deposits in eastern North America only indicates that the coast there was farther to the east than it is now.

A parallel to this channel is apparent in the north-western part of the NORTH AMERICAN continent. For in Alaska, the Tuxedni Sandstone has yielded Bajocian stephanoceratids, which are also known from the Queen Charlotte Islands, the succeeding Chinitna Shale contains *Arctocephalites* and cadocerates, while the Naknek formation has numerous cardiocerates. The Cardioceratan fauna, indeed, is recorded from transgressive strata which extend from Alaska through British Columbia to Wyoming (Map, Fig. 72); it evidently migrated about 3,000 miles southwards from the Arctic regions, a contrast with the northerly direction in Europe. After this

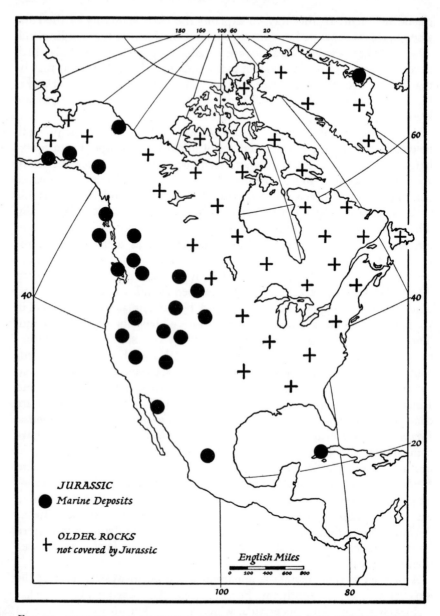

FIG. 72. SKETCH-MAP OF NORTH AMERICA SHOWING THE GENERAL DISTRI-
BUTION OF JURASSIC ROCKS

temporary transgression no marine Jurassic deposits appear in the interior of North America, though small encroachments continue along the Pacific coast, as shown in a series of maps by C. H. Crickmay (1931).

The northern ammonites just mentioned did not reach Mexico where a long succession of Upper Jurassic deposits is the subject of a general review by C. Burckhardt (1930), and of later comments by Spath (1933), and Imlay (1939). The Mexican faunas have much in common with their equivalents in the Mediterranean area of Europe, but naturally there are local differences. The Callovian beds contain many phyllocerates associated with species of *Macrocephalites*, *Reineckeia*, and *Peltoceras* as in Europe; a local feature is the presence of *Neuqueniceras*, a local tuberculate relative of *Reineckeia*, first described from South America. The Oxfordian stage, apparently incomplete, is dominated by perisphinctids especially *Dichotomosphinctes* which probably includes Burkhardt's group of *Per. virgulatus*. Prominent associates are species of *Biplices* and *Prosophinctes*. The chief ammonite genus in the Lower Kimmeridgian Beds is *Idoceras*, developed from the main perisphinctid stock. It is accompanied by aspidocerates like *Nebrodites* and *Waagenia* which also appear to connect with the perisphinctids. Oppelids like *Glochiceras* and *Metahaploceras* are also represented. Though these are all present in Mediterranean assemblages, there is an absence from Mexican records of such common European perisphinctids as *Ataxioceras*, while *Subneumayria* and *Epicephalites* are local elements. Upper Kimmeridgian Beds are characterized by *Subplanites*, *Aulacosphinctes* and by the local oppelid genus *Mazapilites*. These are all associated with aspidocerates and phyllocerates (*Sowerbyceras*) as in the Mediterranean area. The base of the Portlandian stage is marked by *Aulacosphinctoides* of the *bangei* group which is succeeded by early Berriasellids such as *Kossmatia*, *Durangites*, *Micracanthoceras* and the oppelid *Hildoglochiceras*. Higher still, at the top of the Jurassic system, is a large fauna dominated by berriasellids like *Substeueroceras* and *Berriasella* together with the olcostephanid *Proniceras*.

Thus the Mexican faunas show clear relations with their Mediterranean equivalents, particularly those of south-east France and the Jura region. This is hardly surprising if dispersal of the ammonites depended on the pelagic larval stage which could spread by means of the east to west equatorial currents.

Other elements are related to SOUTH AMERICAN forms. The Callovian *Neuqueniceras* has already been mentioned; it is associated in Argentina with typical *Reineckeia* and macrocephalitids. The latter group includes the involute *Macrocephalites steinmanni* which may represent a local Andine race of *M. macrocephalus*; it is connected by transitions with *Eurycephalites*, another local genus which produced an extreme coarse-ribbed offshoot, *Xenocephalites*. The Oxfordian and Kimmeridgian stages seem to be imperfectly represented in South America, but equivalents of the Purbeckian stage are marked by oppelids and berriasellids with local species.

East of the Mediterranean the best known succession is that of Kachh on the west coast of the INDIAN PENINSULA of which the ammonite fauna has been revised by Spath (1924–33). The succession ranges from the Bathonian stage to the top of the System, and is tabulated below.

The Jurassic Succession of Kachh

Umia group (3,000 ft.)		Purbeckian
	Zamia Shales of Nurrha Gudjinsir Beds	} Lower Portlandian
Katrol group (c. 1000 ft.)	Barren Sandstones Katrol Beds Belemnite Marls of Jurun	} Kimmeridgian
Kantecote Sandstone		} Oxfordian
	Dhosa Oolite	
Chari group (1,000 ft.)	Athleta Beds Anceps Beds Rehmanni Beds Macrocephalus Shales	} Callovian
Patcham group (1,000 ft.)	Coral Bed Shelly Limestone (base not exposed)	} Bathonian

No ammonites are recorded from the Patcham Shelly Limestone, but the succeeding coral bed has yielded species of *Macrocephalites*, *Sivajiceras*, *Procerites*, and *Epimorphoceras*. The general association compares well with Bathonian faunas in Europe. The Macrocephalus Shales, interbedded with white compact limestones, have yielded a considerable number of ammonites. The dominant macrocephalitids show a sequence important for detailed correlation; in the upper beds the persistent *Macrocephalites* is joined by species of *Indocephalites*, *Kamptocephalites*, *Dolikephalites*, and *Kheraiceras* of the same family. Most of the types are like those of the English Cornbrash though the species are distinct. There are also oppelids (*Alcidia*, *Chanasia*, *Hecticoceras*) and perisphinctids (*Choffatia*, *Indosphinctes*) which are represented in European faunas of the same age, but *Phylloceras* and *Lytoceras* are only rarely found in these beds. The last macrocephalitids (in the rehmanni zone) are accompanied by derivatives, like *Nothocephalites*, *Eucycloceras*, *Idiocycloceras*, and *Subkossmatia*, which show a tendency towards tabulation of the periphery. By reason of this feature they may be regarded as somewhat analogous to the northern Kosmoceratidae which, however, are quite unknown at Kachh. This local race is also associated with species of *Reineckeia*, which are succeeded by typical coronate forms of the *R. anceps* group. The Callovian perisphinctids of Kachh include a rather special group of heavily ribbed forms, beginning with *Procerites* and *Sivajiceras*, and continuing with such genera as *Obtusicostites*, *Kinkeliniceras*, and *Hubertoceras*; these seem to have a connexion with the European *Proplanulites* which is not recorded from Kachh. While other more widespread genera (e.g. *Choffatia*, *Grossouvria*) continue from lower beds, others (e.g. *Subgrossouvria, Orionoides*) are hardly known out-side Kachh. Certain groups of strongly ribbed oppelids also differ from European forms; these include *Hecticoceratoides, Kheraites,* and *Sindeites,* which are accompanied by the widely distributed *Lunuloceras* and *Hecti-coceras.* The athleta beds are dominated by peltocerates some of which are sufficiently diverse from European forms for Spath to institute the new genera *Pseudopeltoceras, Metapeltoceras,* and *Peltoceratoides;* they include a few forms which approach species described from the renggeri beds of Europe. The Kachh perisphinctids and species of *Pachyceras* from the athleta beds are also similar to European forms, but there is no typical *Erymnoceras* which is so widespread from England to the Caucasus. The association of perisphinctids and peltoceratids continues in the Dhosa Oolite, which is further marked by the maximum development of *Euaspi-doceras.* Another important element in this fauna is provided by a number of genera (*Mayaites, Epimayaites, Dhosaites,* and *Paryphoceras*) grouped in the family Mayaitidae. These are very similar to the earlier macrocephali-tids but there seems to be no connexion between the two groups. Spath regards the Mayaitidae as analogous to the Cardioceratidae which are so well developed in northern latitudes but quite unknown in Kachh. Species of *Epimayaites* continue into the Kantecote Sandstone associated with the perisphinctid genera *Dichotomosphinctes, Perisphinctes, Ataxioceras, Tor-quatisphinctes,* &c. A conspicuous group of aspidocerates (*Neaspidoceras*) is only sparsely represented in Europe.

Thus far there is no break in the Kachh succession. The gradual replace-ment of macrocephalitids by reineckeids, which again overlap the pelto-ceratids followed by euaspidocerates provides a continuous sequence from Bathonian to Oxfordian. At this stage, however, there is a serious hiatus in S. Kachh where the Middle Kimmeridgian Katrol beds rest on the Dhosa Oolite of Oxfordian age, though the Belemnite Beds of Jurun may partly fill the gap elsewhere. In the Katrol beds phyllocerates appear in consider-able numbers for the first time, accompanied by the oppelids *Taramelli-ceras, Glochiceras, Hemihaploceras,* and *Streblites,* comparable with European forms. The chief perisphinctids are species of *Pachysphinctes* and *Katroli-ceras* which appear to be special elements in the Kachh fauna. There are several species of *Aspidoceras* belonging to the *acanthicum* group, as well as *Waagenia* and *Pseudowaagenia,* all typical in mid-Kimmeridgian Beds of Europe. The barren sandstones at the top of the Katrol beds may still belong to the Kimmeridgian stage, but this is uncertain in the absence of ammonites. In any case, the Portlandian and higher beds which continue the succession are only known in NW. Kachh, and they follow immediately on the Oxfordian stage in that district. The commonest ammonites in the Gudjinsir Beds are *Haploceras elimatum* (Oppel) and *Hildoglochiceras pro-pinquum* (Waagen), together with some phyllocerates and a few peris-phinctid species. The Zamia Shales of Nurrha have yielded other species of

Hildoglochiceras and are probably not greatly different in age. Exact correlation with Europe is not possible, for though *H. elimatum* is recorded from the Stramberg Limestone its total range is not known; therefore reference to Lower Portlandian is tentative. The basal bed of the Umia group contains abundant ammonites; the most conspicuous are large, finely costate *Virgatosphinctes* of the *densiplicatus* group, associated with the first berriasellids of the genus *Micracanthoceras* and the olcostephanid *Umaites*, besides occasional phyllocerates and lytocerates. The presence of these forms, together with the absence or scarcity of genera like *Berriasella* and *Aulacosphinctes*, which are definitely known from the summit of the Jurassic elsewhere, indicates that the Umia ammonite bed is to be correlated with lower Purbeckian (or highest Portlandian) strata of the European classification. The Umia plant beds which follow cannot be dated precisely in the absence of ammonites and they are succeeded in NW. Kachh by deposits of Cretaceous age.

The recent revision of the Kachh Cephalopoda by Spath is based on the examination of nearly 7,000 ammonites. They are classified in 556 species, of which only 122 are referred to European forms. The phyllocerates and lytocerates, together numbering only 21 species, are insignificant in view of their dominance at Mediterranean localities. About 60 Kachh species that have affinity with forms typical in deposits of central and western Europe include 18 oppelids and 23 perisphinctids, the two dominant families in Kachh; the remainder are mainly reineckeids and aspidoceratids. There is a total absence from the Kachh faunas of the characteristic mid-European families Kosmoceratidae, Cadoceratidae, and Cardioceratidae. About 400 species are local elements, being special to Kachh and neighbouring areas. These include (1) strongly ribbed oppelids, (2) compressed or evolute developments of the Macrocephalitidae, like the Callovian Eucycloceratidae and the Oxfordian Mayaitidae, (3) heavily ribbed perisphinctids of Callovian age, related to the proplanulitids. They are all highly ornamented groups characteristic of marginal seas. Hence one may infer that marine communication existed between the Mediterranean and Indian Ocean by way of the Persian Gulf and Arabian Sea, but that the Jurassic ammonites of the Indian coastal area developed local peculiarities which give the faunas a highly distinctive aspect.

Ammonites closely related to Kachh forms are recorded from the desert tract of Rajputana, north of Kachh, but only a few limited horizons are known to be represented. The Jaisalmer Limestone has yielded ammonites of the anceps and athleta beds, and the Badasar Sandstone has forms typical of the Upper Katrol and Umia ammonite beds. Similarly in the Salt Range, more than 1,000 miles north of Kachh, ammonites of the macrocephalus beds are preserved in a yellow and crimson matrix identical with the 'Golden Oolite' of Kachh. In the same range Upper Callovian perisphinctids are recorded from Makerwal, and at several localities Upper Kimmeridgian genera have been noted as derived fossils in the condensed deposits of the Neocomian Belemnite Beds. From the Attock District, immediately north of the Salt Range, the Jurassic rocks are restricted to a part of the Oxfordian stage which is dated by perisphinctids and mayaitids comparable with forms from the Dhosa Oolite and Kantecote Sandstone of Kachh. These thin fragments of the Jurassic system evidently represent temporary transgressions of the sea from the south, probably along a depression on the site of the present Indus plains (Map, Fig. 73).

The Jurassic deposits of the Himalayas are equally fragmentary. They begin with the upper part of the Kioto Limestone, known as the Sulcacutus Beds after the abundant belemnite-species; these have yielded an ammonite of the macrocephalus zone. The succeeding Belemnite Bed, which forms the base of the Spiti Shales, contains forms of *Mayaites*, *Epimayaites*, and *Grayiceras* characteristic of the Dhosa Oolite and Kantecote Sandstone of Kachh. Hence there is a gap in the succession representing the greater part of the Callovian stage. The Spiti Shales are further subdivided into the Chidamu Beds and the Lochambel Beds. The former contain species of *Aulacosphinctes* comparable with Upper Katrol species, *Hildoglochiceras* in common with the Zamia Shales of Nurrha, and *Virgatosphinctes* closely related to forms in the Umia ammonite bed. Hence the ammonite assemblage of the Chidamu Beds is heterogeneous, and probably represents diverse faunas of Upper Kimmeridgian and Portlandian ages. It is evident, too, that a considerable hiatus must exist between the Chidamu and the underlying Belemnite Beds. The Lochambel Beds contain many species of *Blanfordiceras*, *Aulacosphinctes*, *Himalayites*, *Paraboliceras*, *Kossmatia*, *Spiticeras*, &c., of late Purbeckian and early Cretaceous age. But again, there is no trace of the rich faunas that in Mexico and South America occur in many hundreds of feet of earlier Purbeckian deposits. Undoubtedly the 500 feet of Spiti Shales represent mere episodes in Upper Jurassic sedimentation, rather than the 'unbroken sequence' of earlier writers. Yet these black shales, enclosing calcareous nodules, are remarkably constant over an immense area, extending from Hazara and north Karakoram to the Everest region, a distance of over 1,500 miles, and the same facies is seen again in the East Indian Archipelago. Consequently there is some reason for believing that this series of Himalayan transgressions came, not from Kachh, but from the direction of the Bay of Bengal.

Westwards from Kachh, Indian relationships in the ammonite faunas can be traced in a number of transgressive deposits along the east coast of Africa. In northern localities of Abysinnia, Somaliland and South Arabia most of the ammonites so far recorded are identified or compared with European species, relationship with Indian forms being slight. Farther south, in Kenya, Jurassic shales and limestones are exposed at intervals along a narrow strip of country near Mombasa, between the Triassic foothills and the Neozoic deposits of the coast. The lowest rocks, of Bajocian

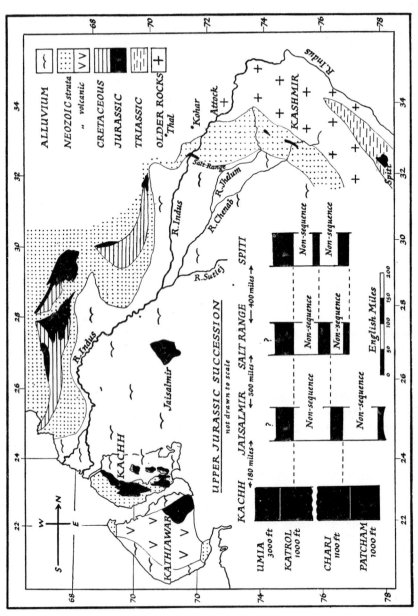

FIG. 73. SKETCH-MAP SHOWING THE DISTRIBUTION OF JURASSIC DEPOSITS IN NORTH-WEST INDIA

age, are similar to the Posidonia Shales of Sicily and south Arabia. The most striking feature is the abundance of phylloceratids which amount to over 70 per cent. of the ammonites collected; lytoceratids also are frequent, but only occasional trachyostracous forms, like *Oppelia*, *Oecotraustes*, *Dorsetensia*, *Stephanoceras*, and *Spiroceras* are present, and they are obviously of Mediterranean type. In view of the dominance of phylloceratids the interbedded Krambe Limestones are of special interest, for they contain several genera of reef-corals, and at one locality they have yielded an ammonite-fauna comparable with the *Macrocephalites triangularis* assemblage of Kachh. Higher in the succession Spath states 'there is the greatest similarity between the Callovian faunas of Mombasa and Kachh', and this is shown especially by the presence of such local elements as *Sindeites*, *Hubertoceras*, *Kinkeliniceras*, &c. The same similarity exists in an Upper Oxfordian fauna with species of *Pachyplanulites*, *Prososphinctes*, and *Torquatisphinctes* in common with the Kantecote Sandstone; also in a Middle Kimmeridgian assemblage with forms of *Waagenia*, *Katroliceras*, *Pachysphinctes*, *Aspidoceras*, &c., typical of the Katrol beds in Kachh.

The same relations are shown in collections from certain localities in Tanganyika which have yielded Kachh ammonites ranging from the Callovian to the Portlandian stage. The highest Jurassic strata at Tendaguru contain deinosaur beds (p. 562) intercalated with the marine deposits from which Spath records Kachh species of *Subdichotomoceras*, *Hildoglochiceras*, and *Haploceras*. These Portlandian strata are directly overlaid by beds which are well up in the Cretaceous system.

In Madagascar all stages from the Bathonian to the Portlandian are represented at various localities by marine deposits, and Bessairie (1936) claims that the combined succession is more complete than that of Kachh. Here it suffices to note that relations with the Indian succession are as close as those of the East African localities just mentioned. The ammonite assemblages of all these localities are sufficiently distinct to form a separate faunal region, and their widespread distribution indicates the existence of an Indian Ocean, connected with the European Mediterranean throughout the Jurassic period, with temporary encroachment on the adjacent land to west and north at various times. We must now examine the evidence concerning the eastern limit of this ocean.

No Jurassic deposits are known in Peninsular India east of Kachh, and the relations of the Namyau Limestones of Burma are uncertain in the absence of ammonites. But certain disconnected observations in the East Indian Archipelago are more definite. Among the ammonites described by Boehm from the Sula Islands Spath has recognized the Callovian *Idiocycloceras*, various forms of the Oxfordian *Epimayaites*, and species of *Uhligites* and *Haplophylloceras* typical of the highest Spiti Shales. Among lamellibranchs from the Oxfordian stage, the coarsely ribbed *Inoceramus galoi* of Boehm is similar to forms recorded from the basal Spiti Shales of the

Himalayas. Indian relations have also been recognized by Spath among ammonites described by Boehm from New Guinea, including the peculiar genus *Paraboliceras* typical of the Spiti Shales.

In Australia deposits of Jurassic age are mainly of freshwater origin, but in western Australia, at Champion Bay and Greenough River, marine Bajocian strata are transgressive on the margin of the ancient shield. The ammonites (revised by Spath in 1939) include local species of *Dorsetensia*, *Normannites*, and *Pseudotoites* the last-named being a peculiar genus of stephanoceratids unknown elsewhere. These, of course, are earlier than the Indian ammonites but Kimmeridgian and Portlandian forms recorded from the North Island of New Zealand include species of *Aulacosphinctoides*, *Uhligites*, *Kossmatia*, and *Berriasella* belonging to groups well represented in the Spiti Shales; the lamellibranch *Inoceramus galoi* is also present. These indicate the continuity of the eastern part of the Indian Ocean during Neojurassic time. Beyond the Australasian region lies the so-called 'Andesite Line', following a sinuous course east of Japan by the Bonin and Ladrone islands, Halmaheira, and New Hebrides, thence curving round the Samoan islands to the east of Tonga and New Zealand. This perhaps marks the margin of the Pacific basin, for 'west of the Andesite Line the Neozoic volcanic rocks are mainly andesites and east of it the unbroken depths of the Pacific extend to the American coast' (Marshall 1911).

LITERATURE

The most recent general work on *The Jurassic System of Great Britain*, published in 1933 by W. J. Arkell, contains illustrations of all the zone-fossils, and an extensive bibliography. From the enormous volume of literature on the Jurassic fossils, the following may be mentioned here.

'The Liassic Rocks of the Radstock District', by J. W. Tutcher and A. E. Trueman, *Q.J.G.S.*, vol. lxxxi, pp. 595–666, 1925, illustrates the modern application of zonal methods to the Lias, gives lists of fossils and numerous references to literature, and figures some distinctive Liassic ammonites. The application of zonal methods to detailed mapping is well shown in Dr. W. D. Lang's large-scale maps of the Dorset Coast illustrating 'The Geology of the Charmouth Cliffs, Beach, and Foreshore', *Proc. Geol. Assoc.*, vol. xxv, pp. 293–360, 1914; and 'The Blue Lias of the Devon and Dorset Coasts', *Proc. Geol. Assoc.*, vol. xxxv, pp. 169–85, 1924.

'The Lias Ammonites of the British Islands' were first collectively described by T. Wright, *Mon. Pal. Soc.*, 1876–87. The Yorkshire types were later reviewed in *Yorkshire Type Ammonites*, vols. i and ii, continued as *Type Ammonites*, vol. iii to vii, by S. S. Buckman, 8vo, London, 1909–28; this publication contains illustrations of over 700 species of Jurassic ammonites, including many forms from the Lias. Revision of other groups of Liassic ammonites is contained in 'Studies in the Ammonites of the Family Echioceratidae', by A. E. Trueman and D. M. Williams, *Trans. Roy. Soc. Edin.*, vol. liii, pp. 699–739, 1925; 'Shales-with-"Beef"', a Sequence in the Lower Lias of the Dorset Coast', by W. D. Lang, L. F. Spath, and W. A. Richardson, *Q.J.G.S.*, vol. lxxix, pp. 47–99, 1923; 'The Ammonites of the Blue Lias', by L. F. Spath, *Proc. Geol. Assoc.*, vol. xxxv, pp. 186–208, 1924; 'The Ammonites from the Belemnite Marls of Charmouth', *Q.J.G.S.*, vol. lxxxiv, pp. 222–3: 1928; 'The Ammonites of the Green Ammonite Beds of Dorset', *Q.J.G.S.*, vol. xcii, pp. 438–55, 1936; 'The Ammonites of the Liassic Family Liparoceratidae', *Brit. Mus. Cat.*, 1938, by the same author. Many species of later age ate described and figured in 'The Inferior Oolite Ammonites of the British Islands', by S. S. Buckman, *Mon. Pal. Soc.*, 1887–1907; in 'Certain Jurassic (Inferior Oolite) Species of Ammonites and Brachiopoda', by S. S. Buckman, *Q.J.G.S.*, vol. lxvi, pp. 90–110, 1910; in 'The English Bathonian Ammonites', by W. J. Arkell, *Mon. Pal. Soc.*, 1951 (in progress); in 'The Ammonite Zones of the Upper Oxford Clay of Warboys, Huntingdonshire', by L. F. Spath, *Bull. Geol. Surv. Gt. Brit.*, No. 1, pp. 82–98, 1939; in 'The Ammonites of the English Corallian Beds', by W. J. Arkell, *Mon. Pal. Soc.*, 1935–48; and in *Ammonites from the Upper Kimmeridge Clay*, by E. Neaverson, Liverpool, 1925. Certain genera described in the last-named work are considered by L. F. Spath to be synonymous with *Pavlovia* established by Ilovaisky in *Les Ammonites du Jurassique superieur du pays de Liapine*, Ouvrages de la section de la Société Imp. Amis Sci. Nat. Moscou, 1917; there appears to be no copy of this paper in English libraries. The ammonite succession in higher stages is described by H. Salfeld in 'Certain Upper Jurassic Strata of England', *Q.J.G.S.*, vol. lxix, pp. 423–32, 1913.

Other molluscan groups are reviewed in 'British Belemnitidae', by J. Phillips, *Mon. Pal. Soc.*, 1865–70; 'The Belemnites of the Belemnite Marls of Charmouth', by W. D. Lang, *Q.J.G.S.*, vol. lxxxiv, pp. 196–222, 1928; 'The Gastropod and Lamellibranch Mollusca of the Belemnite Marls', by L. R. Cox, ibid., pp. 233–45, 1928; 'The Evolution of Certain Liassic Gasteropods, with Special Reference to their use in Stratigraphy', by A. I. McDonald and A. E. Trueman, ibid., vol. lxxvii, pp. 297–344, 1921; 'Liassic Dentaliidae', by L. Richardson, ibid., vol. lxii, pp. 573–96, 1906; *Catalogue of British Jurassic Gasteropoda*, by W. H. Hudleston and E. Wilson, London, 1892, a list of genera and species known in 1892, with their geological distribution and references to descriptions and illustrations; and 'Variation in Gryphaea Incurva (Sow.) from the Lower Lias of Loch Aline, Argyll', by R. M. McLennan and A. E. Trueman, *Proc. Roy. Soc. Edin.*, vol. lxi, pp. 211–32, 1942. 'The British Jurassic Gasteropoda', by W. H. Hudleston, *Mon. Pal. Soc.*, 1887–96, is an incomplete monograph, which contains an account of the gastropods of the Inferior Oolite. Later forms are described in 'Some Gasteropoda from the Portland Rocks of the Vale of Wardour and of Bucks', by W. H. Hudleston, *Geol. Mag.*, vol. xviii, pp. 385–95, 1881. 'British Trigoniae' are described by J. Lycett in *Mon. Pal. Soc.*, 1872–9. Nine species of 'Inferior Oolite Pectinidae' are described and illustrated by E. T. Paris and L. Richardson in *Q.J.G.S.*, vol. lxxi, pp. 521–35, 1915. 'The Mollusca from the Great Oolite', by J. Morris and J. Lycett, *Mon. Pal. Soc.*, 1851–63, deals chiefly with mollusca from Minchinhampton (Glos.) and the coast of Yorkshire. A supplementary monograph by J. Lycett (1863) describes mollusca from the Stonesfield Slate, Great Oolite, Forest Marble, and Cornbrash. 'The Fauna of the Cornbrash' is described by J. F. Blake, *Mon. Pal. Soc.*, 1905–7. A necessary nomenclatural revision of the last three monographs has been undertaken by L. R. Cox and W. J. Arkell, in *A Survey of the Mollusca of the British Great Oolite Series* which was issued by the Palaeontographical Society in 1948 and 1950. 'The British Corallian Lamellibranchia' have also been revised by W. J. Arkell, *Mon. Pal. Soc.*, 1929–37. 'The Fauna of the Basal Shell-Bed of the Portland Stone, Isle of Portland', by L. R. Cox, *Proc. Dorset Field Club*, vol. xlvi, pp. 113–72, 1925, contains new records of mollusca; some are well known in the north of France but not previously recorded from Britain.

British Fossil Brachiopoda, by T. Davidson, Oolitic and Liassic Brachiopoda, 1851, Supplement 1876–78, *Mon. Pal. Soc.* must be supplemented by reference to such papers as 'The Brachiopoda of the Namyau Beds', by S. S. Buckman, *Pal. Indica*, N.S., vol. iii, Mem. 2; *Mem. Geol. Surv. India*, 1917, in which many British brachiopods are described and illustrated, in addition to the Indian forms, and a new classification is proposed; 'The Brachiopods of the Belemnite Marls of Charmouth', by H. M. Muir-Wood, *Q.J.G.S.*, vol. lxxxiv, pp. 245–55, 1928. Other brachiopods are recorded and figured in 'The Stratigraphical Distribution of the Cornbrash', by J. A. Douglas and W. J. Arkell, ibid., vol. lxxxiv, pp. 117–18, 1928, and vol. lxxxviii, pp. 112–70, 1932, and 'The Brachiopoda of the British Great Oolite Series', Part I, Fuller's Earth, by H. M. Muir-Wood, *Mon. Pal. Soc.*, 1936. 'The British Fossil Echinodermata of the Oolitic Formations', by T. Wright, *Mon. Pal. Soc.*, 1857–80, contains descriptions of most species known from the British Oolites, but H. L. Hawkins records three additional genera from the Portland and Purbeck stages in *Q.J.G.S.*, vol. lxxxi, p. cxxviii, 1925. Hawkins has also described 'The Morphology and Evolution of the Ambulacrum in the Echinoidea Holectypoida', *Phil. Trans. Roy. Soc.*, ser. B, vol. ccix, pp. 377–480, 1920.

'British Fossil Corals': Part II, Oolitic Corals, by H. Milne-Edwards and J. Haime, *Mon. Pal. Soc.*, 1851, with a supplement by P. M. Duncan, ibid., 1872, is still an indispensable work. W. J. Arkell has explained 'The Nature, Origin and Climatic Significance of the Coral Reefs in the Vicinity of Oxford' in *Q.J.G.S.*, vol. xci, pp. 77–110, 1935; this work contains numerous references to literature on Jurassic corals in Europe and elsewhere. Liassic corals are described by P. M. Duncan in Supplement Part 4 of 'British Fossil Corals', *Mon. Pal. Soc.* 1868, and R. F. Tomes has reviewed 'The Madreporaria of the White Lias of the Middle and Western Counties of England' in *Q.J.G.S.*, vol. xl, pp. 353–75, 1884.

Many Jurassic fossils from the European mainland were originally described in such works as *Palaeontologie Française: Terrain Jurassique*, by A. d'Orbigny, 1840–55; *Der Jura* by F. A. Quenstedt, Tübingen, 1858; *Die Ammoniten des Schwäbischen Juras*, by the same author, Stuttgart 1882–5; *Beiträge zu einer Revision der Ammoniten des Schwäbischen Juras*, by J. F. Pompeckj, Stuttgart, 1893–6; 'Cephalopodi Sinemuriani dell' Appennino Centrale', by G. Bonarelli, *Pal. Italica*, vol. v, pp. 55–83, 1899; 'Ammoniti del Lias Medio dell' Appennino Centrale', by A. Fucini, *Pal. Italica*, vol. v, pp. 145–85, vol. vi, pp. 17–74, 1899–1901; 'Cephalopodi Liassici del Monte di Cetona', *Pal. Italica*, vol. xi, pp. 93–146, 1905. Also *Die Juraformation Englands, Frankreichs, und des Südwestlichen Deutschlands*, by A. Oppel, 1856–8; *Description des ammonites des calcaires du Château de Crussol, Ardèche*, by F. Fontannes, 1879; *Description de la faune jurassique du Portugal* by P. Choffat, 1893; 'Monographische Beschreibung der Ammonitengattung Perisphinctes', by J. Siemiradzki, *Palaeontographica*, vol. xlv, pp. 69–296, 1898–9; 'Die Gliederung des Oberen Juras in Nordwesteuropa', by H. Salfeld, *Neues Jahrb. Min.* &c., B-Bd. xxxvii, pp. 125–246, 1914, and many other classical works. Full references to these, and an excellent review of Upper Jurassic faunas in Europe and the Mediterranean area, are given by L. F. Spath in 'Revision of the Cephalopod Fauna of Kachh (Cutch)', *Pal. Indica*, N.S., vol. ix, Mem. 2, 1924–33.

The Indian Jurassic ammonite-faunas are fully described in the last-named work, and are correlated with corresponding faunas in East Africa, Madagascar, the East Indies, and New Zealand. Later investigations around the Indian Ocean are described in further works by L. F. Spath, namely, 'Jurassic and Cretaceous Ammonites of the Attock District', *Pal. Indica*, N.S., vol. xx, 1934, 'Bajocian Ammonites and Belemnites from Eastern Persia (Iran)', *Pal. Indica*, N.S., vol. xxii 1936, 'Jurassic Ammonites from Western Australia', *Journ. Roy. Soc. West. Austr.*, vol. xxv, pp. 123–34, 1939, and by H. Besaire in 'Recherches géologiques à Madagascar: La Géologie du Nord Ouest', *Mém. Acad. Malgache*, fasc. xxi, 1936.

Some North African forms are reviewed by L. F. Spath in 'Jurassic Ammonites from Jebel Zaghuan, Tunisia, *Q.J.G.S.*, vol. lxix, pp. 540–80, 1913. The same author describes 'A New Ammonite Genus (Shenarpites) from the Lias of Baluchistan', in *Ann. Mag. Nat. Hist.*, ser. 10, vol. xvii, pp. 641–5, 1936, and comments on the associated forms. The fauna has features in common with the Liassic fauna of Madagascar described by A. Thevenin in *Ann. Palaeont.*, vol. iii, pp. 105–43, 1908. Long ago A. Rothpletz recorded Liassic ammonites from the East Indies in *Palaeontographica*, vol. xxxix, pp. 57–106, 1892; more recently, J. Wanner and E. Jaworski have described 'Lias Ammoniten von Jamdena und Celebes', in *Neues Jahrb. Min.*, &c., vol. lxvi, pp. 199–210, 1931. Liassic rocks and fossils from New Zealand are described by C. T. Trechmann in 'The Jurassic Rocks of New Zealand', with an appendix on the ammonites by L. F. Spath, in *Q.J.G.S.*, vol. lxxix, pp. 246–312, 1923.

A summary of 'The Jurassic History of North America' is given by C. H. Crickmay in *Proc. Amer. Phil. Soc.*, vol. lxx, pp. 15–102, 1931, and C. Burckhardt has written an 'Étude Synthétique sur le Mésozoïque Mexicain' in *Mém. Soc. palaeont. Suisse*, vol. xlix, pp. 1–123, and vol. 1, pp. 123–280, 1930–1, which is amplified by R. W. Imlay's 'Upper Jurassic Ammonites from Mexico', *Bull. Geol. Soc. Amer.*, vol. l, pp. 1–78, 1939, and *Journ. Palaeont.*, vol. xvii, pp. 527–43, 1943. 'The Jurassic Ammonite Fauna of Cuba' has been described by M. O'Connell in *Bull. Amer. Mus. Nat. Hist.*, vol. xlii, pp. 643–92, 1920, and further information on 'Oxford Ammoniten von Cuba' is furnished by E. Jaworski in *Neuen Jahrb. Min.* &c., B-Bd. 83, pp. 87–137, 1940. *Some American Jurassic Ammonites of ... the Family Cardioceratidae* are described by J. B. Reeside in U.S. Geol. Surv., Prof. Paper No. 18, 1919. Records from Alaska, cited by G. C. Martin in 'The Mesozoic Stratigraphy of Alaska U.S.', *Geol. Surv.*, Bull. 776, 1926, need nomenclatural revision, but L. F. Spath has described 'The Invertebrate Faunas of the Bathonian-Callovian Deposits of Jameson Land (E. Greenland) in *Meddelelser om Grønland*, Bd. 87, No. 7, 1932, and 'The Upper Jurassic Invertebrate Faunas of Cape Leslie, Milne Land', *Medd., Grønland* Bd. 99, Nos. 2 and 3, 1935–6. Ammonites from certain horizons in East Greenland compare closely with 'Ammonites from Spitzbergen' described by L. F. Spath in *Geol. Mag.*, vol. lviii, pp. 347–56, 1921, and forms studied later by D. Sokolev and W. Bodylevsky in 'Jura- und Kreide-Faunen von Spitzbergen', *Skrifter om Svalbård og Ishavet*, No. 35, 1931. Other Greenland forms may be compared with certain 'Ammoniten der Unteren Wolga-Stufe' described by A. Michalski in *Mém. Comm. Géol. St. Pétersbourg*, vol. viii, pp. 331–497, 1890. 'The Lower Jurassic Rocks of East Greenland', with illustrations of the most important fossils, are described by A. Rosenkrantz in *Meddelelser om Grønland*, Bd. cx, 1934.

The scattered references to Jurassic deposits in South America are collected by H. Gerth in *Geologie Sudamerikas*, vol. ii, Berlin, 1935.

While this volume was in the Press a new collection of 'The Bajocian Ammonites of Western Australia' has been described by W. J. Arkell and P. E. Playford, *Phil. Trans. Roy. Soc. London*, ser. B, vol. 237, pp. 547–605, 1954. The ammonites are assigned to the mid-Bajocian genera *Sonninia*, *Witchellia*, *Fontannesia*, *Otoites*, *Pseudotoites* and *Zemistephanus*. The last two genera are not recorded from any of the well-known Bajocian outcrops of the Old World. The Australian genus *Pseudotoites* is now shown to be represented also in the Moluccas, British Columbia, Alaska and Argentina, while *Zemistephanus*, formerly known only from Canada, Alaska, and the United States, is now recorded from Western Australia. This distribution favours the concept of free migration across the Jurassic Pacific Ocean.

XIII

CRETACEOUS FAUNAS

THE following table shows the broad classification of Cretaceous strata now in general use, together with the older lithological divisions:

Upper Cretaceous	Senonian	.	.	.	. Upper Chalk
	Turonian	.	.	.	. Middle Chalk.
	Cenomanian .	.	.	. Lower Chalk
Lower Cretaceous	Albian .	.	.	.	. Gault and Upper Greensand.
	Aptian	.	.	.	. Lower Greensand
	Neocomian .	.	.	. Speeton Clay and Wealden.

In the Lower Cretaceous, as in the Jurassic, ammonites provide the safest means of correlation. Difficulties are encountered, however, owing to the discontinuous distribution of marine Neocomian and Aptian deposits (many of which also are unfossiliferous) and to confusion in the nomenclature of the fossils. While ammonites are fairly common in the Lower Chalk, they become rare in higher strata. Consequently they are not in general use as zone-fossils for the Upper Cretaceous, their place being taken by echinoids, brachiopods, and other fossils.

NEOCOMIAN FAUNAS

British Neocomian strata are exposed in two areas, each of which presents a distinctive facies. At Speeton on the coast of Yorkshire the strata consist of clays containing marine fossils throughout, while the variable series of clays, sandstones, and limestones in Lincolnshire and Norfolk are also of marine origin. These beds rest non-sequentially on an eroded surface of Kimmeridge Clay, and there is no evidence of Portland or Purbeck strata. In the south of England the Wealden Beds, of lacustrine origin, are generally regarded as representing the Neocomian, though palaeontological evidence is meagre. Still, the striking lithological change from Purbeck limestones and marls to the sandstones of the Wealden Beds furnishes a convenient line of division between Jurassic and Cretaceous deposit in that area. In the Midland counties Aptian deposits rest upon various horizons of the Jurassic.

Until 1924 the marine Speeton Clays, classified on the vertical range of various belemnites, were thought to present an unbroken succession from the Upper Jurassic to the Aptian. Work on the ammonite faunas by L. F. Spath has shown, however, that the formation lacks not only Purbeck, Portland, and uppermost Kimmeridge deposits, but also several

zones represented at the base of the Neocomian of other countries. Moreover, several non-sequences occur within the Speeton Clay itself, while the
succession in Lincolnshire and Norfolk is still more fragmentary. The following table, abridged from Spath's detailed zonal scheme shows the
larger faunal divisions represented in this country, grouped according to the
accepted European classification.

Substage	Ammonite-fauna	Speeton	Lincs. and Norfolk
BARREMIAN	Heteroceratan	Cement Beds	
	Paracrioceratan		Snettisham Clay
		B (lower)	...
	Haplocrioceratan		Tealby Limestone (= lower zones)
HAUTERIVIAN	Simbirskitan	C 1–6	Tealby Clay (= upper zone)
	Crioceratan	C 7	...
	Lyticoceratan	C 8–11, D 1–2	Claxby Ironstone
VALANGINIAN	Hoplitidan	Not known	...
	Polyptychitan	D 3–6 (= middle zones)	Hundleby Clay
INFRA-VALANGINIAN	Platylenticeratan	Not known	...
	Subcraspeditan		Spilsby Sandstone
	Spiticeratan		...

The Spiticeratan ammonite fauna is not known neàrer than the south of
France and is typically developed in the Himalayas. The oldest British
Neocomian deposit is the Spilsby Sandstone of Lincolnshire, which contains representatives of the **Subcraspeditan Fauna.** The index-genus
Subcraspedites, comprising more or less compressed, round-ventered ammonites with biplicate ribs which become feeble externally, includes *S.
plicomphalus* (J. de C. Sow.) and *S. stenomphalus* (Pavlow). Many lamellibranchs also occur, one of the most interesting being *Aucella volgensis*
Lahusen, whose presence was considered good evidence of boreal conditions
until the wide distribution of the genus in many latitudes became known
and rendered the idea untenable. *Belemnites lateralis* Phillips has also
been recorded from the Spilsby Sandstone.

The lowest ammonite-bearing beds of the Speeton Clay yield members
of the **Polyptychitan Fauna.** The genus *Polyptychites* (Pl. XV), comprising large inflated ammonites, ornamented on the umbilical border by
elongated tubercles which give rise to bundles of peripheral ribs, was formerly confused with the homoeomorphous genus *Gravesia* from the Kimmeridge Clay. Species of *Polyptychites* are also found in the Hundleby Clay
of Lincolnshire. Associated with the inflated forms are smaller ammonites

without tubercles; these, formerly grouped together as '*Craspedites fragilis*', are now assigned to the genus *Dichotomites*, which appears to range up into Hauterivian strata. Both at Speeton and in Lincolnshire the members of the Polyptychitan fauna represent only two zones in the middle of the Valanginian succession, and the slightly later Hoplitidan fauna is unrecognized at these localities.

The **Lyticoceratan Fauna** contains species of *Polyptychites* and *Dichotomites*, along with members of the incoming genera *Lyticoceras* and *Leopoldia* (Pl. XV), as its chief ammonites. Forms like *Lyticoceras regale* (Bean) (Pl. XV) and *L. oxygonium* (Neum. and Uhlig) were formerly ascribed to the genus *Hoplites* because of their generally compressed form and their narrow, flattened venter, but they show differences in developmental and sutural features. The genus *Acanthodiscus*, comprising compressed, round-ventered ammonites with strong simple ribs, also appears with late members of the fauna. Another of the olcostephanid genera, *Subastieria*, exemplified by *S. sulcosa* (Pavlow) (Pl. XV), with highly coronate whorls, gives rise to *Parastieria*, typified by *P. peltoceroides* (Pavlow) (Pl. XV), by division of the ribs into transverse lines of tubercles. The baculoid genus *Bochianites*, recorded from bed D 2 at Speeton, is widely distributed (being known from Europe, South Africa, Himalaya, and Columbia) and of considerable importance in correlation. The Claxby Ironstone of Lincolnshire, resting non-sequentially on the Spilsby Sandstone, has yielded fragments of *Lyticoceras*; but since it also encloses the later genus *Simbirskites*, Spath infers that the formation includes two deposits of different age. The ammonites, however, are rare and poorly preserved, and further investigation is desirable.

Fossils of other groups are often more abundant than ammonites. Belemnites of the *lateralis* group, now assigned to the genus *Acroteuthis*, are of common occurrence. Among lamellibranchs, the oyster *Exogyra sinuata* (J. Sow.) and the large scallop-shell *Camptonectes cinctus* (J. Sow.) (Fig. 76) are distinctive, while *Trigonia ingens* Lycett is typical of the Claxby Ironstone but is not recorded from the Speeton Clay. Other bivalves, and some brachiopods such as '*Terebratula*' *praelonga* J. de C. Sow. and '*T.*' *faba* (d'Orb), are plentiful in the Lincolnshire deposit but unknown at Speeton, where *Nucula*, *Lingula*, &c., are abundant. These faunal differences may be correlated with differences in conditions of deposition as reflected also in the lithological characters of the sediments.

The succeeding **Crioceratan Fauna** is marked by the abundance of *Crioceras*, a genus of uncoiled ammonoids with two types of costae. These appear to have originated, probably from a lytoceratid stock, independently of *Distoloceras*, an uncoiled hoplitid form which appears with the previous fauna. They are associated with numerous capricorn crioceratids now ascribed to the genus *Aegocrioceras* (Pl. XV), with which they are connected by transitional forms. Some perisphinctoid ammonites in this fauna, related to the slightly later *Simbirskites*, have been grouped under the generic term *Speetoniceras*. Other fossils include the belemnoid *Hibolites jaculum* (Phill.) and the echinoid *Echinospatagus cordiiformis* Breyn., ascribed to a southern origin, together with *Exogyra sinuata* (J. Sow.) and '*Terebratula*' *sella* (J. de C. Sow.).

The **Simbirskitan Fauna** is named after the genus *Simbirskites*, a group of coronate ammonites that are very similar to some of the earlier olcostephanid forms, e.g. *S. speetonensis* (Young and Bird) (Pl. XV). *Craspedodiscus*, a genus of discoid shells that persist into the succeeding fauna, is connected with compressed species of *Simbirskites*. *C. discofalcatus* (Lahusen) is illustrated in Plate XV. These simbirskitids are accompanied by species of *Spitidiscus*, typified by the distinctive *S. rotula* (J. de C. Sow.), an almost smooth form with rounded whorls bearing numerous strong constrictions. The sandy Tealby Clay of Lincolnshire with *Hibolites jaculum* (Phill.), *Exogyra sinuata* (J. Sow.), *Perna mulleti* Desh., and *Simbirskites* aff. *kleini* (Neum. and Uhlig), represents the upper Simbirskitan zone.

The genus *Hoplocrioceras*, including uncoiled ammonoids with a characteristic bundling of the ribs at the umbilical tubercle, furnishes a name for the **Hoplocrioceratan Fauna.** These uncoiled forms are early accompanied by species of *Craspedodiscus* which culminate in the oxycone *C. clypeiforme* Judd. The last-named genus serves to correlate the Tealby Limestone of Lincolnshire with a part of the Speeton Clay, though the typical hoplocrioceratids are unknown from the limestone. The belemnoid *Oxyteuthis brunsvicensis* Strombeck and allied species were formerly relied upon for this correlation. The Tealby Limestone also contains *Camptonectes cinctus* (J. Sow.) (Fig. 76), *Ostrea diluviana* Linn., and *Exogyra sinuata* (J. Sow.).

The **Paracrioceratan Fauna** of the Lower Barremian is distinguished by another development of crioceratids exemplified by *Paracrioceras*, a genus with highly tuberculate ornamentation. The related genus *Pseudocrioceras* comprises more massive forms with a tendency to produce trituberculation on the fine intermediary ribs as well as on the principal costae. In the Snettisham Clay of north-west Norfolk *Paracrioceras* is associated with *Acrioceras* of the group of *A. tabarellii* (Astier).

The genus *Heteroceras* and its allies of the Heteroceratan fauna of the south of France are unknown at Speeton. The fauna of the Lower Cement Beds of Speeton is, however, provisionally regarded as its equivalent. This assemblage includes various crioceratids, and is succeeded by Aptian faunas containing species of *Deshayesites*, *Aconeceras*, and several uncoiled genera. Spath concludes that the Barremian succession at Speeton is very incomplete. These beds were assigned in former classifications to the 'brunsvicensis zone', from the abundance of the belemnoid *Oxyteuthis brunsvicensis* (Stromb.).

The Wealden Beds of the south of England offer little scope for recognition by palaeontological means. In speaking of the fauna of the Weald Clay, F. L. Kitchin says:

The few species of molluscs usually met with are often so preserved that they do not favour the detection of any slight mutational changes that might be turned to account in stratigraphical comparisons. The fresh-water forms tend to be stereotyped, while evolutionary progress and differentiation, as in the Purbeck beds, was less rapid and of a less pronounced character than in the case of marine assemblages. All these circumstances combine to retard progress in the utilisation of the faunal elements in stratigraphical correlation.

The Wealden Beds, indeed, are still subdivided on lithological grounds as follows:

Weald Clay
Tunbridge Wells Sands
Wadhurst Clay   ⎫ Hastings Sands
Ashdown Sands   ⎭

In these lacustrine deposits plants are often abundant, and some account of the Wealden flora is given in Chapter VIII. Fresh-water shells of the genera *Viviparus*, *Cyrena*, and *Unio* (the large *Unio valdensis* Mantell being perhaps the most distinctive) sometimes attain rock-forming abundance. Vertebrate remains include species of the reptilian genera *Iguanodon*, *Hypsilophodon* and *Ornithopsis*, and the multituberculate *Plagiaulax*.

APTIAN FAUNAS

The Aptian rocks of this country are, in the main, sandy littoral deposits which are peculiarly liable to lithological variation and to local interruptions in the succession of beds. Moreover, their porous nature has often proved detrimental to the satisfactory preservation of fossils. Those useful index-fossils the ammonoids are far from abundant, and much work remains to be done before the Aptian deposits can be accurately classified on a palaeontological basis. So far, only a provisional table of zones has been published, but in order that local developments of the strata can be discussed, this most recent classification is reproduced on page 493.

The lowest ammonite assemblage known in Aptian strata is the **Parancyloceratan Fauna**, so far recognized in this country only in some of the upper beds of the Speeton Clay. The index-genus *Parancyloceras* is an uncoiled form with very characteristic costation, straight, simple ribs which develop tubercles on the peripheral margins. Other uncoiled genera are *Hemicrioceras* and *Toxoceratoides*, the former with feeble bituberculate ribs interrupted on the periphery, the latter a trituberculate form with only slight curvature of the shell. They are associated with the desmoceratid genera *Melchiorites* and *Pseudosaynella*.

	Fauna	Zones	Localities
UPPER APTIAN	Parahoplitan	*aschiltaensis*	Folkestone Sands (lower part) Isle of Wight (Sandrock)
		nutfieldensis	Nutfield; Seend; Pulborough; Shanklin; Bargate Stone
	Tropaeuman	*tovilense* *bowerbanki* *hillsi*	Maidstone I. of Wight (Ferruginous Sands) Hythe Rag; Upware
LOWER APTIAN	Deshayesitan	*consobrinoides* *hambrovi* *weissi* *bodei*	I. of Wight ('Crackers') Atherfield Clay Perna-bed; Speeton B (top) Hunstanton Carstone
	Parancyloceratan	*bidentatus* *rude* *sparsicosta*	Speeton B (top)

The succeeding **Deshayesitan Fauna** is distinguished by the maximum development of *Deshayesites*—somewhat compressed ammonites with flexed ribs which arise and bifurcate at the umbilical margin. These are often associated with species of *Cheloniceras*, such as *C. seminodosum* (Sinzow) and *C. cornuelianum* (d'Orb.), *Dufrenoyia furcata* (J. de C. Sow.), and various uncoiled forms referred to the genus *Ancyloceras*. Early forms of *Deshayesites*, such as *D. bodei* (v. Koenen) and *D. fissicostatus* (Phill.) occur at the top of the Speeton Clay just below deposits of Albian age. A considerable non-sequence, represented by 800 feet of Aptian Beds in the Isle of Wight, is therefore manifest in Yorkshire. The horizon of *D. bodei* (v. Koenen) is also represented in Norfolk by the 'Carstone', which must not be confused with the much later deposit of that name in the Isle of Wight. The 'Perna-bed', containing abundance of *Perna mulleti* Deshayes, and forming the base of the Atherfield Clay in the Isle of Wight, is also on this horizon. The Atherfield Clay itself contains later forms of *Deshayesites*, such as *D. weissi* (Neum. and Uhlig), and is succeeded by the celebrated 'Crackers' Bed with *D. consobrinoides* (Sinzow) and numerous lamellibranchs. The latter include *Trigonia nodosa* J. de C. Sow. (Pl. XIII), *Panopaea gurgitis* (Brongn.), *Opis neocomiensis* (d'Orb.) (Fig. 70) and *Gervillia sublanceolata* (d'Orb.). The lower part of the Hythe Beds near Folkestone has also yielded *P. consobrinoides* (Sinzow).

The earlier of the two Upper Aptian faunas is named the **Tropaeuman Fauna,** from the presence of large uncoiled forms referred to the genus *Tropaeum*. These include crioceratid species as well as ancyloceratid forms; but they are essentially non-tuberculated and are thus distinguished from the uncoiled shells previously mentioned. Early assemblages are indicated by the two species *T. hillsi* (J. de C. Sow.) and *T. bowerbankii* (J. de C. Sow.) which occur in the upper part of the Hythe Beds and in the 'Ferruginous Sands' of the Isle of Wight. A 'lobster bed' in this series of strata contains *Meyeria vectensis* Bell in some abundance. A later Tropaeuman assemblage has for its index-fossil *Ammonitoceras tovilense* Crick, the huge type of which came from the Upper Hythe Beds of Tovil near Maidstone; it is an evolute form distinguished by bituberculate ornament.

The succeeding **Parahoplitan fauna** has the true *Parahoplites* and species of *Acanthoplites* as its chief forms, but ammonites are rare and the Sandgate Beds cannot always be distinguished from the underlying Hythe Beds. At Nutfield in Surrey, beds of Fuller's Earth have yielded *P. nutfieldensis* (J. de C. Sow.), and similar ammonites have been obtained from the calcareous grits known as the Bargate Stone. At Seend in Wiltshire, ferruginous sands have yielded internal moulds of *Toucasia lonsdalei* (J. de C. Sow.), a rudist lamellibranch (unknown elsewhere in Britain) which indicates the probability of a connexion with Mediterranean waters during Aptian time. The famous sponge-gravels of Faringdon in Berkshire contain abundant calcareous sponges such as *Raphidonema faringdonense* (Sharpe), *Barroisia anastomans* (Mantell), *Peronidella ramosa* (F. Römer); the brachiopods *Terebratella menardi* (Lam.), '*Terebratula*' *tornacensis* d'Arch., and '*Rhynchonella*' *latissima* (J. de C. Sow.); the echinoids *Hyposalenia wrighti* Desor, *Goniopygus delphinensis* A. Gras, *Cidaris faringdonensis* Wright, and *C. coxwellensis* Hawkins; many polyzoa, and numerous other fossils. Derived fossils, such as the ammonites *Pectinatites* and *Pavlovia* from the Upper Kimmeridge Clay, also occur.

ALBIAN FAUNAS

The most important ammonite-families of the Albian stage are the Desmoceratidae, Hoplitidae, and Dipoloceratidae, of which the hoplitids are the most familiar and perhaps the most characteristic. Many ammonites that were formerly grouped in the comprehensive genus *Hoplites* (sensu lato) are now more strictly defined under distinct generic names, but they are all considered to be derivatives, through the desmoceratids, of the persistent root-stocks *Phylloceras* and *Lytoceras*. The latter groups are rare in Britain, and, having a long vertical range, are of little value as zonal indexes. Only the hoplitids and the dipoloceratids are used in this connexion, and in order to facilitate discussion their vertical distribution is shown in the table on page 496.

Knowledge of Lower Albian deposits in England has been greatly extended during recent years by the discovery of ammonites in the Folkestone Sands. Previously, these beds were classified as part of the Aptian 'Lower Greensand', but they are now known to enclose the Acanthohoplitan and Leymeriellan faunas. The earlier assemblage has species of *Acanthohoplites* as its chief element. These ammonites are distinguished by the bifurcating ribs which pass over the rounded periphery without interruption; tubercles may be conspicuous at the division of the ribs, but tend to die away on the outer whorls. The **Leymeriellan Fauna** is developed in the regularis zone of Leighton Buzzard in Bedfordshire as well as in the Folkestone Sands. The distinctive ammonite-genus is *Leymeriella* comprising evolute compressed shells with tabulate venter, single costae, and simple hoplitid suture-line. It is associated with involute, inflated, strongly ribbed ammonites of the genus *Sonneratia* and with *Cleoniceras*, involute discoid forms with sharp venters. These ammonites are comparatively rare in Britain, but have long been known from many continental localities. The ammonites are associated with numerous other fossils, gastropods, lamellibranchs, and echinoids, but no detailed investigation of these elements in Britain has yet been undertaken.

The Middle and Upper Albian stages in England correspond generally with the series of clays known as the Gault, the type-succession being that at Folkestone. As long ago as 1874 Price subdivided the Folkestone Gault into some fourteen horizons, which are shown in the table by Roman numerals. The ammonite-succession has since been investigated by L. F. Spath who has placed the nomenclature on a secure basis. It is now seen that the type-succession, though incomplete in some respects, contains several remarkably rich faunas distinguished by the developmental stages attained by various ammonite-groups. Moreover, in some localities, Wiltshire for example, the Upper Gault becomes sandy—a local facies known as the Upper Greensand which has been the cause of much confusion in correlation. Here, as in other cases, detailed palaeontological work has shown that lithological planes do not necessarily coincide with the time-planes determined on the evidence of fossils, and that non-sequences occur in several districts. Thus the problematical Red Chalk of Norfolk belongs in part to the lower part of the orbignyi zone of Folkestone; the malmstone of Devizes represents the auritus zone and rests on Lower Gault; and the ammonite beds of Blackdown (varicosus zone) are overlain by Cenomanian strata.

Ammonite Zones of the Albian Stage

The Roman numerals refer to the succession at Folkestone as described by Price

	Zones and faunas	Subzones		Hoplitidae	Dipoloceratidae
UPPER ALBIAN (= Upper Gault)	*dispar* (Pleurohoplitan)	*dispar -perinflatum*			
		substuderi	XIII		
	inflatum (Hysteroceratan)	*aequatorialis*	XII		
		auritus	XI		
		varicosus	X		
		orbignyi	IX		
MIDDLE ALBIAN (= Lower Gault)	*lautus* (Euhoplitan)	*cristatus*	VIII		
		daviesi	VII		
		lautus-nitidus	VI V		
		subdelaruei	IV		
	dentatus (Hoplitan)	*niobe*	III		
		intermedius	II I c		
		dentatus	I b		
		benettianus	[Wilts.]		
		inaequinodum	[Wilts.]		
		mammillatum	I a		
LOWER ALBIAN (= Folkestone Sands)	*tardefurcata* (Leymeriellan)	*regularis*			
		acuticostata			
		schrammeni	Beds. Kent and Sussex		
	nodosocostatum (Acanthoplitan)	*jacobi*			
		nolam			

Genera (reading across the Hoplitidae and Dipoloceratidae columns): *Protohoplites*, *Pleurohoplites*, *Discohoplites*, *Epihoplites*, *Callihoplites*, *Hysteroceras*, *Mortoniceras*, *Elobiceras*, *Prohysteroceras*, *Neoharpoceras*, *Dimorphoplites*, *Anahoplites*, *Euhoplites*, *Hoplites* (s.s.), *Hystatoceras*, *Dipoloceras*, *Androiavites*, *Manuaniceras*, *Brancoceras*, *Mojsisovicsia*, *Oxytropidoceras*

The lowest horizon of the Folkestone Gault is the mammilatum zone containing the earliest members of the **Hoplitan Fauna.** The index-ammonite is *Douvilleiceras mammillatum* (Schlotheim), an inflated shell with rounded whorls and prominent multituberculate ribs. According to Spath, this ammonite shows affinity with the desmoceratid stock that pro-duced *Protohoplites* (the earliest genus of true Gault hoplitids), which also occurs in the mammillatum zone of Folkestone. *Protohoplites* includes strongly ribbed ammonites in which the peripheral groove typical of hoplitids makes its appearance, the genus being morphologically inter-mediate between *Sonneratia* (with no peripheral interruption of ribbing) and *Hoplites* (in which the ventral groove is well marked). *Douvilleiceras mammillatum* (Schlot.) also occurs in Bedfordshire and Norfolk, and in the Carstone of the Isle of Wight, while another species, *D. inaequinodum* (Quenstedt), known only in Wiltshire, may indicate a higher horizon.

In higher zones, species of the restricted genus *Hoplites* (the group of '*Hoplites interruptus*') become abundant. These more or less evolute shells are highly ornamented and possess a distinct groove on the venter. They are characteristic of the lower beds at Folkestone, i.e. the deposits that con-tain late Hoplitan and early Anahoplitan assemblages.

The hoplitid stock gives rise to two lineages that persist nearly to the top of the Folkestone Gault. One of these, *Anahoplites*, comprises the involute discoid shells, with flattened venter and feeble flexiradiate ornament, that were for long grouped together as '*Ammonites splendens*'. *Anahoplites* leads, in the Lower Gault, to *Dimorphoplites* by increase in the strength of the ornament, and independently in the Upper Gault to *Epihoplites* with similarly strong ribs which, however, meet the periphery almost at right angles and develop rounded ventral tubercles. *Callihoplites*, the group of '*Ammonites auritus*', and *A. catillus* J. Sow., is another offshoot of *Anaho-plites*, tending to smoothness in the outer whorls and to rounding of the periphery. In the highest Albian zones *Callihoplites* gives rise to *Pleuroho-plites*, which, in the raised median line on the periphery, foreshadows the keeled genus *Schloenbachia* of the Cenomanian stage.

A development of *Hoplites* s.s. is *Euhoplites*, which includes the forms known to older geologists as '*Ammonites lautus*' and '*A. tuberculatus*'. This genus, with typical hoplitid ornament and grooved periphery, is probably the forerunner of *Discohoplites* (distinguished by its falcoid radial line) and its Cenomanian ally, *Hyphoplites*, whose whorls become more angular.

Species belonging to the two hoplitid lineages comprise nearly half the total of ammonite species known from the English Gault. Some hoplitid ammonites are shown in Plate XVI.

Throughout the Gault succession there are numerous broken cephalopod shells which show irregular coiling, and which are sometimes grouped as 'heteromorphs'. They form nearly a quarter of the species of Gault am-monoids and all the genera are believed to be derived from the Lytoceratidae and its offshoot, the Macroscaphitidae. The rare *Scaphites circularis* from the varicosum subzone is essentially a *Lytoceras* in most of its features, and, with three other species from the Upper Gault, it leads directly to the more familiar Cenomanian forms of *Scaphites*. The helicoid genera *Mariella* and *Ostlingoceras* from the Upper Gault connect directly with the larger Cenomanian *Turrilites*, and are probably derived (through the more loosely coiled *Pseudhelicoceras* of the Lower Gault) from a macroscaphitid stock. Another group, represented by the genera *Anisoceras*, *Prohelicoceras*, and *Protanisoceras*, has tuberculate ornament and very irregular coiling. Species are common near the base of the Gault at Folkestone, but there is an almost complete absence of these tuberculate forms in higher beds until an abundance of *Anisoceras* occurs in and above the varicosum subzone. A similar habit is seen in *Hamites* (Pl. XVI) which is ornamented by simple ribs. This genus is known almost throughout the Gault, and it is connected through *Lechites* with the straight baculitids of the Cenomanian stage. Unfortunately there are no known passage forms from Lower Albian horizons to connect these uncoiled heteromorphs with their presumed macroscaphitid ancestors.

Of the keeled ammonites comprising the Dipoloceratidae, the most primitive is probably *Brancoceras*, a capricorn form with impersistent keel, which is rare in England. *Dipoloceras*, which strong ornament and high keel (Pl. XVI), and its offshoot *Mojsisovicsia*, are characteristic of the Lower Gault, as also is the more compressed *Oxytropidoceras* with sigmoid ribbing, though this genus is recorded from Lower Albian horizons in south France. The Upper Gault descendants of *Dipoloceras* are marked by peculiarities of ornament and by reduction in height of the keel. Thus *Hysteroceras* (the *varicosum* group) comprises small compressed ammonites with strong simple ribbing and low keel (Pl. XVI). In *Prohysteroceras* the ornament tends to weaken at the sides and there is an increase in whorl-height and involution, producing flat compressed shells which retain a prominent keel. *Elobiceras* includes compressed discoid shells with elevated or acute periphery and spirally notched ribbing. The later genus *Mortoniceras* (the *rostratum* group) shows increase of tuberculation with spiral striation on the tubercles and broad obtuse ribs. *Neokentroceras* is a late development of quadrituberculate *Mortoniceras*, distinguished by exaggerated tuberculation and disappearance of ribbing. *Neoharpoceras*, contemporary with these, is distinguished by its fine and close ribbing, absence of tuberculation or spiral ornament, distinctive peripheral aspect, and complex suture line.

This brief review of the chief ammonite-genera in the profuse assemblages of the Gault affords a basis for summarizing the faunas themselves.

The earliest assemblage grouped in the **Hoplitan Fauna,** as already noted, contains species of *Douvilleiceras*, *Cleoniceras* and *Protohoplites*, as well as the uncoiled lytoceratid *Pictetia* and *Beudanticeras*, a smooth, involute desmoceratid. This faunule is succeeded in the Folkestone Gault by the *dentatus* assemblage—various species of the true *Hoplites* associated with early forms of *Anahoplites* and uncoiled ammonoids ascribed to *Hamites*.

The genus *Hoplites* persists into the lowest zones that contain the **Anahoplitan Fauna,** but is later replaced by *Euhoplites*. The persistent *Anahoplites* is conspicuous and gives rise to *Dimorphoplites*. Keeled ammonites appear, first *Mojsisovicsia* and then *Dipoloceras*, the latter persisting to the top of the Lower Gault. Uncoiled forms referred to *Hamites* and the helicoid *Turrilitoides* also occur. Of special interest is the presence, in the alphalautus zone, of *Engonoceras iris* Spath, a smooth, involute ammonite with septal sutures of ceratitic pattern. Though frequent in America, these 'pseudoceratites' are rare in Europe, and this species is so far unique in this country.

The **Mortoniceratan Fauna** of the Upper Gault is distinguished by the development of specialized dipoloceratids, the genera *Hysteroceras Mortoniceras, Neoharpoceras, Elobiceras* and *Prohysteroceras* (briefly described above) being characteristic. The hoplitids are represented especially by species of *Callihoplites* and *Epihoplites*, while uncoiled forms include members of the genera *Hamites, Pseudhelicoceras, Ptychoceras*, and *Anisoceras*. It may be noted that *Mortoniceras rostratum* (J. Sow.) which has often been quoted as the zone-fossil of the whole Upper Gault is restricted to the aequatorialis zone.

Certain other fossils occurring in the Gault are important from the stratigraphical standpoint. Among these are the lamellibranchs *Inoceramus anglicus* Woods and *I. sulcatus* Parkinson. The former shell is only known from the Upper Gault, while *I. sulcatus* (Fig. 74) has a more restricted range, being confined to the cristatus and orbignyi zones of Spath's classification. The terebratellid *Kingena lima* (Defr.) (Fig. 67) is also met with in the Upper Gault, though it ranges into higher strata. The smooth *Nucula gaultina* Gard. is typical of Lower Gault, but the radially ribbed *N. pectinata* J. Sow. has a longer range. The little belemnoid *Neohibolites listeri* (Mantell), generally quoted under the more familiar name *Belemnites minimus* Lister, has also a long range in the Gault. The 'Crab-bed' in the niobe zone of the Lower Gault contains an abundance of *Palaeocorystes stokesi* Mantell.

The highest Gault of Folkestone contains early members of the **Pleurohoplitan Fauna,** among which the hoplitid genera *Pleurohoplites* and *Discohoplites* are dominant, while the dipoloceratid genus *Neokentroceras* occurs to the exclusion of *Mortoniceras* and its congeners. Later members of this fauna, unknown at Folkestone, occur in the famous Cambridge Greensand of East Anglia. The presence in this deposit of certain fossils typical of the Mediterranean region is especially interesting. They include the round-whorled lytoceratid *Gaudryceras* and the rudistid lamellibranch *Durania mortoni* (Mantell), formerly included in the genus *Radiolites*. Besides its indigenous fossils, which need critical revision, the Cambridge

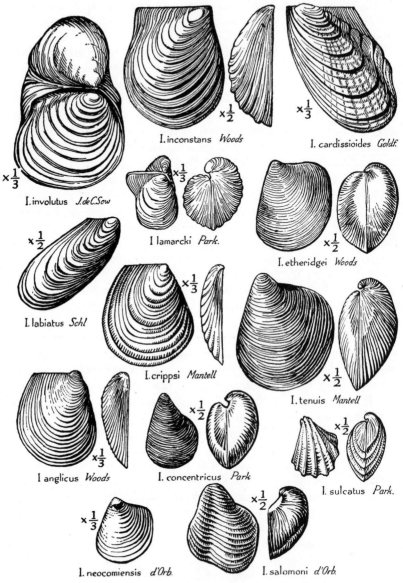

$\times\frac{1}{3}$

I. inconstans *Woods*

$\times\frac{1}{2}$

$\times\frac{1}{3}$

I. cardissioides *Goldf.*

$\times\frac{1}{3}$

I. involutus *J. de C. Sow*

$\times\frac{1}{3}$

I lamarcki *Park.*

$\times\frac{1}{2}$

I. etheridgei *Woods*

$\times\frac{1}{2}$

I. labiatus *Schl*

$\times\frac{1}{3}$

I. crippsi *Mantell*

$\times\frac{1}{2}$

I. tenuis *Mantell*

$\times\frac{1}{3}$

I anglicus *Woods*

$\times\frac{1}{2}$

I. concentricus *Park*

$\times\frac{1}{2}$

I. sulcatus *Park.*

$\times\frac{1}{3}$

I. neocomiensis *d'Orb.*

$\times\frac{1}{2}$

I. salomoni *d'Orb.*

FIG. 74. CRETACEOUS SPECIES OF *INOCERAMUS* (*after* H. Woods)

Distribution and Relationship of Cretaceous Inocerami

(Abridged from Woods)

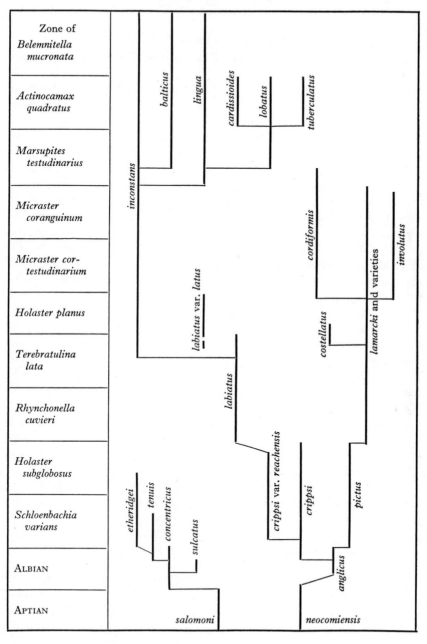

Greensand contains numerous derived fossils, including some 200 species of Invertebrata and an interesting series of vertebrate remains. The latter consist of bones and teeth of reptiles representing the orders Ornithosauria, Dinosauria, Ichthyopterygia, Crocodilia and Chelonia, and of a few birds.

UPPER CRETACEOUS FAUNAS

The Upper Cretaceous strata of north-west Europe are composed almost entirely of the fine-grained, white limestones known as the Chalk, and this deposit underlies a large area in eastern and southern England. Many diverse views have been expressed regarding its origin. The fine-grained, powdery nature of the Chalk formerly led to the conclusion that it was formed at great depths. It was even compared with Globigerina ooze (now forming at depths between 1,000 and 3,000 fathoms), with which it seemed to have certain characters in common, though Foraminifera are, as a rule, conspicuously rare. The discovery of *Echinothuria* (a flexible sea-urchin) in the Chalk of Gravesend seemed to support this comparison, because similar forms now exist in deep waters of the Atlantic Ocean. But such fossils are so rare in the Chalk that the Gravesend specimens are still unique. That occurrence is heavily outweighed in significance by the character of the Upper Cretaceous fauna as a whole, which is not of abyssal depths. Indeed, from the general aspect of the fauna, the Chalk probably belongs to what we have called the continental deep-sea area, and was most likely formed at a depth of not more than 200 or 300 fathoms.

The absence of terrigenous detritus, which is so marked a character of the Chalk, is probably connected with peneplanation of the land and the consequent low gradient of the rivers in Cretaceous time. E. B. Bailey and I. S. Double have independently concluded, from the presence of well-rounded detrital minerals in the Chalk, that such material was wind-borne into the Cretaceous seas, while the first-named author has also inferred the probability of arid conditions in north-west Europe in late Cretaceous time. It may also be mentioned that transport by coast ice was held by Stebbing (in 1897) to explain the occurrence of large boulders of quartzite and other rocks in the Middle Chalk of Betchworth, Surrey.

The Chalk is divided, mainly on lithological grounds, into the Lower, Middle, and Upper Chalk, a classification which seems adequate for general mapping. But, since the formation attains a considerable thickness (1,200 feet), a more detailed subdivision is desirable for many purposes; in boring operations, for example, precision in determining horizon is a matter of much importance. It has been possible to utilize faunal differences at successive levels to establish a series of zonal divisions in the Chalk.

It may be noted that the conditions under which the Chalk was formed were apparently uniform over wide areas; moreover, deposition appears to have been almost continuous, no appreciable gaps comparable with the frequent non-sequences in Jurassic strata having been detected, though the possibility of their occurrence cannot be denied. Consequently the succession of beds, though subject to local variations in lithology and other characters, is fairly regular over wide areas, and the fossils reveal a true and almost unbroken succession of faunas. Indeed, no other formation, except perhaps the graptolitic facies of the Ordovician and Silurian, provides a more complete record of continuous evolution in slowly changing organisms. Thus A. W. Rowe has shown that gradual changes in the test of the sea-urchin *Micraster* can be correlated with successive horizons in the Chalk. In describing the evolution of the lamellibranch *Inoceramus*, H. Woods shows that many species of this genus are restricted to certain horizons. W. D. Lang has studied the coral *Parasmilia*, and G. E. Dibley the palatal teeth of the fish *Ptychodus*, from the zonal aspect. Isolated joints of starfishes and individual plates of crinoids can also be used to determine some horizons.

The zones (tabulated below) are characterized by assemblages of fossils, one species being taken as an index denoting the whole fauna of each particular zone. As a general rule, zones of the Chalk are thicker than those of the Jurassic, and in some cases subzones have been established when such can be easily recognized in the field as denoting constant horizons over considerable stretches of country.

Table of Upper Cretaceous Zones

	Zones	Subzones
Upper Chalk	Ostrea lunata Belemnitella mucronata Actinocamax quadratus Marsupites testudinarius Micraster coranguinum Micraster cortestudinarium Holaster planus	 Marsupites Uintacrinus Hyphantoceras reussianum at base of zone
Middle Chalk	Terebratulina lata Rhynchonella cuvieri	
Lower Chalk	Holaster subglobosus Schloenbachia varians	Actinocamax plenus at top of zone

The several faunas of the Chalk zones show that the depth of the Upper Cretaceous sea was subject to certain variations, and, moreover, the absence of zones and subzones in some districts demonstrates that this apparently homogeneous deposit was not formed continuously. But the widespread transgression already noted continued without conspicuous interruption through most of the period marked by deposition of the Chalk. The depth increased, except for the temporary shallowing marked by the Chalk Rock, until the period represented by the zone of *Micraster coranguinum*. In higher zones the proportional elevation of echinoid shells decreases, and this is taken as evidence of a shallowing of the water. Also the increased importance of gastropods in the zone of *Belemnitella mucronata* supports the evidence afforded by the echinoids. The history of the Cretaceous period, however, is incomplete in this country, since the highest Chalk preserved is succeeded by littoral Eocene deposits which transgress over several Cretaceous zones. In some localities on the Continent of Europe there is a gradual transition in lithological character between the Cretaceous and Eocene deposits.

THE LOWER CHALK

The Lower Chalk, corresponding to the Cenomanian stage of continental authors, comprises two zones, the index-fossils being an ammonite, *Schloenbachia varians* for the lower, and an echinoid, *Holaster subglobosus*, for the higher zone. Recently L. F. Spath has stated that the Lower Chalk can be divided into six horizons, based on the occurrence of ammonites. The indexes suggested, however, are unfamiliar and uncommon species, and further field-work is necessary before the subdivisions can be definitely adopted. Moreover, owing to the relative scarcity of ammonites in the English Chalk (except in the lower part), a series of zones based on the distribution of these shells would be of doubtful utility in this country; its chief merit would lie in enabling a general correlation to be established with Cretaceous deposits of distant lands. Here, the scheme in general use in England will be considered.

The **Zone of *Schloenbachia varians*** is mainly composed of a grey marly chalk known as the Chalk Marl. The basal beds are somewhat variable in lithological character. In southern England they consist of glauconitic sands and marls, including the Chloritic Marl, which is represented in Devon by a coarse calcareous sandstone, and in Yorkshire, Lincolnshire, and north-west Norfolk by a hard pink limestone. Notwithstanding the variations in lithology with which certain faunal differences are connected, the general assemblage of fossils in the varians-zone is distinctive in the following features:

1. The occurrence of the ammonite-genus *Schloenbachia*. This is recognized by its slightly flexed ribs, which usually break up into tubercles, and by its flat and keeled periphery. The index-fossil *S. varians* (J. Sow.) is the most familiar species; some of its varieties, such as *S. subtuberculata* (Sharpe) (Pl. XVII) have lately been elevated to specific rank.

2. The genus *Mantelliceras* is also typical of this zone. *M. mantelli* (J. Sow.) (Pl. XVII) is a somewhat inflated, costate form with tuberculate peripheral margins. The latter feature distinguishes that ammonite at once from *Calycoceras naviculare* (Sharpe) (Pl. XVII), which is a costate form

without tubercles. *Hyphoplites falcatus* (Mantell) has already been noted as a late development of an Albian hoplitid stock.

3. Various heteromorphic ammonoids occur, especially species of *Scaphites* and *Turrilites*, while the straight *Cyrtochilus baculoides* (Mantell) is also distinctive. Until these forms have been critically revised, they can only be used for broad stratigraphical divisions.

4. The ribbed nautiloid *Cymatoceras deslongchampsianus* (d'Orb) is most typical of, though it is not restricted to, the varians-zone.

5. The lamellibranch *Inoceramus crippsi* Mantell (Fig. 74) is characteristic of this and the succeeding zone.

6. Other characteristic lamellibranchs include *Pecten* (*Aequipecten*) *asper* Lam. (Fig. 76), which occurs chiefly in sandy beds, *Lima* (*Plagiostoma*) *globosa* J. Sow., *Plicatula inflata* J. Sow., *Pecten* (*Syncyclonema*) *orbicularis* J. Sow., *Neithea quinquecostatus* (J. Sow.) (Fig. 76), and the ribbed 'mussel' *Septifer lineatus* (J. Sow.).

7. Among brachiopods, '*Rhynchonella*' *grasiana* d'Orb., '*R.*' *dimidiata* (J. Sow.), '*Terebratula*' *ovata* J. Sow., '*T.*' *biplicata* J. Sow. (Fig. 75), and *Terebrirostra lyra* (J. Sow.) (Fig. 67) are typical.

8. The sea-urchins *Salenia petalifera* Desm. (Pl. XVIII). *Discoidea subucula* Klein, *Catopygus columbaris* Lam., and *Pyrina laevis* Ag., frequently occur, especially in the sandy beds.

9. The sponge *Stauronema carteri* Sollas is typical of the Chloritic Marl in some localities in the southern counties: species of *Doryderma*, *Siphonia*, and *Hallirhoa* are common in the basal sands in Wiltshire.

The **Zone of Holaster subglobosus.** In the southern counties the Grey Chalk of the varians zone is succeeded by massive beds of white chalk which form the zone of *H. subglobosus*. Between Yorkshire and the Thames Valley the base of the zone is marked by a bed of hard gritty chalk known as the Totternhoe Stone, from its development near the village of Totternhoe in Bedfordshire; elsewhere the lower limit is rather indefinite. At the top of the zone is a series of greenish-grey marls, the Belemnite Marls, often regarded as a distinct sub-zone. The faunal characters of the *subglobosus* zone may be summarized as follows:

1. The zone is marked especially by the occurrence of *Holaster subglobosus* Leske (Pl. XVIII), which, however, is generally more commonly found in the upper part of the zone.

2. Other distinctive sea-urchins include *Holaster trecensis* Leym., which is especially characteristic of upper beds; and *Offaster sphaericus* Schlüter, which is used as the zonal-index in Lincolnshire, where *H. subglobosus* ranges through the Lower Chalk. *Discoidea cylindrica* Lam. (Pl. XVIII) is another well-known form.

3. *Inoceramus crippsi* Mantell and *I. pictus* J. de C. Sow. are distinctive among lamellibranchs which also include *Pecten* (*Aequipecten*) *beaveri* J. Sow., and a small grypheate form of *Ostrea vesicularis* Lam.

4. The brachiopods '*Terebratula*' *biplicata* J. Sow., '*T.*' *semiglobosa* J. Sow. (Fig. 75), and '*Rhynchonella*' *mantelliana* (J. de C. Sow.) range up from the preceding zone.

5. Acanthoceratan ammonites are frequently found. The typical form is *Acanthoceras rhotomagense* (Defr.); many shells formerly identified as such are now referred to other species, e.g. *A. vectense* Spath (Pl. XVII). They are multituberculate forms with a median row of tubercles on the periphery.

6. The Belemnite Marls are especially distinguished by the occurrence of the belemnoid *Actinocamax plenus* Blainv. and *Inoceramus crippsi* var. *reachensis* Etheridge.

THE MIDDLE CHALK

Most British geologists consider the Middle Chalk to comprise only the two zones of *Rhynchonella cuvieri* and *Terebratulina lata*; but the corresponding Turonian stage of continental authors includes the overlying zone of *Holaster planus*.

The **Zone of *Rhynchonella cuvieri*.**—The base of this zone is formed of a hard nodular chalk (the Melbourn Rock) which contrasts strongly with the marl on which it rests. The higher beds contain fewer nodules and are softer and more massive. The index-fossil *Rhynchonella cuvieri* d'Orb. (Fig. 75) is a fairly stout shell with fairly coarse ribs; the foramen is slightly prolonged, forming a short tube. It is interesting to note that the crura are short, broad, and laminar, forming a contrast with the long, thin, curved, and grooved crura of certain Lower Cretaceous rhynchonellids. The occurrence of *R. cuvieri* is somewhat sporadic but *Inoceramus labiatus* (Schloth.) is found more constantly. Indeed, this lamellibranch has been used by some authors (Barrois and others) as the zonal index. The echinoids *Conulus subrotundus* Mart. and *Discoidea dixoni* Forbes are also typical of this horizon but range into the succeeding zone. *Conulus castanea* (Brongn.) persists from the Lower Chalk. *Mammites nodosoides* Schlüter and other ammonites are recorded from Dorset.

The **Zone of *Terebratulina lata*** is formed of pure white chalk which sometimes contains small black grey-rinded flints. Fossils are not numerous; besides the zonal index, small forms of *Inoceramus lamarcki* Park. are associated with the echinoids of the underlying beds, and also *Hemiaster minimus* Ag. and *Micraster corbovis* Forbes. Ammonites sometimes occur, *Prionotropis*, *Lewesiceras* (Pl. XVII), and *Austiniceras* being the most characteristic genera.

THE UPPER CHALK

The table of zones (p. 503) shows that the Upper Chalk in England contains seven recognizable subdivisions. Comparison with the continental Senonian stage shows that the English succession is not complete, the

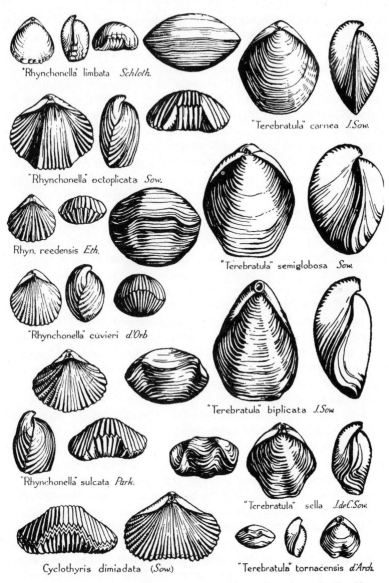

'Rhynchonella' limbata *Schloth.*

"Rhynchonella" octoplicata *Sow.*

Rhyn. reedensis *Eth.*

'Rhynchonella' cuvieri *d'Orb*

'Rhynchonella' sulcata *Park.*

Cyclothyris dimiadata (*Sow.*)

"Terebratula" carnea *J.Sow.*

"Terebratula" semiglobosa *Sow.*

"Terebratula" biplicata *J.Sow*

"Terebratula" sella *J.deC.Sow.*

"Terebratula" tornacensis *d'Arch.*

FIG. 75. SOME CRETACEOUS BRACHIOPODS (*drawn from figures by Davidson, all slightly reduced*)

uppermost portion having been removed by denudation before the deposition of the overlying Neozoic rocks, which transgress the Chalk zones in different localities. Before describing the faunal assemblages of the Upper Chalk, a note may appropriately be given concerning the general method of zoning.

The most characteristic, and often the most common, fossil in the three lower zones of the Upper Chalk is the sea-urchin *Micraster*. A. W. Rowe has shown that gradual progressive changes may be traced in this echinoid from its occurrence in the *Holaster planus* zone upwards. Moreover, these changes may be relied upon to determine zonal position, or even relative horizon within a zone. The chief developmental features are seen in the ambulacra, the mouth-opening and the area immediately behind it, as well as in the general shape of the test. For field purposes the characters of the paired ambulacra provide the most convenient criteria (see Fig. 13, p. 85).

Each of the paired ambulacra is composed of two rows of plates pierced by pores, the latter being situated near the margin of the ambulacrum. Between the two rows of pores is the 'interporiferous area', to which particular attention is now directed. Micrasters from the *Holaster planus* zone (and also from the *Terebratulina lata* zone of the Middle Chalk) do not show any trace of the boundaries of the constituent plates in the interporiferous areas; in other words, these echinoids have 'smooth areas'. In other forms from the planus zone, especially towards the top of the zone, the outlines of the plates are faintly seen giving the appearance known as the 'sutured area'. Higher still, in the *Micraster cortestudinarium* zone, the plates become swollen, their junction is more plainly visible, and a median trough with sloping sides becomes evident; this is the 'inflated' type of area. A further advance is the 'subdivided' area, in which the slope of the plates towards the middle of the ambulacrum gives the appearance of an almost straight groove. The inflated and subdivided types characterize the *M. cortestudinarium* zone and the lower third of the *M. coranguinum* zone. Above this horizon the areas are 'divided'; that is, the median line of the ambulacrum becomes a deep, steep-sided groove between the plates. Further advances occur in Micrasters from zones above the *M. coranguinum* zone, but as these later echinoids are rare, other fossils are employed as zonal guides.

The mouth-opening is placed towards the front on the under surface of the test, and its hind border forms a projecting lip called the labrum. In the lower zonal forms the labrum is very small and the mouth-aperture lies open. At successively higher horizons the labrum tends to project more and more towards the front, until, in forms from the upper part of the *M. coranguinum* zone it completely arches over the aperture. The labrum also changes in shape from broadly triangular in the *H. planus* zone to narrowly oblong in the higher zones; furthermore, it becomes more highly ornamented at successively higher horizons. Compared with low zonal forms the position of the mouth itself in the high-zonal Micrasters is nearer to the anterior notch of the test. Other changes include an increase in granulation of the periplastronal area and the unpaired ambulacrum, a gradual forward movement of the apical system, and a deepening of the ambital notch in high-zonal forms. The more evident progressive changes are indicated diagrammatically in Fig. 13.

Other echinoid genera have not yet been studied so completely with regard to the development of separate features, but the general shape of the test affords some clue to horizon. The following summary of the shape variations of *Echinocorys scutatus* Leske has been made from various scattered observations by A. W. Rowe and other workers on the English Chalk.

Zone	*Shape of* E. scutatus *Leske*
Ostrea lunata . .	. A large depressed form.
Belemnitella mucronata	. A large dome-shaped variety and a small pyramidal form.
Actinocamax quadratus	. A gibbous variety.
Marsupites . .	. Large dome-shaped and pyramidal forms.
Micraster coranguinum	. Large ovate and tall dome-shaped forms.
Micraster cortestudinarium } *Holaster planus* . }	Small gibbous variety.

The echinoid *Conulus* also exhibits successive shape-variations, and H. L. Hawkins regards this genus as a development of *Pyrina*, of which *Echinoneus* is the living homoeomorphous derivative. The latter lives in sheltered places near low-tide mark and is essentially a shallow-water form. *Pyrina* is considered to have had the same general mode of life, and its highest occurrence in this country is in the Chloritic Marl, the last well-defined littoral deposit of the English Cretaceous. In France, however, the genus persists into the Senonian (Upper Chalk), but only where the deposit is full of detrital matter. Thus *Pyrina* is confined to littoral tracts; but *Conulus* shows divergence both in habitat and in general shape, as echinoids show a tendency to become vertically elongate in deep water. Of the species of *Conulus*—

Conulus rhotomagense (Albian) resembles *Pyrina* in its low, elongate test, and probably lived under similar conditions.

Conulus castanea Brongn. (Lower Chalk and Lower Middle Chalk) is still elongate but almost globular.

Conulus subrotundus Mantell (Middle Chalk) is low and rounded in the *R. cuvieri* zone, but taller in the *T. lata* zone.

Conulus albogalerus Leske (Upper Chalk) is relatively low, though conical, in the lower zones, but exceedingly high at the top of the *M. coranguinum* zone.

'The two horizons at which species of *Conulus* attain their greatest height are those that seem to mark the deepest conditions that obtained during the dominance of the Chalk Sea over Britain; while the depressed forms from the lower parts of the Upper Chalk can be correlated with the Chalk Rock uplift' (Hawkins).

The **Zone of** *Holaster planus*. At the base of this zone there occurs a horizon which, by reason of its peculiar fauna, is distinguished as the sub-zone of *Hyphantoceras reussianum*. The fauna has a wide distribution in southern and central England, and has been traced at least as far north as Norfolk. In the south midland counties the beds show a distinctive type of lithology (the Chalk Rock)—hard, cream-coloured limestone, with grains of glauconite and green-coated nodules of foraminiferal limestone; this lithological character, however, is not so widespread as the peculiar fauna. The main features of the fauna are:

1. The presence of numerous cephalopods, of the genera *Nautilus*, '*Ptychoceras*', *Hyphantoceras*, *Cyrtochilus*, *Prionocyclus*, *Lewesiceras*, *Scaphites*, &c. '*Ptychoceras smithi*' Woods, *Hyphantoceras reussianum* (d'Orb.) (Pl. XVII), *Cyrtochilus bohemicus* (Fritsch.), *Scaphites geinitzi* (d'Orb.) (Pl. XVII), and *Prionocyclus neptunei* (Geinitz), are restricted to this horizon; *Lewesiceras cricki* Spath (Pl. XVII) is also typical.

2. The abundance of gastropods, among which *Trochus schlüteri* Woods, *T. beroscirensis* Woods, *Turbo geinitzi* Woods, and *Avellana* cf. *humboldti* Müller, are peculiar to the horizon. Species of *Emarginula*, *Naticina*, *Solariella*, *Pleurotomaria*, and *Aporrhais* also occur, but are represented at other horizons of the Chalk.

3. Common species of lamellibranchs include *Inoceramus lamarcki* Park, *Lima* (*Plagiostoma*) *hoperi* (Mant.), *Spondylus spinosus* (J. Sow.), *Plicatula barroisi* Peron, occurring in beds above and below, while the following are peculiar to this subzone: *Arca* (*Barbatia*) *geinitzi* Reuss, *Inoceramus costellatus* Woods, *Cardium turonense* Woods, *Cardita cancellata* Woods, *Trapezium rectangulare* Woods, *Corbis morisoni* Woods.

The molluscan fauna is similar to that of the same age in northern France, north-west Germany, Saxony, and Bohemia.

4. Sponges are particularly common; sixteen species are recorded, of which five belong to the genus *Ventriculites*.

5. Other fossils include simple corals (*Parasmilia*), brachiopods (both rhynchonellids and terebratulids), the annelid *Serpula*, cirripedes, and fishes (teeth).

From a study of the dominant mollusca, Woods concludes that the Chalk Rock was laid down in shallow water; the comparative richness of the fauna and the proportion of new forms indicate considerable changes of depth; the presence of glauconite supports the conclusion regarding shallow-water conditions.

Above the Chalk Rock the *H. planus* zone consists of soft white chalk with occasional nodular beds of chalk and seams of marl. The presence of *Holaster planus* (Mant.) and of *Micraster* with sutured and feebly inflated areas, is generally sufficient for determination of the zone. A gibbous form of *Echinocorys scutatus* Leske is also typical, and so is *Inoceramus labiatus* (Schlot.) var. *latus*, a wide variety of the species.

The **Zone of *Micraster cortestudinarium*.** The Chalk of this zone is generally soft, white, and blocky; veins of tabular flint and regular courses of flint-nodules often occur. The presence of *Micraster* with inflated and subdivided areas generally suffices for zonal diagnosis. A small gibbous variety of *Echinocorys* is also characteristic, while the large *Holaster placenta* Ag. is typical at the base of the zone. A frequent feature is the profusion of polyzoa and small annelids adherent to the molluscan shells and sea-urchins. The large *Inoceramus involutus* J. de C. Sow., distinguished by its convex left valve, operculiform right valve and spirally curved umbo (Fig. 74), is characteristic of this and the lower part of the overlying zone. *Rhynchonella reedensis* Etheridge (Fig. 75), is a typical brachiopod.

The **Zone of *Micraster coranguinum*.** In lithology this zone resembles the *M. cortestudinarium* zone, but the faunal assemblage presents marked differences. The typical *Micraster* has sharply divided areas. A large ovate form of *Echinocorys scutatus* Leske is characteristic, and *Conulus albogalerus* Leske exhibits a very high conical shape. *Epiaster gibbus* (Lam.) and the belemnoid *Actinocamax verus* Miller are also useful in identifying the horizon. *Inoceramus involutus* J. de C. Sow. persists in the lower part of the zone, while *Inoceramus undulatoplicatus* (an offshoot of the long-ranged *I. inconstans*) is distinctive in possessing divergent radial folds.

The ***Marsupites* Zone** consists, in general, of soft powdery chalk with very few flints. It is distinguished especially by the occurrence of the free-swimming crinoids *Uintacrinus* and *Marsupites*, the former being common in the lower half of the zone, the latter plentiful in the upper part. Both crinoids are of considerable size, but whereas *Uintacrinus* attains greatness by increase in the number of small plates, *Marsupites* retains the primitive number and increases the size of individual plates (Fig. 11). It is hardly necessary to point out that complete crowns are only exceptionally found, the plates usually being scattered. Another crinoid frequently found here is *Bourgueticrinus*, whose barrel-shaped columnals, with elliptical cross-section and twisted axis, are typical even in the absence of the nipple-shaped calyx. The echinoid *Echinocorys scutatus* Leske is represented by large dome-shaped and pyramidal forms. Several species of *Inoceramus* occur, but none are restricted to the zone, *I. inconstans* Woods and its off-shoots *I. balticus* Bohm, *I. lingua* Goldf., and *I. lobatus* Goldf., ranging to higher horizons. The belemnite *Actinocamax verus* Miller persists in the lower part of the zone, but is replaced later by *A. mercyi*, which is allied to *A. granulatus* (Blainv.) of the succeeding zone. A phosphatic chalk of this zone in Buckinghamshire and Berkshire shows certain faunal peculiarities accompanying the unusual lithological characters.

The Chalk of the **Zone of *Actinocamax quadratus*** is usually soft and friable and contains few flints. In the lower part of the zone *A. granulatus*

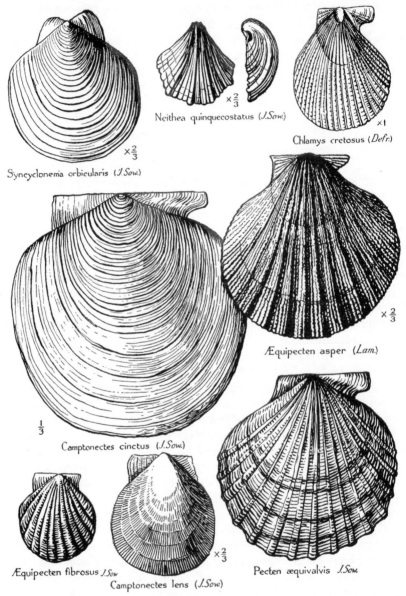

Neithea quinquecostatus (*J. Sow.*) ×⅔

Chlamys cretosus (*Defr.*) ×1

Syncyclonema orbicularis (*J. Sow.*) ×⅔

Æquipecten asper (*Lam.*) ×⅔

Camptonectes cinctus (*J. Sow.*) ⅓

Æquipecten fibrosus *J. Sow*

Camptonectes lens (*J. Sow.*) ×⅔

Pecten æquivalvis *J. Sow.*

FIG. 76. SOME MESOZOIC PECTINIDAE (*drawn from figures by Woods and others*)

(Blainv.), recognized by the finely granulated surface of the guard, is more common than *A. quadratus* Defr., but the latter species, with quadrate alveolar section, is dominant in the higher parts of the zone. In some districts neither species is common, and the faunal assemblage is then recognized by the abundance of the little echinoid *Offaster pilula* Lam., a tumid form with supra-marginal periproct. A gibbous variety of *Echinocorys scutatus* Leske is also characteristic. The typical species of *Inoceramus* are *I. cardissioides* Goldf. and *I. tuberculatus* Woods, which are closely related to *I. lobatus* Goldf. but develop radial folds. This zone in Yorkshire is rendered conspicuous by the abundance and variety of sponges, among which *Coeloptychium agaricoides* Goldf. and *Verruculina reussi* (M'Coy) may be mentioned. The upper beds in Yorkshire have also yielded *Hoploscaphites binodosus* (Römer) and other species of ammonoids.

The **Zone of *Belemnitella mucronata*** usually consists of a soft, white chalk in which the numerous flints often attain a large size, the peculiar concretions known as 'paramoudras' being a feature of the zone in Norfolk. The index-fossil, *Belemnitella mucronata* Schlot., has a parallel-sided guard terminating in a nipple-like point and bearing a ventral alveolar slit. The most notable shape-variations of *Echinocorys scutatus* Leske are large dome-shaped and small pyramidal forms. In the chalk contained in these large echinoids, internal moulds of small gastropods sometimes occur —an instance of 'protective preservation'. *Inoceramus inconstans* Woods, *I. balticus* Böhm., and *I. lingua* Goldf., as well as *Pecten* (*Chlamys*) *cretosus* Defr. (Fig. 76) persist from lower zones, while several brachiopod-species are prominent. Among these the well-known '*Terebratula*' *carnea* J. Sow., '*Rhynchonella*' *limbata* Schlot., '*R.*' *octoplicata* J. Sow. (Fig. 75), *Magas pumilus* J. Sow., and the rare *Trigonosemus elegans* König (Fig. 67), may be mentioned. The first-named species-group has recently undergone revision at the hands of M. R. Sahni, and several new genera and species have been instituted.

The **Zone of *Ostrea lunata*** is known only at one locality in England, namely, at Trimingham on the coast of Norfolk. In its general lithological characters, this Chalk is very like that of the underlying strata, but certain faunal distinctions justify its separation as a definite zone. The most abundant fossil is *Ostrea lunata* Nilssen, a small oyster with a frilled margin and a crescentic outline. The small bun-shaped *Conulus orbignyanus* Ag. and a large depressed form of *Echinocorys scutatus* Leske are distinctive echinoids. Several brachiopods persist from the underlying zone and are joined by two species of *Terebratulina* not known at lower horizons, namely, *T. gisei* Hag. and *T. gracilis* Schlot. While many lamellibranchs and other fossils range up from lower horizons, several of the abundant polyzoa are characteristic of higher zones unknown in England but preserved in the Danish and Belgian succession.

FAUNAL REGIONS

EUROPE. The British succession of Neocomian faunas is closely similar to a corresponding development in north Germany where the marine beds rest on freshwater deposits of Wealden type and thin out towards the west. The ammonites have been described by·Koenen (1902). The lowest ammonite faunas, including species of *Platylenticeras* and *Tolypeceras*, are contained in the Hils Conglomerate of Brunswick. Higher beds, containing an association of *Polyptychites* and *Dichotomites* belong to the polyptychus zone, and are followed by horizons with *Leopoldia* and *Rogersites* which represent the uppermost beds of the Valanginian stage. The Hauterivian sequence seems to be less complete. The Rossfeld and Grodischt Beds yield *Acanthodiscus* and *Lyticoceras*, representing early Lyticoceratan assemblages, but the Crioceratan, Simbirskitan and Hoplocrioceratan faunas are poorly developed. The Barremian substage with criocerates is also incomplete, for certain faunas known elsewhere are not recorded. Hauterivian and Barremian Beds, much like those of Hanover are also known in Heligoland where they rest directly on the Trias. Derived blocks in the Drift of Denmark probably indicate a former extension of Hauterivian horizons in a northerly direction.

In Russia, rocks of Neocomian age are present in three districts, (*a*) the neighbourhood of Moscow and Riasan, (*b*) around Simbirsk farther east, and (*c*) the Petchora area in the far north. The oldest deposits, known as the Riasan Beds, rest unconformably on the Craspedites Beds of the Upper Jurassic; they are glauconitic sandstones with phosphatic nodules. The Riasan Beds contain several species of *Subcraspedites* which resemble forms in the English Spilsby Sandstone. These are associated with the compressed oxynote *Pseudogarnieria*, the hoplitoid genus *Proleopoldia*, and various berriasellids including the characteristic genus *Riasanites*. These deposits are referred to the upper zone of the Infra-Valanginian stage, and are present in the Petchora as well as the Riasan district. The Valanginian stage seems to be well developed and contains various species of *Polyptychites*, associated with many species of the widespread lamellibranch *Buchia*, formerly recorded as *Aucella*. The lower part of the Hauterivian stage appears to be missing in Russia, but the upper part is indicated by an abundance of *Simbirskites* in the Simbirsk district. The Barremian stage seems to be absent.

Within the Arctic Circle, north of the European mainland, Neocomian rocks are reported from Novaja Zemlya, Spitzbergen, and east Greenland. In Novaja Zemlya the record of a species of *Subcraspedites* indicates the presence of an Infra-Valanginian horizon while higher beds, containing *Polyptychites* and *Buchia*, belong to the Valanginian stage; the Hauterivian and Barremian stages are not recorded. From Spitzbergen, Sokolev and Bodolevsky (1931) describe various species of *Polyptychites* which indicate the presence of mid-Valanginian zones; lower beds contain an abundance of *Buchia*, but have yielded no ammonites. According to Frebold (1935) the Hauterivian and Barremian stages are represented by deposits of continental type. In east Greenland, L. Koch (1935) has mentioned several localities which have yielded the Valanginian ammonite *Polyptychites* together with characteristic species of *Buchia*, but higher Neocomian horizons appear to be represented by barren sandstones. Marine deposition in these northern islands during Neocomian time seems to have been due to temporary transgressions of the sea over the land-margin. The Valanginian ammonites so far recorded are closely related to those of Britain, Germany, and central Russia, and doubtless they indicate open marine communication between those areas and the permanent Arctic Ocean.

Comparing these northern faunas with corresponding assemblages from southern Europe, it is evident that the former show a prevalence of trachyostracous ammonites like the polyptychitids and hoplitids, together with heteromorphic forms, but they lack the neocomitids, desmoceratids, lytoceratids, and phylloceratids which are dominant farther south, especially in the Mediterranean region. The name of the Neocomian stage is taken from the Latin name for Neuchâtel in Switzerland, and the sub-stage names Valanginian, Hauterivian, and Barremian are derived from localities in Switzerland and southern France. The typical Neocomian faunas have a wide distribution, for pyritized ammonites of the Valanginian Marls in Tunisia are identical with those of south-east France, and L. F. Spath (1930) records similar forms from southern Persia. Some of the typical genera extend northwards to Poland, Germany, and England where they mingle with northern forms. It is significant that all the sequences are incomplete, even in the Mediterranean region which is commonly but wrongly held to have been a region of continuous deposition.

The impoverished Aptian faunas in the transgressive deposits of England are much better represented in south France, where the sections at La Bedoule, east of Marseilles, and Gargas near Apt, Provence, are respectively typical of the lower and upper subdivisions of the stage. Not only are the thick-shelled Parahoplitidae, Cheloniceratidae, and Ancyloceratidae more numerous and varied here and in North Africa, but they are accompanied by species of the fundamental *Phylloceras*, *Lytoceras*, and Desmoceratidae, besides the widespread genera *Aconeceras* and *Sanmartinoceras* which are unknown or rare at British localities. But some of the finer subdivisions of the stage established in England and Germany have not been recognized in south France owing to condensation of the deposits. The former connexion between the two seas, however, is indicated by surviving strata in west Switzerland and the eastern part of the Paris basin. At the same time, the northern sea, in which the Neocomian Beds of Speeton were accumulated, persisted with fluctuating margins in Yorkshire, north-west Germany, and the Riasan district east of Moscow, and some authors believe that the Russian embayment also connected southward with the Tethys, possibly by way of the Caucasus whence Parahoplitan faunas have been recorded. The Palaeocretaceous deposits of southern Europe show considerable differences in facies, and one of the most remarkable is that known as the Rudist Limestone, which is present at various localities and horizons through Spain, south France, the Apertnines, and Carpathians, as well as North Africa, and which appears again in South Asia. In view of its distinctive character and significance this facies is best discussed separately in the sequel (pp. 541–7).

In parts of the Rhône basin, south-east France, the Aptian, and even lower Cretaceous strata are directly overlaid by Neozoic deposits (see F. Roman, 1936), but in other places, e.g. Escragnolles, Perte du Rhone, &c., the Aptian rocks are followed conformably by the Albian stage. The somewhat variable deposits are often glauconitic sands of slight thickness which indicates slow deposition, and at intervals ammonite beds contain assemblages that are characteristic of several separate horizons elsewhere in less condensed deposits. On the other hand the faunas of some horizons may be altogether lacking. The horizon of Clansayes, or zone of *Diadochoceras nodosocostatum* is taken as the lowest bed of the Albian stage by W. Kilian, L. F. Spath, and M. Breistoffer, but C. Jacob has described the ammonites of this zone from the Luitere Zug as Upper Aptian. In addition to the index-fossil, which is connected directly with the Aptian *Cheloniceras subnodosocostatum*, the fauna includes species of the lytoceratid genera *Jaubertella*, *Tetragonites*, and of the hoplitid genera *Acanthohoplites* and *Hypacanthoplites*. The overlying zone of *Leymeriella tardefurcata* contains *Phylloceras subalpinum*, *Ph. velledae*, various lytoceratid offshoots such as *Kossmatella* and *Tetragonites*, the desmoceratids *Beudanticeras*, *Desmoceras*, and *Puzosia* and thick-shelled derivatives like *Hypacanthoplites milletianus* and species of *Leymeriella*, *Brancoceras*, and *Lyelliceras*. This and the previous zone are grouped together as the Lower Albian. The index *Leymeriella* is widely distributed in Europe, being recorded from England, Denmark (in derived blocks), Germany, south France, Servia, and the Mangyshlak Peninsula; it is also reported from east Greenland and Zululand.

The middle Albian sequence of south France begins with the zone of *Douvilleiceras mammillatum* in which the massive tuberculate index-fossil is associated with the longer-ranged *Beudanticeras ligatum* and *Desmoceras latidorsatum*, along with early hoplitids like *Cleoniceras*, *Sonneratia*, and *Protohoplites*. The higher zones of the stage contain assemblages of the main ammonite-stocks similar to those described above in the English succession, when the appropriate horizons are compared. The hoplitid faunas of central Russia and the Mangyshlak Peninsula, for instance, are closely related to those of certain horizons in the Gault of Folkestone. The Mediterranean faunas, however, contain a greater proportion of the characteristic southern elements, *Phylloceras*, *Lytoceras*, desmoceratids, and lyelliceratids which are abundant as far north as the Carpathians and extend southwards into Algeria and Tunisia. Many sections in south Europe are so condensed that late Albian and early Cenomanian ammonites are intermingled; this circumstance gave rise to the old term Vraconnian which has caused much confusion in stratigraphical correlation.

Some Cenomanian ammonites are related to certain Albian genera just discussed. The commonest genus in the Lower Cenomanian rocks of Europe is *Schloenbachia* (Pl. XVII) comprising strongly keeled forms connected morphologically with the Hoplitidae through the late Albian *Pleurohoplites*, but perhaps derived independently from the Desmoceratidae. The group of *Sch. varians* to which the genus is now restricted, formerly provided the zonal index for the early Cenomanian deposits; it is recorded from the appropriate rocks throughout Europe, but outside this continent it is known only from the Mangyshlak Peninsula and central Persia. Hence the distribution of *Schloenbachia*, like that of the Albian Hoplitidae, indicates that the European area was not a centre for wide dispersal of Cretaceous ammonites, for while these two families are almost restricted to Europe and probably indigenous to the Mediterranean region, the less numerous representatives of other families associated with them are almost universal in marine Cretaceous rocks and are probably immigrants from other seas. Some members of the Schloenbachidae seem to be even more restricted in occurrence, according to available records; *Prionocycloides* and *Algericeras*, for instance, are so far reported only from northern Africa, though *Euhystricoceras*, based on an Algerian type, is represented in England. *Forbesiceras*, another offshoot from an anahoplitid stock, is rare in England, but abundant and widespread in more southerly latitudes. Still another hoplitid derivative is *Hyphoplites* which, with *Discohoplites*, is a direct descendant of the Albian *Euhoplites*, and 'represents the final dissolution of the euhoplitid stock' (Spath). Species of *Hyphoplites* are recorded from England, France, Germany, Switzerland, and the Mangyshlak Peninsula.

In the early Cenomanian deposits of south England, species of *Schloenbachia* are associated with species of *Mantelliceras* (Pl. XVII) and *Submantelliceras*, closely related to the Algerian forms *M. martimpreyi* and *S. aumalense*. Spath (1937) regards these two genera as developed from the lyelliceratid genus *Stoliczkaia* which itself may persist into the lowest Cenomanian horizons. A second offshoot from *Stoliczkaia* comprises the genera *Sharpeiceras* and *Paracalycoceras*, the former of which is not common but is recorded from localities as far apart as England, France, Germany, Tunis, Persia, India, and Portuguese east Africa. A third development from the same source provides first *Calycoceras* and then *Eucalycoceras*, both widespread genera, with a tendency to retain continuous costation across the adult venter (Pl. XVII). Distinctive species of these mantelliceratid genera are recorded from various horizons in the lower half of the old varians zone which is thus dominated by the Mantelliceratan fauna.

The upper half of the varians zone, together with the zone of *Holaster subglobosus*, is marked by the development of the Acanthoceratidan fauna. The family Acanthoceratidae is a collateral derivative from *Stoliczkaia*, and the various genera are distinguished from the mantelliceratids by the tendency to exaggeration of ornament on the adult whorls. *Protacantho- ceras*, with feebly ornamented, compressed whorls, and three peripheral rows of tubercles, is regarded by Spath as a side issue of the stock that pro- duced the true *Acanthoceras*, which is typified by the well-known species *Ac. rhotogamense*, less inflated and less closely ribbed than *Ac. vectense* (Pl. XVII). The highly ornamented *Euomphaloceras* is derived from *Acanthoceras*, and so has no affinity with the mid-Albian *Douvilleiceras* which it resembles superficially. A separate, and later, development from *Acanthoceras* leads to the Turonian genus *Romaniceras*. Most of these genera are widespread through Europe at localities where the appropriate horizons are developed. They also extend into Algeria and Tunisia where the index of the highest Cenomanian horizon is *Neolobites vibrayanus* belonging to the 'pseudoceratitic' family Engonoceratidae; the genus is recorded also from Egypt and south France, but is not known to occur so far north as England. In the southern region, too, strata containing ammonites are often replaced by rudist limestones (see pp. 541–7).

In the lower part of the Turonian stage, corresponding to the Ligerian substage of continental authors, the dominant ammonites belong to the families Metoicoceratidae, Vascoceratidae, Mammitidae, and Prionotro- pidae. The first of these is probably derived from the Cenomanian Mantelli- ceratidae, while the others continue from the acanthoceratid stock of that stage. The Turonian families appear first in the zone of *Actinocamax plenus*; at this level in Dorset and the Paris basin the ammonite fauna includes *Metoicoceras pontieri* and an inflated form of *Neocardioceras*, an early genus of the Prionotropidae which resembles the later *Prionocyclus* except in its crenulate keel. These ammonites are closely allied to a younger assem- blage at the base of the cuvieri zone of Dorset that includes *Metoicoceras whitei* and compressed forms of *Neocardioceras*. Hence L. F. Spath (1926) advocates a return to the old classification in which the base of the Plenus Marls was taken as the lower limit of the Turonian stage. These ammonite assemblages may be grouped as the **Mammitan Fauna;** besides the two genera just mentioned the faunules include the mammitids *Pseudaspido- ceras*, *Mammites*, and *Metasigaloceras* with the vascoceratids *Fagesia*, *Vascoceras*, and *Plesiovascoceras*. Towards the top of the cuvieri zone the desmoceratid *Austiniceras* appears, together with early members of *Lewesi- ceras*, regarded as a separate offshoot from a desmoceratid stock.

The zones of *Terebratulina lata* and *Holaster planus*, equivalent to the Angoumian substage of continental authors, are marked by the **Prionotro- pidan Fauna** in which the dominant ammonites are members of the Prionotropidae. They include the genera *Prionotropis* and *Prionocyclus* which are associated with *Romaniceras*, a late representative of the Acanthoceratidae, and with the desmoceratids *Austiniceras* and *Pseudopuzosia*. The type of the last-named genus comes from the Chalk Rock of south England (p. 510), a peculiar conglomerate which has yielded species of *Puzosia*, *Pseudopuzosia*, *Lewesiceras* (Pl. XVII), *Prionocyclus*, and various heteromorph forms. Of these, the familiar *Scaphites geinitzi* is connected by transitions with older Turonian and Cenomanian species, while *Hyphantoceras reussianum* (Pl. XVII) may be a direct descendant of the Cenomanian *Turrilites*. The genera *Allocrioceras* and *Metaptychoceras* are of uncertain affinity, but the straight *Cyrtochilus bohemicus* is directly related to the Cenomanian *C. baculoides*.

On the European continent Orbigny's Senonian stage was later divided by H. Coquand (1857) into the three substages Coniacian, Santonian, and Campanian, based on typical sections in Cognac, Santonge, and Champagne respectively, and each contains a distinctive assemblage of ammonites. The Coniacian substage, corresponding approximately to the zone of *Micraster cortestudinarium*, is marked by the **Gauthiericeratan Fauna.** The genus *Gauthiericeras* is recorded from localities as far apart as Westphalia, Touraine, and the Rhône basin, Tunisia, the east Alps, and Syria; according to L. F. Spath (1926) it is connected through *Prionocycloceras* with the Turonian *Prionocyclus*. Another widespread genus is *Barroisiceras*; the typical species, *B. haberfellneri*, is recorded from the Gosau Beds of the north-east Alps, from Madagascar and Peru, while other species are known from France and Bohemia. *Peroniceras subtricarinatum*, again, is cited from north France and the Gosau Beds of Austria.

One of the most widely distributed ammonites of the Santonian substage is *Texanites texanum*, founded on an American type which was formerly confused with the Albian genus *Mortoniceras*. The species has lately been found in the zone of *Micraster coranguinum* in south England, and the Alps, Algeria, and Tunisia. Consequently the genus may form the index of the **Texanitan Fauna.** Apart from species of *Texanites* the most conspicuous Santonian ammonites are species of the desmoceratid *Parapuzosia* which are known in England as far north as Yorkshire and continue into the Marsupites zone of Kent and Sussex. *Parapuzosia* produces transitional forms to the widespread *Kossmaticeras* of later zones.

The succeeding **Hoploscaphitan Fauna** occupies a number of Upper Santonian and Lower Campanian horizons, corresponding with the zones of *Offaster pilula* and *Actinocamax quadratus*. The most conspicuous ammonites are members of the Desmoceratidae, including the acute-ventered *Hauericeras pseudogardeni*, recorded from Germany, Galicia, England, France, and Tunisia, besides localities in South Africa, south Asia, and North America. Species of *Hoploscaphites*, known as far north as Yorkshire, are apparently restricted to western Europe.

The **Pachydiscan Fauna** appears in the later half of the Campanian substage and continues into the Maestrichtian stage; its range corresponds roughly with the zone of *Belemnitella mucronata*. Again, desmoceratids are prominent in such genera as *Pachydiscus, Parapuzosia*, and *Menuites*, the last comprising tuberculate forms with scaphitoid coiling. There are also several heteromorphs of the genera *Bostrychoceras, Diplomoceras, Neancycloceras*, and *Glyptoxoceras*, besides the straight, carinate forms of *Eubaculites*. The European ammonites recorded as '*Kossmaticeras*' differ from the typical fine-ribbed forms of the Indo-Pacific region.

Pachydiscus is associated with *Sphenodiscus* in the later **Sphenodiscan Fauna** of the Aquitaine, but the succeeding Danian stage has not yielded ammonites, the only cephalopod being the nautilid *Hercoglossa danicus*.

THE BORDERS OF THE INDIAN OCEAN. It is generally accepted that the European Cretaceous sea, like its Jurassic predecessor, was joined to the Indian Ocean by a route through south-west Asia. In Egypt and Sinai the ancient crystalline rocks of the African continent are bordered by the Nubian Sandstone, a littoral deposit which persists to high Senonian horizons in the south. The Nubian Sandstone is progressively transgressed from the north by marine deposits beginning with the Cenomanian and continuing to the Maestrichtian stage; the marine strata are variable, including oyster beds, and limestones with either ammonites or rudist lamellibranchs. A similar transgression in Syria seems to have begun earlier, judging by the record of *Knemiceras*, which is an Albian ammonite. But in south-west Persia, L. F. Spath (1933) mentions 'a complete succession from uppermost Jurassic into Lower Cretaceous', including a Lower Neocomian fauna with ammonites characteristic of the Valanginian Marls of south France, that is, a typical Mediterranean fauna. Later faunas are said to be more prolific and better preserved, but have not yet been described in detail. There is, however, the record of the mid-Albian *Oxytropidoceras* and *Douvilleiceras* associated with the pseudoceratite *Knemiceras*, and of the Upper Albian genera *Mortoniceras, Prohystericeras*, and *Elobiceras*. Spath (1934) has also mentioned 'a magnificent development of all the Cretaceous formations in south-west Persia'; earlier he had recorded the presence of the Cenomanian *Sharpeiceras* and the group of *Schloenbachia varians* in Persia. Moreover, forty years ago, E. Haug summarized a considerable succession of Neocretaceous rocks, including Cenomanian, Turonian, and Senonian horizons with appropriate ammonites and rudists. It is reasonable to suppose, therefore, that an enlarged Persian Gulf maintained communication between the European sea and the Indian Ocean throughout the Cretaceous period.

This arm of the Cretaceous sea encroached on the ancient tableland of Arabia, for Neocretaceous deposits extend into central Arabia over the Precambrian rocks of the Nejd desert. The Arabian Sea transgressed the same ancient rocks in the Hadramaut, also on Socotra and the Kuria Muria islands where fossils from shelly sandstones and rudist limestones are comparable with Mediterranean forms of Cenomanian to Senonian ages.

The western margin of the Cretaceous Indian Ocean is indicated by transgressive deposits at various places along the eastern coast of Africa. In the north-east of British Somaliland, Barremian ammonites, including holcodiscids, are reported from limestones, but the stratigraphical relations to underlying rocks are unknown (C. B. Brown, 1931). Above the Barremian sub-stage an unexplored interval of 150 feet is followed by limestones containing lamellibranchs that are tentatively referred to the Senonian stage. The earliest Cretaceous ammonites known from Tanganyika Territory are species of the Hauterivian *Olcostephanus* and *Subastieria* associated with holcodiscids and crioceratids. In the same facies are Barremian *Heteroceras* and lytoceratids, and even Aptian *Ancyloceras* and *Procheloniceras*, but L. F. Spath (1939) considers the succession is not likely to be continuous from the Hauterivian to the Aptian stage.

Small and isolated outcrops of Cretaceous strata are exposed at various places in Portuguese East Africa. Little is known concerning the distribution of the beds, for the country is deeply covered with Neozoic deposits; nevertheless, several stages of the Cretaceous system are represented in the available records. The oldest deposits are of Valanginian age, for on Mozambique they have yielded *Rogersites* cf. *schenki* (Oppel) and *Neolissoceras* cf. *grasianum* (Orb.). From another locality, Mahiba Hill, west of Port Amelia, L. F. Spath (1930) cites the presence of *Lytoceras*, *Neocomites*, *Bochianites*, and the belemnoid *Duvalia* as proof of Valanginian age, and states that the cephalopods are closely related to species found in the Uitenhage Beds of South Africa and the Speeton Clay of England. Upper Aptian fossils are known from sandy littoral beds in the vicinity of Delagoa Bay which have yielded the ammonites *Aconeceras* and *Cheloniceras*; species of the same genera are recorded from Mt. Libombo, north-west of Lorenço Marques. Albian ammonites and heteromorphs are described by L. F. Spath (1925) from Catuane, some 40 miles from the present coast in the extreme south of the country. The ammonites include species of *Mortoniceras*, *Hysteroceras*, and *Elobiceras* closely related to European forms from Upper Albian horizons. The fauna also contains interesting heteromorphs, notably *Labeceras* and *Myloceras*. These genera were first described from Australia and are also recorded from Zululand and Madagascar; hence they provide evidence of direct marine communication between the Albian seas of East Africa and Australia. In 1903, P. Choffat described Cenomanian ammonites from the Conducia River, just north of Mozambique, including species of *Acanthoceras* and *Sharpeiceras*. L. F. Spath (1925), however, points out that not only are Albian desmoceratids represented there, but that the fauna includes Senonian fossils also. From Matupoland in the extreme south of the country Spath describes another species of the rare, but widespread *Sharpeiceras*. No Turonian or early Senonian Beds appear to have been described, but Spath records *Submortoniceras* aff. *soutoni* (Baily) from Matupoland, comparable with specimens from the Campanian stage of Zululand. The Maestrichtian *Eubaculites vagina* (Forbes) is reported from localities north of Beira and the mouth of the Zambesi River where lower beds have yielded only oysters. Portuguese geologists ascribe the uppermost Cretaceous Beds of Cheringoma, which contain two species of the nautilid *Hercoglossa*, to the Danian stage. It is evident therefore that most of the Cretaceous stages are represented in Portuguese East Africa, and the apparent gaps may be filled by future discoveries. But in a country which extends some 1,200 miles from north to south, the apparent succession may represent a series of independent local transgressions.

Farther south, Albian and Cenomanian fossils have been described from Manuan Creek, a tributary of the Umsinene River which flows into the northern part of False Bay, St. Lucia Lake. From Albian Beds at this locality, L. F. Spath (1921) lists species of *Dipoloceras*, *Manuaniceras*, *Mortoniceras*, *Lyelliceras*, and *Puzosia*. The collections indicate the presence of Middle and Upper Albian horizons. H. Besairie (1930) has further recorded the peculiar heteromorphs *Labeceras* and *Myloceras* associated with *Mortoniceras aequatorialis*. Ammonites from strata near the junction of Manuan Creek and the Umsinene River include species of *Phylloceras*, *Puzosia*, *Tetragonites*, *Gaudryceras*, *Desmoceras*, *Turrilites*, *Forbesiceras*, and *Acanthoceras* which are clearly of Cenomanian age. The last-named genus is represented mainly by new, perhaps local, species, but some widespread forms, e.g. *Ac. hippocastanum* (J. Sow.) and *Ac. newboldi* Kossmat, are also recorded. These indicate Upper Cenomanian horizons, and apparently there is no trace of *Mantelliceras* faunas typical of lower Cenomanian Beds. No Turonian ammonites are yet known from Zululand, but the stage may be represented by certain lamellibranch and echinid assemblages. Senonian beds appear in the southern side of the Manuan Creek Valley. The Coniacian substage is indicated (Spath 1921) by *Peroniceras* cf. *dravidicum* and two other species of the genus recorded by G. C. Crick (1907). This author also describes species of *Gaudryceras*, *Diplomoceras*, and *Baculites* which Spath refers to the Campanian substage, along with *Kossmaticeras bhavani* and *Placenticeras* cf. *subkaffrarum*. Besairie (1930), however, believes the last to be a Coniacian species, and states that the closely related *Pl. kaffrarum* Eth. is associated with *Peroniceras subtricarinatum* in the district north-west of False Bay. Besairie also records from the same area species of *Submortoniceras* associated with *Canadoceras newberryanus* (Meek) and *Eubaculites* cf. *vagina* (Forbes) which certainly appear to be of Campanian age.

At the mouth of the Umzamba River in Pondoland, horizontal Cretaceous strata, comprising limestones and shales with a basal conglomerate, rest unconformably on the Table Mountain Sandstone of Palaeozoic age. The fossils are referred by H. Woods (1906) to the Upper Senonian, and, in a revision of the ammonites L. F. Spath (1921) describes species of *Haueri-*

ceras, Phylloceras, Gaudryceras, Submortoniceras, Tetragonites, Pseudophyl-lites, Schlüteria, Kossmaticeras, Pachydiscus, Hoploscaphites, Diplomoceras, Baculites, &c. These are identical or comparable with forms that occur in the well-known Campanian and Maestrichtian deposits of the classical areas, such as the Charente, Dordogne, and Cotentin in France, Nagorzany in Poland, and the eastern coast of Peninsular India. The Pondoland deposits evidently represent a late Senonian transgression, the first marine encroachment here since Devonian time.

In South Africa the Neocomian strata comprised in the Uitenhage Beds of Cape Province have long been known, but extended discussion ensued before their precise age was certainly established. The basal deposits (Enon Beds) consist of sandstones, marls, and conglomerates containing *Estheria* and fragments of wood. These are succeeded by the Wood Beds of freshwater or estuarine origin, yellow sandstones, thin limestones and shales with remains of land plants, a few lamellibranch shells, and occasional bones of deinosaurs. Then come the Sunday's River Beds, consisting of clays, shales, and sandy limestones with marine fossils; the invertebrates have been described by F. L. Kitchin (1908), and the twenty species of ammonites so far recorded have been reviewed by L. F. Spath (1930). Apart from the preponderance of lamellibranchs, the outstanding feature of the ammonite-fauna is the abundance of gigantic species of *Rogersites* unknown elsewhere, associated with species of *Leopoldia*, and the heteromorphs *Distoloceras* and *Bochianites*. This association of genera is very similar to the Lytioco-ceratan fauna of bed D 2 in the English Speeton Clay (p. 490); hence the Sunday's River Beds are equivalent to the Upper Valanginian zone of *Saynoceras verrucosum* in south-east France. But it is worthy of note that phylloceratids and lytoceratids, both abundant in Mediterranean faunas, are extremely rare in the Uitenhage assemblage, only one specimen of *Phylloceras rogersi* Kitchin, and one of *Eodesmoceras haughtoni* Spath representing these ancestral stocks at the time of Spath's revision. Though the Uitenhage Beds attain a maximum thickness of 2,000 feet, they represent a local transgression of short duration, and no younger Cretaceous deposits are known in the district.

The Cretaceous succession is more completely developed in Madagascar, where the outcrop extends roughly parallel with the western coast almost the length of the island; only a few small patches representing Neocretaceous horizons appear on the eastern side of the central Precambrian ridge. The Mesozoic geology of Madagascar is best known by the works of H. Besairie and his colleagues (1930, 1936), and certain ammonite-faunas have been discussed by L. F. Spath (1933, 1939).

The sequence begins in north-west Madagascar where the Infra-Valan-ginian ammonites *Kilianella, Thurmannites,* and *Subthurmannia* are said to occur abundantly in limestone bands of the Belemnite Marls. These beds have no equivalent on the opposite African coast, but as early as 1907

E. Haug cited the abundance of the belemnoid *Duvalia* as evidence of direct marine communication with the Mediterranean area. Later Valanginian ammonites from the succeeding Rogersites Beds near Ambiky include species of *Phylloceras*, *Neolissoceras*, *Rogersites*, *Sarasinella*, *Neocomites*, *Distoloceras*, and *Bochianites*, and evidently represent the Uitenhage fauna of the South African mainland. The Hauterivian substage may be represented in the south-west at Menarandroy by belemnite beds containing *Duvalia dilatata* which are transgressive over Kimmeridgian strata; Barremian and Lower Aptian Beds, however, are not certainly known. Near Amborimadinga transgressive strata contain species of *Deshayesites*, and *Cheloniceras* is recorded from the district of Antsalova; the record of a local species of *Hypacanthoplites* perhaps indicates the presence of Lower Albian Beds. Numerous well-preserved ammonites have been obtained from Middle Albian strata in south-west Madagascar, including species of *Phylloceras*, *Lytoceras*, *Puzosia*, *Cleoniceras*, *Beudanticeras*, *Desmoceras*, *Douvilleiceras*, *Manuaniceras*, and *Oxytropidoceras*. From Ambarimaninga L. F. Spath (1939) mentions a particularly interesting association which includes *Douvilleiceras mammillatum* with numerous examples of *Lemuroceras aburense* and *L. indicum*, besides heteromorph species. The last named species were first described from an undetermined horizon in north-west India, and referred to the Aptian genus *Pseudhaploceras*. The Madagascan association, however, shows that *Lemuroceras* is an Albian form, and it provides good evidence of easy communication between the Albian seas of western India and Madagascar. Upper Albian Beds at Montagne des Français have yielded not only species of *Mortoniceras* and *Hysteroceras* similar to those from the Upper Gault of Folkestone, but also the heteromorphs *Labeceras* and *Myloceras* which provide a link with Australia.

Two fossiliferous bands have yielded Cenomanian ammonites. At Diego Suarez the lower one contains pyritized examples of *Mantelliceras* and *Forbesiceras*, and the same horizon is present at Antsandoky. The record of *Acanthoceras rhotomagense* from the same district seems to indicate Upper Cenomanian Beds, but *Ac. newboldi* and *Turrilites costatus* are said to occur at both levels. At several places in west Madagascar Lower Turonian Beds enclose characteristic species of *Fagesia*, *Mammites*, *Neoptychites* associated with *Inoceramus labiatus*. Strata assigned to the Upper Turonian yield only occasional specimens of *Metaplacenticeras*, the most typical fossil being *Inoceramus andersoni* Eth. In the Senonian stage, early Coniacian horizons are well represented at Mont Carré by beds containing typical species of *Barroisiceras* and *Placenticeras*, the former being associated in some places with *Inoceramus*. No Upper Coniacian fossils are yet reported from Madagascar, and a volcanic episode is intercalated hereabouts in the succession. East of Mitraiky a fauna containing *Texanites* represents the Lower Santonian, but higher horizons of the substage are not indicated in the records. A sequence at Andrakaraka shows three divisions; the lowest beds contain

Submortoniceras delawarense (Morton) an early Campanian species; the middle beds yield *Hopliplacenticeras vari* and *Pseudophyllites indra* (Forbes), also of Campanian age; and the upper beds enclose species of *Pachydiscus* characteristic of early Maestrichtian Beds in Europe. The highest Cretaceous deposits in the island are comprised in the Chalk of Andrafiavelo which has yielded *Eubaculites vagina, Bostrychoceras schloenbachi,* and other Maestrichtian species, including the lamellibranch *Cardita beaumonti.* The Cretaceous Beds along the eastern coast all belong to this stage, which is here transgressive on the Precambrian gneiss.

The Cretaceous deposits of Madagascar, even if they represent a number of local transgressions at intervals along the 1,000 miles of coast-line, combine with the corresponding beds on the African mainland, to show that the Mozambique Channel was a seaway throughout Cretaceous time, as it was during the Jurassic period. Likewise the many palaeontological links with India and Australia indicate that, contrary to the views of several older authors, the Indian Ocean was already in existence throughout Mesozoic time.

The northern margin of the Indian Ocean in Cretaceous time can be traced in a general way by means of local and ephemeral transgressions over the former coast-line of southern Asia, eastwards from the ancient seaway of south-west Persia. In Baluchistan the lowest Cretaceous Beds rest on limestones of Callovian age (p. 482); they comprise the so-called 'Belemnite Beds' which contain enormous numbers of *Hibolites subfusiformis* generally in fragmentary condition. They compare well with corresponding beds in Madagascar, and, like them are referred to the Valanginian beds of the Neocomian stage. There follow the so-called Hemipneustes Beds, named after the dominant echinid in the sandy limestones of indefinite Neocretaceous age. The succeeding shaly beds contain ammonoids such as the peculiar *Indoceras baluchistanense* Noetling, together with species of *Sphenodiscus* and *Pachydiscus* which are also found in the Maestrichtian Beds of Europe. Rudist limestones are also recorded, and the succession ends with sandstones containing *Cardita beaumonti* perhaps of Danian age. This broken succession is in strong contrast with the complete sequence in south Persia, and evidently indicates temporary encroachment of the sea on the continental area now represented by Afghanistan.

The Neocomian belemnite beds are widespread from Baluchistan through Waziristan to the Samana and Salt Ranges. Here again, *Hibolites subfusiformis* is the most characteristic fossil, and occurs in great numbers in the condensed glauconitic beds. From the Salt Range L. F. Spath (1939) has described a considerable number of ammonites; some of them are local forms, but others, including species of *Olcostephanus, Rogersites, Neocomites, Blanfordiceras,* &c., show relations with Valanginian faunas of the Mediterranean area and Madagascar. It may be significant that certain ammonites which represent low horizons of the substage at Makerwal

and Chichali are lacking in the collections from localities east of the Indus
where Upper Valanginian Beds rest on Upper Jurassic strata. A belemnite
bed on Kadimak Mountain just north of Thal has yielded an isolated
Olcostephanus, related to *Ol. astierianus* (Orb.), belonging to the same late
Valanginian horizon. This belemnite bed in the Samana Range is succeeded
by a white, siliceous sandstone, about 700 feet in thickness, passing up into
a glauconitic bed which has yielded phosphatized ammonites similar to
those from the mammillatum bed of the English Gault. *Douvilleiceras mammillatum* is, in fact, the commonest Samana species; its associates are
undoubtedly of Middle Albian age and there is no sign of Aptian or even of
Neocomian fossils later than the Valanginian Belemnite Bed (Spath 1930).
In the Attock district the Oxfordian stage (p. 481) is succeeded by so-
called 'Guimal Beds' of slight thickness which have yielded species of
Blanfordiceras and *Spiticeras* belonging to 'a narrow horizon at the limit
of the Jurassic and Cretaceous systems' (Spath 1934). A compact limestone
immediately above has furnished specimens of the mid-Albian *Oxtropido-
ceras*. Spath (1930) has also described a larger assemblage of the same age
from Hazara. Here the most prolific genera are *Lyelliceras* and *Douvilleiceras*, accompanied by species of *Desmoceras*, *Puzosia*, *Cleoniceras*, *Brancoceras*, *Mojsisovicsia*, *Oxytropidoceras*, *Dipoloceras*, and various heteromorphs.
These remnants of the Albian stage are followed at both localities by an unconformity which, in Spath's opinion, 'indicates a considerable break in the
succession, corresponding probably to a period of emergence rather than
to a mere change in the submarine erosion level'. The uppermost Albian
dispar zone is absent, and, as G. P. Cotter stated in 1927, there is no trace
of Cenomanian deposits; the record of '*Am. mantellii*' by Middlemiss in
1896 seems to have been a mistaken interpretation of *Lyelliceras*. The
Albian stage is overlaid by the *Cardita beaumonti* beds of Danian age.

In the central Himalayas the Lochambel Beds of the Spiti Shales contain
species of *Berriasella*, *Blanfordiceras*, and *Spiticeras* which range above
and below the limit between the Jurassic and Cretaceous systems, though
confined to a narrow horizon. The Spiti Shales are overlaid at a number of
places by the yellow Guimal Sandstones, some 300 feet in thickness; these
have yielded fragmentary ammonites among which Spitz (1914) records
Olcostephanus of the *atherstoni* group, typical of Upper Valanginian zones.
The same author also figures a fragment which L. F. Spath (1930) believes
to be an Aptian *Dufrenoyia*. The prolific Albian fauna of Hazara, however,
seems to be lacking entirely in the Guimal Sandstone. There follows about
250 feet of limestones and shales containing belemnites, rudist lamellibranchs, and foraminifera. These beds, known as the Chikkim Series, are
probably of Senonian age, and they are succeeded in Spiti by a great thickness of unfossiliferous sandstone which is said to be Flysch-like in character.
It is evident that the Cretaceous succession in the central Himalayas, like
that of other regions in northern India, is very fragmentary. Only occasional

horizons of the Neocomian and Aptian stages are present, the Albian, Cenomanian, and Turonian seem to be missing entirely, though Senonian rocks are recorded in some places. Evidently northern India was subjected to temporary local transgressions of a sea which, according to the evidence of the ammonites, lay to the south-west, and communicated with the Himalayan region through a depression on the site of the present State of Baluchistan.

In Assam the Cretaceous rocks of the Khasi Hills lie nearly horizontal on the denuded edges of the Precambrian Shillong Series. The most persistent member is a coarse sandstone, some 200 feet in thickness, which encloses small coal-seams. A few beds near Cherrapungi contain marine fossils, including species of *Pachydiscus* referable to the Maestrichtian stage, and E. Spengler (1923) states that the Cretaceous transgression in Assam begins with this stage. Few details are known of Cretaceous rocks in Burma. L. F. Spath (1936) has described a Turonian ammonite, *Mammites daviesi*, from Ramri Island. The upper part of the 'Axial Group' in the Arakan Yoma has yielded the lamellibranch *Cardita beaumonti* but no ammonites. The rocks are chiefly unfossiliferous sandstones of Flysch type with some intercalations of volcanic rocks.

Off the coast-line indicated by these transgressive deposits from Baluchistan to Burma lies the ancient land-mass of Peninsular India, which provides evidence of similar temporary encroachments of the Cretaceous Indian Ocean. The earliest is shown by beds of Barremian age intercalated in the Upper Gondwana Series near the eastern coast, especially in the Madras area. The Neocomian age of the ammonites was noted by W. Waagen in 1875, but subsequent writers, even as recent as C. S. Fox (1931), have assigned the rocks to the Jurassic system. L. F. Spath (1933) has since reviewed the evidence, and has referred the ammonites to a late Neocomian (Barremian) date. In the Budavada Beds the new genus *Pascoeites* is associated with *Holcodiscus* and is believed to be 'allied to those Hauterivian-Barremian groups that are connected with the Holcodiscidae on the one hand, and with the Hemihoplitidae on the other'. Species assigned to *Hemihoplites* are present at other localities. The same association of *Pascoeites* and *Holcodiscus* is present in the Ragavapuram Shales with the addition of *Lytoceras* cf. *vogdti* and *Gymnoplites*. The last genus also resembles *Holcodiscus* but acquires a smooth outer whorl. Hence the assemblages from the Ragavapuram Shales, the Budavada Beds, and other local units are essentially alike, and Spath concludes, 'it seems probable that there is an enormous gap between the Lower Gondwanas and the Rajmahal plant-beds of Peninsular India, involving at least the whole of the Jurassic and perhaps not only the Rhaetic but also the lowest Cretaceous'. At the same time the evidence suggests that the sea was not far distant from the present eastern coast-line of India.

At the northern foot of the Ukra Hills in Kachh, strata above the Umia

(Tithonian) Beds have yielded several ammonoids of Upper Aptian age, and L. F. Spath (1931) has described *Colombiceras waageni*, *Cheloniceras* aff. *martini* (Orb.) and *Tropaeum* aff. *australis* (Moore). The last species is also recorded from Australia, and the first is related to South American forms of the genus which is probably an offshoot of the Parahoplitidae. The relations of the rocks to the underlying Umia Beds are uncertain owing to lack of ammonites in these beds which are disturbed by faulting and igneous intrusions. There appears to be a stratigraphical gap, and the Aptian Beds seem to represent a temporary local transgression over the Jurassic strata. Certain Cretaceous rocks which overlie Upper Jurassic strata in the desert tract of Rajputana, especially near Abur and Jaisalmir, have also yielded ammonites. These were first referred to the Aptian genus *Pseudohaploceras*, but the same species have since been recorded from Albian strata in north-west Madagascar, and interpreted as a separate desmoceratid offshoot, *Lemuroceras*. This north-western transgression was therefore prolonged until mid-Albian time. A much later encroachment is shown by Cretaceous strata in the neighbouring province of Sind. Here the lowest limestones contain echinids (*Hemipneustes*) and mollusca (including *Hippurites*) which are probably of Senonian age. They are succeeded first by sandstones, shales, and limestone with obscure reptile-bones, then by olive-coloured shales enclosing *Cardita beaumonti*, and finally by basaltic lava-flows of the Deccan type.

In the Narbada Valley several small outcrops of Cretaceous rocks are present along an east to west line from the plains of Gujrat to Barwaka, about 240 miles from the present coast. These rocks, known as the Bagh Beds, comprise 50 to 80 feet of argillaceous nodular limestone above un-fossiliferous sandstone which rests unconformably on the Precambrian foundation. The fauna is mainly of sea-urchins, which R. Fourteau (1918) identified with European and North African species of Albian age. But E. W. Vredenburg (1908) had already described three ammonites belonging to the genera *Placenticeras* and *Coilopoceras* which are typically Turonian forms. The Bagh Beds therefore provide evidence of a temporary transgression from the west during Turonian time, long before the extrusion of the Deccan basalts which have protected them from denudation.

On the south-eastern margin of the Indian Peninsula, south of Madras, are a few small outcrops of marine Cretaceous deposits which rest unconformably on Upper Gondwana and Precambrian rocks, and dip eastward under the alluvium of the Coromandel coast. In the Trichinopoli area, where the longest succession is seen, the beds are grouped in four stages. They begin with the Utatur Beds, mainly argillaceous deposits which contain three distinct assemblages of ammonites. The oldest association includes the significant and widely distributed *Mortoniceras inflatum*, *Stoliczkaia dispar*, and *Mariella bergeri*, together with desmoceratids and *Phylloceras* of longer stratigraphical range. E. Haug (1908) recognized this horizon as equivalent to the 'Vraconnian' Beds of Europe, or, in modern parlance, to the uppermost Albian zone of *Stoliczkaia dispar*. In supporting this view L. F. Spath (1930) points out that the almost universal genus *Hysteroceras* is already extinct and that the Indian *Mortoniceras* has a later aspect than species from Upper Albian horizons in East Africa. Cenomanian ammonites are well represented in the Middle Utatur Beds by numerous species of *Mantelliceras*, *Calycoceras*, and *Acanthoceras*, which have been compared with those in the Rouen Chalk of France. The Upper Utatur Beds contain species of *Romaniceras*, *Mammites*, *Fagesia*, and *Neoptychites*, some of which are identical or comparable with Turonian forms of Europe and North Africa.

The Trichinopoli Beds which follow begin with shelly limestones containing species of *Prionocyclus*, *Lewesiceras*, *Scaphites*, and *Cyrtochilus*; these undoubtedly represent younger horizons of the Turonian stage. Later beds of the Trichinopoli group contain ammonites which represent certain horizons of the Senonian stage in Europe. *Peroniceras dravidicum*, associated in the middle beds with *Placenticeras tamulicum* and *Madrasites bhavani*, is closely related to the Coniacian *Per. westphalicum*. *Hauericeras sugatum* and other desmoceratids, together with *Kossmaticeras theobaldianum*, *Bostrychoceras indicum* and other forms in the Upper Trichinopoli Beds are usually taken to represent the Santonian substage of the European classification, and this view is supported by Haug's citation of the crinoid *Marsupites* at the top of the stage. Haug says there is no indication of the Campanian substage, but L. F. Spath (1926) cites *K. theobaldianum* as an index fossil of a Campanian horizon. Species of *Kossmaticeras* are also listed from the Aryalur stage, associated with *Hauericeras*, *Pachydiscus*, *Brahmaites*, *Menuites*, *Bostrychoceras*, and *Eubaculites* in an assemblage which is related to Maestrichtian faunas of Europe and East Africa. Higher beds in the stage yield *Sphenodiscus siva* and *Indoceras baluchistanense* which represent the Sphenodiscan fauna of Spath's classification. Finally, the Niniyur stage is without ammonites but contains the nautilid *Hercoglossa danicus* typical of the Danian Beds of Europe. Near Pondicheri these Maestrichtian and Danian Beds, there known as the Valudayur stage, rest directly on the Precambrian gneiss. The fauna is closely similar to that of the Aryalur and Niniyur Beds farther south, but includes *Pseudophyllites indra* which does not appear in the lists from the Trichinopoli district. It is evident that the Neocretaceous transgression, beginning in late Albian time, persisted in southern India to the Maestrichtian period.

Cretaceous fossils are recorded from several islands in the East Indian archipelago, but, owing to intense disturbance of the rocks, little is known concerning the stratigraphical relations of the horizons they indicate. H. Brouwer (1925) states that Palaeocretaceous beds are known with certainty only on Sumatra, the Sula islands, and New Guinea. From Sumatra he cites the Valanginian ammonite genera *Neocomites*, *Thurmannites*, *Kilianella*,

Oosterella, and *Astieria* (= *Olcostephanus*), besides lamellibranchs and sea-urchins. The record of *Himalayaites* and *Bochianites* from the Sula islands indicates the presence there of Infra-Valanginian and possibly higher beds, as in the Spiti Shales of the Himalayas with which the beds are often com-pared. The same author reports equivalent beds from the River Tarwarin near the north coast of New Guinea. In West Borneo the ammonites *Knemiceras* and *Schloenbachia* are reported from sandstones which some-times begin with a basal conglomerate; they indicate the presence of Albian and possibly Cenomanian horizons. Neocretaceous deposits seem to have a more extended development, but are often foraminiferal and radiolarian rocks without ammonites. Such deposits are known from Java, Borneo, Celebes, Misool, Halmaheira, and Timor. Nevertheless, ammonites are reported from some of the islands. The Cenomanian *Mantelliceras* and *Acanthoceras* are known from the Strickland River in New Guinea. The Senonian *Pachydiscus*, in association with *Inoceramus*, *Radiolites*, and sea-urchins, is recorded from Misool. A fauna comparable with that of the Aryalur Beds of south India is reported from south-east Borneo.

Marine Cretaceous rocks are present in narrow outcrops along the mar-gin of the ancient shield in northern and western Australia. On the main-land near Port Darwin, radiolarian shales containing belemnites and ichthyosaurian remains are followed by shales with loosely coiled am-monoids of the genera *Labeceras* and *Scaphites*. These represent the aequatorialis zone of the Upper Albian, and the first-named genus has already been mentioned from Portuguese East Africa and Madagascar. At Point Charles and Melville Island sandstones with *Acanthoceras* and *Ino-ceramus* represent Upper Cenomanian horizons. A similar succession is indicated by boring records south of Shark Bay (T. W. E. David, 1932) and by outcrops in the Gascoyne area of western Australia (Clarke, 1938). Farther south, younger beds in the Gingin area north-east of Perth, include the Gingin Chalk, famous for the occurrence of the echinoderms *Marsupites*, *Uintacrinus*, and *Micraster*, which brings it into comparison with the Marsu-pites zone of the Upper Chalk in England. The additional record of *Para-puzosia* confirms this correlation with the Santonian substage of Europe.

It is evident that these numerous local extensions of the Indian Ocean over the adjoining land-areas during Cretaceous time represent only a comparatively small increase of its present area. The Indian Ocean of that period was evidently connected with the Pacific Ocean through the East Indian archipelago, as shown by the presence of marine Cretaceous beds on some of the islands. Moreover, there is no evidence that land ever existed between Australia and Antarctica.

THE BORDERS OF THE PACIFIC OCEAN. Cretaceous deposits, still almost horizontal, occupy an extensive area in the eastern half of Australia, extending from Cape York to the Lake Eyre basin and New South Wales. The fossils were first described in detail between 1902 and 1913 by

R. Etheridge jun., and the ammonites have since been reviewed by F. W. Whitehouse (1926–7).

The oldest marine horizon so far known is the Morven Bed which has yielded a single ammonite belonging to the genus *Simbirskites*. This is the only evidence indicating the presence of Hauterivian deposits in Australia, for, in most places, freshwater beds of the Walloon Series underlie the marine representatives of the Aptian Stage.

The succeeding Roma stage of Queensland, comprising bluish-grey clays with concretions, has furnished a number of Aptian ammonites which are distributed in three horizons. The lowest beds which contain the loosely coiled genera *Australiceras* and *Toxoceratoides* are considered by Whitehouse (1926) to represent a high horizon in the Lower Aptian of the European succession. Some species of *Australiceras* are very close to *Tropaeum* which is recorded in association with the smooth oxynote *Aconeceras* from the middle division of the Roma stage. In later beds *Aconeceras* is replaced by its costate derivative *Sanmartinoceras* which is accompanied by the ribbed desmoceratid *Aioloceras*. The ammonite succession therefore is consistent with that in the corresponding Aptian beds of Europe. All three horizons are stated to be present in the opal fields of New South Wales and the Stuart Range of South Australia where unusually large specimens of *Tropaeum imperator* are recorded. In the Styx and Burrum coalfields the Maryborough marine beds, which Whitehouse correlates with the lower part of the Roma stage, are followed by non-marine sandstones and shales with intercalated coal-seams.

The Tambo stage of Queensland has yielded species of *Puzosia, Beudanticeras, Mortoniceras, Prohysteroceras, Hamites, Aleteceras, Myloceras,* and *Labeceras*. The species of *Mortoniceras* and *Prohysteroceras* belong to groups that are typical of the aequatorialis zone in the Upper Albian of England. *Myloceras* and *Labeceras* have already been noted (p. 521) from the western margin of the Indian Ocean, and are of considerable significance in attesting the existence of an open Indian Ocean during late Albian time. The Tambo stage has been proved in a borehole at Patchawarra, south Australia, where blue clays contain *Labeceras* and *Hamites*; this horizon is followed by freshwater beds of the Winton stage which is thought to represent the Cenomanian stage. No ammonites of Lower and Middle Albian age are known from Australia, and the gap between the Roma and Tambo stages is said to be marked in some places by a conglomerate composed largely of belemnites and other fossils derived from the Roma Beds. This may perhaps be interpreted as a result of extensive submarine erosion.

This great marine transgression over the eastern half of Australia was thus of brief duration. The earliest Aptian zones are lacking, early and mid-Albian horizons are represented only by products of submarine erosion, and though late Albian deposits are widespread, no Neocretaceous Beds are recorded.

Several ammonites from New Caledonia, about 700 miles east of the Queensland coast were referred by W. Kilian and P. Reboul (1905) to the Valanginian genera *Polyptychites*, *Rogersites*, &c. Further study, however, led Kilian (1909) to believe that these specimens represent forms of the late Senonian genus *Kossmaticeras*, and both E. Haug (1911) and L. F. Spath (1921) mention the presence of *Madrasites bhavani* which is characteristic of Upper Trichonopoli and Aryalur horizons in south India.

New Zealand is often said to have had the same geological history as New Caledonia, but an earlier Cretaceous transgression is evident. H. Woods (1917) recognizes two well-marked horizons in the Cretaceous deposits of Canterbury and Marlborough provinces. The older beds, with an estimated thickness of about 10,000 feet, begin with a conglomerate, and this is followed by sandstones, mudstones, and limestones. The fauna is compared with that of the Lower Utatur (uppermost Albian) Beds of south India; it includes the ammonoid genera *Gaudryceras* and *Pseudhelicoceras*, besides *Inoceramus concentricus* and other lamellibranchs. The newer beds, containing a straight ammonoid compared with *Eubaculites vagina*, together with species of *Kossmaticeras*, are referred to the upper part of the Senonian stage. L. F. Spath (1921) remarks that species of the kossmaticeratid genera *Madrasites*, *Gunnarites*, and *Grossouvreites* are typical of late Senonian horizons throughout the Indo-Pacific region, whereas most of the European species recorded as '*Kossmaticeras*' belong to another group to which the name *Pseudokossmaticeras* has since been given.

From the islands of Seymour and Snow Hill off the coast of Grahamland, more than 4,000 miles south-east of New Zealand, Neocretaceous strata which compare palaeontologically with the Upper Trichinopoli and Aryalur Beds of south India, have been described by W. Kilian and P. Reboul (1909). The ammonite fauna is remarkable for the great development of *Kossmaticeras* and its allies, many species being identical or comparable with the Indian forms. These are associated, as in India, with other desmoceratids such as *Pachydiscus* and *Hauericeras*, with rare heteromorphs including *Pseudophyllites* and *Diplomoceras*, and with occasional specimens of the lytoceratid *Gaudryceras*.

A similar Maestrichtian or late Campanian fauna is recorded by W. Paulcke (1905) from southern Patagonia; the assemblage again includes the widespread species of *Kossmaticeras*, *Pachydiscus*, *Gaudryceras*, and *Eubaculites*, together with forms that show close relations with *Hoplitoplacenticeras*. But at various places farther north in this region older Cretaceous faunas have been described from time to time. The Neocomian stage is represented by Infra-Valanginian and Valanginian horizons near Lake Argentino and Lake Pueyrredon; the faunas contain such widespread genera as *Berriasella*, *Substeueroceras*, *Himalayaites*, *Blanfordiceras*, *Spiticeras*, and *Neocomites*, as well as the purely local berriasellids *Favrella* and *Hatchericeras*. Higher horizons appear around Lake San Martin where the Hauterivian *Leptoceras* and *Leopoldia*, the Aptian *Uhligella* and *Sanmartinoceras*, the Albian *Beudanticeras* and *Cleoniceras* are among the ammonites recorded. Farther north, in the Neuquen territory of Argentina, C. E. Weaver (1931) has described a succession of ammonite-faunas which apparently represent Infra-Valanginian and Hauterivian horizons.

On the island of Quiriquina in Concepcion Bay, Chili, sandy limestones and glauconitic marls, with a well-preserved molluscan fauna of Neocretaceous age, are transgressive on metamorphic schists. The ammonites include species of *Pachydiscus*, *Kossmaticeras*, and *Eubaculites* already noted as characteristic of the Maestrichtian stage.

Most stages of the Cretaceous system have been noted in the Andes of Peru and Colombia, but the zonal record is apparently incomplete. Horizons of the Neocomian stage are indicated by the ammonite genera *Spiticeras*, *Neocomites*, &c. in Valanginian strata near Lima. Barremiar ammonites include species of *Pulchellia* and the closely related *Karstenia*; the first of these also occurs in Spain and north Africa, and is probably a desmoceratid derivative through *Paraspiticeras*. Rudist Limestones containing *Requienia* and *Agria* are referred to the Aptian stage which is also represented by limestones and marls containing ammonites and echinids; the ammonites include desmoceratids and parahoplitids, among which *Colombiceras*, a local offshoot from *Parahoplites*, is noteworthy. Albian cephalopods are represented by species of *Gaudryceras*, *Lyelliceras*, *Douvilleiceras*, *Knemiceras*, *Pervinquieria*, *Oxytropidoceras*, &c. Records of the Cenomanian genera *Acanthoceras* and *Neolobites* are followed by the Turonian *Mammites* and *Vascoceras*. Among the Senonian genera recorded are *Buckiceras*, *Heterotissotia*, *Gauthiericeras*, *Barroisiceras*, *Lenticeras*, and *Tissotia*, along with the lamellibranch *Roudairea*. Full details of the succession await further investigation, and the records from Ecuador and Venezuela are still more incomplete.

Passing, for the moment, the Cretaceous succession of Mexico which has close relations with the Atlantic region, a series of transgressions from the Pacific Ocean is indicated by the Cretaceous deposits of California and Oregon. The lower members of the succession, described by F. M. Anderson (1938), occupy certain embayments extending for some 200 miles in a meridional direction. In some of them the Knoxville Beds of Neojurassic age had already accumulated. The Palaeocretaceous Shasta stage, resting with slight discordance on Knoxville Beds, begins with the Paskenta Beds, a group of sandy shales which has yielded ammonites of Infra-Valanginian and Valanginian age. Among the genera, *Substeueroceras*, *Berriasella*, *Spiticeras*, *Dichotomites*, *Neocomites*, *Simbirskites*, *Polyptychites*, and *Bochianites* may be noted, along with a constant abundance of the lamellibranch *Buchia*, often recorded as *Aucella*. Some of these are immigrants from the north, and others have affinities with Mexican and South American forms. The overlying Horsetown stage of sandstones and shales ranges from

Hauterivian to Albian in the European classification. The earliest beds, with species of *Neocraspedites*, *Hoplocrioceras*, and *Lytoceras*, are followed by Barremian Beds with a representative crioceratid fauna. Aptian horizons are indicated by the ammonites *Parahoplites*, *Cheloniceras*, *Tropaeum*, &c., and early Albian horizons by *Acanthoplites*, *Douvilleiceras*, and *Oxytropido-ceras*. Most of the Albian stage is apparently cut out by unconformity, above which the Chico Series is transgressive; it is discordant on the Horsetown Beds, and in the Coast Ranges and Sierra Nevada it rests directly on Jurassic strata. Records of ammonites from the lower part of the Chico Series include Cenomanian forms referred to species of *Acanthoceras* and *Metacalycoceras*. F. M. Anderson (1931) has described species of *Fagesia* from the middle portion, and the same, or associated, beds contain species of *Metaplacenticeras*, *Lewesiceras*, and *Prionotropis* as well as *Inoceramus labiatus*, all characteristic Turonian fossils. The upper beds of the series contain ammonites which, according to E. Haug, have Maestrichtian affinities; they include species of *Pachydiscus* and *Baculites*, with others whose generic identity is not apparent from the lists. Taken as a whole, the Californian sequence is broken, and presumably indicates two or three separate local transgressions.

A further transgression appears on the western coast of Canada (Map, Fig. 77). On the Queen Charlotte Islands there is a thick series of Cretaceous sandstones, shales and conglomerate which rests unconformably on Jurassic strata, the whole being disturbed by faulting and folding. The lower portion contains coalseams, but the Skidegate Beds at the top of the sequence have yielded ammonites, species of *Gaudryceras*, *Beudanticeras*, and *Pervinquieria*, which indicate a late Albian horizon. The younger Nanaimo Beds of Vancouver Island and the adjacent mainland are also partly marine and partly coal-bearing in character. Several marine fossils were long ago described by J. F. Whiteaves, and the series as a whole has been regarded as a possible extension of part of the Californian Chico Series.

Cretaceous rocks occupy considerable areas in Alaska. Over much of the Pacific coastal region they lie conformably on late Jurassic rocks which they resemble in the abundance of *Buchia* (= *Aucella*), though of different species. In central Alaska and the Yukon Valley the basal Cretaceous deposits rest with slight discordance on Triassic or older strata. In his excellent summary of Alaskan Mesozoic stratigraphy, G. C. Martin (1926) records ammonites from the Chinitna Valley and attributes them mainly to the Neocomian stage; it seems, however, that the lists are in need of critical revision. But in general the Alaskan Aucella-faunas may be regarded as equivalent to the similar assemblages in British Columbia and California, and they provide a link between the North Pacific occurrences and those in the Arctic regions and northern Russia. The Neocretaceous stages in Alaska also consist of clastic rocks, with coal-seams at some horizons.

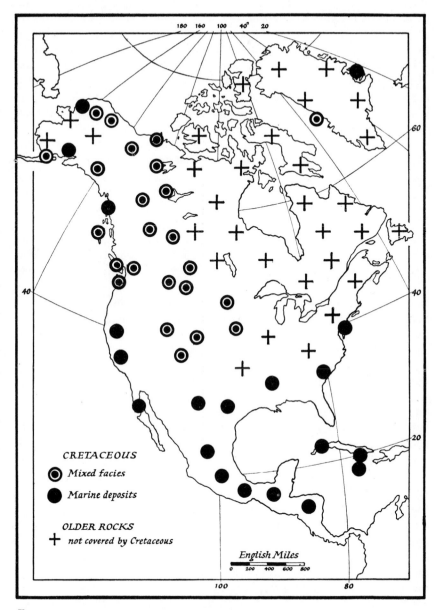

CRETACEOUS
⊙ Mixed facies
● Marine deposits

OLDER ROCKS
✛ not covered by Cretaceous

English Miles
0   200   400   600   800

FIG. 77. SKETCH-MAP SHOWING GENERAL DISTRIBUTION OF CRETACEOUS
ROCKS IN NORTH AMERICA

G. C. Martin records Cenomanian and Turonian rocks in the Lower Yukon and Koyukuk valleys, and Senonian deposits in the Upper Yukon and Chinitna valleys, but again the fossil-lists seem to lack precision.

In north-western Canada Cretaceous rocks are widespread in the Lower Mackenzie Valley; a thick series of sandstones and shales has yielded fossils at some places, but the rocks have not yet been mapped in detail. P. S. Warren (1937) has recognized Aptian deposits west of the Great Bear Lake by the presence of two ammonite species named and described by J. F. Whiteaves and now referred to the genera *Beudanticeras* and *Deshayesites*. There is also a mid-Albian horizon with *Beudanticeras, Gastroplites, Lemuroceras*, and other ammonites tentatively referred to *Puzosia* and *Sonneratia*. Higher in the sequence Warren (1947) has recorded a Turonian fauna with *Inoceramus labiatus* and the ammonoids *Scaphites* and *Watinoceras*, the last genus being regarded as a useful index for basal Turonian rocks. These faunas are considered to be migrant from the Arctic Ocean, but no evidence for direct connexion has yet been recorded lower in the Mackenzie Valley. The Albian horizon has, however, been recorded from the Peace and Athabasca rivers in Alberta, and the Turonian horizon is described by L. S. Russell and R. W. Landes (1940) from a few places in the southern Alberta Plains. Higher in the Cretaceous succession, marine shales known as the Bearpaw formation are intercalated in a series of freshwater deposits; the ammonoids include *Baculites compressus, Placenticeras meeki, Acanthoscaphites nodosus*, and other species of these genera. The Bearpaw formation, which is correlated with the Campanian substage of Europe, occupies considerable areas in south Alberta, Saskatchewan and Manitoba.

The same development extends southwards into the States of Montana, Wyoming, the Dakotas, Nebraska, Kansas, Colorado, and Utah. The general sequence of strata consists of a lower series of non-marine sands and clays with coal-seams, followed by an alternating series of marine and lacustrine strata. The lower non-marine beds, known as the Dakota Series, have yielded a flora which is marked by the presence of numerous dicotyledonous angiosperms. The succeeding Colorado Series comprises a number of formations which may perhaps be taken as analogous, but not equivalent, to the European stages; the formations bear local names in the several States. The oldest is the Graneros formation of Kansas which contains species of *Acanthoceras* indicating equivalence with part of the Cenomanian stage. The Greenhorn formation of Kansas, next in succession, has yielded to A. L. Morrow (1935) species of *Mammites, Pseudaspidoceras, Tragodesmoceras* and *Baculites* by which it is correlated with Lower Turonian horizons of Europe. The corresponding Mosky Sandstone of Wyoming and Montana encloses *Metoicoceras whitei*. The Carlile formation which follows contains the later Turonian genera *Prionotropis* and *Prionocyclus* associated with species of *Vascoceras, Placenticeras* and *Baculites*. The Niobrara shales at the top of the Colorado Series, enclosing

Scaphites vermiformis and *Baculites asper*, may be of Coniacian age; the fauna extends to the Cody Shale of the Oregon basin in Wyoming, and the middle part of the Mancos Shale in New Mexico and Utah. The Montana Series begins with the Telegraph Creek Beds and Eagle Sandstone of Montana from which species of *Submortoniceras, Placenticeras, 'Scaphites'* and *Baculites* are recorded by J. B. Reeside (1927); these beds appear to correspond with horizons of Santonian and Campanian age in Europe. Similar assemblages are recorded from the upper part of the Cody Shale in Wyoming, and the lower part of the Pierre Shale of Dakota. A Sphenodiscan fauna of Campanian or Maestrichtian age is found in the upper part of the Pierre Shale and continues into the Fox Hills formation in Montana, south Dakota, Wyoming, and New Mexico. The system ends with the non-marine Lance or Laramie Series which is discussed in Chapter XIV in connexion with its unique assemblage of fossil reptiles.

In Texas the Cretaceous succession is almost entirely marine, and, as G. Scott (1926) and W. S. Adkins (1933) have shown, it is fairly complete above the Neocomian stage. The visible base is the Travis Peak formation with *Parahoplites furcatus* which represents part of the Aptian stage. Various Albian horizons are recognized in the overlying Fredericksburg and Washita formations ending with the dispar zone at the top. Then follows the Woodbine sands with plant remains, above which the Eagleford formation resumes the marine succession with representatives of the Cenomanian genera *Acanthoceras* and *Turrilites*. The upper part of the Eagleford Beds have yielded Turonian ammonites, including species of *Prionocyclus, Neocardioceras, Coilopoceras*, and *Romaniceras*. The Austin Chalk, which is transgressive in some places, contains species of *Barroisiceras, Placenticeras*, and *Texanites*, representing Coniacian and Santonian faunas. The Taylor Shale and Novarro formation, with species of *Pachydiscus* and *Sphenodiscus* are correlated with Campanian and Maestrichtian horizons. The lower part of the Midway formation is referred by G. Scott (1934) to the Danian stage. The Texan succession is closely similar to that of Mexico in which, however, some Neocomian faunas are represented.

THE BORDERS OF THE ATLANTIC OCEAN. The Caribbean region was regarded by E. Suess as the western extension of the Tethys, and C. Burckhardt (1930) has since described the close relations between the Mesozoic faunas of Mexico and those of the Mediterranean basin. The two regions were certainly in direct marine communication, possibly in the path of the transatlantic equatorial currents of the period. The Caribbean waters extended over the Mexican area, and may have connected with the Pacific Ocean during part of Cretaceous, as well as Jurassic, time. In the north, as we have seen, they extended into Texas, and at some time may have connected directly with the Arctic Ocean by way of the Great Plains. Cretaceous deposits are also present along the northern border of the Gulf of Mexico as far east as Georgia.

In the Greater Antilles marine Cretaceous deposits are transgressive over disturbed and metamorphosed rocks which are usually ascribed to the Palaeozoic group. In Cuba, Jamaica, San Domingo, and Haiti the most conspicuous rocks are rudist limestones (p. 545), but ammonites of Turonian and Senonian age have been described from Jamaica by L. F. Spath (1925), from Cuba by M. G. Rutten (1936) and from Haiti by J. B. Reeside (1947). The Haiti fauna, including species of *Texanites*, *Pachydiscus*, and *Paralenticeras*, is compared by Reeside with a similar assemblage from south-west Venezuela.

Some 2,500 miles to the south-east, Cretaceous rocks in eastern Brazil are transgressive over the margin of the ancient shield. The earliest Cretaceous beds in Bahia have yielded freshwater mollusca, fishes, and reptiles, and, in the south of the province are overlaid by a limestone containing the Upper Albian ammonite *Elobiceras*. In Sergipe, mid-Albian limestones have yielded species of *Mortoniceras*, *Douvilleiceras*, and *Oxytropidoceras*. The presence of Cenomanian horizons is uncertain, but Turonian limestones with *Vascoceras*, *Pseudaspidoceras*, and *Inoceramus* are recorded in Sergipe. An Actaeonella Limestone in Pernambuco is referred to the Lower Senonian and a higher limestone with the lamellibranch *Roudairea* is assigned to the Campanian substage. Maestrichtian horizons are represented in Parahyba and Rio Grande do Norte by limestones containing *Sphenodiscus* and *Pachydiscus*.

Across the South Atlantic Ocean, more than 3,000 miles east of Bahia, an assemblage of Upper Albian ammonoids has been described by L. F. Spath (1922) from Lobito Bay, Angola. Species of *Mortoniceras* are most abundant and are associated with forms of *Prohysteroceras*, *Elobiceras*, *Stolickzaia*, desmoceratids and heteromorphs, but, as in most transgressive deposits, *Phylloceras* and *Lytoceras* are apparently absent. S. H. Haughton (1925) has described species of *Libycoceras*, *Bostrychoceras*, and *Baculites* which indicate the presence of late Senonian horizons in the same region. This is the most southerly development of Cretaceous rocks recorded from the western coast of Africa.

Ammonites from several horizons in the Cretaceous system have been recorded by J. Lombard (1930) from localities on the French Congo coast. They include the late Albian *Elobiceras* from Corisco Bay and Elobi Island, the Turonian genera *Choffaticeras*, *Pseudotissotia*, and *Fagesia* from the neighbourhood of Libreville, the Coniacian *Barroisiceras*, *Gauthiericeras*, and *Peroniceras* from Sette Cama, and the Santonian *Texanites* from Fernand Vaz. In the littoral belt of the Cameroons, Cretaceous rocks, which rest directly on the Precambrian foundation, have yielded the Turonian *Puzosia*, *Hoplitoides*, *Neoptychites*, and the Coniacian *Barroisiceras*, *Peroniceras*, *Tissotia*, and *Pseudotissotia*.

In 1911 J. D. Falconer described Turonian deposits in the valleys of the Benue and Gongola Rivers of northern Nigeria, and H. Woods referred the ammonites to new species of *Vascoceras, Pseudaspidoceras,* and *Hoplitoides.* The last-named genus was also recorded from Southern Nigeria. At that time no earlier Cretaceous rocks were known in Nigeria, but in 1928 L. F. Spath described Albian ammonoids from Ishiago, 109 miles east of Port Harcourt. Most of them are quadrituberculate forms of *Pervinquieria* resembling those in the Upper Gault of south England, and they are associated with species of *Elobiceras* and *Stoliczkaia,* the latter being confined in England to the uppermost Albian horizon. Species of *Elobiceras, Pervinquieria,* and *Prohysteroceras* are also recorded from the southern province. Doubtless this extension of Albian deposits came from the Atlantic Ocean, for the Mediterranean transgression over North Africa reached the Saharan region only in Cenomanian time; the later Turonian rocks may, however, indicate a connexion of Atlantic and Mediterranean waters. The existence of Albian deposits on the margins of Brazil, Angola, and Nigeria leads to the view that the South Atlantic ocean existed as such throughout Cretaceous time, though its limits in places were some distance seaward of the present coasts of South America and West Africa.

In the North Atlantic region the coast between Nigeria and Morocco has provided little evidence of marine Cretaceous encroachment; a sea-urchin of the Maestrichtian genus *Physaster* from Dakar, Senegal, appears to be the only record. The Cretaceous deposits of the European embayment have already been discussed (pp. 514–20). On the American side Cretaceous rocks are sparsely developed near the present coast of the eastern United States. Here, in a belt from Long Island across New Jersey, Delaware, and Maryland into Virginia, the lower half of the system is represented by the plant-bearing beds of the Potomac Series. The succeeding marine beds begin with the Matawan formation with species of *Placenticeras, Submortoniceras, 'Scaphites'* and *Baculites,* representing late Senonian horizons. Then follows the Monmouth Series which C. Schuchert (1943) correlates with the Maestrichtian stage on the evidence of *Belemnitella* and Sphenodiscan ammonites. The Rancocas formation, for long included in the Cretaceous, has, since 1928, been transferred to the Eocene. Proceeding north-eastward along the coast nothing further is seen of Cretaceous deposits until Greenland is reached, indicating that the coast-line of that period was situated seaward of its present position.

On the west coast of Greenland, at Disko Island and Nugsuak Peninsula, plant-beds and basaltic volcanic rocks are associated with marine sediments containing *Inoceramus* and other mollusca, but no ammonites. This assemblage indicates a late Senonian age; it is the earliest marine fauna known in Davis Strait, and it provides a limiting date for the existence of the Strait as an arm of the sea.

Ammonites of various Cretaceous horizons have been collected during the last two decades from the east coast of Greenland between lat. 72° and 75° N., but only a preliminary account of the faunas, by L. F. Spath (1946), is so far available. The succession begins with conglomerates and shales from which the Infra-Valanginian *Subcraspedites* is recorded. A higher assemblage in the Neocomian stage consists mainly of an undescribed genus which may be an offshoot of the family Craspeditidae. Ammonites from the middle of the Valanginian substage are recorded from Kuhn Island and Wollaston Foreland; the genera *Lytoceras, Neocraspedites, Polyptychites, Euryptychites*, and *Dichotomites* are represented, and only two species are common to the two faunas. Among Aptian ammonites, three species, *Lytoceras polare* Ravn, *Deshayesites boegvadi* Rosenkrantz, and *Sanmartinoceras groenlandicum* Rosenkrantz are based on well-preserved specimens from Wollaston Foreland and Kuhn Island; they indicate the presence of Lower Aptian horizons. The abundance of *L. polare* shows that conditions in east Greenland were favourable to that typically Mediterranean genus. The Albian stage is represented by ammonites from several different horizons and localities. An early horizon of the stage is indicated by a rich *Leymeriella* fauna, comprising species of *Puzosia, Beudanticeras, Leymeriella*, and *Arcthoplites*. The base of the Middle Albian is indicated by moulds from Albrecht Bay assigned to *Hoplites* (s.s.). Another fauna contains species of *Dipoloceras, Euhoplites*, and *Dimorphoplites*, in addition to the common genus *Arcthoplites*; the numerous fragments of *Euhoplites* are comparable with the abundant forms in the upper part of the English Lower Gault. Some badly preserved impressions of *Gastroplites* from the west of Sabine Island may belong near the top of the Middle Albian, and another small fauna, indifferently preserved, and including a doubtful *Hysteroceras*, may be approximately the same age. No typical elements of Upper Albian faunas are known from Greenland. Impressions of Cenomanian ammonites from Traill Island, and Geographical Society Island are referred to *Schloenbachia*, and a late Turonian horizon is represented by crushed ammonites identified as *Scaphites* aff. *lamberti* (Gross.) and *Prionotropis* cf. *woolgari* (Mantell). It is evident that the western coast of Greenland was subject to small temporary transgressions of the sea, and therefore that the permanent ocean was not far distant.

Much the same succession is described by H. Frebold (1935) from islands on the Barents Shelf, namely Spitzbergen and Novaia Zemlya. The Cretaceous sequence begins with sandy shales in which nodules containing species of *Polyptychites* indicate a mid-Valanginian horizon. The Hauterivian and Barremian substages are represented in Spitzbergen by plant-bearing beds, but no Neocomian deposits above the Valanginian are known in Novaia Zemlya. The presence of marine Aptian horizons in Spitzbergen is shown by such typical genera as *Deshayesites* and *Aconeceras*, besides a heteromorph referred to *Crioceras*. These are followed by conglomerates and sandstones containing the mid-Albian ammonite *Sonneratia* cf. *jachromensis* Nikitin.

It seems clear, as pointed out by L. F. Spath (1934), that communication between the Arctic and Atlantic Oceans was effected, not merely by a narrow Shetland Strait as formerly supposed, but through the wide channel between Greenland and Scandinavia which is still open sea. Farther south the transgressive Cenomanian and late Senonian deposits of Morven and Mull in west Scotland, and of Antrim, north-east Ireland, represent separate extensions of Atlantic waters over the margins of western Britain, while an eastern arm of the same sea overflowed the coast of Yorkshire and connected through Denmark and Germany with the Mediterranean embayment.

During the Cretaceous period the great oceans must have been much as they are today apart from oscillations of the margins shown by the numerous temporary transgressions. When the smallest horizons are compared the ammonite assemblages show the same elements around all the oceans but with far greater abundance and variety in low as compared with high latitudes. This indicates a freedom of migration, which is not possible at the present day, for it was facilitated by the absence of glacial conditions at the poles.

THE RUDIST LIMESTONE FACIES. We have already noted (p. 516) that at many places in south Europe the Cretaceous deposits include limestones that contain the peculiar sessile lamellibranchs known informally as 'Rudists'. The earliest rudist genus is *Diceras* which is found in the Kimmeridgian stage of the Jurassic system, with other species in higher stages. The valves are twisted into two close spirals, and one of them, usually the left valve, is fixed by the umbonal region to some external support. The fixed valve, whether right or left, has a single hinge-tooth which fits into a socket situated between the two teeth of the free valve. Thus in the Upper Jurassic and Neocomian genus *Valletia*, which is fixed by the right valve, one of the teeth in this valve is vestigial, while the free left valve is provided with two hinge-teeth. This condition is universal among the more specialized rudist families of the Cretaceous system. It is evidently an adaptive modification, though the mechanical advantage of having two teeth in the free valve and only one in the fixed valve, is not apparent.

Other genera of the Diceratidae appear in early Cretaceous deposits, notably *Toucasia* and *Requienia*, in which the fixed left valve is spirally coiled while the free right valve is reduced to a more or less flattened lid or operculum. The familiar *Requienia ammonia* is characteristic of the 'Urgonian' Limestones of south-east France which were at first regarded as a separate stage, but are now recognized as representing a reef-like phase of the Neocomian and Aptian stages. *R. ammonia* is often associated with other rudists that are classified in the family Monopleuridae, e.g. *Monopleura, Agria, Matheronia, Pachytraga*, in which the right valve is long and conical, and the smaller left valve is almost flat; the ligament occupies a groove normal to the junction between the two valves. Other forms, like *Praecaprina* and *Offneria* of the family Caprinidae, are somewhat similar in external form, but the wall of the shell is traversed by longitudinal canals, and is often very thick, with only a small living-space for the animal. Such assemblages are typically developed in the south of France (Provence, Languedoc), and the subalpine chains of the Jura Mountains, and extend all round the Mediterranean region in the appropriate facies. Occasionally individuals are found in more northerly latitudes, as, for instance, *Toucasia lonsdaleia* in the Aptian Beds of Wiltshire, England. Where the facies is typically developed the rudists are commonly associated with the pectinid *Vola atava*, the thick-shelled gastropod *Nerinaea renauxiana*, and the cassidulid sea-urchin *Pygaulus*.

The rudist genera just mentioned persist upwards in similar deposits which are probably the equivalents of the Albian stage. The caprinid forms are increased by the addition of *Caprina* in which the free valve is large and coiled. The associated monopleurids include species of *Ethra* and *Pachytraga*, possibly also *Horiopleura*, *Polyconites*, and *Sauvagesia*. Again, this rudist fauna is best known in south Europe, from the Pyrenees and Spain to the Forest of Bakony, and also from North Africa. In the uppermost Albian deposits of Isère, France, the so-called Vraconnian stage of older authors, there appears *Durania delphinensis* which L. Moret (1936) describes as the first representative of the great family Radiolitidae. This is a solitary shell found in glauconitic sands and never forming reef-like colonies; it has a conical fixed valve, flattish free valve and the middle layer of the shell has a cellular structure. The genus persists through the remainder of the Cretaceous succession in south France and many other regions.

The rudist assemblage of the Cenomanian stage is much like its Albian predecessor, but there is a great extension of the genus *Durania* from south Europe, including Serbia, into north Africa, and northwards to north France, south England, and Westphalia. The English species *D. mortoni* (Mantell) shows a very pronounced cellular structure in the outer layer of the shell. The monopleurid *Gyropleura cornucopia* (d'Orb.) also, is recorded from the Chloritic Marl of Dorset and Wiltshire, and with *Durania* provides evidence of direct marine communication between the Mediterranean and British areas. The monopleurid genus *Caprotina*, typical of Cenomanian horizons in south Europe, shows a tendency towards submergence of the ligament in the shell-wall. It also shows a considerable development of 'accessory cavities' separating the muscle-platforms and teeth from the shell wall. This feature is accentuated in the caprinid form *Caprinula* which, like the persisting *Caprina*, has coiled valves. *Caprinula* is characteristic in Cenomanian and Turonian horizons, especially in Portugal and Sicily.

In the Turonian stage there is a decided change in rudist assemblages. Many genera of the earlier families are lacking, though the non-colonial radiolitid *Durania* persists and reaches a northerly limit in the Middle Chalk of Kent and Wiltshire, England. In south Europe it is associated with the true *Radiolites* which has symmetrically arranged hinge-teeth and submerged ligament. The caprinids are still represented by *Plagioptychus*, and the monopleurids by *Bayleia* and *Gyropleura*. The first members of the Hippuritidae appear abruptly in late Turonian horizons of the Mediterranean region, and the family persists through the remainder of the Cretaceous system. These forms have a conical fixed valve with three longitudinal grooves externally, and a flat lid-like free valve furnished with two very unequal and prominent processes for the attachment of the adductor muscles. This family is represented in the Turonian stage by the genus *Vaccinites* which is widely distributed through south Europe, eastwards through Austria into south Asia.

The Radiolitidae and Hippuritidae provide the majority of Senonian genera, *Hippurites* (s.l.) being particularly widespread, especially in the famous Hippurite Limestone of the Mediterranean borders. Various forms of the group appear in succession so that the Coniacian, Santonian, and Campanian substages can be recognized by characteristic species. These are now usually assigned to separate genera or subgenera, namely *Hippurites* (s.s.), *Vaccinites*, *Hippuritella*, *Orbignya*, *Batolites*, and *Pironaea*. They are accompanied by species of the radiolitid genera *Sphaerulites*, *Radiolites*, *Praeradiolites*, *Biradiolites*, and the recumbent *Bournonia*. The solitary *Durania* persists along with the monopleurid *Agria*. Some of the species attain considerable size, but the latest radiolitids and hippuritids found in the Garumnian (Danian) stage of northern Spain are no larger than some of the earlier members of the genera. The rudists are not known to survive Cretaceous time, but evidently excessive growth cannot have been the sole cause of their extinction.

The greatest number of known rudist species is recorded from S. European localities, particularly south France, Italy, the Alpine region and the Balkans. Similar faunas are known south of the Mediterranean at certain horizons in Algeria, Tunis, Tripoli and Egypt. Thence the rudist limestone facies extends into adjoining parts of Asia. In Syria the Lebanon Limestone has yielded species of *Eoradiolites*, *Caprinula*, &c., along with the Cenomanian ammonites *Acanthoceras* and *Neolobites*; a higher limestone carrying the Turonian *Mammites* has a rudist horizon with *Durania*, *Biradiolites*, &c. E. Frech has cited species of *Radiolites*, *Biradiolites*, *Sauvagesia*, and *Sphaerucaprina* from the Neocretaceous limestones of the Taurus and Pamphylia, and a Bithynian fauna described by J. Boehm (1927) includes the genera *Praeradiolites*, *Radiolites*, *Biradiolites*, *Durania*, *Hippurites*, and *Sabinia*. *Durania* is also recorded from Armenia.

Rich assemblages of rudists are known from Persia. Species of *Hippurites* (s.l.) from Bakhtiyari were described by S. P. Woodward as early as 1855. From this district and Luristan H. Douvillé has since recorded species of *Radiolites*, *Praeradiolites*, *Biradiolites*, *Durania*, *Hippurites*, *Lapeirouseia*, besides the last surviving caprinid. This was originally named *Polyptychus morgani*, but the genus was preoccupied and the shell is now accommodated in the new genus *Trechmannella* established by L. R. Cox (1933). This large recumbent form is also present in eastern Persia where the 'Hippurite Limestone' ranges from the Cenomanian to the Senonian stage; O. Kuhn (1932) records species of the hippuritid genera *Vaccinites, Hippuritella, Orbignya*, and *Pironaea* together with *Èoradiolites, Durania, Lapeirouseia* and *Osculigera*, the last two being specialized radiolitids related to *Sauvagesia*. In southern Persia, Cenomanian, and Turonian strata have yielded species of *Caprinula, Durania*, and *Sauvagesia*, while *Vaccinites* and *Trechmannella* are recorded from Maestrichtian Beds in Oman. We may note here that *Radiolites* and caprinids are reported from a brown limestone on the island of Semha, Socotra; its age is indicated by the presence of the ammonite *Placenticeras simonyi* in the overlying sandy marl. In Tanganyika, *Monopleura* and *Toucasia* are recorded from the Aptian stage, and *Radiolites* from a Turonian sandstone south-west of Dares Salaam.

Eastern Persia and Oman seem to be on the eastern margin of the area in which rudists are of common occurrence; farther east these fossils are rare and sporadic in distribution The Seistan district of Baluchistan provides only two hippuritids, referred to *Vaccinites* and *Pironaea*, and probably of early Senonian age. H. Douvillé has described *Sphaerulites, Eoradiolites*, and *Apricardia* from a locality south of Herat, Afghanistan, and *Horiopleura* and *Praeradiolites* from Gilgit in the Pamirs. Romanowsky recorded species of *Caprina, Caprotina*, and *Radiolites* from Ferghana, to which Douvillé has added *Biradiolites* and *Apricardia*. Lower Cretaceous shales in south-west Tibet have yielded *Praeradiolites*, while *Bournonia* and *Plagioptychus* are recorded respectively from Campanian and Maestrichtian Beds in central Tibet. Only two rudists are described from the Neocretaceous strata of south India, and one of these is stated by Douvillé to be indeterminable; the other is a *Bournonia* from the Ariyalur stage. H. Brouwer (1925) mentions the presence of Senonian rudists in the East Indian Archipelago, particularly of *Radiolites* from the islands of Borneo and Misool. The Cretaceous deposits of east Asia are of continental type, but a rudist shell from Japan is referred to the genus *Praecaprotina*, and may be of Cenomanian age. In spite of their rarity in the Far East, the rudists seem to show close relations throughout the eastern hemisphere.

In the western hemisphere early rudists are known from the Fredericksburg formation of Texas which is approximately equivalent to the Albian stage of Europe. At the top of the formation the Edwards Limestone has yielded species of *Toucasia, Requienia*, and *Monopleura* which compare closely with the corresponding European forms. Species of the same genera are recorded by T. S. Jones (1938) from the Aurora Limestone of Sierra de la Pina, Mexico, which is also of mid-Albian age. In South America *Requienia* is cited by various authors from beds correlated with the Aptian stage in Venezuela and Peru. It is significant that many genera characteristic of the Urgonian facies in Europe are not recorded from these American deposits.

A well-defined assemblage of hippuritids, radiolitids, and caprinids has been described from Neocretaceous strata in the West Indies, particularly Jamaica and Cuba. C. T. Trechmann (1924) states that *Hippurites* is extremely rare in Jamaica, and the specimens of *Orbignya* so far described are so indifferently preserved that they cannot be determined specifically. The genus *Barrettia* is the most highly specialized and also the largest of the hippuritids, attaining a height of 2 feet and a diameter of more than 1 foot; its thick shell has a remarkable cellular structure. *Praebarrettia* is more like the European *Pironaea* but tends to develop the structure of *Barrettia*. These two genera are based on Jamaican types and evidently represent a local development of the Hippuritidae. Most of the radiolitids are referred to local species of *Biradiolites*; the genera *Bournonia* and *Lapeirouseia* are only sparsely represented. There is also the gigantic *Titanosarcolites*, sometimes 6 feet in length, in which the outer shell-layer is traversed by a series of longitudinal canals; this shell was formerly placed in *Caprinula*, but Trechmann regards it as a radiolitid which adopted a recumbent habit. *Antillocaprina* shows a monopleurid arrangement of the hinge-teeth, and probably does not belong to the caprinids, which are represented in Jamaica by species of *Plagioptychus*. The Barrettia Beds are underlaid by a sandstone containing the ammonoids *Baculites* and *Pachydiscus* of Campanian or later age (L. F. Spath, 1925); the rudist fauna is therefore referred to the Maestrichtian substage. Most of these genera are present in assemblages from Cuba (H. J. Macgillvary, 1937) where two additional hippuritids, *Parastroma* and *Torreites* are developed, apparently from the *Barrettia* stock; small species of *Biradiolites* and *Bournonia* are associated with large forms of these genera, with the giant *Titanosarcolites* and with *Durania* and *Sauvagesia*. Outside the Caribbean region representatives of *Barrettia* and *Biradiolites* are cited from Guatemala, *Barrettia*, *Titanosarcolites* and the peculiar radiolitids *Tampsia* and *Chiapasella* from Mexico. *Titanosarcolites* has also been described by L. W. Stephenson (1938) from the Kemp Clay of Texas. This is the most northerly record for a named species, but fragmentary rudists in the Niobrara and Montana formations at various localities indicate a geographical range for the group as far north as Montana (lat. 47° N.). This distribution compares well with the northerly range of *Durania* in England. It is clear that this late assemblage of American rudists has comparatively few genera in common with Europe, and most of these are radiolitids from which peculiar end-forms are developed. It is doubtful if any of the American caprinids can rightly be referred to European genera, and the abundant end-forms of the hippuritids are peculiar to America. Thus the sedentary rudists of the Caribbean area show an isolated development in contrast with the contemporary free-swimming cephalopods; in view of the widespread distribution of European rudist types in southern

Stratigraphical Distribution of Rudist Genera in the Eastern Hemisphere

	Stages	Hippuritidae	Caprinidae	Diceratidae	Monopleuridae	Radiolitidae
7	MAESTRICHTIAN	Pironaea 6–7	Trechmannella 7			Bournonia 6–7
6	SENONIAN	Batolites 6 Orbignya 5–6 Hippuritella 5–6	Sabinia 6 Sphaerucaprina 5–6			Biradiolites 5–7
5	TURONIAN	Vaccinites 5–7 Hippurites (s.s.) 5–6	Plagioptychus 4–5		Bayleia 5	Radiolites 5–7 Sphaerulites 4–6
4	CENOMANIAN		Caprinula 4–5 Caprina 2–4	Apricardia 4–5	Caprotina 4–5	Praeradiolites 4–6 Sauvagesia 4–5
3	ALBIAN		Offneria 2–3	Matheronia 2–4	Pachytraga 1–3	Durania 3–7 Eoradiolites 3
2	APTIAN		Praecaprina 2	Requienia 1–2 Toucasia 1–4	Horiopleura 2 Gyropleura 2–5 Monopleura 2	
1	NEOCOMIAN			Valletia 1	Agria 1–7	
	UPPER JURASSIC			Heterodiceras Diceras		

Asia, the peculiarities of the Central American assemblage appear to be incompatible with the theory of 'Continental Drift' advocated by Wegener and Dutoit.

LITERATURE

The zonal palaeontology of the Cretaceous system was hardly begun before the early years of the present century. Consequently many of the earlier writers could not state precisely the vertical ranges of the fossils they described. Also the older diagnoses of genera and species are, in many cases, too wide according to modern standards and are gradually undergoing revision. In the following list the chief works containing illustrations of fossils are cited, and where possible the titles of critical reviews are also given.

'Mollusca of the Chalk', by D. Sharpe, *Mon. Pal. Soc.*, 1853–6. This monograph was left incomplete and the ammonoids have, for some years, been in need of revision. Dr. L. F. Spath has proposed new generic and specific names for forms from the Upper and Middle Chalk in 'Ammonites from the English Chalk', *Geol. Mag.*, vol. lxiii, pp. 77–83, 1926, and for those from the Lower Chalk and the Aptian in 'The Ammonite Horizons of the Gault and Contiguous Deposits', Summary of Progress for 1922, pp. 139–49, *Mem. Geol. Surv.*, 1923. In 'The Ammonites of the Gault', by L. F. Spath, *Mon. Pal. Soc.*, 1921–43, besides the description and illustration of some 300 species of ammonoids, there is a useful discussion of the palaeontological and stratigraphical conclusions, with a full list of references to literature. Dr. Spath has also revised the nomenclature of the ammonites described by A. Pavlow and G. W. Lamplugh, 'Argiles de Speeton', *Bull. Soc. Imp. Nat., Moscow*, vol. v, pp. 214–76, 455–570, 1892, in 'The Ammonites of the Speeton Clay and the Subdivisions of the Neocomian', *Geol. Mag.*, vol. lxi, pp. 73–89, 1924. 'Some Ammonoidea from the Lower Greensand', by L. F. Spath, *Ann. Mag. Nat. Hist.*, ser. 10, vol. v, pp. 417–64, 1930, is a preliminary revision of about fifty species of English Aptian ammonites, but the larger species still await illustration. C. W. and E. V. Wright have reviewed 'The Cretaceous Ammonite Genera Discohoplites and Hyphoplites' in *Q.J.G.S.*, vol. civ, pp. 477–97, 1949.

Extra-British Cephalopods are described and figured in *Les Ammonites Jurassiques et.Cretacees*, by F. Roman, Paris, 1938. African forms are discussed by L. F. Spath in 'Cretaceous Cephalopoda from Zululand', *Ann. S. Afr. Mus.*, vol. xii, pp. 217–321, 1921; in 'Cretaceous Ammonites from Angola', *Trans. Roy. Soc. Edin.*, vol. liii, pp. 91–160, 1922; in 'Upper Albian Ammonites from Portuguese East Africa', *Ann. Transvaal Mus.*, vol. xi, pp. 179–200, 1925; in 'The Albian Ammonoidea of Nigeria', *Geol. Surv. Nigeria*, Bull. No. 12, pp. 51–54, 1928; 'The Cephalopoda of the Uitenhage Beds', *Ann. S. Afr. Mus.*, vol. xxviii, pp. 131–57, 1929. A magnificent memoir entitled 'Recherches Geologiques à Madagascar, 1. La Geologie du Nordouest', by H. Besairie, *Mem. Acad. Malgache*, vol. xxi, pp. 1–259, 1936, contains excellent figures of many Madagascan ammonites. Indian faunas are described by L. F. Spath in 'The Jurassic and Cretaceous Ammonites and Belemnites of the Attock District', *Pal. Indica.*, N.S., vol. xx, Mem. 4, pp. 1–38, 1934, and 'The Cephalopoda of the Neocomian Belemnite Beds of the Salt Range', ibid., vol. xxv, Mem. 1, 1939. Many later forms are described and figured in 'The Cretaceous Fauna of Southern India', by F. Stoliczka, *Pal. Indica*, 1861–73, and 'The Fauna of Baluchistan', by F. Noetling, ibid., 1897, but the generic names need revision. 'The Cretaceous Ammonoidea of Eastern Australia' are described and figured by F. W. Whitehouse in *Mem. Queensland Mus.*, vol. viii, pp. 195–242, 1926, and vol. ix, pp. 109–20, 1927. From the Antarctic region, W. Kilian and P. Reboul discuss 'Les Cephalodes des Iles Seymour et Snow Hill' in *Wissens. Ergebn. Schwedischen Sud-*

polar Expedit. 1901–3, vol. iii, part 6, Stockholm 1909, and 'Die Cephalopoden der Oberen Kreide Sudpatagoniens' are described by W. Paulcke in *Ber. Natur. Ges. Freiburg*, vol. xv. 1907. C. Weaver discusses Palaeocretaceous faunas from central Argentina in *Mem. Univ. Washington*, vol. i, 1931, and other South American faunas, with references to literature, are listed by H. Gerth in *Geologie Sudamerikas*, vol. ii, 1935.

In 'Étude synthetique sur le Mesozoique Mexicain', *Mem. Soc. palaeont. Suisse*, vol. 1, pp. 125–280, 1930, C. Burckhardt has summarized the Mexican succession, and later R. W. Imlay has described 'Lower Neocomian Fossils from the Miquihuana Region, Mexico', in *Journ. Palaeont.*, vol. xi, pp. 552–74, 1937. L. F. Spath discusses 'Senonian Ammonoidea from Jamaica' in *Geol. Mag.*, vol. lxii, pp. 28–32, 1925; M. G. Rutten lists ammonites in the 'Geology of the Northern Part of Province Santa Clara, Cuba, in *Geog. geol. Medediel*, No. 11, Utrecht, 1936, and J. B. Reeside records *Upper Cretaceous Ammonites from Haiti* in U.S. Geol. Surv., Prof. Paper No. 214 A, 1947. The modern reading of the Texan Cretaceous succession is given by G. Scott in 'A New Correlation of the Texan Cretaceous', *Amer. Journ. Sci.*, ser. 5, vol. xii, pp. 157–61, 1926; and by L. W. Stephenson in 'Correlation of the Upper Cretaceous or Gulf Series of the Gulf Coastal Plain', ibid., vol. xvi, pp. 485–96, 1928. W. L. Moreman has discussed the 'Palaeontology of the Eagleford Group of North and Central Texas' in *Journ. Palaeont.*, vol. xiv, pp. 192–220, 1942. F. M. Anderson has described *Lower Cretaceous Deposits in California and Oregon* in Geol. Soc. Amer., Spec. Paper No. 16, 1938; and has recorded 'The Genus Fagesia in the Upper Cretaceous of the Pacific Coast' in *Journ. Palaeont.*, vol. v, pp. 121–6, 1931. J. B. Reeside has discussed the *Cephalopoda of the Eagle Sandstone and Related Formations in the Western Interior of the United States* in U.S. Geol. Surv., Prof. Paper No. 151, 1927; and A. L. Morrow has described 'Cephalopods from the Upper Cretaceous of Kansas' in *Journ. Palaeont.*, vol. ix, pp. 463–73, 1935. Neocretaceous ammonite faunas are listed by L. S. Russell and R. W. Lander in *Geology of the Southern Alberta Plains*, Canada Geol. Surv. Mem. 221, 1940. Farther north, P. S. Warren has recorded an 'Aptian Horizon in the Cretaceous of the Lower Mackenzie Valley' in *Journ. Palaeont.*, vol. xi, pp. 69–72, 1937, and has described other 'Cretaceous Fossil Horizons in the Mackenzie Valley' in *Journ. Palaeont.*, vol. xxi, pp. 118–23, 1947. G. C. Martin gives lists of Cretaceous ammonites in his *Mesozoic Geology of Alaska*, U.S. Geol. Surv. Bull. 776, 1926, but the nomenclature needs revision. 'Preliminary Notes on the Cretaceous Ammonite Faunas of East Greenland', by L. F. Spath in *Medd. Groenland*, vol. cxxxii, no. 4, 1946, may be compared with the summary given in *Geologie von Spitzbergen*, by H. Frebold, 1935.

Other groups of mollusca are reviewed in 'The Gault Aporrhaidae', by J. S. Gardner, *Geol. Mag.*, vol. xii, pp. 49–56, 124–30, 198–203, 291–8, 392–400, 1875; 'The Mollusca of the Chalk Rock', by H. Woods, Part I, *Q.J.G.S.*, vol. lii, pp. 68–98, 1896, Part II, ibid., vol. lxxx, pp. 377–404, 1897; 'The Cretaceous Lamellibranchia of England', by H. Woods, *Mon. Pal. Soc.*, 1899–1913; 'The Evolution of the Genus Inoceramus in the Cretaceous Period', by H. Woods, *Q.J.G.S.*, vol. lxviii, pp. 1–20, 1912. General accounts of the specialized rudist lamellibranchs have been written by L. R. Cox, 'The Evolutionary History of the Rudists', *Proc. Geol. Assoc.*, vol. lxiv, pp. 370–88, and by H. Douville, 'Les Rudists et leur évolution', *Bull. Soc. geol. France*, vol. i, pp. 319–58, 1935. Detailed studies within the group have been published by O. Kuhn in 'Rudistae from Eastern Persia', *Rec. Geol. Surv. India*, vol. lxvi, pp. 151–79, 1932; by L. Moret in 'Revision du genre Durania', *Trav. Lab. geol. Univ. Grenoble*, vol. xviii, pp. 157–80, 1936; by C. T. Trechmann, 'The Cretaceous Limestones of Jamaica and their Mollusca', *Geol. Mag.*, vol. lxi, pp. 385–410, 1924; by H. J. Macgillavry, *Revisional Studies in*

Rudistid Palaeontology, Univ. of Utrecht, 1937; and by L. W. Stephenson, *A New Upper Cretaceous Rudistid from the Kemp Clay of Texas*, U.S. Geol. Surv., Prof. Paper, No. 193 A, 1938.

The Cretaceous Brachiopoda were first collectively described by T. Davidson in 'British Brachiopoda', vol. i, Part II, *Mon. Pal. Soc.*, 1851; Supplement, ibid., 1874. Certain groups have since been revised in 'Morphology and Zonal Distribution of some Chalk Terebratulids', by M. R. Sahni, *Ann. Mag. Nat. Hist.*, ser. 9, vol. xv, pp. 353–85, 1925; and, by the same author, 'The British Chalk Terebratulidae', *Mon. Pal. Soc.*, 1929; also by N. E. Pettit, 'The Rhynchonellidae of the British Chalk', ibid., Part I, 1950 (in progress).

The echinoderms are monographed in 'The British Fossil Echinodermata from the Cretaceous Formations', vol. i. Echinoidea, by T. Wright, *Mon. Pal. Soc.*, 1864–82; vol. ii. Asteroidea and Ophiuroidea, by Sladen and Spencer, ibid., 1891–1908. A. W. Rowe has since made 'An Analysis of the Genus Micraster', *Q.J.G.S.*, vol. lv, pp. 494–547, 1899. The application of evolutional stages in *Micraster* to stratigraphy is further explained in 'The Zones of the White Chalk of the English Coast', by A. W. Rowe, with Cliff Sections and Index, by C. D. Sherborn: I. Kent and Sussex, *Proc. Geol. Assoc.*, vol. xvi, pp. 289–368, 1901; also vol. xvii, p. 190, 1901; II. Dorset, ibid., vol. xvii, pp. 1–76, 1902; III. Devon, ibid., vol. xviii, pp. 1–51, 1904; IV. Yorkshire, ibid., vol. xviii, pp. 193–296, 1904; V. Isle of Wight, ibid., vol. xx, pp. 209–352, 1908. W. K. Spencer has summarized 'The Evolution of the Cretaceous Asteroidea', in *Phil. Trans. Roy. Soc.*, ser. B, vol. 204, pp. 99–177, 1913.

Other groups of invertebrate fossils are described in 'Growth Stages in Parasmilia', by W. D. Lang, *Proc. Zool. Soc. London*, pp. 285–307, 1909; 'Fossil Sponges', by G. J. Hinde, *Brit. Mus. Cat.*, 1883; 'The Entomostraca of the Cretaceous Formation in England', by T. R. Jones, *Mon. Pal. Soc.*, 1849; a supplementary monograph by T. R. Jones and G. J. Hinde was published in 1890.

Information concerning the numerous fossil fishes is given in 'The Fossil Fishes of the English Wealden and Purbeck Formations', by A. S. Woodward, *Mon. Pal. Soc.*, 1916–19; 'The Fossil Fishes of the English Chalk', by A. S. Woodward, *Mon. Pal. Soc.*, 1902–12; 'The Teeth of Ptychodus and their Distribution in the English Chalk', by G. E. Dibley, *Q.J.G.S.*, vol. lxvii, pp. 263–77, 1911. The land-vertebrates are discussed in Chap. XIV of the present work.

XIV

MESOZOIC LAND-FAUNAS

THE land-animals of the Triassic system are closely related to certain of their Permian forerunners discussed in Chapter IX, and likewise are known only from a small number of widely scattered regions.

Among the Stegocephalians the small Lepospondyli, Phyllospondyli, and Adelospondyli are no longer in evidence, but an important group of labyrinthodonts is characteristic of Triassic rocks. In a survey of the rhachitomous and stereospondylous amphibia, D. M. S. Watson (1919) shows that 'even with known forms there is a complete gradation of structure between the orders which merely mark evolutionary stages'. We have noted that the dominant genera in Permian rocks are in the rhachitomous grade, which persists, in the family Rhinesuchidae, into early Triassic horizons. *Rhinesuchus* itself, with several species from African localities (R. Broom, 1912; S. H. Haughton, 1915), is also represented in the early Trias of Vologda, north-west Russia.

A more advanced genus, *Wetlugasaurus*, originally described from the Palaeotriassic rocks of Wetluga River, north Russia (Riabinin, 1930), has since been recorded from east Greenland (Save-Soderbergh, 1935), and Watson (1942) states that it, or a close ally, is represented among undescribed material from East Africa. These rhachitomous genera lead to the stereospondylous family Capitosauridae which includes aquatic forms like *Capitosaurus* recorded from the Lower Trias of Germany, Siberia, and South Africa, and the later, but closely related, *Cyclotosaurus*, known from Germany, England, Australia, and more doubtfully from Spitzbergen (Woodward, 1932). The Neotriassic Metoposauridae appear to be very similar in structure. The family is represented in Germany by *Metoposaurus*, but the other genera so far described (*Buettneria*, *Anaschisma*, &c.) are from localities in North America. The largest of all labyrinthodonts, *Mastodonsaurus*, recorded from the Keuper Series of Wurtemburg, England (Miall, 1874) and other parts of Europe, is regarded by Efremov (1940) as a probable descendant of *Benthosuchus*, so abundant in the Neopermian rocks of Russia. A rather different group of broad-skulled stereospondyls contained in the Brachyopidae, and including the Indian *Brachyops* (T. Huxley, 1859; R. Broom, 1915), the African *Batrachosuchus* (R. Broom, 1903) and the German *Plagiosternum* (E. Fraas, 1889), may be derived from the Russian *Dwinasaurus* of Neopermian age (Watson, 1919). The Russian *Benthosaurus* and its allies, of similar age (Efremov, 1929), seem to indicate the ancestry of the Triassic family Trematosauridae, members of which are widely distributed. *Trematosaurus* has left abundant remains in the Bunter Sandstone of north Germany (Burmeister, 1840) and a distinct species is described from the Kalmuck Steppe, Siberia. *Tremato-suchus* is represented in South Africa (S. H. Haughton, 1915; Watson, 1919) and Rybinsk, Russia (Riabinin, 1927). The doubtful *Gonioglyptus* (T. Huxley, 1865) and *Glyptognathus* (Lydekker, 1882) are based on bones from the Panchet Beds of India. The genera *Lyrocephalus, Lonchorhynchus, Platystega, Tertrema* of Wiman (1914), and *Aphaneramma* (A. S. Woodward, 1904) form an assemblage in the Mesotriassic rocks of Spitzbergen; the first of these genera is also recorded from east Greenland (Save-Soder-bergh, 1935).

Many of the earliest reptiles are still so imperfectly known that their classification is only provisional, but it is generally agreed that the main groups can be diagnosed by reference to the arrangement of the roofing bones in the temporal region of the skull. The anapsid reptiles, represented by the Cotylosauria, have a continuous cranial roof like their stegocephalian ancestors, and, as we have noted (p. 363), are mainly restricted to Permian rocks. There is, however, one Triassic family, the Procolophonidae, de-rived from the Russian nyctiphuretids, which is widely distributed in South Africa, Europe, and North America. Genera of this family include *Procolophon* from the Karroo system (Upper Beaufort Beds) of South Africa (R. Owen, 1876; D. M. S. Watson, 1914), *Telerpeton* from the Triassic Beds of Elgin, Scotland (Boulenger, 1904), *Sclerosaurus* from the Lower Trias of Switzerland (Meyer, 1837), *Trilophosaurus* from the Upper Trias of Texas, U.S.A. (E. C. Case, 1928). We may note here that the Chelonia (turtles) first appear in the Upper Keuper of Germany, showing all the typical features of the order which are not greatly modified during all their subsequent history; the turtles are now generally regarded as most nearly related to the Cotylosauria.

In the synapsid (therapsid) type of skull, represented in many of the Thermorpha, the roofing bones of the temporal region form a single broad arch with a single temporal vacuity on each side. This group again is mainly distributed in Permian strata (pp. 371–3) but some genera are known from early Triassic horizons. These include the dicynodont *Lystrosaurus* from the Middle Beaufort Beds of South Africa and equivalent strata in India, China, and Indochina. Several other dicynodont genera are recorded only from the Middle Beaufort Beds of South Africa, and the Upper Beaufort Beds of the same region contain species of the specialized *Kannemeyeria*; the allied genus *Stahleckeria* has been described (Huene, 1931) from the Triassic rocks of Brazil. A number of cynodont genera, notably *Cynogna-thus*, also appear in the Upper Beaufort Beds, following earlier members of the same family: most of them are not known outside Africa, but *Gompho-dontosuchus* (Huene, 1928) represents the group in the Trias of Brazil.

We are not directly concerned here with the parapsid condition in which a single temporal vacuity on each side occupies a position nearer the median line of the skull, for it is best known in the marine ichthyosaurs, placodonts, and sauropterygians. But the diapsid reptiles, with both lateral and upper temporal vacuities on each side of the skull, are of extreme importance. The oldest diapsid forms known are *Youngina* and its allies from the late Permian rocks of Africa (R. Broom, 1914, 1926). These are placed in the order Thecodontia (suborder Eosuchia), a generalized group of small crawling animals, with short snout, large orbits, and well-developed dermal armour. From them may be derived the small lizard-shaped reptiles which are placed in the suborder Pseudosuchia, and distributed in three families. The Aetosauridae, typified by the well-known *Aetosaurus* from the Keuper Series of Germany (O. Fraas, 1877), include also the German *Dyoplax* (O. Fraas, 1867), with the North American *Typothorax*, *Stegomus* (Marsh, 1896), and *Stegomosuchus* (Huene, 1922). In the Ornithosuchidae the dermal armour consists of two rows of narrow plates on the back; *Ornithosuchus* and *Erpetosuchus* (E. T. Newton, 1894) are present in the Trias of Elgin, Scotland, *Saltoposuchus* (Huene, 1921) in that of Wurtemburg, *Euparkeria* and *Browniella* (R. Broom, 1913) in that of South Africa. The third family, Sphenosuchidae, is so far represented only by *Sphenosuchus* (S. H. Haughton, 1915) from the Stormberg Beds of South Africa; the pectoral arch of this form is very like that of the crocodiles, and, with other features, provides evidence that this group has a pseudosuchian ancestry.

The thecodonts have certain features in common with the Rhynchocephalia of which three families appear in the Trias, two of them being restricted to that system. Members of the Triassic family Rhynchosauridae have a strangely discontinuous geographical distribution according to available records. The genus *Rhynchosaurus* (R. Owen, 1842) is known by skeletons from the Keuper of Shropshire, England (T. H. Huxley, 1887) and by footprints in the Keuper rocks of other English localities. Similar footprints in the Triassic strata of Massachusetts, U.S.A., are known as *Antipus* (Hitchcock, 1858). The genus *Hyperodapedon* (T. Huxley, 1869, 1887) is based on a stout skeleton from Elgin, Scotland, and fragments of other species are cited from the Trias of Devonshire, Warwickshire and the Maleri Beds of India (A. S. Woodward, 1932). *Stenometopon* (Boulenger, 1904) is a closely allied genus from the Trias of Elgin, Scotland. Several genera (*Scaphonyx*, *Cephalonia*, *Cephalastron*, *Cephalastronius*, and *Scaphonychius*) are recorded (Huene, 1929) from Triassic rocks on the Rio Grande do Sul, Brazil. There are no records of rhynchosaurians from South Africa, but the Karroo beds of Cape Province have yielded *Howesia* and *Mesosuchus* (R. Broom, 1906, 1913) which, according to S. H. Haughton (1925) belong to a closely related, though distinct, family. The apparent absence of Rhynchosauridae from Africa has led Huene (1929) to postulate a transPacific land-connexion to explain their presumed migration from India to South America, while Dutoit (1937) cites the same circumstance to support the continuity of his hypothetical southern continent. Actually, of course, the evidence is so incomplete that argument is futile until further discoveries have been made. The third family, Sphenodontidae, has a longer range than the other groups of rhynchocephalians, for genera are known from all three Mesozoic Systems, and one representative, *Sphenodon*, is still living in New Zealand. A. S. Woodward (1932) lists three Triassic genera, namely *Brachyrhinodon* from Elgin, Scotland, *Polysphenodon* from Hanover, and *Palaerodon* from South Africa, but the group is too imperfectly known to be of use in our discussion.

The lightly built pseudosuchians almost certainly include the ancestors of the deinosaurs, which differ only slightly in general structure, apart from the limbs. The **Deinosauria** form a large and varied group, which first appears in the Triassic rocks, becomes dominant in Jurassic land-faunas, and finally vanishes at the end of Cretaceous time. Records of these tetrapods are numerous in the Mesozoic systems and the known genera provide some information regarding life-provinces, though many gaps remain to be filled by future investigation. We must therefore discuss the deinosaurs in some detail.

The group comprises two distinct natural orders that apparently developed from the Pseudosuchia independently of the crocodiles and birds. One of these orders, the Saurischia, is already represented in Triassic rocks by carnivorous forms classified in the suborder Theropoda. The skeleton of these animals is lightly constructed and the jaws are armed with sabre-like teeth set in sockets. The fore-limbs, bearing prehensile claws, are always shorter than the hind-limbs, and most theropods moved habitually on the hind legs. The pelvic girdle has the triradiate form usual in reptiles, and the bones of the massive tail region are laterally compressed.

The theropods persist into Jurassic rocks and are there accompanied by another saurischian suborder termed the Sauropoda. These deinosaurs are closely related to the theropods as shown by the triradiate form of the pelvis and other features common to the two groups. But the sauropods had very different habits of life as shown by the organization of the skeleton. They are large quadrupedal forms, with long neck, short but massive trunk, and long tail; the skull is small and the jaws contain simple, spatulate teeth indicating herbivorous habits. The Jurassic sauropod genera are grouped in five families, the Cetiosauridae, Brachiosauridae, Morosauridae, Atlantasauridae, and the Diplodocidae.

The second order, Ornithischia, also includes both bipedal and quadrupedal forms, but all of them are distinguished from saurischian types by several skeletal features—especially by the quadrate form of the pelvis, the pubis having not only a forward process for abdominal support, but also a prominent posterior one parallel with the ischium. The bipedal types constitute the suborder Ornithopoda in which the forelimbs are always shorter than the hind-limbs, and the bones may be either solid or hollow.

The skull is more solidly built than in the bipedal theropods, and the dentition is generally reduced in the front of the jaws. The teeth are spatulate or leaf-like in shape indicating herbivorous habits and the forward parts of the jaws are invested in horny sheaths or beaks. There is considerable variation in the size of these animals, but they are never as big as the largest theropods.

Closely similar to the Ornithopoda in characters of the horny beak, the teeth, and structure of the pelvis are certain quadrupedal forms. By reason of this difference in habit, and also because parts of the body are covered with a series of heavy bony plates or spines, the skeletons of these animals are greatly different in general appearance from those of their bipedal relatives. It is convenient therefore to follow W. E. Swinton (1934) and treat them as a distinct suborder, the armoured deinosaurs, though A. S. Woodward (1932) includes them with the bipedal forms in one order Orthopoda. Only one family, the Stegosauridae, is known from Jurassic rocks, but others appear in the Cretaceous system.

Thus we can distinguish four deinosaurian groups with different habits of life:

1. the bipedal, carnivorous theropods,
2. the quadrupedal, herbivorous and amphibious sauropods,
3. the bipedal, herbivorous ornithopods, and
4. the quadrupedal, herbivorous, armoured deinosaurs.

Whereas only the first group is known from Triassic rocks, remains of all four suborders have been obtained from various horizons in the Jurassic system. It is now our task to examine the records from various parts of the world. Many of these records are based on fragmentary material consisting of isolated bones which have been transported, by streams or other agencies, far from the original habitat of the animals. So again we must base our discussion on the generally accepted lists of A. S. Woodward (1932) which may be supplemented by those of W. E. Swinton (1934).

THE TRIASSIC DEINOSAURS

The remains of theropods found in various Triassic rocks are classified in several families and these may be grouped according to the general habit of the animals. Large, heavy theropods are exemplified by the genus *Plateosaurus* (Meyer, 1837; Jaekel, 1913); the type-species from the Keuper Series of Germany is about 6 metres in length; other species are recorded from the Keuper of Germany and France, and from the Stormberg Beds of South Africa (R. Broom, 1911). The last-named horizon has yielded other remains for which R. Broom (1911) has established the genus *Gryponyx*. No bones of deinosaurs are known from the red sandstones of the English Trias, but footprints of various types are commonly found at certain localities. Among them are large spoors, shaped somewhat like the human hand, and usually recorded under the name *Cheirotherium*. A. S. Woodward (1932) tentatively places them with the pseudosuchian thecodonts, but D. M. S. Watson (1914) gives good reasons for reference to the Theropoda, possibly in near relation to *Plateosaurus*. Similar footprints are known from various parts of France, Germany, and Spain. The teeth of Plateosauridae are spatulate in shape and constricted at the base of the crown; other teeth, isolated from the skull but associated with vertebrae, are laterally compressed to two sharp edges with the apex curving backwards. Such teeth from the Muschelkalk and Keuper of Germany form the basis of the genus *Zanclodon* (Pleininger, 1846) which is also represented by a jaw from the Rhaetic Beds of Bridgend, South Wales (E. T. Newton, 1899). Other imperfectly known theropods placed in the family Zanclodontidae are *Teratosaurus* (Meyer, 1861) from Wurtemburg, and *Gressleyosaurus* (Rutimeyer, 1856) with species from Neotriassic rocks in Switzerland, England (H. G. Seeley, 1898), and Germany. A few genera from the Stormberg Beds of South Africa are also placed in the same family, namely *Euskelesaurus* (T. Huxley, 1866), *Melanorosaurus* (S. H. Haughton, 1924), *Gigantoscelus* and *Eucmenesaurus* (Hoepen, 1920).

Small, lightly built Theropoda are distributed in three families. The Anchisauridae is typified by *Anchisaurus* (Marsh, 1892) from the Triassic rocks of Connecticut and Massachusetts, U.S.A., while *Ammosaurus* from the former State is closely related. Isolated bones and teeth from the Magnesian Conglomerate of Bristol, England, are referred by Riley and Stutchbury (1836) to the genus *Thecodontosaurus*, and various comparable fragments are recorded from Germany, North America, Brazil, and South Africa. *Agrosaurus* (Seeley, 1891) from north-east Australia, *Massospondylus* (Owen, 1854) from the Maleri Beds of India and the Stormberg Beds of South Africa, together with the African genera *Hortalotarsus* (Seeley, 1894), *Gyposaurus* and *Aetonyx* (R. Broom, 1911), *Dromicosaurus* and *Aristosaurus* (Hoepen, 1920) are placed in the same family (A. S. Woodward, 1932). Another family, Hallopodidae, is also based on an American form (unfortunately without skull) named *Hallopus* (Marsh, 1896) from the Neotriassic rocks of Colorado, U.S.A. Other genera, more completely known, are the German *Procampsognathus* (E. Fraas, 1914) and *Pterospondylus* (Jaekel, 1913), and the Scottish *Scleromochlus* (Woodward, 1907). Two other genera, *Podokesaurus* (M. Talbot, 1911) from Massachusetts, U.S.A., and *Saltopus* (Huene, 1910) from Elgin, Scotland, are based on parts of skeletons without skulls, and are placed in a separate family Podokesauridae. Another small form, *Halticosaurus* (Huene, 1908) from the Keuper of Germany, is included in the family Coeluridae which is better represented in Jurassic and Cretaceous rocks.

We are here concerned mainly with the geographical distribution of these reptiles, taking into account their probable relationships. From this point of view the available records, scanty though they are, seem to justify a general inference. It is important, however, to realize that the records refer, in the main, to a few regions where the appropriate continental rocks are exposed and well-explored, namely western Europe, South Africa, and parts of North America. In addition, isolated localities in India, China, Australia, and Brazil have furnished a few records. So it may be that our general inference is no more than a false impression created by the incompleteness of the palaeontological record.

It will be noted in the foregoing paragraphs that large, heavy theropods are known only from Europe and South Africa, though lightly built forms are apparently distributed more widely. We may note further that few of the genera are recorded from more than one region. *Plateosaurus* is common to Europe and Africa, and the South African *Massospondylus* is also reported from India (Lydekker, 1888) but most (if not all) other genera are apparently confined to the continent in which they were first discovered and described. This may be an effect of the incomplete character of the records which is emphasized by the apparent absence of sauropods, ornithopods, and armoured deinosaurs from Triassic rocks. But even allowing for wider distribution than the records show, it would seem that the Triassic continents were not connected closely enough to allow of easy migration. In other words, the continental areas of Triassic time were more or less separate units. Consideration of the better-known deinosaur faunas of Jurassic strata will enable us to assess, in greater degree, the significance of this impression.

THE JURASSIC DEINOSAURS

GREAT BRITAIN. Over most of the British area the surviving Jurassic rocks are of marine origin and could not be expected to yield much evidence concerning the land-living deinosaurs. Deposits of several horizons, however, have yielded fragmentary remains which collectively give some idea of the fauna which inhabited the neighbouring land-area. The earliest of these horizons is the Lower Lias from which representatives of two of the great suborders have been obtained. A tooth from the Lower Lias of Dorset is recorded as *Magnosaurus lydekkeri* (Huene, 1932), a tibia from Warwickshire as *Sarcosaurus andrewsi* (Huene, 1932), and a pelvis from Leicestershire as *S. woodi* (Andrews, 1921). These are all assigned to the theropod family Megalosauridae, large bulky forms with compressed, curved, and serrated teeth. The Lower Lias of Dorset has also furnished remains of the earliest armoured deinosaur so far known. This species, *Scelidosaurus harrisoni* (Owen, 1862) is based on part of the hind limb, but the later discovery of an almost complete skeleton shows that this quadruped, about 15 feet long, possessed rows of small tubercles and keeled scutes extending along the back of the body (Swinton, 1934).

No remains of deinosaurs are so far recorded from higher horizons of the Lias, but the Inferior Oolite of Dorset has yielded part of a skeleton which Huene (1926) has named *Megalosaurus nethercombiensis*. Reptilian bones were noted in the Stonesfield Slate of Oxfordshire by Buckland as early as 1824, and afterwards referred to *Megalosaurus bucklandi* by Meyer (1832). Another species, listed as *M. bradleyi* (A. S. Woodward, 1910), from the Great Oolite of Gloucestershire, differs from other megalosaurs by the indication of a small horn on the skull just above the narial opening. This brings the form into apparent relationship with an American genus, *Ceratiosaurus* to be mentioned later (p. 559). In addition to these theropods there are records of sauropods from the Great Oolite based mainly on isolated vertebrae and teeth, but nevertheless attesting the presence of the suborder in the British area. In 1871, J. Phillips described vertebrae of *Cetiosaurus glymptonensis* and a nearly complete skeleton of *Cetiosaurus oxoniensis* from Oxfordshire; teeth from Wiltshire, described by Owen (1841) under the name *Cardiodon rugulosus*, may perhaps belong to the same genus. *Bothriospondylus*, based on vertebrae from Bradford, Wiltshire, is an allied genus with cavernous dorsal vertebrae. The armoured deinosaurs are represented by a femur of *Omosaurus vetustus* (Huene, 1910) from the Great Oolite of Oxfordshire. This form is closely allied to *Stegosaurus*, a genus known from higher beds.

The Oxford Clay, famous for its assemblage of marine reptiles discovered by A. N. Leeds and described by C. W. Andrews, has also furnished remains of deinosaurs. Parts of a megalosaurian skeleton from Weymouth form the type-specimen of *Megalosaurus parkeri* (Huene, 1926) remarkable for the unusual length of the neural spines, while bones from Oxfordshire and Dorset have long been referred to *M. bucklandi* (Meyer, 1832). *M. cuvieri* (Owen, 1842) represented by the greater part of a skeleton from Oxford, is often referred to a separate genus *Streptospondylus* (Huene, 1926). The sauropods are represented by *Cetiosaurus leedsi* (Hulke, 1887). This is a form of considerable size, with long neck and tail; its length is estimated at about 50 feet. A. S. Woodward (1905) states that the spongy texture of the bones distinguishes it from *Ornithopsis* to which the species was originally assigned. The first evidence of iguanodont deinosaurs from the Oxford Clay is provided by a femur from Great Gransden, Hunts., known as *Cryptodraco eumerus* (Seeley, 1875). Another femur, later obtained from Peterborough, is described by Lydekker (1889) under the name *Camptosaurus leedsi*; this genus has a wide geographical distribution. Remains of armoured deinosaurs are represented by the lower jaw of *Sarcolestes leedsi* (Lydekker, 1893) which shows the sigmoid curvature of the dentition typical of these forms, and also by parts of the skeletons of *Stegosaurus durobrivensis* (Hulke, 1887) and *St. priscus* (Nopcsa, 1911), all from Peterborough. The last-mentioned genus has an armour of bony scutes which, along with spines, appear to have been placed vertically with their bases embedded in the thick skin.

Representatives of all four deinosaur groups are also known from the

Kimmeridge Clay. The theropod *Megalosaurus bucklandi*, already cited from lower horizons, persists in the records, and a tooth from Wiltshire is referred to *M. insignis* (Deslongchamps, 1870). An ilium from Oxfordshire, listed as *Iliosuchus incognitus* (Huene, 1932) is also placed in the Megalosauridae. Among sauropods the family Brachiosauridae is closely allied to the Cetiosauridae already mentioned, but differs in the extreme excavation of the vertebrae and in the relative proportions of the fore and hind limbs. British examples of brachiosaurs include *Gigantosaurus megalonyx* (Seeley, 1869) typified by vertebrae and limb-bones from Ely, vertebrae of *Bothriospondylus suffosus* (Owen, 1875) from Swindon, and humeri of *Ornithopsis humerocristatus* (Hulke, 1874) and *O. manseli* (Lydekker, 1888) from Dorset. The iguanodont ornithopods are represented by the genus *Camptosaurus* to which is assigned a nearly complete skeleton from Oxfordshire originally described as *Iguanodon prestwichi* (Hulke, 1880). Bones of an armoured deinosaur from Wiltshire are described as *Omosaurus armatus* (Owen, 1875) and a spine from the same county is listed as *O. hastiger* (Owen, 1875).

The list of British deinosaurs compiled by Swinton (1934) shows no record of these animals from the Portland Stage. Moreover, in spite of the prevalence of freshwater beds in the Purbeck stage, the records from these rocks are meagre, and are confined to the Middle Purbeck Beds of Dorset. The Megalosauridae are there represented by *Nutethes destructor* (Owen, 1854), the species being based on the left ramus of a lower jaw containing recurved teeth with serrate margins. Another incomplete jaw with spatulate teeth, referred to *Iguanodon hoggii* (Owen, 1874) represents the ornithopods, while jaws of *Echinodon becklesi* (Owen, 1861) are assigned to the Stegosauridae. No sauropod remains seem to be recorded from the Upper Purbeck Beds.

Speaking generally, the British Jurassic rocks contain remains of land-living deinosaurs which in most cases have been transported into the area of marine deposition. They attest the presence of all four major groups of deinosaurs on the land bordering the sea during the greater part of Jurassic time. These records furnish a suitable basis for discussing the geographical distribution of the various Jurassic genera in other parts of the world.

WESTERN EUROPE. Remains of deinosaurs are recorded from the marine strata of northern France which accumulated between the landmasses of Armorica, the Ardennes and the Central Plateau. The fossils, however, appear to be even more fragmentary than the British examples. The Lias of Franche Comté has yielded bones of *Megalosaurus*. This genus is also recorded from the Bathonian strata of Caen in Normandy from which remains of the sauropod *Cetiosaurus* have been obtained. The Kimmeridgian stage of Le Havre and Boulogne has yielded bones attributed to *Megalosaurus*, along with those of sauropods referred to *Bothriospondylus* and of the ornithopod genus *Camptosaurus*. Furthermore, Nopcsa (1911) has described an armoured form, *Omosaurus lennieri*, on material from the Upper Kimmeridgian of Cap de la Hève. The genus *Morosaurus* has been recorded from the Portland and Purbeck stages of Boulogne.

Records from the marine strata adjacent to the Iberian meseta are similar. *Megalosaurus* is recorded from the Lias of Ruedes, Asturia, the Lusitanian near Crasto, and the Portlandian of Mont Lambert. *Morosaurus* is listed among the Oxfordian and Kimmeridgian fossils, and *Iguanodon* (or, perhaps, *Camptosaurus*) from the Oxfordian of Cap d'Espiche. These meagre records are thus consistent with those of western Europe as a whole.

Farther east, bones referred to *Cetiosauriscus greppini* have been described by Huene (1927) from Kimmeridgian rocks in Switzerland, while the famous Lithographic Stone of Bavaria has yielded the unique skeleton of the theropod *Compsognathus* (Wagner, 1864). This is a small form about 2 feet long which contrasts strongly with the massive *Megalosaurus* and its allies; the skeleton is lightly built and the nature of the teeth together with the presence of claws on the digits indicates carnivorous habits, which are further suggested by the inclusion of remains of a small skeleton within the body cavity (Huene, 1925). This Bavarian fossil thus demonstrates the presence in Europe of a theropod family so far known by one specimen from a single locality.

NORTH AMERICA. Early Jurassic deposits of continental origin are scarce in North America, and consequently little is known of the deinosaurs of this age. The oldest form so far recorded is the sauropod *Dystrophaeus* described by Cope (1877) from the Red Beds of south-east Utah, which may be equivalent in age to the Dogger of Europe.

The Upper Jurassic Morrison Beds of Colorado and adjacent States consist essentially of freshwater marls, some of which have yielded deinosaur bones in extraordinary abundance. It is perhaps significant that in some quarries sauropods are most conspicuous, the theropods, ornithopods, and armoured forms being comparatively rare, while in others, often within a short distance, the predominant forms are orthopods with but few sauropods and theropods (see Osborn, 1904; Gilmore, 1909; Stovall, 1938). In this feature Lull (1910) sees evidence that the sauropods and orthopods occupied different habitats, and we have already mentioned structural characters which indicate that the sauropods were amphibious and the orthopods mainly dry-land forms. In any case, the American deinosaurs provide interesting comparisons and contrasts with the fragmentary remains obtained from corresponding strata in Europe, and the Morrison fauna is worth discussing in some detail.

The best known theropod is *Allosaurus* (Marsh, 1877) or *Antrodemus* (Leidy, 1870) of which a nearly complete skeleton about 5 metres long is known from Colorado. This genus is the American analogue of the European *Megalosaurus* from which it differs in several skeletal features. Another form, *Ceratosaurus* (Marsh, 1884) differs from typical megalosaurs in the presence of small dermal ossifications along the back and of a horn-core on the nasal bones; the latter feature has already been noted in a small British megalosaur (p. 557). In contrast to these massive forms, the family Coeluridae comprises small and slender theropods with small skull and long neck; it includes *Coelurus* (Marsh, 1879) and *Ornitholestes* (Osborn, 1917) from Wyoming and *Tichosteus* (Cope, 1877) from Colorado, the first-named also being cited from Maryland. Another slender form, *Ornithomimus* (Marsh, 1890) is known from Colorado by the hind foot and other fragments, and a jaw named *Labrosaurus* (Marsh, 1884) is placed with it in the family Ornithomimidae.

The European sauropods are members of the two allied families Ceticsauridae and Brachiosauridae which are both represented in the Morrison Beds of the western States of America by the genera *Haplacanthosaurus* (Hatcher, 1903) and *Elosaurus* (Peterson and Gilmore, 1902) in Colorado, *Elosaurus* and *Pleurocoelus* (Marsh, 1888) in Wyoming, and the last-named genus in Maryland. Of these only *Pleurocoelus* is tentatively recorded from Europe, on the basis of teeth and vertebrae from the Wealden Beds of Sussex, England. An allied family, Morosauridae, is typified by *Morosaurus* (Marsh, 1878) a large form from Wyoming about 50 feet long, with a short, high skull and fore limbs shorter than the hind limbs. Fragments of this or some closely allied genus have been recorded from the English Wealden Beds. Very similar forms from Colorado, *Camarasaurus* (Gilmore, 1925; Lull, 1930) and *Amphicoelus* (Cope, 1877) are classified in the same family, as also is *Barosaurus* (Marsh, 1890) with larger neck and shorter tail, from south Dakota. A fourth family, the Atlantosauridae, distinguished from the foregoing by certain skeletal differences, comprises the type-genus *Atlantosaurus* (Marsh, 1877) from Colorado and Wyoming, and the well-known *Apatasaurus* (Marsh, 1877) or *Brontosaurus* (Marsh, 1879; Gilmore, 1936) from Wyoming. The latter attained a length of some 65 feet and is marked by the very small skull, long neck, short trunk with air-cavities in the vertebrae, solid and heavy limbs and long tail. Vertebrae from Utah known as *Uintasaurus* (Holland, 1924) are referred to the same family. *Diplodocus* (Marsh, 1884; Holland, 1906), known from both Colorado and Wyoming, is even longer than *Apatasaurus*, but the body is more slender and there are several differences in skeletal features, for instance the narial opening is placed at the top of the skull, so this form is classified in a monotypic family.

The Orthopoda are known in the Morrison Beds by *Laosaurus* and *Dryosaurus* (Marsh, 1878) from Colorado and Wyoming, small lightly built forms which are provisionally classified by A. S. Woodward (1932) in the Hypsilophodontidae, but their premaxillae are still unknown. The armoured deinosaurs are represented by *Stegosaurus* (Marsh, 1877) with small elongated skull, short fore limbs, long hind limbs, and dermal armour of erect, flattened bony plates extending in two rows along the back of the body (Gilmore, 1914). *Diracodon* (Marsh, 1881) from Wyoming is possibly the young of *Stegosaurus*.

In comparing the Jurassic deinosaur faunas of North America with those of Europe, two facts are at once apparent. In the first place the fragmentary records from the Lower Lias of Britain show the presence of theropods and armoured deinosaurs, sauropods appear in the Great Oolite, and ornithopods in the Oxford Clay. As the armoured forms are accepted as derived from the bipedal ornithopods, it follows that all four suborders must have been differentiated already in early Jurassic time, though little evidence is available from America. In the second place, where comparison can reasonably be made, namely in the Upper Jurassic (G. G. Simpson, 1926), the assemblages of North America show remarkable differences from those of Europe. No known genus of theropods is common to the two continents, though analogous genera of the Megalosauridae are present in both. The development of a nasal horn-core in a British species of *Megalosaurus* (p. 557) may be a secondary sexual character without significance in regard to relationship with the American genus *Ceratosaurus* (Swinton, 1934). The Coeluridae and Ornithomimidae appear to be purely American families in the Jurassic period, and though representatives of the former are recorded from the early Cretaceous Wealden Beds of England, the identification is regarded as too uncertain to be of value (Swinton, 1936). Among the sauropods, both cetiosaurs and brachiosaurs are again represented by different genera in the two continents, for the English record of the American form *Pleurocoelus* is very uncertain. Moreover, the great atlantosaurs and *Diplodocus*, according to present evidence, are peculiar to America. The remains of ornithopods are often too incomplete for comparison, but Gilmore (1909) states that *Camptosaurus prestwichi* (Hulke, 1880) from the English Kimmeridge Clay is closely related to *C. nanus* from the Morrison beds of the western United States. The only genus of armoured deinosaurs recorded from both continents is *Stegosaurus* which is listed from the English Oxford Clay and the Morrison Beds of western America.

Many of these faunal differences may be due to the fragmentary nature of the fossils and consequent faulty interpretation of their relationships. It should be noted, however, that the evidence so far available hardly supports land-connexion, much less contiguity, of North America and Europe during Jurassic time.

EAST AFRICA. A rich deinosaur fauna found in delta deposits associated with transgressive marine beds at Tendaguru in Tanganyika Territory has been described by Fraas (1908), Janensch (1925, 1929), Hennig (1924), and Parkinson (1930). The beds are classified as follows:

Trigonia schwarzi zone.	Cretaceous.
Upper deinosaur bed.	⎫
Trigonia smeei zone.	⎪
Middle deinosaur bed.	⎬ Portlandian.
Nerinaea zone.	⎪
Lower deinosaur bed.	⎭

The age of these beds has been much debated, but ultimately the question depends upon correlation of the marine beds. Now L. F. Spath (1933) has cited a species of the ammonite *Subdichotomoceras* from the *Nerinaea* horizon, while he records another species of the same genus associated with *Haploceras elimatum* (Oppel) and *Hildoglochiceras kobelli* (Oppel) from the *Trigonia smeei* Beds. Hence these beds are of Portlandian age. Above the upper deinosaur bed there is a considerable gap in the succession, for the *Trigonia schwarzi* horizon is Middle Neocomian to Aptian, the Valanginian being absent. The named deinosaurs are from the middle and upper beds, and, as the two faunas include identical genera and species, they can be discussed together as a unit.

The theropod remains are too fragmentary for more than general identification, though bones are tentatively attributed to *Megalosaurus, Allosaurus*, and *Ceratosaurus*. A smaller form, named *Elaphrosaurus bambergi* (Janensch, 1925) is referred to the Coeluridae.

Among the sauropods, two species of *Brachiosaurus, B. brancoi* and *B. fraasi*, named by Janensch (1914) are found at both horizons; they are immense forms, estimated at 60 to 80 feet long, with fore limbs longer than the hind limbs. *Dicraeosaurus*, represented by *D. hansemanni* in the middle beds and *D. satleri* in the upper bed, is usually classified with the Morosauridae, but Huene places the genus in a separate monotypic family; the neural spines are more deeply forked than in the American *Morosaurus* a feature which Swinton (1934) attributes to a rather different muscular arrangement associated with a comparatively short neck. Another sauropod genus, known by two species *Tornieria africana* and *T. robusta* (Fraas, 1908) is also assigned to the Morosauridae; it is estimated to have been 20 feet high at the shoulder. A distinct species, *T. dixeyi* (Haughton, 1928) has been described from Nyasaland.

The only ornithopod so far described is *Dysalotosaurus lettow-verbecki* (Pompeckj, 1922), a small form not much larger than a cat, from the middle deinosaur bed; it is referred to the family Hypsilophodontidae.

The armoured forms are represented at both middle and upper horizons by *Kentrurosaurus aethiopicus* (Hennig, 1924), a large form estimated at 17 feet long, having an armour of spines on the forward part of the back and on the tail, with small flat plates on the middle of the back. This animal is closely similar to *Stegosaurus*.

With reference to this assemblage, Gilmore (1939) states that 'the Tendaguru fauna with the armoured *Kentrurosaurus*, the long-spined sauropod *Dicraeosaurus* and the long-forelimbed *Brachiosaurus* (an American genus), in its broad aspect resembles the Morrison fauna of North America'. On the other hand, Nopcsa (1934) considers that both *Kentrurosaurus* and *Tornieria* had common ancestors with European types, but evolved on distinct lines of their own.

THE CRETACEOUS DEINOSAURS

The Cretaceous deinosaurs follow a continuous development from the Jurassic forms, but there are some general features that must be noted. The four great groups persist, and certain families continue from the Jurassic into the Cretaceous, but there are others which are not known below the younger system. Among the theropods, the Megalosauridae survive into the Lower Cretaceous but are not certainly known in the higher beds of the system, where the Deinodontidae, Spinosauridae, and Ornithomimidae are typical families. The sauropod families Brachiosauridae and Morosauridae likewise range into the Lower Cretaceous; thereafter the suborder is only known by the Titanosauridae which are widespread in the southern hemisphere but of sporadic distribution elsewhere. The ornithopods are represented in the Upper Jurassic and Lower Cretaceous by the Iguanodontidae which have few survivors in higher beds. The family is mainly replaced in the Upper Cretaceous by the Trachodontidae which are found chiefly in North America though some remains have also been discovered in other parts of the world. The armoured Stegosauridae appear to have become extinct by Cretaceous time but their place is taken by the Acanthopholidae, the Nodosauridae and the Ceratopsidae, heavily armoured forms which survived until the end of the period. Our review of the principal genera follows the plan adopted for the Jurassic deinosaurs.

GREAT BRITAIN. The early Cretaceous Wealden Beds of southern England, entirely of freshwater origin, have yielded an important fauna of deinosaurs. The twenty-seven species recorded from these beds include members of all the four suborders, and the assemblage is best represented in the comparatively small area of the Isle of Wight (Swinton, 1936). Many of the remains are scattered and fragmentary, doubtless owing to transport by streams, but in some cases the skeletons are almost complete and cannot have travelled far from the original habitat.

The presence of large massive theropods is attested only by fragments. A right metatarsus from Sussex is the type of *Megalosaurus oweni* (Lydekker, 1889), and numerous bones from the Isle of Wight are referred to this species. Huene (1926) refers certain megalosaurian vertebrae from Sussex to a separate genus *Altispinax* on account of the unusual height of the neural spines, but this feature may not be of generic significance. A few large vertebrae from the Isle of Wight are attributed to *Streptospondylus cuvieri* (Owen, 1842) which is typically found in the Oxford Clay. Smaller bones, referred to the family Coeluridae, represent lightly built theropods some 5 or 6 feet long which are named as follows:

Aristosuchus pusillus (Owen, 1876), known by vertebrae and associated pubes previously referred to the genus *Coelurus* (Marsh, 1884).
Calamospondylus foxi (Lydekker, 1889) based on cervical vertebrae.

Thecocoelurus daviesi (Seeley, 1888), based on incomplete anterior end of cervical vertebra.

Thecospondylus horneri (Seeley, 1882) founded on a sacrum from the Hastings Sand of Kent.

Among sauropods, *Ornithopsis hulkei* (Seeley, 1870) is known from the Isle of Wight by most of the skeleton apart from the skull; the vertebrae are remarkable for the large air-cavities in the centre giving a structure which combines mechanical strength with lightness in weight. Several species of the genus have been described, and the remains known as *Pelorosaurus conybeari* (Mantell, 1850) may also be referable to *Ornithopsis*. Teeth and vertebrae of a small sauropod, *Astrodon valdensis* (Lydekker, 1890) are referred tentatively to an American genus, but the identification is regarded as very uncertain (Swinton, 1936). The sauropod fossils so far cited belong to the family Brachiosauridae, and the allied family Cetiosauridae is possibly represented by vertebrae from Tetham listed as *Cetiosaurus brachyurus* (Owen, 1841). This author described other vertebrae as *C. brevis*, but the species was later transferred to the genus *Morosaurus*. The relationships, however, are very doubtful, for while Huene (1932) believes the bones to be megalosaurian, Swinton (1936) compares them with vertebrae of the American forms *Apatasaurus* and *Camarasaurus*. Vertebrae of *Titanosaurus* from the Isle of Wight represent the earliest known occurrence of the Titanosauridae which is better represented in the Upper Cretaceous of the southern hemisphere. The bones are too worn to be specifically determinable but they are important as attesting the presence of the genus in the British area.

Two families of the Ornithopoda are represented in the Wealden Beds. The first is typified by *Hypsilophodon foxi* (Huxley, 1870), of which two almost complete skeletons, about 5 feet high, have since been described (Swinton, 1936b). This form is one of the few ornithopods with teeth in the front of the upper jaw, and the skin was reinforced with small flat bony plates, thus suggesting some affinity with the armoured deinosaurs. The second family of these bipedal herbivores is named after *Iguanodon* which is represented by several species. *I. mantelli* (Meyer, 1832), with a long and narrow skull, has a wide distribution in southern England. This form apparently attained a maximum length of about 20 feet, but it is surpassed in size by *I. bernissartensis* (Boulenger, 1881) which is some 35 feet long and has a short, broad skull. *I. atherfieldensis* (Hooley, 1925), known by an almost complete skeleton about 20 feet long, has been redescribed by Swinton (1933). Other species, such as *I. dawsoni* (Lydekker, 1888), *I. fittoni* (Lydekker, 1889), and *I. hollingtonensis* (Lydekker, 1889) are less completely known, but they show considerable variation within the genus. Certain bones from the Wealden Beds are listed as *Camptosaurus valdensis* (Lydekker, 1889) but their reference to the American genus seems of doubtful validity. Again, little is known about the general characters of two small iguanodonts named *Vectisaurus valdensis* (Hulke, 1879) and *Sphenospondylus gracilis* (Lydekker, 1888), which are founded mainly on vertebrae from the Isle of Wight.

Three distinct genera and species of armoured deinosaurs are known from the English Wealden Beds. *Hylaeosaurus armatus* (Mantell, 1833) is founded on a large portion of the skeleton contained in a slab of rock from Sussex. This is a quadrupedal form of considerable size armed with two rows of bony spines along the back, and bony plates elsewhere on the body and tail. The skull is unknown, but the jaw named *Regnosaurus northamptoni* (Mantell, 1845) from Sussex is referred to *Hylaeosaurus* by Owen (1857). This genus is assigned to the family Acanthopholidae, while two other species are classified with the Nodosauridae. One of these, *Polacanthus foxi* (Hulke, 1881), probably about 15 feet long, is represented by vertebrae, ribs, bones of the hind limbs and portions of the dermal armour, but the skull and fore limbs are missing. The armour consists of a continuous shield of fused bony plates over the pelvic region, with a double row of conical spines on the back and of divergent sharp-edged plates on the tail. The third species, originally referred to *Hylaeosaurus* and later named *Polacanthoides ponderosus* (Nopcsa, 1929), is known only by a scapula and humerus of nodosaurian type.

Only one deinosaur is known from British Aptian deposits, namely *Deinodocus mackesoni* (Owen, 1884) from the Lower Greensand of Hythe, Kent. This species is based on the humerus and ulna which were fully described by A. S. Woodward (1908) as belonging to a large, slightly built sauropod with remarkably slender fore limbs. Later (1932) in assigning *Deinodocus* to the Brachiosauridae, Woodward remarks that it is perhaps identical with *Ornithopsis*.

Several deinosaur genera are recorded from the Cambridge Greensand, representing the top of the Albian stage (Seeley, 1879). The assemblage is remarkable because no theropod remains are cited, and the sauropods are only represented by a single caudal vertebra, known as *Macrurosaurus semnus* (Seeley, 1876), which is referred to the Titanosauridae. While *Iguanodon* itself is not recorded, other species of the same family are known at this horizon. *Anoplosaurus curtonotus* (Seeley, 1879) is represented by a lower jaw, vertebrae, ribs, shoulder girdle and limb bones, and *Eucercosaurus tanyspondylus* (Seeley, 1879) by part of the vertebral column. The presence of Trachodonts, which are the ecological, if not genetic, successors of the Iguanodonts, is shown by the record of a single tooth named *Trachodon cantabrigensis* (Lydekker, 1888) and another species, *Syngonosaurus macrocercus* (Seeley, 1879) based on part of a vertebral column. The armoured deinosaurs are three species of *Acanthopholis*, based mainly on characters of the vertebrae. Considering the assemblage as a whole one notes that it differs more from that of the Wealden Beds than the latter differs from the deinosaur associations of the Upper Jurassic.

Remains of deinosaurs are rarely found in the Upper Cretaceous rocks of Britain. This is explained by the characters of the chalk, a marine deposit formed off the coasts of the Welsh, Irish, and Scottish areas which probably formed land of low altitude only occasionally traversed by streams. The Chalk Marl of Folkstone has furnished scutes, teeth, parts of the skull and limb bones of the armoured *Acanthopholis horridus* (Huxley, 1867), and the Totternhoe Stone of Hitchin has yielded a tooth, referred to *Craspedodon hilli* (E. T. Newton, 1892), of the same type as those of its forerunner *Iguanodon*.

THE EUROPEAN CONTINENT. One of the most remarkable occurrences of early Cretaceous deinosaurs in Europe is that of Bernissart, near Mons in Belgium. Here, twenty-nine skeletons of *Iguanodon*, together with remains of fishes, turtles, crocodiles, and land-plants, were found entombed in Wealden Beds which occupy a deep ravine in the Coal Measures. Evidently the ravine was a gorge in Wealden time, and corpses of *Iguanodon* were carried down by a stream and preserved in the deposits of a quiet pool. The specimens have been described by Dollo (1882–4) and many of the skeletons are attractively exhibited in the Brussels Museum.

The genus *Stenopelix* (Meyer, 1857) from the Wealden of north Germany is provisionally classified by A. S. Woodward (1932) in the Hypsilophodontidae. The Aptian Beds of southern France have yielded remains of a titanosaur, *Aepyosaurus* (Gervais, 1900).

A theropod, *Erectopus superbus* (Sauvage, 1914) is recorded from the Gault of northern France. The teeth of this form resemble those of *Megalosaurus* but, as most of the bones differ, Huene (1926) separates the species from that genus and Woodward (1932) places it in the family Deinodontidae.

In western Europe the Upper Cretaceous Maestrichtian Beds of Belgium have furnished bones of the ornithopod genus *Craspedodon*, the trachodont *Orthomerus dolloi* (Seeley, 1883) and an uncertain theropod referred provisionally to *Megalosaurus*. The titanosaur *Hypselosaurus priscus* (Matheron, 1869), associated with an egg, is recorded from the Danian Beds of southern France, while *Titanosaurus* itself is reported from the famous locality of St. Chinian (Deperet, 1900).

Farther east, a number of reptilian remains is recorded from the Gosau Beds of Austria; these were reviewed long ago by Seeley (1881) and some nomenclatorial corrections have since been made by Nopcsa (1923). The assemblage includes crocodiles and chelonians as well as deinosaurs. Three groups of deinosaurs are represented but no sauropods have been found. Teeth of theropod type were referred by Seeley to *Megalosaurus pannonensis*; Huene (1926) doubts if the genus survived to the Upper Cretaceous, though he offers no alternative determination. Among beaked forms there is the small iguanodont *Rhabdodon* (Matheron, 1869) which includes the *Mochlodon* of Seeley (1881) and this author described the species *M. suessi* (Burzel, 1871), founded on a dentary bone, as an '*Iguanodon* in miniature'.

Another form, *Orthomerus gracilis* (Seeley, 1881) based on the distal half of a femoral shaft, is referred to the Trachodontidae. Of the armoured forms the most important is *Struthiosaurus*, a genus of the Acanthopholidae, and A. S. Woodward (1932) refers the *Crataeomus* of Seeley to the same genus. *S. austriacus* (Burzel, 1871) is based on the hind part of the skull while *S. pawlowitschii* (Seeley) and *S. lepidophorus* (Seeley) are founded on characters of the vertebrae, scapulae and limb bones. *Hoplosaurus ischyrus* Seeley is another armoured form of which the scapula, humerus and vertical dermal plates are known. From this brief summary it is evident that the Gosau deinosaurs are known only by fragments of animals which have apparently been transported for some distance from their original habitat.

A similar fauna from beds at a higher horizon is recorded by Nopcsa (1923) from Transylvania. Here the marine Senonian stage is succeeded by brackish water deposits which pass up into freshwater beds referred to the Danian stage. The latter have yielded a crocodile, *Crocidilus affuveliensis* Matheron, an archaic tortoise, *Kallobotion bajazidi* (Nopcsa, 1923), related to Wealden forms, and four deinosaur species. *Rhabdodon priscum* (Matheron, 1869) is one of the last survivors of the iguanodonts, and *Titanosaurus dacus* Nopcsa is likewise one of the few sauropods that survive in the Upper Cretaceous of the northern hemisphere. *Orthomerus transylvanicus* Nopcsa is usually regarded as a trachodont, but Nopcsa considers it to be the survivor of a primitive ancestral type and places it with an American genus in a new family Protrachodontidae. *Struthiosaurus transylvanicus* (Nopcsa, 1915) is probably a late development of *Acanthopholis*, a genus already noted from the Cambridge Greensand of England. These Transylvanian deinosaurs are all of small size, and Nopcsa regards the assemblage as a remnant of an older and richer, but less-known fauna. He points out that central Europe was an archipelago in Cenomanian time, with islands occupying the sites of (1) Britain and Normandy, (2) western Spain, (3) central Germany, (4) the Alps, Hungary, Thrace, and Macedonia, (5) the Dobrudja and southern Russia, and (6) southern France, Corsica, and Sardinia. After a retreat of the sea during the mid-Senonian Carpathian orogeny, further transgression along new channels isolated the fauna of Transylvania, and led to dwarfing of the deinosaurs while the tortoises became gigantic. In a later paper Nopcsa (1934) considers that the separation of Europe from the rest of the world by an epicontinental sea led to evolution of the European Cretaceous tetrapods along special lines of their own.

AFRICA. It is hardly possible to assess the relationships of the few Cretaceous deinosaurs at present known from the African continent, though theropods, sauropods and ornithopods are certainly represented. The earliest known form is a titanosaur, *Algoasaurus baneri* (Broom, 1904), known by fragments of the scapula, femur, and vertebrae from Lower Cretaceous Beds near Uitenhage in Cape Province. Cretaceous strata in Madagascar have yielded bones similar to those of *Megalosaurus* together with *Titanosaurus madagascarensis* (Deperet, 1896), more recently transferred to the genus *Laplatasaurus* by Huene (1929). The iguanodont *Kangnasaurus* described by Haughton (1915) from the uppermost Cretaceous rocks of the Orange River, north-east of Steinkopf in Namaqualand, seems to be a very late survivor of the family.

The Cenomanian rocks of Egypt have furnished the titanosaur *Aegyptosaurus* (Stromer, 1915) and two theropods. Of the latter, *Carcharodontosaurus* is referred to the Deinodontidae, while *Spinosaurus aegyptiacus* (Stromer, 1915) is unique in the extraordinary development (up to 6 feet in length) of the neural spines on the dorsal vertebrae. Nopcsa (1934) thinks this form may be a descendant of the European *Altispinax*, but if so, it seems likely that the Egyptian form developed on its own independent lines, for nothing similar is known elsewhere. Moreover, the associated crocodiles *Stomatosuchus* (Nopcsa, 1926) and *Libyosuchus* (Nopcsa, 1928) are peculiar forms unknown outside Egypt.

THE INDIAN PENINSULA. The isolation of Africa is emphasized by the circumstance that the Cretaceous deinosaurs so far recorded from Peninsular India show no close relations with African forms. Several of the theropods described by Huene and Matley (1933) are not known elsewhere. Of these *Indosuchus* and *Indosaurus* are referred to the Allosauridae, *Campsosuchus* to the Campsognathidae, *Laevisuchus, Jubbulpuria, Coeluroides*, and *Dryptosauroides* to the Coeluridae, and *Ornithomimoides* to the Ornithomimidae. With the exception of the Campsognathidae, these families are morphologically similar to, but not necessarily genetically connected with, North American groups. Similarity with North American faunas is also shown by the presence in India of a nodosaur *Lametasaurus indicus* (Matley, 1924, 1931), for the family Nodosauridae is best known from the western U.S.A. and Canada. The Indian sauropods have, however, attracted most attention for they include the type-species of *Titanosaurus*, together with species of *Antarctosaurus* and *Laplatasaurus*, genera which were originally described (Huene, 1927) from the Upper Cretaceous rocks of Patagonia. On this evidence Huene (1933) advocates a land-bridge from south-east Asia through the Sunda Archipelago, Australia and Antarctica to South America. But, as Rastall (1929) has pointed out, there is no physical or topographical evidence in support of such a connexion. Moreover Huene's hypothesis takes no account of the possible relations of the theropods from the same series of beds.

SOUTH AMERICA. Chief interest is centred in the Upper Cretaceous Beds of Argentina and Patagonia, for the Lower Cretaceous rocks of Brazil have yielded only the coelurid theropod *Brasiliosaurus* (Huene, 1931) and the crocodile *Goniopholis* (see A. S. Woodward and Mawson, 1907). The Upper Cretaceous deinosaurs of Patagonia include *Titanosaurus australis* (Lyddeker, 1893) and *T. robustus* (Huene, 1927), *Laplatasaurus araukanus* Huene, *Antarctosaurus wichmannianus* Huene and *A. giganteus* Huene belonging to genera which are also known from India. Other titanosaurs from Patagonia are *Argyrosaurus superbus* (Lydekker, 1893) and *Campylodon* (?) *ameghinoi* (Huene, 1929), while *Notoceratops bonarellii* (Huene, 1929) is tentatively referred to the armoured group Ceratopsidae. The Argentine forms are the deinodont *Genyodectes serus* (A. S. Woodward, 1907) and the armoured *Loricosaurus scutulatus* (Huene, 1929), which is probably a nodosaur. The ceratopsian and nodosaurian forms just mentioned belong to typical North American families, and the question arises as to possible relations between the South American titanosaurs with certain sauropods that have been described from Upper Cretaceous rocks in North America (Gilmore, 1939).

NORTH AMERICA. Cretaceous deposits of continental type occupy large tracts in North America, extending from New Mexico in the south to Peace River Canyon, B.C., in the north, and from the Great Plains in the east to California in the west. Deinosaur remains of prime importance, including many almost complete skeletons, have been unearthed at numerous localities in this region by the labours of several expeditions during the last few decades. At least five horizons have yielded extensive faunas. (1) The oldest fauna is from the Arundel formation of eastern Maryland. The assemblage was originally regarded as Jurassic by Marsh (1896) and Hatcher (1903), but the formation is referred to the Lower Cretaceous by W. B. Clark (1897) and R. S. Lull (1911). The fauna includes remains of theropods, the sauropod *Astrodon*, and the armoured deinosaur *Priconodon*. In a restudy of the Arundel deinosaurs, C. W. Gilmore (1921) finds that the theropods include a species of *Ornithomimus*, which belongs to a typically Upper Cretaceous family. The deinodonts, doubtfully referred to the genera *Coelurus* and *Dryptosaurus* are less certain, but the armoured *Priconodon* shows certain resemblances with the Upper Cretaceous genus *Palaeoscineus*. The palaeobotanical evidence, however, does not support such a late age for the deposit. (2) The deinosaurs obtained from the Cloverly Formation of south-east Montana by an expedition of the American Museum of Natural History have not yet been fully described. Gilmore (1939) records an armoured theropod, a camptosauroid form and other unnamed genera and species. This fauna is also referred to the Lower Cretaceous. (3) The earliest fauna referred to the Upper Cretaceous is from the Mesa Verde formation of south-west Wyoming. According to Gilmore (1939) the assemblage includes an iguanodont, a trachodont, a ceratopsian, and another armoured deinosaur, none of which had then been fully described. (4) At higher horizons deinosaur faunas are recorded over a wide area extending from New Mexico to Alberta. The beds are correlated as follows:

NEW MEXICO	MONTANA, &c.	ALBERTA
	Lance	
		Edmonton
	Two Medicine and Judith	Belly River
Ojo Alamo	River	

We may first discuss the Canadian deinosaurs which have been described in numerous papers by B. Brown (1914–16), L. M. Lambe (1902–20), W. A. Parks (1920–8), C. M. Sternberg (1929–35) and C. W. Gilmore (1924). The theropods are represented in the Belly River Beds by members of three families. The deinodont *Gorgosaurus* (Lambe, 1917) is known by most of the skeleton; it is a large form, some 29 feet long, with a large head armed with prominent sharp teeth, three-toed hind limbs and two-fingered fore limbs bearing claws. This form is succeeded in the Edmonton Beds by a closely similar genus *Albertosaurus* (Parks, 1928) which is sometimes regarded as identical with *Gorgosaurus*. The small coelurid theropods are represented in the Belly River beds by *Chirostenotes* (Gilmore, 1924). The same formation has also yielded a nearly complete skeleton of a slender form about 13 feet long, known as *Struthiomimus* (Osborn, 1917) which has a small and lightly constructed skull, toothless jaws, long neck, slender limbs, specialized digits armed with claws, and long tail with closely articulated terminal portion.

The Canadian ornithopods of the family Hadrosauridae readily fall into two great groups according to the form of the skull. The flat-headed hadrosaurs are represented in the Belly River Beds of Alberta by a species of *Kritosaurus* (Brown, 1910) a genus founded on material from the equivalent Ojo Alamo Beds of New Mexico. The form named *Gryposaurus* (Lambe, 1914) is included in *Kritosaurus* by Gilmore (1916), Parks (1920), Lull and Wright (1942). The two species thus recorded from the Belly River Beds are succeeded at the Edmonton horizon by *Edmontosaurus* (Lambe, 1917) and by the distinct but closely related form first assigned by Gilmore (1924) to the genus *Thespesius* but now placed in *Anatosaurus* (Lull and Wright, 1942). In *Prosaurolophus* (Brown, 1916) from the Belly River Beds, and its successor *Saurolophus* (Brown, 1912) from the Edmonton formation the nasal bones are prolonged backwards to form a hollow spine. Several other genera are distinguished as crested hadrosaurs by the formation of a large hollow crest on the hinder part of the skull. In *Corythosaurus* (Brown, 1914; Gilmore, 1923) the nasal and premaxillary bones extend backwards from the short facial portion to form a great hollow crest, the cavity of which is continuous with the nasal cavity. The crest of *Lambeosaurus* (Parks, 1923) is even more pronounced, and the premaxillaries project backwards over the occipital elements; that of *Parasaurolophus* (Parks, 1922) is prolonged backward into a parallel-sided appendage which is longer than the entire cranium. These three genera in the Belly River Beds are replaced in the Edmonton Beds by *Hypacrosaurus* (Brown, 1913; Gilmore, 1924), and *Cheneosaurus* (Lambe, 1917) which may well be the products of autochthonous evolution.

Mention should be made of two other ornithopods, namely *Troödon* and *Thescelosaurus*, from the Belly River and Edmonton Beds respectively. The former, which includes the *Stegoceras* of Lambe (1918), is very similar to the European *Hypsilophodon* in skeletal characters, but the skull bones are thickened, the premaxillaries bear teeth, and the teeth are like those of armoured deinosaurs. This curious mixture of characters has aroused much controversy regarding the relationships of the genus, which Gilmore (1924) has placed in a separate family Troödontidae. This author and Sternberg (1933) have suggested that *Troödon* lived on the higher ground above the marshy deltas in which the remains were buried. *Thescelosaurus* also is classified with the Hypsilophondontidae by reason of the skeletal characters and the presence of teeth on the premaxillaries, but again the teeth resemble those of armoured forms (Parks, 1926).

The armoured deinosaurs of Alberta belong to two distinct families. The Nodosauridae comprise low, broad forms with a heavy armour of flat or keeled scutes over the whole upper surface of the body. *Ankylosaurus magniventris* (Brown, 1908), 17 feet long and 6 feet broad, has a heavy triangular skull bearing flat plates fused to its surface, and a continuous series of keeled oval plates arranged symmetrically over the neck, body, and tail, the plates being consolidated at the end of the tail to form a heavy club. An imperfect skeleton named *Dyoplosaurus acutosquameus* (Parks, 1924) is like *Ankylosaurus* in general characters but is readily distinguished by the shape and other details of the skull; moreover, the tail-club is about 4 feet long and is formed by the fusion of 10 or 11 caudal vertebrae, ending in a rigid knob of fused dermal plates. *Scolosaurus cutleri* (Nopcsa, 1928), founded on a unique skeleton in the British Museum, is nearly 18 feet long, and is armed with transverse rows of polygonal plates bearing large blunt spines. In general the nodosaurs are thought to have lived in deltaic lowlands, subsisting on the soft vegetation so abundant in this habitat (Sternberg, 1933).

The second family of armoured forms is the Ceratopsidae, comprising huge massive forms with a large skull armed with one or more horns on the facial region. The parietal and squamosal bones are prolonged backwards to form a projecting neck-frill which is often perforated by so-called 'fontanelles', and ornamented on the border by dermal bones or spines. There is no bony armour on the body region. Several genera in the Belly River Beds are distinguished by variations in the peculiar features of the skull. *Monoclonius nasicornis* (Brown, 1914, 1917), known by a complete skeleton about 17 feet long, has a prominent straight horn on the nose, incipient horn-cores over the orbits, and long openings in the neckfrill which has dermal bones along its borders. The skull of *Centrosaurus* (Lambe, 1905) is very similar but the large nasal horn curves forward, the orbital horns are more prominent, and strong curved processes project over the frill-openings. *Styracosaurus* (Lambe, 1913) has a large straight nasal horn, and the margins of the frill are prolonged into conspicuous spinose processes. In *Chasmosaurus belli* (Lambe, 1914) all three horns are short and stout, the nasal horn curving backward, and the large fontanelles in the frill are elongated longitudinally. All the horns are small also in *Brachyceratops* (Gilmore, 1917) but *Eoceratops canadensis* (Lambe, 1915) has a skull over 3 feet long with a short nasal horn, larger curved orbital horns and a pair of elongated fontanelles in the neck frill. In the succeeding Edmonton Beds the prominent ceratopsians are *Anchiceratops* (Brown, 1914 A) and *Arrhinoceratops* (Parks, 1925). The former seems to be related to *Monoclonius* but shows a tendency towards reduction in size of the fontanelles in the frill. *Arrhinoceratops* has a short nasal horn, large orbital horns and a large neck frill with circular fontanelles. *Leptoceratops* (B. Brown, 1914), also from the Edmonton Beds, has no horns on the face and the frill has two large oval fontanelles: this genus is regarded as a little-modified survivor of the ancestral group.

Considerable assemblages of deinosaurs closely related to the Canadian faunas have been obtained farther south from the Judith River and Two Medicine formations of Montana (Gilmore, 1917). The genera *Deinodon* and *Struthiomimus* represent the theropods. The peculiar ornithopod *Troödon* is common to the two regions together with the trachodont *Hypacrosaurus*. The nodosaurs *Anklyòsaurus, Dyoplosaurus* and *Palaeoscineus* are likewise recorded from both areas, as well as *Monoclonius, Brachyceratops* and *Styracosaurus* among the ceratopsians. The Ojo Alamo and Kirtland Beds of New Mexico are also correlated with the beds just described. They have yielded remains of the trachodont *Kritosaurus* and of the ceratopsian *Monoclonius*, genera which we have noted from Alberta and Montana. In addition, another ceratopsian *Pentaceratops* (Osborn, 1923) is recorded, together with *Alamosaurus* (Gilmore, 1922) which is probably a titanosaur. The last form is important as attesting the presence of sauropods in the Upper Cretaceous of North America. More recently, Gilmore (1938) has recorded another titanosaur from the North Horn formation of central Utah associated with Upper Cretaceous ceratopsians, theropods, and trachodonts. (5) A higher horizon is shown by the Lance, formerly known as the Laramie, formation which is widespread in Montana, Wyoming, and Colorado. In this formation the history of various deinosaur groups is carried a stage farther. Thus the enormous deinodont *Tyrannosaurus rex* (Osborn, 1905), up to 47 feet long, has a great skull some 4 feet in length and the jaws are armed with numerous sabre-like teeth 4 to 6 inches long; this genus illustrates the maximum development of the theropods. The presence of small members of the group is shown by *Ornithomimus* (Marsh, 1896), a slender form with lightly constructed skull and limbs, foreshadowed by the allied *Struthiomimus* in older beds. Among the Lance ornithopods is *Thescelosaurus* which has already been noted from the Edmonton Beds of Alberta. The crested trachodonts are apparently absent, but the family is represented by *Trachodon* itself, a conservative type with a long depressed skull. The Lance formation has also yielded some remarkable ceratopsians. *Torosaurus* (Marsh, 1892) from Wyoming, with a short nasal horn, large orbital horns, and large circular fontanelles in the neck-frill, is regarded by Gregory and Mook (1925) as the logical outcome of the line of development shown by *Arrhinoceratops* and *Chasmosaurus* in the Upper Cretaceous of Alberta. Other forms seem to show development from the Canadian *Eoceratops* or some allied genus. For instance, *Diceratops* (Lull, 1905) has two orbital horns but no nasal one, and the frill-openings are undergoing secondary closure. Again, *Triceratops* (Marsh, 1889), a widely distributed form from Montana, Wyoming, and Colorado, has large orbital horns, sometimes 3 feet in length, a small nasal horn and a large un-perforated neck-frill ornamented on the margin by a row of dermal bones. The skull of *T. prorsus* (Marsh, 1890) from Wyoming attains a length of 6 feet, and skeletons show that the animal must have reached a length of 25 feet. Thus in bulk and, according to Swinton (1934), in appearance also, *Triceratops* may have been comparable with the living African rhinoceros. Having reached this acme of development, the horned deinosaurs became extinct, for none are known to have survived later than the Cretaceous period.

Surveying the Cretaceous deinosaurs of North America, the most re-markable forms are the trachodonts, the nodosaurs, and the ceratopsians which are almost unknown elsewhere. Only in central Asia are comparable forms known, and these have been discovered in recent years during a series of exploratory expeditions.

ASIA. Thirty years ago few deinosaurs were known from Asia, but im-portant discoveries have since been made by expeditions to the Gobi desert in Mongolia organized by the American Museum of Natural History. These have been summarized by F. K. Morris (1936). The Cretaceous de-posits of the region are of continental type, accumulated in shallow basins between the adjacent highlands; they generally rest almost horizontally on upturned Jurassic or older rocks. There are numerous gaps in the suc-cession and correlation of the deposits in the separate basins is difficult, for it depends upon the discovery and investigation of the deinosaur re-mains. Representatives of all four groups have been obtained from the Lower Cretaceous rocks of Oshih, Ondai Sair, and Ongong, and from the Upper Cretaceous Beds of Iren Dabasu and Djadochta. These records are supplemented by reference to occasional specimens from other Asiatic localities.

The Oshih Beds have yielded remains of three genera. The theropod *Prodeinodon* is compared by Osborn (1930) with *Megalosaurus* from the English Wealden Beds, and with the American *Dryptosaurus*. The giant sauropod *Asiatosaurus* is said to be allied to the Camarasauridae of Colorado. The beaked deinosaurs are represented by the larger part of two skeletons, about 5 feet long, which are referred to *Psittacosaurus mongoliensis* (Osborn, 1924). This form has a deep broad skull with highly arched profile and a compressed toothless beak; the jaws have but few teeth, and the large orbits contain a ring of sclerotic plates as in the American *Trachodon*. A similar, but more slightly built, bipedal deinosaur from the Ondai Sair formation is named *Protiguanodon mongoliense* (Osborn, 1924). This form is not related to *Iguanodon*, but both Asiatic genera are regarded as specialized members of a primitive stock related to the ceratopsians. The two genera are associated at one horizon at Haratolgay (42° N., 107° E.), Inner Mongolia (C. C. Young, 1931), so the Oshih and Ondai Sair formations are now regarded as roughly equivalent in age. The Ongong formation of the Gobi desert also contains deinosaur bones and teeth, among which the sauropod *Mongolosaurus haplodon* (Gilmore, 1933) has been distinguished. This form has been compared with the American *Diplodocus* and *Pleurocoelus*, but is not closely related to either. Morris (1936) agrees with Spock (1930) that these beds are about the same age as the Oshih formation. The presence of another sauropod, *Helopus zdanskyi* (Wiman, 1929), in the Mengyin formation of Shantung suggests that beds of similar age are present in China, and Grabau (1924) regards them all as equivalent to the Wealden Series of Europe.

The two Upper Cretaceous formations contain deinosaur assemblages of different composition, probably belonging to different habitats. From the lake-deposits of Iren Dabasu three theropods and a trachodont have been named and there are also remains of nodosaurs, crocodiles, chelonians, fishes and lamellibranchs. The theropods include a small sharp-toothed deinodont which Osborn (1930) compares with the genus *Dromacosaurus* from Alberta. Gilmore (1933) finds a resemblance between the larger deinodont *Alectrosaurus* and the Canadian genus *Gorgosaurus*, and the same author has shown that *Struthiomimus asiaticus* is closely related to *S. altus* from the Belly River Beds of Alberta. The trachodont *Bactrosaurus* is placed in the same subfamily as *Stephanosaurus* from the same Canadian horizon. *Bactrosaurus* also has close relations with *Tanius* (Wiman, 1929) a trachodont from the Upper Cretaceous of Shantung, and *Nipponosaurus* (Nagao, 1936) from the island of Saghalien. Another form from the Iren Dabasu Beds is referred provisionally to the genus *Mandschurosaurus* (Riabinin, 1930) the type of which comes from the River Amur in Siberia, and is regarded by Nopcsa (1929) as belonging to an ancestral stock of the trachodonts.

In contrast with the Iren Dabasu fauna, that of Djadochta has no trachodonts, but some remarkable theropods and a primitive ceratopsian together with a small crocodile and a mammal are entombed in the wind-blown sands of the formation. The theropods are specialized types, *Velociraptor* and *Saurornithoides*, the latter being classified as a coelurid, and *Oviraptor* as a deinodont. The skull of the last-named genus is lightly built and toothless; the animal is thought to have subsisted on eggs of ceratopsians with which its remains were found associated. The armoured form, *Protoceratops* (Granger and Gregory, 1923), is the most primitive ceratopsian known, and is the first record of the group outside North America. It is represented by a number of specimens which show various stages in individual development from egg to adult. The triangular skull has large orbits and the neck-frill is pierced by two large fontanelles; there are no horns on the facial region. *Protoceratops* has so many resemblances to the Lower Cretaceous bipedal form *Psittacosaurus* from the same region, that the latter may be the ancestral form of the ceratopsian group. Most of the North American ceratopsians differ greatly from the Mongolian form but there is one genus, *Leptoceratops* (Brown, 1914) that shares many features with it. The skull is of the same general type, but in the latter genus three of the cervical vertebrae are fused together to give stronger support for the heavy skull; in *Protoceratops* there is no such fusion. On account of the close resemblance of these two deinosaurs the Djadochta formation may be tentatively correlated with the Edmonton Beds of Alberta, while, as we have already noted, the Iren Dabasu formation has some relation to the Belly River Beds of Alberta. Even if this correlation has to be modified, there is no doubt that close relation exists between the Cretaceous deinosaurs of North America and those of eastern Asia. On the other hand there seems to be no such relation with the faunas of Europe, Africa, and India, each of which appears to have developed on independent lines.

LITERATURE

Space will not allow an adequate review of the vast literature on Mesozoic vertebrate land-animals. The foregoing chapter is based essentially on the generally accepted lists of genera by A. Smith Woodward in the Zittel-Eastman *Textbook of Palaeontology*, vol. ii, 1932. These are supplemented by W. E. Swinton's volume on *The Deinosaurs*, 1934, and the same author's paper on 'The Deinosaurs of the Isle of Wight, *Proc. Geol. Assoc.*, vol. xlvii, pp. 204–20, 1936. For more detailed reference the author and date of each genus given in the foregoing pages will enable the literature to be traced in the appropriate volume of the standard bibliographical lists mentioned below. *Bibliography and Catalogue of the Fossil Vertebrata of North America*, by O. P. Hay, U.S. Geol. Surv., Bull. 179, 1902; or *2nd Bibliography*, &c., vol. i (1929) *Fishes and Amphibia*, vol. ii (1930) *Reptiles, Birds, and Mammals*, Carnegie Inst. Washington, Publ. No. 390. *Bibliography of Fossil Vertebrates, 1928 to 1933*, by C. L. Camp and V. L. Vanderhoof, Geol. Soc. Amer., Special Paper No. 27, 1940; *1934 to 1938*, by C. L. Camp, D. N. Taylor, and S. P. Welles, ibid. No. 42, 1942; *1939 to 1943* by C. L. Camp, S. P. Welles, and M. Green, Geol. Soc. Amer., Memoir No. 37, 1949. A bibliographical list of 479 items is given in the textbook of *Vertebrate Palaeontology* by A. S. Romer, 2nd edition, Chicago, 1945.

XV

OLDER NEOZOIC FAUNAS

IN the south-east of England the White Chalk is succeeded by a group of deposits (known collectively as the Neozoic) that have scarcely a feature in common with the rocks on which they rest. The purely marine Cretaceous rocks are overlain by a series of sands and clays of shallow marine, brackish, and freshwater origin, while the varied fauna of the Chalk simultaneously disappears and is not seen again.

But these changes imply far more than a decrease in depth of water. It has already been noted that no representatives of the uppermost Cretaceous limestones of Denmark and Belgium are found in England. Moreover, detailed mapping has shown that the English Neozoic deposits rest upon the bevelled edges of various Chalk zones. Thus there is a wide gap in the stratigraphical succession, due mainly to denudation of the Mesozoic deposits before the Neozoic strata were laid down. This explains the great difference in aspect between the Cretaceous and Neozoic faunas of this country—a contrast that is not so strongly marked in certain continental occurrences.

In the marine Neozoic faunas, gastropods and lamellibranchs are extremely abundant, and, in general, approximate closely to existing assemblages, though most of the species are extinct.

Foraminifera are abundant, and certain large specialized forms (*Nummulites* and its allies) are utilized as zone-fossils in districts where they are found. The short-tailed decapod crustacea become a conspicuous element in the faunas. Fishes are, with few exceptions, of the modern 'bony' type, while the reptiles are represented only by groups which survive in living faunas. The entire absence of ammonites and marine saurians, together with the rarity of crinoids, brachiopods, cephalopods, and (in British deposits) of corals and echinoids, is in striking contrast with Mesozoic life-assemblages.

The freshwater deposits often contain remains of mammals and plants. The latter are mainly dicotyledonous flowering plants, and many are now confined to warm climates. The mammalian fossils serve, to some extent, as criteria for stratigraphical subdivision, though their fragmentary condition is often disconcerting to the general field-worker.

The Neozoic deposits were subdivided by Lyell into four series based upon the percentage of living species of mollusca found in the several faunas. Nowadays the position of a bed is fixed by the association of several species which experience has shown to be characteristic of certain stratigraphical horizons. Though the Oligocene Series has been differentiated since his day, the classification of Lyell remains but little modified and may be summarized thus:

Neozoic systems	Series	Typical Areas
Newer or Neogene	Pleistocene Pliocene Miocene	Britain north of Thames East Anglia ? Absent in Britain
Older or Palaeogene	Oligocene Eocene	Hampshire basin London and Hampshire basins

It has been claimed that these subdivisions cannot be regarded as systems of the same palaeontological value as those into which the Mesozoic and Palaeozoic rocks have been divided. Consequently they have been grouped into Palaeogene and Neogene systems, as shown in the table. The Palaeogene System comprising the Eocene and Oligocene Series is discussed in the present chapter.

Palaeogene strata in England appear at the surface in two areas known as the London basin and the Hampshire basin respectively. These form part of a much larger area of deposition which includes Belgium and northern France. The disposition of the present outcrops is due to their occurrence in synclinal areas, formed by Miocene earth-movements and separated by subsequent denudation of the intervening anticlines.

Since the deposits (and consequently the nomenclature) differ in the two British areas, a summary of classification is given in the table below, together with the terms employed on the Continent as being applicable to the older Neozoic deposits of the whole west European area.

Classification of British Neozoic Rocks

	London basin	Hampshire basin	Continental stages
Oligocene		Hamstead Beds Bembridge Beds Osborne Beds Headon Beds	} Rupelian
Eocene	Bagshot Sands { Upper / Middle / Lower London Clay Oldhaven and Blackheath Beds Woolwich and Reading Beds Thanet Sands	Barton Beds Bracklesham Beds Bagshot Sands Bognor Beds } Plastic Clays	Bartonian Ledian Lutetian } Ypresian } Landenian

The oldest Neozoic strata of England are the Thanet Beds, which occupy a restricted area in northern Kent, typically in the Isle of Thanet. They are mainly pale-coloured sands, but the lower part is darkened by the abundance of glauconite grains; at the base, resting on the eroded surface of the Chalk, is a layer of greenish loam containing unworn green-stained flints, derived (by solution of the surrounding matrix) from the underlying chalk. The Thanet Beds are equivalent to the lower part of the Landenian Stage of Belgium, the Montian of that country being unrepresented in England. The lower Landenian, of marine origin, is divided into three zones whose stratigraphical significance in this country may be tabulated thus:

3. Zone of *Cyprina scutellaria* (Lamarck)   { Bottom Bed of Woolwich Stage.

2. Zone of *Phalodomya konincki* Nyst   } Thanet Beds.
1. Zone of *Cyprina morrisi* (J. de C. Sow.)

Though generally poor in fossils, the Thanet Beds have yielded the index-species *Cyprina morrisi* (J. de C. Sow.) and *Pholadomya konincki* Nyst (Fig. 78), also *Ostrea bellovacensis* Lam., *Pectunculus terebratularis* Lam., species of *Protocardia*, *Thracia*, *Modiola*, and shark's teeth referred to the genus *Lamna*. These beds, therefore, indicate the return of shallow-water marine conditions to the area now forming south-eastern England.

The Bottom Bed of the Woolwich Stage is truly marine, and is marked by the appearance of *Cyprina scutellaria* (Lam.). Other characteristic species are *Pectunculus terebratularis* Lam. and *Protocardia plumsteadiana* (J. Sow.).

The succeeding **Woolwich and Reading Stage** (Upper Landenian) presents two distinct facies, the estuarine Woolwich Shell Beds, and the freshwater Reading Beds. The former, consisting principally of well-bedded shelly clays, are well developed in the central part of the London basin, and contain a characteristic molluscan assemblage. Lamellibranchs are represented by species of *Cyrena*, such as *C. cuneiformis* (J. Sow.) and *C. cordata* Morris (Fig. 80). Gastropods include the well-known *Melania* (*Brotia*) *inquinata* Defrance and *Potamides* (*Tympanotomus*) *funatus* (J. Sow.) (Fig. 80), besides species of *Viviparus*. The Reading Beds—current-bedded gravels and sands, mottled clays and freshwater limestones—are practically barren of fossils. These variable deposits form a broad fringe on the western side of the Woolwich Beds.

The **Blackheath Beds,** representing the lower part of the Belgian Ypresian Stage, consist of sands and pebble-beds, for the most part strongly current-bedded. They are of marine origin, and represent renewed encroachment of the sea, during which currents scoured into the soft Woolwich Beds and eventually deposited the material of the Blackheath Beds on the eroded surface thus formed. The Blackheath Beds contain an extensive

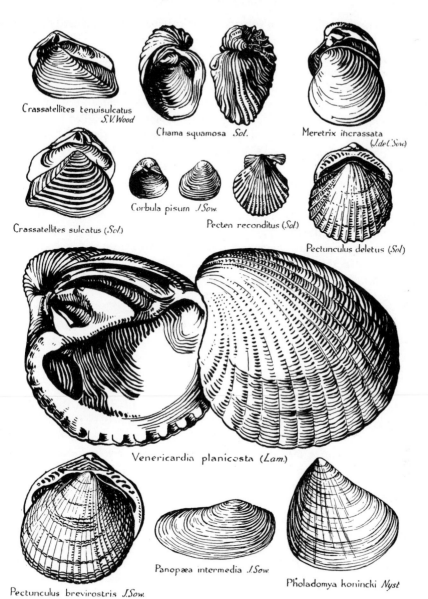

Crassatellites tenuisulcatus
S.V. Wood

Chama squamosa *Sol.*

Meretrix incrassata
(J.del Sow.)

Crassatellites sulcatus *(Sol.)*

Corbula pisum *J.Sow.*

Pecten reconditus *(Sol.)*

Pectunculus deletus *(Sol)*

Venericardia planicosta *(Lam.)*

Pectunculus brevirostris *J.Sow.*

Panopæa intermedia *J.Sow.*

Pholadomya konincki *Nyst*

FIG. 78. BRITISH EOCENE LAMELLIBRANCHS (*drawn from figures by S. V. Wood and from specimens*). *About two-thirds the natural size*

fauna consisting mainly of estuarine and marine mollusca; these have been separated into four groups:

(*a*) Certain freshwater and estuarine molluscs living in the Landenian 'lagoon' (represented by the Woolwich Beds) persisted in the Ypresian sea; most of these became modified, usually reduced in size, under salt-water conditions. Such survivals include: *Melanopsis buccinoidea* Férussac, *Brotia inquinata* (Defr.), *Tympanotomus funatus* (J. Sow.) (Fig. 80), *Cyrena cuneiformis* (J. Sow.), *Ostrea bellovacensis* Lam., and *Ostrea tenera* J. Sow.

(*b*) Some marine species found in the Blackheath Beds also occur in the Thanet Beds, but were presumably excluded from the Woolwich Beds by the unfavourable character of the prevailing physical conditions. Such species are: *Pectunculus plumsteadiensis* J. Sow., *Corbula regulbiensis* Morris, *Cyprina scutellaria* (Lam.), *Dosiniopsis orbicularis* (Morris), *Aporrhais sowerbyi* (Mantell) (Fig. 79).

(*c*) Certain marine species appear for the first time and become more abundant in the higher parts of the Blackheath Beds. These new forms determine the age of the deposit and link its fauna with that of the overlying London Clay. They include the gastropods *Actaeon turgidus* (Deshayes), *Calyptraea* cf. *aperta* (Solander) (Fig. 79), *Natica* (*Naticina*) *labellata* Lam. (Fig. 79), *Pseudoliva* spp., and the lamellibranchs *Arca modioliformis* Deshayes, *Cytherea* (*Caryatis*) *obliqua* Deshayes, *Corbula arnouldi* Nyst, *Panopaea intermedia* (J. Sow.) (Fig. 78), and a slightly oblique variety of *Pectunculus plumsteadiensis* J. Sow., near to *P. brevirostris* J. de C. Sow.

(*d*). A few species are almost restricted to the Blackheath Beds, and, as they are represented by well-developed shells, seem to have thrived particularly well under the conditions then obtaining; such are *Neritina globulus* (Férussac), *Natica infundibulum* Watelet, *Cyrena tellinella* Fér. and Desh., and the true *Pectunculus plumsteadiensis* J. Sow.

The **London Clay** is a truly marine deposit, the result of sedimentation in a sea whose depth has been estimated at not more than 100 fathoms. Most of the fossils are mollusca, many of which show close affinity with those of the Blackheath Beds. For instance, *Aporrhais sowerbyi* (Mantell), *Naticina labellata* Lam., *Ostrea bellovacensis* Lam., and others, are common to the two deposits. Other forms make their appearance and afford a means of differentiating the faunas. Since a zonal classification has not yet been definitely established, the subdivisions utilized in the Memoirs of the Geological Survey, namely, the Basement Beds, the Main Mass, and the Top Beds, are adopted here. There are differences in faunal composition that suggest variation in depth at which these clays were formed. The Main Mass contains fossils that are not recorded from either the Basement Beds or the Top Beds, while the two latter have many forms in common. The Top Beds have, however, some distinctive newcomers. The most characteristic fossils of these three divisions are listed below.

CHARACTERISTIC FOSSILS OF THE LONDON CLAY

BASEMENT BEDS—shallow conditions estimated at 50 fathoms:

Gastropoda: *Aporrhais sowerbyi* (Mantell), *Naticina labellata* Lam., *Pyrula nodulifera* G. B. Sowerby.

Lamellibranchia: *Pectunculus brevirostris* J. de C. Sow., *Protocardia plumsteadiana* (J. Sow.), *Caryatis obliqua* (Deshayes), *Corbula regulbiensis* Morris, *Ostrea bellovacensis* Lam., *Panopaea intermedia* (J. Sow.) (Fig. 78).

The annelid *Ditrupa plana* J. Sow. is regarded by some authors as especially characteristic.

The MAIN MASS—suggests deeper water; about 100 fath.

Cephalopoda: *Nautilus imperialis* J. Sow., *N. centralis* J. Sow.

Gastropoda: *Fusus porrectus* Solander, *Naticina labellata* Lam., *Voluta nodosa* J. de C. Sow., large species of *Pyrula*, e.g. *P. smithi* (J. de C. Sow.), species of *Pleurotoma, Phorus, Cassis,* and other genera.

Lamellibranchia: *Pectunculus decussatus* J. Sow., *Modiola elegans* J. Sow., *M. simplex* J. de C. Sow., *Pinna affinis* J. Sow., *Protocardia nitens* (J. Sow.), *Pteria arcuata* (J. de C. Sow.).

TOP BEDS—recurrence of shallow conditions.

Many fossils of Basement Beds and Main Mass, together with the following distinctive newcomers:

Gastropoda: *Pyrula nexilis* (Solander), *Litiopa sulculosa* Edwards MS., *Murex (Poirieria) spinulosus* Desh., *Pisiania (Streptolathyrus) zonulata* Edwards MS.

Lamellibranchia: *Pseudamusium corneum* (J. Sow.), *Modiola depressa* J. Sow.

Echinoidea: *Hemiaster branderianus* (Forbes).

These are overlaid, in the London area, by the sandy Claygate Beds, which contain few fossils. Obscure moulds have been referred to *Cyprina morrisi* (J. de C. Sow.), a shell that occurs in the Basement Beds but not in the Main Mass of the London Clay.

Compared with equivalent faunas of south Europe, the scarcity of echinoids in the London Clay is noticeable, though species of the tropical or subtropical genera *Coelopleurus, Hemiaster,* and *Schizaster* have been recorded. They present an aspect comparable rather with the Chalk Marl fauna than with later Cretaceous assemblages; this is due probably to factors of physical conditions. The echinoids of the London Clay are of small size, showing that they lived under unfavourable conditions.

At Bognor in Sussex, the London Clay is represented by beds of clay and calcareous sandstone with abundant fossils. The most conspicuous shell is *Pectunculus brevirostris* J. Sow. (Fig. 78), with broad and depressed radial ribs, which are transversely striated.

The **Bagshot Sands** of the London area are almost unfossiliferous. The equivalent strata of the Hampshire basin consist of yellow and white sands with bands of laminated clay. The upper beds contain layers of white pipeclay, which are of interest in containing numerous leaves of plants. These are mainly dicotyledonous angiosperms, and the leaves have been assigned to the genera *Aralia, Ficus, Laurus, Quercus,* and others, the whole flora indicating a warm temperate climate. At Studland in Dorset, the fern *Acrostichum lanzeanum* Visiani is abundant; nowadays the genus *Acrostichum* is restricted to the mangrove-swamps of south-eastern Asia (see p. 346).

The **Bracklesham Beds** contain a rich fauna of marine mollusca and other organisms. The most satisfactory faunal subdivision is based on the vertical distribution of the large specialized Foraminifera included in the genus *Nummulites.* On this basis the Bracklesham Beds are divided into a lower zone of *Nummulites laevigatus* and an upper zone of *N. variolaris.* The lower beds of the succeeding Barton stage are marked by the presence of another form, *N. wemmelensis.* It may be useful for purposes of reference to summarize here the distinguishing characters of these Foraminifera, more especially as some confusion has arisen in the past.

N. laevigatus (Bruguière) is the megaspheric form of the microspheric *N. lamarcki* d'Arch. It attains a diameter of about 16 millimetres, and is lenticular in shape; the external surface is reticulate, but may be granulose in young individuals. Internally it is distinguished by its thick spiral lamina and its curved chamber walls, the length of the chambers exceeding their height. It ranges through the whole of the Lutetian Stage.

N. variolaris (Lamarck) is very small and inflated, with radiating striae on the external surface; internally it shows a thick spiral lamina, and the length of the chambers is about equal to their height.

N. orbignyi (Galeotti), and its microspheric form *N. wemmelensis* de la Harpe, are small flat forms with central boss and fine radiating striae; the spiral lamina is very thin and the chambers are arcuate. These forms have often been confused with *N. elegans* Sow. and its megaspheric form *N. planulatus* (Lam.), which are characteristic of the Ypresian and are not known from British strata. The last-named nummulites are almost flat, and have a thick spiral lamina with radiating striae; the chamber-walls are thin, and are curved only at their junction with the contiguous whorl.

The zone of *Nummulites laevigatus* contains many shells that individually have no precise stratigraphical significance, since they range into contiguous strata. Some, however, are highly characteristic in their association. In general, the fauna of the Lower Bracklesham Beds, with its giant Nummulites, its Bullas, Cones, Cowries, and Harp-shells, associated with a wealth of corals, differs more from the Upper Bracklesham assemblage than the latter does from the Lower Barton fauna. The large convolute gastropod *Cypraea tuberculosa* (Duclos), with flattened base and a few tubercles on its otherwise smooth body-whorl, is typical of the zone, though apparently rare. Another characteristic (though rare) cowry is *Cypraea globularis* Edwards, recognized by its globular shape and the prolongation of its aperture into a narrow and straight anterior canal. The cone-shells include the large *Conus deperditus* Brug. (Fig. 79) and other species, while several members of the genus *Voluta* (sensu lato) emphasize the sub-tropical character of the fauna. Various long turreted shells with oval apertures belong to the genus *Turritella*; *T. imbricataria* Lamarck is ornamented by conspicuous spiral lines of diminutive tubercles, crossed by faint transverse striae, and is readily distinguished from other associated species. Among lamellibranchs, *Venericardia planicosta* (Lam.) (Fig. 78) is conspicuous; its large thick shell bears broad radial ribs, and is furnished with an extremely high hinge-plate with massive teeth. The small oyster *Ostrea flabellula* Lamarck is easily recognized by its lunate shape and ribbed valves. The corals include the massive perforate form *Litharea websteri* (Bowerbank), whose colonies sometimes attain considerable size. *Oculina conferta* M.-Edw. and Haime is also a compound encrusting form with circular corallites. Another aporose coral, somewhat similar to the last in its irregular habit, is *Diaphelia papillosa* M.-Edw. and Haime, distinguished by its large columella and denticulated septa. The small, simple *Turbinolia sulcata* Lamarck is easily recognized by the thin sharp costae on its outer surface, and the columella, whose pointed apex rises above the septa; this coral ranges into higher strata. The rare occurrence of sea-urchins is of much interest, though their vertical range is somewhat uncertain. J. W. Gregory recognizes four species from the Bracklesham Beds, namely, *Coelopleurus dixoni* Gregory, *Echinopedina edwardsi* (Forbes), *Scutellina lenticularis* (Lamarck), and *Schizaster d'urbani* Forbes. They are generally small in size, but give evidence of a warm climate.

The zone of *Nummulites variolaris* is marked especially by the presence of *Cerithium (Campanile) giganteum* Lamarck, a large shell which sometimes attains a length of 18 inches. This is associated with various other gastropods, such as the spinose *Murex minax* Solander, the tuberculate *Voluta nodosa* J. de C. Sow., and *Clavilithes longaevus* (Solander) (Fig. 79), a 'fusoid' shell with smooth whorls that develop a horizontal shelf near the sutures. The shell-beds of various Eocene horizons contain numerous species of the genus *Pleurotoma*; in the zone under discussion members of the species-group *P. denticulata* Basterot are common, and may be distinguished by the length of the spire, the pronounced transverse striations, and the obtuse tuberculate keel on the shoulders of the whorls. Among lamellibranchs the well-known *Corbula pisum* J. Sowerby (Fig. 78) is often abundant; the small inflated shells of this species are smooth externally and have a characteristic arrangement of the hinge-teeth. *Pecten (Pseudamusium) corneus* (J. Sow.) is also abundant but generally fragmentary; this thin, flattened shell is practically smooth and the ears are nearly equal. Altogether, over 500 species of mollusca have been recorded from the Bracklesham Beds, and the fauna is decidedly tropical in character.

The lower limit of the **Barton Beds** is defined by the incoming of *Nummulites orbignyi* (Galeotti) and its microspheric form *N. wemmelensis* de la Harpe, the characters of which have already been noted (p. 582). These nummulites appear to be restricted to the basal beds of the Barton Stage, and the customary threefold division of the beds is therefore based on the vertical distribution of certain molluscan assemblages.

The Lower Barton fauna includes many species which, like *Voluta athleta* (Solander), *Hippochrenes amplus* (Solander), *Chrysodomus errans* (Solander), *Pisania interrupta* (Pilkington), *Rimella rimosa* (Solander), *Meretrix elegans* (Lamarck), and *Corbula pisum* J. Sowerby, range up from the Bracklesham Stage. But the absence of many of the larger species of *Conus, Cypraea, Harpa, Bulla, Cassis,* and other genera common in the Bracklesham Beds, together with the appearance of new forms, gives a distinctive character to the Barton molluscan assemblage. Speaking generally, the later fauna is less tropical in aspect, and an incursion of colder waters from the north has been invoked to explain the difference. It is noticeable, too, that the incoming forms are mostly of small size, the only large species first appearing in the Barton Beds being *Voluta luctatrix* (Solander). This shell is distinguished by its elevated spire and angular spinose whorls; also the columella is slightly folded (Fig. 79). The Barton Beds are famed for their Volutes, and among other species are *V. ambigua* (Solander), whose conical spire and convex whorl-shoulders give a characteristic regularity of form, and *V. (Athleta) athleta* (Solander), an unmistakable shell with rather short spire, smooth, ventricose body and spreading spines on the whorl-shoulders (Fig. 79). Perhaps the most abundant shell is the little *Mitra parva* J. de C. Sow. (Fig. 79), fusiform in shape, with a long, narrow aperture and folded columella; this species, however, ranges up from the Bracklesham Beds. A distinctive and abundant newcomer is the diminutive *Strombus (Canarium) bartonensis* (J. Sow.) (Fig. 79), whose outer margin is slightly expanded and much thickened. The spirally ornamented 'whelk' *Cominella canaliculata* (J. de C. Sow.), with a short posterior groove to the aperture, is also confined to the Lower Barton fauna. Among the many fusiform shells assigned to *Pleurotoma*, the large *P. rostrata* (Solander) (Fig. 79) may be cited as characteristic of this horizon; it has a long spire, a long anterior canal, its sinus is at the posterior margin of the whorl, the whorls are very convex with a single row of oblique tubercles near the middle, bordered by concave margins that bear spiral ornament crossed by lines of growth. This shell is associated with many smaller species of *Pleurotoma*, of which *P. microdonta* Edwards and *P. varians* Edwards are typical Barton forms. Other gastropods restricted to this horizon are *Cassis ambigua* (Solander), *Acera striatella* (Lamarck), and *Volvaria acutiuscula* J. Sow. The most typical lamellibranch is *Crassatellites sulcatus* (Solander) (Fig. 78), whose elongate trigonal valves, with a diagonal ridge near the posterior end, recall those of the Mesozoic genus *Trigonia*; the ornament consists of strong elevated ridges separated by deep furrows.

The fossils mentioned above are the most typical and conspicuous forms. Mingled with them, in the Lower Barton Beds, is a great number of minute

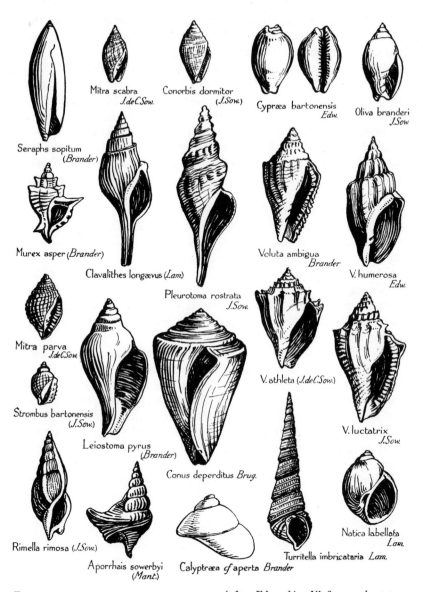

Mitra scabra
J. de C. Sow.

Conorbis dormitor
(J. Sow.)

Cypræa bartonensis
Edw.

Oliva branderi
J. Sow

Seraphs sopitum
(Brander)

Murex asper *(Brander)*

Clavalithes longævus *(Lam.)*

Pleurotoma rostrata
J. Sow.

Voluta ambigua
Brander

V. humerosa
Edw.

Mitra parva
J. de C. Sow.

Strombus bartonensis
(J. Sow.)

Leiostoma pyrus
(Brander)

Conus deperditus *Brug.*

V. athleta *(J. de C. Sow.)*

V. luctatrix
J. Sow.

Rimella rimosa *(J. Sow.)*

Aporrhais sowerbyi
(Mant.)

Calyptræa *cf* aperta *Brander*

Turritella imbricataria *Lam.*

Natica labellata
Lam.

FIG. 79. BRITISH EOCENE GASTROPODS (*after Edwards*). *All figures about two-thirds the natural size*

but adult shells, 'some of which occur in such incredible profusion that an ounce of the sand may contain hundreds of individuals of a species, whilst others are so rare that only solitary examples are known'.

The fauna of the Middle Barton Stage (the well-known Barton Clay) is nearly as rich as the preceding assemblage, comprising some 300 species. The most conspicuous fossils, however, are not confined to these beds, and may be separated into groups according to vertical range.

(a) Some of the largest species range from the Bracklesham Beds right through the Barton Beds, but attain their finest development in the Barton Clay. Such species include *Hippochrenes amplus* (Solander), *Clavilithes longaevus* (Solander), *Leiostoma pyrus* (Sol.) and *Murex asper* Solander (Fig. 79).

(b) The range of other forms passing up from the Bracklesham Beds does not extend beyond the Middle Barton. Of these, *Chrysodomus antiquus* (Solander), *Pyrula nexilis* (Solander), *Cassidaria nodosa* (Solander), and *Lampusia arguta* (Solander) may be cited.

(c) Among shells restricted to the Barton Beds, many, such as *Voluta luctatrix* (Solander) (Fig. 79), *Crassatellites sulcatus* (Sol.), and *Limopsis scalaris* (J. de C. Sow.), are best developed in the middle series; while others, like *Voluta ambigua* (Solander) and *Pleurotoma rostrata* (Solander) (Fig. 79), are not known in later beds.

(d) Several small but well-known species, such as *Conorbis dormitor* (Solander) (Fig. 79) and *Cominella deserta* (Solander), make their first appearance here. The first-named, though allied to *Conus* by the straight, narrow aperture, approaches *Pleurotoma* in the elevated spire and the produced anterior portion of the whorls; the ornament consists of thin, sharp, concentric ridges. *C. deserta* (Sol.) is a small 'whelk' with prominent sutural ridges; its surface is ornamented by intersecting spiral and transverse striae.

(e) Finally, some species appear to be peculiar to the Middle Barton, but are neither conspicuous nor abundant; e.g. *Chrysodomus lima* (J. de C. Sow.) and *Tellina ambigua* J. de C. Sow.

The molluscan element is by far the most important part of the known fauna of the Barton fauna, though other fossil-groups are present. The precise horizon of some of the rarer fossils is unfortunately uncertain. Thus, of the four known species of sea-urchins, only one, *Hemiaster branderi* (Forbes) is definitely stated to occur in the Barton Clay. The other three, *Eupatagus hastingsiae* Forbes, *E. excentricus* Gregory, and *Maretia grignonensis* (Desmarest), are recorded simply from the Barton Beds. Several species of the coral *Turbinolia* have been described, as well as various Ostracoda and Foraminifera, while the Vertebrata are represented by teeth and bones of fishes, crocodiles, turtles, and the cetacean *Zeuglodon*.

The most fossiliferous horizon in the Upper Barton Series is the famous Chama-bed, so named from the great abundance therein of the familiar lamellibranch *Chama squamosa* Solander (Fig. 78), which is associated with many other equally distinctive fossils. *Crassatellites tenuisulcatus* S. V. Wood (Fig. 78), more elongate than *C. sulcatus* (Solander), and having finer ribs which do not extend over the posterior area, is confined to this upper series. *Pectunculus deletus* (Solander) is also typical of the Upper Barton Series; it is almost circular, and has sharp radial ribs crossed by concentric striae (Fig. 78). Another lamellibranch abundant at Barton is *Pecten reconditus* (Solander); this shell has eighteen to twenty-four convex ribs, which are generally smooth but sometimes imbricate (Fig. 78). These bivalves are accompanied by many others, including species of *Tellina*, *Anomia*, and *Cardita*. The gastropod assemblage also is strikingly different from earlier Barton faunas. The scarcity of *Pleurotoma* is very noticeable, while species of *Turritella*, *Cypraea*, *Conus*, *Mitra*, *Murex*, and *Typhis* become more conspicuous; this is probably the reflection of a physical change towards clear-water conditions. Several of these species appear to be restricted to the Upper Barton Beds. *Conus scabriculus* Solander and *C. lineatus* Solander are both small shells with elevated spires, the former being ornamented by fine tuberculate spiral ribbing, the latter by smooth, regular, transverse lines. A characteristic species of *Voluta* is *V. humerosa* Edwards (Fig. 79), a shell with elevated spire and flattened whorls, ornamented by thick, round ribs that develop into tubercles on the shoulders of the last two whorls. The small *Mitra scabra* J. de C. Sow. (Fig. 79) differs from allied species in possessing a deep anterior notch; the ornament consists of irregular longitudinal ribs crossed by sharp transverse striations, giving a roughened appearance to the surface of the shell. *Cypraea bartonensis* Edwards (Fig. 79) is a fairly small shell whose spire is more evident than in most cowries; the inner lip is thickened anteriorly by a prominent callus, and the posterior canal is strongly marked. Another convolute form is seen in the peculiar *Seraphs sopitum* (Solander) (Fig. 79), a thin shell with large smooth body-whorl, long, narrow aperture (slightly dilated anteriorly) and smooth, straight columella. The spinose *Typhis pungens* (Solander), which persists from the Bracklesham Series, is here accompanied by the more exaggerated *T. fistulosus* (Brocchi). *Oliva branderi* J. Sow. (Fig. 79), a smooth shell with short spire, large body-whorl, deep anterior notch, and obliquely folded columella, is characteristic of, but not peculiar to, Upper Barton Beds.

The **Oligocene** strata of Britain are seen only in the Isle of Wight and Hampshire, where they present a succession of freshwater and estuarine deposits, broken at intervals by marine beds. The lithological features are subject to rapid change in a lateral direction, and subdivision on a palaeontological basis is difficult, because the freshwater faunas tend to become stereotyped and show little evolutional change. The customary divisions are purely stratigraphical, and little can be done but to describe the general aspect of the faunas. The accompanying table shows a generalized classification of the beds, and gives some idea of the lithological and faunal changes in the succession.

Oligocene of Isle of Wight

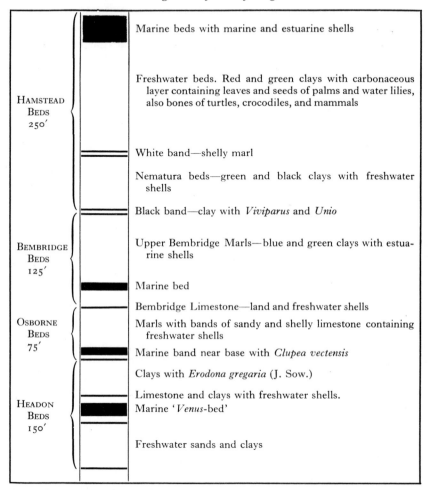

	Marine beds with marine and estuarine shells
HAMSTEAD BEDS 250′	Freshwater beds. Red and green clays with carbonaceous layer containing leaves and seeds of palms and water lilies, also bones of turtles, crocodiles, and mammals
	White band—shelly marl
	Nematura beds—green and black clays with freshwater shells
	Black band—clay with *Viviparus* and *Unio*
BEMBRIDGE BEDS 125′	Upper Bembridge Marls—blue and green clays with estuarine shells
	Marine bed
OSBORNE BEDS 75′	Bembridge Limestone—land and freshwater shells
	Marls with bands of sandy and shelly limestone containing freshwater shells
	Marine band near base with *Clupea vectensis*
HEADON BEDS 150′	Clays with *Erodona gregaria* (J. Sow.)
	Limestone and clays with freshwater shells. Marine '*Venus*-bed'
	Freshwater sands and clays

The Headon Beds are divided into three stages, of which the lower and upper are entirely brackish and freshwater deposits, while the middle stage contains marine as well as estuarine strata. All these divisions are highly fossiliferous. The freshwater limestones contain abundant gastropods which possess the thin, fragile shells usual in this habitat. The most conspicuous forms are *Limnaea longiscata* Brongn. (Fig. 80), a shell with long pointed spire and oval aperture, and *Planorbis euomphalus* J. Sow. (Fig. 80), a well-known discoid, smooth form. Other species of these genera, together with *Viviparus lentus* (Solander) (Fig. 80), a turbinate shell with rounded apex, rounded whorls and a subcircular aperture, are also common. Among lamellibranchs, species of *Erodona* and *Cyrena* are abundant in the lower and upper stages. It is interesting to note that species of the first-named genus exist today in the great rivers of South America.

Many of the marine mollusca are species that persist from the Barton Beds, but others are peculiar to the Oligocene. Perhaps the most conspicuous shell is *Meretrix (Sinodia) incrassata* (J. de C. Sow.) (Fig. 78), which ranges up from the Middle Barton, attains its maximum abundance in the Middle Headon, and persists to the Bembridge Beds. It was formerly assigned to the genus *Venus*, and gave its name to the well-known 'Venus-bed', where it is the predominant fossil. It is a rounded shell ornamented with concentric striae; it has a long ligament, large thick hinge-plate, and a specialized arrangement of the hinge-teeth. *Ostrea velata* S. V. Wood is abundant at certain horizons, where it forms 'oyster beds'. Other noteworthy lamellibranchs are *Cyrena obovata* (J. Sow.), *Nucula headonensis* Morris, and *Trigonocoelia deltoidea* (Lamarck). The last-named is a small shell with inflated trigonal valves; its hinge is curved, and bears five or six teeth on each side.

Conspicuous among the gastropods are several species that have been variously referred to *Cerithium* and *Potamides*. Of these, *Batillaria concava* (J. Sow.) and *Potamides vagus* (Solander) [= *C. pseudocinctum* auctt.] may be cited as typical. The presence of these, together with such shells as *Melanopsis fusiformis* J. Sow., *Neritina aperta* J. de C. Sow., and *N. concava* J. de C. Sow., is suggestive of brackish rather than salt-water conditions. Other beds contain a fauna indicative of marine conditions, such molluscan shells as *Murex sexdentatus* J. de C. Sow., *Pisania labiata* (J. de C. Sow.), *Voluta suturalis* Nyst and *V. geminata* J. de C. Sow., being associated with corals. *Voluta spinosa* (Linn.) ranges from the Barton, and *Ancilla buccinoidea* Lamarck from the Bracklesham Beds.

The Osborne Beds are a varied series of brackish water strata (chiefly red and green marls), with intercalated bands of shelly and sandy limestones. Little can be said concerning the sparsely distributed molluscan species, which all occur in the contiguous stages. The most interesting faunal records are those from a marine band near the base of the series, which contains the fishes *Diplomystus vectensis* (Newton), *Amia colenutti* Newton, and a species of *Lepidosteus*. The first-named was formerly assigned to *Clupea*, which includes the modern herrings, while the 'ganoid' genera *Amia* and *Lepidosteus* now survive only in the rivers of central America and the southern part of the United States. These fishes, together with prawns referred to the genus *Propalaemon*, appear to be distinctive of the Osborne Beds. Other fossils include remains of crocodiles, turtles (*Trionyx*) and mammals—*Palaeotherium* (a perissodactyl with a skull like that of the tapir) and *Theridomys* (a rodent).

The **Bembridge Limestone** is a white limestone constituted largely of freshwater molluscan shells like *Limnaea longiscata* Brongn., *Planorbis*

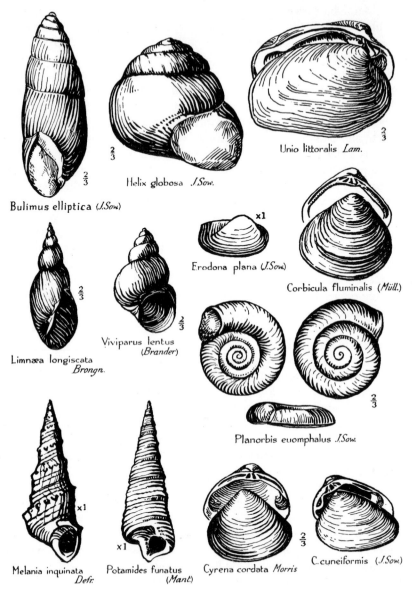

Bulimus elliptica (*J.Sow.*)

Helix globosa *J.Sow.*

Unio littoralis *Lam.*

Limnæa longiscata
Brongn.

Viviparus lentus
(*Brander*)

Erodona plana (*J.Sow.*)

Corbicula fluminalis (*Müll.*)

Planorbis euomphalus *J.Sow.*

Melania inquinata
Defr.

Potamides funatus
(*Mant.*)

Cyrena cordata *Morris*

C. cuneiformis (*J.Sow.*)

FIG. 80. NEOZOIC NON-MARINE MOLLUSCA (*drawn from figures by Edwards and S. V. Wood*)

euomphalus J. Sow., and *P. discus* Edwards. Associated with these are numerous land-shells such as *Glandina costellata* (J. Sow.), elongate oval in form, with large body-whorl and high spire, *Bulimus elliptica* and *Helix globosa* J. Sow., similar to living snails in their conical form, rounded whorls, and oblique crescentric aperture (Fig. 80). The shell substance, however, has often disappeared, leaving only the internal mould to mark the occurrence of these fossils. Several mammalian genera are recorded, including the swamp-dwelling ungulates *Hyopotamus*, *Chaeropotamus*, and *Anoplotherium*, allies of the living *Hippopotamus*. Nucules of *Chara*, which are abundant, are the only plant remains usually preserved.

The overlying Bembridge Marls have at their base a marine bed containing some shells that are not known to occur at lower horizons. These include *Ostrea vectensis* Morris, *Arca websteri* Morris, and *Panopaea minor* Morris. The lithological and faunal characters of the Bembridge Marls proper point to estuarine or deltaic conditions of deposition. The molluscan fauna is poor in species but prolific in individuals. The chief genera are *Cyrena*, *Melania*, *Melanopsis*, and *Viviparus*. Various plants have also been recorded (see p. 347).

The lower **Hamstead Beds** consist mainly of mottled clays that seem to have been deposited in fresh or only slightly saline water. They yield few fossils except drifted plants and bones of reptiles. At the base is the thin 'Black Band', a blackish carbonaceous clay containing seeds of aquatic plants and shells of freshwater mollusca, the most abundant shells being *Viviparus lentus* (Solander) and *Unio gibbsi* Morris. The succeeding clays are sometimes known as the Nematura Beds, but this name is more usually restricted to a thin band somewhat higher in the sequence. The latter is marked by the occurrence of the diminutive thin shells of *Stenothyra* (*Nematura*) *pupa* (Nyst), which are turbinate in form and have a contracted aperture. The 'White Band' is impersistent, but where present is rendered conspicuous by means of white shell-marl composed mainly of comminuted *Cyrena* and *Potamides* shells. In the succeeding clay-series is a firm dark clay known as the Waterlily Bed, which contains leaves of *Nelumbium* and palms. The Lower Hamstead Beds are thus closely related to the Bembridge Marls, and some authorities have suggested the union of these two series, restricting the term Hamstead Beds to the upper marine series. The latter, containing *Ostrea callifera* Lamarck, *O. cyathula* Lamarck, *Meretrix lyelli* (Morris), and *Voluta rathieri* Hébert as their chief fossils, are very incompletely represented in England as compared with the equivalent Stampian Stage of the Continent.

The Palaeogene strata of south-eastern England thus give evidence of the varied physical conditions consequent upon several oscillations in the relative level of land and sea. The Thanet Beds mark the beginning of marine deposition on a floor composed of eroded Cretaceous strata. The succeeding Woolwich Beds are estuarine in character, and are fringed on the landward side to the west by the freshwater Reading Beds. A return of marine littoral conditions is reflected in the Blackheath Beds, and the London Clay was also formed in muddy coastal waters. The overlying Bracklesham and Barton Beds were deposited in a clearer sea which supported corals and echinoids as well as an abundance of molluscan species. The remnants of Oligocene strata preserved in the Isle of Wight record alternations of marine (or brackish) and freshwater conditions which are conspicuously reflected in the fossil assemblages of the various beds. It may be added that the general appearance of the faunas suggest a sub-tropical climate, the molluscan genera inviting comparison with those living at present in the Indo-Pacific seas.

FAUNAL REGIONS

The two great faunal regions of the Cretaceous period, discussed in Chapter XIII, seem to have their analogues in Palaeogene fossil records. In the tropical regions the most conspicuous, if not the most abundant, elements of Palaeogene faunas are large nummulitic Foraminifera, reef-corals, and sea-urchins. Certain molluscan genera are virtually restricted to the tropical areas, but many others are represented also in the extra-tropical region to which some genera are almost confined, while reef-corals and nummulites are usually absent. It is convenient to discuss the distribution of these phyla separately.

THE FORAMINIFERA. The stratigraphical sequence and zonal distribution of the Eocene Foraminifera have been investigated in Aquitaine, south France, by H. Douvillé (1919) and others, more fully than elsewhere in Europe. Indeed, H. Gerth (1935) has chosen the section near Biarritz as a standard by which to compare the development in Europe with that in other parts of the world. In south France the Lower Eocene Beds contain radiate species of *Nummulites*, such as *N. atacicus* and *N. planulatus*, a granulose species of the same genus, *N. aquitanicus*, small granulose species of *Assilina*, *A. granulosa* and its megalospheric form, *A. leymeriei*, small thin species of *Discocyclina* like *D. archiaci*, and elliptical forms of *Alveolina*, e.g. *A. subpyrenaica*. Lutetian horizons yield abundance of radiate *Nummulites* such as *N. complanata*, *N. perforata*, &c., and large granulose forms as *N. laevigatus*. Species of *Assilina* show increase in size, e.g. *A. exponens* and its megalospheric form *A. mammillata*, as also do those of *Discocyclina*, e.g. *D. pratti*, and the elliptical forms of *Alveolina*, e.g. *A. oblonga*. At the base of the Ledian Stage there is an abrupt change in the general aspect of the nummulitids, the Upper Eocene beds being marked by small radiate species like *N. variolaris* and *N. contorta-striatus*. These are associated with large smooth forms of *Assilina* and fusiform species of *Alveolina*. Higher in the series reticulate species of *Nummulites* appear and *Discocyclina* becomes extinct. Reticulate species of *Nummulites*, such as *N. intermedius* and *N. fichteli*, along with small radiate forms like *N. vascus* and *N. bouillei* persist into Oligocene strata. They are associated with new orbitoid forms of the comprehensive genus *Lepidocyclina*. The first to appear are assigned to the sub-genus *Eulepidina* of which *E. dilatata* is a typical species. Both *Eulepidina* and reticulate *Nummulites* are represented in the Aquitanian Stage, the large *E. raulini* being specially characteristic. Later in the sequence *Nummulites* virtually disappears and *Lepidocyclina* is represented by small shells assigned to the sub-genus *Nephrolepidina*, e.g. *N. morgani* and *N. tournoueri*. The characteristic *Miogypsina* appears at about this level. Above the Burdigalian Stage, such large Foraminifera, *Heterostegina*, *Cycloclypeus*, *Orbiculina*, *Borelis*, as still persist have no particular stratigraphical significance.

Similar assemblages at the appropriate horizons have been recorded at other places in south Europe, including the Minervois, south of the Montagne Noire, the Swiss Alps, the Pyrenees, and the Cantabrian coast. The age value of orbitoid genera has been questioned by Italian geologists who assert the presence of *Discocyclina*, *Lepidocyclina*, and *Miogypsina* in Eocene strata of the Apennines and Sicily. South of the Mediterranean also, J. Flandrin (1934) has described an assemblage from Algeria in which abundant lepidocyclines are associated with Upper Eocene nummulitids; some authors, e.g. H. Gerth (1935), interpret this as representing a considerable succession in which fossils of various horizons have been mingled during erosion of the older beds. J. Bourcart and E. Davis (1933), however, record a complete sequence from Upper Eocene to Miocene in western Morocco in which *Lepidocyclina* associated with *Discocyclina* appears in beds below those containing the late Eocene *Nummulites fabiani*. So it seems that either the nummulitids in question survived longer than usual, or that the lepidocyclines appeared earlier in these regions; it may be noted here that, according to T. W. Vaughan (1924), *Lepidocyclina* was already established in American Eocene strata. Nummulitids reported from mid-Eocene Beds in Senegal by J. Flandrin and F. Jacquet (1937) include *N. heeri* and a variety of *N. gizehensis*, and the late Eocene *Discocyclina pratti* is recorded from Nigeria by R. B. Newton (1911). Neither nummulitids nor orbitoids are known farther south in West Africa; this coast nowadays is washed by the cold Benguella current which flows northward from the Southern Ocean.

With regard to the northern limit of the large Foraminifera, the group is only sparsely represented in northern France. Lower Eocene forms, such as *Nummulites planulatus*, *N. murchisoni*, and *Alveolina oblonga* are known from the coast of Brittany near Lorient, and *Assilina* and *Discocyclina* have been found by dredging off Gavres (L. Dangeard, 1928). Mid-Eocene deposits which underlie freshwater beds of Upper Eocene age at Gourbeauville, Manche, have yielded *Nummulites brongniarti* to J. Bourcart (1922). In the Paris basin, the Ypresian group of *N. planulatus-elegans*, and the Lutetian *N. laevigatus* and *Alveolina subulosa* are followed by the diminutive *N. variolaris* which, in its turn, is replaced by the small *N. orbignyi*. These forms are also present in the Bracklesham and Barton Beds of Hampshire

(p. 582). The Lower Eocene faunas of north Germany, Denmark, and Holland resemble that of the London clay in England, and higher strata are practically unknown there. In the Kressenberg *Nummulites planulatus* is the only Lower Eocene form recorded by M. Schlosser (1925), but the Middle Eocene fauna includes large nummulites and *Discocyclina*. In general, it may be said that the northern limit of the large Foraminifera in Europe lies not far north of the 50th parallel of latitude.

The Neozoic Foraminifera of Egypt, revised by J. Cuvillier (1930, 1933), provide an important link with those of Europe and south-west Asia. The earliest species of *Nummulites* in the Farafra Beds are the small primitive forms *N. fraasi* and *N. deserti*. The succeeding Libyan Stage of Lower Eocene age, has yielded species of *Nummulites* (*N. atacicus*, *N. globulus*), and *Alveolina* (*A. oblonga*, *A. lepidula*), some of which are present in corresponding deposits of Syria, Palestine, Europe, and India. The most typical species in the Lower Mokattam Beds of Middle Eocene age is the large *Nummulites gizehensis* which is equally abundant in Syria and Palestine; it is known in Armenia, Irak, and India, and extends westwards to the Dardanelles, Verona, Algeria, and Senegal. The Upper Mokattam Beds yield nummulitids only in their lower part, *N. beaumonti* and *N. scheinfurthi* being typical; the former appears to extend as far west as Algeria and eastwards to Assam (L. M. Davies, 1940). From Oligocene marine beds near Mariout, J. Cuvillier (1938) has recorded the orbitoid *Lepidocyclina dilatata*, a species which has long been known from Aquitaine and India.

The Eocene succession in north-west India, well known from the researches of W. L. F. Nuttall (1925-6) and L. M. Davies (1927-40) in Baluchistan, Sind, Punjab, and Kachh, may be taken as a standard for south Asia. The sequence begins with the Ranikot Beds which, in their upper part, contain radiate species of *Nummulites* including *N. nuttalli* formerly confused with the European *N. planulatus*, small granulose forms of *Assilina* such as *A. ranikoti*, small thin species of *Discocyclina* like *D. ranikotensis*, together with *Alveolina oblonga*, *Alv. globosa* and species of the peculiar rotaline genus *Dictyoconoides*. For long known only in Sind, these beds have now been recorded by L. M. Davies at Thal in the Frontier Province, at widely separated places in the Himalayan region and Tibet, and on the western border of Persia. In Sind and Baluchistan the succeeding Laki Beds have yielded to Nuttall (1925) radiate *Nummulites* such as *N. atacicus* and *N. mamilla*, associated with *Assilina granulosa*, *Alveolina oblonga*, *Alv. subpyrenaica*, &c. These two faunas are closely related, and show great similarity with the Lower Eocene faunas of south France and Italy, several species being identical with Mediterranean forms. *Nummulites atacicus* persists in the Lower Khirthar Beds, where it is accompanied by another radiate form *N. obtusus* and by medium-sized *Assilina* such as *A. exponens*. The nummulites of the Middle Khirthar Beds include both radiate (e.g. *N. atacicus*, *N. beaumonti*), and granulose forms (*N. acutus*, *N. laevigatus*, and *N. gizehensis*) but the former group become small and scarce towards the top of the sequence. They are associated with large species of *Discocyclina*, *Assilina*, *Alveolina*, and *Dictyoconoides*. These faunas include several species in common with the Lutetian faunas of south Europe. Most of the nummulitids known from the Upper Khirthar Beds (L. M. Davies, 1940), e.g. *N. carteri*, *Assilina papillata*, *Dictyoconoides kohatensis*, seem to be variants of Middle Khirthar types, but two forms, apparently of some stratigraphical significance, seem to be restricted to the upper beds. The large *Nummulites millecaput* has a restricted vertical range at the base of the sequence and according to J. Flandrin (1938) has a similarly limited range at the top of the Middle Eocene in Algeria; it is also reported from Switzerland, Crete, and Syria. The smaller *N. beaumonti*, originally described from the Upper Mokattam Beds of Egypt, is recorded also from Assam and Burma. On the evidence of these two forms L. M. Davies correlates the Upper Khirthar Beds of India with the Auversian Stage of Europe. No Upper Eocene strata appear to be present in north-west India, and a widespread unconformity above the Khirthar Beds is mentioned by F. R. C. Reed (1921). The Oligocene Series begins with the Nari Limestone which contains the large reticulate nummulites *N. intermedius* and *N. fichteli* commonly associated with the orbitoid *Eulepidina dilatata*; these occur also in the Oligocene deposits of south Europe. The succeeding Gaj Beds have yielded *Lepidocyclina blanfordi* and are regarded as equivalent to early Miocene horizons of Europe. Large Foraminifera do not appear to be known in higher strata in India.

The close relation of the Indian Palaeogene Foraminifera with assemblages from the Mediterranean borders of Syria, Palestine, Egypt, Algeria, Italy, and south France, is also shown in a considerable sequence of nummulitic deposits in Persia described by R. K. Richardson (1924). The Eocene faunas are much like those of India, but the Oligocene strata contain a greater variety of Foraminifera than the Nari Beds of India. The oil-bearing Asmari Limestone, which may include early Miocene horizons, has abundant species of *Lepidocyclina*, *Cycloclypeus*, *Amphistegina* and *Heterostegina*, besides *Nummulites intermedius* and numerous alveolines. The later Miocene fauna of the Fars Beds consists mainly of small miliolines, the larger Foraminifera being absent. It is perhaps significant that the Persian and Indian faunas include some forms that are not known in Europe, for example, the genera *Dictyoconoides*, *Alveolinella* and the species *Lepidocyclina sumatrensis*. Apparently the foraminiferal fauna of the Indian Ocean had become differentiated to a considerable degree.

Typical faunas are recorded also from fragmentary sequences which at several places transgress the eastern margin of the African continent. From Somaliland W. L. F. Nuttall and A. G. Brighton (1931) have described Lower Eocene faunas containing local species of *Dictyoconoides* in association with more widely spread alveolines, such as *Alveolina subpyrenaica* and

Alv. globosa. An overlying fauna of Middle Eocene age includes *Nummulites discorbinus, N. somaliensis, N. hormoensis, Dictyoconus aegyptiacus, Dictyoconoides kohatensis.* Higher faunas are represented by the Oligocene *Nummulites intermedius,* also by *Lepidocyclina sumatrensis* and *Miogypsina irregularis* of Lower Miocene age. J. Cuvillier (1938) has recorded a nummulite from Lower Eocene beds in south Arabia which he refers to the widespread species *N. planulatus.* Miocene Foraminifera are recorded from the island of Pemba whence A. M. Davies (in Stockley and others, 1927) has described species of *Amphilepidina, Miogypsina,* and *Trillina.* The first of these is almost confined to the Indo-Pacific region, while *Trillina,* originally described from Australia, is also known in the Philippine Islands and Persia. At Lindi, in Tanganyika Territory, Eocene limestones with *Nummulites perforatus* and species of *Alveolina* are recorded by P. Oppenheim (1916), following the discovery by E. Scholz (1911) of Oligocene and Miocene horizons with such species as *Nummulites intermedius, N. fichteli,* and *Lepidocyclina formosa.* Farther south H. K. Hodson (1928) has recorded Lower Miocene forms of *Amphilepidina, Lepidocyclina, Cycloclypeus,* and *Miogypsina* from Portuguese East Africa. On Madagascar P. Lemoine (1911) records *Nummulites lucananus, Assilina granulosa, Alveolina elliptica* and other species from Eocene rocks near Diego Suarez in the north of the island, while *Nummulites atacicus* and *Alveolina elliptica* are reported by H. Besairie (1930) from Betioky Province in the south. Miocene species, including *Amphilepidina gallieni* recorded also from Pemba, were long ago recorded by R. Douvillé (1904) from Andravy in northern Madagascar. From the Bathurst district in Cape Province the Upper Eocene species *Discocyclina pratti* and a small *Nummulites* have been recorded by F. Chapman (1930) from beds in the Alexandria series which was formerly regarded as of Miocene or Pliocene age.

In southern India Upper Eocene sandstone revealed by boring at Pondicheri has yielded to R. Furon and P. Lemoine (1938) specimens of *Discocyclina pratti* and underlying limestones have furnished the widespread *Assilina granulosa.* The latter species is reported by G. H. Tipper (1911) from the Andaman Islands, and by G. P. Cotter (1912) from the Negraio Beds of Burma, in both localities associated with *Nummulites atacicus.* Upper Eocene Beds in Burma contain *N. beaumonti,* and the Miocene beds which lie unconformably on Eocene strata in the Andaman Islands have an abundance of *N. niasi.* E. J. Wayland and A. M. Davies (1923) have recorded Miocene species of *Orbiculina* and *Spiroclypeus* from the northern part of Ceylon.

The records so far quoted seem sufficient to show the essential continuity of the Indian Ocean which extended during early Neozoic time some distance over its present margin on the African coast, and to a greater distance in north-west India. For, though the Neozoic deposits in the latter area are usually considered to have been accumulated in a hypothetical 'Himalayan geosyncline', the fragmentary sequences at various localities seem more in accord with local transgressions from the Indian Ocean. The evident affinities with European faunas are best explained by connexion with the Mediterranean through Persia and Palestine.

The waters of the Indian Ocean also flooded a considerable part of the present Indonesian archipelago, for nummulitic deposits are known on many of the islands. We may follow H. Gerth (1935) in taking the succession in Java, described by H. Douvillé (1912) and H. W. Doornink (1932), as a standard for the region. Early Eocene limestones near Djoka, containing *Nummulites gerthi* associated with *Pellatispira* and the orbitoid *Discocyclina*, are correlated tentatively with the Ranikot Beds of north-west India. Limestones in the Djiwo hills yield *Assilina granulosa*, *Nummulites aturicus*, and *N. obtusus* which are typical of the Lower Khirthar Beds in India. These species of *Nummulites* persist in higher strata where they are accompanied by *N. gizehensis* and alveolines like *Borelis javana*; this fauna is comparable with that of the Middle and Upper Khirthar Beds of Sind. The Nanggoelan Beds of Java, containing the Upper Eocene *N. variolaris* and species of *Discocyclina* seem to have no counterpart in India. The Tjidjengkol Beds with *N. intermedius* and *N. fichteli* evidently correspond with the Indian Nari Beds and the Oligocene Series generally; the orbitoid genera *Eulepidina* and *Pliolepidina* appear in the upper horizons of these beds. Higher faunas are more fully developed than in India; they compare with the Miocene succession in Persia, and some species are known at other localities on the western border of the Indian Ocean. Thus *Nephrolepidina sumatrensis* is well known in Persia and *Miogypsina thecidaeformis*, first described by Rutter (1911) from Borneo, is recorded also from Pemba Island. There is also a development of the peculiar genera *Flosculinella* and *Alveolinella* which gives special character to Miocene faunas of the Indian Ocean from Java to Persia. Above the Miocene the only genus of the large Foraminifera is *Cycloclypeus* which persists to the present day and has no precise stratigraphical significance. Parts of the Javan succession are represented in various islands of the Malay archipelago, namely, Sumatra, Nias and the Mentawei islands, Christmas Island, Borneo, the Philippines, Celebes, Timor, New Guinea, and New Hebrides.

South of the archipelago nummulitids are known in Australia. Here the Eocene strata are of freshwater origin, but marine Oligocene beds with *Lepidocyclina dilatata* are recorded by F. Chapman (1927) from Western Australia. Miocene beds in Victoria contain *Lepidocyclina tournoueri*, *L. marginata*, and *Amphistegina lissoni*. Chapman (1932) has also described a rock containing *Assilina* and *Discocyclina* from the vicinity of Mount Oxford in South Island, New Zealand.

North of the Philippine Islands the large Foraminifera extend by Formosa, through the Riu Kiu Islands to Japan. Upper Eocene Beds in Riu Kiu have yielded to T. Nagao (1928) small nummulites and species of *Pellatispira* and

Discocyclina. In Kyushu, Japan, Nagao has discovered Middle Eocene beds with *Nummulites* and *Discocyclina,* while S. Hanzawa (1935) records Miocene forms of *Miogypsina, Lepidocyclina* and *Cycloclypeus.* Hence in the Pacific Ocean the known distribution of these large Foraminifera extends to about 33° N. latitude. Between this limit and 30° S. latitude various nummulitids and orbitoids are reported from several islands in the Pacific Ocean. For instance, W. S. Cole (1939) records *Nephrolepidina parva,* and species of *Miogypsinoides* and *Spiroclypeus* from Lower Miocene beds in Guam (13° N.). C. A. Matley and A. M. Davies (1927) describe Miocene species of *Amphistegina, Lepidocyclina,* and *Cycloclypeus* from Vitu Levu, Fiji (18° S.). Species of *Lepidocyclina* and *Spiroclypeus* are also recorded by P. Marshall (1927) from Mangaia, Cook Island (22° S.), but the record from New Zealand already mentioned is much farther south (40° S.).

In North America deposits containing large Foraminifera are known from the neighbourhood of San Francisco (37° N.) in California and extend at intervals from the Pacific coast through Mexico to the Gulf coastal region of Texas, Louisiana and Mississippi, Alabama, Georgia, and Florida (Map, Fig. 81). They have a considerable range in Cuba, the Cayman Islands, Jamaica, Haiti and Puerto Rico, Antigua, St. Bartholomew, and other islands of the Antilles to Trinidad and Curaçoa, as well as the Panama Canal region of central America. Important assemblages have been described from Venezuela, Colombia, south-west Ecuador and north-west Peru, the southern limit being approximately 5° S.

We may discuss this great region as a unit, for the several assemblages of Foraminifera characteristic of distinct horizons are very uniform throughout its extent, and recent researches have tended to confirm the general conclusions expressed by T. W. Vaughan in 1924. In America nummulitids do not appear until the Middle Eocene, and then are very rare; moreover, there are no large species comparable with *Nummulites laevigatus, N. aturicus,* &c., of the Old World. Small nummulitoids, however, range from Middle Eocene to Middle Oligocene horizons, the earliest being *N. matleyi* described by T. W. Vaughan (1929) from the Yellow Limestone of Jamaica. Even this is suspect, for S. Hanzawa (1937) has transferred it to a new genus *Pellatispirella* which he places with *Pellatispira* in a new family Pellatispiridae. Other species of *Nummulites* are recorded from Upper Eocene Beds of the Gulf coastal region, Cuba and St. Bartholomew, and from the Oligocene Series of Cuba. The genus *Assilina* does not seem to be represented in America, though *Operculina* ranges from Middle Eocene to Miocene horizons. *Heterostegina* extends from Middle Eocene to Miocene in Florida, Antigua, Jamaica, and Panama, but *Helicolepidina,* which may be identical with *Spiroclypeus* of the eastern hemisphere, seems to be restricted to Upper Eocene deposits, though widely distributed from the Gulf region to Ecuador and Peru.

Unlike the nummulitids, the orbitoids are plentiful in the Palaeogene

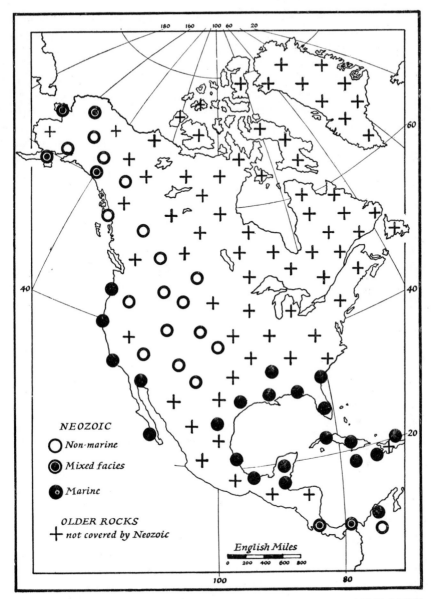

FIG. 81. SKETCH-MAP SHOWING GENERAL DISTRIBUTION OF NEOZOIC ROCKS
IN NORTH AMERICA

rocks of tropical and subtropical America. *Discocyclina*, ranging through the Eocene Series, is recorded from California, Mexico, Louisiana, Georgia, Alabama, Florida, Cuba, St. Bartholomew, Panama, Ecuador, and Peru, but the stellate subgenus *Asterocyclina* is confined to Upper Eocene deposits in America though it is known as low as the Lutetian Stage in Europe. *Lepidocyclina* and its allies range from Upper Eocene to the top of the Oligocene Series, and in some localities, e.g. California, persists to early Miocene horizons. Four of the subgenera are abundant in Upper Eocene beds, two of them, *Polylepidina* and *Pliolepidina*, being restricted to that horizon, the other two, *Lepidocyclina* s.s. and *Nephrolepidina*, persisting through the Oligocene Series. *Eulepidina* is particularly characteristic of Middle Oligocene horizons. Some of the species are widely distributed through the Gulf area. For instance, an association that includes *Lepidocyclina yurnagunensis*, *L. gigas*, *Nephrolepidina undosa*, and *Eulepidina favosa* is recognized in Middle Oligocene deposits from Georgia to Mexico, also from Cuba, the Cayman Islands, and Jamaica to Antigua. Some species may have a more extended geographical range, as certain forms found in Cuba and Mexico are closely similar to the European species *L. marginata* (Michelotti). Species of *Miogypsina* are also abundant in some Oligocene faunas in America; we may note especially a form from the Meson Beds of Mexico which W. L. F. Nuttall (1933) regards as apparently identical with *M. complanata*, a species first described by Schlumberger (1900) from Aquitanian deposits in France, and recorded by A. Silvestri (1910) as rare in Oligocene beds in Italy. This peculiar genus becomes extinct about midway through the Miocene Series, not long surviving *Lepidocyclina*.

The American Palaeogene Foraminifera show considerable differences from the contemporary assemblages in the Indo-Pacific and Mediterranean regions. But as a few American species seem to be identical or comparable with European forms, the coastal areas of America were probably nearer to those of Europe than to those of Malaya. Some bottom-living Foraminifera, which are large enough to be compared with the Palaeogene orbitoids, still live in shoal waters of tropical and subtropical seas, and T. W. Vaughan (1933) assumes that the Neozoic forms occupied a similar habitat. Migration across the deep ocean must have been accomplished by pelagic larvae which could be transported for considerable distances by ocean currents. Vaughan concludes that such transatlantic migration would be possible by means of the equatorial currents, provided that shoal-areas within 100 metres of the surface existed at intervals of a few hundred miles; it is not necessary to postulate extensive mid-Atlantic land-areas. *Lepidocyclina* and its allies appear to have originated in tropical or subtropical America during Eocene time and subsequently to have migrated to Europe. The nummulitids, on the other hand, probably originated in the Old World, for they are largely confined to the Mediterranean and Indo-Pacific regions.

THE REEF CORALS. The distribution of the large Foraminifera just discussed is paralleled by that of the reef-building corals; indeed T. W. Vaughan (1933) states that the two groups are often associated in Neozoic limestones of the tropical and subtropical regions. The corals, however, are not such constant constituents of the rocks, nor so intensively studied as the Foraminifera, but, unlike the latter, they do provide evidence with regard to faunal regions in later Neozoic time. There are four main regions of Neozoic deposits in which reef-corals are conspicuous; we may therefore discuss the Mediterranean, Indian, Malayan, and Antillean regions in the order named.

The Mediterranean region has been the most thoroughly investigated in Europe, and several successive coral-faunas have been described, the species of which are distributed in more than a hundred genera. Lower Eocene deposits in Europe contain few corals, but numerous reef-building forms are recorded from strata of Middle and Upper Eocene age at Frimli and San Giovanni Ilarione in north-east Italy, Corbières in south France, the vicinity of Barcelona, and Herzegovina in the north-west Balkans. Similar faunas of Oligocene age have long been known from Crosaro and Castel Gomberto in north Italy, Reit on the borders of Bavaria and Tyrol, Oberburg in Styria, and several localities in the eastern Alps.

These faunas are all closely related and may be discussed together. There is unfortunately much nomenclatorial confusion, but this is somewhat reduced by J. W. Wells (1936). It seems clear that many genera persist from Mesozoic deposits in which they are already established, while others appear for the first time in Eocene and Oligocene strata. The genus *Stylophora* represents a family of massive corals in which the corallites are embedded in vesicular tissue; some species are recorded from Jurassic rocks, and others are widespread in the Palaeogene deposits of south Europe. *Astrocoenia* and *Stylocoenia* of the family Astrocoenidae are similar in general habit and distribution. Among the Eusmiliidae, the simple forms *Trochosmilia*, *Coelosmilia*, and *Parasmilia* persist from Cretaceous horizons, but *Euphyllia* and *Dichocoenia* are apparently new genera, as are various branching Astrangiidae. Massive colonies of the Orbicellidae have been cited as *Heliastraea*, *Phyllocoenia*, and *Orbicella*, but, according to Wells (1936), these names are all synonymous with the genus *Montastraea* of Blainville (1830). *Solenastraea* and *Antiguastraea* of the same family are conspicuous in the European Oligocene fauna, and the type of *Antiguastraea*, common in equivalent rocks of the West Indies, provides an important link between the Oligocene coral-faunas of Europe and North America. The fasciculate *Calamophyllia* and *Rhabdophyllia* together with the massive *Goniastraea* of the family Faviidae, already represented in Mesozoic strata, are joined by *Hydnophora* and *Leptomussa* in the European Palaeogene deposits. The fungid *Cyathoseris*, forming low expanded colonies, is another coral that persists from Cretaceous rocks; it is accompanied in the Oligocene rocks of Bavaria and Italy by *Mesomorpha*,

Siderastraea, the simple *Trochoseris*, and other genera. *Cyathomorpha* is also a fungid type, but it has the general appearance of an *Orbicella* and T. W. Vaughan (1919) has transferred it to the family Oulastraeidae.

There are also several corals with porous septa usually classified in the order Perforata, but W. D. Lang (1917, 1938) believes this cribriform or perforate condition to have arisen independently in the morphological development of numerous lineages. The condition is well known in some Jurassic corals, e.g. *Microsolenia* is a cribriform development of *Thamnastraea*. Neozoic forms include *Actinacis* and *Astraeopora* of the family Acroporidae which continue from Cretaceous to Oligocene strata where they are joined by *Dendracis* and *Acropora* of the same family. Among the massive Poritidae, *Porites*, already established in Cretaceous horizons, accompanies *Alveopora* and *Goniopora* (often cited as *Litharaea*) in the Neozoic deposits.

There are few corals in the Eocene and Oligocene deposits of the Paris basin, but some of the reef-building genera just discussed are represented as far north as Belgium and south England. The Middle Eocene corals of Belgium described by M. Glibert (1930) are mainly simple forms but include massive colonies of *Astrocoenia* and *Goniopora*. These two genera, together with species of *Stylocoenia, Dendrophyllia, Solenastraea, Acropora, Dendracis, Porites*, are described by P. M. Duncan (1866–72) from the Bracklesham and Brockenhurst Beds of Hampshire and the Isle of Wight, the most northerly record of the group. The corals seem to be drifted fragments though some of them are tolerably well preserved. This northern limit of the reef-corals coincides approximately with that of the large Foraminifera.

In Egypt, as in south Europe, the Middle Eocene is much richer in reef-corals than the lower deposits. From the Libyan Stage of Upper Egypt J. W. Gregory (1898) has described species of *Coelosmilia* and *Goniopora* (cited as *Litharaea*) which are closely allied to European types. A species of *Stylophora* from the Upper Eocene of the Fayûm is brought into comparison with a form from south France. In Somaliland M. H. Latham (1929) has described species of *Stylophora, Tubicora, Stylina, Astrocoenia*, and *Dendracis* from Eocene strata, and of *Stylophora, Circophyllia, Favia, Orbicella, Columnastraea*, and *Porites* from Oligocene beds. Some of these species are identical with European forms, and may indicate a connexion with the Mediterranean by way of Egypt, though the Red Sea as such did not exist at the time.

A considerable succession of coral faunas from Sind, north-west India, is described by P. M. Duncan (1880). The sequence begins in Cretaceous strata, from which species of *Stylophora, Rhabdophyllia*, and *Goniopora* (cited as *Litharaea*), in addition to simple corals, are recorded. Some fifty species from the succeeding Ranikot Beds include such reef-building corals as *Stylophora, Astrocoenia, Stylocoenia, Diploria, Leptoria, Pironastraea*,

Pavona (cited as *Reussastraea*), *Goniopora* (cited as *Litharaea*), and *Porites*, besides simple forms. Several of the species are identical or comparable with forms described from Italy and the Alpine region. J. W. Gregory (1930) has described a similar early Eocene assemblage from the Samana Range some 500 miles north of Sind; it indicates an extension of the Indian Ocean over the low-lying area of the Punjab. A smaller assemblage from the Khirthar Beds of Sind includes species of *Stylophora*, *Astrocoenia*, *Calamophyllia*, *Hydnophora*, and *Porites*; it is comparable with the Ranikot fauna though many of the corals are local species. The Oligocene corals of the Nari Beds form a similar generic association, also related to that of the Mediterranean borders.

The Palaeogene coral-faunas of the Malayan Archipelago are very incompletely known; present knowledge, summarized by H. Gerth (1933), is based largely on a small collection from south-east Borneo described by K. Fritsch in 1875. The generic association including *Stylophora*, *Stylocoenia*, *Astrocoenia*, *Actinacis*, and *Dendracis*, is comparable with that of the Ranikot Beds, but the species are in general distinct. An Eocene coral-fauna from New Guinea, described by J. W. Gregory and J. B. Trench (1916), includes local species of *Stylophora*, *Leptoria*, *Stylina*, *Plesiastraea*, *Dachiardia*, *Kobya*, *Actinacis*, *Porites*, and *Montipora*. Again there is some generic resemblance with the Sind fauna, but some of the most typical genera in the latter are absent from the New Guinea collection. It may be noted that *Montipora* is restricted to the Western Pacific, Indian Ocean, and Red Sea, and is not represented in the Eocene fauna of Sind. Some of these discrepances may disappear after further exploration, if one may judge by the large number of genera listed by H. Gerth (1931) from the Neogene deposits of the Malayan region (p. 638).

Numerous fossil corals from several of the West Indian islands were described by P. M. Duncan in various papers between 1863 and 1868. Modern knowledge of the corals, however, is largely due to the extensive researches of T. W. Vaughan during the first three decades of the present century. The earliest reef-fauna is preserved in a limestone of Upper Eocene age on the island of St. Bartholomew; species of *Stylophora*, *Astrocoenia*, *Leptoria*, *Antilloseris*, *Dendracis*, *Actinacis*, and *Goniopora* are conspicuous forms. A few of the species are found in equivalent deposits of Jamaica, and one of them, an *Astrocoenia*, in the Brito Beds near the Pacific coast of Nicaragua. These beds are shown to be of Upper Eocene age by the resemblance of a *Discocyclina* to a species from the Ocala Limestone of south Georgia and Florida. Corals from the Ocala Beds have nothing in common with the St. Bartholomew fauna, but Vaughan (1919) believes this to be due to difference of habitat, particularly to temperature of the water. Vaughan (1924) follows P. Oppenheim (1901) in correlating the coral fauna of St. Bartholomew with that of the Priabonian Beds of Italy.

No reef fauna of Lower Oligocene age seems to be known in the West

Indies or Central America, though the Vicksburg Beds in the States of Mississippi, Alabama, and Florida contain a limited fauna correlated by Vaughan (1900) with that of Veneto in north Italy. The numerous corals of Middle Oligocene age in Antigua, Puerto Rico, south Hispaniola, Cuba, Georgia, Alabama, Florida, east Mexico, Panama, and Arube represent the greatest known development of American coral-reefs. The chief genera, *Stylophora, Pocillopora, Stylocoenia, Astrocoenia, Euphyllia, Orbicella, Antiguastraea, Goniastraea, Favia, Hydnophora, Trochoseris, Mesomorpha, Mysetoseris, Cyathomorpha, Astraeopora, Actinacis, Goniopora, Porites,* and *Alveopora* have a wide distribution in the region. In the abundance of *Stylophora, Astrocoenia, Antiguastraea,* and *Cyathomorpha* this fauna is much like that of Castel Gomberto in Italy, and Vaughan (1919) states that some species are closely related, though not identical as P. M. Duncan supposed. The resemblance of the two faunas has often attracted attention and some authors have postulated a land-area across the Atlantic along the shores of which the corals were able to migrate. After a study of coral larval stages T. W. Vaughan (1933) believes that the requirements for transatlantic migration would be met by a series of shoals a few hundred miles apart, and that great land-bridges are not necessary for corals and orbitoid foramini-fera to have achieved their known geographical distribution.

There is a considerable development of reef-corals also in the Upper Oligocene limestones of Anguilla, Panama, Cuba, and the Tampa Beds of Florida (Vaughan, 1919). The coral genera recorded are *Stylophora, Pocillopora, Astrocoenia, Orbicella, Stylangia, Goniastraea, Pavona, Acropora, Astraeopora, Goniopora,* and *Porites,* an association which has much in common with that of the preceding stage.

The Eocene and Oligocene faunas under discussion comprise three categories of corals. (1) Genera now extinct, including such forms as *Trochosmilia, Antilloseris, Actinacis,* and *Dendracis.* (2) Some of the genera now live only in the Pacific region, for example, *Stylophora, Antillia, Goniastraea, Leptoria,* and *Goniopora.* (3) Others, like *Astrocoenia* and *Orbicella,* still live in the Antillean region, some of them, e.g. *Favia* and *Porites,* also in the Indo-Pacific Ocean. The distribution of these corals, together with the fact that some of the Palaeogene species are common to the West Indies and the Pacific coast of Panama shows that there was marine connexion between the Atlantic and Pacific Oceans during Palaeogene time, probably across the site of the present Isthmus of Panama. The development of the coral-fauna in Neogene time is discussed in the next chapter.

ECHINOIDEA. All the orders and most of the families of living sea-urchins are already established in the Mesozoic systems. At the end of Cretaceous time many genera became extinct, and their place was gradually filled by the development of new forms during the Neozoic era. Hence, while the continuity of echinoid evolution is maintained, there is considerable difference between the Mesozoic and Neozoic assemblages. One striking feature they have in common is the persistence of the order Cidaroida which is almost unchanged since Triassic time. The genus *Cidaris* s.l., with numerous species in littoral deposits of Jurassic and Cretaceous age, is widely distributed in the Neozoic strata of tropical and subtropical regions, and it still exists in North Atlantic waters; it probably represents the radicle stock from which the other orders have arisen.

We may discuss first the echinoid fauna of the Indian Ocean, because in general it seems to have developed autochthonously throughout Neozoic time. The assemblages were first described by P. M. Duncan and W. P. Sladen (1882–6), and their account was revised by E. W. Vredenburg in 1906. The earliest association is contained in the Upper Ranikot Beds of Sind, approximately equivalent to the Ypresian Stage of west Europe. Species of *Cidaris* and *Rhabdocidaris* represent the radicle stock, while the diademoids *Salenia* and *Cyphosoma* persist, in different species, from Cretaceous horizons. Two other genera of regular sea-urchins are recorded, namely, the curiously ornamented *Dictyopleurus*, representing the Temnopleuridae, and the large *Eurypneustes*, a member of the Strongylocentrotidae. Among the Irregulares the order Holectypoida is represented by the thick-shelled genus *Conoclypeus* and the Cassidulidae by *Eurhodia, Eolampas, Plesiolampas*, and *Cassidulus*, the last three surviving from the Cretaceous System. Several genera of the spatangoid family Brissidae are present; *Hemiaster* and *Linthia* persist from Cretaceous strata, *Prenaster, Ditremaster*, and *Schizaster* are essentially Palaeogene developments.

A similar association of genera is present in the succeeding Laki Beds which correspond with the lower horizons of the Lutetian Stage in Europe. Here the cidarids are represented by *Leiocidaris* and *Porocidaris*, the diademoids by *Cyphosoma* and *Micropsis*, and the temnopleurids by *Arachniopleurus*. The holectypoid *Conoclypeus* persists with one species and is accompanied by *Amblypygus* of the same family. The fibulariid *Echinocyamus*, persisting from Cretaceous strata, has five species in the Laki Beds. Of the cassidulids, *Eolampas* persists from Ranikot horizons and is joined by seven species of *Echinolampas* and two of *Rhynchopygus*. The family Brissidae also has increased representation with seven species of *Hemiaster*, two of *Schizaster* and the appearance of *Macropneustes, Metalia*, and *Brissopsis*, while *Eupatagus* represents the allied family Spatangidae.

In the Khirthar Beds of Sind, correlated with Middle Lutetian horizons of Europe, no cidaroids or diademoids are recorded except one species of *Cyphosoma*, and the temnopleurids are likewise wanting. *Conoclypeus* persists from the Laki Beds with three species. The fibulariid *Echinocyamus* does not appear in the lists, its place being taken by the larger and flatter *Sismondia*. The cassidulid *Echinolampas* is still well represented but *Rhynchopygus* is lacking; newcomers of the same family are *Echinanthus* and *Ilarionia*. The Brissidae include species of *Micraster*, a late survivor from the Cretaceous, *Linthia* and *Schizaster*. The Oligocene fauna of the Nari

Beds in Sind is largely a development of genera already present in the region. The most frequently occurring forms are species of *Schizaster*, *Echinolampas* with the temnopleurid *Paradoxechinus* (formerly assigned to *Temnechinus*), and the highly specialized spatangid *Breynia*. The large *Clypeaster apertus* from Kachh was regarded by Duncan and Sladen as an Eocene species, but Vredenburg (1906) states that the type-specimen is partially covered with shells of *Nummulites intermedius* which establishes its Oligocene age. The Gaj Beds of Sind are closely related to the underlying Nari Beds and are usually correlated with the Lower Miocene of Europe. One of the most abundant sea-urchins is *Breynia carinata* and it is associated with species of *Paradoxechinus*, *Echinolampas*, *Clypeaster*, *Eupatagus*, the echinid *Tripneustes*, the arbacid *Coelopleurus* and the scutellid *Amphiope* (sometimes cited as *Echinodiscus*). Towards the middle of the Miocene period the sea retreated from the whole of northern India.

The echinoid faunas of Eocene deposits around the Mediterranean borders are closely related to the Indian assemblages. In Egypt, the Libyan Stage contains species of the cidaroid *Leiocidaris*, the holectypoid *Conoclypeus*, the cassidulids *Cassidulus*, *Gisopygus*, and *Echinolampas*, the fibulariid *Sismondia*, the brissids *Linthia* and *Schizaster*, and the spatangid *Eupatagus* in variety and abundance. Many of these genera continue into the overlying Mokattam Beds where they are joined by *Porocidaris*, *Brissopsis*, and the temnopleurid *Dictyopleurus*, all of Indian affinities. Records from the western Mediterranean region show that many of the genera have a wide geographical range, though others are curiously restricted. In the Middle Eocene fauna of south France there are species of the widespread holectypoids *Conoclypeus* and *Amblypygus*, with the cassidulids *Eurhodia*, *Eolampas*, and *Ilarionia* in common with the Egyptian and Indian faunas; some genera, however, e.g. *Leiopneustes*, *Saviniaster*, *Codiopsis*, *Circopeltis*, and the early clypeastrid *Biarritzella*, are hardly represented elsewhere. Farther north, the Middle Eocene deposits of the Paris basin have yielded forty-two species of echinoids of which thirty are unknown elsewhere, and none of them are identical with Aquitaine forms. Only one genus, the brissid *Moiropsis*, is confined to the Paris basin; others, like the diademoids *Echinopsis* and *Hebertia* are represented by different species in Brittany, Normandy, Belgium, Germany, and the Alps, and most of them are represented in earlier deposits of south Europe. Some of them, *Coelopleurus*, *Echinopedina*, *Scutellina*, and *Schizaster*, reached England, but the tests are generally small in size. The amber-bearing beds of Samland in east Prussia also yield sea-urchins comparable with Eocene species of *Spatangus* and *Lenita* from the Paris basin, and with *Salenia* and *Scutellina* from the Atlantic border of France. Species of *Lenita*, *Echinolampas*, *Scutellina*, *Hemipatagus*, *Moira*, *Spatangus*, and *Tristomanthus* are present in Oligocene deposits of Germany, especially at Bunde in Westphalia, but the contemporary faunas of the Mediterranean borders contain additional clypeastrids

(*Paratinanthus*), scutellids (*Amphiope, Scutella*), and spatangids (*Moira*). Hence it would appear that a steady stream of migrants made its way northwards from the warmer seas throughout Palaeogene time, and that they reached the limit of distribution attained by the large Foraminifera in central and western Europe. Most of the genera show affinities with Indian forms and indicate marine connexion with the Indian Ocean, possibly through an enlarged Persian Gulf. Others are largely confined to the Atlantic border and must be discussed in relation to North American faunas.

In North America there is some uncertainty about the lower limit of the Neozoic deposits which occupy the coastal plain between Alabama and Texas. J. Gardner (1935) and others regard the Midway Beds as early Eocene in age, though G. Scott (1934) refers them to the Cretaceous Danian Stage. The only sea-urchins reported are rare and local species of the cassidulid *Echinanthus* and the brissid *Linthia*, genera which are known from Cretaceous and Eocene deposits in other parts of the world. Echinoids continue scarce up to the Middle Eocene Claiborne Beds of the Southern States in which important developments are manifest. The Claiborne fauna includes the earliest known members of the Scutellidae; the genus *Protoscutella* is recorded from Mississippi, Texas, and California, while the allied *Periarchus* ranges from north Carolina to Texas. The associates of these forms include species of *Fibularia, Hemipatagus*, and *Schizaster*. The succeeding Jackson and Ocala formations of late Eocene age have yielded a much larger assemblage, especially of irregular sea-urchins. The imperforate scutellids continue to flourish with such genera as *Mortonella* and *Praescutella*, in addition to *Periarchus*. A few species of *Praescutella* are also recorded from western Europe (Brittany, Paris basin, Aquitaine), and on this account G. Stefanini (1924) and A. M. Davies (1934) regard this imperforate group of Scutellidae as originating in the Atlantic region, in contrast to the bilunulate *Amphiope* of Indo-Pacific origin. The holectypoid *Oligopygus* may have a similar history, for C. W. Cooke (1942) cites it from Georgia, Florida, Cuba, Trinidad, and Venezuela, and it appears also in the Eocene of Senegal, West Africa. But *Amblypygus* of the same family appears first in the Laki Beds of India, and, ranging through the Eocene of south Europe, is only recorded from the Upper Eocene in Florida and California. Furthermore, the early Eocene *Conoclypeus* apparently never reached America. The Jackson-Ocala fauna also contains members of the Fibulariidae (*Fibularia* and *Echinocyamus*), Clypeastridae (*Laganidea*), Laganidae (*Rumphia*), Brissidae (*Linthia, Schizaster*), and Spatangidae (*Eupatagus, Hemipatagus, Agassizia*). The last-named genus, found in the Upper Eocene of Florida and the West Indies, is not recorded outside America until the Oligocene, when it appears in Algeria, afterwards spreading northwards in Europe. The Oligocene echinoids of the Vicksburg Beds evidently developed autochthonously, but are reduced in number; the most conspicuous forms are species of *Clypeaster, Cassidulus, Echinolampas*,

Schizaster, Brissopsis, and its ally *Cyclaster.* Similar Palaeogene faunas are recorded by W. Kew (1920) from the Pacific coast of North America; spatangid genera are dominant throughout, and scutellids appear in the Tejon formation of California and Oregon.

Many of these Eocene and Oligocene genera are also present in corresponding deposits of the Caribbean islands, but G. Stefanini (1924) states that no species are common to both regions. The main feature of the West Indian assemblage is the great development of *Clypeaster,* the genus being specially abundant in the Oligocene beds of Antigua. Among the many other associates the cassidulid *Rhynchopygus* and the holectypoid *Echinoneus* are characteristically present, but the scutellids are apparently not represented. This tropical fauna extended southward into South America, for *Oligopygus* and *Rhynchopygus* are recorded from the Upper Eocene in Peru, and Oligocene in Venezuela, and there is considerable similarity with the Palaeogene echinoid assemblage of south Europe, as with the reef-corals and the giant Foraminifera.

MOLLUSCA. Shells of lamellibranchs and gastropods are the most abundant and widely distributed fossils in marine deposits of the Neozoic stages. This is due mainly to the adaptability of different families and genera to a great variety of habitat so that some mollusca are almost certain to be found whatever the lithological character of the deposit.

Notwithstanding the wide differences between Cretaceous and Eocene faunas, the majority of Neozoic molluscan families are already represented in the later Mesozoic rocks, and certain groups had already attained their maximum abundance and distribution before Neozoic time. Some of them have few survivors persisting into Neozoic rocks (e.g. *Gervillia, Trigonia, Cucullaea, Cyprina*) and others are now restricted geographically either to the cooler seas (Astartidae, Cyprinidae, Aporrhaidae) or to more tropical waters (*Nautilus,* Pteriidae, Spondylidae). Many families, which are already important elements in Cretaceous faunas, reach their acme in Neozoic horizons and continue in abundance and variety in living faunas. For instance, the gastropod family Volutidae is represented by many species of several genera (*Volutilithes, Lyria, Scaphella, Volutospina, Caricella*) in the Cretaceous deposits of Europe and south India and is still important in the faunas of tropical seas. The earliest records of Cypraeidae are from late Jurassic rocks of Sicily; they are followed by species of *Gisortia* and *Eocypraea* from the Albian stage of south Europe and south India, with *Transovula, Megalocypraea, Vicetia, Cypraedia, Cypraeorbis, Protocypraea* appearing at higher Cretaceous horizons in both regions (Vredenburg, 1920; Schilder, 1927). Genera of the existing lamellibranch families Chamidae and Veneridae are also widely distributed in Upper Cretaceous deposits. Hence the main dispersal of these and other families seems to have been accomplished already during Cretaceous time, and their geographical distribution in early Neozoic horizons may have been maintained by autochthonous development in the several regions. On the other hand, such families as the Cancellariidae, Conidae, Xancidae, Cymatidae, and Strombidae have few (if any) genera in Cretaceous deposits, and many new forms (e.g. *Eovasum, Strepsidura, Terebellopsis*) appear suddenly at early Neozoic horizons without any evidence of gradual evolution from older forms. These are regarded as migrants from some region at present undetermined and their wide distribution at the earliest horizon from which they are recorded emphasizes the need for caution in interpreting their early history.

After the exhaustive review of *Tertiary Faunas* by A. M. Davies (1934–5), detailed discussion of the Neozoic mollusca would appear superfluous, but two of the main conclusions reached by that author are of importance in our present study. In the first place Davies shows that the distribution of a large and distinctive group of mollusca conforms closely with that of the large Foraminifera, and that a large number of other genera is characteristic of deposits outside the Nummulitic belt. Secondly, the mollusca of later Neozoic rocks provide evidence of oceanic relations that are not so clearly shown by the other groups of fossils we have discussed.

The early Eocene Beds of north-west India are said to be completely conformable on Cretaceous strata, and, as is usual in such cases, there is some difference of opinion regarding the position of the stratigraphical boundary. Hence the *Cardita beaumonti* Beds of Sind are correlated by some authors (e.g. Vredenburg, 1906, 1928) with uppermost Cretaceous (Danian) horizons, by others (L. M. Davies, 1940) with the basal Eocene (Montian) Beds of Europe. This Indian horizon has a distinctive molluscan fauna (H. Douvillé, 1928–9) which, apart from the index-fossil cited, includes species of Cerithiidae (*Campanile, Pyrazus*), Turritellidae (*Haustator, Mesalia*), Strombidae (*Praestrombus*), Cypraeidae (*Cypraeorbis*), Xancidae (*Eovasum, Heligmotoma*), Turridae (*Turricula, Turris*), Volutidae (*Voluticorbis*), Crassatellidae (*Crassatellites*), Lucinidae, and other forms. The faunas of corresponding beds in Baluchistan and Persia are specially marked by a great abundance of Cerithiidae (*Procerithium, Tiaricerithium, Pyrazus, Campanile*) and Thiaridae (*Pyrgulifera, Pseudoglauconia*) associated with Melanopsidae (*Faunus, Morgania*) and Turritellidae (*Turritella, Mesalia*).

In Sind the lower part of the Ranikot Beds has yielded only one marine species, *Ostrea talpur*, but the upper part has a large molluscan fauna in which such gastropod families as Volutidae, Mitridae, Conidae, Harpidae, Fusinidae, Cassididae, Cypraeidae, Strombidae, to name only a few, are represented by more than sixty genera (Cossman and Pissaro, 1909; Vredenburg, 1928). Many of the genera are present in the slightly older Hangu Shales of the Samana Range (L. R. Cox, 1930), but only a few long-ranged species are common to the two horizons, and both lack the distinctive species of the *Cardita beaumonti* Beds. Some widespread genera of

Xancidae (*Eovasum*), Strepsiduridae (*Strepsidura*), Strombidae (*Terebellopsis*), Conidae (*Cryptoconus*), and Fusinidae (*Dolicholatirus*) make an abrupt appearance in the Hangu Shales and continue into younger beds, but nothing is known concerning the place of their origin. The presence of the remarkable strombid genus *Calyptraphorus* in the Ranikot Beds is of interest in view of its wide distribution, for it was originally described from Eocene strata in Alabama, U.S.A., and afterwards recorded from Cretaceous beds of Madras and from the lowest Eocene beds of Belgium and South America. The cerithiid genus *Campanile*, abundant in the Danian rocks of Persia and the Ranikot Beds of Sind is another form which links the early Eocene rocks of India and Europe. Rocks of this age appear to have a wide extension in southern Asia. A molluscan fauna collected by H. Hayden (1907) in Tibet is assigned to the Danian stage by Douvillé (1916). But G. P. Cotter (1926) shows that certain of the Tibetan species of *Voluta, Lyria, Terebellum, Chenopus, Campanile, Velates,* and *Spondylus* are identical with Ranikot species, and L. M. Davies (1938) states that the associated Foraminifera are Upper Ranikot forms. A few gastropods, species of *Athleta* and *Strepsidura*, of similar age are recorded (Vredenburg, 1924) from the lower part of the Laungshe Shales near Yeshin, Burma. Another extension of the Ranikot Beds is indicated by Foraminifera collected from a section near Shamshir i Quili on the western borders of Persia (L. M. Davies, 1938).

The molluscan fauna of the Laki Beds in Sind and Baluchistan (L. R. Cox, 1932) differs considerably from that of the Ranikot horizon, partly because the calcareous Laki Beds indicate physical conditions different from those of the arenaceous Ranikot Beds. Though few species are common to the two horizons, many genera occur in both and there are few newcomers. We may note the earliest occurrence of *Vicarya*, a peculiar genus of Cerithiidae, which for long was known only in Lower Miocene rocks of Sind and certain East Indian islands. The earliest of the cypraeid shells grouped in the genus *Vicetia* occurs in the Lower Laki Beds of Sind, and Cox (1932) describes a specimen of *Cordiopsis incrassata* (J. Sow.) from the Laki Beds of Baluchistan remarking that 'the Indian shell agrees well with specimens from the English Oligocene' and 'the species has not previously been recorded from so low a horizon'. Certain shells, including species of *Velates, Euspirocrommium, Hippochrenes, Terebellum, Ostrea, Spondylus, Lucina (Pseudomiltha), Panopaea,* have a wide distribution in Eocene rocks generally, and the lamellibranch species *Euphenax jamaicensis* occurs in Jamaica as well as in India and Somaliland. Some Laki species, e.g. *Lucina (Loripinus) pharaonis,* are found in Persia and North Africa but not in Europe, *Blagravia sindensis* in Persia and Somaliland, still others (*Lucina metableta, Bicorbula subexarata*) are unknown west of Egypt. A few of the gastropods that show a series of folds on the inner lip are referred to families in which this feature is not usually developed; they comprise species of *Praestrombus, Gosavia,* and *Involuta* which are all recorded from the Laki and Khirthar Beds, but seem to be peculiar to India.

The molluscan fauna of the Khirthar Beds differs little from that of the underlying Laki horizon, and many of the genera persist into the Nari Beds which contain representatives of Conidae, Volutidae, Mitridae, Fusinidae, Strombidae, Cypraeidae, and other families now characteristic of warm latitudes. Many species of the Nari fauna are closely related to shells found in the Oligocene beds of Europe and so provide evidence of close connexion between the two regions. Some forms now living in the Indian Ocean can be traced back to species which first appear in the Nari Beds (Vredenburg, 1928). Thus *Terebra narica* Vredenburg is a forerunner of the living *T. crenulata* (Linn.). *Distorsio reticulata* (formerly referred to the genus *Persona* of Lamarck) is hardly distinguishable from shells still extant in the Indian and Caribbean seas. Vredenburg (1924) also describes a succession of closely related mutations of *Turbinella* ranging from the European and Indian Oligocene species *T. episoma* (Michelotti) which is abundant in the Nari Beds of Sind and Baluchistan, to the *T. fusus* Sowerby which lives in the Andaman seas. The genus *Turbinella* (or *Xancus*) may be an immigrant form for it is known from Eocene strata in Peru. *Harpa narica* is said to be intermediate in some features between the Ranikot species *H. morgani* C. and P. and the living *H. conoidalis* Lamarck, 'of which it perhaps represents an ancestral form'.

From Persia Neozoic strata continue westward into Palestine, Syria, and Egypt, where the Eocene deposits are usually transgressive on Cretaceous rocks. The Libyan stage of Egypt is referred to the Lower Eocene, but the fauna is markedly different from that of the Laki Beds of India, few molluscan species being common to both. Genera of the gastropod families Olividae, Turridae, and Conidae are absent from the Egyptian records, and the Volutidae are only represented by a single species of *Volutocorbis*. Some Libyan genera, *Aturia, Pseudoliva, Heligmotoma, Thersitea, Macrosolen*, &c., are not reported from the Laki Beds. Volutidae and Olividae are still extremely rare in the Middle Eocene Mokattam Beds of Egypt, from which such widespread species as *Gisortia gigantea, Velates perversus, Spondylus radula*, and *Lucina gigantea* are recorded. New forms appearing in the Upper Mokattam Beds include species of *Latrunculus, Mactra, Chione, Carolia, Cucullaea, Trisidos, Architectonica, Turricula*, and *Raetomya*. The last three are represented in the Middle Eocene Beds of Nigeria, and therefore indicate communication, perhaps across the Sahara region, with the Atlantic Ocean. Oligocene deposits in the Fayûm district are estuarine.

Over the greater part of the Mediterranean area marine deposits equivalent in age to the Ranikot Beds of India appear to be absent. In some places the passage from Cretaceous to marine Eocene rocks is represented by freshwater deposits, in others, such as the Alpine region and England, the Eocene beds rest unconformably on the truncated edges of various Cretaceous horizons. Consequently it is extremely difficult, if not impossible, to make direct comparison between early Eocene faunas of the Mediterranean and Indian regions. L. R. Cox (1930) has noted, however, that *Globularia brevispina* and *Terebellopsis*, both known from the Hangu Shales of north-west India, are recorded from early Eocene deposits of Haute Garonne, south France. Again, though no species are common to the early Eocene deposits of India and north-west Europe, the genus *Calyptraphorus* occurs in both the Ranikot Beds and the Calcaire de Mons, also *Campanile* is recorded from the Danian Beds of Persia and the Montian Beds of Belgium.

Some molluscan genera, like *Strepsidura, Streptochetus, Voluta, Cassis, Harpa, Sigaretus* and certain long-ranged species such as *Lambis goniophora, Mesalia fasciata, Corbula exarata* appear first in Europe at Ypresian or Lutetian horizons, though they occur in beds of Ranikot age, or even earlier, in India. Hence some authors incline to the view that such forms originated in the Indian Ocean and spread steadily westwards. But L. R. Cox (1930) points out that this idea of an eastern origin is no longer tenable for the nummulites and, in the present incomplete state of our knowledge, uncertain for the early Eocene mollusca of the Mediterranean area. The Lutetian fauna of Europe is, however, very similar to the contemporary Khirthar fauna of India (L. R. Cox, 1932) as is shown by the wide distribution of such genera as *Velates, Hippochrenes, Terebellum, Cordiopsis, Panopaea,* &c., some species (as *Hippochrenes amplus, Cordiopsis incrassata, Panopaea intermedia, Lucina gigantea*) reaching as far north as England. Most of the species common to the two regions are forms with a long vertical range, for they are found already in the Laki Beds of India, and some of them at Lower Eocene horizons in Egypt, whereas in Europe they are known only from Middle Eocene or even later beds. This of course may be due to the poor representation of Lower Eocene strata in south Europe; it cannot be taken as good evidence for a westward migration from the Indian seas. Nevertheless it seems certain that the wide transgression of the warm Lutetian seas in Europe led to the invasion of north-west Europe by numerous genera from more southerly waters (L. R. Cox, 1930). The northerly limit known to have been reached by the southern forms, namely south England (Wrigley, 1934) and Kressenburg (Schlosser, 1925) is almost coincident with that attained by the nummulites.

The greatest faunal similarity between the two regions is seen in the Upper Eocene and Oligocene stages of Europe and the Nari Beds of India about 90 per cent. of the genera being common to the two regions. Vredenburg (1928) mentions many species, especially from the Oligocene beds of Liguria, which are identical with Nari forms, including species of *Cypraea, Lyria, Turbinella, Murex, Sconsia, Scaphander, Streptochetus, Sassia, Olivella, Lucina.* This close relationship is doubtless connected with the considerable transgression of the Oligocene sea over parts of central Europe which facilitated migration.

The molluscan faunas of the earliest Eocene deposits at Mons and Ciply in Belgium, and near Copenhagen and Rugaard in Denmark show considerable differences from the Mediterranean faunas just discussed. These northern faunas apparently belong to rather different habitats; nevertheless they have many genera, though few species, in common. Some genera, especially at Mons, are warm-water forms which are well represented in Mediterranean and Indian faunas; among them are *Delphinula, Mesalia, Calyptraphorus, Ficus, Drupa, Chama*. Others, like *Astarte, Cyprina, Aporrhais, Pseudoliva*, and *Scaphella*, are more characteristic of cooler habitats, and are hardly known in southern Europe, except in the Volga basin of south Russia. Some of these boreal genera are represented in the Thanet Sands of England, and the Sables de Bracheux of the Paris basin; they do not survive this horizon in France, but in England they persist into the London Clay. Later Eocene faunas in both countries are dominated by warm-water mollusca. The Lower Eocene faunas of north Germany, Denmark, and Holland are comparable with that of the London Clay. A small assemblage of Lower Eocene age from the Kressenberg, Bavaria, in which *Cyprina* and *Dosiniopsis* are associated with *Gisortia, Ficus, Neoathleta, Spondylus*, &c. is said to resemble that of the Paris basin, but the succeeding fauna of Middle Eocene horizons is thoroughly Mediterranean in character. Species of *Cyprina, Astarte, Aporrhais* and other molluscan genera have been described by J. P. Ravn (1904) from strata of Eocene age in east Greenland, and Ravn believes that the Greenland fauna is so closely related to the contemporary fauna in western Europe as to indicate open marine connexion between the two regions during the Eocene period. A mixture of temperate and tropical forms continues in the transgressive Lattorfian Beds of north Germany. According to A. v. Koenen (1889–94) the boreal genera *Scaphella, Thyasira, Astarte, Cyprina*, &c. are greatly outnumbered by southern forms, which include species of *Rimella, Terebellum, Conus, Vulsella, Spondylus*, and other genera. Some of the Lattorfian species are recorded by S. Sokolev (1894) from south Russia, and by P. Gočev (1929) from Bulgaria; in the latter region the mollusca are associated with large nummulites, including *N. orbignyi*. Hence these beds, and also the Lattorfian Beds of Germany, may be of Upper Eocene rather than Lower Oligocene age. Many of the warm-water genera, *Terebellum, Pseudoliva, Clavilithes, Conorbis*, and *Vulsella*, for example, are lacking in the higher Oligocene beds of north Germany, though they persist in contemporary deposits of the Mediterranean borders. Newcomers in these faunas include *Liomesus* in the Rupelian stage of Jutland, and *Ecphora* in the Mainz basin of Germany.

A similar distribution of temperate and tropical genera is evident in the Neozoic deposits of the coastal plain bordering the south-eastern United States from New Jersey to Texas and Mexico. The earliest Palaeogene mollusca are contained in the Midway stage of Texas and Alabama. G.

Scott (1934) believes this molluscan assemblage to be most closely related to that of the Danian stage of Europe which is usually placed at the top of the Cretaceous System. But most authors assign the Midway stage to the base of the Eocene Series, and J. Gardner (1935) has correlated it with the Montian and Landenian stages of Europe. In any case, it inevitably forms the basis of a discussion of Palaeogene faunas of the Atlantic and Gulf coastal plain. The mollusca fall into two categories. In the first place there are genera which now live in the cool waters of the temperate zone; these include such gastropods as *Aporrhais, Pseudoliva, Scaphella,* and the lamellibranchs *Astarte, Cucullaea, Pectunculus,* and *Yoldia.* The second group includes genera like *Strepsidura* and *Volutocorbis* which have already been noted as members of tropical or subtropical faunas. A few of the Midway genera require more than casual mention. The strombid *Calyptraphorus* is represented, not only in the Midway fauna, but also in the early Eocene faunas of Mons and Ranikot; C. W. Cooke (1924) says that the European form appears to resemble more closely the American species of later Eocene stages and therefore may be younger than the Midway species. The gastropods *Perissolax, Laevibuccinum,* and *Caricella* are distinctive American genera. In contrast with the Montian, the Midway fauna has no representatives of the Turbinidae, Neritidae, Ampullospiridae, Conidae, or Hipponycidae, while Cerithiidae and Cypraeidae are very rare. Among the lamellibranchs the genus *Venericardia,* especially the subgenus *Venericor* comprising the widespread group of *V. planicosta,* is well represented. J. Gardner and E. Bowles (1939) have distinguished species of two lineages in the Midway fauna; one of the American forms has considerable resemblance to a species from Mons, Belgium, and may be derived from a common stock. Hence, the American and Belgian faunas give evidence of oceanic connexion, but at a considerable distance in early Eocene time. The succeeding Wilcox stage shows a gradual decline of the temperate genera *Astarte, Cucullaea, Dosiniopsis, Aporrhais, Admete,* which, with the exception of *Cucullaea,* are wanting in the upper beds of the stage. Other genera, like *Calyptraphorus, Perissolax, Caricella, Volutocorbis,* and *Cypraea,* persisting from the Midway Beds, together with members of the Veneridae and Pectinidae, increase in variety and abundance. A feature of the lamellibranch element is the prolific variety of *Venericor,* largely from the two lineages established in the Midway stage, which reach their maximum development in America at this horizon.

The succeeding Claiborne stage has the faunal aspect of the Lutetian stage in Europe, though R. Abrard (1927) states that the bulk of the fauna is distinct with only three species in common. Several Claiborne genera are unknown in the Middle Eocene deposits of Europe though they appear in higher beds in that continent; these are mainly temperate forms like *Yoldia, Macoma, Cardium, Caricella, Scaphella.* Species of *Venericor* are regarded by Gardner and Bowles (1939) as autochthonous derivatives of

Wilcox forms. On the other hand, such warm-water genera as *Pseudomiltha*, *Velates*, *Campanile*, *Terebellum*, *Rimella*, and *Gisortia* are well known in the Lutetian rocks of Europe but are wanting in Alabama, though some are recorded from Jamaica. Considering that the Anglo-Parisian basin lies between 48° and 51° N. latitude and Alabama between 31° and 35° N. latitude, the distribution of the Middle Eocene mollusca seems to indicate that the isothermal lines across the north Atlantic Ocean of the Eocene period were of similar form to the present ones, and maybe that the warm Florida current (or Gulf Stream) already exercised influence on the climate of west Europe during Palaeogene time. The Jackson stage of Mississippi and Alabama, with a similar generic association, is distinguished by a number of characteristic species of *Cypraea*, *Conus*, *Mitra*, *Rostellaria*, *Corbula*, *Nuculana*, *Cardium*, &c. that are commonly associated in the strata. *Turritella* is abundantly represented, and E. Bowles (1939) has shown that the several species continue lines of development that were already established in underlying stages of the same region; a species of the allied *Mesalia* likewise continues a lineage which ranges up from the Midway stage. In contrast with the Claiborne stage, the Jackson contains only three species of *Venericor*, and none of them is abundant; this is the final record of the *V. planicosta* stock. A species of *Velates* is closely comparable with the representatives of this widespread genus in the Priabonian stage of south Europe. The Ocala Limestone of Georgia and Florida is included in the stage.

The Vicksburg Series is generally accepted as equivalent to the Oligocene Series of Europe, but the comparison of faunas is complicated by differences of facies. Few species survive from the Jackson stage, and the fauna comprises an association of distinctive species that can be differentiated from Eocene and Miocene assemblages. Such distinctive forms in the type section in Mississippi include *Pecten poulseni* Morton, *Ostrea vicksburgensis* Conrad, *Pteria argentea* Conrad, *Pitar* (*Lamelliconcha*) *calcanea* (Dall), *Conus alveatus* Conrad, *Xancus wilsoni* Conrad, *Ficus mississippiensis* Conrad. In the coral-reef facies of Alabama, Florida, and Georgia the most characteristic mollusc is *Orthaulax pugnax* (Heilprin), a peculiar strombid whose spire is enveloped in an extension of the outer lip. Other associates of the reef-corals include *Ampullina streptosoma* (Heilprin), *Pecten anatipes* Morton, *Spondylus filiaris* Dall, *Arcoperna inflata* Dall. The Glendon Limestone has an abundance of *Cerithium* unusual in American deposits.

The corresponding faunal succession in the Pacific States of North America is comparable with that of the south-eastern States, but also shows significant differences. B. L. Clark and H. E. Vokes (1935) state that a large proportion of the molluscan species is indigenous, and many of the genetic stocks persist from early Eocene to Oligocene and some even to the present day. The molluscan fauna of the Martinez stage has few species in common with the Midway fauna, but many genera appear in both stages.

Among these are the temperate forms *Leda, Yoldia, Cucullaea, Pectunculus, Aporrhais,* and such warm-water genera as *Venericor, Siphonalia, Cypraea, Ficus, Ovula, Strepsidura,* &c. Some distinctive gastropod genera make their first appearance, for example *Brachysphingus, Cryptochorda, Heterostoma, Perissolax, Priscoficus, Retipirula.* Among lamellibranchs the Tellinidae and Veneridae show greater variety than in the Midway stage, and *Venericor venturensis* is closely similar to the eastern *V. mediaplata.* The Meganos stage of California is broadly equivalent to the Wilcox stage of the Gulf States. The generic association is much the same as in the previous stage, but the nuculid *Acila* and the cassid *Galeodea* appear for the first time and the neptuneid *Siphonalia sutterensis* is abundant. The succeeding Capay stage is correlated with the lower part of the Claiborne stage of Alabama. Several species show close affinity with the Ypresian stage of north France; the widespread *Velates perversus* is common to both, and there are analogous species of *Clavilithes, Gisortia, Turritella,* and other genera. The Domengine stage of California has affinities with the Lutetian stage of Europe, as shown in species of *Harpa (Eocithara), Potamides, Turritella, Typhis, Eocypraea, Keilostoma, Lyria, Cuneocorbula, Cryptochorda,* and *Cryptoconus.*

The Tejon stage of California has no species in common with the Gulf States; a few species are related to analogous forms in the Upper Eocene beds of Europe, but as these all appear to have ancestors in the underlying stage, they may have evolved independently in western America. The only transatlantic route for the migration of such tropical forms would be along the track of the equatorial currents, which would be feasible if shoal waters were present at intervals, and a portal existed through central America. The molluscan assemblage of the Tejon stage includes distinctive species of *Acila, Pectunculus, Lamelliconcha, Crassatellites, Exilia, Ficopsis, Polinices, Conus, Siphonalia,* and *Turritella.* The lower part of the Gaviota stage is linked with the Jackson stage of the Gulf States by its foraminifera and species of *Venericor.* The upper part of the Gaviota stage includes the Lincoln and Blakeley formations of Washington, and the Eugene Beds of Oregon which are generally placed in the Oligocene Series. Precise correlation is difficult because of variation in palaeogeographical, climatic, and bathymetrical factors. Species of *Epitonium, Galeodea, Bruclarkia, Molopophorus, Acila, Pitar* (sub-genus *Katharinella*), *Macrocallista, Thyasira,* and *Mulinia,* are cited by H. G. Schenck (1928) and N. M. Tegland (1933) as important for purposes of correlation. Faunas of the same age are recorded by B. L. Clark and R. Arnold (1923) from Vancouver, and by B. L. Clark (1932) from south Alaska.

Some of the western American genera mentioned above have special interest in that their early Neozoic history, so far as it is known, is restricted to the borders of the Pacific Ocean. The nuculid *Acila* is recorded from the Palaeogene stages of California and north Peru, and only at certain Miocene and Pliocene horizons is it known from Caribbean and Atlantic stations. The neptuneid *Searlesia* is first cited from the Oligocene of California, afterwards from the Miocene of Vancouver, then the Pliocene of England, and now lives in North Atlantic waters. *Bruclarkia*, another genus of the same family, is not recorded outside the Oligocene and Miocene deposits of California. The nassid genus *Molopophorus* is only recorded from Palaeogene and early Miocene stages at Californian localities. The mactrid *Mulinia* is cited by B. L. Clark and R. Arnold (1923) from Oligocene beds on Vancouver Island, by H. G. Schenck (1928) from Oligocene beds in west Oregon, and thereafter is restricted to America. Records of the venerid genus *Chione*, ranging from Oligocene to the present day are mainly American in location. Such records indicate the possible source of certain cryptogenetic genera which became important elements in the Neogene molluscan faunas in other parts of the world.

Tropical mollusca are typically developed in the West Indian islands and in the northern part of South America. C. T. Trechmann (1924) has described the molluscan fauna of the Richmond Beds in Jamaica which contain 'derived' Cretaceous fossils and species of *Velates, Ampullina, Siphonalia, Morgania, Melanatria, Melanopsis, Potamides, Turritella, Ostrea, Carolia, Corbis, Cyrena,* and *Raetomya*. The majority of these seem to be related to forms in the Lower Eocene of Europe and the Ranikot Beds of India, but *Raetomya* is only represented elsewhere by one species in later Eocene beds of Venezuela and Peru, and by another in the Middle Eocene of Egypt, Nigeria, and south-west Africa. The succeeding Yellow Limestone of Jamaica contains a fauna, also described by Trechmann (1923), which includes species of *Velates, Terebellum, Cypraea, Gisortia, Rimella, Conus, Hipponyx,* &c., and has been compared with corresponding assemblages in the Laki and Khirthar Beds of Sind, the Libyan and Mokattam Beds of Egypt, and the Calcaire Grossier of the Paris basin. The White Limestone of Jamaica is correlated by T. W. Vaughan (1919), on the basis of its foraminifera, with the Vicksburg stage of Mississippi, and certain lamellibranchs have been described by L. R. Cox (1941). On the island of Antigua this Oligocene stage is represented by the Antigua Limestone famed for its reef-corals (p. 604) and the specialized gastropod *Orthaulax*; the similar Anguilla Limestone on the island of that name, is placed in the Lower Miocene, to be discussed later. Other Palaeogene faunas of tropical aspect have been described from the islands of Barbados, St. Bartholomew, Trinidad, and also from Venezuela.

A succession of Eocene faunas has been described from north Peru by H. Woods (1922) and A. A. Olsson (1928–30). The Negritos stage, of Lower Eocene age, is marked by an abundance and variety of *Turritella*, especially by *T. negritosensis* Woods, associated with species of *Volutospina, Pseudoliva, Melanatria, Bezanconia, Strepsidura, Olivancillaria, Cerithium, Morgania, Corbula, Meretrix, Ostrea, Leda,* and *Venericor*. The last-named genus is represented in this stage by *V. negritensis* and *V. libreaensis* of Olsson, which are comparable with species in the Wilson stage of Alabama. These are replaced in the overlying Salinas and Parinas stages by *V. pacifica*, *V. parinensis*, and *V. peruviana* of Olsson, which are referred by J. Gardner and E. Bowles (1939) to two different lineages of the Claiborne development. In the Upper Eocene Saman stage *V. clavidens* Grzybowski continues the progressive tendency for the ribbing to become obsolete near the ventral margin of the shell. The generic association in the Salinas and Parinas stages is similar to that in the Negritos stage, but the Turritellas have decreased in importance, and species of *Clavilithes* form a notable addition. The Upper Eocene fauna of the Talaran and Saman stages is less varied and comprises distinctive species mainly of persistent genera, associated with discoid foraminifera. In south-west Ecuador, G. W. Sheppard (1937) correlates the Socorro Sandstone with the Upper Eocene on the evidence of the foraminifera and these are associated with the molluscan genera *Turritella*, *Liotia*, *Oliva*, *Phos*, *Crepidula*, *Pecten*, *Cardium*, *Lucina*, &c. In the Ancon Point Sandstone, referred to the Lower Oligocene, the dominant fossil is the large slender gastropod *Anconia elenensis* of Sheppard, accompanied by species of *Leda*, *Barbatia*, *Thyasira*, and *Polinices*. Higher beds in the Oligocene Series contain species of *Scapharca*, *Chione*, *Lamelliconcha*, *Clementia*, *Macoma*, *Sinum*, *Turritella*, *Pseudoliva*, *Olivancillaria*, &c. Much farther south at Point Malaspina (45° S.) in the Province of Chubut, Argentina, Eocene beds have yielded *Turritella* and *Volutocorbis*, together with a large, coarse-ribbed *Venericor* which Gardner and Bowles (1939) have named *V. austroplata*.

Certain of the Peruvian genera merit further discussion. The gastropod *Gisortia* and the lamellibranch *Carolia* are recorded, not only from Peru, but also from Eocene beds in Jamaica and the Mediterranean region; these occurrences possibly indicate a migration route. Relations with Alabama are shown by the presence of the venerid *Grateloupia* in the Peruvian Eocene beds. *Raetomya*, which is recorded from Upper Eocene beds in Peru, is earlier in Jamaica and Venezuela; the only other species so far known occurs in Middle Eocene rocks of south Nigeria, Egypt, and south-west Africa. It is evident that the Eocene sea off the west of the Brazilian Shield was connected with the North Atlantic Ocean by way of the Caribbean Sea and this may also be the route of communication with the Nigerian area. For *Raetomya* is known from Venezuela and Jamaica, and R. B. Newton (1922), in his monograph on the Nigerian fauna, cites species of *Bulbifusus*, *Buccinorbis*, *Cancellaria* (*Trigonostoma*), and *Crepidula* as constituting relationship with the Eocene faunas of Alabama. A. M. Davies (1934) links the West African transgressions from Nigeria to south-west Africa into 'a definite SE. Atlantic province', but no marine Eocene deposits are yet recorded on the southern margin of the Brazilian Shield. The venerid *Clementia* is known from mid-Eocene Beds in Peru, Colombia,

Burma, and Sind, and from Oligocene Beds in Peru before becoming more widespread in Miocene strata. The earliest records of *Nassa, Dorsanum,* and *Xancus* are from the Eocene Beds of Peru and Java. Some Pacific source doubtless accounts for the distribution of these mollusca but, at present, there is no precise evidence concerning the route of migration across the Pacific Ocean.

LITERATURE

The abundance and beauty of Eocene mollusca attracted attention before geology became established as a science, and many species were described and illustrated in the eighteenth century. Later, various fossil-groups were taken as the subject of monographs, which now form the standard works of reference. 'The Eocene Mollusca', by F. E. Edwards, *Mon. Pal. Soc.,* 1849–77 and 'The Eocene Bivalves of England', by S. V. Wood, ibid., 1861–77, were unfortunately left unfinished, and the majority of Eocene fossils still remain to be illustrated in British literature. A catalogue of 'British Eocene and Oligocene Mollusca', by R. B. Newton, *Brit. Mus. Cat.,* 1891, giving references to foreign illustrations, however, proves a useful compromise.

Some smaller molluscan groups have received special attention, e.g. 'The British Eocene Aporrhaidae', by J. S. Gardner, *Geol. Mag.,* vol. xxi, pp. 529–34, 1884; 'The Classification of the Tertiary Nautili', by L. F. Spath, *Ann. Mag. Nat. Hist.,* ser. 9, vol. xx, pp. 424–8, 1927. A series of papers on 'English Eocene Mollusca', by A. Wrigley, is published in *Proc. Malac. Soc.,* 1925–34.

Other British Palaeogene fossils are described in 'The Echinodermata of the British Tertiaries', by E. Forbes, *Mon. Pal. Soc.,* 1852.

'A Revision of British Cainozoic Echinoids', by J. W. Gregory, *Proc. Geol. Assoc.,* vol. xii, pp. 16–60, 1892.

'British Fossil Corals', by M. Edwards and J. Haime, *Mon. Pal. Soc.,* 1850; Second Series, by P. M. Duncan, ibid., 1866.

'The Tertiary Entomostraca of England', by T. R. Jones and C. D. Sherborn, *Mon. Pal. Soc.,* 1857–89.

'The Foraminifera of the Thanet Beds of Pegwell Bay', by H. W. Burrows and R. Holland, *Proc. Geol. Assoc.,* vol. xv, pp. 19–52, 1897.

'The Fossil Reptilia of the London Clay', by R. Owen and Bell, *Mon. Pal. Soc.,* 1849–80.

An excellent discussion of *Tertiary Faunas* throughout the world by A. M. Davies, 2 vols., London, 1934–5, has full bibliographies of the palaeontological and stratigraphical aspects. It is only necessary here to add references to a few important works published since that date.

T. W. Vaughan and W. S. Cole have issued a preliminary report on *The Cretaceous and Tertiary Larger Foraminifera of Trinidad, British West Indies,* Geol. Soc. Amer., Special Papers No. 30, 1941; it contains a good bibliography and notes on geographical distribution. F. R. S. Henson has monographed 'The Larger Imperforate Foraminifera of South Western Asia', *Brit. Mus. Cat.,* 1948; this work deals with the Lituolidae, Orbitolinidae and the new family Meandropsinidae.

'Eocene and Oligocene Coral Faunas of Washington' are discussed by J. W. Durham in *Journ. Palaeont.,* vol. xvi, pp. 84–104, 1942.

H. G. Schenck has described and illustrated *The Nuculid Bivalves of the Genus Acila* in Geol. Soc. Amer., Special Papers No. 4, 1936. L. R. Cox has described

'Eocene Mollusca from North Western India' in *Ann. Mag. Nat. Hist.*, Ser. 11, vol. i, pp. 161–77, 1938, and 'Oligocene Mollusca from Afghanistan', ibid., vol. v, pp. 362–71, 1940; also 'Lamellibranchs from the White Limestone of Jamaica' in *Proc. Malac. Soc.*, vol. xxiv, pp. 135–44, 1941. J. Gardner and E. Bowles have discussed and illustrated species of *The Venericardia Planicosta Group in the Gulf Province* in United States Geol. Surv., Prof. Paper No. 189 F, 1939.

Several groups of gastropods have been revised as follows: 'Eocene and Palaeocene Turritellidae of the Atlantic and Gulf Coastal Plain of North America', by E. Bowles, *Journ. Palaeont.*, vol. xiii, pp. 276–336, 1939; 'Fossil Turritellas from the Pacific Coast Region of North America', by C. W. Merriam, *Univ. Calif. Publ. Bull. Dept. Geol. Sci.*, vol. xxvi, pp. 1–214, 1941; 'The Fossil Gastropod *Exilia*', by H. Bentson, ibid., vol. xxv, pp. 199–238, 1940; 'The Molluscan Genus *Siphonalia* of the Pacific Coast Tertiary', by J. W. Ruth, ibid., vol. xxvi, pp. 287–306, 1942; 'The Gastropod Subfamily Typhinae', by A. M. Keen, *Journ. Palaeont.*, vol. xviii, pp. 50–72, 1944. Some South American mollusca and foraminifera are described and illustrated in *The Geology of South Western Ecuador*, by G. Sheppard, London, 1937.

XVI

THE LATER NEOZOIC FAUNAS

THE later Neozoic strata, commonly grouped together as the Neogene
System, comprise all formations later than the Oligocene, namely, the
Miocene, Pliocene, Pleistocene, and Holocene. Many authors exclude
the last two series from the Neogene System and place them in a 'Quaternary system' which they seem to regard as of equal rank with the Neozoic
group. But the only essential difference between the Neogene thus restricted and the so-called Quaternary is that remains of man have hitherto
only been found in the latter. Considered generally, the faunas show
continuous evolution within pre-existing animal groups, though distribu-
tional variations, due to migration following changes in climatic conditions,
are often seen. No great faunal change occurred here that is in any way com-
mensurate with the incoming of the Mesozoic reptiles, or with the comparatively rapid rise of the mammals to a dominant position in early Neozoic
time. Hence it is considered that there is no palaeontological justification
for the institution of a 'Quaternary system', and that the deposits now being
formed belong essentially to the Neozoic Group.

It has been noted that Oligocene strata are incompletely represented in
Britain compared with their development elsewhere. It may be further
stated that no deposits containing fossils strictly comparable with extra-
British Miocene faunas have been found in this country. Moreover, there
is physical evidence for believing that the Miocene period was one of considerable change in the relative level of land and sea, and that the British
area was entirely terrestrial during that interval of time. Marine deposits
occur, however, in the south-west of France, in Switzerland, Italy and
Austria, Germany and Belgium; therefore we may link up the British
Palaeogene and Neogene faunas by brief reference to those areas.

The molluscan genera show close affinity with living forms, the European
Miocene assemblage showing more resemblance with the existing fauna
of the Caribbean than with that of the Mediterranean Sea. Echinoids are
conspicuous members of the French, Italian, and Austrian Miocene faunas;
they include species of *Clypeaster*, *Echinolampas*, *Scutella*, and other genera,
many being closely related to West Indian types. The foraminiferal genus
Nummulites is rare in Miocene rocks, but other specialized genera such as
Lepidocyclina and *Miogypsina* appear. These fossils are discussed in some
detail later in the chapter.

British Pliocene deposits, commonly known as the Crag, cover a large
part of East Anglia, and are subdivided as under, in descending order:

Cromer Forest Bed

2. Freshwater beds with comparatively recent flora and fauna.
1. Estuarine beds with a 'mixed' assemblage of mammalian remains.

Icenian Crag

3. Weybourne Crag with abundance of *Tellina balthica* Linn., its first appearance in England.
2. Chillesford Beds with a boreal marine fauna, nearly all being living species.
1. Norwich Crag with a marine fauna of northern type; about 89 per cent. of living species.

Butley Crag

Red Crag of Butley, &c.

Newbourne Crag

Red Crag of Newbourne, &c.

} Increased importance of northern shells.

Walton Crag

2. Red Crag of Oakley, &c. Marked appearance of boreal mollusca.
1. Red Crag of Walton-on-Naze. Southern fauna with rare boreal forms.

Gedgrave Crag

Coralline Crag with molluscan fauna of Mediterranean affinities.

Lenham Crag

2. Lenham Beds—isolated outliers in south England containing some typically Miocene shells.
1. Box-stones at the base of the East Anglian Pliocene. Fauna of Miocene affinities.

Apart from the Coralline Crag, the various subdivisions of the Pliocene deposits in East Anglia have a definite geographical order of occurrence, the oldest in the south, the youngest in the north. The 'Crags' are not seen in super-position, and are regarded as littoral deposits banked up on a shore-line that steadily migrated northwards in consequence of relative uplift in the south.

The most noticeable general features of the Pliocene Mollusca are (1) the decrease in the number of extinct species in the higher beds, and (2) a progressive decrease in the number of southern species and a corresponding increase in the number of northern forms in passing from lower to higher horizons. This is well illustrated in the following table, which shows an analysis, by F. W. Harmer, based on an estimate of the characteristic and abundant species in the several East Anglian Crags.

Analysis of the Molluscan Fauna contained in the various Horizons of the English Crag (Characteristic and Abundant Species only)—Harmer, 1900.

Horizon	Not known living	Southern	Northern
	Per cent.	Per cent.	Per cent.
Icenian	11	7	32
Butley	31	13	23
Newbourne	32	16	11
Walton	36	20	5
Gedgrave	38	26	1

'The figures are to be taken as approximate only, since it is not always easy to draw the line between rare and abundant forms' (Harmer).

The Box-stones.—At the base of the Crags in certain East Anglian localities there is a bed of rounded sandy concretions, associated with phosphatic nodules, phosphatized bones of cetaceans and other mammals, derived Eocene and Mesozoic fossils, and igneous erratics. The 'mixed' character of this bed has already been briefly mentioned (p. 26). The sandy concretions sometimes contain fossils (represented by internal moulds)—hence the term 'box-stones'. The age of this fauna is still a matter of dispute. The assemblage bears considerable relation to that of the Lenham Beds next to be described, but it is not identical, and some authorities refer it to the Miocene.

Among the typical molluscan forms may be cited *Conus (Conospirus) dujardini* (Desh.), *Cassidaria bicatenata* (J. Sow.), *Desmoulea conglobata* (Broc.), *Ficus conditus* (Brongn.), *Voluta auris-leporis* Grat., *V. (Scaphella) lamberti* J. Sow., *Dentalium dentale* Linn., *Cyprina islandica* (Linn.), *Isocardia lunulata* Nyst, *Panopaea faujasii* Men. de la G., *Pecten (Aequipecten) opercularis* Linn., and *Pectunculus glycimeris* Linn. Though the fauna has been studied in some detail and over a hundred molluscan species have been described, further investigation is desirable.

The **Lenham Beds** occur mainly in a series of isolated hills stretching across the Kentish downs from Maidstone to Folkestone. These are connected, by a line of similar hills through Cassel, Tournai, Grammont, Brussels, and Louvain, with the continuous outcrop of Diestian Sands in eastern Belgium. Some outliers north of London are also referred to this horizon. The Lenham Beds have yielded over seventy species of mollusca, which include some that do not occur in the Coralline Crag, but are plentiful in Upper Miocene strata of continental Europe. And while R. B. Newton regards the Lenham Beds as Miocene, F. W. Harmer writes: 'The Lenham-Diestien beds, it is true, contain some characteristic Miocene

or Lower Pliocene fossils unknown from either the Coralline or the Caster-
lien zones, but they include also a considerable proportion of a more recent
character which would seem out of place in a typical Miocene deposit.'
The appearance of these new forms would appear to outweigh the importance of Miocene survivals, and so the Lenham Beds are here considered as
definitely of Pliocene age.

Perhaps the most characteristic shell of the Lenham deposits is *Ringi-
culella lenhamensis* R. B. Newton. It is a turreted form with a more or less
cylindrical contour; its surface is almost smooth, only obscure transverse
striae being present. This fossil is unknown in other deposits. One of the
most abundant Lenham shells is *Andara [Arca] diluvii* (Lamarck), distinguished from other ark shells by its strong radial ribs, deep sulcations,
concentric striae, and more or less distant lines of growth; this species has
a wide range in Miocene deposits but is not recorded from the Coralline
Crag or later deposits of Britain. *Cardium papillosum* Poli, with minutely
papillose ribs and concentrically striated furrows, is also plentiful in the
Lenham Beds; it now lives in the Mediterranean Sea, and is known from
the Pliocene deposits of Italy and the south of France, but not from the
East Anglian Crags. The turreted gastropod *Terebra acuminata* Borson,
with slightly raised sutural bands and flexuous striations, has a wide range
in Miocene deposits and is common to the Lenham Beds and the Italian
Pliocene. The fusiform *Clavatula jouanneti* (Desmoulins), once referred to
the genus *Pleurotoma*, has depressed whorls, thickened at the sutural margins and ornamented by spiral striations; it is widely distributed in European Miocene strata, and apparently makes its last appearance in the British
Lenham Beds. Another shell formerly assigned to *Pleurotoma* is *Drillia
obeliscus* (Desmoulins), which has a turriculate spire and short body-whorl,
its transverse costae being crossed by fine spiral striations; this form ranges
up from the Miocene into the Lenham Beds but is not known from younger
strata. Many other Lenham shells occur in Miocene Beds and range up into
the Pliocene Crags; they include *Scaphella lamberti* J. Sow. (Fig. 16),
Capulus ungaricus (Linn.), *Trivia europaea* (Montagu), *Pyramidella plicosa*
Bronn, *Aporrhais pes-pelicani* Linn., *Ficus reticulata* (Lam.), *Actaeon tornatilis* (Linn.), *Astarte omalii* Lajon (Fig. 83), *A. basteroti* Lajon, *Cardita
(Glans) senilis* (Lam.) (Fig. 83), *Cyprina rustica* (J. Sow.), and *Panopaea
menardi* Desh. Species which first appear in the Lenham Beds and continue
into later Pliocene strata include the trochoid gastropods *Eumargarita
trochoidea* (S. V. Wood), *Gibbula cineraria* (Linn.), *Calliostoma zizyphinus*
(Linn.), and *Ampullotrochus miliaris* (Brocchi), as well as *Xenophora crispa*
König and the turreted *Scala subulata* J. de C. Sow. Among new lamellibranchs are *Yoldia oblongoides* (S. V. Wood), the mussels *Vulsella barbata*
(Linn.) and a variety of *Mytilus edulis* Linn., and the oyster *Ostrea princeps*
S. V. Wood. The appearance of these and other newcomers seems to
determine the Lower Pliocene age of the Lenham Beds. The possibility that

these deposits represent the *rémanié* of various horizons redeposited during a later period must, however, not be overlooked.

The **St. Erth Beds,** a thin series of sands and clays occupying a restricted area in Cornwall, may appropriately be mentioned here. These beds are generally admitted to be older than the Red Crag; and they may be earlier than the Coralline Crag, since their fauna includes a greater proportion of southern species than does that of the latter. Indeed, northern shells are virtually absent, while south European forms are prevalent, and many of the species are unknown elsewhere but belong to southern genera. A large number of the gastropods are minute shells, including such genera as *Rissoa, Odostomia, Turbonilla, Eulima, Alvania,* and *Cingula.* These belong mostly to forms whose favourite habitat is the Laminarian zone (0–14 fathoms), where they live among the luxuriant seaweeds that flourish at such depths. The occurrence of these genera has been taken to indicate that the St. Erth Beds were deposited under such conditions. But this view has been challenged on the ground that littoral genera such as *Patella* and *Littorina* are absent, while the fine-grained and evenly stratified beds and the unworn shells point to deposition under quiet conditions. There is much to be said for the suggestion that the St. Erth Beds were formed in deeper water (40 fathoms, according to Reid), and that the shells of these herbivorous gastropods were drifted there from their original home near the shore.

The genus *Trochocochlea*, comprising imperforate trochoid shells with a rhomboid aperture, thickened columella, and a tubercle on the inner lip, is represented at St. Erth by four species. The genus is unknown at other British localities, but occurs in the Italian Neogene deposits and lives in the present Mediterranean Sea; its occurrence at St. Erth has been cited in support of the view that the Cornish deposit is older than any of the Eastern Crags. Some of the trochids are peculiar to St. Erth, but others, like *Calliostoma zizyphinus* (Linn.), *C. bullatus* (Philippi), *Gibbula adansoni* (Payr.) (Fig. 82), and *G. adriaticus* (Philippi), occur also in the East Anglian Pliocene. Three species of the little ribbed cowries that form the genus *Trivia* are also common to the Cornish and East Anglian deposits. A large number of species were formerly referred to *Pleurotoma* but are now referred to such genera as *Mangilia, Raphitoma, Haedropleura,* and *Donovania.* Small species of *Potamides* and *Bittium* (formerly included in *Cerithium*) are also present; the variety *trinodosa* Eth. and Bell of *Bittium reticulata* (Da Costa), a small, elongate, turreted shell with granulated ornament, rounded base and very short canal (Fig. 82), is one of the most abundant forms of the St. Erth fauna. *Turritella erthensis* Harmer is also very common, but apparently peculiar to St. Erth; it is a large form distinguished by the prominent, sharp ridges which ornament the whorls in the longitudinal direction (Fig. 82). Another of the most abundant St. Erth shells, *Nassa semireticosa* Eth. and Bell (Fig. 82), seems to be unknown elsewhere; this form is distinguished from its allies by its comparatively coarse sculpture. Two other species, *N. emiliana* (Mayer) and *N. turonica* (Desh.), persist from the Miocene and range into the East Anglian Crags; still other forms, like *N. mutabilis* (Linn.), are unknown there, but occur in the Italian Neogene rocks. 'Taken as a whole, the St. Erth Nassas are strikingly different from those of the English Crag' (Harmer). *Natica catenoides* S. V. Woods (Fig. 82) is one of the larger shells common to St. Erth and the eastern counties, but for the most part the Cornish species of *Natica* have short, depressed spires, and show little relation with those of the Crag. *Euthria cornea* (Linn.), a fusiform shell with inconspicuous ornament, is often cited as a St. Erth fossil but is not common there, and is unknown elsewhere in Britain, though widespread (both fossil and living) in Mediterranean countries. Among lamellibranchs, *Cardium papillosum* Poli has already been noted as occurring in the Lenham Beds and the Mediterranean Neogene deposits, while *Cardita aculeata* Poli has a similar distribution. The St. Erth fauna also contains many foraminifera and ostracods, besides a few polyzoa and rare remains of echinoids, sponges, a tunicate, a holothurian, and fishes.

The **Gedgrave** or **Coralline Crag** is mainly of organic origin. It consists of sand mingled with the comminuted shells of marine organisms, or with calcareous material derived from their decomposition. In some places layers of unbroken shells occur, but more often the sands are current-bedded and contain only broken shells and drifted material. Again, 'polyzoa sometimes occur in the position of growth, and evidently assisted in arresting the comminuted material in which they are now embedded. Thus the Coralline Crag was formed as reefs or sandbanks in the then existing Crag sea, not very far from land but at some distance from any river discharging into it. The polyzoa flourished when any change of current diverted the drifting material, and died when choked by sediment' (Boswell).

In general, the Gedgrave fauna is of a distinctly southern type. Most of the species still living are found in the Mediterranean Sea or along the western coasts of France and Portugal. Species that are now typical of northern regions are, as a rule, not found in the Coralline Crag. While, for general purposes, the Gedgrave fauna may be regarded as a well-defined assemblage, some conspicuous mollusca, especially the species-group of *Nassa reticosa* (J. Sow.), appear in the upper beds and extend into the Red Crag. On this account the Boyton Crag is sometimes regarded as a separate stage, later than the main mass of the Coralline Crag.

The shells of the bivalved mollusca are very prominent in the Coralline Crag. One of the most abundant is *Cardita* (*Glans*) *senilis* Lam. (Fig. 83), an oblique shell with strong rugose, sometimes squamose, ribs, and thick striated hinge-teeth; this shell, along with many others, persists from the Miocene and passes up into the Red Crag. *Cardita* (*Miodon*) *scalaris* (J. Sow.) is a smaller shell, distinguished by its close-set nodulous ribs and concentric striations. *Cyprina islandica* (Linn.) (Fig. 83), ranging from the Miocene to the present day, sometimes forms the bulk of certain bands in the Coralline Crag; it is a large tumid shell with slightly incurved beaks, and is smooth except for the concentric lines of growth. Species of *Pecten* are also conspicuous, and include *Flexopecten tigrinus* (Müll.) (Fig. 83), a form with broad costae ornamented by fine, curved and diverging striae; *Pseudamusium gerardi* (Nyst), a planoconvex shell, almost smooth but having fine radiating striae near the margins; and *Aequipecten opercularis* (Linn.), with strong imbricated radial ribs crossed by concentric striae. Of the genus *Astarte*, the well-known *A. omalii* Lajon (Fig. 83), a somewhat trigonal shell with broad concentric ribbing, is perhaps the most abundant. It is accompanied by other species, such as *A. basteroti* Lajon., an almost smooth shell with a few concentric ridges confined to the umbonal region, and *A. incerta* S. Wood, distinguished by its fine, regular, concentric ornament. *Pectunculus glycimeris* (Linn.) hardly needs description, since the subcircular shell with its curved line of numerous hinge-teeth (the central teeth being obsolete) is familiar to all students.

Many of the most conspicuous gastropods of the Coralline Crag have little stratigraphical significance, for some persist from the Miocene, while others are found at all horizons in the Crags. For instance, *Voluta* (*Scaphella*) *lamberti* J. Sow. (Fig. 16), is found in East Anglia from the Lenham Beds to the Butley Crag; it is a large, subfusiform shell with conical spire, rounded apex, large body-whorl and plaited columella, closely allied to, if not identical with, *V. miocaenica* Dollf. and Daut. from the south European Miocene. The limpet-like, but spirally coiled *Calyptraea chinensis* Linn. has even a longer range, namely, from the Miocene to the present day. The large *Turritella* (*Haustator*) *incrassata* J. Sow. is common in the Coralline Crag, but less so thereafter; its flat whorls are ornamented by a few prominent ridges and spiral striae. *Scala foliacea* (J. Sow.) (Fig. 82) may also be taken as typical of the Gedgrave fauna, where it is abundant, though it also occurs in the Red Crag; it is easily recognized by its oblique lamelliform ribs. *Natica multipunctata* S. Wood is common to all horizons of the Crag, but is peculiar to the Anglo-Belgian Pliocene; this large shell has an expanded aperture and a large open umbilicus traversed obliquely by a strong, coarse ridge.

It is the smaller and less abundant constituents that give character to the Gedgrave fauna. These include species of many genera already noted as occurring in the St. Erth Beds. *Pleurotoma* and its allies (*Oligostoma, Drillia, Clathurella, Mangilia,* and *Raphitoma*), species of *Murex, Cerithiopsis, Aporrhais, Trivia, Erato, Cassidaria, Scala, Turbonilla, Rissoa, Trochus,* and the 'limpets' *Capulus, Emarginula, Calyptraea, Fissurella,* and *Patella* combine to give the strong southern facies so often quoted for this fauna. *Terebratula grandis* Blum. (Fig. 14) is the only conspicuous brachiopod. The echinoids, rare because of their fragility, are no less definite, though they complicate the problem of accounting for geographical distribution. Besides forms like *Echinus*, *Echinocyamus*, *Spatangus*, and *Echinocardium*, that are widely distributed in western Europe, there are other genera, *Rhynchopygus*, *Temnechinus*, and *Agassizia*, that are typically shallow-water dwellers of tropical America. These are absent from the Mediterranean Pliocene, while the characteristic echinoids of that area are not found in the English Crags. The resemblance with the American forms is so close that J. W. Gregory postulates direct communication between the Crag seas and the central American area. The corals also are said to have West Indian affinities. The geographical distribution of Pliocene faunas thus needs further discussion in order to unravel the somewhat conflicting evidence furnished by the several animal-groups (see pp. 636–55).

The **Red Crag** rests either unconformably on the London Clay, or on the flanks of the Coralline Crag. The beds, of comparatively insignificant thickness, appear to have been formed as beach-deposits, or as sandbanks in close proximity to the shore, since they are strongly current-bedded and the fossils show the features of drifted material. The shells are not in the position of growth, lamellibranchs being represented by single valves, or broken into fragments. Similar shell-banks are being formed, under the influence of the prevailing westerly winds, along the coasts of Holland at the present day, but no such accumulations are forming on the East Anglian coast. Harmer concludes that during the Red Crag period the Atlantic cyclones crossed western Europe farther to the south than at present, causing the prevalence of easterly rather than westerly gales.

In the older part of the Red Crag are found many mollusca that are abundant in the Coralline Crag, but the general faunal aspect is modified by the appearance of northern species. Proceeding to later beds, the fauna is gradually and steadily changed by the invasion of more boreal species, until its character eventually becomes entirely northern. The conclusion is reached that tectonic movements cut off connexion with the southern seas, and at the same time opened up communication with northern seas.

The first northern forms to reach East Anglia appear to be the shells that form the species-group of *Nassa reticosa* (J. Sow.). These are large shells compared with other species of *Nassa*, and have somewhat variable ornament consisting of strong, rounded transverse ribs, reticulated by longitudinal striations (Fig. 82). They are most abundant in the Red Crag, but appear rarely in the main mass of the Coralline Crag. Their frequency, however, gives character to the higher Gedgravian Beds of Boyton, which are sometimes referred to a distinct subdivision, the Boyton Crag.

In the **Walton Crag,** many other species of *Nassa*, especially the granulate forms like *N. propinqua* (J. Sow.), *N. granulata* (J. Sow.), and *N. elegans* (J. Sow.), appear, and are characteristic of the Red Crag as a whole. Some of these species are still living in south European seas, but it is noteworthy

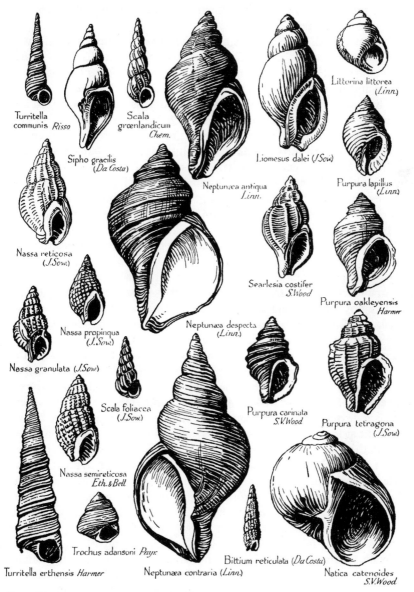

Turritella communis *Risso*

Scala grœnlandicum *Chem.*

Littorina littorea (*Linn.*)

Sipho gracilis (*Da Costa*)

Neptunæa antiqua *Linn.*

Liomesus dalei (*J.Sow.*)

Purpura lapillus (*Linn.*)

Nassa reticosa (*J.Sow.*)

Searlesia costifer *S.Wood*

Purpura oakleyensis *Harmer*

Nassa propinqua (*J.Sow.*)

Neptunæa despecta (*Linn.*)

Nassa granulata (*J.Sow.*)

Scala foliacea (*J.Sow.*)

Purpura carinata *S.V.Wood*

Purpura tetragona (*J.Sow.*)

Nassa semireticosa *Eth.&Bell*

Trochus adansoni *Payr.*

Bittium reticulata (*Da Costa*)

Natica catenoides *S.V.Wood*

Turritella erthensis *Harmer*

Neptunæa contraria (*Linn.*)

FIG. 82. BRITISH PLIOCENE GASTROPODS (*mainly from figures by Harmer*). *All about two-thirds of the natural size*

that *N. propinqua* now inhabits North American waters but is not known in the Mediterranean.

Associated with these is the sinistral *Neptunea contraria* (Linn.), which is abundant at Walton and gradually dies out in the later Crags, where it is replaced by other species of *Neptunea*. The genus *Purpura* is another newcomer, and its species show considerable variation. *P. tetragona* (J. Sow.) (Fig. 82), most abundant at Walton and Oakley, is easily recognized by its decussate ornament; this shell shows much variation in the slopes of the sutural shoulders. Early varieties ascribed to *P. lapillus* (Linn.) often show closer relation with *P. tetragona* than with the typical *P. lapillus* of existing seas (Fig. 82), and certain varieties of this shell are said to have some stratigraphical constancy. *P. oakleyensis* Harmer (Fig. 82), a tumid shell with expanded outer lip and strong varices, is most abundant in the Waltonian Crag of Oakley, but is rare thereafter, and is not recorded from the Icenian Crag. Another early variety, *P. carinata* S. V. Wood (Fig. 82), is distinguished by its spiral carination and thereby approaches the larger species *P. incrassata* (J. Sow.).

Despite the appearance of these northern forms, southern species are still dominant in the Red Crag of Walton, which is closely related to the Coralline Crag by the frequent occurrence of *Raphitoma*, *Eulimene*, *Clathurella*, *Trochus*, and many other equally significant genera. The Crag of Oakley, more northerly in geographical situation and slightly later in age, contains nearly all the Walton species, but also some, more distinctly boreal and Arctic forms, that are unknown or rare at Walton. While *Neptunea contraria* (Linn.) is still abundant, the Oakley Crag is specially marked by the appearance of the Arctic *Neptunea despecta* (Linn.) (Fig. 82) and its varieties. This is a dextral shell with prominent carinated ornament, and it becomes dominant at later horizons. Other newcomers in the Oakley Crag are members of the gastropod-genera *Buccinum*, *Trophon*, *Sipho*, and *Bela*, with species of the bivalved genera *Tellina* (*Macoma*) and *Mactra*. Lack of space prevents adequate description here of this rich fauna, since more than 700 species have been recorded. A few other forms may be mentioned as attaining great abundance in the Walton Crag, though they also occur at later horizons. *Liomesus dalei* (J. Sow.) (Fig. 82), a strong and almost smooth 'whelk', now living along the Norwegian and Scottish coasts, is especially characteristic of Walton horizons, though frequently found in the Coralline Crag. *Searlesia costifer* (S. Wood) (Fig. 82) is another distinctive 'whelk', its thick shell being strongly ribbed. The lamellibranch *Dosinia exoleta* (Park.) (Fig. 83), rare in the Coralline but abundant in the Red Crag, is readily distinguished by the numerous crowded concentric ribs which ornament its biconvex shell. The familiar cockle is portrayed in *Cardium parkinsoni* J. Sow., which often attains a large size, and has rather flattened, slightly imbricated ribs. *Corbulomya complanata* (J. Sow.) (Fig. 83), a thick, somewhat quadrate shell with truncated posterior end, is restricted in range to the Walton and Newbourne divisions of the Red Crag.

In the succeeding **Newbourne Crag** the southern element is not so preponderant, and the fauna has a larger proportion of northern and living species. The life-assemblage of the Butley Crag, highest of the Red Crag horizons, has a distinctly northern and recent aspect. Along with many species typical of the Red Crag as a whole, there are some whose abundance in these higher horizons is particularly noteworthy. The bivalved genus *Tellina* (*Macoma*), easily recognized by the characters of the hinge (which possesses two cardinal but no lateral teeth) is represented by the thick-shelled oblique *T. obliqua* J. Sow. (Fig. 83) and the thin, smooth, somewhat trigonal *T. praetenuis* Woodw. Species of *Mactra* are also frequent throughout the Red Crag. The Waltonian *M. arcuata* J. Sow. is replaced in the higher Crags by *M. ovalis* J. Sow., whose smooth shell is elliptical and nearly equilateral. The associated *M. constricta* S. Wood has a thick shell with a similar shape during immaturity, but the adult has a contracted ventral margin. The outline of *Cardium angustatum* J. Sow. differs from most species of the genus in its transversely elongate form with a posterior constriction, while *C. groenlandicum* Chem. of the Butley Crag is distinguished by the relative smoothness of the thin and fragile shell. A striated variety of the boreal *Neptunea antiqua* (Linn.) appears, but *N. despecta* predominates. Distinct varieties of *Purpura lapillus* (Linn.) are characteristic of these horizons, and *Scala groenlandica* (Chem.) of the Butley Crag, a thin, fragile shell with obtuse transverse ribs, is another immigrant from the north. *Sipho gracilis* (Da Costa) is a solid turreted shell ornamented by feeble spiral ridges; its canal of moderate length has an oblique notch (Fig. 82). This northern shell ranges through the Red Crag stages.

The threefold division of the **Icenian Crag** is shown in the table of succession on p. 622. The lowest of these divisions, known as the Norwich Crag, is a variable series of sands and gravels which cover a considerable area in Norfolk and Suffolk. The marine molluscan fauna has a recent aspect; nearly 90 per cent. of the species are still living, while most of the typical Red Crag fossils are absent. The shells are generally smaller, thinner, and more fragile than those of the Red Crag—characters that may be due to a decrease in salinity of the water. Land and freshwater species occur locally, having presumably been drifted by streams. It is concluded that the Norwich Crag originated in widespread shallow and brackish waters resembling the present Baltic Sea. It may be added that the fauna is impoverished in character, since only some forty species are really abundant (out of a total of 150 recorded forms), and these are somewhat sparsely distributed.

Few shells are restricted to the Norwich Crag, but some are more abundant in it than in earlier beds. For instance, *Littorina littorea* (Linn.), typically a Pleistocene and Recent species, is occasionally found in the upper

Tellina obliqua *J.Sow.*

Nucula cobboldiæ *J.Sow.*

Yoldia lanceolata (*J.Sow.*)

Corbulomya complanata (*J.Sow.*)

Mactra ovalis *J.Sow.*

Dosinia exoleta (*Park.*)

Pecten tigrinus *Müll.*

Cyprina islandica (*Linn.*)

Astarte omalii *Lajon.*

Astarte basteroti *Lajon.*

Pecten gerardi *Nyst.*

Cardita senilis *Lam.*

FIG. 83. BRITISH PLIOCENE LAMELLIBRANCHS (*mainly from figures by S. V. Wood*).
All about two-thirds of the natural size

part of the Red Crag, but first becomes abundant in the Norwich Crag. Certain varieties of this shell that occur in the Norwich and Weybourne Crags are unknown in the existing fauna, and are regarded as due to growth in waters of slight salinity. The sinistral *Neptunea contraria* (Linn.) is practically absent, while *N. despecta* (Linn.) is far from abundant in the Norwich Crag. *N. antiqua* var. *striata* S. V. Wood is, however, characteristic, this variety differing from the typical living species in the comparative coarseness of its striate ornament. *Turritella communis* Risso (Fig. 82), a northern form, which should be distinguished from the older and extinct southern *T. tricarinata* (Brocchi) from the Italian Neogene, is abundant in the Norwich Crag and later deposits. It is distinguished by its convex whorls ornamented by fine spiral ribs.

The Chillesford Beds are sands and clays resting indifferently on the Red and Norwich Crags. Plotted on a map, the localities form a sinuous belt increasing in width northwards, 'as if representing the bed of a former muddy estuary' (Harmer). The fauna differs considerably from those of the Norwich and Weybourne Crags, but this may be due to differences in physical conditions of the habitat. The molluscan shells are mostly thin and fragile, and the lamellibranchs often have the valves united in the position of life. The bivalved mollusca include *Nucula tenuis* (Montagu), *N. (Acila) cobboldiae* J. Sow. (Fig. 83), *Yoldia lanceolata* (J. Sow.), *Y. oblongoides* (S. Wood), *Cardium groenlandicum* Chem., *Mactra ovalis* J. Sow., *Mya truncata* Linn., and *Tellina calcarea* Gmelin, while *Turritella communis* Risso is the chief gastropod.

The Weybourne Crag, only known in the north of Norfolk, contains a meagre molluscan fauna of some fifty species. Only six of these are extinct, and the remainder are now living in the seas bordering north-west Europe. Of the non-British forms, four are Arctic and seven are Scandinavian species. The most characteristic shell (unknown in earlier beds) is *Tellina (Macoma) balthica* Linn., individuals of which often outnumber those of all the other species.

The **Cromer Forest Bed,** developed along the east coast of Norfolk, consists of an estuarine deposit (the Forest Bed proper), lying between two freshwater beds. The local and discontinuous Lower Freshwater Bed is composed of peat and peaty clays containing land and freshwater shells, besides plant-remains. The peaty loams of the Upper Freshwater Bed also enclose similar remains, together with bones of small mammals (voles and shrews). This bed lies in erosion-hollows of the Forest Bed, the upper surface of which is weathered into a soil and penetrated by roots. The estuarine Forest Bed, a series of clays, sands, and gravels, contains a mixture of marine and freshwater shells, mammalian bones, drifted stumps of trees, and seeds of many plants. The marine species, few in number, all occur in the Weybourne Crag, and include the extinct forms *Melampus pyramidalis* (J. Sow.), *Tellina obliqua* J. Sow., and *Nucula cobboldiae* J. Sow. Some sixty species of land and freshwater shells are recorded, and about half of these occur in the Icenian Crags. Some extinct forms like *Pisidium astartioides* Sandb. and *Nematura runtoniana* Sandb. are unknown in older beds, and with the living, non-British species *Corbicula fluminalis* (Müller), *Hydrobia marginata* Mich., and *Valvata fluviatilis* Colb., have a distinctly southern range. The presence of these shells in the Forest Bed, among Arctic marine mollusca, is usually regarded as due to a river flowing from the south-east, probably a continuation of the Rhine. In this connexion reference may be made to Reid's suggestion that the northern character of the marine fauna may not altogether be due to climatal changes. When communication with southern seas was closed by the tectonic movements, the southern species could not be replenished, while constant immigration of northern forms was assured, apart from the cooling influence of northern currents. On the other hand, the dispersal of freshwater species would be from the south, along the rivers flowing through the newly raised land-area.

The mammalian remains found in the Forest Bed are also of a 'mixed' character, and no difference of mineralization between the derived and indigenous forms is apparent. Some species like *Elephas meridionalis* Nesti (the southern elephant), *Hippopotamus amphibius* Linn., and *Rhinoceros etruscus* Falc., are southern types, but there are also *Elephas antiquus* Falc. (the northern straight-tusked elephant), *Ovibus moschatus* Zimm. (the musk-ox), and perhaps *Elephas primigenius* Blumenb. (the northern mammoth). Remains of carnivores are less significant with regard to climate than are those of herbivores, since the range of the latter depends upon the available vegetation. But the presence in the Forest Bed of *Machairodus* (sabretoothed tiger), together with *Canis lupus* Linn. (wolf), *Ursus spelaeus* Blum. (cave-bear), *Hyaena crocuta* Erxl., *Gulo luscus* Linn. (glutton), may be noted. As P. G. H. Boswell has remarked, 'small wonder it is, therefore, that the age of the Forest Bed fauna has long been in dispute'.

Though Pleistocene deposits in Britain are mainly of terrestrial origin—englacial boulder clay and morainic material left by glaciers, cave-deposits, and valley gravels—yet glimpses of the marine fauna are given by the occurrence of molluscan shells in some of the glacial beds. During their passage across the Irish Sea and North Sea basins the glaciers removed portions of the sea-bed and transported the material, often to a considerable height above sea-level. The shells contained in the resulting deposits mostly belong to living species typical of the seas round the northern parts of our islands, mollusca that are now restricted to the southern coasts being only exceptionally found. The most abundant species are:

Gastropods.—*Turritella communis* Risso, *Purpura lapillus* (Linn.), *Nassa reticulata* (Linn.), *Littorina littorea* (Linn.), *Buccinum undatum* Linn., *Trophon clathratum* (Linn.).

Lamellibranchs.—*Astarte borealis* (Chem.), *Cardium edule* Linn., *Cyprina islandica* (Linn.), *Mya arenaria* Linn., *M. truncata* Linn., *Panopaea norvegica* (Spengler), *Pecten islandicus* Müller, *Saxicava rugosa* (Pennant), *Tellina balthica* Linn.

The shells are often comminuted, but in certain beds (not formed by glacial agency) are perfectly preserved in the position of life. Thus in the Lower Pleistocene *Leda-myalis* Bed of Norfolk, the index-fossil as well as *Mya arenaria* Linn. and *Astarte borealis* (Chem.) may all be found with their valves united.

The Drift deposits of Wexford, the Isle of Man, and Selsey (Sussex), have attracted attention because they enclose shells that are not generally present in Pleistocene Beds. The fauna of the Wexford Gravels has, on the whole, a northern and Pleistocene character, and includes abundant specimens of *Nassa incrassata* (Ström.), *N. reticulata* (Linn.), and many species of northern *Trophon*, together with *Buccinum undatum* Linn., *Ocinebra erinacea* (Linn.), and *Scala similis* (J. Sow.). A thick, strongly ridged variety of *Purpura lapillus* (Linn.) commonly occurs, as well as a sinistral *Neptunea*—not the southern Crag shell *N. contraria* (Linn.), but a short, tumid form allied to the Arctic species *N. deformis* Reeve. The abundance and variety of *Trophon* is remarkable; they 'seem to form a special group different from that either of any recognized horizon of our Pliocene or Pleistocene deposits, or of the existing seas of Great Britain or Scandinavia' (Harmer). The shells of the Manx Drift are also mostly of recent and northern character, but some, as well preserved as the majority, show affinity with Pliocene forms. Certain extinct pre-Pleistocene species give a character to this Manx fauna, 'which does not altogether agree with that of any recognized British horizon'. These shells include species of *Nassa*, such as *N. reticosa* (J. Sow.), *N. granulata* (J. Sow.), *N. elegans* (J. Sow.), a variety of *Searlesia costifer* S. Wood, and other species of the genus; varieties of *Sipho curtus* (Jeffreys) and *S. tortuosus* (J. Sow.), *Fusus longiroster* (Brocchi), *Murex rudis* Borson, and *Potamides tricinctum* (Brocchi). Some authors regard the Wexford and Manx deposits as residual concentrates of morainic material derived from beds of various ages, but others regard them as Pleistocene deposits of a character unknown elsewhere.

The Selsey Drift contains over 200 species of well-preserved marine mollusca, besides numerous species of other groups. Many of the mollusca are of a well-marked southern character, and are said to have no equivalent in British post-Pliocene deposits.

The Pleistocene marine fauna merges insensibly into the closely related assemblage of the present day. To the geologist, Holocene faunas are of interest chiefly from the ecological and geographical standpoints. These have already been discussed broadly, but attention may here be drawn to the fact that many southern species, living along the west coasts of England and in the English Channel, are not found in the North Sea. In the latter area the tidal currents are from the north, and they meet the southern current near the Straits of Dover.

FAUNAL REGIONS

The differentiation of tropical and temperate belts, demonstrated in Chapter XV for the Palaeogene period by the distribution of foraminifera, reef-corals, sea-urchins, and mollusca, can be traced through Neogene time to the present day. Furthermore, the relations of various fossil-assemblages in several regions of the world show that important geographical changes took place within the Neogene period. In the European area, the Atlantic marine embayment, which had persisted from the Mesozoic era, but which was somewhat reduced in Palaeogene time, now became further reduced by cumulative deposition and orogenic processes. Miocene freshwater strata are prevalent in a great tract which extends from the Scandinavian Shield and Russian platform, through Germany, northern and central France to Spain. Farther east, after a marine episode in early Miocene time, the Vienna basin and the greater part of the Balkans, together with the low ground around the Black and Caspian Seas, became covered with deposits of freshwater origin. The fossils in this region are mainly terrestrial molluscan and mammalian remains; the latter are discussed separately in Chapter XVII. Hence for the first time Europe became a continental area. Around its margins three separate areas of marine deposition are evident. The area of the present North Sea extended southwards over Denmark, north Germany, and the Netherlands, with a Pliocene extension over East Anglia. Atlantic waters encroached over the margins of western France, forming small embayments in Anjou and Aquitaine, and a still smaller one in the Iberian meseta near Lisbon. The Mediterranean Sea covered most of Italy, the margins of South Spain, Balearic Islands, Corsica, Sardinia, Sicily, Crete, and Cyprus, also the margins of Morocco, Tunisia, and Egypt. In discussing the Neogene faunas of these regions, and of the marginal deposits around the extra-European continents we shall follow the plan of the previous chapter, and consider the distribution of foraminifera, reef-corals, sea-urchins and mollusca separately.

FORAMINIFERA. The nummulites are of slight importance in Neogene faunas, for, after their prolific development in Palaeogene strata, they disappear entirely after the lowest (Aquitanian) stage of the Miocene Series. The orbitoids, however, are represented in that stage by large species of *Lepidocyclina*, particularly of the subgenera *Nephrolepidina*, *Eulepidina* and *Amphilepidina*. These give way to smaller species in the Burdigalian stage, and thereafter they vanish altogether. *Miogypsina* also continues from the Oligocene Series and is present in great abundance at early Miocene horizons, but does not long survive the Lepidocycline forms.

Like their Palaeogene predecessors these early Miocene orbitoids are very plentiful in tropical and subtropical regions. In south Europe they are present in south France and Spain, in Italy from the Vicentin, along the slopes of the Apennines to Calabria, Malta, and eastwards to Cyprus. The northerly limit of this region is obscured by the development of terrestrial and freshwater deposits, but orbitoids are not recorded north of Aquitaine, that is, about 47° N. latitude.

Lepidocyclina and *Miogypsina* are represented in Egypt and south-west Persia, sometimes by species which are identical or closely comparable with Mediterranean species. But around the Indian Ocean they are associated with other foraminifera, like the miliolid *Trillina* and the alveoline *Flosculinella*, which are not known from the European localities. Assemblages containing these forms are recorded from transgressive Miocene deposits on the East African coast, in Somaliland, Kenya, Tanganyika, Pemba Island, Madagascar, and Portuguese East Africa to 23° 30' S. latitude. On the northern margin of the Indian Ocean they appear in the Gaj Beds of Sind and equivalent horizons in Ceylon, Burma, and several islands of the Malayan Archipelago, namely, Sumatra, Mentawei, Java, Borneo, and New Guinea.

In the Pacific Ocean species of *Lepidocyclina* and often *Miogypsina* are recorded from the Philippines, Formosa, and Japan (to 40° N. lat.), from Guam, Fiji, and New Hebrides. Species of *Lepidocyclina* are known from the shores of the Great Australian Bight and in Victoria, while *Miogypsina* is recorded as abundant at Whangarei (36° S. lat.) in the Auckland district of New Zealand.

The chief American source for these fossils is the Carribean area, including Mexico, Panama, Cuba, Jamaica, Carriacou, Trinidad. They also extend to the south-eastern mainland of the United States and to California. In South America they are recorded from Venezuela, north Peru, and south-west Ecuador. Doubtless their further extension southward was prevented by the cold Humboldt Current flowing northward from the Antarctic Seas.

REEF-CORALS. It may be recalled that during Palaeogene time a varied fauna of reef-building corals had developed in four regions, namely, the Indian Ocean, the Mediterranean Sea, the Caribbean area and the Pacific Ocean. It is evident, from the number of genera these regions had in common, that a considerable degree of communication existed between them. Nowadays the reef-corals of the Indian and Pacific Oceans are so much alike that they form one Indo-Pacific unit; the Atlantic fauna is much impoverished in comparison, and reef-corals no longer live in the Mediterranean Sea. It is now our task to discuss the reasons for this remarkable change, and our discussion may conveniently begin with the Indo-Pacific fauna.

In Sind, many of the Palaeogene reef-genera, like *Stylophora*, *Calamophyllia*, *Orbicella* (*Montastraea*), *Plesiastraea*, *Porites*, &c., persist into the Gaj Beds which represent a low horizon of the Miocene Series. The Gaj fauna is clearly distinguished by the increased development of certain genera which had hitherto been subordinate elements in the reef-faunas. The Eusmiliidae acquire new importance in the presence of *Antillia, Leptomussa,* &c. which, with the astrangid genera *Cladocora* and *Echinopora,* are already represented in the Palaeogene coral-faunas of south Europe. The Faviidae are represented by species of *Platygyra* (formerly *Leptoria*) and *Monticulastraea,* the latter often showing striking resemblance to the living *Hydnophora.* Among fungid corals the simple forms *Cycloseris* and *Agaricia* show some variety, and the perforate genera *Porites* and *Astraeopora* are conspicuous. Further development of reef-corals in Sind was prevented by the accumulation of terrestrial deposits, but farther west Miocene strata in eastern Egypt have yielded to J. W. Gregory (1898, 1906) massive colonies of *Stylophora, Stylocoenia, Montastraea, Solenastraea, Prionastraea, Plesiastraea, Leptastraea, Favia,* and *Acanthastraea.* Many of them are closely similar to Indian and European forms and must have had a common origin. Later reefs, resting on gravels of torrential origin, probably represent a considerable part of late Pliocene and Pleistocene time. They lie above sea level on both sides of the Red Sea and Gulf of Suez, and J. Walther (1888) has described in detail the raised reefs in the peninsula of Sinai. Among the corals cited by Gregory (1906) from these beds are species of *Stylophora, Heliastraea, Echinopora, Galaxea, Leptastraea, Prionastraea, Solenastraea, Porites,* all related to living forms in the Red Sea and the Indian Ocean. Apart from an isolated record of badly preserved Miocene corals, including *Hydnophora* and *Porites,* in south Ceylon, the most important Neogene reef-fauna is that of the Malayan Archipelago. Here H. Gerth (1931) has provided an impressive list of genera and species; further, he has written, in another paper, his interpretation of the evolution of the reef-corals.

The Neogene reef-corals of the Malayan Archipelago are distributed among about eighty genera, but these were not all living at the same time. We may consider some of the main features in their development, leaving aside the simple corals of the Trochosmilidae which, after a rich development in Palaeogene faunas, became extinct during Neogene time. Of the massive Eusmiliidae only a few species of different lineages survive the Palaeogene; some forms, like *Coelocoenia* show similarity with Antillean species, while the living genera *Euphyllia* and *Caulastraea* can only be traced back to the Pliocene. Some Neogene species of the stylinid *Galaxea* show little difference from living forms of the genus. The branching Calamophyllidae, now extinct, are abundantly represented in Palaeogene faunas, but only *Rhabdophyllia* is known in the Miocene of Borneo. The Lithophyllidae are better known, for *Antillia* persists from the Palaeogene rocks of the Caribbean and Mediterranean areas, and is represented by a number of species throughout the Neogene of Java and Borneo; *Indophyllia* is also recorded from Miocene horizons in those islands. The Mussidae are represented in the older Miocene by members of the genus *Hydno-*

phyllia which is well developed in Palaeogene faunas of the Mediterranean region; the branching *Mussa* and the massive *Symphyllia* first appear in the Pliocene fauna of the East Indies, but their precise ancestry is not yet apparent. The family Faviidae show a wealth of forms from Miocene to the present day with little difference in structure; indeed, several of the Neogene forms are placed with living species, e.g. in the genera *Coeloria* and *Maeandra*. On the other hand, the genus *Monticulastraea*, first described from India but later found in Borneo and Sumatra, is said to throw some light on the origin of the living *Hydnophora*, which first appears in late Miocene horizons. *Platygyra*, formerly quoted as *Leptoria*, which is recorded in Eocene faunas of New Guinea, is reported from the Miocene of Borneo and Pliocene of Java. The Astraeidae show a marked decline in importance after the Miocene which has a considerable variety of forms, and *Cyphastraea* has already disappeared by Pliocene time. Several fossil species of the astrangid *Echinopora* hardly differ from living species. The ancient family Astrocoenidae, represented by fossil and living species of *Stephanocoenia* and *Astrocoenia*, is recorded as rare in the Miocene of Java and Borneo. The Oulastraeidae of T. W. Vaughan show a superficial likeness to the Astraeidae; the genus *Diploastraea*, which appears in the Miocene of Borneo and is still living, seems to be related to the Palaeogene genus *Cyathomorpha* of the Caribbean and Mediterranean regions. Several colonial genera of the Fungidae occur in the Neogene faunas of the Archipelago including species of *Leptoseris*, *Comoseris*, and *Pironastraea*, and some of them merge gradually into their living representatives. *Siderastraea* has a range from Oligocene time to the present day in both Atlantic and Indo-Pacific faunas; species found in the Miocene of the Archipelago are also known from equivalent deposits on the Mediterranean borders. In the family Stylophoridae, the typical genus *Stylophora* has a variety of species from Palaeogene horizons onwards, but they disappear entirely from the Atlantic region after Miocene time. *Stylophora* seems to have given rise to the two Neogene genera *Pocillopora* and *Seriatopora*, the latter only known in the Indo-Pacific region. The predominant corals in living reef-faunas are often grouped in the Perforata, but they probably represent a number of independent lineages which have developed a porous skeleton. In the family Acroporidae the Palaeogene *Dendracis* survives in the East Indies as late as Miocene horizons. The branching *Acropora* also dates from Palaeogene time and has the greatest number of species among modern reef-builders, but the massive *Astraeopora* has no living representatives. The Poritidae are represented in late Palaeogene strata by *Porites* and *Goniopora*, and Neogene members show a greater diversity of form. *Dictyaraea*, with finely branched colonies, is well developed in Miocene horizons of the Archipelago, but vanishes suddenly at the end of the Pliocene Series. The constant interchange of species between the Indian and Pacific Oceans has resulted in virtual uniformity of living reef-faunas from

East Africa and South Asia, through the East Indian Archipelago to Japan, Hawaii, and the western coast of central America.

In contrast with the strong development of the Neogene reef-fauna in the Indo-Pacific region that of the Mediterranean borders shows a marked decline through Miocene horizons. Among the forty reef-corals known from the Neogene strata of south Europe, only the Astraeidae are really conspicuous; the Fungidae are less numerous than in earlier stages, the Stylophoridae and the Poritidae are also poorly developed. For example, F. R. C. Reed (1939) has described species of *Cyphastraea*, *Montastraea* (cited as *Heliastraea*), *Leptastraea*, *Plesiastraea*, *Prionastraea*, *Solenastraea*, and *Porites* from the Vindobonian stage of Cyprus. Species of the same genera have long been known from the Vienna basin and Moravia, also from north Italy and Aquitaine. These corals may represent autochthonous development from Priabonian and Rupelian forms already noted, for A. M. Davies (1934) says the assemblage is not found in the Indian region. It still has considerable similarity with the contemporary Caribbean fauna, though such distinctive forms as *Antiguastraea* and *Cyathomorpha* have vanished. Eventually, by the end of Pliocene time, reef-corals disappeared entirely from the Mediterranean faunas. This is consistent with isolation of the area, which prevented the immigration of species from other seas, and with evidence of climatic change shown by the appearance of northern types of mollusca, to be discussed later (p. 651).

In the Caribbean region there is a considerable development of reef-corals in early Miocene limestones of Anguilla, Cuba, Panama, and the Tampa Beds of Florida, whence T. W. Vaughan (1919) records species of *Stylophora*, *Pocillopora*, *Astrocoenia*, *Montastraea* (as *Orbicella*) *Stylangia*, *Goniastraea*, *Pavona*, and the perforate genera *Acropora*, *Astraeopora*, *Goniopora*, *Porites*. This assemblage compares closely with that of the Oligocene Series in the Antillian region, though it lacks such distinctive genera as *Antiguastraea*, *Cyathomorpha*, &c. Other genera are wanting in the coral-fauna of the Bowden Marl in Jamaica, such as *Astrocoenia*, *Astraeopora* to name only two. On the other hand, the Bowden fauna contains new forms of *Stylophora*, *Stephanocoenia*, *Antillia*, *Thysanus*, *Siderastraea*, *Acropora*, *Goniopora*, *Porites*, including two species still living in the Caribbean region. Vaughan refers this and similar assemblages from San Domingo, Cuba, and Florida to the Miocene Series. It should be noted that these faunas contain such genera as *Stylophora*, *Pocillopora*, *Antillia*, *Favites*, *Syzygophyllia*, *Pavona*, and *Gonipora* which now live only in the Indo-Pacific reefs. Further, the record of *Septastraea matsoni* from Colombia, a species nearly related to *S. marylandica* of the Virginian Miocene, suggests interoceanic connexion between the Atlantic and the Pacific in Miocene time.

A Pliocene fauna in the Caloosahatchie Marl of Florida contains species of *Archohelia*, *Dichocoenia*, *Maeandrina*, *Cladocora*, *Phyllangia*, *Solena-*

straea, Septastraea, Thysanus, Siderastraea, and *Porites.* T. W. Vaughan (1917) remarks that this fauna contains no genera now confined to the Indo-Pacific region, and infers that during Miocene time the Atlantic became separated from the Pacific Ocean by a land-area extending from North to South America. A late Pliocene coral-fauna from Carrizo Creek, California, is an association of *Eusmilia, Dichocoenia, Solenastraea, Maeandra, Siderastraea,* and *Porites.* Only one of these, namely, *Porites,* is at present known on the western coast of America, but all six are found in the Gulf of Mexico and the Caribbean Sea. The fauna is therefore purely Atlantic in character and indicates a temporary interoceanic connexion.

The Caribbean coral-fauna has altered little since the elimination of the Pacific connexion. Pleistocene reefs are extensively developed in central America, the West Indies, and Florida, and it is hardly possible to distinguish the species from those of living reefs which occupy the same areas. The coral-faunas of the Atlantic are now entirely isolated from those of the Indo-Pacific region; communication to the north is cut off by the cold waters of the Arctic Ocean, to the south by cold currents flowing northward from the Southern Ocean along the western coasts of South America and Africa. As a result of this isolation the Caribbean coral-reefs have developed a remarkably uniform fauna with certain distinctive characters. There is not a single species in common with the Indo-Pacific fauna, and though the West Indian fauna has a few genera that are not known in the Pacific, there is no family of corals restricted to the Caribbean region. We may note, however, the rich development of Eusmiliidae in which the genera *Stephanocoenia* and *Eusmilia* are peculiar to the West Indies. Other exclusively Caribbean genera include *Manicina, Dendrogyra,* and *Maeandrina*; indeed, *Maeandrina strigosa* is said to be one of the most important reef-builders in the West Indies and Florida. On the other hand, there is a scarcity or even absence in the West Indies of several families, and consequently many genera, that flourish in Indo-Pacific waters. The simple Fungidae are entirely absent and the foliaceous colonies of the family, represented among living corals only by *Agaricia,* are poorly developed. The Stylophoridae are completely absent in living reefs, though *Stylophora* and *Pocillopora* are well developed in Miocene strata of Florida and the West Indies. The Perforata also are poorly developed on living reefs of the Caribbean region, only a few species of *Porites* and *Acropora* remaining from a larger representation in Miocene strata. As a whole the Caribbean coral-fauna may be regarded as an impoverished Pacific fauna that has developed a pronounced local character as the result of isolation.

The coral-fauna of Bermuda (32° N. lat.) is a detached colony of the more hardy species that have migrated from the West Indies by the agency of the Florida Current which has carried their free-swimming larvae northeastward. Twenty species are listed by A. E. Verrill (1901), and probably most of them have come directly from the Bahamas, over 700 miles away.

The genera represented are *Maeandrina, Favia, Montastraea, Plesiastraea, Madracis, Oculina, Mussa, Agaricia, Siderastraea,* and *Porites. Maeandrina labyrinthiformis* is the predominant reef-builder, being relatively more abundant here than in the West Indies. The absence of all varieties of *Acropora muricata* is conspicuous; for these are among the most prolific of West Indian reef-corals; other genera lacking are *Dendrogyra, Dichocoenia, Eusmilia, Stephanocoenia,* and *Solenastraea.* These differences may be due to varying capacity of the several species to endure the comparatively low temperature in winter. Bermuda lies within the marginal belt of W. M. Davies (1928) the northward extension of which is explained by the warmth of the Florida Current.

In South America coral-reefs occupy an area around Cap San Roque, Brazil, and their southern limit is marked by the coastal reefs of Abrolhos (18° S. lat.). A. E. Verrill (1901) states that the reef-corals are few in number (only sixteen species are listed), but of more than ordinary interest because several of them combine in a single species features which usually give character to two or more distinct genera. Perhaps of more immediate interest in the present discussion is that the course of the ocean currents is northward along the Brazilian coast, and the reefs are separated from the West Indies by the enormous volume of freshwater from the Amazon which coral larvae cannot pass. Nevertheless, Verrill considers that the original home of species common to the two regions must have been on the Brazilian coast.

We have now traced the development of coral-reef faunas through Neogene time, a period first of orogenic activity, and then of climatic change. Neither of these seems to have disturbed the continuity of reef-building though each had its local effects. The isolation of the Mediterranean area from the Indian Ocean was perhaps an effect of the Alpine orogeny, and the emergence of the Panama isthmus may be its counterpart in the western hemisphere. After the separation of the Atlantic and Indo-Pacific reef-faunas the north and south polar ice-caps began to accumulate and extended in Pleistocene time to about 45° lat. on either side of the equator. There is some uncertainty about the limits of the coral-reef belt at this period, but the suggestion of R. A. Daly (1934) that reef-building stopped completely or suffered serious decline cannot be entertained. Pleistocene reefs are known in Florida and the West Indies, and the development of reef-corals in the Caribbean area shows no lack of continuity. Likewise in the Indo-Pacific region, especially in the Malayan Archipelago there is abundant evidence of continuous development. Indeed, H. Gerth (1930) ascribes the great increase in Perforate corals in that region to adaptation consequent on rapid changes in sea-level during the Pleistocene period.

ECHINOIDEA. We have already noted (p. 606) that the Gaj Beds of Sind, which are usually correlated with the Aquitanian stage of Europe, contain species of *Paradoxechinus*, *Echinolampas*, *Amphiope*, *Clypeaster*, *Breynia*, and *Eupatagus*, belonging to stocks that were already established in the region. Towards the middle of the Miocene period the sea retreated from the whole of northern India, and later deposits there are of continental origin. From marine Pliocene beds on the coast of Baluchistan, however, P. M. Duncan and W. P. Sladen (1886) have described species of the temnopleurids *Salmacis* and *Temnopleurus*, while similar deposits on islands in the Persian Gulf have yielded *Clypeaster* and *Laganum* in abundance, associated with *Amphiope* and *Breynia*. Pleistocene echinoids described by A. G. Brighton (1931) from the Farsan Islands, Red Sea, include species of *Echinometra*, *Heterocentrotus*, *Clypeaster*, *Laganum*, *Fibularia*, *Paraster*, *Brissus*, and *Maretia*; all these species still live in the Indo-Pacific waters.

Similar associations are known from transgressive deposits on the western margin of the Indian Ocean. The Lower Miocene rocks of Pemba Island have furnished G. M. Stockley (1927) with extinct species of *Coelopleurus*, *Temnopleurus*, *Clypeaster*, and *Echinolampas* identical with Indian forms, and a species of *Schizaster* which was previously known from Tanganyika. The Pliocene echinoids described by the same author from the neighbouring island of Zanzibar are mainly species of *Temnopleurus*, *Clypeaster*, *Laganum*, and *Brissus* which are identical or comparable with forms known to be living in adjacent seas. Neogene strata in Madagascar have yielded species of *Cidaris*, *Heterocentrotus*, and *Eupatagus*.

Proceeding to the eastern part of the Indian Ocean, A. M. Davies (1923) has recorded species of *Clypeaster* from Miocene beds in Ceylon, that are closely related to forms in the Gaj Beds of north-west India. The Pegu stage of Burma has yielded certain echinoids which have been reviewed by E. D. Currie (1939). Species of *Amphiope*, *Echinolampas*, *Paraster*, and *Breynia* are referred to or compared with species from the Gaj stage of Sind. A new species of *Dicoptella* from eastern Prome and Pegu River, where it occurs in some abundance, is compared with a form from the Upper Miocene of Java. H. Gerth (1922) has reviewed the Neogene sea-urchins of Java which include members of the genera *Coelopleurus*, *Temnopleurus*, *Sismondia*, *Brissus*, *Brissopsis*, *Meoma*, *Maretia*, *Breynia*. The general aspect of all these faunas is that of the Indo-Pacific fauna of the present day, allowing for differences due to the course of evolution since Miocene time.

Neogene faunas are also recorded from marginal transgressions in Victoria, along the shores of the Great Australian Bight, and in western Australia. The earliest is found in the Balcombe stage of Victoria which may be equivalent to the Aquitanian stage of Europe, if not, perhaps, somewhat earlier. It is followed by the Janjuc stage which includes the Batesford Limestone containing Burdigalian species of *Lepidocyclina*. The Kalimna stage represents the Pliocene series. The echinoid element of these stages, reviewed by P. M. Duncan (1887), differs in several features from other

develop lunules. Three genera of this group successively become dominant with slight overlap in vertical range, and provide the most characteristic sea-urchins of the western States from California to British Columbia. The true *Scutella* persists from the Oligocene Series, and attains its maximum development in the Vacqueros and Monterey stages of California, regarded as early Miocene in point of age; *Scutella* is here associated with two species of *Cassidulus*. In later Miocene strata *Astrodapsis* becomes dominant in place of *Scutella*, and in the Etchegoin stage is replaced by *Dendraster* which is dominant at late Pliocene horizons. The widespread *Strongylocentrotus* appears in Californian Pliocene deposits and becomes abundant in the Pleistocene whence the quadrilunulate scutellid *Mellita* is also recorded. The presence in the Pliocene of Carrizo Creek, California, of an exceptional association of *Tripneustes*, *Clypeaster*, and *Encope* with reef-building corals (p. 641) is interpreted as evidence of a temporary connexion with the Caribbean Sea during some part of Pliocene time.

A varied assemblage of sea-urchins from various islands in the Antillean region is reviewed by R. T. Jackson (1922). The earliest Miocene horizon is represented by the Anguilla Limestone in the island of Anguilla, correlated with the Aquitanian stage of Europe. Species of *Cidaris*, *Echinometra*, *Sismondia*, *Clypeaster*, *Echinoneus*, *Echinolampas*, *Agassizia*, *Paraster*, *Brissopsis*, *Macropneustes*, and *Brissus* are recorded from the Anguilla Limestone. Some of the species are also present in the Emperador Limestone of Panama, and equivalent horizons in Cuba, Puerto Rico, and the Dominican Republic. About one-third of the species are reported from the Antigua stage of the Oligocene Series (p. 608), and others appear to range upward into later Miocene horizons. On a general view there appears to have been continuous development of the fauna within the Caribbean region. *Clypeaster* is very conspicuous with a number of species, and the living type of the genus *C. rosaceus* (Linn.) is reported from Pliocene deposits in Cuba and Puerto Rico. The perforate scutellids *Encope* and *Mellita* are rare, according to West Indian records, but several fossil species are recorded from the Panama Canal Zone, and the genera are represented in the living fauna on both the east and west coasts of tropical America. A species of *Echinoneus* present in the Anguilla Limestone is still living in the West Indies as well as in the Pacific Ocean. Species of *Echinolampas*, especially *E. semiorbis* Guppy, are distinctive in the Anguilla Limestone, and are found also in Cuba, Puerto Rico, and Panama, but 'none of the fossil species is at all near to the recent species of the West Indies'. *Paraster* persists from Palaeogene horizons, but is not recorded above the Miocene and is not represented in the living fauna of the West Indies. *Brissopsis antillarum* Cotteau is the Anguillan forerunner of the Pliocene and living *B. atlantica* Mortensen; similarly *Brissus exiguus* Cotteau from the Anguilla Limestone is succeeded by the Pliocene *B. brissus* (Leske) which still lives in the adjacent seas. The several Eocene species of *Eupatagus* represented in the St. Bartholomew Limestone are much reduced in number by Miocene time, and all the West Indian species are very different from the single living species in Australian waters. It is evident that, apart from the extinction of some forms and the development of others, the general constitution of the Caribbean fauna was fairly constant throughout Neozoic time. Moreover as with the corals (p. 641) certain genera now restricted to the Indo-Pacific region vanish from eastern America after Miocene time.

The northern limit of this tropical fauna is rather indefinite because of the varying limits of distribution of different genera. About a dozen echinoid genera are recorded by C. W. Cooke (1942) from Miocene strata in the south-eastern United States, but only *Scutella*, *Encope*, and *Clypeaster* in common with the West Indies. *Scutella* is represented in Miocene strata in Florida and Maryland, Miocene species of *Encope* are recorded from Florida, North and South Carolina, while *Clypeaster* is very rare in the Chipola stage of Florida. Of the genera which are present in the south-eastern States, but not known fossil in the West Indies, *Echinocyamus* is recorded from the Chipola stage in Florida, North and South Carolina, *Lovenia* from the Miocene of Florida, and *Echinocardium* in Miocene strata from Maryland to South Carolina. Hence there seems to be some distinction between tropical and subtropical Neogene faunas as in Europe. But in the Caribbean area the tropical fauna was not exterminated by the progressively cooler conditions during Pliocene and Pleistocene time, for geographical conditions favoured its extension southward. The echinoid fauna in the Miocene rocks of Venezuela, about 1,200 miles south of Florida, includes such genera as *Tripneustes*, *Encope*, *Clypeaster*, *Echinolampas*, *Pericosmus*, *Agassizia*, and *Schizaster*. After isolation from the Pacific Ocean in Miocene time by the emergence of the Isthmus of Panama, the tropical sea-urchins of the Caribbean area developed independently, and the living assemblage shows little difference generically from that of the Miocene Series of the West Indies.

MOLLUSCA. Reverting to the Miocene rocks of north-west India, a considerable number of genera, including *Terebra*, *Conus*, *Oliva*, *Volutospina*, *Lyria*, *Mitra*, *Cassis*, *Cypraea*, *Strombus*, &c., persist from the Nari into the Gaj Beds, thus demonstrating the general continuity of faunal development. A few of the Gaj forms, notably species of *Conus* and *Galeodea*, are recorded also from the Lower Miocene deposits of Europe. The window-pane oyster *Indoplacuna* seems to be a Miocene derivative of the Eocene *Carolia* which in its turn is derived from an unnamed Khirthar species of *Anomia*: in the Gaj Beds *Indoplacuna* is accompanied by *Placuna* (or *Placenta*) which survives in the Indian Ocean. The venerid lamellibranch *Clementia* is a newcomer in the Indian succession, though it is recorded in Eocene and Oligocene rocks of America. Another immigrant form is the gastropod *Nassa*; the earliest records of this genus are from Eocene Beds of Alabama, Peru, and Java, but it is first represented in

Indian deposits by four species in the Gaj Beds of Sind. E. W. Vredenburg (1924) remarks that the resemblance between the Miocene molluscan faunas of India and the Caribbean region may perhaps be explained by mutual interchange across the Pacific Ocean before the emergence of the Isthmus of Panama. Some of the Gaj Bed species, like *Mitra chinensis* Gray and *Calyptraea chinensis* (Linn.), cannot be distinguished by any precise characters from their living representatives in the Indian seas. Others, such as *Cypraea prunum* J. de C. Sow., *Architectonica affine* (J. de C. Sow.), *Antigona granosa* (J. de C. Sow.) are closely similar to allied species, *Cypraea nivosa* Linn., *Architectonica maxima* (Philippi) and *Antigona puerpera* (Linn.), respectively, still existing in the adjacent seas.

The proportion of shells identical or comparable with those of living species is considerably larger in the Pliocene fauna of the Mekran coast in Baluchistan (Vredenburg, 1928) and Karikal in south-east India (Cossmann, 1900–11). The fauna is also interesting in that it contains species of *Volutospina* and *Clavilithes* persisting from early Eocene horizons; the former genus becomes extinct at the end of Pliocene time, but the latter still lives in Java. There are also some immigrant forms. One of these is *Xancus pirum*, the living 'chanka' of Ceylon, recorded fossil from Karikal; the same genus is represented in the Mekran Beds of Baluchistan by *X. mekranensis* Vred., the last member of an autochthonous series which begins in the Nari Beds with *X. episoma* Michelotti (Vredenburg, 1924). A supposed boreal immigrant, referred to *Neptunea* by R. B. Newton (1905) is now assigned by Vredenburg (1928) on the basis of better material, to the genus *Cymia*. This may be another migrant from the eastern Pacific coast, for the genus is represented in the Eocene beds of the West Indies and in the Miocene strata of Peru.

Marine deposits of various Neogene stages are recorded in south Persia and the Bahrein Islands by L. R. Cox (1936), the Farsan Islands in the Red Sea by L. R. Cox (1931), the coastal belt of Somaliland by Gregory and others (1925) and B. Brown (1931), in Kenya by L. R. Cox (1930) and J. Weir (1938), in Zanzibar and Pemba Islands by G. W. Stockley (1927), and Madagascar by R. Douvillé (1901). In all these instances the molluscan faunas are comparable with those of equivalent rocks in north-west India. Similar relations are shown by Miocene fossils from Ceylon described by G. W. Wayland and A. M. Davies 1923, Assam (Vredenburg, 1921), Burma (Vredenburg, 1928), Java (K. Martin, 1911), Celebes (G. F. Dollfus, 1915), New Guinea (Wylie *et alia*, 1930), and Fiji Islands (C. A. Matley and A. M. Davies, 1927). The general aspect of the fossil molluscan faunas at these widely separated places around the Indian Ocean is that of the living fauna in the adjacent seas, allowing for modification by evolutional processes, loss by extinction and gain by the migration of exotic forms.

The living fauna of the Indo-Pacific Ocean is remarkable in containing many molluscan genera that persist through the Neozoic strata of India, but which do not survive after the Oligocene stage in most other regions. Among them are members of the Fissurellidae (*Rimula, Scutus*), Trochidae (*Delphinula, Liotia*), Cerithiidae (*Pyrazus*), Strombidae (*Rimella, Terebellum*), Fusinidae (*Clavilithes*), Corbidae (*Corbis*), Solenidae (*Cultellus*), Veneridae (*Sunetta*), Vulsellidae (*Vulsella*), Spondylidae (*Plicatula*). Hence it seems reasonable to infer that the bulk of this modern fauna has developed autochthonously in the Indian Ocean since Cretaceous time. This is also consistent with the coral and echinoid faunas noted earlier.

The Miocene mollusca of the southern coasts of Australia show considerable affinity with Indo-Pacific faunas, and, in addition, some genera indicate relations with faunas of other regions. Among gastropods the Volutidae show an unusual variety of forms. The Indo-Pacific genus *Lyria* is widespread in Miocene faunas of India, Europe, and North America, besides the Balcombe stage of south Australia. The Balcombe species of *Leptoscapha* represents a genus which is otherwise recorded only from the Eocene of the Paris basin. The old-established *Scaphella*, still widespread in Miocene faunas, is recorded from the Balcombe Beds of Victoria, but the equally ancient *Volutospina* is not reported in Australia until the Kalimnan stage. The fusinid genus *Clavilithes* is another survivor from Palaeogene time; its range extends through Miocene horizons in south Australia to the Pliocene of Java and the living Indo-Pacific fauna. The family Muricidae is represented by numerous genera, most of which are widespread already in Palaeogene faunas, for example, *Pteropurpura, Chicoreus,* and *Phyllonotus,* (all formerly included in *Murex* s.l.), *Ocinebra, Hadriania, Trophon, Typhis*. Large species of the cypraeid genus *Cypraeovula* are represented in abundance in the Miocene beds of south Australia, and a related group of species forms the genus *Umbilia* peculiar to Australia; these are associated with the small *Trivia* and *Erato* of widespread distribution. Other gastropod families well developed in Miocene strata of Australia are the Conidae (*Conus, Hemiconus*), Cancellaridae (*Trigonostoma, Sveltella, Merica, Uxia, Bonellitia*), Turridae (*Turris, Bela, Drillia, Mangilia, Borsonia*), and Cymatiidae (*Sassica, Distorsio*). Among lamellibranchs, the abundance of *Cardita, Eucrassatella, Myochama, Cleidothaerus,* and the persistence of the ancient genera *Cucullaea* and *Trigonia* may be noted. In contrast with this wealth of forms, the Strombidae has only one species of *Anachis* and *Atilia,* the Nassidae only one *Nassa,* the Thaididae only a *Sistrum* and a *Concholepas,* and the southern Struthiolariidae only two species of *Pelicaria*.

The molluscan faunas of Neogene strata in New Zealand differ considerably from those of Australia. They consist largely of an autochthonous element composed of genera which can be traced back through the Palaeogene sometimes to late Cretaceous (Wangaloan) strata. Such genera include the forerunners of forms now inhabiting the adjacent Southern Ocean. The assemblage is reinforced by Indo-Pacific forms, but this element is less pronounced than in southern Australia as is shown for instance by the rarity of Volutidae and Cymatiidae in New Zealand. As a whole the Miocene faunas of New Zealand are of subtropical aspect though no reef-corals are developed. In contrast, the Pliocene faunas lack many genera, e.g. *Cucullaea, Spondylus, Pyrazus, Galeodea, Typhis, Conospirus, Olivella,* &c., which are conspicuous in the earlier faunas. Most of these are now restricted to tropical and subtropical seas, and their disappearance is considered by C. A. Fleming (1944) to indicate extinction as a result of the northward advance of Antarctic waters in late Miocene and early Pliocene time. Concurrently, mollusca of southern affinities such as *Chlamys delicatula* and certain genera of Malletiidae (*Neilo*) and Struthiolariidae (*Struthiolaria, Pelicaria, Callusaria*), appear in the Nukumarua stage of North Island. The Castlecliffe Beds, of latest Pliocene age, are marked by the sudden appearance of subtropical mollusca of east Australian origin such as the naticid *Eunaticina*, the cymatiid *Cabestana* and the cassid *Xenophalirum*, which have no ancestors in earlier strata of New Zealand. These forms were presumably transported by a branch of the warm south equatorial current which, according to G. E. R. Deacon (1936), still flows along the east coast of Australia, then eastward across the Tasman Sea to the northern shores of New Zealand. The immigration of eastern Australian species is said to have continued to the present time. Five faunal provinces, based on the distribution of living mollusca, are recognized which show differences between the extremes of subtropical in the north, to Antarctic influence in the south. New Zealand lies athwart the convergence of warm Pacific water and cold Antarctic water, and the variations in its Neozoic molluscan faunas are evidently due, in large part, to fluctuations of the convergence.

West of the Indian Ocean many Oligocene genera persist into Miocene strata of the Mediterranean region, but several of them like *Crassatella, Delphinula, Athleta,* hardly survive the Miocene stage in Europe. Some species, e.g. *Cypraea leporina, Trigonostoma crassicosta, Melongena lainei, Chlamys pusio* (Linn.), and the long-ranged oysters *Ostrea latimarginata* Vredenburg, *O. virleti* Deshayes, and *O. gryphioides* (Schlotheim), are very close to forms described from the Gaj Beds of India by E. W. Vredenburg (1928), but the proportion of shells comparable with Indian forms is much smaller in the Miocene than in the preceding stage. Along with these forms there are important newcomers in Mediterranean deposits; *Indoplacuna* and *Clementia* are Indian genera whose temporary presence in Mediterranean strata is taken as evidence of sporadic migration from the eastern seas. Abundant gastropods of the family Nassidae (*Nassa, Dorsanum,* &c.), appear abruptly in the Lower Miocene strata of Europe; a few are already recorded from Eocene beds in America and Java, and from Oligocene beds in Japan, but the route of their migration is not yet determined. Genera of Thaididae appear successively, *Iopas, Cymia,* and *Coralliophila* in Aquitanian beds, *Stramonita* in Burdigalian, *Acanthina, Concho-*

lepas, Vitularia, and *Nucella* in Vindobonian beds. This family, like the Nassidae, may possibly be of Transatlantic origin, but the early records are too discontinuous for certainty (A. M. Davies, 1935). The Cancellariidae and Columbellidae are already represented in late Cretaceous and Eocene faunas, but they show a striking expansion in the Miocene strata of Europe and Asia. The genus *Ecphora* from the Upper Oligocene and Miocene stages of Germany appears to be more certainly a Transatlantic migrant. The arrival of these and other immigrants emphasizes the great difference in development of Mediterranean and Indian faunas from Miocene time onwards.

The Lower Pliocene (Astian) fauna of northern Italy described by Bellardi and Sacco (1872–1904) has many descendants of Miocene forms, but we note the absence of such families as Volutidae, Harpidae, and Olividae, especially of some genera, like *Clavilithes, Tibia, Rimella* which had persisted from Eocene to Miocene horizons. Some other Miocene genera are only feebly represented, e.g. *Nerita, Haliotis, Acanthina* but the Conidae and Pectinidae retain their importance. The assemblage as a whole has practically no relationship with the molluscan fauna of the contemporaneous Mekran Beds in Baluchistan, and oceanic connexion between the Mediterranean and Indian seas appears to have been completely severed as at the present day, probably as a result of the upheaval of the Persian mountain ranges.

A further reduction among autochthonous forms is seen in the succeeding Calabrian and Sicilian stages but *Nassa, Cancellaria, Terebra, Cerithium, Turritella, Chama,* and other genera persist in abundance. These survivors are accompanied by some significant newcomers like *Cyprina islandica* (Linn.), *Pecten maximus* (Linn.), *Chlamys islandicus* (Müller), *Mya truncata* Linn., *Neptunea sinistrorsa* Deshayes, *Buccinum undatum* Linn. These are regarded as boreal species that spread southwards as a result of colder climatic conditions which gradually extended over Europe during Pliocene time. Though some of the exiled Mediterranean genera are found again in raised beaches of postglacial age, others, like the single species of *Conus* are only feebly represented in Mediterranean waters.

Nearly half the molluscan species in the Miocene Beds of north Germany are autochthonous forms (Kautsky, 1925) and most of the remainder are closely related to the equivalent fauna in the Mediterranean area, especially to that of the Vienna Basin. Even so, Strombidae, Cypraeidae, Doliidae, Pectinidae are rare in the German Miocene faunas, though Muricidae, Columbellidae, and Nassidae are well represented. The northern genera *Astarte* and *Thyasira* are recorded as far south as Ottnang in Austria (Hornes, 1875). No Pliocene deposits are known in Germany except in the Island of Sylt where an early Pliocene fauna includes a species of *Conus* resembling the Miocene form *C. antediluvianus* together with *Corbulomya complanata.* The earliest Pliocene fauna in Belgium, belonging to the

Diestian stage, includes *Astarte omalii* Lajon., *Lucina borealis* (Linn.), *Isocardia cor*, *Ringicula succinea*. This fauna is represented in the Lenham Beds of south-east England (R. B. Newton, 1915); about half of the Lenham mollusca are referred to living species, the majority of which still live in British seas though a few are now confined to Mediterranean waters, e.g. *Cardium papillosum* Poli, *Pitar rudis* Poli, *Manupecten pes-felis* (Linn.), *Pectunculus pilosa* (Linn.), *Semicassis saburon* (Bruguière). The whole fauna has a marked relation to Miocene assemblages. The Casterlian Beds of Belgium and the Coralline Crag of east England (F. W. Harmer, 1914–25) have a marked preponderance of warm-water genera (*Sinum*, *Cassidaria*, *Ficus*, *Terebra*, *Cardita*, &c.) associated with a few boreal forms (e.g. *Buccinum*, *Liomesus*, *Trophon*, *Yoldia*, *Cyprina*, *Mya*). This fauna is represented far to the north in blocks of limestone dredged from the North Sea east of the Orkney Islands and described by R. B. Newton (1917). In the upper beds of the Coralline Crag, and the lower beds of the Red Crag (equivalent to the Scaldisian Beds of Belgium) a number of new forms appear, including *Neptunea contraria* (Linn.), *Dosinia exoleta* (Park.), *Searlesia costifer* (S. Wood), *Nucella lapillus* (Linn.), and *Corbulomya complanata* (J. Sow.). The higher beds of the Red Crag, not represented in Belgium except in borings, show a gradual change in the fauna, an increase in northern forms (species of *Buccinum*, *Neptunea*, *Sipho*, *Volutopsis*, *Macoma*, &c.) and a decrease in Mediterranean species. Derived fossils from the Red Crag occur in the glacial deposits of Aberdeenshire (Jamieson, 1882) and thus afford further evidence of a northern distribution. Some of the English Pliocene species, e.g. *Acila cobboldiae* (J. Sow.), *Mya truncata* Linn., *Searlesia alveolata* (J. Sow.), *Nucella tetragona* (J. de C. Sow.), *Trophon muricatus* Montague, are thought to have migrated from North Pacific waters (A. M. Davies, 1934) along with certain echinoids already noted (p. 645), perhaps by way of the North Atlantic Ocean.

In North America the Miocene faunas of the Caribbean area afford a convenient basis for discussion. The earliest (Aquitanian) deposits include the Anguilla Limestone of Anguilla Island, the Thomonde Beds of Haiti, and the Cercado Beds of San Domingo. The Bowden Marls of Jamaica, the Gurabo stage of San Domingo, and equivalent beds in Costa Rica are correlated with the Helvetian stage of Europe.

The Miocene faunas of the West Indies have often been compared with those of Europe, but the latter include certain genera which indicate that conditions of life were rather different. The West Indian fauna is purely tropical, but the Miocene faunas of the Mediterranean region, including Aquitanian, contain such temperate genera as *Mytilus*, *Astarte*, *Cardium*, *Macoma*, *Aporrhais* which are not found in the West Indian strata. Nevertheless, a large proportion of genera is common to the two regions, including *Leda*, *Arca*, *Plicatula*, *Lucina*, *Nemocardium*, *Martesia* among lamellibranchs, and *Distorsio*, *Bursa*, *Phos*, *Xancus*, *Murex*, *Oliva*, *Lyria*, *Cassis*,

Sconsia, Morum, Conus (several groups), *Ficus, Strombus, Cancellaria* among gastropods. This assemblage perhaps depends on the length of the free-swimming larval stage in the various genera.

A general survey of the faunas is given by W. P. Woodrirg (1925–8) in his extensive monograph on the molluscan fauna in the Bowden Beds of Jamaica, correlated with the Helvetian stage of Europe. The Bowden fauna contains about 600 molluscan species, among which members of the Turridae, Conidae, Mitridae, Columbellidae, Rissoinidae, Naticidae, Epitonidae, Trochidae, Fissurellidae, Arcidae, Pectinidae, Lucinidae, and Tellinidae are conspicuous. Nearly 90 per cent. of the Bowden genera are now living in West Indian waters, and many of them are already represented in the Anguilla Limestone, and in the Alum Bluff horizons of Florida which are equivalent to the Aquitanian stage of Europe. Woodring states that the majority of the Bowden species have developed autochthonously from Palaeogene ancestors, though records of Oligocene deposits are far from complete in the West Indies. Twenty genera are now extinct, representing about 6 per cent. of the fauna; among these are the peculiar strombid *Orthaulax* which persists from Oligocene horizons, and the naticids *Ampullina* and *Ampullinopsis*. About 5 per cent. of the Bowden genera are exotic, their modern representatives living in the Pacific or Indo-Pacific region. The presence in the Bowden Beds of such genera as the nuculid *Acila*, the venerid *Clementia*, the subgenera *Aphera* and *Naronia* of the genus *Cancellaria*, and the thaidid *Cymia*, to name only a few, doubtless indicates a temporary extension of their usual range. These genera disappeared from the West Indian faunas at or soon after the close of Miocene time, following the exclusion of Pacific waters from the Caribbean sea by the emergence of the Isthmus of Panama. As a result of this isolation the Pliocene and modern molluscan faunas of the West Indies have developed autochthonously, and are relatively impoverished in comparison with their Miocene predecessors.

Farther north, the Alum Bluff stage of Florida has yielded a Lower Miocene fauna of subtropical aspect which has been monographed by J. Gardner (1926–47). The lowest assemblage, the Chipola fauna, is much like the preceding Tampa fauna of Aquitanian age. It has more than 400 species, three-quarters of them peculiar to it. The gastropod element is predominant, the Turridae being the most conspicuous family, and there is an abundance of *Orthaulax gabbi* Dall which is taken as the index-fossil. Among lamellibranchs the Arcidae and Cardiidae are well represented but no species become dominant. Locally, a shallow-water phase is developed with about fifty species of mollusca among which large species of *Ostrea*, *Pecten*, and *Anomia* are the only common forms. The Chipola fauna is comparable with the Burdigalian fauna of the Mediterranean region in regard to the development of *Arca, Cardita, Venericardia, Lucina, Divaricella* which are conspicuous on both sides of the Atlantic Ocean, but *Astarte*, so well represented in south Europe, is not recorded in the Chipola fauna, and the venerid genera are different. The succeeding Oak Grove fauna has less than half the number of species; a number of tropical genera has disappeared, and species of *Busycon, Strombus, Turritella, Anadara, Pectunculus,* and *Chione* appear in abundance. The fall in temperature indicated by this assemblage is maintained in the Shoal River fauna next in succession in which the northern invaders, including *Astarte,* become more numerous, though relations with the West Indies are shown in the diversity of *Cancellaria, Conus,* and *Spondylus.* The molluscan fauna of the slightly later Chesapeake stage in Virginia and Maryland has been compared with that of Middle Miocene Beds in north Germany, but it lacks numerous warmwater gastropods which are present in the German fauna, though *Ecphora* is common to both. Such cool-water genera as *Mya, Trophon, Siphonalia, Neptunea* appear in the Maryland fauna, and a similar assemblage is contained in the later Duplin Marls of North Carolina. The Pliocene Beds of Calooshatchie, Florida, also have some Caribbean genera, together with species of *Astarte, Macoma, Mulinia, Mytilus, Panopaea, Busycon, Ocinebra, Scaphella* and other genera characteristic of cool water. It is evident that present day conditions of climate along the east coast of North America were initiated in early Pliocene time.

On the Pacific coast of North America the Miocene Series is represented by the Vaqueros and Temblor stages of California. A number of genera already established in Oligocene strata of the region continue into the Vaqueros stage, for example, *Chione, Crassatella, Dosinia, Mulinia, Bruclarkia*; others, like *Acila, Yoldia, Molopophorus, Searlesia* are unknown in the Vaqueros, but return in the Temblor stage. W. Loel and W. H. Corey (1932), however, state that the greater part of the Miocene fauna of California can only be derived from more southerly, tropical, sources. Some of the newcomers, such as *Clementia, Diplodonta, Spisula, Bursa,* and *Nassa* are recorded from Palaeogene strata in Peru, while others, like *Lyropecten* and the Californian variety of *Ostrea haitensis,* indicate Caribbean relations. Certain genera, *Conus, Ficus, Cancellaria, Nassa,* and *Thais,* for example, which are sparingly represented in the Vaqueros, show a decided increase in number of species in the Temblor stage, where they are joined by many new species of *Crepidula, Oliva, Olivella, Pyramidella,* and other genera. Thereafter the tropical genera gradually decline, and in the Etchegoin stage, of Pliocene date, the molluscan assemblage includes such species as *Cancellaria dalliana, C. simplex, Conus owenianus, Neverita recluziana, Polinices callosa, Trophon kermainus, Pectunculus septentrionales, Mulinia densata, Lyropecten crassicardo, Patinopecten oweni,* and approaches nearly to the existing north Pacific fauna.

In central America the Gatun fauna of the Panama Canal zone is closely related to the Bowden fauna of Jamaica and its correlatives. In Colombia it has the same Caribbean aspect but includes the Pacific nuculid genus *Acila.* Again, the Miocene faunas described by A. A. Olsson (1932) from north Peru show relations with those of the Caribbean area, but also certain differences. In the early Miocene Zorritos stage the genera *Columbella*, *Oliva*, *Mitra*, and the thaidids *Chorus* and *Cymia* are among survivors from Oligocene strata, but the Volutidae are absent from the records. Members of Lucinidae and Olividae are unknown in the Cardalitos stage of mid-Miocene date, and the later Tumbez stage is marked by the appearance of the mactrid *Mulinia*, and an increase in the Cancellaridae, perhaps indicating connexion with the Californian region.

The Coquimbo Beds of Chile, of late Miocene or early Pliocene age, situated in 27°–30° S. latitude, have a number of tropical genera, *Conus*, *Mitra*, *Murex*, *Distorsio*, *Pseudoliva*, *Ficus*, *Cassis*, *Lucina*, *Cardita*, *Cucullaea*, &c., but fewer than the Peruvian strata just mentioned. The thaidids *Acanthina* and *Concholepas* are almost restricted to East Pacific locations, and the genera *Mytilus Crepidula* and *Struthiolariella* are characteristic of cooler waters.

The Navidad Beds of Chile, and the Patagonian mollasse, which are probably of Miocene age, may be discussed together, for they have about sixty species in common. The faunas contain some subtropical genera, as, for example, *Phyllonotus*, *Terebra*, *Ficus*, *Dolium*, but no members of Cypraeidae, Cassidae, Conidae, Olividae, or Mitridae are recorded. Among lamellibranchs *Ostrea hatcheri* is the most distinctive form, and species of *Cardita* and *Crassatella* are abundant. Other molluscan genera invite comparison with Miocene faunas of Australia and New Zealand. Species of *Cucullaea*, *Limopsis*, *Chione*, *Proscaphella*, and *Verconella* suggest relations with Australian faunas, while connexions with New Zealand are indicated by *Malletia*, *Sigapatella*, *Crepidula*, and *Struthiolariella*. The last-named genus covers the South American shells which are closely related to *Struthiolaria* and its allies in New Zealand and the Southern Ocean.

In reviewing the evidence provided by Neozoic faunas along the Pacific coasts, J. W. Durham (1950) concludes that during early Eocene time the marine isotherm of 20° C. was north of 49° N. lat.; since then it has gradually moved southward until, in the Pliocene age, it approached its present position, and only minor oscillations, both northward and southward, are evident in Pleistocene time. He notes the similarity of Neozoic faunas from Ecuador, Peru, and East Indies, to the tropical faunas now living in adjacent seas, and also the tropical or subtropical aspect of early Neozoic faunas from south France and Italy, despite their geographical position well north of the present tropics. The Eocene tropical belt must have been much wider than its modern successor, a condition which is incompatible with the positions of the continents and poles postulated by the exponents of 'Continental Drift'. Hence it appears that during Neozoic time the continents and poles must have occupied approximately the same positions as they do at the present day.

LITERATURE

The chief sources of information concerning the late Neozoic fossils of Britain are the following:

'The Crag Mollusca', by S. V. Wood, *Mon. Pal. Soc.*, 1848–82.

'The Pliocene Mollusca of Great Britain', by F. W. Harmer, 2 vols., ibid., 1914–25. This work contains descriptions of the chief groups of Gastropoda.

'The Conchological Features of the Lenham Sandstones of Kent and their Stratigraphical Importance', by R. B. Newton, *Journ. Conch.*, vol. xv, pp. 56–84, 97–118, 137–49, 1916.

'The Post-Pliocene Non-marine Mollusca of the South of England', by A. S. Kennard and B. B. Woodward, *Proc. Geol. Assoc.*, vol. xvii, pp. 213–60, 1902. Those of Ireland, ibid., vol. xxviii, pp. 109–90, 1917.

'British Fossil Brachiopoda, Tertiary Species', by T. Davidson, *Mon. Pal. Soc.*, 1855; Supplement, ibid., 1874.

'The Tertiary Entomostraca of England', by T. R. Jones and C. D. Sherborn, ibid., 1857–89.

'The Fossil Polyzoa of the Crag', by G. Busk, ibid., 1859.

'The Foraminifera of the Crag', by T. R. Jones *et alia*, ibid., 1866–97.

The excellent discussion of *Tertiary Faunas* throughout the world, by A. M. Davies, 2 vols., London, 1934–5, has full bibliographies of the palaeontological and stratigraphical aspects. It is therefore only necessary here to add important works published since that date.

The Molluscan Fauna of the Alum Bluff Group of Florida, by J. Gardner, U.S. Geol. Surv., Prof. Paper No. 142 A–H, pp. 1–638, 1926–47, is illustrated by 62 plates; *Mollusca from the Miocene and Lower Pliocene of Virginia and North Carolina*, by the same author, ibid., 199 A–B, pp. 1–310, 1943–8, has 38 plates of illustrations. Certain Australian mollusca, Neozoic and living, are discussed in papers by B. C. Cotton, *Rec. South Austr. Mus.*, vols. viii and ix, 1949. J. Weir has described 'Additions to the Neogene Molluscan Faunas of Kenya' in *Mon. Geol. Dep. Hunterian Mus. Glasgow*, vol. v, pp. 65–81, 1938.

'Fossil Corals from Central America, Cuba and Porto Rico', with an account of the American Tertiary, Pleistocene and Recent Coral Reefs, by T. W. Vaughan, *U.S. Nat. Mus., Bull.*, vol. ciii, pp. 189–524, 1919, may be read in conjunction with *Corals from the Gulf of California and the North Pacific Coast of America*, by J. W. Durham, Geol. Soc. Amer., Mem. 20, 1947, and 'The Nomenclature and Type Species of Some Genera of Recent and Fossil Corals', by J. W. Wells, *Amer. Journ. Sci.*, ser. 5, vol. xxxi, pp. 97–134, 1936. H. L. Clark describes the composition and origin of the isolated *Echinoderm Fauna of Australia* in Carnegie Inst. Wash. Publ. 566, 1946.

'The Ecology of Modern Marine Organisms with Reference to Palaeogeography' is discussed by T. W. Vaughan in *Bull. Geol. Soc. Amer.*, vol. li, pp. 433–68, 1940, and J. W. Durham discusses the evidence concerning 'Cenozoic Marine Climates of the Pacific Coast' in ibid., vol. lxi, pp. 1243–64, 1950.

XVII

NEOZOIC MAMMALIAN FAUNAS

I. FORERUNNERS OF THE NEOZOIC MAMMALS

THE land faunas preserved in Neozoic rocks are remarkably different in general character from those of the Mesozoic systems. The great reptilian families of the Deinosauria, some of which persisted to late Cretaceous time, have vanished without leaving descendants. On the other hand, several orders of placental mammals are first found in early Eocene strata, and at higher horizons gradually become adapted for life in various habitats. They have evidently evolved from some of their Mesozoic predecessors, and, though the available records are very incomplete, we must review the early history of the mammals before we can begin to understand the significance of the geographical distribution of Neozoic forms. A revision of the Mesozoic mammals by G. G. Simpson (1928, 1929) embodies the modern interpretation of these rare fossils.

It is generally agreed, after the researches of R. Broom (1905, 1910, 1914) and others, that the early mammals are closely related to, or even derived from, the theromorph reptiles which are best known from their great development in the Karroo system of South Africa (see Chap. IX), but which are also widely distributed in Europe, Asia, and America. It seems significant that the upper (Triassic) part of the Karroo system has yielded an imperfect skull, known as *Tritylodon* (Owen, 1884), which Simpson refers to the Multituberculata. This is a specialized group of Allotheria, perhaps independently derived from the reptiles and having only the remotest relationship with any later mammals. According to Simpson 'they certainly are not marsupials, nor can they possibly be considered as placentals'. More information is given by a nearly complete skull, described as *Bienotherium* (Young, 1940), recently discovered in Yunnan, south China. It is closely allied to *Tritylodon*, and D. M. S. Watson (1942) considers that both genera are technically cynodont reptiles. To the Multituberculata are tentatively assigned the small teeth, of similar pattern to those of *Tritylodon*, recorded from the Rhaetic Bone-Bed of Wurtemburg (Plieninger, 1847) and England (Owen, 1871) under the name *Microlestes*. This name, however, is preoccupied in Coleoptera, and the teeth are now placed by Simpson (1928) in the genera *Thomasia* and *Microleptes*. Two other genera, *Dromatherium* and *Micronodon*, represented by small mandibles from Neotriassic rocks in North Carolina, U.S.A., were formerly considered as mammals (Osborn, 1886–7), but Simpson (1926) is convinced that they belong to cynodont reptiles.

The Multituberculata are represented in the Mesojurassic Stonesfield Slate of Oxfordshire, England, by jaws and teeth known as *Stereognathus ooliticus* (Charlesworth, 1854). According to Simpson (1928) this form appears to be a late survivor of the group already noted from the Rhaetic Beds. Other forms from the Stonesfield Slate (Goodrich, 1894), the earliest true mammals yet known, belong to two separate groups. *Amphilestes* and *Phascolotherium* are placed in the order Triconodonta which again are neither marsupials nor placentals, but probably represent 'an unsuccessful sidebranch of the Mammalia not related to any later forms' (Simpson, 1928). The remaining genus, *Amphitherium*, is referred to the Pantotheria, an order which Simpson believes to 'represent the ancestry of both marsupials and placentals without itself belonging to either group'. This assemblage from the Stonesfield Slate is the only mammalian fauna of Mesojurassic age so far known.

A more varied assemblage of mammals, first described by Owen (1871), is known from the Purbeck Beds of south England associated with dwarf crocodiles (Owen, 1879) and other fossils. The Multituberculata are represented by the genera *Plagiaulax*, *Ctenacodon*, *Bolodon*, and the triconodonts by *Triconodon* and *Trioracodon*. The pantotheres include the genera *Peramus*, *Peraiocynodon*, *Amblotherium*, *Kurtodon*, *Peraspalax*, *Phascolestes*, all more or less specialized in different ways. A fourth group, the Symmetrodonta, represented by *Spalacotherium* and *Peralestes* is remotely allied to the pantotheres, but tends away from the ancestry of marsupials or placentals while the pantotheres were tending towards it (Simpson, 1928). Certain of these genera are known from the slightly earlier Morrison Beds of Wyoming, U.S.A. (Simpson, 1926), namely *Trioracodon*, *Ctenacodon*, *Amblotherium*. Others (Simpson, 1928) seem to be closely allied; for example, the American *Tinodon* resembles the English *Peralestes* and *Spalacotherium*; the Purbeck *Phascolestes* and *Peraspalax* are comparable with *Dryolestes* and *Laolestes* from the Morrison Beds. But there are several forms, like the predaceous triconodonts *Priacodon*, *Aploconodon*, *Phascolodon*, the carnivorous symmetrodont *Amphidon*, the herbivorous multituberculate *Psalodon* and such presumably insectivorous pantotheres as *Paurodon*, *Archetrigon*, *Tathiodon*, *Kepolestes*, *Herpetairus*, *Melanodon*, *Malthacolestes*, *Miccylotyrans*, *Euthlastus*, *Pelecopsis* which are unknown in England. This compares with reptilian distribution (p. 561) and seems to indicate only limited communication between the two regions at this period of time.

Little is known of the Cretaceous mammal fauna of Europe. Several teeth have been found in the Wealden Beds of Kent, but the only example definitely identified is referred to *Loxaulax* (Simpson, 1928) related to the Purbeck *Plagiaulax*. The plagiaulacids seem to have given rise to the family Ptilodontidae, members of which are common in the Upper Cretaceous rocks of North America (Simpson, 1929). The Laramie (Lance) Beds of Dakota, Wyoming, &c. have yielded species of *Cimolomys*, *Meniscoëssus*, &c., and the family is represented in basal Eocene Beds by *Neoplagiaulax* in Europe, *Liotomus* and *Ptilodus* in North America. There are apparently no survivors of the Triconodontia and Symmetrodonta, and the Pantotheria are replaced by their descendants the Didelphidae and the Insectivora. The former group, comprising the earliest marsupials, are known from the Lance Beds by isolated teeth and fragmentary jaws of *Pediomys*, *Hyssodon*, *Delphodon*, *Ectoconodon*, *Thlaeodon*, *Alphodon*, *Cimolestes*, *Diapharodon*, and *Stagodon*. The same group is represented by *Eodelphys* in the Belly River Beds of Alberta. The earliest definite insectivores are represented by rare specimens of *Gypsonictops* in the Lance Beds, possibly also by *Telacodon* and *Batodon* whose affinities are uncertain (Simpson, 1927).

Several skulls of small mammals have been recovered from wind-blown sands of Neocretaceous age at Djadokhta, Mongolia (Simpson, 1925). They are associated with deinosaur remains which we have already noted (p. 574). The mammals so far described are the multituberculate *Djadokhtatherium*, related to *Ptilodus* and its allies, and the insectivores *Deltatheroides* and *Zalambdolestes* intermediate between primitive Insectivora and primitive Carnivora (Gregory and Simpson, 1926). Concerning the last two genera Simpson (1928) says, 'Though it is clear that they could have been derived from Pantotheria, even the very early forms from the Djadokhta formation of Mongolia are no longer pantotheres but definite insectivores.'

Thus only the Insectivora among Mammalian orders have so far been traced back to their Mesozoic ancestors, the Pantotheria, which flourished in Europe and North America if not also in Asia. But early Eocene families of the Insectivora seem to show affinities with rodents and primates. The creodonts likewise are said to share relations with the insectivores and are connected with the later carnivores by the development of carnassial teeth in many genera. The skeletal structure of still another group, known as the Condylarthra, shows certain creodont features and the two groups probably arose from a common ancestral stock. The Condylarthra undoubtedly gave rise to the primitive Ungulata from which perissodactyls, artiodactyls, and possibly subungulates arose as a result of adaptation to diverse habitats.

Fossil mammals, often known only by fragmentary specimens, are often difficult to classify and different opinions may be held by several competent observers. The relations of the chief genera and their range in time are stated by A. S. Woodward (1925) in volume iii of the Zittel-Eastman textbook. The history of Neozoic mammalian faunas is treated exhaustively in *The Age of Mammals* by H. F. Osborn (1910), but in the forty years that have elapsed many important discoveries have been made and amplification in the light of later literature is necessary. It is proposed, therefore, briefly to review the main features in the mammalian history of the several continents separately.

2. EUROPEAN FAUNAS

The earliest Neozoic land-fauna known in Europe is from a river deposit resting on marine beds of Landenian age at Cernays in the neighbourhood of Rheims (Gaudry, 1898). The mammals recorded include the last allotherian genus *Neoplagiaulax* which has also been recorded from basal Eocene beds in North America. There are several creodonts, some more primitive than others. For instance, *Dissacus* and *Hyaenodictis* are large, long-limbed forms in which the dentition shows no differentiation of carnassial teeth. The first-named genus is also recorded from slightly later Eocene beds in North America. *Arctocyon* represents a specialized branch of the creodont stock, similar to the bears in many respects, but not genetically related to them. Some of the Cernays fossils are classified tentatively as dilambdodont insectivores, but the relationships of the small *Adapisorex* and *Adapisoriculus* are entirely uncertain, and the genera are not known outside Europe. Also of *Plesiadapis* and *Protadapis* A. S. Woodward (1925) remarks that 'the shape of the jaw and the nature of the dentition indicate that we probably have to deal with the ancestral stock of rodents'. The condylarthran genus *Pleuraspidotherium* may possibly have relations with later European perissodactyls, while the small artiodactyl *Orthaspidotherium* seems to be the ancestor of *Anoplotherium* which is abundant in the Upper Eocene of Europe.

The genera *Plesiadapis*, *Protadapis*, and *Hyaenodictis* are also recorded from the slightly younger (Landenian) beds of Erquelines and Orsmael in Belgium (Dollo and Teilhard, 1924), and the 'Sparnacian stage' of northern France. But here they are accompanied by forms which are not known from the Cernays Beds. The newcomers include well-developed creodonts such as *Sinopa* and *Palaeonictis* in which the anterior molars function as carnassial teeth. True rodents occur in the simplicidentate genera *Paramys* and *Plesiarctomys*, the former being represented by several species in the Eocene of North America. Some perissodactyl ungulates are recorded, including *Lophiodon*, a forerunner of the tapirs, and *Propachynolophus*, an early member of the Equidae probably derived from a condylarthran stock. Another four-toed equine genus, *Hyracotherium* is represented by two species in the Lower Eocene of England (Owen, 1841). The artiodactyl *Protodichobune* is reported from the Lower Eocene of Epernay (Stehlen, 1909). The amblypod genus *Coryphodon*, widely distributed in Lower Eocene Beds of North America, is also found in northern France, Belgium, and England. In the Teredina Sands of Epernay, also referred to the Ypresian stage, there are further species of *Lophiodon* and a new hyracothere genus *Pachynolophus*. The source of the immigrants is unknown in most cases, but some, like *Coryphodon*, are more abundantly represented in North America. Their migration is probably to be explained by regression of the sea increasing the land areas, as for instance in the deposition of the estuarine and fluvatile Woolwich and Reading Beds above the marine Thanet Sands of south-east England. A similar regression from east Russia may have provided a land-route from Asia to Europe and so, as A. M. Davies (1934) suggests, some of the cryptogenetic forms may have originated in Asia.

Though marine strata of Middle Eocene age are transgressive in many parts of Europe, there are important areas where non-marine deposits are developed. The Bracklesham Beds of Hampshire, in England, the upper beds of the Calcaire Grossier in the Paris basin, and in the Dept. of Indre (central France) include freshwater deposits from which mammalian remains have been obtained. Planorbis Limestones, found at Buchsweiler in north Alsace, in Baden, Bavaria, Switzerland, and south France (Languedoc and Provence), have also yielded considerable mammalian assemblages. The Equidae provide the most important fossils; the lophiodonts continue from the Lower Eocene in the genera *Lophiodon* and *Chasmotherium* (Deperet, 1903; Stehlin, 1903), and several new genera (*Propalaeotherium*, *Paloplotherium*, *Palaeotherium* for example), represent a development of the autochthonous hyracotherine stock. With the perissodactyls we must also note the lower jaw named *Brachydiastematherium* (Boekh and Maty, 1876) from the Upper Eocene of Transylvania; it is the earliest European representative of the Titanotheridae, a family of large ungulates developed principally in North America, but Osborn (1929) regards it as a distinct European development from a common northern source. Artiodactyls are only sparsely represented in the lower Lutetian Beds; *Meniscodon* (Dichobunidae), *Dacrytherium* and *Catodontherium* (Anoplotheriidae) seem to continue stocks that are already present in the Cernays fauna. New elements appear, however, in higher beds of the Lutetian stage. *Cebochoerus* is the earliest member of the Suidae (pigs), and *Rhagatherium*, one of the earliest anthracotheres; these early members of the two families are closely allied, and may have arisen from a common condylarthran stock, possibly the Mioclaenidae. The creodonts are represented by the hyaenodont genera *Proviverra*, *Prorhizaena* and *Galethylax* which may have developed from an earlier European form such as *Sinopa*.

The mammalian fauna of Upper Eocene age, taken as a whole, differs only slightly from that of the Middle Eocene. The perissodactyls again form the most conspicuous element. The Bartonian fauna of Hordwell in Hampshire, and that of Languedoc are notable for the absence of lophiodonts, but the hyracotheres flourish in the genera *Paloplotherium*, *Anchilophus*, *Lophiotherium*, and *Palaeotherium*. The Paris gypsum deposits have yielded entire skeletons of *Palaeotherium* with the dimensions of a rhinoceros, while crushed skulls, isolated bones and teeth have been obtained from the lignitic marl of Debruge in Vaucluse, from the lower Phosphorites of Quercy, from the Bembridge Limestone of the Isle of Wight, and from the so-called Bohnerz deposits of the Swabian and Franconian Alps. The artiodactyls gradually become more numerous. The Suidae are represented by *Choeropotamus* in addition to *Cebochoerus* already established in the Middle Eocene. The Anthracotheres, *Haplobunodon* and *Rhagatherium* also continue from older horizons. The Anoplotheriids *Mixtotherium*, *Catodontherium*, *Dacrytherium*, and *Leptotheridium* already present in older beds are now accompanied in the Gypsum of Montmartre and the Quercy Phosphorites by the robust *Anoplotherium* and the smaller *Diplobune*. The slender-footed xiphodonts reach the end of their development with *Xiphodon gracile* Cuvier in the supragypseous marls of Paris, the Headon Beds of Hampshire and the Bohnerz of Switzerland. A closely allied family Coenotheriidae is represented for the first time in the Phosphorites of Quercy by the genus *Oxacron*, and the chevrotain *Gelocus* is also a newcomer. A fauna of the same age at Debruge (Vaucluse) includes the rodent *Theridomys* which is regarded as possibly ancestral to the hystricomorphs. Several hyaenodont creodonts appear for the first time, including *Hyaenodon*, *Pterodon*, *Quercytherium*, *Cynohyaenodon*, and are associated with various Miacidae such as *Miacis* and *Viverravus*. A member of the last-named family probably gave rise to the most primitive canid genus *Cynodictis* represented by several species in the Gypsum Beds of Paris, the Phosphorites of Quercy and the Lignites of Debruge. Some of the European deposits have yielded remains of primate genera such as *Adapis*, *Cryptopithecus*, *Microchoerus*, and *Necrolemur* which represent the early lemurs.

The dominant mammals of European Oligocene deposits are the anthracotheres. The genus *Ancodus* is especially abundant in the rich fauna of Ronzon, Haute Loire. At Hamstead, Isle of Wight, *Ancodus*, formerly recorded as *Hyopotamus* (Owen, 1848), is associated with *Anthracotherium*, species of which are also known from the sands of Fountainebleau, the limestone of Brie, the Phosphorites of Quercy, the asphalt deposits of Lobsann in Alsace, the Bohnerz of Swabia and the lignites of Bohemia and northern Italy. *Ancodus* is associated with the anoplothere *Diplobune* at Calaf near Barcelona, and other Eocene artiodactyls which range into the Oligocene are *Amphimeryx*, *Caenotherium*, *Plesiomeryx*, *Metriotherium*, *Dichobune*, and *Gelocus*. Newcomers include the giant pig *Elotherium* recorded from Ronzon, Lobsann, and the Quercy Phosphorites, forerunners of the deer *Bachitherium* and *Prodremotherium* also from the Phosphorites. The perissodactyls include the last of the hyracotheres, *Paloplotherium* and *Palaeotherium* but also primitive hornless rhinoceroses. Forms of the latter group are generally referred to the genus *Aceratherium*, but some species perhaps belong to *Ronzotherium* known principally from teeth found at Ronzon. The carnivores are represented by the creodont *Hyaenodon*, besides *Amphicyon*, *Cynodon* and *Cephalogale*, supposed ancestors of the bears, and numerous mustelines like *Palaeoprionodon*, *Stenoplesictes*, *Stenogale*, and *Plesictis*. The rodent *Theridomys* is widespread and is accompanied in the Phosphorites by *Trechomys*, *Protechimys*, *Cricetodon* and *Eomys*;

the first European lagomorph, *Titanomys*, is recorded from Middle Oligocene marls of the Auvergne. Thus while there are numerous survivors from the Eocene, the Oligocene mammalian fauna is distinguished by many newcomers some of which are probably immigrants.

Mammals of Lower Miocene age are contained in freshwater deposits that are intercalated with marine beds of the Aquitanian stage in south France. The fauna is best known at St. Gerard le Puy in the Limagne Valley, north-east of the French Central Plateau (Viret, 1929). It is also represented in various freshwater limestones of the Mainz basin, Bavaria, and Switzerland. It includes many species of genera that are already present in the underlying Oligocene deposits, and many of the new forms are merely advanced developments of autochthonous types. Among the perissodactyls there are the tapir *Palaeotapirus*, the hornless rhinoceros *Aceratherium* and its two-horned ally *Diceratherium*, and the peculiar *Chalicotherium* with claw-like terminal phalanges. The hornless artiodactyl genera *Amphitragulus* and *Dremotherium* seem to connect the Oligocene chevrotains (*Gelocus*, &c.) with the later antlered Cervidae. The anthracoceres are much reduced in importance; such genera as *Anthracotherium* and *Microbunodon* are no longer seen but *Brachyodus* is a new type. *Palaeochoerus* (Suidae) and *Caenotherium* survive from Oligocene horizons. Among carnivores also there are numerous surviving genera such as the canids *Amphicyon* and *Cephalogale*, the viverrid *Herpestes* and several mustelines (*Potamotherium, Amphictis*, &c.). The Oligocene genera *Cricetodon* and *Titanomys* are among the numerous rodents, and the Didelphyidae are recorded for the last time in Europe.

A slightly later fauna, of Burdigalian age, is well known from the neighbourhood of Orleans on the southern edge of the Paris basin (Mayet, 1908), from Simorre (Gers) in south-west France, from localities in Bavaria, Bohemia, and the Vienna basin. This fauna is remarkable chiefly for the first appearance in Europe of the Proboscidae. The most widespread form is *Tetrabelodon*, a genus with skull like that of the elephant but with the symphysis of the lower jaw much elongated. In the sands near Orleans it is associated with an allied form *Deinotherium* in which the mandibular symphysis is curved downward and carries a pair of backwardly directed tusks. These immigrants can only have come from Africa, as well as the anthropoid ape *Pliopithecus* which is recorded from south-west France, Switzerland, and Bavaria. A new perissodactyl *Anchitherium*, the first European member of the Equidae since the extinction of the Oligocene hyracotheres, is known from localities in France, south Germany, and Austria. A new rhinoceros, *Brachypotherium*, is recorded but *Aceratherium* and *Diceratherium* survive from older horizons. The anthracothere *Brachyodus*, widely represented by *B. onoideus* is another autochthonous development from Oligocene forms, as also are the carnivores *Amphicyon, Cephalogale*, and *Plesictis*.

The preceding faunas are generally restricted to a comparatively few localities, but higher assemblages of Middle Miocene age are widely spread over central Europe. Among the principal localities are Sansans, Gers (Filhol, 1891), La Grive St. Alban, Isère (Deperet, 1892), and St. Gaudens, Haute Garonne in south France, Steinheim in Wurtemburg, Genigen in Bavaria, Eibiswald in Styria, Mte. Bamboli in Tuscany (Major, 1873). All these faunas contain numerous forms that are closely related to their Lower Miocene predecessors in Europe.

The proboscideans *Tetrabelodon* and *Deinotherium* persist as well as *Anchitherium, Chalicotherium*, and various tapirs, rhinoceroses, carnivores, rodents, and insectivores. But there are also some interesting newcomers. Among Suidae, *Listriodon* (a descendant of *Dolichochoerus*), *Hyotherium* and *Sus*, derived from *Palaeochoerus*, show genetic connexion with earlier forms. Deer, like *Micromeryx* and *Dicrocerus*, provided with simple antlers, seem to be developments from the earlier hornless *Amphitragulus*. Along with Lower Miocene genera of Canidae, Viverridae, and Mustelidae there are *Trochictis* a forerunner of the badger, *Ursavus* the first true bear, *Machairodus*, the sabre-toothed tiger, which is preceded by the Oligocene *Eusmilus*, and the first species of the true *Felis*. The primate *Dryopithecus*, recorded from France and Spain, is perhaps a development of *Pliopithecus* and may be the common ancestor of the living orang and chimpanzee. *Oreopithecus* from Mt. Bamboli, Tuscany, is a forerunner of the European baboon now existing on the Rock of Gibraltar and in North Africa.

The mammalian fauna next in succession, that of the Pontian stage in eastern Europe, is even more widespread. It is especially well developed at Pikermi in Greece (Gaudry, 1862–7) and the Isle of Samos (Major, 1894). Remains of it are found in Macedonia (Schlosser, 1921), at various localities in the Black Sea provinces (M. Pavlow, 1914; Borissiak, 1915; Khomenko, 1914; Alexijeiv, 1916), in Turkey (Malik and Nafiz, 1913), in Roumania (Athanasin, 1907 ; and Simionescu, 1930), in Hungary (Petho,1885 ; Kormos, 1911 ; Kadic and Kretzoi, 1927), and Sicily (Seguenza, 1907). It is known as far west as Concud in the province of Teruel, Spain (A. S. Woodward, 1903), and the neighbourhood of Lisbon. In France some of the mammals are recorded from Concuron and Mont Leberon in Vaucluse (Gaudry, 1873) and from the neighbourhood of Lyons. Such remains are scarce farther north; in south Germany they are only reported from Eppelsheim near Worms (Kaup, 1832–9) and certain localities in the Swabian Alps (Schlosser, 1902). The Pontian stage is often referred to the Lower Pliocene, but the balance of evidence seems to favour an Upper Miocene age (A. M. Davies, 1934).

A considerable part of the fauna consists of forms already established at subjacent horizons or of genera autochthonously derived from these types. There are in addition some important elements which must be regarded as immigrants from lands outside Europe. It is convenient to take the fauna of Pikermi as a standard for discussion. Of Proboscidea, the autochthonous genera *Tetrabelodon* and *Deinotherium* are associated with the first *Mastodon*, but this differs from *Tetrabelodon* only in the shortened mandibular symphysis and atrophied lower incisors. The hyracoid *Pliohyrax*, however, has no European predecessors but belongs to a family characteristic of the Oligocene fauna of Egypt (Andrews, 1906, 1907). The perissodactyls are represented in part by already established genera of tapirs (*Tapirus*), rhinoceroses (*Aceratherium*, *Brachypotherium*) and chalicotheres (*Chalicotherium*). But new forms are exemplified by the two-horned rhinoceros *Atelodus* and the three-toed horse *Hipparion*; these probably migrated from Asia. The last-named genus is so widespread and abundantly preserved that the mammalian assemblage is generally known as the Hipparion fauna. The artiodactyl element at Pikermi is enriched by the presence of numerous giraffes and antelopes. The former comprise species of *Helladotherium*, *Samotherium*, *Palaeotragus*, and *Giraffa*, genera that are entirely absent from western Europe. The antelopes are represented by *Palaeoryx*, *Protoryx*, and *Protragelaphus*, in addition to *Palaeoreas*, *Tragocerus*, and *Gazella*, which are known also in central and western Europe. The latter group may be autochthonous descendants of earlier forms like *Dremotherium*, but the first three genera are usually regarded as Asian immigrants. Among carnivores (Pilgrim, 1931) the widely distributed *Hyaena* and the viverrid *Ictitherium* appear in Europe for the first time, and are also regarded as immigrants from the east, but such indigenous types as *Machairodus*, *Pseudoaelurus*, and *Felis* persist from older beds. The primitive bear *Hyaenarctos* may be a development from the indigenous cyonodonts. There are few rodents, as might be expected from the torrential origin of the deposits (A. S. Woodward, 1901); the chief forms are the beavers *Castor* and *Dipoides* and the lagomorph *Lepus*, all of which are found fossil in Europe and north America, the last two also in Asia. The Old World baboons are represented abundantly by *Mesopithecus* which is also known from Macedonia, Hungary, south Russia, and Persia.

The Lower Pliocene fauna (Deperet, 1893) is best known on the Central Plateau of France; at Perpignan and Montpellier it is found in deposits that rest conformably on marine beds of Lower Pliocene age, and at Trevoux it succeeds the Pontian fauna in a series of freshwater deposits. Members of the same assemblage have been described from the Red Crag of eastern England (Osborn, 1922). As a whole the fauna is connected with the Pontian fauna by the persistence of *Hipparion*, *Palaeoryx*, *Mastodon*, and other herbivores, of *Machairodus*, *Hyaenarctos*, and other carnivores, while the genera *Dolichopithecus*, *Semnopithecus*, and *Macacus* continue the development of cynopithecine primates. Several persisting species, especially of *Machairodus*, *Hyaena*, *Ursus*, *Mastodon*, *Tapirus*, and *Gazella*, serve to connect this fauna with younger assemblages. A curious case of discontinuous distribution is shown by the raccoon *Parailurus*, recorded from the

Pliocene lignite of Transylvania and the Red Crag of England, for all the other members of the family are North American, with the exception of *Ailurus* living in the Himalayan region.

The Upper Pliocene mammalian fauna is typically developed in France at Perrier in the Auvergne, and at Chagny in the Laon Valley. Many of the most characteristic species are known from the Val d'Arno in Tuscany (Major, 1885) and the Norwich Crag of England (Osborn, 1922); some are recorded from Transylvania and Roumania. The fauna as a whole bears a strong resemblance to its Lower Pliocene predecessor, for most of the deer and antelopes, pigs and tapirs, rhinoceroses and proboscideans, rodents and carnivores, belong to genera already present in Lower Pliocene deposits. But a more modern aspect is introduced by the association of *Elephas meridionalis* with *Mastodon arvernensis*, the replacement of *Hipparion gracile* by *Equus stenonis*, and by the first appearance of *Bos*, though Major (1885) contends that *Bos etruscus* Falconer from Val d'Arno may belong to the more primitive *Leptobos*. Haug (1911) takes the arrival of these new types, *Elephas*, *Equus*, and *Bos* (including *Bison*) as marking the beginning of Pleistocene time, and Hopwood (1935) supports the suggestion. But, as A. M. Davies (1934) has shown that general acceptance would seriously reduce the value of the Pliocene series as a stratigraphical unit, the current classification is followed here.

The earliest Pleistocene fauna in Britain is that of the Cromer Forest Bed on the coast of Norfolk. The fauna is described by E. T. Newton (1882) and analysed by H. F. Osborn (1922). Many forms of the preceding Pliocene Crags are unknown in the Forest Bed, notably the genera *Mastodon*, *Hipparion*, *Tapirus*, *Gazella*, *Antilope*, *Ailurus*, and *Hyaenarctos*. But some Pliocene forms survive, as for instance, *Elephas meridionalis*, *Elephas antiquus*, *Rhinoceros etruscus*, *Equus stenonis*, *Cervus carnutorum*, *Hyaena striata*, *Hyaena antiqua*. These survivals are species that occur also in the Pleistocene deposits of south France and Italy. They are accompanied in the Cromer Forest Bed by other forms that now make their first appearance in Britain, e.g. *Elephas primigenius*, *Rhinoceros megarhinus*, *Equus caballus*, *Hippopotamus amphibius*, *Sus scrofa*, *Bison bonasus*, *Caprovis savini*, *Ovibos moschatus*, *Alces latifrons*, *Cervus capreolus*, *Cervus elaphus*, *Ursus spelaeus*, *Felis spelaea*, and various rodents. Similar early Pleistocene faunas with strong Pliocene element are described from Mauer near Heidelberg (Soergel, 1912), Mosbach, &c.

Many of these mammals are not seen in the younger Pleistocene cave-deposits and valley-gravels of Britain. During the prevalence of glacial conditions the fauna consisted of species that are nowaday confined to northern latitudes, together with some forms that are now extinct. The later Pleistocene mammals of Britain are therefore usually grouped according to their modern distribution with regard to habitat (Osborn, 1910; W. B. Wright, 1937). Among the extinct forms we may note first the elephants.

Elephas meridionalis is characteristic of Upper Pliocene deposits throughout central and southern Europe (e.g. Auvergne and Val d'Arno) and is recorded from interglacial deposits in the Alps. *Elephas antiquus* occurs in late Pliocene and early Pleistocene deposits of Britain (K. S. Sandford, 1925) and Europe generally (Deperet and Mayet, 1923). According to Vaufry (1929) the dwarf elephants *E. mnaidriensis*, *E. melitensis*, and *E. falconeri* in the older Pleistocene deposits of Sicily, Malta, Cyprus, Crete, and Sardinia, are all races of *E. antiquus*. The third form, *E. primigenius*, commonly known as the mammoth, is widely distributed in Pleistocene deposits throughout the northern parts of Europe and Asia. Complete carcases found embedded in the frozen ground of Siberia show that the body was covered with long hair. The mammoth is said to have lived on into postglacial time; certainly it was a contemporary of Magdalenian man, as engravings on bone implements bear witness. The successive appearance of these three elephants provides a rough means of subdividing the Pleistocene deposits in western Europe (Hopwood, 1935, 1940).

The Pleistocene rhinoceroses of north-west Europe are considered by Wright (1937) to fall into four species. *Rhinoceros etruscus* Falconer (= *R. merckii* of various authors) is very abundant in the Pliocene deposits of Val d'Arno, north Italy, and is the typical rhinoceros of the Norfolk Forest Bed; it is also known from France and Spain. *Rhinoceros megarhinus* also is widely distributed in Pliocene and Pleistocene deposits of France, Germany, and England. *Rhinoceros hemitoechus* Falconer (= *R. leptorhinus* Owen) is known from a number of British caves and from the brick-earths of the Thames Valley. The woolly rhinoceros (*R. tichorhinus* of Cuvier) often associated with *Elephas primigenius*, is recorded in Pleistocene deposits from the Arctic regions, throughout Russia, Germany, and France to the Alps and Pyrenees. All these forms are distinct from the living species of Africa and Asia.

A few of the European Pleistocene mammals are now restricted to warmer climates. The hippopotamus, now confined to the rivers and lakes of Africa, is widely distributed in the Pleistocene deposits of Europe. Reynolds (1922) mentions fifty-three localities in Britain where the hippopotamus has been recorded from river deposits and twelve from caves or fissures; the majority are in the Thames Valley and the eastern counties, but the range extends westwards to Torquay and North Wales, and northwards to Overton in Yorkshire. The most notable localities in Europe are Val d'Arno (north Italy), and Sicily where enormous masses of bones were accumulated in cave-deposits near Palermo (Falconer, 1860). Early writers regarded the fossil form as a distinct species but the view is now generally held that it cannot be separated from the living species *Hippopotamus amphibius*. We may note also the dwarf hippopotami from the Mediterranean islands, for example *H. pentlandi* in Sicily and *H. minutus* in Malta. There are also two prominent carnivores whose remains are found in the Pleistocene cave-deposits of Europe and whose successors now live in warmer countries. Bones of the lion are recorded from many localities in central and southern Europe, including caves in Britain as far north as Yorkshire (Dawkins and Sanford, 1866). Some writers regard the cave-dwelling form as a distinct species, *Felis spelaea*, but it is more generally regarded as a variety of the living *Felis leo*. The latter is now confined to Africa (excepting Egypt and the Cape Province) and districts bordering the Persian Gulf in Asia. Similarly the hyaena in Pleistocene time ranged over continental Europe from Spain and Sicily to Poland, and its remains have been recorded from many caves in England and Wales (Reynolds, 1902), but apparently, like the cave-lion, it did not reach Scotland or Ireland. Notwithstanding the difference in habits between the cave-dwellers and the living species, there is no definite distinction (except perhaps in size) between the skeletons of *Hyaena spelaea* and *H. crocuta*. The latter lives only in Africa south of the Sahara.

Living representatives of a third group of Pleistocene mammals are characteristic of the steppes of eastern Europe and western Asia. One of the most significant of these is *Saiga tartarica* Pallas (the Saiga antelope), remains of which are recorded from Pleistocene deposits in Bohemia, Belgium, England, south France, and Portugal (Reynolds, 1939). The Saiga now inhabits the steppes of south Russia and south-west Siberia, migrating between the east Urals and Turkestan. The Asiatic wild ass (*Equus hemionus*) of the Kirghiz and Aralo-Caspian steppes is recorded from the Pleistocene deposits of Germany, and the wild horse (*E. caballus ferus*) is also abundant in Pleistocene deposits (including the loess) of middle Europe. Several rodents are known from Pleistocene deposits far west of their present habitation in the steppes. The jerboa (*Alactaga jaculus*), for example, is recorded from the Pleistocene of Germany but is now strictly limited to the steppe country of European Russia and adjacent parts of Asia. Species of *Spermophilus* (susliks), *Arctomys* (marmots), *Cricetus* (hamsters) and other genera in Middle European deposits testify to similar wanderings during Pleistocene time.

The three groups so far considered are associated in European Pleistocene deposits with a number of mammals now characteristic of the Arctic tundras. The most conspicuous of these is the reindeer *Rangifer tarandus* (Linn.) whose Pleistocene range extends far into central Europe, along the northern front of the Alps and Pyrenees into Spain (Reynolds, 1938). The remains of reindeer are commonly associated with those of the mammoth and woolly rhinoceros. With the return of milder climatic conditions in post-glacial time, the reindeer gradually reverted to its present circumpolar distribution. The musk-ox (*Ovibos moschatus*), also widespread in the Pleistocene deposits of central Europe as far south as the Dordogne in France, is now restricted to the Arctic regions of Canada and Greenland (Reynolds, 1934). Among the smaller mammals, the arctic fox (*Canis lagopus*), the lemmings (*Lemmus, Dicrostonyx*) (Hinton, 1926) and others show comparable changes in habitation. The glutton (*Gulo luscus*) and the elk (*Alces machlis*), not so characteristic of actual tundra, but having a decidedly northern range, are also widespread in Pleistocene deposits of central and western Europe, the latter persisting into post-glacial deposits.

With the amelioration of climate in post-glacial time, most of these northern and eastern invaders gradually withdrew to their present locations, leaving a few stragglers mingled with the indigenous types in the impoverished faunas of the present day. The activities of mankind have undoubtedly increased the impoverishment, but on the other hand, domestication and breeding has added some variety to the fauna, especially among the Bovidae (Reynolds, 1939).

3. AFRICAN MAMMALIAN FAUNAS

The earliest Neozoic mammals known in Africa come from Upper Eocene beds in the Fayûm district of Egypt (C. W. Andrews, 1906). This horizon has yielded only two genera, *Moeritherium* and *Barytherium*, both primitive proboscideans. The former is a tapir-like animal with the second incisors in both jaws enlarged, the upper pair forming strong tusks, and the molars have two transverse ridges, each composed of two cusps, and a small hind lobe or talon. In the Lower Oligocene beds of the same district (Andrews, 1906), *Moeritherium* is accompanied by *Palaeomastodon* in which the proboscidean characters are more pronounced. The same beds have yielded the great *Arsinoitherium* with a horned skull somewhat like that of a rhinoceros in size and form, but the hind limb resembles that of the elephant. There are also several hyracoids, including *Geniohyus, Bunohyrax, Mixohyrax, Saghatherium*, and *Megalohyrax*, which display considerable variety in form and size. Though their ancestry is still uncertain, the animals so far mentioned, and also the aquatic sirenians associated with them, seem to be indigenous to Africa. On the other hand, some genera in the same rocks probably originated in Europe. These include the anthracothere *Ancodus*, the creodonts *Pterodon* and *Apterodon*, the rodents *Phiomys* and *Metaphiomys*, also primitive anthropoid mammals, *Parapithecus* and *Moeripithecus* which seem to retain prosimian features in the jaws and teeth.

Miocene beds in Moghara, Egypt (Fourtau, 1920) have yielded a small number of mammals, including the hornless rhinoceros *Aceratherium*, and the anthracothere *Brachyodus* along with the proboscidean *Tetrabelodon* and the anthropoids *Prohylobatus* and *Dryopithecus*, an assemblage closely similar to contemporary European faunas. Two species of the distinctive proboscidean *Deinotherium* are described by C. W. Andrews (1911) from Lower Miocene beds near Karungu, east of Lake Victoria where they are associated (Andrews, 1914) with remains of the hyracoid *Myohyrax*, the anthracothere *Merycops*, tragulids resembling

Prodremotherium and *Dorcatherium*, a rodent *Paraphiomys*, and a feline carnivore referred to *Pseudaelurus*. *Deinotherium* is also reported (Haug, 1911) from a locality north of Lake Rudolph along with other genera which Hopwood (1929) has assigned to a much younger fauna. A collection from Kenya, mentioned (but not described) by Hopwood (1929) contains similar tragulids and others resembling *Bachitherium* as well as several rodents. This fauna also contains unnamed creodonts, and the same group is represented in an assemblage from Namaqualand, south-west Africa (Stromer, 1926) by the new genus *Metapterodon* which is stated to resemble the earlier *Pterodon* and *Apterodon* of Egypt. A large part of this fauna, however, consists of rodents which include the lagomorph *Austrolagomys*. The hyracoids are represented by *Myohyrax* and *Protypotheroides*, pigs by *Diamantohyus* and a form near to the genus *Propalaeochoerus*, the antelopes by *Propalaeoryx*, and a form compared with the European genus *Strogulognathus*. It is clear that the Miocene mammals of Africa, so far as they are known, belong largely to immigrant families, only the proboscideans and hyracoids being indigenous. Two special features, however, are worthy of note. One is the early appearance of *Deinotherium*, but this may be due to autochthonous development of the Oligocene stock already established in Egypt. The other is the persistence of creodonts, for these animals are not known in Europe above the Oligocene stage; Hopwood (1929) considers there is no reason why they should not persist in a 'backwater' such as Africa where competition would be limited.

Later faunas, from late Pliocene and Pleistocene deposits in Algeria, have been described by Pomel (1893–8) and partially revised by Joleaud (1917). In a summary of these assemblages, Osborn (1915) cites elephants, rhinoceroses, zebras, asses, giraffes, wild cattle, buffalo, antelopes, gazelles, gnus, elands, hippopotami, wart-hogs, lions, and hyaenas. In central Africa some of these genera, namely *Rhinoceros*, *Giraffa*, *Buffelus*, *Hippopotamus*, *Phacochoerus*, together with *Hipparion* are recorded by Haug (1911) from the neighbourhood of Lake Rudolph, and referred by Hopwood (1929) to a Pleistocene age. In 1923 C. W. Andrews recorded a phalangeal bone of a chalicothere from Pleistocene deposits near Lake Albert in Uganda, and later Hopwood (1926) described remains of *Elephas*, *Rhinoceros*, *Equus*, *Hipparion*, *Sus*, *Hylochoerus*, *Hippopotamus* and several antelopes from the same beds. Andrews (1916) and Hopwood (1926) have also recorded *Hippopotamus*, *Metridiochoerus*, *Phacochoerus*, *Bos*, *Elephas*, and *Simopithecus* from Homa Mountain east of Lake Victoria. Deposits of Middle Pleistocene age at Olduvai, Tanganyika Territory, have yielded a large quantity of bones described by Reck (1914, 1926, 1928, 1937), Dietrich (1916, 1925, 1928, 1937), Hopwood (1937), Schwarz (1937); the assemblage includes *Hipparion*, *Equus*, *Elephas*, *Rhinoceros*, *Hippopotamus*, numerous antelopes, giraffes, buffalo, and pigs. *Hippopotamus* and *Mastodon* are reported (Hopwood, 1927) from deposits of similar age near Lake

Nyasa. In Rhodesia, workings at the Broken Hill Mine have yielded many of the genera already mentioned (Mennell and Chubb, 1907) associated with stone implements. Fraas (1907) has described teeth of zebra, hippopotamus, *Mastodon* and *Damaliscus* from the Vaal River gravels, and Haughton (1921) has added teeth of *Elephas* (*Loxodon*) and *Griquatherium* (a large giraffoid) to the records from that deposit. W. B. Scott (1907) has described new species of *Elephas, Rhinoceros, Hippopotamus, Bubalis,* and two unnamed antelopes from Pleistocene deposits on the coast of Zululand.

These records prove that a varied fauna of uniform character is widespread in the Pleistocene deposits of Africa so far explored. But the weight of available evidence tends to show that only the proboscideans and the hyracoids are truly indigenous to the continent. All the other groups appear to be immigrants. Thus, the Equidae as a group originated outside Africa, but the zebra may have developed autochthonously within the family. The rhinoceroses have a wide distribution in earlier deposits of Europe and elsewhere. The hippopotamus is first known in Pliocene deposits of Asia, and appears to have entered Africa at a later date. The cavicorn ruminants show a great development in the Upper Miocene rocks of south Europe, and appeared there much earlier; some of them may have migrated directly into Africa during Oligocene time, as indicated by the Miocene *Propalaeoryx* of Namaqualand. The origin of the suid genera *Phacochoerus, Hylochoerus,* and *Metridiochoerus* is unknown, but they probably developed from an immigrant stock, for in Europe Suidae are known as far back as Middle Eocene deposits. A note-worthy feature of these African Pleistocene faunas is the persistence of *Hipparion*, which is not known in Eurasia and North America above the Pliocene stage.

In other respects the Pleistocene fauna of Africa contrasts strongly with the contemporary fauna of Europe, for Africa was not affected directly by glacial conditions, and northern species are absent. The climate, however, was probably cooler and wetter than now, and a varied fauna flourished even in the north of the continent. At the end of the European Ice Age the climate gradually became drier, the Saharan region was transformed into a desert and many members of the fauna became restricted to the region farther south, leaving only the present impoverished remnant in North Africa. The modern fauna of central Africa includes many bovine genera known from the Siwalik Series of India; these are evidently immigrants from Asia. There are also some interesting survivors of ancient stocks; for instance, *Okapia* is a primitive hornless giraffid allied to the Miocene genus *Palaeotragus*, the water chevrotain (*Hyaemoschus*) is closely related to the Miocene genus *Dorcatherium* and the aardvack (*Orycteropus*) is a development from the Miocene *Palaeorycteropus*.

The existing fauna of Madagascar is worthy of special comment because it does not resemble the present fauna of Africa, also because it includes a curious mixture of ancient and modern types. Among the older types we may note a peculiar group of insectivores, the Centetidae, which is now restricted to the island, with the exception of one genus *Solenodon* living in Cuba, and closely related to *Potamogale* of West Africa. According to A. S. Woodward (1925) these can only be considered as related to certain insectivores from the Oligocene Series of North America. W. D. Matthew (1915) explains their presence in Madagascar as the result of a casual dispersal, perhaps before Neozoic time. There are numerous lemurs, some of considerable size; these appear to have radiated from a single group (W. K. Gregory, 1916) into a number of peculiar forms, two of which (now extinct) simulated the ungulates and the higher apes in several significant features. A. S. Woodward (1925) considers that this group can only be derived from the Adapidae of the European Eocene fauna. The peculiar carnivore *Cryptoprocta* has similarities with the Miocene genus *Proailurus* which Filhol (1881) regards as the ancestor of the Felidae, and the viverrids are allied to *Cynodictis*, also a European genus of Oligocene age. A dwarf form of *Hippopotamus* is a late entrant from the African continent, and the only other ungulate *Potamochoerus* (the river-hog) was possibly introduced by man. As we have already noted, there is evidence that Madagascar has been separated from the mainland at least since Permian time. The peculiarities of the living Madagascan fauna, therefore, are quite likely due to sporadic settlement of a few species at different times as suggested by Arldt (1907) and Matthew (1915).

4. ASIATIC MAMMALIAN FAUNAS

Present knowledge of early Neozoic mammals in Asia is largely the result of investigation by members of the central Asiatic Expedition organized by the American Museum of Natural History during the years 1921–5. The geological results have been summarized by Berkey and Morris (1927) and the mammalian fossils have been described by Granger, Matthew, Osborn, Simpson, Colbert, and others cited below. We have already noticed (p. 659) certain mammals of Neocretaceous age discovered in the Gobi Desert, Mongolia. Other localities in the same region have yielded a number of Neozoic faunas. The earliest of these, from the Gashato Beds (Matthew and Granger, 1925) is of the same general type as the European Cernays fauna. A small multituberculate, *Prionessus*, seems to be related to the *Meniscoëssus* recorded from the Laramie Beds of North America, but the other genera cannot be traced back to their Mesozoic antecedents. Rodents are represented by *Baenomys*, and possibly also by *Eurymylus*; the latter, however, may be related to the modern Tupaiidae (tree-shrews). There is a creodont, *Hyracolestes*, and the form named *Sarcodon* may be another creodont, or possibly a carnivorous marsupial. *Phenacolophus* is probably a condylarth. The most abundant, and most surprising, form is *Palaeostylops*, a primitive notoungulate, which, according to Simpson (1937), is a possible ancestor of *Arctostylops* from the Lower Eocene of

Wyoming. The same group is represented in the Eocene of South America by *Notostylops*, but this form is said to be on a different line of descent. *Prodinoceras*, a forerunner of the Eocene uintatheres, is closely allied to *Probathyopsis* from the Clark Fork Beds of Wyoming, U.S.A. Though the Asiatic fossils are similar in a general way to the early Neozoic forms of Europe and North America, many of them have peculiarities of their own, and Simpson (1937) regards them as isolated side-branches from the common ancestral stock, possibly specialized for their own particular habitat.

Several localities have yielded faunas of Eocene age, probably equivalent to those of the Bridger Beds (Upper Eocene) of North America. A considerable assemblage of carnivores, perissodactyls and artiodactyls is recorded from Irdin Manha (Matthew and Granger, 1925 E), and another from slightly later beds at Shara Murun (Matthew and Granger, 1925 D) has some genera in common with the former. There are several creodonts; the more primitive forms, without carnassial teeth, include the large *Andrewsarchus* with a skull some 3 feet long (Osborn, 1924) and *Hapalodectes* which is also recorded from early Neozoic beds in North America. The more specialized hyaenodonts are represented at Irdin Manha by *Paracynohyaenodon*, *Hyaenodon*, *Propterodon*, and at Shara Murun by *Pterodon*; other species of the last three genera are known from Upper Eocene Beds in Europe. Species of the widely distributed genus *Miacis* are also in the collection from Irdin Manha. It is the development of the Ungulata, however, that provides the best means of correlation with other regions. Among perissodactyls, the lophiodont tapirs are represented at Irdin Manha by *Teleolophus*, *Lophialetes*, and *Desmatotherium*, the last genus being recorded from Eocene beds in North America. The group is also represented in a slightly earlier deposit at Arshanto by the small *Schlösseria* and in the Shara Murun Beds by a species of *Deperetella*. The lophiodonts have some affinity with the Rhinocerotidae, and *Caenolophus* (with species from both Irdin Manha and Shara Murun) is an early member of the hyracodont rhinoceroses, a group previously known only from North American deposits. Another hyracodont, *Teilhardia*, from a red clay of similar age at Tukkum (Matthew and Granger, 1926) may be the ancestor of the Oligocene form *Ardynia*. An allied group, the amynodonts, is also represented at Shara Murun. The records from Irdin Manha include remains of the chalicotheres *Eomoropus* and *Grangeria* (Colbert, 1934) and it seems likely that this family had its origin in Asia. An important link with the North American Eocene fauna is shown in the presence of the titanotheres *Protitanotherium*, *Dolichorhinus*, *Telmatotherium*, and *Manteoceras*, the first two genera being recorded by different species at Irdin Manha and Shara Murun (Osborn, 1929). A further affinity with American forms is indicated by certain artiodactyl genera; these are *Gobiohyus* an early peccary, and *Archaeomeryx*, a hypertragulid which is said to be more directly ancestral to higher ruminants than any form known in the Eocene faunas of

America or Europe (Matthew, 1928). Another genus, *Eudinoceras* (Osborn, 1924) is an early amblypod, not very different from the Lower Eocene *Coryphodon* known from Europe as well as North America.

The absence of Equidae and anthracotheres from the Mongolian collection is noteworthy, because both groups are present in European Upper Eocene strata, and both are well developed in later deposits of North America and Europe. Moreover, anthracotheres are present in some quantity in the Pondaung Sandstone of Burma (Pilgrim and Cotter, 1916). This deposit lies below the marine Yaw stage which is referred to the Upper Eocene. The anthracothere genera *Anthracohyus*, *Anthracothema*, and *Anthracokeryx* are considered to be the most primitive types so far known (Pilgrim, 1928) and Burma is thought to be near the original centre of differentiation of this important family. Other elements of the fauna (Pilgrim, 1925) are lophiodont tapirs (*Indolophus*, *Chasmotherium*), an amynodont rhinoceros (*Metamynodon*) and a titanothere (*Sivatitanops*); these groups are represented in the Eocene beds of Mongolia, but by different genera.

The Lower Oligocene deposits of Ardyn Obo, Mongolia, rest directly on granite and gneiss of the ancient rock-floor (Berkey and Morris, 1927). The mammalian fauna (Matthew and Granger, 1923, 1925) is broadly comparable with that of Shara Murun but is probably younger. The widely distributed creodont *Hyaenodon* persists from the Upper Eocene and is associated with the oxyaenid *Ardynictes* (Matthew and Granger, 1925 B). Among the rodents is *Desmatolagus*, an early lagomorph and possibly an ancestral type. The tapirs are represented by *Paracolodon* and *Colodon*, the latter genus typified by a species from Oligocene beds in North America. The hyracodont rhinoceros *Araynia* is probably derived from the earlier *Teilhardia*, and the amynodonts (Osborn, 1924) are represented by *Cadurcotherium*, the type of which comes from the Oligocene Phosphorites of Europe. The titanotheres *Brontops* and *Menodus* show an advance on the earlier forms of Shara Murun (Osborn, 1929). We may note in passing the peculiar *Embolotherium* from the slightly later beds of Ulan Gochu. The skull of this genus has a single bony horn which is broadly expanded at the distal end. Osborn considers this form to represent a purely Asiatic development from unknown ancestors which probably lived farther north in central Asia. The peculiar chalicotheres, with two genera in earlier beds, are recorded (Matthew and Granger, 1925 c) in a species of *Schizotherium* from Ardyn Obo, the genus having been established (Gaudry, 1877) on fragmentary remains from the Quercy Phosphorites of France. The artiodactyl remains are referred (Matthew and Granger, 1925 c) to local species of the tragulid genera *Lophiomeryx* and *Miomeryx*, the former being represented also in the Oligocene of Europe. The anthracotheres are again almost lacking, only one doubtful tooth being recorded. A noteworthy feature of the fauna as a whole is the increased affinity to European assemblages as compared with the earlier faunas.

Oligocene strata along the Hsanda Gol at Loh, Mongolia (Berkey and Morris, 1927) have yielded a fauna in which species of carnivores, insectivores and rodents are most numerous. The carnivores (Matthew and Granger, 1924) include the specialized creodont *Hyaenodon*, together with several forms of early mustelids (*Bunaelurus, Palaeoprionodon*) and somewhat doubtful canids (*Cynodictis, Cynodon*). The form referred to *Viverravus* is probably one of the ancestral Miacidae. The ungulates are less prominent. The only perissodactyls recorded are the long-necked rhinoceros *Baluchitherium* and another form doubtfully referred to *Epiceratherium*. The artiodactyl *Eumeryx* is described as possibly a direct ancestor of the deer. Worn fragments of *Baluchitherium* are also recorded (Matthew and Granger, 1923) from a deposit of gravel at the top of the Houldjin bluff, south of Iren Dabasu, associated with similarly worn fragments of *Cadurcotherium*, *Caenopus*, *Entalodon* and indeterminate carnivores. Again, a species of *Baluchitherium* is associated with a mastodon *Serridentinus* in Miocene strata at Loh (Osborn, 1924 G). In the slightly later beds at Tung Gur *Serridentinus* is associated with another proboscidean *Platybelodon* (Osborn, 1936), the three-toed horse *Anchitherium*, the chalicothere *Macrotherium* (Colbert, 1934), various artiodactyls, such as the suid *Listriodon*, the cervids *Dicrocerus* and *Stephanocemas*, the giraffid *Palaeotragus* (Colbert, 1936), the bovid *Oioceros*, and many carnivores (including *Hemicyon*, *Amphicyon*, *Machairodus*, and the early hyaenid *Crocuta*). Among these forms *Anchitherium gobiense* (Colbert, 1939) is a large species comparable with the European *A. aurelianense*; the two species of *Macrotherium* are related to forms from Grive St. Alban (France) and India; the Mongolian *Listriodon* is close to European and Indian species of Miocene age (Colbert, 1934); the species of *Oioceros* are 'distinctly more primitive than the Pontian species' (Pilgrim, 1934); and *Crocuta tungurensis* is close to the Indian Miocene species *C. carnifex* which is ancestral to *C. eximia* of the Pikermi Beds. Hence the Tung Gur fauna of Mongolia compares well with Middle and Upper Miocene faunas in Europe and India, though it includes no specimens of the plains-dwelling *Hipparion*.

Baluchitherium, one of the largest of land animals, is named after Baluchistan (C. F. Cooper, 1923) where it is found in the early Miocene Gaj Series of the Bugti Hills. It is associated there with a considerable number of other ungulate genera, a few proboscideans, and carnivores (Pilgrim, 1912). The chief perissodactyls are rhinoceroses ascribed to the genera *Cadurcotherium*, *Diceratherium*, *Aceratherium*, *Teleoceras*, and *Paraceratherium*. A few worn chalicothere teeth form the basis of the genus *Phyllotillon*, and another may belong to *Schizotherium* already noted from Europe and Mongolia. Among artiodactyls there is a large representation of anthracotheres (F. C. Cooper, 1924) comprising species of *Anthracotherium, Brachyodus* and several other genera (e.g. *Hyoboops*, *Hemimeryx*) unknown outside India, and based on rather fragmentary remains. *Brachyodus* is known also from Oligocene beds in Egypt associated with the proboscidean *Palaeomastodon*. In the Bugti Beds it is accompanied by *Hemimastodon* which is only an advanced *Palaeomastodon* and evidently an immigrant from Africa along with *Deinotherium*. The artiodactyls include *Palaeochoerus* and *Bugtitherium* which represent the Suidae, *Prodremotherium* (an early tragulid) and *Progiraffa*, a primitive giraffe apparently derived from a tragulid ancestor (Pilgrim, 1911). The carnivores, *Pterodon*, *Amphicyon*, and *Cephalogale* appear to be allied to European Oligocene types. The slightly later Muree Beds in their lower part have also yielded *Anthracotherium*, *Brachyodus*, and *Teleoceras*. In Japan the Hiramaki Beds of Eastern Mino contain the last-named genus in association with *Anchitherium* and *Tetrabelodon*.

Later Neozoic faunas in northern India are contained in the Siwalik Series which extends for about 1,500 miles from the Salt Range eastwards along the southern foothills of the Himalayas. These flood-plain deposits are several thousands of feet in thickness and Pilgrim (1913) has recognized in them a number of distinct assemblages comparable with Upper Miocene and Pliocene faunas of Europe. Colbert (1935) and Lewis (1937) have discussed the correlation with American deposits and have expressed disagreement with certain of Pilgrim's conclusions. Consequently, at the present time we can only indicate the stratigraphical position of the Siwalik faunas in a general way.

The earliest assemblage, that of the Kamlial Beds, includes *Deinotherium* and the four-tusked elephant *Tetrabelodon*, the rhinoceroses *Aceratherium*, *Teleoceras*, the chalicothere *Phyllotillon*, the anthracotheres *Brachyodus*, *Hyoboops*, *Hemimeryx*, the cervuline *Propalaeomeryx*, the suid *Hyotherium* and the carnivore *Amphicyon*. Many of these genera are present in the succeeding Chinji horizon of the Salt Range where they are accompanied by more specialized pigs such as *Listriodon*, *Potamochoerus*, and *Sus*, by the robust three-toed horse *Hipparion*, by antelopes, by the last creodont (*Dissopsalis*) and by the hyaenid *Crocuta*. The fauna of Nagri (Salt Range) and Perim Island is not very different in composition, but it includes the remains of a large giraffe (*Bramatherium* or *Hydraspitherium*) and the traguline *Dorcatherium*. These faunas are comparable generally with Middle Miocene assemblages of Europe.

The fauna of the Dhok Pathan Beds is the richest of all the Siwalik faunas. It is correlated by Pilgrim (1913) with the Pontian (Upper Miocene) fauna of Pikermi in Greece with which it has many genera and some species in common. The three-toed horse *Hipparion* is especially abundant. The proboscideans *Tetrabelodon* and *Deinotherium* persist and are joined by *Mastodon* and *Stegodon* which mark an advance towards the modern elephants. There are several types of rhinoceroses, including species of *Aceratherium*, *Teleoceras*, and the true *Rhinoceros*. Among artiodactyls the persisting Suidae *Sus* and *Listriodon* are accompanied by the specialized anthracothere *Merycopotamus*; this last form is said to be a possible ancestor of *Hippopotamus* which now appears for the first time. Besides many deer and numerous antelopes (Pilgrim, 1937) there are giraffes (*Giraffa*) with their strange allies *Hydaspitherium* and *Vishnutherium*. A large assemblage of carnivores includes the persisting canids *Amphicyon* and *Hyaenarctos*, related to Miocene types of Europe. The felids comprise machairodonts like *Paramachairodus* and *Aeluropsis*, besides the more typical *Felis*. There are also several types of hyaenas, some primitive forms (*Ictitherium*) resembling earlier viverrids, others similar to the modern *Crocuta*. It is evident that the Dhok Pathan fauna bears much resemblance to the Pontian fauna of Pikermi and Samos.

In the Tatrot fauna, of Lower Pliocene age, several genera persist from earlier beds including *Hipparion*, *Merycopotamus* and *Hippopotamus*, the last being represented in abundance, and *Stegodon* predominates over *Mastodon*. There is a sudden influx of bovine genera such as *Amphibos*, *Hemibos*, *Leptobos*, while *Sivatherium* is a bizarre development of the large giraffids. The succeeding Pinjor fauna is marked by the first of the true elephants, *Elephas planifrons*, and is therefore comparable with the Upper Pliocene fauna of western Europe. This elephant is associated in the Pinjor beds with *Stegodon*, *Equus*, *Rhinoceros*, *Leptobos*, *Hemibos*, antelopes, *Merycopotamus*, *Hippopotamus*, and other genera. An assemblage from Ceylon (Deraniyagala, 1937, 1942) including *Elephas*, *Hippopotamus*, *Merycopotamus* and deer, may belong to this horizon. The highest Siwalik fauna, found in the Boulder Conglomerate, is characterized by the association of *Bos* and *Equus* with species of *Elephas*. Another newcomer is *Camelus sivalensis*, representing an immigration from the east. Survivors or developments from previous faunas include *Stegodon ganesa* (the last of its genus), *Dicerorhinus* and *Rhinoceros*, *Hippopotamus*, *Sivatherium*, *Hyaena*, and *Felis*. This assemblage is assigned to the Lower Pleistocene by Pilgrim (1913) and Colbert (1935). A fauna of approximately the same age and containing remains of *Stegodon*, *Elephas*, *Rhinoceros*, antelope, giraffe, *Bos*, *Hippopotamus*, *Hipparion* and *Felis* is recorded from Palestine (Gardner and Bate, 1937). An assemblage from the ancient alluvium of the Narbada Valley, referred to a Middle Pleistocene age, includes *Elephas antiquus* and *Equus namadicus* together with extinct species of *Rhinoceros*, *Hippopotamus*, *Cervus*, *Bos*, *Bubalis*, *Sus*, and *Ursus*. The fauna of Trinil, Java, which has become so famous by the occurrence of *Pithecanthropus*, is a similar assemblage of extinct species (Selenka and Blanckenhorn, 1911). During Pleistocene time many of the Siwalik mammals, especially the great carnivores, various elephants, *Sivatherium* and other highly specialized ungulates, became extinct, and the modern fauna of the Indian region, though still impressive, is a mere remnant of the mighty host that formerly roamed over southern Asia.

We have space to mention only a few of the modern survivors in order to emphasize the diversity of their palaeontological histories. The Indian elephant (*Elephas indicus*) belongs to a family whose earliest known member occurs in the Upper Eocene deposits of Egypt; later members migrated to the Indian region by Miocene time after which the genus *Elephas* developed numerous species in the Siwalik area. The Indian elephant differs considerably from the African form (*Loxodon africanus*) in the structure of the molar teeth, ears, trunk, and other features, and has a different ancestry. The one-horned rhinoceros, *Rhinoceros indicus*, now living in south India, compares closely with species in the Siwalik Beds, as also does the smaller *Rhinoceros sondaicus* which ranges from Bengal through Burma, and the Malay Peninsula to Sumatra and Java. The Sumatran rhinoceros, *Ceratorhinus sumatrensis*, belongs to a line which has been traced back to *C. sansaniensis* and *C. simorrensis* of the French Miocene deposits. These forms are all generically distinct from the two-horned *Atelodus bicornis* of the African continent. The tapir (*Tapirus*) now has three species living in Malaya, Sumatra, and Borneo, and two other forms in Central and South America. This discontinuity of distribution is explained by extinction in intermediate regions of a family that was formerly widespread over the lands of the northern hemisphere. The Camelidae are now restricted to Asia and North Africa. Apart from the South American llamas, only two species, the one-humped Arabian camel (*Camelus dromedarius*) and the two-humped Bactrian camel (*C. bactrianus*), remain of a family that evolved mainly in North America, but became extinct there during Pleistocene time while the Asiatic immigrants survived. The muntjacs (*Cervulus*) comprise a group of small deer living in southern and eastern Asia and adjacent islands; their ancestry is unknown, but the cervulines may be allied to *Dremotherium* which is known from European Miocene deposits. The allied musk-deer (*Moschus* and *Hydropotes*) inhabit the highlands of central Asia, and the first genus is recorded from the Siwalik deposits of north India. The chevrotain (*Tragulus*), living in south India and Malaya, has skeletal characters very similar to those of *Dorcatherium* from the Miocene and Pliocene of Europe and India. Several carnivores are doubtless indigenous, but the Himalayan Panda (*Ailurus*) is an isolated genus of the Procyonidae; other living members of the family are restricted to America where the earliest form is *Phlaocyon* of Miocene age. The palaeontological history of the group in Asia is unknown but the genus *Parailurus* is recorded from Pliocene deposits in Transylvania and England. These examples must suffice to show that the Asiatic fauna contains diverse elements, some indigenous, others immigrant from Africa and North America at various periods, and some of these developed autochthonously after their arrival in Asia.

Elsewhere in Asia the records are less complete, but the Upper Miocene Hipparion fauna is widely distributed. A considerable number of animals has been described from Maragha in north-west Persia by Lydekker (1886), Rodler and Weithofer (1890), Gunther (1899–1900), Mecquenem (1924–5), many species being common to this locality and Pikermi. Orlov (1936, 1939) has recorded a Hipparion fauna from Pavlovdar in west Siberia which includes giraffes, deer, antelopes, carnivora, along with numerous *Hipparion*, rhinoceroses and beavers. Many elements of the same fauna are known from northern China and Mongolia, including species of *Hipparion* (Sefve, 1927), the rhinoceroses *Chilotherium, Diceratherium, Dicerorhinus, Sinotherium* (Ringstrom, 1924), the proboscideans *Tetrabelodon* and *Mastodon* (Hopwood, 1935), the giraffes *Palaeotragus, Samotherium,* and *Honanotherium* (Bohlin, 1926), *Antilospira* (Teilhard and Young, 1931) and such carnivores as *Hyaenarctos, Hyaena, Machairodus, Indarctos, Ictitherium* (Zdansky, 1924). The lower part of the Irrawaddy Series in Burma, containing *Hipparion* and *Aceratherium* probably belongs to the same horizon. Evidently, the Hipparion fauna is very uniform at widely separated localities between eastern Asia and central Europe, though naturally there are some variations. For instance, the carnivores *Eomellivora* and *Plesiogulo* of China are missing from the corresponding fauna in Europe, and the Felidae are represented in China by certain large types also unknown in Europe. On the other hand, the European *Helladotherium* together with the Indian *Hydaspitherium* and *Bramatherium* are lacking in China, though *Palaeotragus* and *Samotherium* are common to both regions. These discrepancies may be due to the accidents of collecting, to differences in habitat, or possibly to the distance separating Europe and China.

Records of Pliocene faunas are also wide-spread. The upper part of the Irrawaddy Series in Burma, with species of *Mastodon, Stegodon, Hippopotamus,* and *Bos*, is comparable with the Tatrot beds of the Upper Siwalik Series. Farther north, the extensive Pliocene and early Pleistocene deposits of north China have yielded important faunas. In Central Shansi, *Mastodon* and *Stegodon* survive from Pontian into Pliocene Beds (Licent and Trassaert, 1935) with *Chilotherium, Rhinoceros, Gazella, Hipparion,* and a new antelope, *Antilospira*. The Upper Pliocene fauna of Nihowan (Teilhard and Piveteau, 1930) contains species of *Equus, Hipparion, Camelus, Rusa, Cervus, Gazella, Bison,* &c. Pleistocene deposits in northern Manchuria, enclosing remains of *Elephas, Bos, Bubalis, Spirocerus, Gazella, Cervus, Camelus, Rhinoceros, Equus, Hyaena, Canis,* indicate an extensive northern range for these genera. The Pleistocene faunas of north Siberia (Obrutschev, 1926) are similar to those of the glaciated areas in Europe. Immense numbers of mammoth tusks representing the extinct *Elephas primigenius* have been exported as a source of ivory from these northern latitudes, and other extinct forms include *Rhinoceros tichorhinus* and *Elasmotherium sibiricum*, the latter possibly derived from the earlier Chinese genus *Sinotherium*. These are associated with living species of *Rangifer, Alces, Saiga, Bison, Ovibos, Equus, Gulo, Canis, Ursus, Felis*, and smaller mammals. The precise ancestry of these northern forms is obscure, but the mammoth and woolly rhinoceros, possibly also *Elasmotherium*, most likely represent developments from stocks of Indian origin which migrated northwards. *Saiga* and also the central Asiatic chiru (*Pantholops*), are regarded by Teilhard and Young (1931) as the survivors of the true Asiatic stock of antelopes, represented in the Pontian deposits of China by *Pachygazella*, and independent of western Asiatic and African types. Kusnezov (1938) believes that the present composition of the Arctic fauna is determined not so much by climatic conditions as by nutritional interrelations of organisms, especially of the plant life which is mainly dependent on the seasonal variation of daylight.

5. NEOZOIC MAMMALIA OF NORTH AMERICA

The earliest Neozoic fauna so far discovered comes from the Puerco Beds of the San Juan basin in New Mexico (Cope, 1888). This horizon succeeds the Neocretaceous Lance Beds, and the two faunas have little or nothing in common. The Puerco fauna (Matthew, 1937) contains a few Multituberculata such as *Catopsalis*, *Taeniolabis* (often cited as *Polymastodon*) and *Eucosmodon*, along with the didelphid marsupial *Thylacodon*. The genera *Wortmania* and *Onychodictis* represent the herbivorous taeniodonts, a purely North American group usually classified with the edentates, though they differ from these in having enamel-covered teeth. There are several creodonts, *Carcinodon*, *Toxolophus*, *Oxyclaenus*, *Protogonodon*, *Eoconodon*, all belonging to the Arctocyonidae, a group of omnivorous forms with sharp canine but no carnassial teeth. Matthew regards this group in the broad sense as the central stock from which other creodont families are derived, and probably the Condylarthra also. This last group includes the genera *Ectoconus*, *Periptychus*, *Conacodon*, *Anisonchus*, *Hemithlaeus*, all assigned to the family Periptychidae comprising small animals in which creodont and ungulate characters are combined. This Puerco fauna has no known equivalent elsewhere and we can only make a comparison with the fauna of the overlying beds.

The Torrejon Beds are separated (Wortman, 1897) from the original Puerco Beds because they contain a distinctive vertebrate fauna; this also has been revised by W. D. Matthew (1937). The Multituberculates show little change, but the Insectivores are more varied, being represented by *Prodiacodon*, *Acmeodon*, *Palaeoryctes*, *Mixodectes*, and *Pentacodon*. The taeniodonts *Conoryctes* and *Psittacotherium* show some degree of specialization in the dentition. Among creodonts, all the known arctocyonid genera (*Chriacus*, *Tricentes*, *Triisodon*, *Mixoclaenus*, *Deltatherium*, *Goniacodon*, *Claenodon*, and *Neoclaenodon*) are new; the Mesonychidae (with blunt hoof-like extremities) are represented by *Dissacus* and *Microclaenodon*; the Miacidae by *Didymictis*. The last family comprises small carnivores equipped with carnassial teeth, and some of its members are possible ancestors of the dogs and bears. The condylarth family Periptychidae already established in the Puerco Beds, continues with the genera *Peripty-*

chus, Anisonchus and the new form *Haploconus*. These are accompanied by the more specialized *Tetraclaenodon*, the earliest member of the Phenaco-dontidae, and the Mioclaenid genera *Mioclaenus* and *Ellipsodon*. Though abundantly represented in North America the two families Periptychidae and Phenacodontidae are unknown in European deposits. Another animal with condylarth affinities is *Pantolambda* which, having short limbs and spreading feet, is regarded by Osborn (1910) and Matthew (1937) as ancestral to the massive Amblypoda of Eocene horizons.

The succeeding Tiffany Beds were formerly included in the Wasatch Beds, but Granger (1917) shows that they are separated by an erosional un-conformity, and the mammalian fauna resembles that of the Torrejon rather than the Wasatch Beds. Indeed, the Tiffany fauna, as recently de-scribed by G. G. Simpson (1935) is essentially a continuation of the Torre-jon assemblage. The dwindling Multituberculata are represented only by *Ectypodus* and *Ptilodus*, the didelphid marsupials by *Peradectes*. The Insec-tivores include members of the Leptictidae (*Leptacodon, Xenacodon*) and Plesiadapidae (*Plesiadapis*), the latter having a highly specialized dentition similar to that of rodents (A. S. Woodward, 1925). The genera *Labidolemur, Carpodaptes, Navajovius* are early primates showing affinity to lemurs. The persisting creodont *Chriacus* and a possible *Dissacus* are accompanied by a new form *Thryptacodon*. The condylarth *Periptychus* also persists but is overshadowed by its derivative *Phenacodus*. Many of the Tiffany genera are present in the slightly later fauna of the Fort Union (Clark Fork) Beds of Montana and Wyoming (Granger, 1914), and a similar assemblage is de-scribed (L. S. Russell, 1929) from the Paskapoo Beds of Alberta, Canada.

Some Tiffany genera, *Plesiadapis, Dissacus* for instance, are recorded also in the Cernays fauna of Europe, and others seem to be closely related, for example, *Chriacus* to *Arctocyonides, Neoclaenodon* to *Arctocyon, Ptilodus* to *Neoplagiaulax*. But the forms in common are not the most abundant elements in the faunas, and we have already noted the absence of peripty-chids and phenacodonts from Europe. It seems therefore that communica-tion between the two faunas was indirect or remote.

American authors (e.g. Matthew, 1928; Simpson, 1937) emphasize the fact that these early Neozoic faunas contain no representatives of modern mammalian orders, but consist essentially of specialized members of more ancient orders that did not survive the Eocene age. They consider that this important faunal distinction justifies the institution of a major subdivision of the Neozoic strata to rank with the accepted stages of Lyell. They have therefore adopted the term 'Palaeocene' originally used by Schimper (1874) for basal Eocene floras. European geologists do not readily endorse this view, perhaps because equivalent strata are only sparsely preserved outside North America. Only the Cernays horizon of France, the Gashato Beds of Mongolia and the Rio Chico Beds of Patagonia are equivalent to the Tiffany Beds of North America. Moreover, the term 'Palaeocene' is unfortunate in itself, for it is often confused by students with the term 'Palaeogene' which is used in Europe as a system for the old established Eocene and Oligocene Series.

Eocene mammalian faunas are extensively developed in North America, the earliest of them in the Wasatch Beds of Wyoming, Utah, and New Mexico. The Wasatch fauna (Cope, 1874–7; Matthew and Granger, 1915–18) as at present known, comprises some forty-six genera of which only five are recorded from older beds. Four of these are creodonts, a group which has a varied representation in the fauna. The persisting *Chriacus* and *Thryptacodon*, together with the new *Anacodon* represent the Arctocyonidae. The Mesonychidae have one survivor, *Dissacus*, and two new genera *Pachyaena* and *Haplodectes*. The Miacidae, also with one Palaeocene survivor (*Didymictis*) develop a number of new forms, including *Miacis*, *Viverravus*, *Uintacyon*, *Vassacyon*, *Vulpavus*. Two new families Oxyaenidae and Hyaenodontidae make their appearance, the hyaenodont *Sinopa* being recorded also from western Europe. The condylarths are much reduced in number, the principal form being *Phenacodus* which continues up from the Tiffany Beds, while the new genus *Meniscotherium* may be related to the *Pleuraspidotherium* of the European Cernays fauna. The robust species of *Coryphodon* which represent the Amblypoda are likely descendants of the smaller *Pantolambda* of the Torrejon Beds and are distinguished by the elongation of their canine teeth; *Coryphodon* is also represented in the Lower Eocene of western Europe. An early development of perissodactyls is seen in the first tapirids *Heptodon*, *Systemodon*, and the first Equid *Eohippus*; the last-named form has tetradactyl extremities and is comparable with the European *Hyracotherium* of similar age. *Lambdotherium* and *Eotitanops* from the slightly later Wind River Beds are the oldest known genera of titanotheres; they are small, slender-limbed forms, apparently immigrants, for they have no recognized ancestors in earlier beds (Osborn, 1929). *Diacodexus*, *Wasatchia*, and *Bunophorus* are primitive artiodactyls in the Wasatch fauna. Another noteworthy genus is *Arctostylops* which is the only North American member of the Notoungulata. It is possible that this form is derived from the Mongolian *Palaeostylops*, but contemporary notoungulates are also known from South America. So it may be that both *Arctostylops* and *Palaeostylops* indicate migration from, rather than to, South America (Simpson, 1937). But, as with other forms, such as the reputed armadillo *Palaeanodon*, the data so far available are too fragmentary for any positive conclusion with regard to place of origin. It seems clear, however, that the Palaeocene faunas of North America contain few forms that can be regarded as ancestors of the new elements that make up the bulk of the Wasatch fauna. The latter can only be explained as immigrants though their place of origin is still unknown.

The succeeding Bridger Beds of Wyoming contain a fauna made famous by the researches of Leidy (1869), Marsh (1877), and Cope (1885). The creodont family Arctocyonidae seems to be absent, but several genera of the Miacidae survive from Wasatch horizons, and are joined by species of *Oodictis* and *Palaearctonyx*; the hyaenodont *Tritemnodon* accompanies the persisting *Sinopa*; the Oxyaenidae are represented by new genera (*Patriofelis*, *Machairoides*, *Thinocyon*, and the Mesonychidae by *Mesonyx*, *Synoplotherium*, and *Harpalogestes*. The most conspicuous insectivores are *Tillotherium* and *Anchippodus* of the family Tillodontidae, unusually large forms with powerful incisor teeth; smaller members of the order include *Pantolestes* and *Phenacops* which appear to be autochthonous developments in their respective families. The condylarths have now given place entirely to their ungulate successors. The most abundant perissodactyls are species of the delicate lophiodont tapir *Helaletes* which are accompanied by the light-limbed hyracodont rhinoceros *Hyrachyus*. The Equidae are represented by *Orohippus* which hardly differs in skeletal characters from its predecessor *Eohippus*, but its premolar teeth show a tendency to assume molar form. The broadheaded, hornless titanothere *Palaeosyops* has left abundant remains, but the allied *Limnohyops* is comparatively rare; the skull of *Telmatotherium* is longer, with tusk-like canine teeth, that of *Manteoceras* (abundant in Upper Bridger horizons) shows slight bony prominences above the orbits. The dichobunid artiodactyls, already established in the Wasatch Beds, continue in the genera *Homacodon*, *Microsus*, *Sarcolemur*, *Helohyus*, and *Lophiohyus*. The Lower Eocene *Coryphodon* is replaced by *Uintatherium* with tusk-like canine teeth and bony protuberances on the skull; these large amblypods are particularly abundant in the Upper Bridger Beds (Marsh, 1884). Among the minor elements of the fauna we may note the lemuroid primates *Anaptomorphus Washakia* and *Omomys*, with the rodents *Sciuravus* and *Paramys*, the last-named being recorded also from the Lower Eocene of France. The genus *Metacheiromys* succeeds the Lower Eocene *Palaeanodon* as a representative of the edentates (Simpson 1931).

The Uinta Beds of Utah, and equivalent horizons in Wyoming, contain a vertebrate fauna (Scott and Osborn, 1890) apparently developed from that of the Bridger Beds. Similar assemblages are recognized in the Duchesne Beds of the Great Basin, the Middle Sespé Beds of south California (Stock, 1932) and in Upper Eocene strata of Saskatchewan (Russell and Wickenden, 1933). The creodonts are represented by the large specialized oxyaenid *Limnocyon* and giant mesonychids like *Harpalogestes* and *Mesonyx*. These are accompanied by the first true canids (*Procyonodictis*) which probably evolved from certain miacid creodonts. The great amblypod ungulates are represented by the four-horned *Eobasileus*, the last member of the order. Among perissodactyls the titanotheres *Telmatherium* and *Manteoceras* persist; they are associated with *Protitanotherium*, a relative of *Manteoceras* showing more prominent horn-development, with *Mesatirhinus* and its derivative *Dolichorhinus* which have very narrow skulls. The hyracodont rhinoceros (*Hyrachyus*) of the Bridger Beds is replaced by *Triplopus*, and the amynodont group appears for the first time in the genus *Amynodon*. The tapirid *Isectolophus* survives from older beds, but the equids are now represented by *Epihippus*, which is still four-toed, but all the premolar teeth except the first have acquired the form of molars. A noteworthy newcomer is *Eomoropus*, an early chalicothere; the same genus (with others) appears in the Irdin Manha Beds (Upper Eocene) of Mongolia. There is an increase in variety of the artiodactyls and we may note especially the appearance of two new families. *Bunomeryx* is sometimes placed (Osborn, 1910) with the Bridger genus *Homacodon* in the family Dichobunidae, but A. S. Woodward (1925) classifies it with the Uinta forms *Leptotragulus* and *Protylopus* as a primitive member of the Camelidae. *Camelomeryx* may be related to these forms, but it seems to foreshadow the peculiar *Protoceras* of later horizons. Another purely North American family is the Agriochoeridae, now represented for the first time in *Protoreodon* and *Protagriochoerus*, which may perhaps be offshoots of the same root-stock as the Camelidae.

The next fauna is referred to the Oligocene Series, and we may pause to consider the relations of the American Wasatch, Bridger, and Uinta faunas to European assemblages. The Wasatch fauna has a few genera in common with the Lower Eocene fauna of Europe, notably the creodont *Dissacus* and the ungulate *Coryphodon*. Other forms are closely related or have reached a comparable stage of development, as for instance the American *Eohippus* and the European *Hyracotherium*. It may be significant that the types shared by the two regions are not the most abundant forms. Again, the European pleuraspidotheres appear earlier than the related meniscotheres of America and the phenacodonts are much earlier in America than in Europe. In spite of the difference in generic lists from the two regions, Matthew (1928) states that the North American and European faunas start from a common source and are almost identical at the beginning of Eocene time. Thereafter they become progressively divergent and eventually (in the Upper Eocene) quite distinct, each evolving on more or less parallel lines, but specializing with regard to distinct families. Thus, while the European *Hyracotherium* develops into *Palaeotherium*, *Paloplotherium*, and other genera without importance in the phylogeny of the horses, the American equids are represented progressively by *Eohippus*, *Prohippus*, and *Epihippus*, apparently a direct line of equine development which is carried further in later deposits. Europe has its tragulids which are unknown in America, and the American uintatheres, hypertragulids, and agriochoerids do not appear in Europe. Hence the two continents seem to have been without direct land-connexion throughout Eocene time. But Mongolian Eocene faunas show affinities to both, for they include representatives of chalicotheres, titanotheres, hypertragulids, and tragulids, besides groups which have long been known in both European and American Eocene deposits. Hence we may infer that Asia provided a migration route between Europe and North America; it may even have been a centre of dispersal from which some northern groups of animals migrated westwards to Europe and eastwards to North America.

The Oligocene Series is represented in Nebraska, Dakota, Montana, Colorado, and Wyoming by the White River Beds. The fauna of this stage (Scott and Osborn, 1887–90) is largely derived from the preceding indigenous fauna, but some new elements are immigrants. Remains of creodonts are confined to the lower beds and comprise gigantic hyaenodonts such as *Hyaenodon* and *Hemipsalodon* comparable with European forms. Among true carnivores the canids *Daphaenus* and *Galecynus* (the latter resembling the European *Cynodictis*), the first American mustelid (*Bunaelurus*) and the felid *Dinictis* persist through the stage; in the higher beds *Hoplophoneus* and *Eusmilus* are more clearly related to the machairodonts, and the canids become more varied with the appearance of *Nothocyon*, *Protemnocyon*, and other genera. Several groups of perissodactyls seem to have developed autochthonously. The tapir *Colodon* survives from the Uinta Beds, and in higher horizons is accompanied by *Protapirus*. The three-toed horse *Mesohippus* appears to be a direct development from *Epihippus*, and it is joined by the larger and more advanced *Miohippus* in the higher beds of the stage. The persisting hyracodont rhinoceroses are represented by *Hyracodon*, the amynodonts by *Metamynodon*; the true rhinoceroses make their appearance with *Trigonias* and *Leptaceratherium* in the lower beds, *Caenopus* continuing through the stage, and *Subhyracodon* foreshadowing the pair-horned *Diceratherium* in higher horizons (Wood, 1927). The most characteristic animals of the Lower White River Beds are the great titanotheres of which entire skeletons, numerous skulls, and abundance of scattered bones have been collected (Osborn, 1929). The chief genera in the so-called Titanotherium zone are *Menodus* (formerly cited as *Titanotherium*), *Megacerops*, *Teleodus*, *Brontops*, *Allops*, *Diploclonus*, and *Brontotherium*. These forms are considerably specialized as compared with their predecessors in the Uinta beds; they now reach the climax of their development and do not survive into higher beds. This great development, which is also known in the Cypress Hills of Saskatchewan (Cope, 1891; Lambe, 1908) contrasts strongly with the meagre development in south-east Europe, but the family is well developed in Mongolia (Osborn, 1929) and is represented in Burmese Eocene deposits (Pilgrim, 1925). The chief artiodactyl families of the White River Beds are the Suidae, Anthracotheriidae, Agriochoeridae, and Cervicornia. The Suidae include peccaries (*Perchoerus*) and giant pigs (*Archaeotherium*, *Elotherium*), presumably immigrants from the Old World, for no earlier American forms are likely ancestors. The first American anthracotheres in the Titanotherium Beds were originally referred to the European genus *Ancodus*, but they are smaller forms which differ in structure of the feet and teeth; hence Troxell (1921) has separated them under the name *Aepinacodon*; they persist to the Upper White River Beds where they are accompanied by larger forms referred to *Anthracotherium*. Pilgrim (1940) considers these immigrants as probable derivatives of earlier Asiatic genera. The Agriochoeridae, already established in the Uinta Beds, continue in the genera *Agriochoerus* and *Oreodon*. Remains of the latter are exceedingly abundant in the middle division of the White River Beds, often known as the Oreodon zone. In the upper division two genera of the same family, *Eporeodon* and *Leptauchenia* make their first appearance, the latter being particularly characteristic. This family may belong to the radicle stock that produced the Camelidae which are represented in White River faunas by *Proebrotherium* and *Paratylopus*. The hypertragulids also continue from their Upper Eocene predecessors, with *Hypertragulus* and *Leptomeryx* persisting through the stage. The Upper White River Beds are specially characterized by the remarkable four-horned deer *Protoceras*, remotely related to the hypertragulids, but not descended from any known American ancestor (Osborn, 1910). The smaller mammals include lagomorph rodents (*Palaeolagus*) perhaps immigrant from Asia, and such insectivores as *Leptictis* and *Ictops* of the extinct family Leptictidae, together with *Domnina*, *Protosorex*, and *Proterix* representing the Talpidae (moles), Soricidae (shrews), and Erinaceidae (hedgehogs) respectively.

The fauna of the White River Beds, therefore, is essentially an autochthonous development from indigenous types, though a few Asiatic immigrants appear. Subdivision is possible by the abundance of certain types at three horizons. Elements of the Protoceras fauna, notably *Miohippus* and identical species of diceratherine rhinoceros, are present in the Lower John Day Beds of Oregon, but fossils are not plentiful in those beds. Further developments of the American mammalia are shown in the middle and upper parts of the John Day Beds which are regarded as equivalent to early Miocene horizons of Europe.

The fauna of the John Day Beds (J. C. Merriam and W. J. Sinclair, 1907) is almost entirely a development from that of the White River Beds, with very little admixture of exotic elements. The Carnivora include numerous canids (*Nothocyon*, *Temnocyon*, *Mesocyon*, *Enhydrocyon*); the first raccoon (*Phlaocyon*) which connects the family Procyonidae with the Oligocene canid *Cynodictis*; a few mustelids (*Oligobunis*, *Megalictis*, *Aelurocyon*) and felids (*Archaelurus*, *Nimravus*, *Hoplophoneus*). There are numerous rodents of which we may mention *Entoptychus*, *Meniscomys*, and *Palaeocastor*, representing the Geomyoidea, Aplodontoidea, and Castoridae respectively; the first true rabbit (*Lepus*) replaces the Oligocene *Palaeolagus*. The most important perissodactyls are the Equidae, and it is generally agreed that a gradual transition exists from *Mesohippus* and *Miohippus*, persisting from the White River Beds, to certain forms that were originally assigned to the European genus *Anchitherium*. The American anchitherine species are nowadays classified in distinct genera of which the earliest is

Kalobatippus. This appears in the upper division of the John Day Beds, and it agrees with *Anchitherium* in most of its characters, but is distinguished by its long slender limbs and by details of tooth-structure. There seems to be no doubt that these equids evolved primarily in North America, and that *Anchitherium* is immigrant in Europe; hence the John Day Beds must be earlier than the Upper Miocene of France. Other perissodactyls include rhinoceroses, chiefly the pair-horned *Diceratherium*, regarded as a development of *Subhyracodon*, and the chalicothere *Moropus* which is apparently related to the Miocene *Macrotherium* of Europe and is probably an immigrant from Asia. Forms belonging to the artiodactyl family Agriochoeridae provide means for discriminating horizons in the field. The middle division of the John Day stage is marked by abundant remains of *Eporeodon*, while *Promerycochoerus* is confined to the upper division. *Agriochoerus*, *Meseoreodon* and *Leptauchenia* persist through the sequence. Of other artiodactyls, *Hypertragulus* is a frequent type in the middle division accompanied by *Allomeryx* and the strange *Syndyoceras*. The primitive camel *Paratylopus* also survives from older beds; the suids are represented by *Elotherium* and *Dinohyus*.

Later developments of the American mammals are seen in a number of faunas collected from scattered localities in the Western Plains. Though closely connected by certain elements, these faunas are probably not strictly contemporaneous, and they have been described under various local names. The Lower Rosebud Beds of Dakota (Matthew and Gidley, 1904) contain *Promerycochoerus*, *Mesoreodon* and *Leptauchenia*, and are therefore correlated with the Upper John Day Beds of Oregon. The Gering and Monroe Creek Beds of Nebraska (Petersen, 1906) are probably of the same age. *Promerycochoerus* is present in the Lower Harrison Beds of Nebraska accompanied by species of *Kalobatippus* and *Moropus* which are larger and more advanced than the John Day forms. In the Upper Harrison Beds *Promerycochoerus* is accompanied by its probable derivative *Merycochoerus*; the dominant equid *Parahippus* is associated with the short-limbed *Hypohippus*; the camelid *Oxydactylus* and the hypertragulid *Blastomeryx* are also developments from native families.

The Mascall Beds of Oregon, separated from the John Day Beds by basaltic lavas (Merriam and Sinclair, 1907) have few genera in common with the older beds, but the survivors include *Promerycochoerus* and *Paratylopus*. Among newcomers we may note the first of the true equines or grazing horses, *Merychippus*, a more progressive type than its associate *Parahippus* (the last of the browsing horses) in that the adult molar teeth are prismatic in shape. The hornless deer *Dromomeryx*, and the camelid *Miolabis* are also recorded in the small assemblage known. The Deep River Beds of Montana have yielded a larger fauna (W. B. Scott, 1893). These beds form the Ticholeptus zone of Cope (1880) so named from an abundance of the agriochoerid *Merychyus*, often cited as *Ticholeptus*. The fauna shows autochthonous development of several other families. The horses are represented by *Merychippus* and *Hypohippus*. Among rhinoceroses the short-limbed *Teleoceras* and *Aphelops* have a habit more like the hippopotamus than the rhinoceros. With the camelid *Protolabis* is the long-necked form *Alticamelus* having a superficial resemblance to the giraffe. The antlered *Merycodus* is an early member of the Antilocapridae (prong-horned antelopes), a family unknown outside North America. The canid *Amphicyon*, according to Matthew (1924), is directly descended from the Oligocene *Daphaenus* through *Daphaenodon* of the Harrison Beds. We may note also the peculiar mylagaulids, unique among rodents in developing a horn on the skull. Remains of proboscideans (*Tetrabelodon*) represent migrants, probably from Asia, and invite comparison with Middle Miocene forms of Europe. The Sheep Creek Beds of Nebraska, also yielding *Merychippus* and *Merycodus*, are approximately equivalent in age. Similar fossils recorded from the Snake Creek Beds of western Nebraska (Matthew and Cook, 1909) are said to be associated with more advanced forms; but the deposits are ancient flood-gravels probably representing more than one stage (Merriam, 1917), the material having been repeatedly reworked and the fossils of various horizons mingled together (Matthew, 1924).

It has become evident that the continuous development of the Equidae provides the most reliable means for correlating the Neozoic faunas of North America with those of other continents. It is generally agreed that species of the Miocene *Merychippus* are ancestral to the three genera *Protohippus*, *Pliohippus*, and *Hipparion*, the first two being in the direct line to *Equus*, the modern horse, the last a side-line which left no descendants. The three are contemporaneous in some deposits, and *Hipparion* is of special importance in our study of life-provinces because it is present, as an immigrant form, in Upper Miocene deposits of Europe and Asia. The earliest American records of *Hipparion* are in the Burge Beds of Dakota, the Ricardo and Mint Canyon Beds of California (J. C. Merriam, 1919), the Clarendon Beds of Texas (Matthew and Stirton, 1930). In discussing the correlation of North American Neozoic deposits, Pilgrim (1940) correlates these with the Chinji Beds of north India, which have yielded the earliest Asiatic *Hipparion*, and hence with the Upper Sarmatian Beds of Europe. At higher horizons, such as the Thousand Creek Beds of Nevada (Merriam, 1917), the Rattlesnake Beds of Oregon (Merriam, 1925), the middle Snake Creek Beds of Texas and New Mexico (Matthew and Stirton, 1930), *Hipparion*, accompanied by *Pliohippus* and *Protohippus*, becomes more abundant, and provides evidence for correlation with the European Pontian Beds. There are also carnivores, such as the canid *Simocyon*, the ursids *Hemicyon* and *Indarctos*, the mustelids *Taxidea*, *Plesiogulo*, and *Eomellivora*, which show affinities with forms that are conspicuous in the Pontian fauna of Europe and Asia. Hence, Pilgrim (1940) regards the American deposits under discussion as roughly equivalent to the Pontian Beds of Eurasia, despite the absence of the Bovidae, Cervidae, Suidae, Rhinocerotidae, and Proboscidea which are so typical of that horizon in Europe. No explanation of this discrepancy seems possible at present, and Pilgrim could only suggest that the migration route through Alaska may have presented difficulties to these animals. The fauna of the Thousand Creek Beds includes two large antelopes *Ilingoceros* and *Sphenophalos* (Merriam, 1909) which replace the earlier antilocaprid *Merycodus* (Furlong, 1927); *Sphenophalos* has also been found in the Rattlesnake Beds (Merriam, 1917). The peccaries are represented by *Prosthennops*, the camelids by *Procamelus* and *Alticamelus*. Several species of teleocerine rhinoceroses survive.

In referring these faunas to an Upper Miocene age, Pilgrim (1940) differs from most American authors (e.g. Stirton, 1934) who have assigned them to various Pliocene horizons. In North America there is difficulty in distinguishing between these two stages because the faunas show almost continuous development; moreover, the deposits are so scattered and limited in area that agreement has not yet been reached with regard to a stratigraphical boundary-line. Specialization of the Bovidae, Equidae, and Proboscidae seem to afford the best means of distinguishing Pliocene and Pleistocene faunas, though both *Elephas* and the bovines arrived late in North America. However, it is generally agreed that the faunas of the Blanco Beds of Texas (Merriam, 1917), the Tehama Beds of California (Russell and Vanderhoof, 1931), the Hagerman Lake Beds of Oregon (Vanderhoof, 1933), and the topmost Snake Creek Beds of Nebraska (Matthew, 1924) are of Pliocene age.

The Blanco Beds probably correspond to a mid-Pliocene horizon. They have yielded the canid *Borophagus* and the mustelid *Canimartes*; the equids *Pliohippus*, *Protohippus*, and *Neohipparion* persist; the artiodactyls include a large cursorial peccary (*Platygonus*) and the large camelid *Pliauchenia*; the most advanced proboscidean is the short-jawed *Stegomastodon*. In addition, there are the edentates *Glyptotherium*, *Megalonyx*, and *Mylodon*, which indicate a migration of South American animals. It is evident that the two Americas were joined at this period—an important geographical change. The Hagerman Lake Beds, containing the more advanced horse *Plesippus*, and the Tehama Beds, in which *Plesippus* is associated with *Hyaenognathus*, *Camelops*, *Platygonus*, *Odocoileus*, *Stegomastodon*, and a megalonychid edentate, are perhaps a little later, but still approximately mid-Pliocene. We may notice here the Alachua Clay of Florida which overlies marine beds of early Pliocene age (Dall, 1892). This deposit is notable for the persistence of the rhinoceroses *Teleoceras* and *Aphelops*; other fossils include remains of *Hipparion*, *Mastodon*, *Procamelus*, and *Odocoileus* (Leidy, 1896; Simpson, 1930).

The equid genus *Plesippus* is very near to the modern horse *Equus*, and the latter is present in many deposits between Alaska, Florida, and Cali-

Y y

fornia. These include the famous Hay Springs Quarry in Nebraska (Matthew, 1902), Peace Creek Beds in south-west Florida (Leidy, 1889), the Rock Creek Beds of Texas (Gidley, 1900), the Twelve Mile Creek Beds of Kansas (Williston, 1897), the Silver Lake Beds of Oregon (Cope, 1889), the Rancho La Brea Beds (Merriam, 1906), and the Irvington Beds of California (Stirton, 1939), to name only a few of the localities. These deposits are referred to early Pleistocene horizons by Osborn (1910), but many of them have yielded *Elephas colombi* which is closely related to the northern mammoth (*Elephas primigenius*) of mid-Pleistocene age, and may be a local variant of it (W. B. Scott, 1924). Indeed, *E. primigenius* itself is known from various places between Alaska and British Columbia in the north and New England in the south-east; it is regarded as a late immigrant from Asia, by way of a Bering land-bridge. *Elephas imperator*, known from the western plains between Nebraska and Mexico, is perhaps earlier, and *Mastodon americanus* represents the survival of a genus that had become extinct in the Old World by the end of Pliocene time. Several species of horses, but not *Equus caballus*, are described from Pleistocene deposits in North America, and seem to show the development of local races in this indigenous family. Other autochthonous forms are camels and llamas, peccaries (*Platygonus*), and many carnivores. The Virginian deer (*Odocoileus*) is not exactly autochthonous, but it has a long American ancestry, and persists from the Pliocene with little change. There are many Eurasian types which are not known in North America below the Pleistocene deposits. Such mammals include the moose (*Alces*), the bison (*Bison*), the Rocky Mountain 'goat' (*Oreamnos*), the musk-ox (*Ovibos*) with its Californian allies *Euceratherium* and *Preptoceros*, the wapiti (*Cervus*), the reindeer (*Rangifer*), the bear (*Ursus*). *Cervalces* is not known in the Old World, but Scott (1924) believes it to be almost certainly an immigrant from east Asia. We must note also the South American edentates *Megalonyx*, *Megatherium*, and *Mylodon* which arrived in North America during Pliocene and persisted into Pleistocene time.

According to Osborn (1910) the Pleistocene deposits of North America can be subdivided into four successive faunal zones, (1) the Equus zone, (2) Megalonyx zone, (3) Ovibos-Rangifer zone, (4) Cervus zone, but the lines of separation are not clearly defined. They are based largely on present knowledge of the arrival of immigrants and may partly overlap one another. The appearance in the third zone of *Ovibos*, *Rangifer*, and the northern mammoth (*Elephas primigenius*), which spread southwards into the Middle States, apparently coincides with the maximum glaciation of the region. Meanwhile the greater part of the large indigenous fauna of North America gradually vanishes; the sabre-tooth cats, the tapirs, the camels and horses, one by one disappear, as also do the elephants and mastodon of Asiatic origin, and the South American sloths and edentates.

The survivors form the bulk of the modern fauna which varies considerably from north to south through the great latitudinal extent of the continent. In the arctic region, the Polar bear (*Thalarctos*), the Arctic fox (*Vulpes lagopus*), musk-ox (*Ovibos*), caribou (*Rangifer*), lemming (*Lemmus*), and marmot (*Marmotta*) are typical, and are all of Asiatic origin. Farther south, the coniferous forest belt follows a sinuous course from Alaska to New England. Here again the mammals are largely of Old World origin, some of them descendants of Pliocene immigrants. They include various deer (*Cervus*), the moose (*Alces*), the Rocky Mountain 'goat' (*Oreamnos*), mountain sheep (*Ovis*), bison (*Bison*), wolverine (*Gulo*), grey wolf (*Canis*), weasels, martens, bears, red foxes, otters, and large numbers of rodents; some of these forms extend into the Arctic region. There are also some native American elements, and even one genus of South American origin, namely *Erethizon*, the Canadian porcupine. The greater part of the United States forms the Sonoran region which is mainly south of the 43rd parallel but reaches 48° N. lat. in the Western Plains and Great Basin. Among the characteristic mammals are opossums (*Didelphys*), grey foxes (*Urocyon*), coyote (*Canis latrans*), timber wolf (*Canis occidentalis*), skunk (*Mephitis*), caxomistle (*Bassariscus*), coati (*Nasua*), raccoon (*Procyon*), pumas, lynxes, some bears, peccary (*Tagassu*), prong-horned antelope (*Antilocapra*), American deer (*Odocoileus*) and armadillo (*Tatusia*). Some of these range into the forest belt farther north. The fauna of the Mexican lowlands shows greater affinity with that of South America next to be discussed.

From the foregoing brief summary, it is evident that the outstanding features in the history of North American mammalian faunas are: (1) the autochthonous development of many great fami ies between Palaeocene and Pleistocene time, (2) occasional immigration from Asiatic sources at various periods and from South America during Pliocene and Pleistocene time, (3) widespread extinction of various native and immigrant elements late in Pleistocene time.

6. NEOZOIC MAMMALS OF SOUTH AMERICA

Fossil mammals have long been known from South America. Over a century ago Charles Darwin (1839) collected certain forms, which were described by Owen (1840), from the Neozoic deposits of Patagonia. But the great bulk of material now known from the continent is due largely to the work of the brothers Ameghino and of R. Lydekker during the last two decades of the nineteenth century. Later investigators include W. B. Scott (1903, 1910), Gaudry (1904, 1909), W. J. Sinclair (1906, 1909), and G. G. Simpson (1935).

The most ancient fauna so far known in the continent, and also the most recently discovered, is contained in the Rio Chico Beds of central Patagonia (Simpson, 1935). The assemblage includes primitive marsupials of a synthetic didelphid-dasyurid type (*Polydolops*) which are very different from anything known elsewhere, and represent an aberrant group of unknown antiquity and origin. The xenarthran edentates are represented by isolated armadillo scutes. Forms which seem to be condylarths very nearly allied to the North American phenacodonts are exemplified in the genus *Ernestokokenia*, but these are imperfectly known; others show certain characters of the litopterns and astropotheres which we shall discuss later. The most abundant remains are those of primitive notoungulates (e.g. *Henricosbornia*), perhaps less specialized than the Mongolian *Palaeostylops* or the *Arctostylops* of Wyoming, but on a different line of descent. Compared with later faunas in the same region the Rio Chico assemblage is decidedly primitive, but already is distinctly differentiated into several of the major groups peculiar to South America (Simpson, 1937). The origin of the fauna is a complex problem. The presence of notoungulates in North America and Asia would seem to suggest migration from Asia to the Americas, but the Asiatic *Palaeostylops* does not represent (even structurally) the ancestry of the contemporary South American types, and it is still possible on the available evidence that migration was from south to north. In any case, the Rio Chico fauna shows that South America, or at least Patagonia, was already isolated from the northern hemisphere in Palaeocene time, and had then been isolated long enough for a marked degree of differentiation to have taken place in its mammalian groups.

The Casa Mayor Beds of the same region have yielded a fauna which continues the peculiarities of the preceding assemblage. It is often known as the Notostylopean fauna from the abundance of small notoungulates especially *Notostylops*. Though small, this form is considerably specialized in dentition, and with several other genera (*Catastylops*, *Isotemnus*, &c.) is placed in the suborder Entelonychia. An allied group, the Astrapotheroidea, including *Trigonostylops*, *Albertogaudrya*, *Proplanodus*, have tusk-like canines, and simple, low molar teeth rather like those of the rhinoceros. Still other forms (*Notopithecus*, *Oldfieldthomasia*, &c.) are less specialized, with superficial resemblance to rodents, and are classified in the suborder Typotheria. The Pyrotheria are larger animals with short skull and specialized limb-bones; they are represented in the Casa Mayor Beds by *Carolozittelia* which attained the size of a tapir. Thus the Notoungulata rapidly became differentiated, for only one of the established suborders is absent from this fauna. A number of other genera has been founded on isolated molar teeth which bear similarity to those of condylarths. Such forms (*Didolodon*) are referred to the Litopterna, an extinct suborder of the true ungulates, which is unknown outside South America. Unfortunately the skeletal features of these early forms are very imperfectly known, but they appear to simulate those of perissodactyls. There are marsupials of diverse types. Small forms (*Polydolops* and its allies) with high, sectorial premolars, may be regarded as specialized types of the Coenolestidae, a family still living in Ecuador. Others, *Procladosictis*, *Pseudocladosictis*, for example, are predaceous forms like creodonts, and represent the earliest of the so-called

Sparassodonta (Ameghino, 1904). It is evident that this fauna shows little (if any) relation to the northern faunas discussed above, for insectivores, creodonts, and condylarthrans are apparently absent. Consequently, correlation is difficult, but the concensus of opinion (Windhausen, 1931; Simpson, 1937) favours the view that the Casa Mayor Beds correspond to some part of the Eocene stage of the northern hemisphere.

Higher in the succession are the Astraponotus Beds. What is known of the somewhat sparse fauna shows a general advance on the preceding assemblage. It is notable for the presence of *Eomorphippus* and *Interhippus* which are the earliest known representatives of the notoungulate suborder Toxodontia. Among other notogunulates, the astrapotheres are continued in *Astraponotus* and *Edwardocopeia*, the entelonychids in *Carolodarwinia* and *Stenogenium*, the typotheres in *Guilelmoscottia*. The litopternine ungulates are similar to those of the Casa Mayor Beds. Remains of edentates indicate the presence of several families, but they are in a fragmentary condition.

The mammals of the Deseado Beds of Patagonia show a further development of the indigenous groups. The bulk of the fauna consists of hoofed animals, and the litopterns are now differentiated into two families which originate in the primitive forms of the preceding horizons. The Macraucheniidae, which in later members have elongated skull, long neck, low-crowned teeth, and digitigrade extremities, are represented in the Deseado fauna by teeth called *Coniopterneum* and *Protheosodon*. In the Proterotheriidae the skull is more tapering and the extremities (in later forms at least) show reduction in the number of digits; *Eoproterotherium* and *Deuterotherium* are recorded from the Deseado Beds. The Typotherian notoungulates are usually small but *Eutrachytherus* is larger than the majority of them. The Toxodonts, with *Coresodon*, *Pronesodon*, and *Leontinia*, show specialization of the teeth, the incisors becoming chisel-shaped and the molars prismatic. These characters are taken (Scott, 1924) to indicate that grazing habits are beginning to replace browsing habits of life. There are varied entelonychids and astrapotheres, the latter group including relatively large forms such as *Parastrapotherium* and *Liarthrus*. The large massive *Pyrotherium* with tusk-like incisors and short limbs is eminently characteristic of the fauna and represents the maximum development of the Pyrotheria. Ameghino (1902) has related this form to the Proboscidea, and it has also been compared with the Australian Pleistocene marsupial *Diprotodon*, but there can be no relationship with these two groups. Edentates are only scantily represented in the fauna. The only predaceous animals are marsupials, such as *Proborhyaena* and *Pharsophorus*, some species attaining considerable size. Jaws of small herbivorous forms may represent early members of the existing Coenolestidae. The Deseado fauna also contains the earliest rodents recorded from South America, namely the hystricomorph genera *Cephalomys* and *Eosteiromys*. It may be recalled that the hystricoids appear first in the Eocene deposits of Europe and that the group seems to be lacking in North America before the Pliocene. On this account a direct land-bridge between South America and the Old World, independent of North America, has been suggested. But this view is at variance with the evolution and distribution of other mammalian orders, besides being highly improbable on isostatic grounds (Matthew, 1915). It would seem that the relationship of the New and Old World porcupines must be more remote than it appears, and that the two groups developed independently, for no other hypothesis seems to explain their distribution.

The succeeding Patagonian Series has in its upper portion the celebrated fauna of the Santa Cruz Beds. At the base of the series in some localities certain transgressive beds contain a fauna which is distinguished from that of the Santa Cruz horizon by the persistence of some early groups. We may note especially the primitive horse-like toxodonts *Perhippidium*, and *Stylhippus*, together with the leontinid genus *Colpodon*, variously classified with the toxodonts or the entelonychids. The early typothere *Archaeohyrax* also persists in these basal beds (Roth, 1908). Otherwise, this Colpodon fauna is closely related to the Santa Cruz fauna which is far richer in species and more widely distributed. The latter contains a varied assemblage of hoofed animals. The most abundant are the toxodonts *Adinotherium* and *Nesodon*, heavily built forms ranging in size from a sheep to a tapir respectively and with small, three-toed feet. The small typotheres *Protypotherium*, *Intratherium*, and *Hegetotherium* show little change from their predecessors in lower horizons. The entelonychid *Homalodontotherium* has a skull much like that of the toxodont *Nesodon*, but the feet have five digits armed with blunt claws. The pyrotheres have become extinct, but the astrapotheres are represented by the grotesque *Astrapotherium* with short dome-like skull, tusk-like canine teeth, and heavy five-toed feet; the several species vary in size, the smallest about as large as a wild boar, the largest probably bigger than a rhinoceros. The litoptern ungulates continue their development in the families Macraucheniidae (*Thesodon*) and Proterotheriidae (*Proterotherium*, *Diadiaphorus*, *Thoatherium*). All are three-toed forms, the latter family with side-digits much reduced as in Miocene horses of the northern continents; indeed, *Thoatherium* is almost monodactyl, a remarkable instance of convergent evolution. The edentates are also abundant and diversified. The majority of the Gravigrada (ground-sloths) belong to the Mesonychidae and are represented by small forms such as *Hapalops*, *Eucholoeops*, *Schismotherium*, *Hyperleptus*, some of which are recorded from older beds. The Mylodontidae are poorly represented by a few forms (*Nematherium*, *Analcitherium*); they are very like members of the Megalonychidae in the structure of the skull. Armadillos abound in the genera *Peltephilus*, *Stegotherium*, *Proeutatus*, most of them aberrant types of which no descendants are known. The contemporary glyptodonts *Propalaeohoplophorus*, *Cochlops*, *Eucinepeltus*, are all small and seem to approach the armadillos in many features, thus suggesting a common origin for the two families. There is an extraordinary variety of rodents, but they are all hystricoids referable to the existing South American families Erethizontinae, Capromyinae, Octodontinae, Chinchillinae, and Caviinae. The presence of *Necrolestes* is noteworthy because it is the first and only record of insectivores in South America; in features of the skull, teeth, and extremities the genus resembles the existing Chrysochloridae ('golden moles') of South Africa. Another striking feature of the Santa Cruz fauna is the great abundance of marsupials. The common Didelphidae (opossums) are exemplified by *Microbiotherium*, and there are small herbivorous forms such as *Abderites, Epanorthus, Metaepanorthus, Paraepanorthus, Garzonia*, and *Halmarhiphus*. Certain predaceous marsupials fill the place taken by the true Carnivora on the northern continents. The genus *Prothylacinus*, as large as a wolf, is similar to the existing Tasmanian *Thylacinus* and is classified with it in the family Dasyuridae. Another large form of the same family is the massive cat-like *Borhyaena* which is even more specialized in features of the skull and dentition. *Cladosictis* and *Amphiproviverra* serve as examples of smaller carnivorous marsupials. Unlike previous faunas the Santa Cruz assemblage is known far beyond the limits of Patagonia, for fragments of *Nesodon* are recorded from Bolivia (Douglas, 1914) and of *Astrapotherium* and the toxodont *Gyrinodon* from Venezuela (Stehlin, 1928; Hopwood, 1928). Most authors correlate the assemblage with Miocene faunas of the northern continents.

The limits of the South American Miocene stage are very doubtful, and the Parana Beds of Argentine may be either Upper Miocene or Lower Pliocene in age. The major part of the mammalian fauna consists of autochthonous genera already established in the Santa Cruz fauna, including toxodonts, typotheres, litopterns, hystricoids, edentates, and marsupials. In addition, representatives of true carnivores (dogs, racoons, and bears) are reported but the identifications are based on very fragmentary material. Similar evidence is given by the later horizons of Catamarca and Monte Hermoso in Argentina. These records evidently indicate the opening of a route for migration, presumably from North America, for we have already noted the presence of South American elements in the Pliocene faunas of the south-western States of that continent.

A larger proportion of migrant elements is contained in an Upper Pliocene fauna from the Tarija Valley in Bolivia (Boule and Thevenin, 1920). Here, in addition to the indigenous litopterns (*Macrauchenia*), toxodonts (*Toxodon*), ground-sloths, armadillos, glyptodonts, and rodents, there are carnivores, peccaries, llamas, tapirs, horses, and mastodons. Besides the true *Equus*, the horses include two peculiar genera, *Hippidium* and *Onohippidium*, with curious modification of the skull and short limbs; these forms are regarded as a development from the North American *Pliohippus*.

This mixture of immigrant and autochthonous forms continues in the

Pampas Beds of the great Argentine plains, which correspond to the Pleistocene stage of the northern continents. These aeolian and deltaic deposits have yielded an abundance of mammals in a remarkably perfect state of preservation. Among the indigenous forms, the litopterns are represented only by *Macrauchenia*, larger and more heavily built than a camel with which it has a superficial resemblance. The notoungulates are much reduced in variety, the last surviving groups being the typotheres (*Typotherium, Pachyruchos*) and the toxodonts (*Toxodon*). The hystricoid rodents are species of *Dolichotis, Viscaccia, Hydrochoerus, Ctenomys, Myopotamus*, and other genera still living. There is a great variety of edentates, some attaining gigantic size. The gravigrade genera *Megatherium, Mylodon*, and *Megalonyx* vary in size from a tapir to an elephant. The glyptodonts, with huge carapace and enormous tail-sheath, are exemplified by *Glyptodon, Sclerocalyptus, Daedicurus*, and other genera, and are especially numerous and varied in the Pampas Beds. Armadillos also are numerous in Brazilian and Argentine deposits; some genera are still living, but others, like the huge *Chlamydotherium*, are extinct.

The Pampean carnivores are all immigrants, though, as we have noted, some of the genera may have arrived in South America during Pliocene time. Of bears, the only genus known is the short-faced *Arctotherium*; sabre-toothed cats (*Smilodon*), and species of *Felis* allied to the puma and jaguar represent the Felidae. The Canidae are numerous in species of *Canis, Palaeocyon*, and *Dinocyops*. Of immigrant horses there are species of the true *Equus* (but not *E. caballus*) and also members of the extinct genera *Hippidium* and *Hyperhippidium*, offshoots of the northern *Pliohippus*. The artiodactyls include peccaries (*Prosthennops*), llamas (*Palaeolama*), and numerous deer (*Paraceros, Odocoileus*, &c.) all closely related to North American types. Several species of *Mastodon* have been found in Brazil, Argentine, and Bolivia, but, according to present records, *Elephas* only penetrated from the north as far as French Guiana.

This famous Pampean fauna, of which several elements were vividly described by Charles Darwin and Owen over a century ago, became seriously depleted by extinction towards the end of Pleistocene time. The ground-sloths, glyptodonts, litopterns, notoungulates, horses and mastodons all disappeared. The present South American fauna, which has developed from the survivors, still shows a strange mixture of autochthonous forms and northern immigrants. The latter may be readily identified, for, as Scott (1924) points out, they seem almost out of place among the indigenous forms. In this modern assemblage hoofed mammals are not numerous. The only perissodactyl is the tapir (*Tapirus*), a northern immigrant which is now restricted to the tropical region of South and Central America. The horse is not native, for it was introduced by Spanish settlers in the sixteenth century and spread rapidly in the wild state (Darwin, 1839). Artiodactyls are more varied, but again are all descendants of comparatively recent migrants from North America. The peccary (*Tagassu*) extends from Texas and Central America into Paraguay. There are two members of the Camelidae, namely the guanaco (*Auchenia huanacus*) of the Peruvian Andes, and the vicuna (*Auchenia vicunia*) of Bolivia; these are modified descendants of North American ancestors. Various deer (Cervidae) include species of *Odocoileus, Blastocerus, Hippocamelus, Mazama, Pudua*, all of North American origin and distinct from Old World types. The rodents are astonishingly varied, the indigenous porcupines alone being classified in twenty-nine genera; there are many true squirrels, but few hares and rabbits, while marmots and beavers are entirely lacking. The typical sloths, anteaters, and armadillos have developed autochthonously from truly indigenous families as have also the marsupials. This last group includes numerous species of opossums in greater variety than the North American forms, and two species of *Coenolestes*. Considerable discussion has centred round the last-named genus because its dentition resembles that of the diprotodont marsupials of Australia (Osgood, 1921). Some authors (e.g. Dederer, 1909; Broom, 1912; Regan, 1914) however believe that this feature may have developed independently from polyprotodont ancestors. The numerous carnivores are all modified descendants of northern families. The canids belong to genera, such as *Cerdocyon* and *Icticyon*, not represented elsewhere. Mustelids are not numerous; there are some otters (*Lutra*) and a few skunks (*Spilogale, Conepatus*), but no badgers or weasels. Raccoons (*Procyon*) have a wide geographical range, but the spectacled bear (the only ursid of South America) is confined to the high lands of Peru and Chili. The felines include the jaguar, ocelot, and puma, but the lynx does not range so far south.

The fauna of Central America has many features in common with that of South America but is less varied; it may be considered as transitional to that of the Sonoran region. The West Indian islands are poor in mammals; they have only a few rodents, insectivores, and bats. Despite the proximity of Florida there are no North American perissodactyls, artiodactyls, or carnivores. With few exceptions the affinities of the Antillean mammals appear to be with Central or South American forms (Anthony, 1925–6), as also are those of Pliocene ground-sloths on Cuba (Matthew, 1919). Schuchert (1935) follows Barbour (1916) in postulating former land-connexion with the adjacent continent, but Matthew (1915) believes that the islands have been colonized by casual drift at various times, the direction having been determined by the equatorial ocean-current.

Considering the South American mammalian faunas together, the main features appear to be determined by a long period of isolation lasting from Palaeocene to Pliocene time. During this period descendants of the Palaeocene animals developed autochthonously and became extremely diversified by processes of radiative adaptation. During Pliocene time South America again became united to North America and mammals migrated in both directions from one of these regions to the other. In South America the northern forms mingled with the indigenous fauna and many of them persisted into Pleistocene time while intermigration continued. Then occurred a great extinction of the greater part of the native fauna together with many of the immigrants. The survivors form the bulk of the modern fauna.

7. THE MAMMALS OF AUSTRALASIA

The living fauna of the Australian region is unique, in that, apart from the peculiar monotremes and a few stray forms (dingo, mice, rabbit, &c.) of recent (probably human) introduction, all the indigenous mammals are marsupials. Indeed, the Australian fauna includes all the living marsupials except the American Didelphidae (opossums) and Coenolestidae, the latter being restricted to a small area in South America. Pleistocene forms known from various parts of Australia are closely related to living genera of the same continent, but only one genus (*Wynyardia*) is known from an earlier (Upper Miocene) stage.

The marsupials are usually classified in two suborders: (1) Polyprotodontia, with three or four pairs of lower incisor teeth, (2) Diprotodontia with only one pair of lower incisors which are usually enlarged. The Australian polyprotodonts include the predaceous Dasyuridae, the insectivorous Myrmecobiidae, the rodent-like Peramelidae, and the Notoryctidae (marsupial moles). The diprotodonts of this region comprise the Macropodidae (kangaroos and wallabies), the arboreal and flying Phalangeridae, and the Phascolomyidae (wombats). It is evident that members of the order have developed a wide variation in size, form, and habits of life, similar to the adaptive radiation of the placental mammals in the northern continents. Some of the extinct Pleistocene genera are much larger than any of the living forms; for instance, the skull of the phalangerid *Thylacoleo* approximates to that of a lion in size, and typical species of the phascolomyids *Nototherium* and *Diprotodon* are about as large as rhinoceroses (Owen, 1877). The genus *Wynyardia*, from Upper Miocene deposits in Tasmania, has characters of Polyprotodontia and Diprotodontia combined in the skull and limbs, but its precise relations are uncertain because the dentition is imperfectly known. It seems probable that the diprotodonts are descendants of certain polyprotodonts that have become adapted to a mixed or herbivorous diet (A. S. Woodward, 1925).

The peculiarities of the Australasian mammalian fauna are explained on the view that the region has long been isolated geographically and that, in consequence, the marsupials have evolved autochthonously, probably since Cretaceous time. But we have to consider the fact that fossil marsupials are abundant in Patagonia, especially in the Miocene beds of Santa Cruz. The polyprotodont Didelphidae (opossums) have a long history in America, and forms close to modern types are recorded as far back as the Cretaceous in North America and the Eocene in Europe. Hence this persistent family represents a conservative stock that may well have had a world-wide distribution at the beginning of Neozoic time. In the Eocene strata of Patagonia certain forms (e.g. *Procladisictis*) show a combination of didelphid and dasyurid features. These are followed in the Santa Cruz Beds by predaceous forms (Borhyaenidae) which so closely resemble the living *Thylacinus* of Tasmania that they have been referred to the same family (Thylacinidae). Matthew (1915) states, however, that the resemblance is not closer than that between parallel adaptations in some distinct families of Carnivora developed independently from unspecialized common ancestors. Hence he believes that there is no closer affinity between the Borhyaenidae and the Thylacininae than a common origin in didelphid ancestors. There has also been much controversy concerning the South American Coenolestidae which have a dentition resembling that of the Australian diprotodonts. This family can be traced back to the Palaeocene Beds of Patagonia, if *Polydolops* and its allies are truly related to the living *Coenolestes*. Though many authors have classified the group in Diprotodontia, Dederer (1909) and Broom (1912) believe that the peculiar dentition has developed independently from American polyprotodont ancestors. Hence it is probable that the true Diprotodontia have developed autochthonously in Australasia, and are only remotely related to the American forms. The supposed affinities of these marsupials have been used as an argument for a former land-connexion between the two continents by way of Antarctica. But if the two groups evolved independently as outlined above, their distribution affords a valid argument against such a connexion. The same reasoning applies to the case of the struthious birds, the ostrich, emu, and rhea of Africa, Australia, and South America respectively, the distribution of which has been cited in support of similar land-connexions. It is appropriate to recall that the only land-vertebrates known on the Antarctic continent are penguins, and there is no evidence that mammals ever existed there. Moreover, Rastall (1929) has reminded us that, though connexion between South America and Antarctica does not present insuperable difficulties from the physiographical point of view, there is a gap of some 2,000 miles of deep water between the Ross Sea and Australia where the topography reveals nothing comparable with the islands and shallow water of the Southern Antilles.

The Australian region is bounded on the north-west by the Indomalayan province of the Oriental region. The boundary is known as 'Wallace's line', and extends across the chain of the Sunda Islands between Bali and Lombok, along the Macassar Strait between Borneo and Celebes, thence eastwards south of the Philippines. Some doubts have been expressed as to the validity of this line; for instance, C. T. Simpson (1900) and H. A. Pilsbry (1916) have shown that it does not determine the limits of freshwater mussels and land-snails respectively. Kampen (1909) asserts that no sharp boundary exists for the whole fauna, and postulates a transition area in which the Oriental and Australian faunas are mingled. Matthew (1915) in effect obliterates the line by adopting as a subregion, this Australo-Malayan area which includes the islands east of the line as far as the Australian continent. Raven (1935), however, shows that the distribution of living mammals is consistent with a definite barrier along the line in question. Some East Indian mammals have crossed the line in an easterly direction, especially bats, shrews, rats, and mice. Some of these, together with other forms, like the dingo, have doubtless been transported, accidentally or deliberately, by human agency. But there are far more Asiatic mammals whose wanderings appear to have been checked at Wallace's line, including chevrotain, muntjac, tapir, rhinoceros, bear and other carnivores, porcupines, pangolin, tree-shrew, hedgehog, squirrel, gibbon, orang. Hence the line, which is sometimes regarded as the eastern limit of the ancient Asiatic continent, seems to be a definite barrier for the great majority of Malayan animals on the one side, and for the marsupials on the other.

Nothing is known of early Neozoic mammals in Australia, but, like Europe, Asia, and the Americas, that continent must have had its quota of Palaeocene forms, probably derived in common from known Cretaceous types. In Europe, Asia, and North America a new type of fauna begins to appear in Palaeocene deposits, and consists of new or modernized groups clearly derived from a fauna of Palaeocene type. Only placental mammals are involved in this change; where known, the new types appear to be immigrants from some unknown source, and they replace the older types completely during Eocene time. Since then, in the view of G. G. Simpson (1937) there has not been any other major spread of mammals, or any great change in faunal type. Apart from changes due to long-continued evolution, intermigration and extinction, the mammals now peopling the northern continents are essentially those that appeared in the Eocene invasion. In South America the change was long delayed; the northern immigrants did not arrive in the habitat of the ancient fauna until Pliocene time. In Australia, owing to longer isolation of the continent, the change never took place (apart from the agency of man) and the indigenous mammalian fauna represents the adaptive radiation from an ancient marsupial stock.

LITERATURE

In the foregoing text references to the author and date of each genus are given but space does not allow full details of all these to be stated; they may be sought in the appropriate *List of Fossil Vertebrates* mentioned above on p. 575. The standard textbooks of a quarter of a century ago now need amplification, as, for example, *The Age of Mammals* by H. F. Osborn, New York, 1911; *A History of Land Mammals in the Western Hemisphere*, by W. B. Scott, New York, 1913; and the volume on 'Mammalia' by A. S. Woodward in the Zittel-Eastman *Textbook of Palaeontology*, vol. iii, London, 1925. Hence some of the important later works which form the basis of the present chapter should be noted. *A Catalogue of the Mesozoic Mammalia*, by G. G. Simpson, British Museum (Nat. Hist.), London,

1928, and *American Mesozoic Mammalia*, by the same author, Mem. Peabody Mus., Yale Univ., vol. iii, pp. 1–171, 1929, embody the modern interpretation of the earliest mammalian fossils. Many genera of early Neozoic mammals discovered in Mongolia and discussed on pp. 672–5 are described in detail by W. Granger, W. K. Gregory, W. D. Matthew, H. F. Osborn, G. G. Simpson, and others in papers in *Amer. Mus. Novitates*, and *Bull. Amer. Mus. Nat. Hist.* during the years 1921–40.

From the great number of works dealing with particular groups of animals we may select for mention *The Titanotheres of Ancient Wyoming, Dakota and Nebraska*, by H. F. Osborn, U.S. Geol. Surv., Mon. lv (2 vols.) 1929; *The Phylogeny of North American Equidae*, by R. A. Stirton, Univ. Calif. Publ. Dept. Geol. Sci., vol. xxv, pp. 165–98, 1940, which amplifies R. S. Lull's 'Special Guide No. 1' from the Peabody Mus. Nat. Hist. 1931, and the well-known 'Guide' from the British Museum (Nat. Hist.), London; *The Pontian Bovidae of Europe*, described by G. E. Pilgrim and A. T. Hopwood, Brit. Mus. (N.H.) London, 1928; C. W. Andrews's *Descriptive Catalogue of the Tertiary Vertebrata of the Fayûm, Egypt*, issued by the Brit. Mus. (N.H.) London, 1906, containing an account of the earliest ancestors of the elephants, may be supplemented by such general reviews of the group as that by R. S. Lull, Special Guide No. 2, of the Peabody Mus. Nat. Hist. 1913, and a similar work from the British Museum, London. The later members of the group in Britain are described in 'British Fossil Elephants', by A. Leith Adams, *Mon. Pal. Soc.*, 1877–81, and 'The Fossil Elephants of the Upper Thames Basin', by K. S. Sandford, *Q.J.G.S.*, vol. lxxxi, pp. 62–86, 1925.

Other British fossil mammals are described in 'The British Pleistocene Mammalia', vol. i: Felidae, by W. Boyd Dawkins and W. A. Sandford, *Mon. Pal. Soc.*, 1866–72, vol. ii, Hyaenidae, Ursidae, Canidae, and Mustelidae, by S. H. Reynolds, ibid., 1902–12, vol. iii, Hippopotamus, Giant Deer, Red Deer, Reindeer and Roe, *Ovibos, Alces*, and Bovidae, by S. H. Reynolds, ibid., 1922–39.

'British Fossil Cetacea from the Red Crag', by R. Owen, *Mon. Pal. Soc.*, 1870–89.

'The Vertebrata of the Pliocene Deposits of Britain', by E. T. Newton, *Mem. Geol. Surv.*, 1891.

'The Vertebrata of the Forest Bed Series of Norfolk and Suffolk', by E. T. Newton, *Mem. Geol. Surv.*, 1882.

'British Fossil Voles and Lemmings', by M. A. C. Hinton, *Proc. Geol. Assoc.*, vol. xxi, pp. 489–507, 1910.

A valuable review by G. G. Simpson entitled 'The Beginning of the Age of Mammals' is published in *Biol. Reviews* (Cambs. Phil. Soc.), vol. xii, pp. 1–47, 1937.

XVIII

GENERAL RELATIONS OF THE CONTINENTS AND OCEANS: A SUMMARY OF CONCLUSIONS

I. THE CONTINENTS

THE fact that the present continents have grown around the ancient shields, mainly by the gradual accretion of marine sediments, implies that the shields have generally been separated by some extent of ocean. This inference is supported to a considerable degree by the generic differences in the tetrapod faunas of the several continents from Carboniferous time onwards. Early land-floras are not so distinct; indeed, Devonian and early Carboniferous associations, as far as they are known, show a surprising uniformity the world over. Later Carboniferous floras of Europe have many genera, and even species, in common with those of North America and Asia, and the Permian Glossopteris flora is equally uniform and widespread through the southern continents. Hence, in considering past relations of the continents we have to assess the significance of specific identities in the floras against that of generic differences in the tetrapod faunas. We have noted that plants have means of dispersal (by the agency of wind and water) which are denied to tetrapod animals, and the eminent botanist J. C. Willis (1908) attributes the uniform and widespread distribution of early cryptogam floras to dispersal of their spores by winds. He considers that the distribution of the later seed-plants was checked by the more specialized methods of dispersal and by ecological factors like differences of climate and habitat. In a later work (1910) Willis holds that arms of the sea form adequate barriers to plant dispersal, an opinion previously expressed by W. T. Blanford (1890) and many others. This, however, is hardly consistent with our later knowledge of the development of the present flora on the island of Krakatoa for instance. Moreover, the distribution of fossil floras (Seward 1931) leads us to think that much has yet to be learned about the possibilities of plant-dispersal. In any case, it is clear that we must rely mainly on the evidence of tetrapod faunas with regard to continental relationships, and this must be checked and supplemented by such evidence as is furnished by marine faunas concerning the extent of the oceans at the appropriate periods of time.

A great deal has been written about past continental relationships, but most of the statements are vague and speculative; some, indeed, have long been discredited by competent authors but are still perpetuated in certain recent literature. Until lately no definite criteria had been formulated which would enable degrees of faunal resemblance to be assessed, but G. G. Simpson (1943) has now compiled some analyses of data referring to living and fossil mammals. He points out that no two local faunas are likely to be composed of exactly the same species, even if near each other and not separated by any climatic or geographical barrier. For instance, only 65 per cent. of the mammalian species living in Ohio are found in Nebraska, 500 miles distant, though 82 per cent. of the Ohio genera are represented in Nebraska. This is taken as the degree of resemblance that should appear in fossil faunas from opposite points on different continents that were, according to the Theory of Continental Drift, in former contact. The degree of faunal similarity to be expected between the distant parts of united continents is illustrated by reference to the mammals living in Florida and New Mexico, 1,000 miles apart; 18 per cent. of the Floridan species and 67 per cent. of the genera occur in New Mexico. This compares well with the 26 and 64 per cent. respectively of recent French mammals also living in North China, 5,000 miles away. New Mexico and Venezuela, 3,000 miles apart, are two areas connected by a land-bridge since Pliocene time; originally the faunas were completely different, but now that intermigration is essentially complete and faunal equilibrium established, 5 per cent. of the New Mexican species and 24 per cent. of the genera are recorded from Venezuela. Simpson says that resemblances far less than this have repeatedly been given as conclusive evidence for drifted or transoceanic continents, but the example shows that the evidence leads to no such conclusion. He further remarks that radically different faunas thousands of miles apart and with only imperfect land-connexions (Canada and Patagonia, for example) may and often do contain some identical and related species, the importance of which can easily be over-rated.

These data refer only to land-mammals but Simpson believes them to be similar for most land vertebrates, and we shall use them as a guide in the interpretation of the relationships of certain fossil reptilian as well as mammalian faunas. It must be borne in mind, however, that their application to fossil faunas is less certain than for living associations; past faunas are, in the very nature of the case, less completely known. Now let us discuss the fossil tetrapod faunas of each continent in turn, taking the European succession as a basis.

EUROPE. The Baltic Shield, including much of Scandinavia and the Baltic States of Russia, has horizontal marine deposits of Cambrian, Ordovician and Silurian age at intervals on and around its margins (Map, Fig. 84). Another stable area is that comprising the Outer Hebrides and northwest Highlands of Scotland, where the Torridon Sandstone of Pre-Cambrian age rests horizontally on the eroded surface of crystalline gneiss, and is succeeded eastwards by marine Cambrian deposits. The original westward extent of this area is not known but it need not have been great and the area may represent an outlying island.

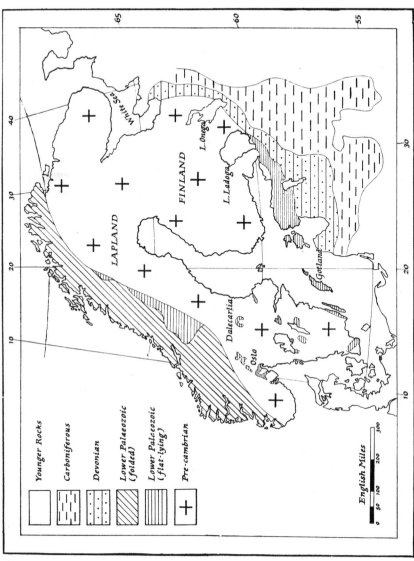

FIG. 84. GEOLOGICAL SKETCH-MAP OF NORTH-WEST EUROPE SHOWING THE DISPOSITION OF PALAEOZOIC ROCKS AROUND THE PRECAMBRIAN SHIELD

The non-marine sediments of the Old Red Sandstone cover large areas of the folded Highland region in Scotland; in the Midland Valley farther south, over considerable tracts in Ireland and the western Midlands of England they succeed marine Silurian strata. These deposits, with armoured fishes and land plants as their chief fossils, provide no evidence of tetrapod animals. Similar deposits of the same age are present in the Belgian Ardennes and occupy large tracts in the Baltic States of Russia, especially in Livonia (Map, Fig. 42).

The Lower Carboniferous strata of Scotland and the north of England are largely of non-marine type, and have yielded remains of the oldest British tetrapods—amphibians already differentiated into four distinct orders. The Upper Carboniferous rocks show a southward extension of the Coal Measures over marine Carboniferous Limestone as far as Bristol and South Wales. Marine bands at intervals in the Coal Measures indicate that deposition in general was near sea level, and the marine bands represent the eustatic flooding of low-lying land. The amphibians of the Coal Measures seem to be direct autochthonous descendants of the earlier stocks. Similar forms are recorded from the Coal Measures of intermontane areas in central Europe, especially in Bohemia. The amphibians are mainly aquatic animals, and the anthracosaurs may be regarded as a typically European development. Occasional stragglers from dry-land habitats indicate the early stages of reptilian organization.

The Lower Permian Rothliegende of Germany and France contains remains of amphibians and reptiles which likewise seem to represent autochthonous development from Carboniferous stocks. The succession is cut short in this region by the incursion of the Zechstein Sea (Map, Fig. 57). But later Permian strata in eastern and northern Russia furnish a practically continuous series of tetrapod faunas which provides evidence of the development of several amphibian and reptilian orders. One of these faunas extends far to the west, for it is known from north-east Scotland. The Russian Upper Permian strata also demonstrate the replacement in that region of the *Callipteris-Walchia* flora (which is a continuation of the northern Carboniferous flora), by the Glossopteris flora which is widespread in southern regions. The highest Permian deposits of Russia contain labyrinthodont amphibians which have every appearance of being the direct ancestors of stereospondylous forms known in Triassic rocks of that country, also of Germany, England, and Scotland. Related labyrinthodonts are also recorded far to the north in the Triassic rocks of Spitzbergen.

Beginning in Triassic rocks, deinosaurs and rhynchocephalians provide new reptilian developments, perhaps arising from the Pseudosuchia, small lizard-shaped land-reptiles which are well represented in the Trias of Germany and Scotland. The deinosaurs form the main element in Mesozoic land faunas and their drifted remains are present in considerable variety in the marine Jurassic and Cretaceous deposits of Europe. These reptiles differ considerably in size and habit; both carnivorous and herbivorous types are adapted for life in various habitats. The order reaches its acme in the lacustrine deposits of Upper Jurassic and Lower Cretaceous age. The more fragmentary record from later Cretaceous rocks gives evidence of further specialization. Nopcsa (1923) recognizes the isolation of Europe during Cretaceous time and describes an extreme instance of an assemblage in Transylvania derived from earlier forms isolated on an island.

The Jurassic flora, best illustrated in the Great Oolite of the Yorkshire coast in England, is of a cosmopolitan type. Indeed, the Yorkshire flora is said to be closely similar to an association described from Grahamland in the Southern Ocean. The Cretaceous flora continues the same features but is further marked by the first indubitable appearance of angiospermous flowering plants.

The disposition of Neozoic rocks in Europe indicates the persistence of archipelagic conditions during the early part of the era (Map, Fig. 71). The dominant mammals are represented in strata of different ages at many scattered localities according to oscillations of the sea-border. The earliest Eocene mammals of the Paris basin show considerable resemblance with corresponding faunas of North America. But while 45 per cent. of the European genera are represented in North America, no species are common to the two regions. Simpson (1943) interprets this as an indication that the two faunas are derived from a common source which was connected with Europe and North America by a long or a restricted route. Thereafter the faunas are more distinct, and, in particular, the abrupt appearance of new types without obvious ancestry indicates successive migrations from outside sources. In Miocene strata the appearance of proboscideans shows connexion with Africa. The spasmodic distribution of various Equidae, with short autochthonous development, is consistent with repeated migrations from Asia. The influx of the Pontian fauna in south-east Europe, gradually decreasing towards the west, points to derivation from the same source, with land-connexion between Europe and Asia increasing to its present maximum condition. The southward extension of northern animals during the Pleistocene Ice Age, with its subsequent retreat, needs no other continental connexion.

NORTH AMERICA. The great mass of Precambrian rocks that forms the Canadian Shield (including Greenland) has numerous flat-lying, marine deposits of Lower Palaeozoic age on and around its margins (Map, Fig. 85). As in Europe the earliest non-marine rocks are of Devonian age and of Old Red Sandstone type: the main outcrops are in eastern Canada and east Greenland. The principal fossils are armoured fishes and land plants very similar to those of Europe, but the rocks of east Greenland (about 73° N. lat.) have yielded primitive tetrapods not far removed in structure from crossopterygian fishes; these are the oldest land animals so far discovered.

The Carboniferous Coal Measures of Nova Scotia, Ohio, and Illinois have yielded tetrapod faunas associated with floras of Westphalian type. The tetrapod genera described from Nova Scotia are not recorded elsewhere, but the more varied assemblage of Linton, Ohio, is comparable with the amphibian faunas of Ireland and Bohemia. Two of the American genera are represented in Europe by closely allied species and the faunas are said to be closely similar in general aspect, though the Bohemian assemblage

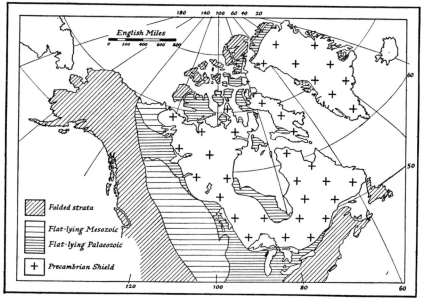

FIG. 85. GEOLOGICAL SKETCH-MAP OF CANADA SHOWING THE DISPOSITION OF PALAEOZOIC ROCKS AROUND THE PRECAMBRIAN SHIELD

contains more advanced branchiosaurs. It is this general resemblance, added to the close similarity of the floras, that has led numerous authors (e.g. Haug, 1908, Watson, 1921) to postulate a North Atlantic continent, or a continuous land-bridge from Britain to Canada during part, at least, of Carboniferous time. But the two genera common to Europe and North America represent only about 12 per cent. of the seventeen genera listed from Linton. Even if any generalization can be drawn from these small assemblages, this proportion is certainly not sufficient to be taken as evidence for a North Atlantic continental connexion. The hypothesis is still more uncertain when one remembers that the amphibians in question are aquatic or marsh dwelling forms. If a land-bridge is necessary to account for the floral similarity in the two continents, it is probably to be restricted to the ridge (now largely submarine) between Greenland and Britain, by way of Iceland and the Faröe Islands.

The Permian tetrapods of North America are all obtained from deposits of Lower Permian age, equivalent to the Rothliegende of central Europe, and Romer (1935) has shown that they represent autochthonous development from the preceding Carboniferous stocks. Williston (1909) and Case (1915) believed that the distinctness of the North American fauna indicates an isolation of the continent from Europe nearly as complete as that of today. The Lower Permian flora of North America, well developed in the Appalachian region, Kansas, Oklahoma, Texas, New Mexico, and Colorado, is very similar to the *Callipteris-Walchia* association of Europe. In Oklahoma and Texas, however, it contains a large fern-like plant, *Gigantopteris*, which is not known in European floras (D. White, 1912). *Gigantopteris* was first discovered in early Permian strata in China and subsequently found at other localities in the Far East of Asia, including Korea and Sumatra (Map, Fig. 53). The slightly later flora of the Hermit Shale in Arizona (D. White, 1929), in addition to *Callipteris* and *Walchia*, contains several plants that are identical with, or related to, species from the distinctive Permian flora of Kusnezk and other localities in Northern Asia, and some which have a strong likeness to plants of the *Glossopteris* flora characteristic of the southern continents and India. This introduces the possibility of connexion between North America and Asia, but unfortunately we have no knowledge of Permian tetrapods from Asiatic deposits. The peculiar distribution of the Gigantopteris flora is an argument against Continental Drift, for according to this theory North America should be contiguous with Europe at the time when a similar relation across the Pacific is demanded.

The higher Permian strata of North America have yielded no tetrapods and the few records of Triassic labyrinthodonts and cotylosaurian reptiles differ generically from the European lists. The presence of dicynodonts, specialized thesodonts and early deinosaurs is proved by records from Arizona; the first group, best known from abundant specimens in South Africa, is now recorded from widely separated regions in the northern hemisphere. In the far north, early Triassic labyrinthodonts from east Greenland are congeneric with species from Spitzbergen and Russia.

Another gap in the history of North American tetrapods is due to the scarcity of early Jurassic deposits on the continent. But the later freshwater Morrison Beds of Colorado, Wyoming, and adjacent States have yielded deinosaur remains in great abundance and variety. The Morrison assemblage has hardly a genus in common with the European fauna (p. 561) and we have concluded that the evidence certainly does not support extensive land-connexion, much less contiguity, of North America and Europe during Jurassic time. The vast tracts of non-marine Cretaceous deposits, extending from New Mexico and California to Alberta and British Columbia have also yielded deinosaurs of primary importance in our discussion. They include extraordinary, specialized forms of trachodonts, nodosaurs, and ceratopsians which are almost unknown elsewhere. Some comparable forms recently discovered in central Asia seem to indicate a westward land-connexion probably by the Behring Peninsula.

Apart from deposits in the coastal belts, the Neozoic strata of North America are all of continental origin (Map, Fig. 81), and have provided a tolerably continuous series of mammalian remains. From our discussion in Chapter XVII it is clear that many great families of land-mammals developed autochthonously in North America between Palaeocene and Pleistocene time. In no other continent can the evolution of land mammals be traced in such detail. Occasional immigration from Asiatic sources at various periods is indicated by such events as the sudden appearance of peccaries and anthracotheres in Oligocene beds, of elephants in Miocene deposits, musk-ox, reindeer, and bear in Pleistocene beds, to name only a few examples. These migratory movements are believed to have taken place over the obvious Behring route. An influx of South American edentates in Pliocene beds of the southern States is sufficiently explained by the emergence of the Panama Isthmus which still joins the two American continents.

The history of the fossil tetrapods thus goes far to prove that the continent of North America has been essentially isolated from other continents since Carboniferous time. Occasional immigrations of Asiatic animals are amply explained by the discontinuous emergence of the Behring connexion (now inoperative). The slight affinity with European faunas in late Carboniferous and early Eocene times may require the now obscure route from Greenland by way of Iceland and the Faröe Islands to Britain. These two, and the still operative Panama Isthmus, seem to be the only connexions from North America to other continents warranted by the available evidence of the tetrapods.

ASIA differs from the other continents in having two nuclei, apart from the ancient mass of Arabia which geologically belongs to Africa. In the south the Indian Peninsula (Map, Fig. 86), has a foundation of Precambrian rocks which seems to have formed a land surface since early Palaeozoic time. For, with the exception of a marine band in the Upper Carboniferous rocks of Bengal, and a few marginal deposits of Mesozoic age, the sedimentary rocks of the Peninsula are of continental origin. The Angara nucleus of north-east Siberia, augmented by the emergence of early Palaeozoic rocks at the end of Silurian time, is limited southwards by the folded arcs of Sayan and Baikal. The intervening area, occupied largely by marine Palaeozoic deposits, has been welded to the continental mass by successive orogenic movements of late Palaeozoic, Mesozoic, and Neozoic ages. As a result, the marine Mesocarboniferous deposits of China, for example, are succeeded by a great coal-bearing series of sandstones and shales, and, apart from short marine transgressions of Permian and Triassic age (Map, Fig. 63), the greater part of China has been part of the continent ever since. During late Palaeozoic time the marine depression of the Ural region became upfolded to connect Asia and Europe. Farther south marine conditions persisted until Miocene time when the Alpine orogeny completed the union of the two continents.

The coal-bearing beds of Carboniferous and Permian age in India and

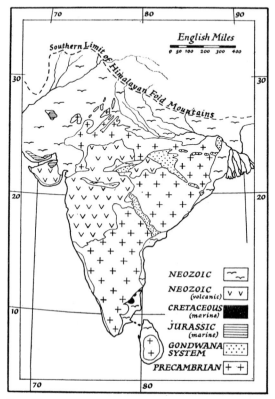

NEOZOIC

NEOZOIC *(volcanic)*

CRETACEOUS *(marine)*

JURASSIC *(marine)*

GONDWANA SYSTEM

PRECAMBRIAN

FIG. 86. GEOLOGICAL SKETCH-MAP OF THE INDIAN PENINSULA SHOWING THE RELATION OF PALAEO-ZOIC AND LATER ROCKS TO THE PRECAMBRIAN FOUNDATION

China have so far yielded few fossil tetrapods, though land plants are abundant. The Carboniferous flora of China has close resemblance to that of Europe and North America and the Permian 'Cathaysian' flora is recorded (Halle, 1937) as far south as Sumatra (Map, Fig. 53). The Permian Glossopteris flora of India is closely similar to that of Africa and Australia, and it is also recorded from the northern Dwina in Russia. A different flora is characteristic of Permian deposits in the Angara region, namely, the *Gigantopteris* flora, which extends southwards to the Yangtze Valley, and is recorded also from Sumatra; a similar flora occurs in Texas. The earliest of the Asiatic tetrapods are two genera of rhachitomous labyrinthodonts from the Lower Permian of Kashmir, which are also represented in corresponding beds of Europe. Fragmentary remains of labyrinthodonts from the Lower Triassic beds of India are of uncertain affinities but the anomodont reptile *Lystrosaurus* from the same beds has species in the Trias of Indo-China, China, and, more abundantly, in Africa. More primitive forms in Russian deposits, however, probably indicate the ultimate origin of the genus. Higher Triassic deposits in India have yielded the reptiles *Hyperodapedon*, *Parasuchus*, &c. which are akin to corresponding European forms. The obvious route to or from the west is by way of Arabia and Afghanistan where continental deposits of appropriate age are known. These scanty records certainly do not justify the statements of close affinity with the great African fauna which are made in some of the textbooks.

The Cretaceous reptiles lately described from the Lameta Beds of Peninsular India include a number of deinosaurs. Several theropod genera are referred to families that have a long range in North America. The nodosaurs, with one local genus in India, are best known from Canada and the western States. The sauropods, apart from the type-species of *Titanosaurus*, are referred to genera that were originally described from the Upper Cretaceous rocks of Patagonia. But the actual relationship between the Indian and South American faunas may be more apparent than real, for other members of the same family are known from North America, western Europe, Egypt, Madagascar, and South Africa. Moreover, the earliest deinosaurs recorded from Lower Cretaceous deposits in Mongolia are closely related to North American forms. They include beaked deinosaurs that are members of a primitive stock related to the later American ceratopsians, also a sauropod morphologically similar to certain American genera. Upper Cretaceous beds in Mongolia have yielded theropods and a ceratopsian comparable with Canadian forms. There is no doubt that close relation exists between the Cretaceous deinosaurs of North America and central Asia. The most obvious land-connexion is the Behring route (now broken), in spite of the great distance between Mongolia and Canada, but the relations of the Indian titanosaurs are still obscure.

The Neozoic mammals of Mongolia, from various horizons between early Eocene and Miocene, emphasize further the relationship of Asian with North American faunas. The Mongolian collections include representatives of the creodonts, tapirs, rhinoceroses, peccaries, titanotheres, hypertragulids, amblypods and other groups which all show continuous evolutional series in the North American rocks. Migration from North America to Asia admits of no doubt. Some North American groups developed autochthonously in Asia after migration, and some of these, e.g. the camels, survived the great Pleistocene extinction only in Asia. The presence of mastodons in Asiatic Miocene beds indicates affinity with African and European faunas. Connexion between Europe and Asia approached its present maximum at this time, and the famous Pontian fauna of Greece has many genera, and even some species, in common with the Siwalik faunas of India.

AFRICA, south of the Sahara, has undoubtedly been a land-area since Devonian time, at least. For the sedimentary rocks overlying the Precambrian foundation are entirely of freshwater or subaerial character, apart from a few marine transgressions that extend only a short distance inland (Map, Fig. 87). The northern border of the African Shield, in the Saharan region, consists of a considerable thickness of marine strata which resemble those of southern Europe. The southern border of the Shield includes marine Devonian and Cretaceous rocks the former of which are involved in the Cape folding. Deposits of Mesozoic and Neozoic age at intervals on the western and eastern coasts represent transgressions of the sea at various periods of time.

Rocks of the non-marine Karroo system cover vast tracts of the Shield in the Cape Province (Map, Fig. 55), the Belgian Congo and numerous smaller areas scattered as far north as Abyssinia. The Dwyka tillite at the base of the system attests widespread glaciation extending through 35 degrees of latitude, or more than 2,000 miles from north to south, during the later part of Carboniferous time. The succeeding Ecca and Beaufort Series provide an abundant flora and a long, almost continuous, series of tetrapods. The former is the well-known Glossopteris flora which extends through the southern continents and India, and even to the Upper Permian deposits of northern Russia. For many years this flora has been taken to indicate continuity of these widely separated land masses in late Palaeozoic time, thus forming the Gondwanaland Continent of Suess.

The abrupt appearance of tetrapods at the base of the Beaufort Series is evidently due to immigration. The labyrinthodont amphibians and various groups of reptiles which compose the faunas are distributed in some 145 genera and over 90 per cent. of these are not yet recorded outside Africa. This high proportion of restricted forms may merely indicate that conditions for fossilization were unusually favourable, but many authors have inferred either an undetermined southern source for the fauna, or an autochthonous development from the original migrants. Later discoveries of similar reptiles in north Russia disclose that many of the older Russian forms are more primitive than their African relatives which may, therefore, have had a northern origin. If this be so, there is no need to derive the Indian and Chinese, to say nothing of the Scottish, dicynodonts, from an African source. The Upper Beaufort Series contains genera of labyrinthodonts which also occur in the Lower Trias of Europe and are possibly derived from forms represented in the Upper Permian of Russia (p. 372). The latest cotylosaur, *Procolophon*, has its nearest ally in the Triassic rocks of north-east Scotland (p. 401), and there are European genera among the deinosaurs of the Stormberg Series (p. 544). Hence there seems no need to uphold an unknown southern source of origin for these tetrapods, when so many possible ancestors or collaterals were already established in northern faunas.

An assemblage of deinosaurs from late Jurassic deposits in Tanganyika

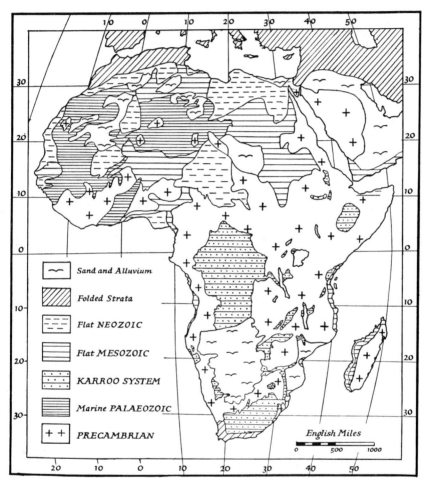

FIG. 87. GEOLOGICAL SKETCH-MAP OF AFRICA SHOWING THE RELATION OF PALAEOZOIC AND LATER ROCKS TO THE PRECAMBRIAN FOUNDATION

Territory (p. 561) contains named species of six genera; the only one recorded outside Africa is represented in the Morrison Beds of North America. The African assemblage as a whole is said to resemble the Morrison fauna in its broad aspect, but this statement is too vague to have any value. Nopcsa (1934) is more definite in claiming that two of the genera had ancestors in common with European types, but evolved on independent lines in Africa. The few scattered records of deinosaurs from Cretaceous deposits in Africa do not allow any reliable generalization, though, again, some forms show signs of independent specialization.

A survey (Chap. XVII) of the Neozoic mammals of Africa shows that the only truly indigenous groups are the proboscideans and the hyracoids which first appear in the Upper Eocene and Lower Oligocene deposits of Egypt. Already in the latter rocks immigrant creodonts, anthracotheres, rodents and anthropoids are established. Miocene and Pliocene strata of various regions yield additional Eurasian immigrants from which the animals now characteristic in the African fauna have developed.

The peculiar and restricted fauna of Madagascar (p. 672) is due to such a degree of isolation as allowed only sporadic settlement of a few species at different periods of time.

It is clear therefore that the fossil tetrapod faunas of Africa all show affinities with those of Eurasia. The land-connexion thus implied, probably through Arabia, is nowadays lessened by the formation of the Red Sea during Pliocene time. No other connexion seems to be warranted by the evidence of the tetrapods.

SOUTH AMERICA has for its nucleus the great Brazilian Shield, extending from the Rio de la Plata in the south to the Venezuelan Andes in the north. An embayment in the lower part of the Amazon Valley is occupied by flat-lying marine deposits of Silurian and Devonian age; transgressive Cretaceous and Neozoic rocks occur on the coast of Brazil (Map, Fig. 88). These apart, the sedimentary rocks on the Shield are of continental origin. The largest area is occupied by the Santa Catherina system, similar and equivalent to the Karroo system of Africa. Both systems contain identical species of the Glossopteris flora, but the tetrapods on the two continents differ considerably. Of the tetrapods of the Santa Catharina system A. S. Woodward (1935) says,

> The little Mesosauria found in the Permian of Brazil seem to be so essentially identical with those of the Lower Karroo formation of South Africa that they have actually been quoted as proof of a former direct connection between South America and South Africa; but in the Coal Measures of both North America and Europe there are possible ancestors from which they might have been derived in different directions. In somewhat later formations in Brazil there are also dicynodonts which are specially characteristic of the South African Karroo: but typical dicynodonts have lately been found in Arizona and they have long been known from Europe and from Asia, so that these again might be independent immigrants from the north. The recent discovery in Brazil of numerous large Rhynchosauria, which have not hitherto been met with in South Africa, favours the supposition that the two early Mesozoic faunas in question did not live on one continuous land-area.

This view is supported by G. G. Simpson (1943) who states that only 8 per cent. of the genera and 43 per cent. of the families of known reptiles from the Triassic rocks of South America are also known from the Trias of South

ALLUVIUM ~

NEOZOIC : : :

FOLDED STRATA

FLAT CRETACEOUS

SANTA CATHARINA
SYSTEM

FLAT PALAEOZOIC

PRECAMBRIAN +

English Miles
0 100 200   400   600

FIG. 88. GEOLOGICAL SKETCH-MAP OF SOUTH AMERICA SHOWING THE DIS-
POSITION OF PALAEOZOIC AND LATER ROCKS AROUND THE PRECAMBRIAN
SHIELD

Africa. He says, 'These figures are decidedly inconsistent with any direct union of corresponding parts of South America and Africa. The resemblance is greater than between South America and Africa today, but its small degree opposes a direct land-connection, even a connection by a direct bridge.' With these definite pronouncements on this much-debated topic by eminent specialists on fossil vertebrates it is surely unnecessary to comment on opposing statements by authors who have no special competence in the palaeontological field, or on the attempts of others (e.g. J. W. Gregory, 1929, 1930; Nopcsa, 1934) to explain the distribution of certain South American tetrapods by trans-oceanic land-bridges. In the light of present knowledge, it is clear that the idea of a great southern continent, extending over South America, Africa and beyond, was originally founded on insufficient evidence; now it rests only on the similarity of the floras, and this seems capable of a different interpretation (pp. 335–6).

Records of later Mesozoic tetrapods come mainly from the Upper Cretaceous rocks of Patagonia. These include four genera of titanosaurs some of which are otherwise recorded only from India. Other genera of the same family are, however, known from Europe, Asia, North Africa, Madagascar, and recently from New Mexico. In view of the last-named record the transpacific land-bridge advocated by Nopcsa (1934) will eventually prove to be unnecessary. It is pertinent to mention that Simpson (1935) postulates a connexion with North America during a part of Cretaceous time to account for the advent of marsupials in South America.

The history of South American mammals, discussed in Chapter XVII, shows that some orders spread from North America during late Cretaceous or earliest Eocene time. Then, until the Miocene age, autochthonous development of Eocene stocks demonstrates the complete isolation of South America from the rest of the world. Immigration of proboscideans, artiodactyls, and perissodactyls from North America followed the emergence of the Panama Isthmus in late Miocene time. The survivors and descendants of the indigenous genera and of the immigrants form the present mixed fauna of the continent.

AUSTRALIA. As in Europe and North America, the earliest sedimentary rocks of continental origin on the Australian Shield are red sandstones of Devonian age (Map, Fig. 89). The fishes contained therein show a surprising uniformity with European forms, and one genus is recorded only from Australia and Spitzbergen. Lower Carboniferous rocks contain the Rhacopteris flora which is widespread in the northern continents. On the other hand the Permian deposits of Australia yield the Glossopteris flora, several species being identical with Indian and African forms. But marine faunas of Permian and Triassic age on the island of Timor are closely related to corresponding faunas in India, Madagascar, and North America. Hence an extent of ocean separated Australia from India and Africa during at least part of Permian and Triassic time.

The earliest tetrapods so far recorded in Australia are labyrinthodont amphibians from the Triassic rocks of New South Wales. The genus *Bothriceps* belongs to a family which has representatives in the Trias of India, Europe, and South Africa. Later forms of *Capitosaurus* and *Cyclotosaurus* are similar to species from the Trias of Siberia, Europe, and Africa. There are few records of deinosaurs. A terminal phalangeal bone is referred to the European genus *Megalosaurus*, and a giant sauropod from Jurassic deposits in Queensland is placed in the Brachiosauridae, a family represented also

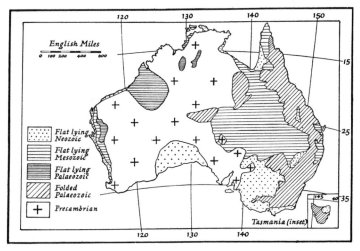

FIG. 89. GEOLOGICAL SKETCH-MAP OF AUSTRALIA SHOWING THE RELATIONS OF PALAEOZOIC AND LATER ROCKS TO THE PRECAMBRIAN NUCLEUS

in North America and Europe. Despite their Eurasian similarities the records are too scanty to provide a definite inference with regard to connexion with the northern continents, or with Africa during Mesozoic time.

Neozoic mammals are hardly known in Australia before the Pleistocene age, but it is generally accepted that the unique marsupial fauna still existing has evolved autochthonously from an ancient stock isolated geographically since the Cretaceous period. The marsupials of South America are not directly related to Australian forms and there is no justification for the land-bridge between the two continents advocated by Huene (1929), Gregory (1930), and Nopcsa (1934). There is no evidence, either, for an alternative route through Antarctica.

The placental mammals of Australia, chiefly rodents, certainly came from Asia, probably during Miocene and Pliocene time. Hence we may conclude, in the words of Simpson (1943), 'The faunal relationships of Australia are completely and simply explained by the view that Australia has had about its present relationships to other continents since the

Cretaceous at least, that the marsupials entered by the island route from Asia, and that rodents entered later over the same route.

II. THE OCEANS

On the evidence of fossil land animals we have arrived at the conclusion that the continents have always had more or less their present relationships to each other since the Carboniferous period. Land-connexions between adjacent continents have fluctuated from time to time, as shown by the degree of similarity or variation between appropriate faunas at corresponding horizons in the succession of strata, and, though the evidence is by no means complete, such land connexions seem to have been limited to those which are operative or obvious at the present day. All other land-bridges are merely speculative.

We have now to consider whether the oceans show the same degree of permanence as the continents. This is more difficult to prove or refute, for we have to depend almost entirely on the fragmentary evidence provided by marine deposits that now form part of the land-areas. We have seen, however, that these deposits are primarily due to the transgression of oceanic waters over the continental margins, and that the marine faunas in the coastal belts of the great oceans often show striking resemblances which are not due entirely to facies. It seems desirable therefore, at the risk of some repetition to summarize the evidence discussed in the foregoing pages, concerning each of the oceans in turn.

There is also the important question of size, especially with regard to the Atlantic and Pacific Oceans. There seems to be general agreement that the total amount of water on the surface of the earth has remained virtually constant through the ages. Additions of magmatic water from volcanic material makes only a small proportional difference to the total. Marine transgressions at any one period have always been relatively small, and have been estimated to account for only about one-eighth of the water. Hence the remaining seven-eighths must have been accommodated in ocean basins of almost the same capacity as the present ones. These could not have been converted into land areas without drowning the continents and exterminating the land flora and fauna living thereon; there is no evidence of such a widespread catastrophe in the palaeontological record. On these grounds we regard as untenable the idea of Haug (1911) and others that the present sites of the Atlantic and Pacific Oceans were formerly occupied by great continents. On the other hand, Wegener (1923) views Palaeozoic geography as a single 'Pangaea' surrounded by a single great ocean, and Dutoit (1937) only differs in allowing a narrow strait in place of the present Atlantic Ocean. The size of these oceans, however, must always have been considerable to account for (1) the area covered by the marginal transgressive seas, and (2) the conspicuous specific differences in related forms of the respective faunas on the western and eastern borders of the oceans.

With regard to the faunal similarities and differences there are few data of quantitative character in the literature, but those concerning the general features of the faunas seem sufficiently definite to prove the principle. We shall note these at their appropriate places in the discussion.

THE ARCTIC OCEAN. Thanks to the work of several expeditions to Arctic lands, including Alaska (P. S. Smith, 1939), Greenland (Koch, 1929, 1935), and Spitzbergen (H. Frebold, 1935), knowledge of the geology and palaeontology of the region has been greatly extended in the last three decades. Most of the systems are represented around the margins of the Arctic Ocean by deposits laid down in temporarily transgressive seas, which indicate the presence of permanent ocean at no great distance (Map, Fig. 90). There is evidence, too, that this stable Arctic Ocean has been connected with the Atlantic and Pacific Oceans since early ages. We have noted (p. 147) transgressive Palaeocambrian deposits on the coasts of north Siberia and north-west Greenland. The fauna in the latter locality closely resembles that of the interior and western States of North America with which it must have had direct marine communication. One possible route lies by way of east Greenland which has yielded a similar fauna, and the Olenellid trilobites of north-west Scotland indicate a connexion with the North Atlantic between Scotland and Greenland. Similar evidence is given by the faunas in the transgressive Ordovician rocks of Spitzbergen, Bear Island, north-west Scotland, and north Greenland. Contemporary erosion has caused gaps in the Silurian succession of north Greenland which, with the widespread occurrence of similar rocks in the Arctic archipelago of north America, attests a considerable extension of the Arctic Ocean on to the Canadian Shield. Above the Devonian rocks (of Old Red Sandstone type) in Spitzbergen there are marine Carboniferous deposits and a similar transgression is displayed on Bear Island and in Timan; in east Greenland the Lower Carboniferous is represented by sandstones containing plants of the Rhacopteris flora and is followed by marine beds of later Carboniferous age. On Clavering Island, east Greenland, late Permian rocks contain the ammonoids *Medlicottia* and *Cyclolobus*, and the fish fauna is closely similar to that of the English Marl Slate and the German Kupferschiefer (Aldinger, 1937, Westoll, 1941). In Spitzbergen marine Triassic rocks are said to follow Permian strata with apparent conformity, the system ending with plant beds of Rhaetic age. Early Triassic Beds in east Greenland contain ammonoid genera that are known elsewhere only in corresponding beds of the Himalayas; in the absence of further evidence the route of communication can only be conjectured. The Rhaetic plant-beds of east Greenland are followed by a series of marine deposits representing numerous Jurassic horizons from the Middle Lias to the Portland stage, and a fairly continuous succession of Cretaceous rocks of Neocomian and Aptian age. On Spitzbergen the Jurassic strata begin with Aucella Beds of Oxfordian age which are followed by certain horizons of the Kimmeridge

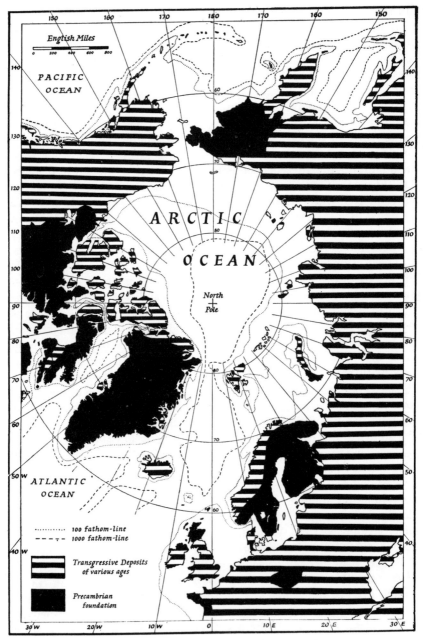

Fig. 90. SKETCH-MAP OF THE ARCTIC OCEAN WITH THE AREAS COVERED BY
THE SEVERAL PALAEOZOIC AND MESOZOIC TRANSGRESSIONS

and Portland stages. The Kimmeridge ammonites of Spitzbergen are very similar to those of Scotland and there is considerable generic similarity among the Jurassic and Lower Cretaceous ammonites of east Greenland and England, though the Arctic assemblages are always comparatively impoverished and some genera are peculiar to the boreal seas. This resemblance clearly indicates open marine communication between the Arctic, Barents, and Greenland seas on the one hand, and the North Atlantic Ocean and the North Sea on the other. Continuation of this marine passage in later Cretaceous time is indicated by the considerable degree of resemblance between the molluscan faunas of that age in east Greenland and north-west Europe. A marine molluscan fauna of Upper Cretaceous age on the islands off west Greenland is the first indication of Davis Strait as an arm of the sea. The oceanic connexion after Cretaceous time is not easy to trace, for Neozoic rocks in Greenland and Spitzbergen are either volcanic rocks or coalbearing sandstones of continental type. Nevertheless, the sea passage doubtless continued as such, judging by the degree of difference shown by the tetrapod faunas of Europe and North America, with the possible exception of the Palaeocene assemblages. On the whole, then, the area between Greenland and west Europe has always been occupied by the sea, with the possible exception of short intervals in Devonian, early Permian, late Triassic, and early Neozoic time.

To find a counterpart of the North Atlantic communication with the Arctic Ocean it is necessary to go to the extreme west of the Canadian Shield. Here in the Mackenzie Valley several horizons of Cambrian strata have yielded trilobites that show affinities with those of north-west Greenland and British Columbia. Resser (1929) writes of 'sketchy reports' concerning numerous Cambrian outcrops in north Asia, but says the faunas are all related to those found in western North America. Ordovician and Silurian graptolites of various horizons are recorded from north-west Greenland, Alaska, Yukon Territory, and British Columbia; according to Ruedemann (1929) these show Pacific affinities but nothing appears to be known of these organisms in the Arctic Archipelago or north Asia. Silurian limestones of Wisconsin and Illinois contain certain shelly elements comparable with those of west Europe, but unknown in the eastern States of America. Weller (1898) suggested migration through the Arctic seas, but Foerste (1929) points out that recent investigations have failed to disclose these organisms in the wide-spread Silurian deposits of the Arctic regions. Hence, though marine communication through the Mackenzie Strait is certain, its application to certain organisms remains to be proved. Thick and widespread Mesodevonian deposits in Alaska contain such characteristic fossils as *Calceola* and *Stringocephalus*, but these cosmopolitan forms give no definite information as to migration routes. Special interest, therefore, attaches to the distribution of Neodevonian goniatites. A varied assemblage is described from a horizon in the Timan Peninsula, north Russia, and

3 A

the same fauna is represented at Novaia Zemlya, and localities in Arctic Siberia. Two genera of the same fauna are reported from the Mackenzie Valley and Alberta, Canada, one of them (*Timanites*) being unknown in the famous Naples fauna of New York. Fusulina limestones of Upper Carboniferous age in British Columbia are comparable with the Russian deposits, and higher strata in Alaska are said to contain Artinskian or Gshelian fossils. Transgressive rocks of late Triassic age in north-west America contain *Pseudomonotis subcircularis* which is closely related to *Ps. ochotica* of the Sibeiran coast. The evidence for this Yukon passage during Jurassic time is less clear than that for the Atlantic connexion, and Crickmay (1931) states that it was inoperative before Bajocian time. The occurrence of occasional *Phylloceras* and *Lytoceras*, with abundant macrocephalitids, cadoceratids, and cardiocerates in Alaska and Siberia, shows that connexion was open for part of the period, and that the main migration was from north to south. Crickmay shows the strait continuing in Neocomian time but thereafter the Cretaceous rocks of Alaska and the Mackenzie district, an alternation of marine and freshwater deposits, indicate only intermittent communication with the Arctic Ocean. Canada has no marine Neozoic strata, and communication between the Arctic and Pacific Oceans through the Yukon strait was ended. Thenceforward north-west America became important as a route for the migration of land-mammals, though as W. D. Matthew (1908) shows, the Behring Strait became an open marine passage at various periods as at the present day.

Evidence of a third outlet (now a land area) is given by the Palaeozoic rocks of the Ural Mountains. This folded mountain-system has a pronounced meridional trend, beginning in the north with the Pai Khoi Range (69° N.; 63° E.) and extending southwards to the Mugojary Range (48° N.; 58° E.) near the Aral Sea. The highest summits, 1,600 to 2,000 metres in the north and 1,000 to 1,600 metres in the south, are in a central belt of crystalline schists assigned to a Precambrian age. Cambrian strata in the area are mainly clastic rocks without fossils, but limestones with calcareous algae and archaeocyathids are present at some localities. Early Ordovician trilobites are recorded from Pai Khoi, and later genera from the Kinderly River in the south Urals are prominent in corresponding beds of Scandinavia. Along the western slopes of the Urals, Silurian beds have yielded graptolites belonging to several zones but the record is incomplete; there are also limestones with brachiopods and corals. Devonian strata are well developed on the western slopes; at certain localities in the central and southern Urals the upper series contains goniatites of several horizons most of which are also recorded from the Timan Mountains, Novaia Zemlya and Arctic Siberia. A fairly complete succession of Carboniferous rocks has furnished abundant goniatites, brachiopods, and fusuline foraminifera, especially in the south Urals, and is followed by the early Permian Artinsk horizon long famous for its ammonoids. Younger Permian (as well as the succeeding Triassic and Jurassic) deposits are of continental type. Still higher in the succession flat-lying Cretaceous strata are transgressive over the folded Palaeozoic rocks, and Gorsky (1937) suggests that 'the Boreal and Southern Seas were joined together along the Eastern slope of the Urals'. A later transgression carries Eocene and Oligocene strata over the eroded surface of the Cretaceous beds, but from the Oligocene onwards only freshwater deposits are developed. The Ural region, therefore, was a marine channel during most of Palaeozoic time, and again during late Cretaceous and early Neozoic ages. In its early history the depression probably communicated with the Altai region, and possibly even extended farther eastwards to the Pacific Ocean.

THE NORTH ATLANTIC OCEAN. There is a considerable body of evidence that the Atlantic Ocean separated Europe and North America throughout the Lower Palaeozoic era. The early Cambrian strata of Britain and the European mainland, carrying the *Callavia*, *Paradoxides*, and *Olenus* faunas in ascending order, extend from localities near the present Atlantic coasts of Norway and Wales, France and Spain, eastwards to places in western Russia and Poland. This distribution evidently indicates a huge shallow embayment of the North Atlantic Ocean. On the western side similar faunas in the same order of succession, and having considerable generic identity, are known from south-east Canada and the eastern coasts of the United States. There can be no doubt that these faunas belong to the two coastal areas of a single ocean. The question is complicated by the presence of a different fauna, marked by the trilobite *Olenellus*, in early Cambrian rocks of the north-west Highlands of Scotland, a fauna which has generic similarity with that of west Newfoundland, the interior of North America, and Greenland. B. N. Peach (1912) held that the two faunas were separated by a stretch of deep ocean which neither could cross, but J. W. Gregory (1929) thought that the difference is so pronounced that a narrow land-barrier across the Atlantic is necessary. Gregory's hypothesis seems untenable because, as we have noted in Chapter III, brachiopod species of the *Callavia* and *Olenellus* faunas mingle in east Greenland, the *Paradoxides* fauna extends into north-west Vermont to cover lower strata carrying the *Olenellus* fauna, and the Neocambrian deposits of England and Wales have yielded occasional trilobites belonging to typical North American genera. The distribution of the two faunas is doubtless due to differences in the circulation of ocean currents in the early Atlantic Ocean, but opinion is divided with regard to the necessity of continuous coasts, or interspaced shoals for the dispersal of benthonic organisms like trilobites and brachiopods.

It is evident that similar geographical conditions also influenced the distribution of many genera of invertebrates which are common to the Ordovician rocks of west Europe and eastern North America. Among trilobites, the trinucleids and telephids are particularly apt examples, for many of their associates in North America are also confined to a narrow tract extending north-east and south-west along the eastern side of the present continent. These probably migrated from the European region, but many of the most prominent trilobite-genera in the Baltic area are unknown in America, perhaps owing to unequal capacity for migration. The graptolite faunas on the two sides of the Atlantic have many genera, and even some species, in common; Ruedemann (1934) suggests that these organisms radiated from a 'Sargasso Sea' in the North Atlantic Ocean of the period. The cystids (Bather, 1913), starfishes (Spencer, 1950) and cephalopods (Bather, 1913) also show resemblances that demand an extent of ocean between Europe and North America. At the same time there are distinct local developments which indicate that the two continents were separated by a considerable distance. On this question Schuchert (1928) said that the faunal similarities of the two regions should be identities if the continents were close together as Wegener postulates in his theory of Continental Drift. 'Many of the marine faunas, for instance, should have, not five per cent. of identical species, as is actually the case, but between 50 and 75 per cent. which is not true at all.' In particular there are few identical species, apart from graptolites, in the Ordovician faunas of Newfoundland and Ireland, though many genera are common to the two regions. This indicates an Atlantic Ocean which must have been of considerable width.

The same degrees of resemblance and difference are presented by the Silurian faunas of the two regions, especially in the graptolite, trilobite, and coral assemblages that we have discussed in Chapter V. The brachiopod fauna of Anticosti shows limited relations with those of England and Sweden, but the fauna of Newfoundland is not closely related to that of Ireland. We have also noted (p. 232) the presence of certain crinoid genera in Europe and North America which probably indicates an Atlantic communication, though some of those found in the central United States are not yet recorded from the well-searched rocks of New York State; their absence here may be altogether fortuitous.

The general character of the Devonian rocks in Europe and North America shows that considerable geographical changes have intervened, doubtless an effect of the Caledonian orogeny. In Europe, non-marine deposits of the Old Red Sandstone type occupy considerable tracts in Britain north of lat. 51° 30', also in the eastern Baltic States of Livonia and Latvia. Similar deposits occupy areas of south-east Canada in much the same latitude. The armoured fishes (Chap. VI) and land plants, which are the characteristic fossils, are so closely related in all these localities, that many authors have postulated an 'Old Red Continent' occupying the North Atlantic basin. But, as we are aware from present-day geography, the presence of non-marine or continental deposits on each side of this basin does not prove that the ocean was not in existence; the truncated outcrops merely prove that the coast-lines were farther out towards the continental slope. Many of the fishes are found in marine as well as in non-marine deposits, and all probably originated in oceanic waters. The marine Devonian faunas of Europe and North America are largely autochthonous developments from the preceding Silurian faunas. Nevertheless, the degree of resemblance is so considerable that some intermigration must have taken place. We may note especially the close similarity of Neodevonian goniatites in west Europe and North America; all the American genera, except one, are known in Europe which seems to have been the chief centre of development of the group. These fossils are rare in the Carboniferous Limestones on both sides of the Atlantic, but they show generic relationships in the shales of early horizons of the Coal Measures. The later American forms are not represented in the west European deposits because marine bands are not developed there so late as in America. Other groups of fossils also have many genera in common on both sides of the ocean. We have noted this in the corals and crinoids, but certain American genera of the latter group often develop peculiar modifications that are unknown in Europe (pp. 307–8).

In Europe marine deposits of the Permian and Triassic systems, apart from the peculiar Zechstein and Muschelkalk of Germany and adjacent countries, are almost restricted to the Alpine region. Likewise in North America marine rocks of these systems are known only in the south and west of the continent. Hence Koken (1907) and other authors conclude that all the Atlantic basin north of a line from Spain to Florida was occupied by land during the period in question. We have noted (p. 556) that this view is not justified by the testimony of the land-reptiles, and, though direct evidence is lacking, it seems reasonable to suppose that the 'New Red' lands did not extend beyond the present continental shelf on either side. Because of similarity of Permian and Triassic ammonoids in Sicily and Texas, the Mediterranean 'Tethys' is commonly held to have been continuous across the Atlantic area, joining up with the sea over Texas. To us it seems that this transoceanic Tethys merely marks the path of the equatorial current. This follows also from the similarity of Jurassic ammonites in south Europe and Mexico. There is evidence of a northern connexion with the Arctic Ocean during Jurassic time. The presence of marine Liassic deposits in west Scotland and north Ireland proves that the north-western part of the British area was already dissected and invaded by the sea, while the ammonites clearly indicate connexion with the Alpine-Mediterranean embayment of the Atlantic Ocean which extended well into North Africa. The shoreline of eastern North America, however, was still outside the present coast, but the marine faunas of the Antillean region and Mexico have a large preponderance of genera identical with those of southern Europe. These conditions continued during early Cretaceous time and the English Gault has yielded occasional ammonites belonging to characteristic American genera. In north-west Europe peculiar conditions gave rise to the Chalk of the Upper

Cretaceous, and remnants of this rock extend to the coasts of north Ireland and west Scotland: contemporaneous sandy deposits indicating the proximity of a coast-line are present at places in central Europe, e.g. Saxony.

The archipelagic condition of central Europe continued into Neozoic time, deposits of this age following the Mesozoic rocks in the basins between the Palaeozoic horsts (Map, Fig. 71). Many of the reef-building corals, echinoids and mollusca of the Mediterranean region show close resemblance to contemporaneous forms of the West Indies. These and other groups of marine organisms, such as the nummulitic foraminifera, are often said to require a continuous coastline for migration, but W. T. Vaughan (1924) states that a series of shoals would serve the purpose. The evidence of the marine faunas is therefore consistent with that of the land-mammals which is distinct enough to rule out direct transoceanic land-bridges.

On the whole, therefore, the palaeontological evidence, though it is far from continuous, indicates that neither the hypothetical Atlantic continent, the legendary Atlantis, nor the idea of Continental Drift can be justified in the present state of our knowledge as far as the North Atlantic Ocean is concerned.

THE SOUTH ATLANTIC OCEAN. There is little direct evidence for the existence of a South Atlantic Ocean in early Palaeozoic time. No marine rocks of Lower Palaeozoic age are known in West Africa between the Guinea coast and the Cape Province, nor in eastern South America between the Amazon and Patagonia. But, as J. W. Gregory (1929) points out, this absence of marine deposits does not prove the non-existence of a South Atlantic Ocean; it merely proves that the ocean was less wide than at present. We have noted (p. 144) that Neocambrian deposits in Argentina and Bolivia contain trilobites belonging to genera that are widespread in corresponding strata of European localities. This seems to require a seaway, west and north of the Brazilian Shield, connecting with the North Atlantic Ocean: the route of communication, however, is still unknown. Ordovician graptolites and trilobites (pp. 187–8) from Bolivia also have affinities with European forms, but Silurian rocks resting on the Precambrian floor of the Amazon Valley have yielded an assemblage of brachiopoda and mollusca which has been compared with the fauna of the Medina Sandstone in North America. It is clear that our limited knowledge of these early South American faunas does not permit any definite pronouncement concerning oceanic relationships.

Devonian rocks of the Amazon Valley have furnished a distinctive fauna of trilobites, brachiopods, and other fossils which is closely related to that of corresponding beds in the Falkland Islands and South Africa (p. 268). The same fauna is now known from localities in south Brazil, Uruguay, and north Argentina, besides Peru and Bolivia. Fossils from Devonian Beds near Accra on the Gold Coast of West Africa (p. 269) are said to have affinities with the Bokkeveld fauna of South Africa, and also with the

Hamilton fauna of North America. Some trilobites of the southern fauna are also recorded from the Sahara where they are associated with European types. The rocks containing this distinctive fauna can best be regarded as transgressive deposits from the South Atlantic Ocean, for their presence near the coast of south Brazil seems to rule out the extensive transoceanic land-bridge between South America and Africa which was suggested by earlier authors. Apparently the South Atlantic and Pacific Oceans were connected much farther north than at the present day.

The range of the Glossopteris flora over Brazil and Africa is usually taken to indicate continuous land across the South Atlantic region during Permian and Triassic time. This view, however, is inconsistent with the evidence of the tetrapod faunas of the two continents (p. 714) which are distinct enough to rule out the idea of direct land-connexion. There are two other occurrences which seem to point in the same direction. One is the presence of marine Triassic deposits in south-east Brazil, far away from the main outcrop of marine Trias in western South America, and separated from it by the non-marine Santa Catharina system. The other is the distribution of the small aquatic reptile *Mesosaurus*, which is restricted to the coastal regions of Brazil and South Africa: it is not certain, however, that this reptile is a marine form.

No Jurassic rocks are known on the borders of the South Atlantic Ocean, but the presence of a Cretaceous sea is indicated by marine deposits of Albian to Senonian age on the coasts of West Africa and Brazil. In Nigeria Albian deposits are followed by Turonian rocks of similar lithological type, but in Cameroon the Turonian stage rests directly on the Precambrian foundation. In Angola the lowest Cretaceous deposits of marine origin belong to the Albian stage, and higher beds are of Senonian age. Hence these represent temporary and local transgressions from the South Atlantic Ocean: connexion with the Mediterranean Sea across the Sahara is confined to the later horizons, for nothing earlier than Cenomanian is known in the Sahara. On the Brazilian coast, transgressive deposits of Albian, Turonian, and Senonian age are known at Rio Grande do Norte, Pernambuco, Sergipe, and Bahia. The ammonite faunas are closely related to those of corresponding horizons in West Africa, Madagascar, and Zululand. There is no doubt, therefore, concerning the existence of the South Atlantic Ocean during the greater part of Cretaceous time.

Early Neozoic deposits, ranging between Palaeocene and Middle Eocene, are found on the coasts of Togo, Cameroon, Angola, and Luderitz Bay. A. M. Davies (1934) says of them, 'The whole region seems to constitute a definite SE. Atlantic province.' Later Neozoic deposits of Angola, however, are not sufficient to establish regional relationships, and the zoo-geographical anomalies so often quoted are inadmissible as evidence in ignorance of their palaeontological history. In any case the presence of a South Atlantic Ocean has not been disputed for this period.

In summary, there is no incontrovertible evidence that the South Atlantic Ocean was occupied by land since Devonian time, and the absence of earlier marine deposits on the present coasts is no proof that the ocean did not exist in those early periods. There are definite indications of its existence during Devonian, Triassic, Cretaceous, and Neozoic time, and there seems no reason to doubt its general stability in the intervening periods.

THE INDIAN OCEAN. It is commonly asserted that the site of the Indian Ocean was occupied until Cretaceous time by a continental tract uniting India with Africa and Australia. The marine deposits of various Palaeozoic and Mesozoic horizons which have been recorded from localities in Persia, northern India, &c. are said to have accumulated in a 'Himalayan geosyncline' connecting the Mediterranean Sea in the west with the south-west Pacific in the Far East—an extension of the 'Tethys' along the northern border of 'Gondwanaland'. We have noted (Chap. IX) that the fossil land faunas of Africa, India, and Australia, as far as they are known, give no conclusive support to the hypothesis of Gondwanaland. We must now summarize the evidence of the several marine faunas on the question of the 'Himalayan geosyncline'.

The early Mesocambrian Redlichia fauna (p. 153) seems specially significant, for it is apparently restricted to the northern and eastern margins of the Indian Ocean. The fauna is recorded from south-west Persia, the Salt Range of Punjab, the Himalayas of Spiti, from Indo-China and Australia, with a northerly extension to China and Korea. Its westward range is unknown, for no Cambrian deposits are reported from the east coast of Africa. Apart from the presence of the small brachiopod *Botsfordia* it has nothing in common with any known Cambrian fauna in Europe or North America. Hence it forms a distinct biogeographical province apparently radiating from the Indian Ocean. Different relationships are shown by certain trilobites from Mesocambrian deposits in Spiti and Kashmir; the former include *Oryctocephalus* also recorded from British Columbia, Nevada, and Queensland, the latter have abundant *Tonkinella*, a genus also reported from Indo-China, Korea, and British Columbia. These records, therefore, show relationships with the Pacific Province, extending to North America. Hence the Indian Ocean of Upper Cambrian time had some connexion with the Pacific probably by way of south-east Asia. These fragmentary records obviously represent only a small part of the Cambrian succession though the system is reputed by some authors to be tolerably complete in the Himalayan region.

The Ordovician and Silurian systems are also represented in the central Himalayas and Burma by an extensive development of clastic sediments, but again the fragmentary palaeontological records seem to indicate that considerable gaps exist in the sequence. According to F. R. C. Reed (1912), fossils from Ordovician beds of the central Himalayas show marked affinities with the Trenton fauna of North America. This seems to indicate marine communication across the Pacific Ocean. But Reed (1906) also describes an Ordovician fauna from the Northern Shan States in Burma with pronounced European relationships and without any definite American elements. We still have to admit with Reed (1910) that 'it is not clear by what route the immigration of American types can have proceeded, nor how it crossed the strong European wave which seems to have flooded Eastern Asia'. Somewhat similar relations are shown by the Silurian assemblages so far described. That of the central Himalayas has a considerable development of Palaeosilurian corals with American affinities, whereas those brachiopods which have more than local significance seem closely related to European forms. The strong European relationship shown by the Burmese faunas is not, however, developed. We have noted (p. 223) that in Australia and New Zealand also an admixture of European and North American species is associated with local elements. In particular, the remarkable cosmopolitan distribution of graptolite species is demonstrated by the presence of identical forms in Europe, Burma, and the Pacific borders of Australasia, but these fossils are not recorded from the central Himalayas.

No Palaeodevonian fossils are so far recorded from the Himalayan region, yet the rich, early Devonian fauna of Bohemian type, which has been described from the Urals and the Altai, is well represented in the Zebingyi Beds of Burma. Later Devonian faunas have a wider distribution for they are described from numerous places in south Asia between the Urals and China including Persia, Afghanistan, Turkestan, Pamir, Chitral, the Himalayas, and Yunnan. It is worthy of note that certain widespread fossils characteristic of definite horizons in Europe are absent from the records of some Asiatic regions; for instance, no Devonian goniatites are recorded from Himalayan localities though a series of Neodevonian assemblages is described from Western Australia. Hence the statement of Teichert (1942) that the Australian goniatites migrated from Europe along the 'Himalayan geosyncline' seems to lack foundation.

In the central Himalayas (Bashahr and Spiti) the Devonian Limestones are said to pass up into Palaeocarboniferous shales and limestones which enclose a typical European flora and fauna. In Kashmir marine Carboniferous beds directly overlie the barren Muth Quartzite which may be of Silurian age: they contain brachiopods which are referred to European species associated with endemic forms.

Thus the Palaeozoic faunas so far known from south Asia seem to indicate temporary transgressions of local extent emanating from a more stable ocean of which the site is not fixed by the available evidence. There is also the possibility of a transgressive sea across central Asia connecting the Arctic, by way of the Urals and Altai with the Indian region.

Permian faunas around the Indian Ocean furnish more conclusive evidence of regional relationships. Near the base of the system in the Salt Range and Kashmir is an assemblage of marine mollusca including the peculiar lamellibranch *Eurydesma* associated with species of *Conularia*, *Pleurotomaria*, and *Martiniopsis*. (Reed, 1932, 1936). This Eurydesma fauna is represented also in corresponding beds in New South Wales and south-west Africa. The seaway between South Africa and the other two regions must have been round the southern end of Africa, for there is no evidence of marine deposits across the Precambrian block farther north, and the Eurydesma fauna is not known from North Africa. Hence the existence of an Indian Ocean during early Permian time is indicated. The distribution of certain elements in later faunas supports this conclusion. The type of fauna contained in the Productus Limestone of north India is very widespread, extending from the Urals to Japan across Central Asia (Tschernyschew, 1904), but the upper part is distinguished by the presence of the ammonoids *Cyclolobus*, *Xenaspis*, and *Medlicottia*. These are also known in the Upper Permian of Madagascar and Timor which were doubtless in direct marine communication across the Indian Ocean.

Similar evidence is provided by the distribution of Triassic ammonoids. Sections of marine Trias, though nowhere complete, have long been known in the Salt Range and the Himalayas. The known horizons in the marine Trias of Timor have faunas closely related to those of corresponding beds in India, and the Flemingites fauna is also represented in Madagascar. J. A. Douglas (1929) has described a fauna of different type from east Persia where the most conspicuous element is the scallop *Indopecten*. This compares closely with certain forms from the East Indies, but the genus is not known from the Himalayas. Afghanistan is known to have been land at this period, and the route connecting Persia with the East Indies is shown by the presence of *Indopecten* in the Triassic rocks of Oman (G. M. Lees, 1928); thence it would lie south of India through an open Indian Ocean.

The standard of reference for Jurassic rocks in the Indian region is the section in Kachh which provides a tolerably complete succession from the Bathonian to the Portlandian stage (p. 478). Liassic strata are present in Persia, Baluchistan and Madagascar. Many of the ammonites have close relations with forms long known from south Europe, but some are apparently peculiar to the borders of the Indian Ocean. The Liassic genus *Bouleiceras*, for instance, is only known from Baluchistan and Madagascar; this fact led Haug (1910) to postulate direct marine connexion between these two localities. The long outcrop of Triassic, Jurassic, and Cretaceous rocks near the western coast of Madagascar clearly indicates the existence of the Mozambique Channel throughout most of the Mesozoic era, though the sea did not overflow the coasts of Zululand and Portuguese East Africa until Cretaceous time. Farther north, Jurassic deposits, beginning with the Bathonian stage, indicate temporary transgressions over the coastal margins of Kenya, Tanganyika, Somaliland, Abyssinia, and Arabia. Many of the ammonites of East Africa are closely related to Kachh species (Chap. XII) but a fair proportion is referred to south European forms. Though

Persia is still incompletely explored many Jurassic horizons are known to be present, and they indicate that marine communication existed between the Indian Ocean (Madagascar, East Africa, and Kachh) and the Mediterranean Sea, by way of an enlarged Persian Gulf. The Cretaceous succession is also well represented in Persia, and points to a continuance of similar geographical conditions.

Apart from Kachh the Jurassic sections in India are very incomplete. Strata representing a few Middle and Upper Jurassic horizons occur in Rajputana and Attock, and in a review of the Indian Jurassic ammonites Spath (1927—43) concludes that the deposits of these localities represent a series of marine transgressions from Kachh northwards through the low-lying Indus plains. Ammonites characteristic of the highest Jurassic horizons are present in the Spiti Shales of the Himalayan region. The fossils and deposits here are more closely related to those of the Sula islands in the East Indies, and seem to indicate a separate series of transgressions from the south-east. This interpretation of the Jurassic rocks in northern India introduces a controversial note, for it has been stated (e.g. Reed, 1921) that in the central Himalayas marine conditions seem to have continued uninterruptedly from Permian to Cretaceous, producing a thickness of 7,000 feet of strata in unbroken sequence. But the fragmentary palaeontological succession shows that marine occupation of the Himalayan area was sporadic, unlike that of Kachh which was nearly continuous. Similar conditions are illustrated by the record of Cretaceous rocks in north India.

The Cretaceous succession is well represented in Persia, but only fragmentary sections are seen in north-west India. In Baluchistan Neocomian horizons are succeeded by deposits of Danian age. In Hazara and the Samana Range only fragments of the Neocomian and Albian stages are preserved and the Himalayan succession shows only a slight thickness of early Neocomian deposits. It is significant that no Cenomanian beds are known in this region, for deposits of that stage are transgressive in many parts of the world, though detailed work has shown that in many cases the transgression actually began before the Cenomanian. A temporary transgression of late Neocomian age is shown in the Madras area of Peninsular India by Barremian ammonites from marine beds that are intercalated in the Upper Gondwana Series. These prove that the main ocean was probably not far from the present eastern coast-line of the Peninsula in early Cretaceous time. The outlier at Trichinopoli has Upper Albian deposits at the base and the succession seems complete onwards to the Danian stage. At Pondicherry, however, the section begins with transgressive Campanian or Maestrichtian strata. Fossils of the same age are recorded from Cherrapungi, Assam, where the Cretaceous beds lie nearly horizontally on the eroded edges of Precambrian rocks. These instances suffice to show that the marine transgressions are extremely local and often of short duration.

Furthermore, recent work on the Himalayan fossils has shown such considerable gaps in the succession that the old idea of a continuous 'Himalayan geosyncline' has been seriously shaken. The facts seem to be better explained by a series of temporary marine transgressions from a stable Indian Ocean. On this view the Mesozoic Arabian Sea would only differ from its present successor in communicating with the Mediterranean Sea through an enlarged Persian Gulf, and in extending temporarily at various times into the East African and Himalayan regions.

Similar conditions seem to have continued into early Neozoic periods, for marine strata extend from the coast of Sind and Kachh to the North West Frontier Province. The early Eocene Ranikot Beds are known as far north as Thal and Tibet, while higher Eocene and some Oligocene strata are recorded in Thal and the Himalayas. Miocene and later deposits of the Himalayan region, known as the Siwalik Series, consist of alluvial detritus derived from the subaerial waste of the newly elevated mountain range.

THE PACIFIC OCEAN, 64 millions of square miles in extent, is the largest single geographical feature of the earth's surface. Its great size alone renders its history most difficult to interpret. Moreover, its 3,000 islands are usually small, and are composed of basalt or coral; they give very scanty information concerning ancient sediments. Nevertheless there is no real evidence, but only uncertain inference, that the Pacific area has ever been occupied by land of continental size as Haug, Gregory, and others have held. It is most convenient to discuss the western and eastern borders of this ocean separately.

We have already noted (p. 153) that the early Mesocambrian *Redlichia* fauna is recorded from numerous localities in east Asia, between Indo-China and Korea, as well as from Australia, India, and Persia. Hence we may be reasonably certain of connexion at this time between the Indian and west Pacific seas. Later Cambrian faunas of China are more distinct from the known Indian assemblages and in particular most of the typical Chinese trilobites are unknown in India (p. 154). The distribution of the various horizons indicates some fluctuation of the Cambrian coast-line in China, and the south-eastern part of the country, consisting of Precambrian rocks, was probably an island. The Ordovician deposits of China show a westward transgression over the Precambrian foundation as far as east Kansu and south-west Szechuan, with a central ridge of non-deposition along the site of the Tsinling Range. The separation into two basins is shown by the shelly faunas; the northern one has affinities with North American, the southern one with Burmese assemblages. The distribution of Ordovician graptolites indicates transgression from the direction of the Pacific Ocean, contrary to the interpretation of Grabau (Map, Fig. 33). The Silurian graptolites of China point to similar conditions, but the associated shelly deposits are restricted to an embayment over central and southern

China (Map, Fig. 38). It is doubtful if this embayment had any connexion with the Indian Ocean to the south-west by way of Burma.

As a result of post-Silurian earth-movement the sea retreated still farther from northern and eastern China, and marine deposits of Devonian age are confined to transgressive strata in south-west China (Map, Fig. 43). These range from the Eifelian to the Famennian stage of the European succession, and the faunas include such widespread elements as the coral *Calceola*, the goniatite *Manticoceras*, the brachiopods *Stringocephalus burtini*, *Hypothyridina cuboides*, and *Spirifer verneuili*. The goniatite provides a link with the Western Australian transgression and indicates that the migratory route from the Arctic region may have been through Pacific waters or through the transgressive seas of Central Asia. In south-west China marine Carboniferous rocks extend north-eastwards as far as Lushan in the Province of Kwangsi, but there are only non-marine deposits in south-east China. Farther north, transgressive Mesocarboniferous strata occupy considerable tracts from Shansi, Honan, and the Nanking Hills to Manchuria; this basin is separated from the southern area by a wide ridge of older rocks. J. S. Lee (1939) states that these northern deposits are evidently connected with central Asiatic strata by way of the 'Nanshan geosyncline' which was undoubtedly in free communication with the Urals, as shown by the almost identical faunas. In the higher Carboniferous strata, coalbearing shales and sandstones are intercalated with the marine limestones, and throughout Permian time north China was a site for the accumulation of continental deposits (Map, Fig. 59). Marine strata, especially fusuline limestones and goniatite-shales, continue in south China in the central Yangtze Valley and the south-western provinces. We have noted earlier (p. 388) that certain fusulinid genera (*Parafusulina*, *Neoschwagerina*, *Sumatrina*, *Verbeekina*) are also represented at localities in south Asia, e.g. Sumatra, Indochina, north-west India, Afghanistan, Turkestan. The coral genera *Waagenophyllum* and *Wentzelella* have a similar distribution in their appropriate facies. Moreover, the distinctive Loping fauna of Neopermian age includes the peculiar brachiopods *Richthofenia*, *Leptodus*, and *Oldhamina* which are most characteristic of Permian deposits in south Asia, though they have now been discovered elsewhere. Hence there are cogent reasons for supposing that the Permian faunas of south China had communication with those of the Indian Ocean, but there is the further possibility of a trans-Pacific connexion which remains to be discussed (p. 736).

In south China Neopermian coalbearing strata are succeeded by thin-bedded limestones which enclose ammonoids of Palaeotriassic age, and Mesotriassic genera are recorded from Yunnan and Kweichow. These indicate an early Triassic transgression which did not encroach on the south-east uplands. Later Triassic rocks of south China, and all the Trias of north China are of non-marine origin. Apart from marine Jurassic deposits near Hongkong and in east Yunnan, all the Jurassic, Cretaceous, and Neozoic strata throughout China are of continental type.

The Chinese geological succession therefore indicates that the marine strata of the country all represent transgressions of the sea, partly from the south across Burma, partly from the Pacific Ocean to the east. This view is well summarized by J. S. Lee (1939) though he unaccountably adheres to the older conception of a 'Cathaysian geosyncline'. From Jurassic time onward all China has been a land area.

Farther north, the rocks of Japan give evidence of repeated marine transgressions. The oldest marine sediment yet identified is of Neodevonian age, and marine limestones of Mesocarboniferous age play an important part in the stratigraphical development of central Japan. The marine Trias of south-west Japan has yielded ammonoids of the Anisian stage, and Norian fossils are also recorded. On the mainland of Manchuria Palaeotriassic and Mesotriassic ammonoids indicate an encroachment of the sea in the Ussuri district. Late Liassic ammonites are reported from the south-east and north-west coasts of Japan, as well as from the Manchurian mainland near Vladivostock. Higher beds are of continental type with freshwater shells and land plants, but include some marine beds with Mesojurassic (perhaps Oxfordian) ammonites. Lower Cretaceous beds are represented on various islands; resting unconformably on much older rocks, the base is not a constant horizon and the whole represents a transgression from the direction of the Pacific Ocean. The Neocretaceous Cenomanian and Senonian stages are represented at several localities, but the Turonian stage has not been satisfactorily recorded. The Senonian ammonites are said to be closely allied to Indian and west American forms. On Saghalien Island the Cretaceous beds are chiefly non-marine, plant-bearing deposits which lie directly on the crystalline foundation. There are, however, some intercalated marine beds which indicate temporary transgressions corresponding to Cenomanian and Senonian horizons.

On the eastern side of the Pacific Ocean the Cambrian succession in the western states of North America is based on the three major assemblages of trilobites known as the *Olenellus*, *Zacanthoides*, and *Dikelocephalus* faunas after the most characteristic genus in each. These faunas show considerable differences, but still fundamental similarities when compared with western Pacific faunas. *Olenellus* is not known in eastern and southern Asia, but the slightly later *Redlichia* is a close ally. The Chinese genera *Drepanura*, *Damesella*, *Blackwelderia* are unknown in America, and the American *Ogygiopsis* and *Neolenus*, equally typical of Mesocambrian horizons, are unknown in Asia. At the same time *Oryctocephalus* and *Zacanthoides* are recorded from Middle Cambrian rocks in Nevada, Idaho, British Columbia, Korea, and north India, and *Tonkinella* from the last three localities. The Neocambrian genera *Dikelocephalus* and *Saukia* seem to be restricted to North America, but their allies *Briscoia* and *Calvinella* are also recorded from East Asia. It is significant that many Chinese trilobites were originally referred to American genera by Walcott (1913). Lately there has been a tendency to refer the American and Asiatic forms to separate genera, but the relations between the two groups seem so close that direct, though far distant, marine communication is indicated.

The Ordovician graptolites of North America include many cosmopolitan species, but the presence of *Cardiograptus* and *Oncograptus*, first described from Australia, is taken by Ruedemann (1928) to indicate radiation from a 'Sargasso Sea' in the Pacific Ocean (p. 189). The shelly faunas of Ordovician deposits in North America and northern China are closely related, presumably influenced by the circulation of north Pacific ocean-currents. The same degree of relationship, however, does not extend to south China where the shelly faunas show closer affinity to those of Burma and north India. It seems likely that the Pacific connected with the Indian Ocean over this region during Ordovician time.

It has long been recognized that the Silurian faunas of North America have the same general characters as those of Europe and Asia (Frech, 1902), all belonging to a great 'Periarctic fauna' (Reed, 1910). The similarity between the faunas of the American Interior (e.g. Illinois, Iowa, Wisconsin, Arkansas) and those of northern Europe is shown particularly by certain species of crinoids, brachiopods, and corals which are not recorded from the well-searched areas of the eastern states. The evidence suggested to S. Weller (1898) some degree of communication through the Arctic Ocean. Subsequent discoveries of Silurian rocks in Alaska and the Mackenzie Valley support this view in principle but the particular fossils just mentioned have not yet been found in those regions. Farther south, in the western States, marine Silurian rocks are present near the Pacific coast, but the actual existence of a North Pacific Ocean in Silurian time is difficult to prove owing to the absence of Silurian rocks in north China. In South America the Silurian faunas contain many species identical or allied with those of North America. In eastern Australia many corals and other fossils have affinities with European species and thus link up with the Burmese faunas.

The early Devonian fauna of North America seems to have developed from the restricted Neosilurian fauna of the same region. Later (Meso-devonian) faunas include species of European type, and rocks of appropriate age in British Columbia and Alaska serve to connect the Interior of America with northern Russia by way of the Arctic Ocean. This may be the route by which the brachiopod *Stringocephalus* and the goniatite *Timanites* reached north-west America, for these genera are not recorded among the numerous forms invading New York State from the Atlantic region (Miller, 1938). Certain American elements described by F. R. C. Reed (1922) near the junction of Meso- and Neodevonian deposits in south Asia indicate trans-Pacific communications, though not necessarily extending over the whole area of the present ocean. A few North American forms are mingled with many species of Rhenish type in Queensland and New Zealand but there appears to be little affinity with the austral Devonian fauna of South America which apparently radiated from the South Atlantic Ocean.

The north-west passage connecting the Arctic Ocean with the transgressive seas of the middle and western States of North America was apparently operative during Carboniferous time. This is well shown by the distribution of the distinctive bryozoon *Archimedes* in the Lower Carboniferous of the Middle States, Alaska, north Russia, and Spitzbergen. The succession of goniatites in the Pennsylvanian Series of the United States is a close counterpart of the Russian sequence. Fusuline foraminifera also are abundantly represented in the marine Pennsylvanian rocks and C. O. Dunbar has emphasized their close relationship to Russian forms (p. 312). The Carboniferous fauna of South America, so far as it is known, appears to have close affinities with that of North America, and therefore with the Russian assemblage.

The shrinkage of the oceans in late Carboniferous and early Permian time, consequent on the widespread glaciation of the southern continents, has resulted in a scarcity of Permian marine deposits on the present land surface. Those of Texas and Mexico, however, have yielded numerous cephalopods which show generic similarity with those of Timor. This may reasonably be taken to indicate migration across or around the Pacific Ocean. No species appear to be identical in the two regions and we may infer that the distance between them was considerable, perhaps of the same order as at present. Species of the reef-coral *Waagenophyllum* in the Permian rocks of Texas and British Columbia are closely related to species from southern and eastern Asia, and the specialized brachiopods *Leptodus* and *Richthofenia* show comparable affinities (p. 390). Some species of bryozoa from Vancouver Island are said to be identical with forms described from Timor and the Salt Range of north India (Fritz, 1932). Certain genera of the fusuline foraminifera also, notably the specialized *Neoschwagerina* and *Polydiexodina*, are common to the southern United States, Mexico, and south Asia (p. 389) though some Asiatic forms are not yet known in America. Dunbar (1932) suggests that oriental fusulines migrated round the north-western margin of the North Pacific and entered the Cordilleran region from the north. However this may be, it is clear that there is substantial evidence for the existence of a wide Pacific Ocean during Permian time and Smith (1935) suggests that two embayments spread over the western United States and Canada respectively (Map, Fig. 58).

The Triassic cephalopod assemblages of western North America and Timor show close generic similarity when contemporaneous horizons are compared (p. 410). Again specific differences demand a wide expanse of ocean or a roundabout route between the two regions, and gaps in the American sequence suggest oscillations of the coastal margin. A junction of the Pacific and Indian Oceans is shown by the distribution of marine Triassic rocks in the East Indies (Map, Fig. 62). The presence of *Pseudomonotis ochotica* and its associates around the coasts of the north Pacific, but almost unknown elsewhere, has long been taken as an indication of the unity of this ocean during Triassic time. The description of Triassic coral-reefs in Alaska (60° N. lat.) by J. P. Smith (1912) is noteworthy, because Wegener (1923) places the North Pole of Triassic time close by (50° N. lat.) in the north-west Pacific, though the record of these reefs was available to him.

A series of maps by C. H. Crickmay (1931) demonstrates in a convincing manner that north Pacific waters extended over the margins of western North America at intervals during Jurassic time. In addition, the presence of boreal ammonoids at many localities along the Rocky Mountains, between Alaska and Colorado, indicates communication with the Arctic Ocean. The most extensive of these Arctic transgressions is of Oxfordian date; thereafter no marine deposits are known in the interior of the continent. In California the Oxfordian faunas are mostly made up of perisphinctids related to types characteristic of low latitudes and unknown farther north. The higher Jurassic beds between California and Alaska are marked by the presence of the lamellibranch *Aucella* in species closely comparable with Arctic forms. The existence, along the Pacific borders, of small faunas belonging to Kimmeridgian and Tithonian horizons indicates that marine waters lingered here long after they had retreated from the area now occupied by the Rocky Mountains. H. Gerth (1935) postulates a Pacific origin for the marine Jurassic deposits of the Andean region of South America, and the distribution of marine strata in the East Indies shows that a connexion between the south-west Pacific and Indian Oceans persisted during Jurassic time.

Transgressive Cretaceous deposits of various horizons along the western margin of the North American continent, in Alaska, north-west Canada, British Columbia, and California, are discussed in Chapter XIII. There is still an abundance of *Buchia* (*Aucella*), and, among ammonoids, such northern immigrants as *Polyptychites*, *Simbirskites*, &c., are associated with genera that are closely related to Mexican forms of the equatorial zone. In South America also, Cretaceous ammonoid faunas of several horizons are recorded from incomplete sections in Colombia, Peru, Chili, and Patagonia. Most of the genera are migrants from the equatorial belt, but some are purely local elements with a restricted distribution. When strictly contemporaneous faunas are compared, it is apparent that the Pacific faunas are composed of the same elements as those of the Atlantic and Indian regions, allowing for some impoverishment in the faunas of high latitudes. This is a reflection of the greater degree of faunal interchange between the Mesozoic oceans than that between their modern counterparts. Apart from this, the Pacific, like the Atlantic Ocean, must have been much the same as it is at the present time, except that the marginal transgressions were continually changing in size and location.

In early Neozoic time connexion between the Pacific and Atlantic Oceans was continued by the persistence of a seaway across the southern United States and Mexico. The evidence of corals, sea-urchins, and mollusca, discussed in Chapters XV and XVI, shows that this connexion was broken during Miocene time by the emergence of a land-area, corresponding more or less with the present Isthmus of Panama, joining the continent of North America to that of South America. Since that time only slight fluctuations of the coast-line have taken place, the most extensive being due to the abstraction of water from the oceans to form the Pleistocene ice-sheets. The severe climatic conditions then and now in high latitudes have restricted the interchange of faunal elements, and so have allowed some greater precision in the recognition of life-provinces during late Neozoic time.

GENERAL CONCLUSION. It has become evident that the palaeontological features of the several stratigraphical systems afford no support to the hypothesis of large transoceanic land-bridges as advocated by J. W. Gregory (1929-30) and others in the early years of this century. The hypothesis, though based on incomplete evidence, was held to explain certain apparent anomalies in palaeontological evidence, but some of these have been otherwise resolved as a result of subsequent exploration. It is equally certain that the theory of Continental Drift, envisaged by A. Wegener (1921) and A. Dutoit (1937), is inconsistent with the facts of palaeontological history, and that the theory is bolstered up by faulty interpretations of faunal relationships, some already discredited by competent palaeontologists. On the contrary, the evidence of marine faunas throughout the ages is consistent with the older view of stable ocean basins with fluctuating margins, and the continental faunas show such a measure of isolation that the land-masses of the globe must have had approximately their present relations during the whole history of the tetrapod animals.

LITERATURE

Full references to many of the works cited in this chapter have been made on previous pages, as in the following list.

Anderson 1938, p. 548; Bather 1913, p. 192; Crickmay 1931, p. 487; Davies 1934, p. 619; Douglas 1929, p. 428; Dunbar 1932, p. 394; Dutoit 1937, p. 353; Gerth 1935, p. 14; Halle 1937, p. 353; Haug 1911, p. 13; Koch 1929, p. 14; Lee 1939, p. 13; Lees 1928, p. 428; Miller 1938, p. 272; Peach 1912, p. 160; Reed 1906, p. 193; Reed 1912, p. 193; Reed 1950, p. 13; Romer 1935, p. 376; Seward 1931, p. 352; Smith 1912, p. 428; Spath 1924-33, p. 486; Teichert 1941, p. 271; Walcott 1913, p. 161; Wegener 1923, p. 353; White 1912, 1929, p. 353; Woodward 1935, p. 376.

The following works have not previously been cited in this volume.

Aldinger, H., 'Permische Ganoidfische aus Ostgrönland', *Medd. Grönland,* vol. cii, No. 3, 1937.

Blanford, W. T., 'The Permanence of Ocean Basins', *Proc. Geol. Soc.* pp. 29–77, 1890.

Foerste, A. F., 'Ordovician and Silurian of Arctic Regions', *Bull. Geol. Soc. Amer.,* vol. xl, p. 225, 1929.

Frebold, H., *Geologie von Spitzbergen,* &c. Berlin, 1935.

Fritz, M. A., 'Permian Bryozoa from Vancouver Island', *Trans. Roy. Soc. Canada,* ser. 3, sec. 4, vol. xxvi, pp. 93–107, 1932.

Gregory, J. W., 'Geological History of the Atlantic and Pacific Oceans', *Q.J.G.S.,* vols. lxxxv and lxxxvi, 1929–30.

Huene, F., 'Ueber Rhynchosaurier und Andere Reptilien aus den Gondwana-Ablagerungen Sudamerikas', *Geol. Palaeont. Abh.* N.S. vol. xvii, pp. 1–62, 1929.

Matthew, W. D., 'Mammalian Migrations between Europe and North America', *Amer. Jour. Sci.,* ser. 4, vol. xxv, pp. 68–70, 1908.

Nopcsa, F., 'The Geological Importance of the Primitive Reptilian Fauna in the Uppermost Cretaceous of Hungary', *Q.J.G.S.,* vol. lxxix, pp. 100–16, 1923.

—— 'The Influence of Geological and Climatological Factors on the Distribution of Non-Marine Fossil Reptiles and Stegocephalia', *Q.J.G.S.,* vol. xc, pp. 76–140, 1934.

Reed, F. R. C., 'Pre-Carboniferous Life-Provinces', *Rec. Geol. Surv. India,* vol. xl, pp. 1–35, 1910.

Resser, C. E., 'Cambrian of the Arctic Regions', *Bull. Geol. Soc. Amer.,* vol. xl, pp. 224–5, 1929.

Ruedemann, R., 'Fossil Evidence of the Existence of a Pacific Ocean in Early Ordovician Time', *Bull. Geol. Soc. Amer.,* vol. xxxix, pp. 299–310, 1928.

—— 'Palaeozoic Plankton of North America', *Geol. Soc. Amer. Mem.* No. 2, 1934.

Schuchert, C., *The Theory of Continental Drift,* Tulsa, 1928.

Simpson, G. G., 'The Oldest Known South American Mammals from the Rio Chico Formation', *Amer. Mus. Novitates,* No. 793, 1935.

—— 'Mammals and the Nature of Continents', *Amer. Journ. Sci.,* vol. ccxli, pp. 1–31, 1943.

Spencer, W. K., 'Asterozoa and the Study of Palaeozoic Faunas', *Geol. Mag.,* vol. lxxxvii, pp. 393–408, 1950.

Tchernyschew, T., 'Upper Palaeozoic Formations of Eurasia', *Rec. Geol. Surv. India,* vol. xxxi, pp. 111–41, 1904.

Vaughan, W. T., 'American and European Tertiary Larger Foraminifera', *Bull. Geol. Soc. Amer.,* vol. xxxv, pp. 785–822, 1924.

Watson, D. M. S., 'Eugyrinus, A Branchiosaur from the Lancashire Coal Measures', *Geol. Mag.,* vol. lviii, pp. 70–74, 1921.

Weller, S., 'The Silurian Fauna Interpreted on the Epicontinental Basis', *Journ. Geol.,* vol. vi, pp. 692–704, 1898.

Westoll, T. S., 'The Age of Certain Permian Fish-Bearing Strata', *Geol. Mag.,* vol. lxxviii, pp. 37–44, 1941.

Willis, J. C., *Flowering Plants and Ferns,* p. 192, Cambridge, 1908.

Woodward, A. S., in discussion on 'Fossils as Indicators of Continental Drift', *Q.J.G.S.,* vol. xci, p. vi, 1935.

PALAEONTOLOGICAL INDEX

Because of its length this index is divided into three sections, listing genera and species of (I) Invertebrate Animals (pp. 741–71), (II) Vertebrate Animals (pp. 772–82), and (III) Plants (pp. 783–85), mentioned in the text.

Numbers in **heavy type** refer to pages on which drawings of fossils appear, and Roman numerals refer to the plates at the end of the volume.

I. GENERA AND SPECIES OF INVERTEBRATE ANIMALS

The Phyla or Classes to which the genera belong are indicated by letters in brackets after the names, thus:

Foraminifera (F), Porifera (P), Graptolithina (G), Anthozoa and Archaeocyathidae (A), Hydrozoa, mainly Stromatoporoids (H), Echinodermata (E), Brachiopoda (B), Bryozoa (Bz), Vermes (V), Lamellibranchiata (L), Gastropoda (S), Cephalopoda (K), Trilobita (T), Eucrustacea (C), Acerata, mainly Merostomata (M).

Acanthastraea (A) 638.
Acanthina (S) 650, 651, 655.
Acanthoceras (K) 517, 521, 522, 529, 530, 533–4, 536–7, 543.
hippocastanum 522.
newboldi 522, 524.
rhotomagense 516, 518, 524.
vectense 506, 518, Pl. XVII.
Acanthoclymenia (K) 267.
Acanthodiscus (K) 490.
Acanthograptus (G) 226.
Acanthohoplites (K) 494, 516, 534.
Acanthopleuroceras (K) 438.
valdani 439, Pl. VIII.
Acanthorhynchia (B) 449.
Acanthoscaphites (K)
nodosus 536.
Acanthothyris (B) 447, 449, 450.
spinosa **458.**
Acaste, or Acastina (T)
downingae 211, **212.**
Acentrotremites (E) 307.
Acera (S)
striatella 584.
Acervularia (A) 231.
goldfussi 246.
luxurians 217.
Acidaspis (T) 176, 190, 204, 219.
kashmirica 221.

Acila (L) 62, 616, 653, 654.
cobboldiae 652.
Aconeceras (K) 491, 515, 521, 531, 540.
Acrochordiceras (K) 415, 416, 417.
enodi 415.
Acrocrioceras (K) 491.
tabarellii 491.
Acropora (A) 602, 604, 639–41.
muricata 642.
Acrosalenia (E) 451, 456.
hemicidaroides 452, Pl. XII.
Acrospirifer (B)
murchisoni 265.
primaevus 252.
Acroteuthis (K) 490.
lateralis 490.
Acrothyra (B)
comleyensis 130.
Acrotreta (B) 138.
socialis 131.
Actaeon (S)
tornatilis 624.
turgidus 580.
Actinacis (A) 602, 603, 604.
Actinocamax (K) 98.
granulatus 511.
mercyi 511.
plenus 503, 506, 518.
quadratus 503, 511, 513, 519.
verus 511.
Actinoceras (K) 94, 139, 191.

Actinocrinus (E) 82, 308.
Actinopteria (L)
arenarea 265.
textilis 265.
Actinostoma (H) 231.
Adacna (L) 62.
Admete (S) 46, 614.
Adontophora (L) 412.
Adrianites (K) 383, 386.
defordi 386.
Aeglina (T) 37.
Aegoceras (K) 470.
Aegocrioceras (K) 490.
capricornum Pl. XV.
Aequipecten (L)
asper 505, **512.**
barbatus 449.
beaveri 505.
fibrosus **512.**
opercularis 627.
Agaricia (A) 638, 641, 642.
Agaricocrinus (E) 308.
Agassiceras (K) 435.
geometricum 437.
Agassizia (E) 607, 628, 646, 647.
Agassizocrinus (E) 307.
Agathiceras (K) 383–4, 386, 391–2.
Agnostus (T) 36, 134, 138, 141, 143, 179.
agnostiformis **133.**
altus 132, **133.**
barrandei 132, **133.**
bifurcatus 134.
callavei **133,** 136.

3 C

Otoites (K) 447.
braikenridgei Pl. X.
sauzei 445.
Overtonia (B) 88.
fimbriata Pl. IV.
Ovula (S) 616.
Owenites (K) 407, 410, 414.
Oxycerites (K)
waterhousei 451.
Oxyclymenia (K) 255.
Oxynoticeras (K) 437, 469.
oxynotum 434, Pl. VII.
Oxyteuthis (K)
brunsvicensis 491.
Oxytoma (L)
costata 452.
Oxytropidoceras (K) 496,
498, 520, 524, 526, 533,
534, 538.

Pachyceras (K) 479.
Pachydiscus (K) 520, 523,
525, 527, 529, 530, 532–
534, 538, 545.
Pachylocrinus (E) 307.
Pachyplanulites (K) 483.
Pachypora (A) 79, 256.
cristata 80.
Pachysphinctes (K) 479,
483.
Pachytraga (L) 541, 542,
546.
Paedumias (T) 126, 145.
clarkei 147.
nevadensis 147.
transitans 147.
Palaechinus (E) 84.
Palaeocorystes (C)
stokesi 499.
Palaeodiscus (E) 84.
Palaeodonta (L) 369, 381.
Palaeolecanites (K) 390.
Palaeolenus (T) 153.
Palaeomutela (L) 369.
Palaeoneilo (L) 269, 423.
Palaeophyllites (K) 408.
Palaeosmilia (A) 75, 274,
276.
murchisoni 277, 283.
regia 279, 284, 285.
Paltopleuroceras (K) 66.
Panopaea (L) 610, 612, 654.
faujasii 623.
gurgitis 494.
intermedia 579, 580–1,
612.
mandibula 464.
menardi 624.

Panopaea (cont.)
minor 591.
norvegica 635.
Papyriaspis (T) 155.
Paraboliceras (K) 481, 484.
Parabolina (T) 143.
spinulosa 135, 137, 144.
Parabolinella (T) 136, 138,
142.
andina 144.
argentinensis 144.
rugosa, 138.
Paracaloceras (K) 467.
Paracalycoceras (K) 517.
Paraceltites (K) 386–7, 390,
392.
Paraceratites (K) 415–16,
418.
antecedens 402.
binodosus 415, 416, 417,
419.
newberryi Pl. VI.
thuillieri 417.
trinodosus 402, 415–16,
419.
Paracoroniceras (K) 435.
gmuendensis 435.
Paracrioceras (K) 491.
Paradoxechinus (E) 606,
643–4.
Paradoxides (T) 8, 62, 129,
141, 143, 152, 155.
abenaceus 144.
aurora 128, 130, 131.
bennetti 144.
bohemicus 141.
davidis 128, 130, 134, 141,
144.
forchammeri 130, 134.
groomi 130.
hicksi 128, 130, 131–2, 134
141, 144.
intermedius 130.
matthewi 144.
mediterraneus 141.
oelandicus 130, 131.
rotundatus 141.
rugulosus 128, 130, 134,
141, 142.
sjogreni 130, 131.
tessini 130, 131, 141, 144.
Parafusulina (F) 384, 386–
388, 391, 733.
kattaensis 390.
Paragastrioceras (K) 383–4,
386, 388.
Paragoceras (K) 412.
Parahomalonotus (T) 253.

Parahoplites (K) 494, 533,
534.
furcatus 537.
nutfieldensis 494.
Parajuvavites (K) 423.
Paralecanites (K) 392.
sextensis 392–3.
Paralegoceras (K) 310, 390.
Paralenticeras (K) 538.
Paralobites (K)
pisum 418.
Parancyloceras (K) 492.
bidentatum 493.
Paranorites (K) 407.
Paraphorhynchus (B) 308.
Paraphyllites (K) 254.
Parapopanoceras (K) 417.
Paraprionites (K) 392.
Parapsiloceras (K) 467.
Parapuzosia (K) 519, 520,
530.
Pararcestes (K) 415.
Parasageceras (K) 417.
Parasalenia (E) 644.
Paraschwagerina (F) 67,
299, 383–4, 391.
Parasmilia (A) 77, 503, 601.
centralis 78.
Paraspirifer (B)
acuminatus 265.
cultrijugatus 265, 265.
Paraspiticeras (K) 533.
Paraster (E) 643, 646.
Parastieria (K) 490.
peltoceroides 490, Pl. XV.
Parastroma (L) 545.
Parastrophia (B) 176.
Paratibetites (K) 424.
Paratinanthus (E) 607.
Paratirolites (K) 413.
Paratrachyceras (K) 426.
Paratropites (K) 420, 422,
426.
Parechioceras (K) 468.
Parinodoceras (K) 439, 469.
Parkinsonia (K) 449.
parkinsoni 445, Pl. X.
Parmorthis (B) 229.
Parodoceras (K) 254.
Parowenites (K) 407.
Paryphoceras (K) 479.
Pascoeites (K) 527.
Patella (S) 627.
rugosa 451, 464.
Paterina (B) 126.
labradorica 127.
Patinopecten (L)
oweni 654.

II. GENERA AND SPECIES OF VERTEBRATE ANIMALS

The letters F, A, R, B, or M in brackets after the genera indicate the classes Fishes, Amphibians, Reptiles, Birds, and Mammals respectively.

Abderites (M) 695.
Acanthaspis (F) 262.
Acanthodes (F) 241, 300.
Acanthoessus (F) 262.
Acanthopholis (R) 565.
  horridus 566.
Acanthostoma (A) 366.
Acentrophorus (F) 109.
Aceraspis (F) 249.
Aceratherium (M) 662–3,
  665, 669, 675–6, 679.
Acmeodon (M) 680.
Acrodus (F) 108, 398.
  minimus 400.
Actinodon (A) 365.
  risinensis 373.
Adapis (M) 662.
Adapisorex (M) 660.
Adapisoriculus (M) 660.
Adelogyrinus (A) 357.
Adelosaurus (R) 366.
Adinotherium (M) 693.
Aegyptosaurus (R) 568.
Aelurocyon (M) 686.
Aeluropsis (M) 677.
Aepinacodon (M) 686.
Aepyosaurus (R) 566.
Aetonyx (R) 555.
Aetosaurus (R) 111, 552.
Agriochoerus (M) 686–7.
Agrosaurus (R) 555.
Ailurus (M) 666, 678.
Alactaga (M) 668.
  jaculus 668.
Alamosaurus (R) 572.
Albertogaudrya (M) 692.
Albertosaurus (R) 570.
Alces (M) 679, 690–1.
  latifrons 666.
  machlis 669.
Alectrosaurus (R) 574.
Algeinosaurus (A) 362.
Algoasaurus (R)
  baneri 567.
Allomeryx (M) 687.
Allops (M) 685.
Allosaurus (R) 559, 562.
Alphodon (M) 659.
Alticamelus (M) 688–9.
Altispinax (R) 563, 568.

Amblotherium (M) 116,
  658.
Amia (F) 53.
  colenutti 589.
Ammosaurus (R) 555.
Amphibamus (A) 362.
Amphibos (M) 677.
Amphicoelus (R) 560.
Amphictis (M) 663.
Amphicyon (M) 117, 662–3,
  675–7, 688.
Amphidon (M) 658.
Amphilestes (M) 116, 658.
Amphimeryx (M) 662.
Amphiproviverra (M) 695.
Amphitherium (M) 116,
  451, 658.
Amphitragulus (M) 663–4.
Amynodon (M) 684.
Anacodon (M) 682.
Analcitherium (M) 694.
Anaptomorphus (M) 683.
Anaschisma (A) 550.
Anatosaurus (R) 570.
Anchiceratops (R) 572.
Anchilophus (M) 661.
Anchippodus (M) 683.
Anchisaurus (R) 555.
Anchitherium (M) **118**, 663,
  664, 675–6, 686.
  aurelianense 675.
  gobiense 675.
Ancodus (M) 662, 669, 685.
Andrewsarchus (M) 673.
Anisonchus (M) 680–1.
Ankylosaurus (R) 572.
  magniventris 571.
Anna (R) 368, 371.
Anningia (R) 371.
Anoplosaurus (R)
  curtonotus 565.
Anoplotherium (M) 591,
  660, 662.
Antarctosaurus (R) 568.
  giganteus 568.
  wichmannianus 568.
Anthodon (R) 368, 372.
Anthracohyus (M) 674.
Anthracokeryx (M) 674.
Anthracosaurus (A) 357.

Anthracothema (M) 674.
Anthracotherium (M) 662,
  633, 675–6, 686.
Antilocapra (M) 691.
Antilope (M) 666.
Antilospira (M) 679.
Antipus (R) 552.
Antrodemus (R) 559.
Apatasaurus (R) 560, 564.
Aphaneramma (A) 551.
Aphelops (M) 688–9.
Aphelosaurus (R) 366.
Aploconodon (M) 658.
Apterodon (M) 669, 670.
Araeoscelis (R) 365.
Archaelurus (M) 686.
Archaeohyrax (M) 693.
Archaeomeryx (M) 673.
Archaeopteryx (B) 115.
Archaeotherium (M) 685.
Archegosaurus (A) 365, 366.
  decheni 365.
  ornatus 373.
Archetrigon (M) 658.
Arctocyon (M) 660, 681.
Arctocyonoides (M) 681.
Arctomys (M) 668.
Arctostylops (M) 672, 682,
  692.
Arctotherium (M) 696.
Ardynia (M) 673, 674.
Ardynictes (M) 674.
Argyrosaurus (R)
  superbus 569.
Aristosaurus (R) 555.
Aristosuchus (R)
  pusillus 563.
Arrhinoceratops (R) 572,
  573.
Arsinoitherium (M) 669.
Asiatosaurus (R) 573.
Asterolepis (F) 240, 250.
Astraponotus (M) 693.
Astrapotherium (M) 694,
  695.
Astrodon (R) 569.
  valdensis 564.
Atelodus (M) 665.
  bicornis 678.
Atlantosaurus (R) 560.

III. GENERA AND SPECIES OF PLANTS

Classification is indicated by the following letters in brackets after the generic names:

A = Angiospermae, G = Gymnospermae, C = Cycadophyta, P = Pteridospermae, F = Filicales, E = Equisetales, L = Lycopodiales, S = Sphenophyllales, B = Bryophyta, T = Thallophyta (Algae and Fungi).

Note that botanical and zoological nomenclature are independent, and some generic names of plants are identical with those given to certain animals.

Abelia (A) 347.
Acacia (A) 345.
Acer (A) 346.
Acitheca (P)
  polymorpha 329.
Acrostichum (F)
  aureum 346.
  lanzeanum 346, 347, 582.
Actinidia (A) 347.
Adiantites (P) 322, 334.
  antiquus 322, **323.**
Agathis (G) 328.
Alethopteris (P) 325, 326, 336.
  lonchitica **323,** 326, 327.
  serli 327, 328.
Alnus (A) 348.
  glutinosa 350.
  viridus 349.
Aneimia (F) 346.
Annularia (E) 325.
  radiata 327.
  spicata 331.
Anomozamites (C) 342.
Aptiana (A) 343.
Aralia (A) 346, 582.
Araucaria (G) 342.
Araucarites (G) 342, 343, 347.
  goepperti 354.
Archaeopteris (P) 248, 319.
Archaeosigillaria (L) 319, 321.
Arthrostigma (L) 319.
Artisia (G) 328.
Artocarpus (A) 344, 346.
Asterocalamites (E) 321.
Asterophyllites (E) 325.
Asterotheca (P) 334.
Asteroxylon (L) 318.
Azolla (F) 347.

Baiera (C) 343, 344.
Bennettites (C) 341.
  saxbyanus 342.

Betula (A) 348.
  alba 350.
  nana 350.
Botryopteris (F)
  antiqua 322.
Brachyphyllum (G) 343.
Brasenia (A) 347.

Calamites (E) 41, 320, 321, 325–6, 329.
  communis 325, 326.
  ramosus 325, 326.
Calamostachys (E) 325.
Callipteris (P) 329, 705, 708.
  conferta 331.
Callixylon (G) 320.
Cantia (A) 343.
Cardiopteris (P) 332, 334.
Carpinus (A) 348.
  laxiflora 348.
Carpolithus (P) 341.
Catalpa (A) 347.
Caytonia (A) 339.
Cephalopteris (P) 319.
Chara (T) 466, 591.
Cheirostrobus (L) 321.
Cinnamonum (A) 44, 344, 347.
Cladophlebis (F) 339, 341, 343, 344.
  denticulata 339, **340.**
Clematis (A) 347.
Clepsydropsis (F) 304.
Coniopteris (F) 339.
  hymenophylloides 339.
Cordaites (G) 326, 328, 332, 334.
  angulostriatus 328.
  hislopi 332, 333.
  principalis 328.
Corema (A) 349.
  alba 349.
  intermedia 349.
Corylus (A)
  avellana 350.

Crataegus (A) 348.
  oxyacantha 350.
Crossotheca (P) 325.
Cupressus (G) 341, 342, 346.
Cycadeoidea (C) 341, 466.
Cycadites (C) 342.
Cyclostigma (L) 319.
  kiltorkense 319.
Cyperus (G) 349.

Dactylotheca (P)
  plumosa **323,** 327.
Dadoxylon (G) 320, 332, 333, 334.
Danaeopsis (P) 331.
Decroidium (P) 331.
Dicksonia (F) 342.
Dicotylophyllum (A) 354.
Dictyophyllum (F) 339, 341.
Dipelta (A) 347.
Diplopora (T) 416.
Diplotmema (P)
  furcata **323,** 327.
Dipteris (F) 44, 339, 342.

Elatides (G) 342.
Elatocladus (G) 343, 344.
Engelhardtia (A) 347.
Epiphyton (T) 157.
Equisetites (E) 337, 338, 343.
  arenaceus 338, 398.
  burkhardti 341.
  columnaris 338.
  keuperiana 398.
  scanicus 338.
Equisetum (E) 321, 325, 338.
Erica (A) 348.
Eucalyptus (A) 44, 346.

Fagus (A)
  bouronensis 354.
Ficus (A) 346, 582.

STRATIGRAPHICAL INDEX

The systems to which the stratal divisions belong are indicated by symbols, thus:

Precambrian (PC), Cambrian (P1), Ordovician (P2), Silurian (P3), Devonian (P4), Carboniferous (P5), Permian (P6); Triassic (M1), Jurassic (M2), Cretaceous (M3); Eocene (N1), Oligocene (N2), Miocene (N3), Pliocene (N4), Pleistocene (N5). Casual references are not indexed.

A few terms now obsolete are mentioned in the text; these are printed below in *italic* type. The names of palaeontological zones are not included here; they may be found by reference to the name of the zone-fossil in the palaeontological index (pp. 741–85).

GEOGRAPHICAL INDEX

The names in this index are purely geographical localities. For instance, Ireland refers to the whole island of that name irrespective of the political partition, and the subcontinent of India includes the political region now known as Pakistan.

In addition to the usual abbreviations of British counties, and North American States, the following symbols are used:

Afr.	Africa	Eng.	England	Pen.	Peninsula
Am.	America	Eur.	Europe	R.	River
Atl.	Atlantic	Ger.	Germany	S.	South
Aus.	Australasia	I. Is.	Island(s)	Scot.	Scotland
Cent.	Central	Mts.	Mountains	U.S.	United States
Co.	County	N.	North	W.	West
Dep.	Department	Oc.	Ocean		
E.	East	Pac.	Pacific		

3 F

PLATE I

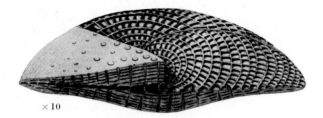

× 10

Spiroclypeus   Miocene

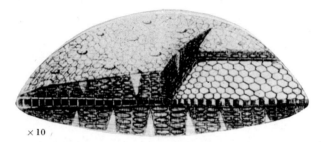

× 10

Lepidocyclina   Upper Eocene to Miocene

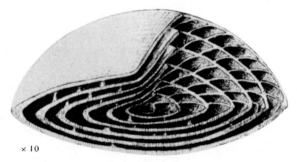

× 10

Nummulites   Eocene and Oligocene

SOME NEOZOIC FORAMINIFERA
Diagrams to show structure
(Reproduced by permission from van der Vlerk and Umbgrove, 1927)

PLATE II

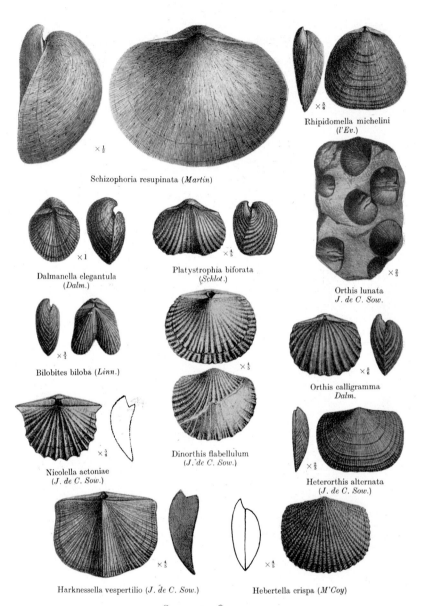

Schizophoria resupinata (*Martin*)

$\times \frac{1}{2}$

Rhipidomella michelini
(*l'Ev.*)

$\times \frac{5}{6}$

Dalmanella elegantula
(*Dalm.*)

$\times 1$

Platystrophia biforata
(*Schlot.*)

$\times \frac{4}{5}$

Orthis lunata
J. de C. Sow.

$\times \frac{2}{3}$

Bilobites biloba (*Linn.*)

$\times \frac{3}{2}$

Dinorthis flabellulum
(*J. de C. Sow.*)

$\times \frac{4}{5}$

Orthis calligramma
Dalm.

$\times \frac{5}{6}$

Nicolella actoniae
(*J. de C. Sow.*)

$\times \frac{3}{5}$

Heterorthis alternata
(*J. de C. Sow.*)

$\times \frac{2}{3}$

Harknessella vespertilio (*J. de C. Sow.*)

$\times \frac{4}{5}$

Hebertella crispa (*M'Coy*)

$\times \frac{4}{5}$

SPECIES OF ORTHIDAE

(after Davidson. Reproduced by permission of the Council of the
Palaeontographical Society)

PLATE III

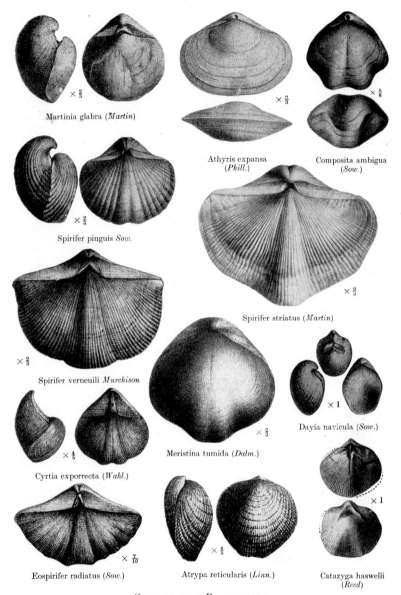

Martinia glabra (*Martin*)

Athyris expansa
(*Phill.*)

Composita ambigua
(*Sow.*)

Spirifer pinguis *Sow.*

Spirifer striatus (*Martin*)

Spirifer verneuili *Murchison*

Dayia navicula (*Sow.*)

Meristina tumida (*Dalm.*)

Cyrtia exporrecta (*Wahl.*)

Eospirifer radiatus (*Sow.*)

Atrypa reticularis (*Linn.*)

Catazyga haswelli
(*Reed*)

SPIRE-BEARING BRACHIOPODS

(Mainly after Davidson, reproduced by permission of the Council of the
Palaeontographical Society)

PLATE IV

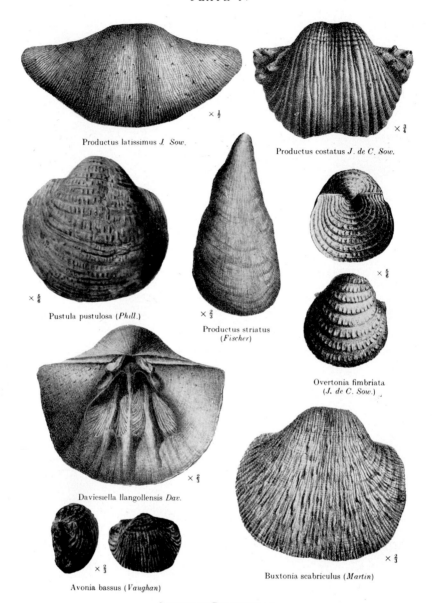

Productus latissimus *J. Sow.*

Productus costatus *J. de C. Sow.*

Pustula pustulosa (*Phill.*)

Productus striatus
(*Fischer*)

Overtonia fimbriata
(*J. de C. Sow.*)

Daviesiella llangollensis *Dav.*

Avonia bassus (*Vaughan*)

Buxtonia scabriculus (*Martin*)

SPECIES OF PRODUCTIDAE
(Reproduced by permission of the Palaeontographical Society and the
Geological Society of London)

PLATE V

Reticuloceras gracile *Bisat*

×1

× ½

Gastrioceras listeri (*Martin*)

×3

Reticuloceras reticulatum
(*Phill.*)

×3

Homoceratoides prereticulatum *Bisat*

×2

Eumorphoceras bisulcatum
(*Girty*)

×2

Goniatites spiralis (*Phill.*)

×4

Homoceras proteum (*Brown*)

CARBONIFEROUS GONIATITES

(after Bisat and from specimens in the Dept. of Geology, University of
Liverpool)

PLATE VI

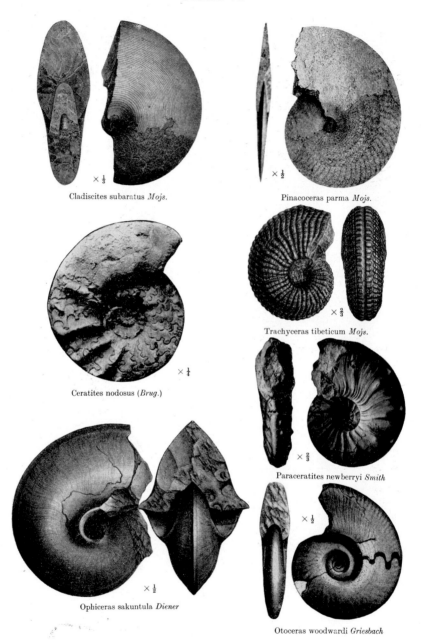

Cladiscites subaratus *Mojs.*

Pinacoceras parma *Mojs.*

Trachyceras tibeticum *Mojs.*

Ceratites nodosus (*Brug.*)

Paraceratites newberryi *Smith*

Ophiceras sakuntula *Diener*

Otoceras woodwardi *Griesbach*

Some Triassic Ammonoids

(Reproduced by permission of the Geological Surveys of India and of the
United States of America)

PLATE VII

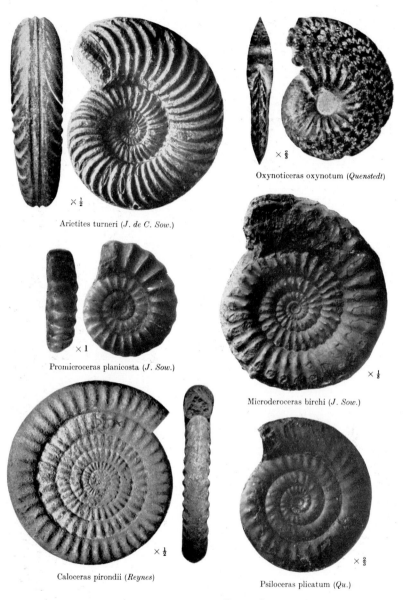

Oxynoticeras oxynotum (*Quenstedt*)

× ½

Arietites turneri (*J. de C. Sow.*)

× 1

Promicroceras planicosta (*J. Sow.*)

× ⅓

Microderoceras birchi (*J. Sow.*)

× ½

Caloceras pirondii (*Reynes*)

× ⅔

Psiloceras plicatum (*Qu.*)

AMMONITES FROM THE LOWER LIAS
(mainly after Buckman and Tutcher)

PLATE VIII

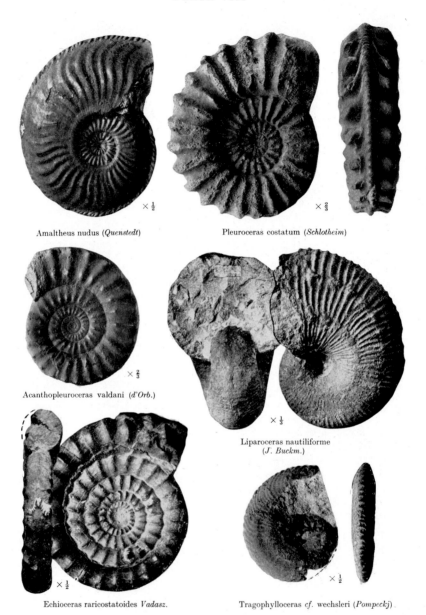

Amaltheus nudus (*Quenstedt*)

Pleuroceras costatum (*Schlotheim*)

Acanthopleuroceras valdani (*d'Orb.*)

Liparoceras nautiliforme
(*J. Buckm.*)

Echioceras raricostatoides *Vadasz.*

Tragophylloceras *cf.* wechsleri (*Pompeckj*)

AMMONITES FROM THE LOWER AND MIDDLE LIAS
(after Buckman and Tutcher and from specimens)

PLATE IX

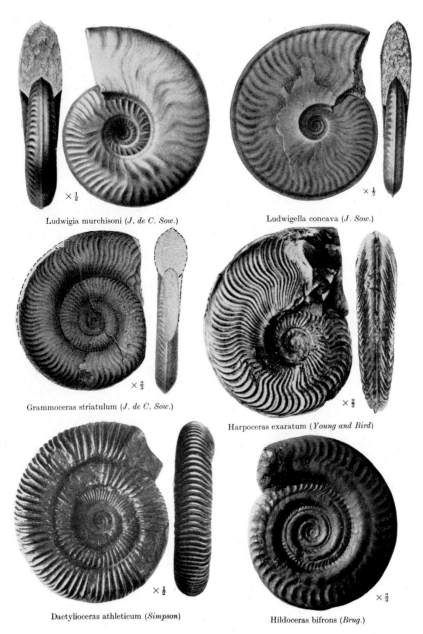

Ludwigia murchisoni (*J. de C. Sow.*)

Ludwigella concava (*J. Sow.*)

Grammoceras striatulum (*J. de C. Sow.*)

Harpoceras exaratum (*Young and Bird*)

Dactylioceras athleticum (*Simpson*)

Hildoceras bifrons (*Brug.*)

AMMONITES FROM THE UPPER LIAS
(after Buckman and Tutcher)

PLATE X

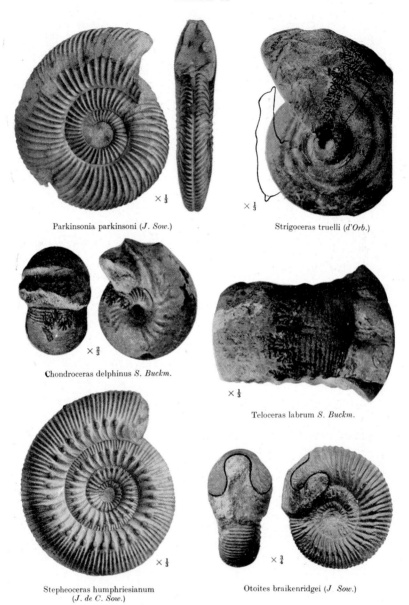

Parkinsonia parkinsoni (*J. Sow.*)

Strigoceras truelli (*d'Orb.*)

Chondroceras delphinus *S. Buckm.*

Teloceras labrum *S. Buckm.*

Stepheoceras humphriesianum
(*J. de C. Sow.*)

Otoites braikenridgei (*J Sow.*)

AMMONITES FROM THE INFERIOR OOLITE
(after Buckman)

PLATE XI

Creniceras cristatum
(*J. de C. Sow.*)

× 1

× 1

Scarburgiceras scarburgense (*Y. & B.*)

× ½

Quenstedtoceras *sp.*

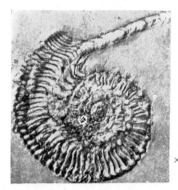

× ½

Kosmoceras acutistriatum *Robson*

× ⅔

Kosmoceras geminatum *S. Buckm.*

× ⅔

× ½

Cadoceras sublaeve (*J. Sow.*)

Proplanulites koenigi (*J. Sow.*)

SOME CALLOVIAN AMMONITES
(mainly after Buckman)

PLATE XII

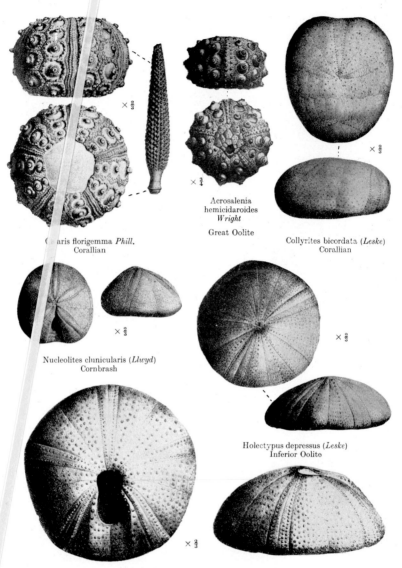

Acrosalenia
hemicidaroides
Wright

Great Oolite

aris florigemma *Phill.*
Corallian

Collyrites bicordata (*Leske*)
Corallian

Nucleolites clunicularis (*Llwyd*)
Cornbrash

Holectypus depressus (*Leske*)
Inferior Oolite

Pygaster ornatus *J. Buckm.*

Inferior Oolite

SOME JURASSIC ECHINOIDS
(Reproduced from Wright by permission of the Council of the
Palaeontographical Society)

PLATE XIII

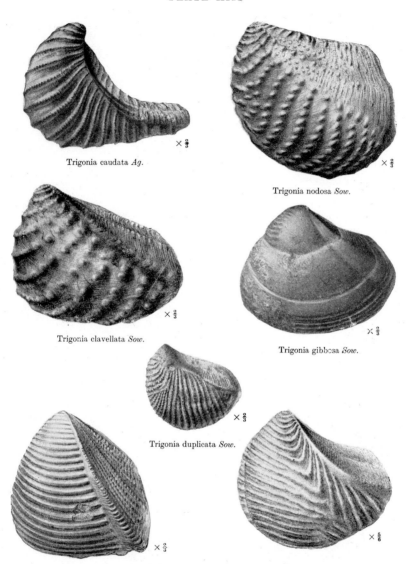

Trigonia caudata *Ag.* × ⅔

Trigonia nodosa *Sow.* × ⅔

Trigonia clavellata *Sow.* × ⅔

Trigonia gibbosa *Sow.* × ⅔

Trigonia duplicata *Sow.* × ⅔

Trigonia costata *Sow.* × ⅔

Trigonia v-costata *Lycett* × ⅚

Some Species of *Trigonia*
(after Lycett. Reproduced by permission of the Council of the
Palaeontographical Society)

PLATE XIV

Rasenia *cf.* involuta *Salfeld*

× ½

Pavlovia pallasioides (*Neaverson*)

× ⅔

Ringsteadia pseudocordatus
(*Blake and Hudleston*)

× ⅓

Prionodoceras superstes (*Phill.*)

× ½

Cardioceras quadrarium *S. Buckm.*

× ⅔

Aspidoceras perarmatum (*J. Sow.*)

× ⅓

OXFORDIAN AND KIMMERIDGIAN AMMONITES
(after Buckman, Neaverson, and from specimens)

PLATE XV

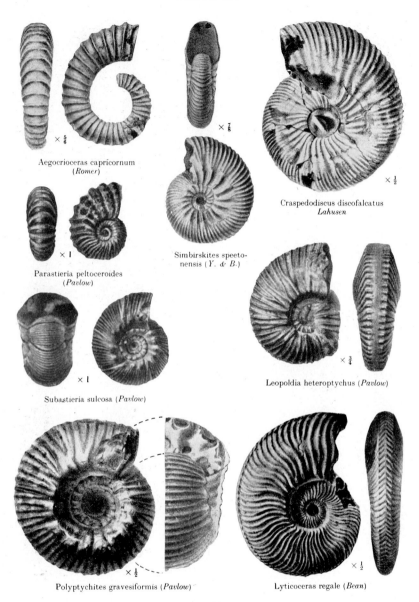

$\times \frac{5}{6}$

Aegocrioceras capricornum
(*Romer*)

$\times \frac{7}{8}$

Parastieria peltoceroides
(*Pavlow*)

$\times 1$

Simbirskites speeto-
nensis (*Y. & B.*)

Craspedodiscus discofalcatus
Lahusen

$\times \frac{1}{2}$

Subastieria sulcosa (*Pavlow*)

$\times 1$

Leopoldia heteroptychus (*Pavlow*)

$\times \frac{3}{4}$

Polyptychites gravesiformis (*Pavlow*)

$\times \frac{1}{2}$

Lyticoceras regale (*Bean*)

$\times \frac{1}{2}$

NEOCOMIAN AMMONOIDS
(after Pavlow and Lamplugh)

PLATE XVI

Callihoplites auritus (*J. Sow.*)

Hysteroceras varicosum
(*J. de C. Sow.*)

Euhoplites lautus (*J. Sow.*)

Dipoloceras cristatum (*d'Orb.*)

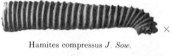

Hamites compressus *J. Sow.*

Anahoplites planus (*Mantell*)

Hoplites *aff.* dentatus (*J. Sow.*)

SOME ALBIAN AMMONOIDS
(mainly after Spath, reproduced by permission of the Council of the
Palaeontographical Society)

PLATE XVII

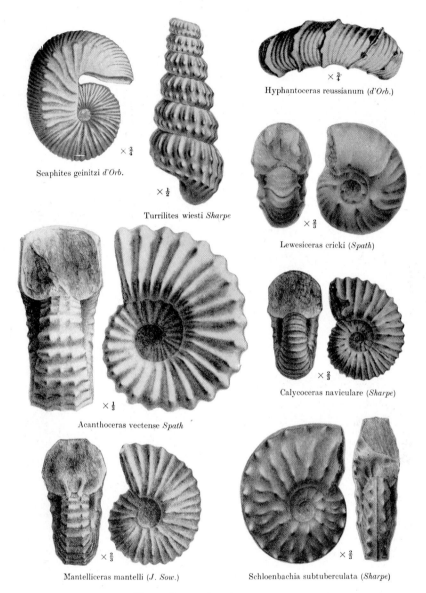

$\times \frac{3}{4}$

Scaphites geinitzi *d'Orb.*

$\times \frac{1}{2}$

Turrilites wiesti *Sharpe*

$\times \frac{3}{4}$

Hyphantoceras reussianum (*d'Orb.*)

$\times \frac{2}{3}$

Lewesiceras cricki (*Spath*)

$\times \frac{1}{3}$

Acanthoceras vectense *Spath*

$\times \frac{2}{3}$

Calycoceras naviculare (*Sharpe*)

$\times \frac{2}{3}$

Mantelliceras mantelli (*J. Sow.*)

$\times \frac{2}{3}$

Schloenbachia subtuberculata (*Sharpe*)

UPPER CRETACEOUS AMMONOIDS

(mainly after Sharpe. Reproduced by permission of the Council of the
Palaeontographical Society)

PLATE XVIII

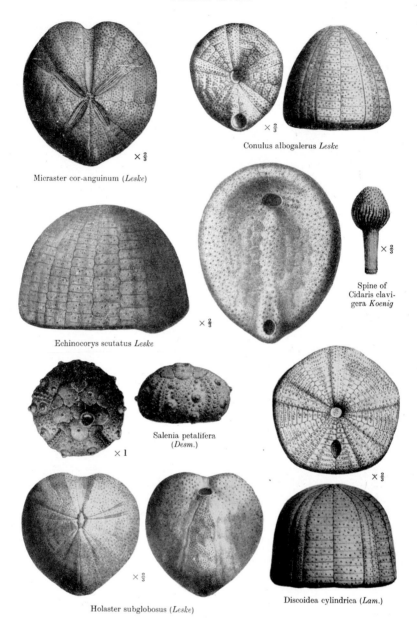

Micraster cor-anguinum (*Leske*)

× ⅔

Conulus albogalerus *Leske*

× ⅔

Echinocorys scutatus *Leske*

× ⅔

Spine of
Cidaris clavi-
gera *Koenig*

× ⅔

Salenia petalifera
(*Desm.*)

× 1

× ⅔

Holaster subglobosus (*Leske*)

× ⅔

Discoidea cylindrica (*Lam.*)

CRETACEOUS ECHINOIDS
(after Wright, reproduced by permission of the Council of the
Palaeontographical Society)